UNIVERSITY OF MAINE LIBRARY
DOCUMENT DEPOSITORY
ORONO, MAINE 04473

HISPANIC FOUNDATION BIBLIOGRAPHICAL SERIES NO. 10

National Directory
OF
Latin Americanists

*Biobibliographies of 1,884 Specialists
in the Social Sciences & Humanities*

Compiled by the Hispanic Foundation
Library of Congress

HISPANIC FOUNDATION • REFERENCE DEPARTMENT
LIBRARY OF CONGRESS
WASHINGTON: 1966

L.C. Card 65-61762

Supported by U.S. Office of Education, National Defense Education Act, Title VI Program

Survey of Personnel With Specialized Knowledge of Latin America, 1963–64

For sale by the Superintendent of Documents, U.S. Government Printing Office
Washington, D.C., 20402 - Price $2 (cloth)

Contents

	Page
INTRODUCTION	1
LIST OF ABBREVIATIONS	7
BIOBIBLIOGRAPHIES	11
INDEX TO SUBJECT SPECIALTIES	335

Introduction

This directory provides biobibliographical information on 1,884 persons in the United States whose experience and professional training qualify them as specialists in the Latin American field. Coverage is highly selective, both by design and because the survey is a pioneering venture. Undoubtedly, despite the determined efforts of the compilers, many well-qualified individuals may have escaped our notice. The procedures by which data for the directory were obtained are discussed at greater length below.

Pressed increasingly by inquiries for current information about individuals with specialized knowledge of Latin America, the Hispanic Foundation decided to revive and broaden a pilot program it had undertaken earlier. As part of a survey of resources in the United States for the study and teaching of Latin America, the Hispanic Foundation had made comprehensive surveys of course offerings and in 1958 had begun to collect biobibliographical data on specialized personnel. The latter activity lapsed for lack of funds.

But, on the basis of this experience, the Librarian of Congress placed a proposal before the Commissioner of Education, who agreed in 1963 to provide financial support for the development of a national directory of Latin Americanists from research funds authorized under Title VI of the National Defense Education Act. In addition to providing data on linguistic skills and other capabilities of specialized manpower, the directory shows, as far as practicable, gaps in the supply of specialists in various academic disciplines. These findings may be especially useful to institutions that are planning area study and training programs aided by funds provided under Title VI of the National Defense Education Act.

From the outset it was hoped that information on two classes of specialized persons could be obtained systematically and comprehensively. The first, and largest, class consists of "area" specialists: individuals whose professional training and experience have provided them with valuable knowledge about Latin America, often to the virtual exclusion of other areas. Furnishing data on the fields of interest and research of these specialists and thereby encouraging communication among them and other scholars with related interests, is one of the main objectives of this directory.

The other class included in the directory consists of specialists whose training is in a field of knowledge that does not always readily lend itself to segmentation on an area basis, but whose personal interest and linguistic abilities would make it feasible and desirable for them to undertake professional pursuits in Latin America. Among them, for instance, are many economists, political scientists, and other social scientists who do not think of themselves as exclusively "Latin Americanists."

Even more marked is the "non-area" nature of training in the physical and natural sciences, pure and applied. Many such "non-area" specialists, however, have adequate language skills in the two major Latin American languages, Spanish and Portuguese, to carry out an investigative, training, or consultative mission.

From the outset it was expected that the Hispanic Foundation would obtain more information on the relatively finite number of "area" specialists than on "non-area" specialists with some Hispanic language abilities. The latter group ranges across all branches of knowledge.

Among "non-area" specialists, the physical scientists form a large and important body. During a preliminary phase of the present effort, in cooperation with the National Science Foundation, the Hispanic Foundation circularized a sample of scientists whose names had been provided by the National Science Foundation. Although responses were encouraging, the Hispanic Foundation decided, in view of the numerous specialties within the scientific fields, to defer systematic coverage of that community. At this time the limitations of funds and staff precluded comprehensive inquiries. And, rather than give an improper impression that relatively few scientists are available for assignments or have an interest in Latin America, we have purposely omitted the few who kindly responded to our earlier inquiries.

In like fashion, after preliminary returns had been analyzed from businessmen, diplomats, and others whose employment brings them into contact with Latin America but who do not possess the academic background and/or professional experience in specific disciplines, it was decided not to include these categories as fields in the directory.

To summarize, a variety of circumstances narrowed the number and scope of the fields from which specialists were selected to appear in the published version of the directory. Somewhat loosely and broadly defined, these fields are the social sciences and the humanities. Table 1 lists the specific fields and shows the number of persons from each represented in this compilation.

The questionnaire technique was the method used in compiling the directory. Initially, Mr. J. Fletcher Wellemeyer was engaged as a consultant to aid in the planning and early operations of the project.

Field	Count
Anthropology	257
Architecture	6
Art	27
City and Regional Planning	8
Communication	7
Economics	286
Education	50
Geography	129
History	389
Journalism	22
Language	66
Law	47
Library Science and Bibliography	68
Literature—Brazilian	29
Haitian	2
Spanish American	179
Music	12
Linguistics	76
Philosophy	15
Political Science	122
Psychology	3
Social Welfare	6
Sociology	74
Statistics	4

Table 1. Fields Represented in Published Directory

He developed and sent a questionnaire to approximately 1,000 persons; personal data, plus a critique of the questionnaire itself, were solicited. The responses, analyzed by Mr. Wellemeyer, resulted in several modifications of the original questionnaire. A revised version, also approved by the Bureau of the Budget, was then prepared and given wider distribution.

From a variety of published and unpublished sources preliminary mailing lists were developed. A number of professional associations graciously permitted directory staff members to search administrative files and use unpublished membership lists. From such printed sources as listings of recent doctoral degrees came other names. Recipients of fellowships in Portuguese and Spanish awarded under Title VI of the National Defense Education Act were also circularized, even though clearly many would not have completed their professional training before the appearance of the published directory.

From the several hundred names thus accumulated, rosters by fields were prepared and circulated to persons whose knowledge of the personnel in each field was deemed to be comprehensive and reliable. These selected voluntary consultants were asked to add further candidates who should be queried, as well as to eliminate from further consideration those persons whose professional and other qualifications did not seem, in their view, to meet the minimum standards of their field.

Questionnaires were then mailed to over 6,000 persons during an 18-month period in calendar years 1964 and 1965. Approximately 3,600 replies were received. Only four persons indicated that they did not wish to be included in the directory; their wishes were followed. No doubt, among those who did not reply are specialists who would meet the criteria for inclusion. We believe that the 1,884 specialists entered in this directory represent a substantial portion of the total number of such specialists.

The biobibliographical data on about 1,700 individuals who responded, but whose names are not included here, are also kept on file in the Hispanic Foundation. These files are open for public reference use, on permission from the Director of the Hispanic Foundation. Among them are questionnaires returned by persons who stated frankly that they did not consider themselves either Latin Americanists or qualified by language ability to work in or on the area. In addition are materials furnished by various others whose qualifications did not wholly meet directory criteria.

These criteria for inclusion in the published directory generally conform to those established for other comparable professional rosters. Our guiding principle was, in cases of doubt, exclude rather than include. The directory was conceived to provide public and private agencies and institutions, often for their staffing and other specific needs, with reliable information on clearly specialized professional personnel. The possibility that persons listed might actually undertake outside assignments played some part in the selection process, but by no means was it a sole determining factor.

U.S. citizens and non-U.S. citizens who are permanently resident in the United States were considered for inclusion. Foreign nationals, even temporarily resident, were normally excluded. Since most of those born before 1895 indicated that they were retired and were not actively seeking further assignments, they were, except for unusual circumstances, omitted.

For persons principally or exclusively associated with academic pursuits, it was reluctantly decided to omit those who had not earned a doctor's degree or its equivalent when our files were closed about February 1, 1965. An exception was made in a few instances where the master's is normally the highest degree in a technical field or subspecialty. The staff of the directory made every effort to ascertain the degree status of numerous Ph. D. candidates, but where there was no positive confirmation that the degree had actually been granted, such persons were omitted from this edition of the directory.

The following parallel criteria were used for those not clearly or primarily engaged in university or other academic pursuits:

1. Achievement, by reason of experience and training, of a stature in the social sciences and humanities at least equivalent to that associated with the doctorate degree, coupled with presently continued activity in such work;
2. Research activity of high quality in the social sciences and humanities as evidenced by publication in reputable scholarly journals; or, research activity of high quality in those disciplines as evidenced by the consensus of the individual's peers;
3. Employment in a position of substantial responsibility requiring specialized knowledge and experience of approximately the extent described for (1) and (2);
4. Strong recommendations for inclusion, on special grounds, by recognized authorities in the same field or activity.

The principal source used for compiling the individual biobibliographical entries was information submitted on the questionnaires. The entries should not be considered as having been officially "verified" by the Library of Congress. When the respondent did not provide complete data, standard biographical reference sources and the Library's collections were used whenever possible to supplement the information.

Entries are arranged alphabetically by name. They are indexed at the close of the volume by general discipline or activity. A person with recognized competence in two fields is listed under each in the index.

The standard entry usually contains the following data, in this order:

Name, birthplace, birthdate;
Major discipline (in uppercase);
Degrees, including honorary degrees;
Professional career (with present position in uppercase);
Fellowships, honors, awards, committees, consultantships;
Membership in professional and honorary organizations;
Research specialties and interests;
Publications (limited to three);
Language knowledge (see below for discussion);
Linguistic studies;
Home and office addresses.

Linguistic knowledge is a major feature in each specialist's biobibliography. The numbers after the languages in the entry is a self-rating, in response to a rather elaborate question developed in consultation with various specialists. Because of its significance to those seeking such specific data, the language-knowledge question is herewith reproduced:

17. **WHAT IS YOUR NATIVE LANGUAGE?** *(If bilingual, indicate both languages)* _____

PRESENT COMPETENCE IN OTHER LANGUAGES: *(Include English if not a native speaker)*
RATE YOURSELF IN ACCORDANCE WITH THE FOLLOWING LANGUAGE PROFICIENCY CODE IN ALL MODERN FOREIGN LANGUAGES IN WHICH YOU HAVE SOME COMPETENCE.

1. HAVE NO PRACTICAL USABLE PROFICIENCY.
2. ABLE TO READ SIMPLE PROSE WITH DIFFICULTY, TO FOLLOW SIMPLE CONVERSATION, TO USE THE LANGUAGE TO GET AROUND, BUT NOT AS A MEANS OF EXCHANGING IDEAS, TO SPELL OUT SIMPLE PHRASES, BUT NO REAL COMMAND OF GRAMMAR AND SYNTAX.
3. ABLE TO READ NON-TECHNICAL MATERIALS AND TECHNICAL WRITING IN ONE'S FIELD, TO UNDERSTAND ORDINARY NATIVE SPEECH, TO CARRY ON AN EXCHANGE OF IDEAS, THOUGH HALTINGLY, TO WRITE WITH DICTIONARY AND OTHER AIDS.
4. HAVE FLUENCY, ACCURACY AND RANGE ADEQUATE FOR ALL NORMAL PROFESSIONAL AND SOCIAL SITUATIONS.
5. HAVE THE FLUENCY, ACCURACY AND RANGE OF AN EDUCATED NATIVE USER OF THE LANGUAGE.

CHECK THE MOST APPROPRIATE NUMBER IN EACH ASPECT OF EACH LANGUAGE.

LANGUAGES	READING					UNDERSTANDING THE SPOKEN LANGUAGE					SPEAKING					WRITING				
	1	2	3	4	5	1	2	3	4	5	1	2	3	4	5	1	2	3	4	5
SPANISH																				
PORTUGUESE																				
FRENCH																				
OTHERS *(List below)*																				

It would not be possible to compile a work of this scope and complexity without the guidance and assistance of many public and private institutions. We would especially like to thank the following institutions for their valuable contributions to the directory: American Anthropological Association, American Economic Association, American Historical Association, Association of American Geographers, Center for Applied Linguistics of the Modern Language Association of America, Conference on Latin American History, National Science Foundation, Overseas Educational Service (New York City), Business Council for International Understanding, Inc. (American University), and the Conference Board-Associated Research Councils. Various officials in the U.S. Office of Education were uniformly helpful on administrative and substantive matters.

Numerous individuals similarly gave generously of their time and knowledge to aid the directory enterprise. We are especially appreciative of help from a long list of professional friends who frankly, discreetly, and anonymously evaluated their colleagues during various selection processes.

Finally, a special word of thanks is due the Ford Foundation. It generously permitted a portion of the funds it made available to the Hispanic Foundation in 1964 for various programs to be used to defray publication costs of the directory.

HOWARD F. CLINE
Director
Hispanic Foundation

List of Abbreviations

A.B.	Bachelor of Arts
Ala.	Alabama
A.M.	Master of Arts
Apr.	April
Apt.	Apartment
Ariz.	Arizona
Ark.	Arkansas
Assoc.	Associate
Asst.	Assistant
Aug.	August
Ave.	Avenue
b.	born
B.A.	Bachelor of Arts
B. Arch.	Bachelor of Architecture
B.B.A.	Bachelor of Business Administration
B.C.L.	Bachelor of Civil Law
B.C.P.	Bachelor of City Planning
B.D.	Bachelor of Divinity
B.F.A.	Bachelor of Fine Arts
Bldg.	Building
Blvd.	Boulevard
B. Mus.	Bachelor of Music
B.S.	Bachelor of Science
B.S.F.S.	Bachelor of Science in Foreign Science
Calif.	California
Chmn.	Chairman
Coll.	College
Colo.	Colorado
Conn.	Connecticut
Ct.	Court
C.Z.	Canal Zone
D.C.	District of Columbia
Dec.	December
Del.	Delaware
Dept.	Department
D.F.	Distrito Federal

Dir.	Director
Div.	Division
Dr.	Drive
D.S.S.	Doctor of Social Science
Dto.	Departamento
Ed. D.	Doctor of Education
Feb.	February
Fla.	Florida
Ga.	Georgia
Ill.	Illinois
Inc.	Incorporated
Ind.	Indiana
Instr.	Instructor
Jan.	January
J.D.	Doctor of Laws
Jur. D.	Doctor of Laws
J.U.D.	Doctor of Canon and Civil Laws
J.S.D.	Doctor of Juristic Science
Kans.	Kansas
Ky.	Kentucky
La.	Louisiana
Lectr.	Lecturer
L.H.D.	Doctor of Humanities
Lit. D.	Doctor of Literature
Litt. D.	Doctor of Letters
LL.B.	Bachelor of Laws
LL.D.	Doctor of Laws
LL.M.	Master of Laws
Ltd.	Limited
M.A.	Master of Arts
M.A.L.S.	Master of Arts in Library Science
Mar.	March
M. Arch.	Master of Architecture
Mass.	Massachusetts
M.C.P.	Master of City Planning
Md.	Maryland
M. Ed.	Master of Education
M.F.	Master of Forestry
M.F.A.	Master of Fine Arts

Mich.	Michigan
Minn.	Minnesota
Miss.	Mississippi
M. Mus.	Master of Music
Mo.	Missouri
Mont.	Montana
M.R.P.	Master of Regional Planning
M.S.L.S.	Master of Science in Library Science
M.S.S.	Master of Social Science
M.S.W.	Master of Social Work
Mt.	Mount
N.C.	North Carolina
N. Dak.	North Dakota
NE.	Northeast
Nebr.	Nebraska
Nev.	Nevada
N.H.	New Hampshire
N.J.	New Jersey
N. Mex.	New Mexico
Nov.	November
NW.	Northwest
N.Y.	New York
Oct.	October
Okla.	Oklahoma
Oreg.	Oregon
Pa.	Pennsylvania
Ph. B.	Bachelor of Philosophy
Ph. D.	Doctor of Philosophy
Pl.	Place
P.R.	Puerto Rico
Prof.	Professor
Rd.	Road
R.F.D.	Rural Free Delivery
R.I.	Rhode Island
Rm.	Room
S.A.	Sociedad Anónima
S.B.	Bachelor of Science
S.C.	South Carolina
S. Dak.	South Dakota

SE.	Southeast
Sept.	September
S.J.D.	Doctor of Juristic Science
Sq.	Square
St.	Street
S.T.B.	Bachelor of Sacred Theology
S.T.D.	Doctor of Sacred Theology
SW.	Southwest
Tenn.	Tennessee
Ter.	Terrace
Tex.	Texas
Th. B.	Bachelor of Theology
Th. D.	Doctor of Theology
U.	University
UNESCO	United Nations Educational, Scientific, and Cultural Organization
U.S.	United States
Va.	Virginia
V.I.	Virgin Islands
Vis.	Visiting
Vt.	Vermont
Wash.	Washington
Wis.	Wisconsin
W. Va.	West Virginia
Wyo.	Wyoming

Biobibliographies

A

ABRAHAM, WILLIAM I., b. Philadelphia, Pa., Mar. 3, 1919. ECONOMICS. A.B., U. of Pa., 1940; M.B.A., U. of Chicago, 1942; Ph. D., Columbia U., 1953. Statistician and economist, United Nations, 1946–61; adviser, Economic Commission for Latin America (Santiago, Chile), 1955–56; PROF., ECONOMICS, N.Y.U., 1961– . Consultant, U.S. Agency for International Development; consultant, National Planning Association; organizer, United Nations Latin American National Accounts Seminar (Rio de Janeiro), June 1959. Membership: American Economic Association; American Statistical Association; International Association for Research in Income and Wealth; Society for International Development. Research: economic development; international economic relations; social accounting; Latin American economic and statistical problems, especially national income accounting. Author: Methods of National Income Estimation (1955); Saving Patterns in Latin America (Economic Development and Cultural Change, July 1964). Co-editor and contributor: Structural Interdependence and Economic Development (1963). Language: Spanish 3,2,2,2; French 2,2,1,1; German 3,3,3,3. Home: 25 Old Mill Rd., Great Neck, N.Y. Office: Graduate School, N.Y.U., Washington Sq., New York 3.

ABRAHAMS, ALLEN E., b. Ithaca, N.Y., Nov. 6, 1926. ECONOMICS AND ENGINEERING. B.S., U. of Md., 1949; M.S., Stevens Institute of Technology, 1954; Ph. D., N.Y.U., 1960. Asst. prof., Oreg. State U., 1960–61; manager, Commercial Development, Witco Chemical Company, Inc., 1961–63; PRESIDENT, A.E.A. INDUSTRIAL AND ECONOMIC SERVICES (BROOKLYN, N.Y.), 1963– ; ASSOC. PROF., INDUSTRIAL MANAGEMENT, POLYTECHNIC INSTITUTE OF BROOKLYN, 1963– . Consultant, Asimow Project, U. of Calif., Los Angeles (Brazil), 1964; consultant on Latin American projects, International Ore and Fertilizer Corporation (N.Y.). Membership: American Association for the Advancement of Science; American Association of University Professors; American Chemical Society; American Economics Association; American Marketing Association; Chemical Industries Association; Society for International Development. Research: technical-economic analysis; economic development; industry and market studies; project feasibility studies for various products in Latin America; small industry development in rural areas in Brazil. Author: Growth of Competition in the Nitrogen Industry (American Chemical Society, Mar. 1961); The Impact of Tariff Revision and International Competition on the Chemical Industry (American Chemical Society, Sept. 1962); Needed: New Disciplines in Chemical Marketing (Proceedings, American Marketing Association, June 1963). Language: Spanish 2,2,1,1; Portuguese 3,3,3,2; French 3,3,2,2. Home: 270 Jay St., Brooklyn, N.Y. 11201. Office: A.E.A. Industrial and Economic Services, Inc., P.O. Box 1181, Brooklyn, 11201.

ABREU, MARIA ISABEL, b. Rio Prêto, Minas Gerais, Brazil, Oct. 8, 1919. BRAZILIAN LITERATURE AND LANGUAGE. Dr. em Direito, U. of Minas Gerais, 1942; M.A., Columbia U., 1957. Education supervisor, Ministry of Education (Brazil), 1944–56; teacher, Municipality of Rio de Janeiro, 1953–56; lectr., Ministry of Education (Brazil), 1955, 1956, 1960; lectr., N.Y.U., 1958–59; education supervisor, Ministry of Education (Brazil), 1959–61; ASST. PROF., PORTUGUESE, GEORGETOWN U., 1961– ; lectr., Loyola U. (Md.), 1962; vis. prof., Columbia U., Summers 1962, 1963. U.S. Dept. of State fellow, 1948; La. State U. fellow, 1949; U. of Chile fellow, 1950; British Council fellow, 1951; CAPES fellow, Columbia U., 1956–58; Research and Bibliography Committee of Portuguese, Modern Language Association. Membership: American Association of Teachers of Spanish and Portuguese; American Association of University Professors; Asociación de Lingüística y Filología de América Latina; Modern Language Association. Research: linguistics applied to the teaching of Portuguese; Portuguese structure for the preparation of text books. Author: Devemos ensinar gramática nos cursos de inglês? (Escola Secundária, Mar. 1961). Language: Spanish 4,3,2,2; Portuguese 5,5,5,5; French 4,2,2,2; Italian 1,1,1,1. Linguistic studies: English; Portuguese; Spanish. Home: Arlington Towers T–544, Arlington 9, Va. Office: Institute of Languages and Linguistics, Georgetown U., Washington, D.C. 20007.

ADAMS, ELEANOR BURNHAM, b. Cambridge, Mass. HISTORY. A.B., Radcliffe Coll., 1931; Centro de Estudios Históricos, U. of Madrid, 1931–32. Investigator, historian, Carnegie Institution of Washington, 1934–49; Div. of Manuscripts, Bancroft Library, U. of Calif., Berkeley, 1950; RESEARCH ASSOC. IN HISTORY, U. OF N. MEX., 1951– . Research: archival research in Mexico; specialization in New Spain, New Mexico, and Maya area. Author: A Bio-Bibliography of Franciscan Authors in Colonial Central America

(1953). Co-author: Don Diego Quijada, Alcalde Mayor de Yucatán (1938) ; Documentos para la historia del México colonial (1955). Language: Spanish 5,5,4,4 ; Portuguese 3,3,2,2 ; French 4,3,3,2 ; Italian 4,3,3,2 ; Latin 3,-,-,-. Home: 413 Bryn Mawr Dr., SE., Albuquerque, N. Mex. Office: Library 217, U. of N. Mex., Albuquerque.

ADAMS, HENRY E., b. Ancon, C.Z., July 23, 1940. BIBLIOGRAPHY. B.S., Georgetown U., 1963. ASST. TO THE EDITOR, HANDBOOK OF LATIN AMERICAN STUDIES, HISPANIC FOUNDATION, LIBRARY OF CONGRESS, 1963- . Membership: Academy of Political Science ; American Historical Association ; Conference on Latin American History ; Inter-American Council (Washington, D.C.). Research: descriptive and applied linguistics ; socio-linguistic study of a Brazilian idiolect. Co-contributor: Bibliography and General Works Section (in Handbook of Latin American Studies, 1964, 1965). Language: Spanish 5,5,5,5 ; Portuguese 5,5,5,5 ; French 4,4,4,4 ; Dutch 1,1,1,1 ; German 2,2,2,1 ; Italian 3,3,4,4. Linguistic studies: Guaymí ; Portuguese. Home: 1630 Fitzgerald Lane, Alexandria, Va. Office: Hispanic Foundation, Library of Congress, Washington, D.C. 20540.

ADAMS, RICHARD EDWARD WOOD, b. Kansas City, Mo., July 17, 1931. ANTHROPOLOGY. B.A., U. of N. Mex., 1953 ; M.A., Harvard U., 1960 ; Ph. D., 1963. Archeologist, Tikal Project (Guatemala), Museum, U. of Pa., 1958 ; salesman, Future Planning Corporation, 1958-59 ; ceramic analyst, archeologist, Peabody Museum, Harvard U., 1961-63 ; ASST. PROF., ANTHROPOLOGY, U. OF MINN., 1963- . U.S. Dept. of State exchange fellow (Mexico), 1953 ; research fellow, Altar de Sacrificios Project (Guatemala), Peabody Museum, Harvard U., 1961-63. Membership: American Anthropological Association ; International Congress of Americanists ; Society for American Archaeology. Research: Middle American archeology ; culture dynamics ; culture change ; analysis of culture patterns. Author: Temple I (str. 5D-1) : Post-Constructional Activities (Tikal Reports, U. of Pa., 1961) ; The Ceramic Sequence at Altar de Sacrificios and Its Implications (Actas, XXXV Congress of Americanists, 1962) ; Seibal: Una secuencia cerámica y un mapa nuevo (Estudios de Cultura Maya, 1963). Language: Spanish 5,5,4,4 ; German 3,2,1,1. Home: 1357 Beech St., St. Paul 6, Minn. Office: Dept. of Anthropology, U. of Minn., Minneapolis 14.

ADAMS, RICHARD NEWBOLD, b. Ann Arbor, Mich., Aug. 4, 1924. ANTHROPOLOGY. A.B., U. of Mich., 1947 ; M.A., Yale U., 1949 ; Ph. D., 1950. Ethnologist, Institute of Social Anthropology, Smithsonian Institution (Guatemala), 1950-51 ; social anthropologist, dir., Institute of Nutrition of Central America and Panama, U.S. Dept. of State (Guatemala), 1951-52 ; scientist, World Health Organization, 1953-56 ; prof., Mich. State U., 1956-62 ; PROF., ANTHROPOLOGY, ASST. DIR., INSTITUTE OF LATIN AMERICAN STUDIES, U. OF TEX., 1962- . Smithsonian Institution grant, 1950-51 ; U.S. Dept. of State grant, 1951-52 ; consultant, U.S. Institute of Social Anthropology Education Mission (Guatemala) ; consultant, Institute of Nutrition of Central America and Panama. Membership: American Anthropological Association ; American Association for the Advancement of Science ; American Ethnological Society ; American Sociological Association ; Sigma Xi ; Society for Applied Anthropology. Research: social and applied anthropology ; public health and nutrition ; Central America. Author: Culture Surveys of Panama-Nicaragua-Guatemala-El Salvador-Honduras (1957) ; A Community in the Andes: Problems and Progress in Muquiyauyo (1959). Co-author: United States University Cooperation in Latin America: A Study Based on Selected Programs in Chile, Bolivia, Mexico and Peru (1960). Language: Spanish 5,5,4,4. Home: 3204 Cherry Lane, Austin, Tex. Office: Institute of Latin American Studies, U. of Tex., Austin.

ADDY, GEORGE MILTON, b. Salt Lake City, Utah, July 6, 1927. HISTORY. B.A., Brigham Young U., 1948 ; M.A., 1950 ; Ph. D., Duke U., 1957. Instr., Brigham Young U., 1957-58 ; asst. prof., 1958-62 ; ASSOC. PROF., HISTORY, BRIGHAM YOUNG U., 1963- . Institute of International Education fellow, 1956 ; Angier B. Duke Memorial fellow, Duke U., 1957 ; American Council of Learned Societies grant-in-aid, 1962. Membership: American Historical Association ; Conference on Latin American History. Research: the enlightenment in Hispanic culture and the 18th century. Author: Reforms of 1771 : First Steps in the Salamancan Enlightenment (Hispanic American Historical Review, Aug. 1961). Language: Spanish 4,3,3,3 ; French 3,2,2,2 ; German 3,1,1,1. Home: 720 No. 1000 East, Provo, Utah. Office: 320A Maeser Bldg., Brigham Young U., Provo.

ADLER, JOHN H., b. Tachau, Czechoslovakia, Nov. 16, 1912. ECONOMICS. Dr. Juris, German U. of Prague, 1937 ; Ph. D., Yale U., 1946. Instr., Oberlin Coll., 1942-44 ; economist, Board of Governors, Federal Reserve System, 1944-45 ; deputy chief, Finance Div., U.S. War Dept. (Austria), 1945-47 ; economist, Federal Reserve Bank (N.Y.), 1947-50 ; economist, International Bank for Reconstruction and Development, 1950-57 ; guest lectr., Centro de Estudios Monetarios Latinoamericanos (Mexico), 1953, 1960 ; economic adviser, International Bank for Reconstruction and Development, 1957-61 ; lectr., School of Advanced International Studies, Johns Hopkins U., 1958- ; DIR., ECONOMIC DEVELOPMENT INSTITUTE OF THE WORLD BANK, 1962- . Membership: American Economic Association ; International Institute of Public Finance ; Royal Economic Society ; Society for International Development. Research: economic development ; public finance, international trade and payments ; Argentina ; Chile. Co-author: Public Finance in a Developing Country—El Salvador. A Case Study (1951) ; Public Finance and Economic Development in Guatemala (1952) ; The Pattern of United States Import Trade Since 1923 (1952). Language: Spanish 3,3,3,3 ; Portuguese 2,1,1,1 ; French 2,2,2,2 ; German 5,5,5,5. Home: 5620 Western Ave., Chevy Chase, Md. 20015. Office: Economic Development Institute, 1818 H St., NW., Washington, D.C. 20433.

AGUILAR, LUIS ENRIQUE, b. Manzanillo, Cuba, June 16, 1926. HISTORY. LL. D., U. of Havana, 1949 ; LL. D., U. of Madrid,

1950; American U. Prof., Oriente U. (Cuba), 1952–56; prof., Columbia U., 1961–62; PROF., LATIN AMERICAN HISTORY, GEORGETOWN U., 1962– . Membership: American Historical Association. Research: historical and social factors that formed the Cuban nation; role of universities in Latin American political life. Author: Pasado y ambiente en el proceso cubano (1957); La agonía de la democracia en Latino América (Cuadernos, Oct. 1962); The Shadow of Cuba (New Leader, Sept. 1962). Language: Spanish 5,5,5,5; Portuguese 3,3,3,1; French 4,4,4,2. Home: 6836 Tulip Hill Ter., Washington, D.C. 20016. Office: Dept. of History, Georgetown U., Washington, 20007.

AGUILERA, FRANCISCO, b. Concepción, Chile, Oct. 3, 1899. SPANISH AMERICAN LITERATURE. B. Humanities, U. of Chile, 1916; B.A., Ind. U., 1920; Yale U., 1922–25, 1930–32. Dir. General, Secondary Education, Ministry of Education, Government of Chile, 1928; asst. prof., U. of Chile, 1928–30; instr., Yale U., 1930–35; asst. chief, Div. of Intellectual Cooperation, Pan American Union, 1935–44; SPECIALIST IN HISPANIC CULTURE, HISPANIC FOUNDATION, LIBRARY OF CONGRESS, 1944– ; editor, Handbook of Latin American Studies, 1948–58; lectr., George Washington U., 1956; CURATOR, ARCHIVE OF HISPANIC LITERATURE ON TAPE, 1958– ; vis. prof., U. of Wash., National Defense Education Act Institute, Summer 1959. Advisory Board, Handbook of Latin American Studies, secretary; Advisory Board, Odyssey Review; Team for Book Survey in Latin America, Franklin Publications, Inc.-Library of Congress, 1961. Membership: Academy of American Franciscan History; American Association of Teachers of Spanish and Portuguese; Hispanic Society of America; Instituto de Estudios Madrileños; Instituto Internacional de Literatura Iberoamericana; Sociedad Geográfica de Lima. Research: poetry; Hispanic literature; Spanish language teaching; Latin American bibliography; inter-American library cooperation. Author: Cervantes in the Library of Congress (1960). Co-author: Introducción a la historia de la América Latina (1928); New World Spanish on RCA Victor Records (1945). Language: Spanish 5,5,5,5; Portuguese 5,4,3,2; French 5,4,3,3. Home: 2817 18th St. NW., Washington, D.C. 20009. Office: Hispanic Foundation, Library of Congress, Washington, 20540.

AHUMADA, RODOLFO, b. San Diego, Calif., Aug. 6, 1927. PHILOSOPHY. B.A., Mexico City Coll., 1950; M.A., 1951; Ph. D., U. of Southern Calif., 1963. Instr., U. of the Americas, 1954–58; instr., U. of Southern Calif., 1960–63; asst. prof., Calif. State Coll., 1963–64; ASST. PROF., PHILOSOPHY, MIAMI-DADE JUNIOR COLL., 1964– . Delegate, Interamerican Congress of Philosophy, 1957; Mexico City Coll. fellow, 1958–59. Membership: American Philosophical Association; International Phenomenological Society; Phi Epsilon Theta; Philosophical Society of the University of Southern California. Research: Latin American thought; philosophy of Andrés Bello and its origins in the Scotch School of Common Sense; concepts of value in the philosophies of Antonio Caso and José Vasconcelos. Author: Descartes and the Relationship of Dreams to the Problem of Reality (1956). Language: Spanish 5,5,5,4; Portuguese 2,2,1,1; French 3,3,2,2; German 2,1,1,1. Home: Apt. 5, 780 NE. 122d St., North Miami, Fla. Office: Dept. of Philosophy, Miami-Dade Junior Coll., 11380 NW. 27th Ave., Miami, Fla., 33167.

AKIN, WALLACE ELMUS, b. Murphysboro, Ill., May 18, 1923. GEOGRAPHY. B.A., Southern Ill. U., 1948; M.A., Ind. U., 1949; Ph. D., Northwestern U., 1952. Field Team Chief, Dept. of Agriculture and Commerce (P.R.), 1950–51; instr., Northwestern U., 1951–52; instr., U. of Ill., 1952–53; PROF., HEAD, GEOGRAPHY, DRAKE U., 1953– . Consultant, Iowa Natural Research Council, 1954–60; Fulbright research scholar, U. of Copenhagen, 1961–62; chmn., International Relations Committee, Soil Conservation Society of America, 1963–64. Membership: Arctic Institute of North America; Association of American Geographers; Iowa Academy of Science; Royal Danish Geograpical Society; Soil Conservation Society of America. Research: water and land resources development; land classification and reclamation. Author: Flood Plain Regulation in Iowa (1961); The Dairy Industry of the San Juan Area (in Symposium on the Geography of Puerto Rico, 1955); Reclamation of the Danish Heath (Journal of Soil and Water Conservation, May-June 1963). Language: Spanish 3,2, 2,3; Portuguese 2,1,1,1; French 2,1,1,1; Danish 4,3,3,3; German 3,2,2,1; Norwegian 4,3,3,3; Swedish 3,2,2,2. Home: 4418 University Ave., Des Moines, Iowa, 50311. Office: Dept. of Geography, Drake U., Des Moines, 50311.

ALDEN, DAURIL, b. San Francisco, Calif., Jan. 12, 1926. HISTORY. A.B., U. of Calif., Berkeley, 1950; M.A., 1952; Ph. D., 1959. Instr., U. of Wash., 1959–60; asst. prof., U. of Wash., 1960–64; vis. asst. prof., U. of Calif., Berkeley, 1962–63; ASSOC. PROF., HISTORY, U. OF WASH., 1964– . Doherty fellow (Brazil), 1957–58; Social Science Reseach Council fellow, 1958; American Philosophical Society summer grant, 1962. Membership: Conference on Latin American History; Pacific Coast Conference of Latin American Studies. Research: colonial Brazil; administrative and economic history of Brazil; Mexico. Author: Manuel Luis Vieira: An Entrepreneur in Rio de Janeiro During Brazil's Eighteenth Century Agricultural Renaissance (Hispanic American Historical Review, Nov. 1959); The Undeclared War of 1773–1777: Climax of Luso-Spanish Platine Rivalry (Hispanic American Historical Review, Feb. 1961); The Population of Brazil in the Late Eighteenth Century: A Preliminary Study (Hispanic American Historical Review, May 1963). Language: Spanish 4,3,3,3; Portuguese 4,4,4,3; French 3,3,1,1. Home: 8002 38th Ave., NE., Seattle, Wash. Office: Dept. of History, U. of Wash., Seattle 5.

ALDRICH, EARL MAURICE, JR., b. Portland, Oreg., Feb. 13, 1929. SPANISH AMERICAN LITERATURE. B.A., U. of Oreg., 1951; M.A., Mexico City Coll., 1952; Ph. D., Ind. U., 1960. Dir., Ind. U. Junior Year to Peru, Universidad de San Marcos, 1959–60; ASST. PROF., SPANISH, U. OF WIS., 1960– . Contributing editor, Handbook of Latin American Studies. Membership: American Association of Teachers of Spanish and Portuguese; Association for Latin American Studies. Research: literature, culture, and history of Peru and Mexico; Peruvian short story. Author: The Quechua World of José María Arguedas (Hispania, Mar. 1962); El don cuentístico de Ciro Alegría (Hispanófila, Sept. 1963); Observations on the Contemporary Peruvian Short Story (Journal of Inter-American Studies, Oct. 1963). Language: Spanish 5,5,5,5; Portuguese 4,3,2,2; French 3,2,2,2. Home: 4905 Waukesha St., Madison, Wis., 53705. Office: Dept. of Spanish and Portuguese, U. of Wis., Madison.

ALEGRÍA, FERNANDO, b. Santiago, Chile, Sept. 26, 1918. SPANISH AMERICAN LITERATURE. Ph. D., U. of Calif., 1947. PROF., SPANISH, U. OF CALIF., BERKELEY, 1947– . Guggenheim fellow, 1947–48. Membership: Instituto Internacional de Literatura Iberoamericana. Research: history and literature of Chile and Central American area. Author: Walt Whitman en Hispanoamérica (1954); Caballo de copas (1957); Breve historia de la novela hispanoamericana (1960). Language: Spanish 5,5,5,5; Portuguese 3,3,3,3; French 3,3,3,3; Italian 3,3,3,3. Home: 55 Arlmonte Dr., Berkeley, Calif. Office: Dept. of Spanish, U. of Calif., Berkeley.

ALEGRÍA, RICARDO E., b. San Juan, P.R., Apr. 14, 1921. ANTHROPOLOGY. B.A., U. of P.R., 1943; M.A., U of Chicago, 1947; Harvard U., 1952–53. Dir., Archaeological Research Center and Museo de Antropología, U. of P.R., 1946–55; DIR., INSTITUTO DE CULTURA PUERTORRIQUEÑA, 1955– . Guggenheim fellow, 1951–53. Membership: American Anthropological Association; American Archeological Society; Hispanic Institute (New York). Research: West Indian archeology and folklore. Author: Historia de nuestros indios (1950); La Fiesta de Santiago apóstol en Loíza Aldea (1954). Language: Spanish 5,5,5,5; Portuguese 3,3,1,1; French 2,2,1,1. Home: 225 Parque St., P.R. Office: Instituto de Cultura Puertorriqueña, San Juan, P.R.

ALERS, J. OSCAR, b. New York, N.Y., Apr. 15, 1933. SOCIOLOGY. B.A., City Coll. (N.Y.), 1955; M.A., Harvard U. 1959; Ph. D., Cornell U., 1965. Research asst., City Coll. (N.Y.), 1954–55; lectr., 1958; research asst., Harvard U., 1958–59; Institute for Social Research, U. of Mich., 1960–61; U.S. AGENCY FOR INTERNATIONAL DEVELOPMENT RESEARCH ASSOC., ANTHROPOLOGY, CORNELL U., 1964– . National Defense Education Act fellow in Latin American Studies, Cornell U., 1961–63. Membership: American Sociological Association. Research: survey research; social factors in economic development in Peru. Author: The Population of Vicos (1964); Evolution and Revolution; Slavery in the Americas (Journal of Social Studies, Spring 1954). Co-author: Attitudes of Whites and Nonwhites Toward Each Other (Sociology and Social Research, May 1956). Language: Spanish 5,5,5,5; Portuguese 3,1,1,1; French 3,3,3,3; German 2,1,1,1. Home: 114 Grandview, Ithaca, N.Y. 14850. Office: Dept. of Anthropology, Cornell U., Ithaca, 14850.

ALERS-MONTALVO, MANUEL, b. San Sebastian, P.R., Dec. 8, 1920. SOCIOLOGY. B.S., City Coll. (N.Y.), 1941; M.A., Columbia U., 1951; Ph. D., Mich. State U., 1953. Rural sociologist, Inter-American Institute of Agricultural Science (Lima, Peru), 1953–55; sociologist, 1955–57; sociologist, head, Economics and Social Science, Inter-American Institute of Agricultural Science (Costa Rica), 1957–62; vis. prof., U. of P.R., 1959, 1961, 1963; PROF., SOCIOLOGY, COLO. STATE U., 1963– . Mich. State U.-Inter-American Institute of Agricultural Science research asst., 1952–53; John Hay Whitney fellow, 1953–54. Membership: American Sociological Society; Rural Sociological Society; Society for Applied Anthropology. Research: cultural change in Costa Rica and Peru. Author: Sociología: Introducción a su uso en programas agrícolas rurales (1960); Estudio sociológico sobre programación en extensión (1963); Social Systems Analysis of Supervised Agricultural Credit in an Andean Community (Rural Sociology, Mar. 1960). Language: Spanish 5,5,5,5; Portuguese 3,3,2,2; French 3,2,2,3. Home: 1504 Pitkin St., Fort Collins, Colo. 80521. Office: Dept. of Sociology, Colo. State U., Fort Collins, 80521.

ALESSANDRO, JOSEPH VINCENT, b. Curwensville, Pa., June 26, 1920. EDUCATION. M. Ed., Pa. State U., 1948; D. Ed., 1954. ASSOC. PROF., EDUCATION, PA. STATE U., 1955– ; dir., Pa. State U. study groups (Latin America), Summers 1958–62; specialist, Survey of Radio Phonics Program, U.S. International Cooperation Administration (Colombia), 1962–63; chief education adviser, U.S. Agency for International Development (Costa Rica), 1963–64. Membership: National Education Association; National Elementary School Principals Association; Phi Delta Kappa. Research: primary and secondary education; educational systems of Latin America. Language: Spanish 4,4,4,4; Portuguese 3,3,3,3; French 2,2,2,2; Italian 5,5,5,5. Home: 209 Homan Ave., State College, Pa. Office: Dept. of Elementary Education, College of Education, Pa. State U., University Park.

ALEXANDER, CHARLES S., b. Santiago, Chile, Dec. 26, 1916. GEOGRAPHY. A.B., U. of Calif., Berkeley, 1947; Ph. D., 1955. Instr., San Francisco State Coll., 1951–52; field work (Venezuela), U. of Calif., Berkeley, 1952; ASSOC. PROF., GEOGRAPHY, U. OF ILL., 1953– ; acting dir., Latin American Studies Center, U. of Ill., 1962–63. Member, Working Group on Geomorphology, Pan-American Institute of Geography and History. Membership: African Studies Association; American Geographical Society; Association of American Geographers; Geological Society of America; Royal African Society; Sigma Xi; Tanganyika Society. Research: physical geography; Venezuela; Mexico; Africa. Author: The Geography of Margarita and Adjacent Islands, Venezuela (1958); The Marine Terraces of Aruba, Bonaire and Curação (Annals, Association of American Geographers, Dec. 1961); Margarita Island, Exporter of People (Journal of Inter-American Studies, Oct. 1961). Language: Spanish 3,3,3,2; French 3,2,2,1; German 3,2,2,1. Home: 2010 Cureton Dr., Urbana, Ill. Office: Dept. of Geography, U. of Ill., Urbana.

ALEXANDER, HUBERT GRIGGS, b. Lincoln, Nebr., Dec. 8, 1909. PHILOSOPHY. B.A., Pomona Coll., 1930; Ph. D., Yale U.,

1934. Instr.-assoc. prof., U. of N. Mex., 1935–48; PROF. CHMN., PHILOSOPHY, U. OF N. MEX., 1948– . Carnegie lectr., Yale U., 1954–55; chmn., 5th Inter American Congress of Philosophy, 1957. Membership: American Philosophical Association; Mountain-Plains Philosophical Conference; Rocky Mountain Council on Lation American Studies; Southwestern Philosophical Society. Research: history of cultures; language, logic, and communication problems; aesthetics; 17th and 18th century Spanish thinkers. Author: Time as Dimension and History (1945). Language: Spanish 3,3,2,2; Portuguese 1,1,1,1; French 5,4,4,3; German 2,2,2,2; Greek 2,-,-,-; Latin 3,-,-,-. Linguistic studies: Navaho. Home: 603 Girard Blvd., NE., Albuquerque, N. Mex. Office: Dept. of Philosophy, U. of N. Mex., Albuquerque.

ALEXANDER, ROBERT J., b. Canton, Ohio, Nov. 26, 1918. ECONOMICS AND POLITICAL SCIENCE. B.A., Columbia U., 1940; M.A., 1941; Ph. D., 1950. Asst. economist, Office of Inter-American Affairs, 1945–46; instr.-PROF., ECONOMICS, RUTGERS U., 1947– ; vis. lectr., Atlanta U., Summer 1949; vis. prof., U. of P.R., Summers 1958, 1959, 1962, Columbia U., 1962–63. Selection Committee, Fulbright Program, 1961–62, and Foreign Area Fellowships, Ford Foundation, 1963–64. Membership: American Economic Association. Research: labor relations and related political and economic problems in Latin America. Author: Communism in Latin America (1957); The Struggle for Democracy in Latin America (1961); Labor Relations in Argentina, Brazil, and Chile (1962). Language: Spanish 4,4,4,3; Portuguse 4,4,3,1; French 4,3,3,2; Italian 3,3,1,1. Home: Box 88A, Route 24, New Brunswick, N.J. Office: Dept. of Economics, Rutgers U., New Brunswick.

ALISKY, MARVIN HOWARD, b. Kansas City, Mo., Mar. 12, 1923. JOURNALISM, COMMUNICATION, AND POLITICL SCENCE. B.A., U. of Tex., 1946; M.J., 1947; Ph. D., 1953. Newscaster, reporter, NBC Regional Network (San Antonio, Tex.), 1947–49; instr., Trinity U. (San Antonio), 1949–50; asst. prof., Ind. U., 1953–57; news correspondent for Ariz. and Mexico, Christian Science Monitor, 1956– ; Latin American news correspondent, NBC Network (N.Y.), Summers 1957, 1963; PROF., COMMUNICATIONS AND POLITICAL SCIENCE, CHMN., MASS COMMUNICATIONS, ARIZ. STATE U., 1957– . News consultant for television (Peru), Summer 1958; U.S. delegate, UNESCO Conference on Mass Media (Quito), Mar. 1960; Smith-Mundt vis. prof., National U. of Nicaragua, Summer 1960; curriculum consultant (Ecuador), 1960; vis. fellow, Princeton U., 1963–64. Membership: American Political Science Association; Association for Education in Journalism; Inter-American Broadcasters Association; Inter-American Press Association; National Society for the Study of Communication; Pi Sigma Alpha; Sigma Delta Chi; Western Political Science Association. Research: journalism and mass communications in Latin America. Author: Latin American Journalistic Bibliography (1958); State and Local Government in Sonora, Mexico (1962). Co-author: The Foreign Press (1963). Language: Spanish 5,5,5,5; Portuguese 3,2,1,1; French 3,3,2,1; Italian 3,2,1,1. Home: 502 Vista del Cerro, Tempe, Ariz., 85281. Office: Dept. of Mass Communications, Ariz. State U., Tempe, 85281.

ALLEGER, DANIEL E., b. East Stroudsburg, Pa., Oct. 18, 1903. SOCIOLOGY. B.S., Pa. State Coll., 1926; M.S., 1943. ASSOC. AGRICULTURAL ECONOMIST, DEPT. OF AGRICULTURAL ECONOMICS, U. OF FLA., 1945– ; chief of party, International Cooperation Administration-U. of Fla. contract (Costa Rica), 1956–60. Consultant, Ministry of Agriculture, Costa Rica. Membership: American Association of University Professors; American Farm Economic Association; Florida Council on Aging; Gerontological Society; International Conference of Agricultural Economists. Research: rural sociology and economics; land tenure; economic development; gerontology. Author: Older People and Their Problems (in 1963 Yearbook of Agriculture, 1963). Co-author: Organización y operación de fincas de caña (1957). Editor: Fertile Lands of Friendship (1962). Language: Spanish 3,3,3,3. Home: R.F.D. 4, Box 168-X, Gainesville, Fla., 32601. Office: 45 B McCarty Hall, U. of Fla., Gainesville, 32603.

ALLEN, CYRIL G., b. Edgerton, Alberta, Canada, Jan. 23, 1919. HISTORY, B.S., Winona State Teachers Coll., 1941; M.A., U. of Minn., 1946; Ph. D., 1949. Instr. U. of Cincinnati,1947–49; asst. prof., Extension Div., U. of Minn., 1949–50; PROF., HISTORY, MANKATO STATE COLL., 1950– . Fund for Advancement of Education fellow (Central America, Mexico), 1954–55. Membership: American Historical Association; Conference on Latin American History; Mississippi Valley Historical Association; Society for the History of Discoveries. Research: Central American history, 19th and 20th centuries; United States-Central American relations. Author: U. of Minn. Latin American History Correspondence Study Courses (1952–53); Felix Belly: Nicaraguan Canal Promoter (Hispanic American Historical Review, Feb. 1957). Language: Spanish 3,3,3,2; Portuguese 3,2,1,1; French 3,1,1,1; German 3,2,1,1,. Home: Waterville, Minn. Office: Dept. of History, Mankato State Coll., Mankato, Minn.

ALLEN, RICHARD, F., b. Norman, Okla., Feb. 21, 1935. SPANISH AMERICAN LITERATURE. B.A., U. of Okla., 1956; National U. of Mexico, Summers 1953–55, 1957; M.A., U. of Md., 1958; Ph. D., 1961. Instr., U. of Md., 1956–61; translator, U.S. Dept. of the Interior, 1958–60; asst. prof., Wake Forest Coll., 1961–62; U. of Toledo, 1962–64; ASST. PROF., SPANISH, IND. U., SOUTH BEND-MISHAWAKA CAMPUS, 1964– . Chmn., Membership Committee, Midwest Council for Latin American Studies; consultant, Libby Owens Ford (Toledo, Ohio). Membership: American Association of University Professors; College English Association; Gamma Theta Upsilon; Modern Language Association; Phi Kappa Phi; Phi Sigma Iota; Sigma Delta Pi. Research: Latin American studies; social and political thought in the novels of Rómulo Gallegos. Language: Spanish 5,5,5,5; Portuguese 3,3,3,3; French 3,3,3,3. Linguistic studies: English; French; Spanish. Office: Dept. of Spanish, Ind. U., South Bend-Mishawaka Campus, South Bend.

ALLEN, ROBERT LORING, b. Trenton, Mo., July 10, 1921. ECONOMICS. A.B., U. of Redlands, 1947; M.A., Harvard U., 1950; Ph. D., 1953. Economist, U.S. Government, 1951–56; assoc. prof., U. of Va., 1956–59; PROF., ECONOMICS, U. of OREG., 1959– ; vis. prof., Universidad de los Andes (Venezuela), 1964–65. Membership: American Economic Association. Research: regional economics; economic history and development; comparative systems; international commerce; economy of Venezuela and the Andean region; higher education in Venezuela. Author: Soviet Influence in Latin America (1959); Las cuentas regionales, anuario (1963). Co-author: Economic Policies Toward Less Developed Countries (1962). Language: Spanish 4,4,4,4; French 2,2,2,2. Home: 3022 Onyx Pl., Eugene, Oreg. Office: Dept. of Economics, U. of Oreg., Eugene.

ALPERT, LEO, b. Boston, Mass., Oct. 31, 1915. GEOGRAPHY AND METEOROLOGY. B.S., Mass., State Coll., Bridgewater, 1937; M.A., Clark U., 1939; Ph. D., 1946. Weather officer, Air Weather Service, U.S. Air Force (C.Z., N.C.), 1941–46; supervisory physical geographer, Latin America, U.S. Army Map Service (Washington, D.C.), 1946–61; consulting meteorologist, private employment, 1946– ; climatologist, Cambridge Research Laboratories, U.S. Air Force (Bedford, Mass.), 1952; tropical specialist, U.S. Army Research Office (Washington, D.C.), 1961–63; CHIEF SCIENTIST, TROPICAL RESEARCH, U.S. ARMY RESEARCH AND DEVELOPMENT OFFICE (C.Z.), 1963– . Consultant, Puerto Rico Water Resources Authority, Ponce Cement Company, United Fruit Company, Brazilian Power and Light Company, Santa María Coffee Growers (Guatemala), Cámara de Café (Ecuador), California Texas Oil Corporation. Membership: American Geophysical Union; American Meteorological Society; Association of American Geographers; Society of American Military Engineers. Research: climatology; tropical environment of Latin America; environmental testing; tropical meteorology. Author: The Climate of the Galapagos Islands (1963); Silver Iodide Cloud Seeding in Puerto Rico (Transactions, American Geophysical Union, Apr. 1955); Total Environmental Observation and Instrumentation Program for the Canal Zone (U.S. Army Research and Development Office, Canal Zone, Nov. 1963). Language: Spanish 3,2,2,2. Home: 542A Curundu Heights, C.Z. Office: U.S. Army Research and Development Office, P.O. Drawer 942, Fort Clayton, C.Z.

ALSOP, JOHN RICHARD, b. Salinas, Calif., Apr. 12, 1930. LINGUISTICS. B.S., U. of Calif., 1953; B.D., Fuller Theological Seminary, 1956; Summer Institute of Linguistics, 1957, 1958. Youth dir., Mayflower Church (Pacific Grove, Calif.), 1956–57; engineer, Calif. State Health Dept., 1957–58; MISSIONARY, LINGUIST, SUMMER INSTITUTE OF LINGUISTICS (MEXICO), 1959– ; teacher, Summer Institute of Linguistics Programs, 1960, 1962–64. Research: descriptive linguistics; computational linguistics; automatic phonemic analysis; Zapotec Indians of the Isthmus of Tehuantepec, Mexico. Author: Index to the Arndt and Gingricht Greek Lexicon (Wycliffe Bible Translators, 1964). Language: Spanish 4,4,4,4; Zapotec 4,4,4,3. Linguistic studies: Zapotec. Home: 417 Lincoln Ave., Salinas, Calif. Office: Summer Institute of Linguistics, Box 1960, Santa Ana, Calif.

ALTEN, IVAN JOHN, b. Budapest, Hungary, June 12, 1916. CITY AND REGIONAL PLANNING. B.A., Royal Hungarian Polytechnic Institute, 1939; M.A., 1940. State architect, State of Virginia, 1940–44; architect-city planner (Richmond, Va.), 1949–56; city planning adviser, U.S. Agency for International Development, 1956–63; ASST. PROF., URBAN PLANNING, MICH. STATE U., 1963– . Membership: American Institute of Architects; American Institute of Planners; American Society of Planning Officials. Research: architecture; history of human settlements; Chile. Author: Kurdish Feudal Economy (1958); Sanandaj—Town Plan (1959); Glossary of Chilean Planning Terms (1962). Language: Spanish 3,4,3,–; French 2,3,2,1; German 5,5,5,5; Hungarian 5,5,5,5; Persian 1,3,2,1. Home: 322 Doty St., Ann Arbor, Mich. Office: School of Urban Planning, Institute for Community Development, Mich. State U., East Lansing.

ALTER, GERALD MILTON, b. Mason City, Iowa, Dec. 15, 1919. ECONOMICS. B.S., Harvard U., 1941; M.P.A., 1948; Ph. D., 1954. Fiscal analyst, U.S. Bureau of the Budget, 1942–45; economist, Federal Reserve Board, 1945–46; economist, U.S. Dept. of Commerce, 1946–47; economist, Federal Reserve Board, 1948–51; asst. to dir., Economic Staff, World Bank, 1953–58; economic adviser, Western Hemisphere, World Bank, 1958–64; DIR. OF OPERATIONS, WESTERN HEMISPHERE, WORLD BANK, 1964– . Fellow, Littauer School, Harvard U., 1941–42; Littauer fellow, Harvard U., 1947–48. Membership: American Economic Association. Research: economic development; economy of Chile, Venezuela, Mexico and Colombia. Author: Development Loans to Private Enterprises in Underdeveloped Countries (1952). Co-author: Economic Development of Venezuela (1961); Latin America's Post War Inflation and Balance of Payments Problems (Federal Reserve Bulletin, Nov. 1948). Language: Spanish 4,4,4,3; French 2,1,1,1. Home: 5124 Linnean Ter., NW., Washington, D.C.

ALTSCHULER, MILTON, b. New York, N.Y., Apr. 9, 1926. ANTHROPOLOGY. A.B., U. of Calif., Los Angeles, 1953; A.M., 1956; Ph. D., U. of Minn., 1964. Instr., U. of Minn. 1961–64; ASST. PROF., ANTHROPOLOGY, U. OF CINCINNATI, 1964– . Doherty fellow (Ecuador), 1958–59; National Institute of Mental Health research grant (Ecuador), 1958–60. Membership: American Anthropological Association; American Ethnological Society; International Congress of Americanists; Society for Applied Anthropology. Research: primitive law and political anthropology; application of linguistic techniques and theories to problems of general cultural analysis. Author: On the Environmental Limitations of Mayan Cultural Development (Southwestern Journal of Anthropology, Summer 1958). Language: Spanish 4,4,4,4; Portuguese 3,2,3,2; French 3,2,3,2; German 3,3,3,3. Linguistic studies: Cayapa. Office: Dept. of Sociology and Anthropology, U. of Cincinnati, Cincinnati, Ohio, 45221.

ALVAREZ-PEDROSO, ANTONIO, b. Havana, Cuba, June 15, 1910. HISTORY AND SPANISH AMERICAN LITERATURE.

LL.D., Havana U., 1934; Ph. D., 1938. Prof. Private School of Law (Havana), 1935-38; prof., Havana Institute, 1938-42; adjunct prof., U. of Havana, 1942-44; prof., U. of Villanueva (Havana), 1946-58; asst prof. U. of Havana, 1952-60; assist. prof., Marshall Coll., 1962-63; ASSOC. PROF., MODERN LANGUAGE, KUTZTOWN STATE COLL., 1963- . Cuban vis. scholar, St. Louis U., 1961-62. Membership: American Association of Teachers of Spanish and Portuguese; Modern Language Association. Research: political and diplomatic relations between the United States and Latin America; Monroe Doctrine and its historic evolution; history and literature of Mexico, Venezuela, Colombia, and Peru. Author: Miguel de Aldama y Alfonso (1948); La civilización maya (Revista de la Habana, May 1946); La civilización azteca (Revista de la Habana, June 1946). Language: Spanish 5,5,5,5. Home: 520 East Walnut St., Kutztown, Pa. Office: Dept. of Modern Languages, Kutztown State Coll., Kutztown.

AMERINGER, CHARLES D., b. Milwaukee, Wis., Sept. 19, 1926. HISTORY. B.A., U. of Wis., 1949; M.A., Fletcher School of Law & Diplomacy, 1950; Ph. D., 1958. Instr., Suffolk U., 1950-51; research analyst, U.S. Dept. of Defense, 1951-59; part-time instr., George Washington U., 1954-55; asst. prof., Bowling Green State U., 1959-63; vis. asst. prof., Pa. State U., 1963-64; ASSOC. PROF., HISTORY, PA. STATE U., 1964- U.S. Dept. of Defense fellow (Mexico), 1956-57; lectr., U.S. Peace Corps, U. of Wis., Milwaukee, 1963. Membership: American Association of University Professors; American Historical Association; Association of Latin American Studies; Conference on Latin American History. Research: United States-Latin American diplomatic history; history of the Caribbean area and the national period; Mexico. Author: The Panama Canal Lobby of Philippe Bunau-Varilla and William Nelson Cromwell (American Historical Review, Jan. 1963). Language: Spanish 4,4,3,4; Portuguese 3,3,3,3; French 2,-,-,-. Office: Dept. of History, Pa. State U., University Park.

ANDERSON, ARTHUR JAMES OUTRAM, b. Phoenix, Ariz., Nov. 26, 1907. ANTHROPOLOGY. A.B., San Diego State Coll., 1930; M.A., Claremont Coll., 1931; Ph. D., U. of Southern Calif., 1940. Assoc. prof.-prof., div. chmn., Eastern N. Mex. Coll., 1938-45; curator, assoc.-in-charge, editor, History and Publications, Museum of N. Mex. and School of American Research, 1945-57; instr., El Camino Coll., 1957-60; ASST. PROF., ANTHROPOLOGY, SAN DIEGO STATE COLL., 1961- . Guggenheim fellow (Spain), 1955, 1960-61. Membership: Pacific Coast Council on Latin American Studies; Sociedad Mexicana de Antropología. Research: pre-Hispanic Mexico; ethnohistory. Co-editor and translator: General History of the Things of New Spain; Florentine Codex, by B. de Sahagún (1950-). Language: Spanish 5,5,5,4; Portuguese 2,2,1,1; French 4,3,3,3; Nahuatl 5,2,2,4. Linguistic studies: Nahuatl. Home: 4411 Hermosa Way, San Diego, Calif. 92103. Office: Dept. of Sociology and Anthropology, San Diego State Coll., San Diego, 92115.

ANDERSON, CHARLES WILLIAM, b. Manitowoc, Wis., June 28, 1934. POLITICAL SCIENCE. B.A., Grinnell Coll., 1955; M.A., Johns Hopkins U., 1957; Ph. D., U. of Wis., 1960. ASSOC. PROF., POLITICAL SCIENCE, U. OF WIS., 1960- . Woodrow Wilson fellow; Danforth fellow; Doherty fellow (Costa Rica), 1958-59; Social Science Research Council grant (Colombia), 1962-63; Social Science Research Council Joint Committee on Latin American Studies; external research consultant, U.S. Dept. of State. Membership: American Political Science Association; American Society for Public Administration; Midwest Conference of Political Scientists. Research: comparative politics; developing areas of Latin America; Mexico; Central America. Author: The Political Economy of Mexico (1963). Language: Spanish 4,4,4,3; Portuguese 3,1,1,1; French 3,2,2,1. Home: 1304 Nishishin Trail, Madison, Wis. 53716. Office: Dept. of Political Science, U. of Wis., Madison, Wis. 53706.

ANDERSON, CONWELL A., b. Sister Bay, Wis., May 24, 1926. HISTORY. B.A., U. of Ala., 1949; M.A., 1950; Ph. D., 1954. Instr., U. of Ala., 1952-54; prof., dean, Mary Hardin-Baylor Coll., 1954-60; PROF., HISTORY, PRESIDENT, JUDSON COLL., 1960- . U. of Ala. graduate fellow. Membership: Conference on Latin American History; Phi Alpha Theta; Sigma Delta Pi. Research: Central America—18th century. Author: Gibraltar: Fortress or Pawn (Southwestern Social Science Quarterly, Dec. 1958). Home and office: Judson Coll., Marion, Ala. 36756.

ANDERSON, DOLE A., b. Sioux City, Iowa, Dec. 4, 1917. ECONOMICS. B.S., U. of Pa., 1940; M.B.A., N.Y.U., 1942; Ph. D., 1950. Instr., N.Y.U., 1941-43; asst. prof., 1946-52; prof., chmn., Instituto Tecnológico de Aeronáutica and Ministério de Aeronáutica (Brazil), 1952-57; economist, J. C. Buckley, Inc. (N.Y.), 1957-59; technical adviser, Universidade da Bahia, Brazil Project, Mich. State U.-U.S. Agency for International Development, 1959-61; CO-DIRECTOR, SÃO PAULO SCHOOL OF BUSINESS ADMINISTRATION, BRAZIL PROJECT, MICH. STATE U.-U.S. AGENCY FOR INTERNATIONAL DEVELOPMENT, 1961- . Membership: Alpha Kappa Psi; American Economic Association; American Society of Traffic and Transportation; Regional Science Association. Research: economic development; transportation economics and management; business administration, particularly curriculum planning for business schools; economy of Brazil. Author: Airline Self-Sufficiency and the Local Air Service Problem (Journal of Air Law & Commerce, Winter 1954); Algunos Aspectos do Desenvolvimento Aéreo no Brasil (Revista Transportes Aéreos, May 1955); The Seasonal Factor in the Brazilian Economy (Revista de Administração de Emprêsas, Oct.-Dec. 1963). Language: Spanish 3,2,2,1; Portuguese 4,5,5,4. Home: American Consul, São Paulo, APO 676, New York, N.Y. Office: Centro de Pesquisas e Publicações, Escola de Administração de Emprêsas, Av. Paulista, 548, São Paulo, Brazil.

ANDERSON, JAMES MAXWELL, b. Seattle, Wash., Apr. 9, 1933. LINGUISTICS. B.A., U. of Wash., 1958; M.A., 1961; Ph. D., 1963. Instr., Instituto Cultural Americano (Mexico, D.F.), 1957; ASST. PROF.,

INSTITUTE OF LANGUAGES AND LINGUISTICS, GEORGETOWN U., 1963– . National Defense Education Act fellow, 1962–63; Fulbright lectr. (Valladolid, Spain), 1964–65. Membership: Modern Language Association; Phi Sigma Iota. Research: Romance languages; structural analysis of syncope in the history of Spanish. Author: Morphophonemics of Gender in Spanish (Lingua, Sept. 1961); Two Analyses of English Consonants (Orbis, 1962); A Study of Syncope in Vulgar Latin (Word, 1964). Language: Spanish 4,–,–,–; Portuguese 2,–,–,–; French 3,–,–,–; German 2,–,–,–; Italian 2,–,–,–. Linguistic studies: English; Spanish. Home: 3616 SW. Othello St., Seattle 6, Wash. Office: Institute of Languages and Linguistics, Georgetown U., Washington, D.C.

ANDERSON, LAMBERT LYLE, b. Chicago, Ill., Mar. 15, 1928. LINGUISTICS. Trainee, Summer Institute of Linguistics (Mexico), 1951–52; TRANSLATOR, LIAISON OFFICER, SUMMER INSTITUTE OF LINGUISTICS (PERU), 1952– . Research: descriptive linguistics; investigation, analysis, translation, and preparation of literacy materials; Ticuna Indians of the Amazon River. Author: Ticuna Vowels: With Special Regard to the System of Five Tonemes (Publicações do Museu Nacional, Brasil, 1959). Language: Spanish 4,4,4,4; Ticuna 4,4,4,4. Linguistic studies: Ticuna. Home: Route 1, Box 333, Oconto Falls, Wis., 54154. Office: Summer Institute of Linguistics, P.O. Box 1960, Santa Ana, Calif., 92702.

ANDERSON, ROBERT R., b. Littleriver, Kans., Apr. 25, 1927. SPANISH AMERICAN LITERATURE. B.A., U. of Denver, 1952; M.A., U. of Ala., 1953; U. of Calif., Berkeley, 1957. Asst. prof., Claremont Men's Coll., 1957–59; U. of Ariz., 1959–61; ASSOC. PROF., ROMANCE LANGUAGES, U. OF ARIZ., 1961– . National Defense Education Act Fellowship Committee, U. of Ariz. Membership: American Association of Teachers of Spanish and Portuguese; Modern Language Association. Research: Spanish American novel; paleography; literature, history, and culture of Mexico. Author: Alfonso X el Sabio and the Renaissance in Spain (Hispania, Sept. 1961). Co-author: Index to El Archivo de Hidalgo del Parral, 1631–1821 (1961). Language: Spanish 5,5,4,4; Portuguese 3,2,2,1; French 3,3,3,3; German 3,3,3,3; Italian 4,3,2,1. Home: 4052 Calle Chica, Tucson, Ariz. Office: Dept. of Romance Languages, U. of Ariz., Tucson.

ANDERSON, ROBERT WILLIAM, b. San Mateo, Calif., July 2, 1926. POLITICAL SCIENCE. M.A., U. of Chicago, 1948; Ph. D. U. of Calif., Berkeley, 1960. Instr., U. of P.R., 1948–50; asst. prof.-assoc. prof., U. of P.R., 1957–62; asst. prof., U. of Calif., Berkeley, 1962–64; acting chmn., Center for Latin American Studies, 1963–64; ASSOC. PROF., CHMN., POLITICAL SCIENCE, U. OF P.R., 1964– . Consultant, Governor's Committee on Civil Rights, Government of P.R., 1958–59; Fulbright lectr. (Peru), 1961. Membership: American Political Science Association; American Society for Public Administration; International Political Science Association; Northern California Political Science Association. Research: political parties in Puerto Rico; comparative public administration in Latin America; Mexico. Author: Los partidos y la representación en el pensamiento político norteamericano (Revista de Ciencias Sociales, Sept. 1959); Los partidos políticos en Puerto Rico: El contenido legal (Revista de Ciencias Sociales, Sept. 1961); Partidos políticos como instituciones: La experiencia puertorriqueña (Memoria del VI Congreso Latinoamericano de Sociología, 1961). Language: Spanish 5,5,5,5; Portuguese 3,3,2,1. Office: Dept. of Political Science, U. of P.R. Río Piedras.

ANDERSON-IMBERT, ENRIQUE, b. Córdoba, Argentina, Feb. 12, 1910. SPANISH AMERICAN LITERATURE. Bachiller, Colegio Nacional de La Plata, 1927; Ph. D., Universidad Nacional de Buenos Aires, 1946. Literary section, La Vanguardia (newspaper), 1931–37; instr., Universidad Nacional de Cuyo, 1940; prof., Universidad Nacional de Tucumán, 1941–47; PROF., ROMANCE LANGUAGES, U. OF MICH., 1947– ; vis. assoc. prof., Columbia U., Harvard U., Princeton U., Duke U., and Smith Coll. Guggenheim fellow, 1954. Membership: American Association of Teachers of Spanish and Portuguese; Instituto Internacional de Literatura Iberoamericana. Research: aesthetics; history of Spanish American literature. Author: El arte de la prosa en Juan Montalvo (1948); Crítica interna (1960); Historia del la literatura hispano-americana (1962). Language: Spanish 5,5,5,5; Portuguese 2,2,2,2; French 2,2,2,2; Italian 2,2,2,2. Home: 1216 Ferdon Rd., Ann Arbor, Mich. Office: Dept. of Romance Languages, U. of Mich., Ann Arbor.

ANDERSSON, THEODORE, b. New Haven, Conn., Feb. 18, 1903. LANGUAGE. B.A., Yale U., 1925; M.A., 1926; Ph. D., 1931. Instr., Yale U., 1927–37; prof., chmn., Romance Languages, American U., 1937–41; assoc. prof.-prof., Wells Coll., 1941–45; chief, Western European Section, Cultural Cooperation, U.S. Dept. of State, 1945–46; assoc. prof., Yale U., 1946–55; assoc. dir.-dir., Master of Arts in Teaching Program, Yale U., 1951–55; assoc. dir.-dir., Foreign Language Program, Modern Language Association, 1955–57; PROF., ROMANCE LANGUAGES, U. OF TEX., 1957–. Educational consultant, Mutual Security Agency (Vietnam), 1952; educational consultant, Ford Foundation (Latin America), 1964–65. Membership: American Association of Teachers of French; American Association of Teachers of Spanish and Portuguese; American Association of University Professors; Comparative Education Society; Modern Language Association; National Education Association. Research: teaching of modern foreign languages; English as a second language; Latin American literature and civilization; foreign languages in the elementary schools. Author: Carlos María Ocantos, Argentine Novelist (1934); The Teaching of Foreign Languages in the Elementary School (1953); The Teacher of Modern Languages (1962). Language: Spanish 4,4,4,4; Portuguese 2,2,1,1; French 4,4,4,4; Danish 3,3,2,2; German 2,2,2,2; Norwegian 3,3,2,2; Swedish 3,3,2,2. Home: 902 Bluebonnet Lane, Austin, Tex. 78704. Office: Dept. of Romance Languages, Batts Hall 112, U. of Tex., Austin, 78712.

ANDIC, FUAT M., b. Istanbul, Turkey, Jan. 31, 1927. ECONOMICS. B.A., U. of Istanbul,

1949; M.A., U. of Mich., 1956; Ph. D., U. of Edinburgh, 1961. Instr., U. of Istanbul, 1949–52; lectr., U. of P.R. (Mayagüez), 1956–59; research fellow, U. of Edinburgh, 1961–62; economist, United Nations (Geneva), 1962–63; ASST. PROF., ECONOMICS, U. of P.R. (MAYAGÜEZ), 1963 ; RESEARCH ASSOC., INSTITUTE OF CARIBBEAN STUDIES, U. OF P.R., 1963–. Institute of Caribbean Studies research grant (French and Dutch West Indies), 1963. Membership: American Economic Association; Royal Economic Society. Research: quantitative research in economic development; the Caribbean area. Author: Distribution of Family Incomes in Puerto Rico (1963) ; Fiscal and Economic Problems of Underdeveloped Countries (Finanzarchiv, 1956) ; A Survey of Ghana's Tax System and Finances (Public Finance, 1963). Language: Spanish 5,5,4,4 ; French 5,5,4,3 ; Turkish 5,5,5,5. Home: 69 De Diego, Oeste, Mayagüez, P.R. Office: Institute of Caribbean Studies, U. of P.R., Río Piedras.

ANDREWS, DAVID HENRY, b. Washington, D.C., Jan. 23, 1933. ANTHROPOLOGY AND SOCIOLOGY. B.A., Ohio Wesleyan U., 1954; M.A., Cornell U., 1959; Ph. D., 1963. Research asst., Cornell U. (Peru), 1960–61; research asst., 1961–62; research assoc. (Peru), 1963–64; RESEARCH ASSOC., ANTHROPOLOGY, CORNELL U., 1964– . Membership: American Anthropological Association; American Ethnological Society; Society for Applied Anthropology. Research: culture change and the process of development; impact of horse complex on indigenous cultures; social structure of Latin America; Peru. Author: Migración e integración en Paucartambo Pasco, Perú (in Migración e Integración en el Perú, 1963). Compiler: Bibliography of Paperback Books on Latin America (1964). Language: Spanish 4,4,3,3. Office: Dept. of Anthropology, 220 Morrill Hall, Cornell U., Ithaca, N.Y. 14850.

ANDREWS, EDWARD WYLLYS, IV, b. Chicago, Ill., Dec. 11, 1916. ANTHROPOLOGY. B.A., Harvard U., 1938; Ph. D., 1942. Archeologist, Carnegie Institution of Washington, 1939–42; U.S. Navy, 1942–46; U.S. Government, 1946–50; ARCHEOLOGIST, MIDDLE AMERICAN RESEARCH INSTITUTE, TULANE U., 1950–; dir., Program of Studies at Dzibilchaltun, Yucatán. Guggenheim fellow, 1952–53; National Science Foundation grant; American Philosophic Society grant; National Geographic Society grant. Membership: American Anthropological Association; Society for American Archaeology. Research: Mesoamerican archeology; hieroglyphic writing; Yucatan peninsula in Mexico. Author: The Archaeology of Southwestern Campeche (1943) ; Excavations at Dzibilchaltun, Northwest Yucatan (Proceedings, American Philosophical Society, 1960) ; Excavaciones en Dzibilchaltun (1962). Language: Spanish 4,4,4,4 ; Portuguese 1,1,1,1 ; French 3,3,3,2. Linguistic studies: Maya. Home: Quinta Mari, Calle 13 No. 203–A, San Cosme, Mérida, Yucatán, México. Office: Middle American Research Institute, Tulane U., New Orleans 18, La.

ANDREWS, NORWOOD HENRY, JR., b. Camden, N.J., Oct. 2, 1934. BRAZILIAN LITERATURE. B.A., Oberlin Coll., 1957 ; M.A., U. of Oreg., 1959 ; Ph. D., U. of Wis.,

1964. ASST. PROF., SPANISH AND PORTUGUESE, VANDERBILT U., 1964– . National Defense Foreign Language fellow, 1959–63. Research: Brazilian novel of transition. Author: An Essay on Camões' Concept of the Epic (Revista de Letras, 1962) ; O Seminarista, de Bernardo Guimarães, romance de transição (Revista de Letras, 1963). Language: Spanish 5,4,3,4 ; Portuguese 5,4,4,4. Office: Dept. of Spanish and Portuguese, Vanderbilt U., Nashville, Tenn. 37203.

ANDREWS, WADE H., b. Ogden, Utah, July 5, 1916. SOCIOLOGY. B.S., Utah State U., 1947; M.S., 1949 ; Ph. D., Mich. State U., 1956. Prof., Ohio State U. and Ohio Agricultural Experiment Station, 1951–63 ; research sociologist, Mich. State U. (Ciudad Juárez, Mexico), Summer 1962; SOCIAL SCIENCE ANALYST, FARM POPULATION BRANCH, U.S. DEPT. OF AGRICULTURE AND COLO. STATE U., 1963– . Consultant, Ohio State Engineering Experimental Station on Highway Research. Membership: American Sociological Association ; Rocky Mountain Social Science Association ; Rural Sociological Society. Research : rural sociology; social change and adjustment in rural communities; population change and its effects on communities; rural and urban migration; community structure in Ciudad Juárez, Mexico. Author: A Case Study of Rural Community Development and Leadership (1958) ; The New Community I, Characteristics of Migrants and Non-migrants in the Rural Fringe of a Metropolitan Area (1963) ; The New Community II, Adjustment of Residents of the Rural Fringe (1963). Language: Spanish 4,4,4,3 ; Portuguese 2,2,2,1 ; French 2,1,1,1. Home: 1112 East Lake Pl., Fort Collins, Colo. 80520. Office: Economic Research Service, U.S. Dept. of Agriculture, Dept. of Sociology, Colo. State U., Fort Collins.

ANGEL, FRANK, JR., b. Las Vegas, N. Mex., Feb. 26, 1916. EDUCATION. B.S., U. of N. Mex., 1947 ; M.S., U. of Wis., 1951 ; Ph. D., U. of Calif., Berkeley, 1959. Dir., Elementary Education and Administrative Services, N. Mex. State Dept. of Education, 1950–54 ; ASSOC. PROF., EDUCATION, U. OF N. MEX., 1955– . John Hay Whitney fellow, U. of Wis. ; consultant, Ministry of Education (Honduras, Costa Rica, Venezuela) ; consultant, U.S. Agency for International Development (Guatemala) ; consultant, N. Mex. State Board of Education ; assoc. dir., Ford Program on University Improvement in Central America, 1962–63. Membership: National Education Association; New Mexico Education Association; Phi Delta Kappa. Research: bilingual education; education of migrant agricultural laborers. Author: Nambé: A Community School in a Spanish-speaking Village (1941). Language: Spanish 5,5,5,5. Home: 1136 Pear Rd., SW., Albuquerque, N. Mex. Office: Coll. of Education, U. of N. Mex., Albuquerque.

ANGELES, PHILIP, b. Mexico, D.F., Oct. 15, 1909. SPANISH AMERICAN LITERATURE. B.A., Lehigh U., 1929 ; M. Ed., Instituto Científico de México, 1963 ; M.A. National U. of Mexico, 1934; Ph. D., 1948. Teacher, American School Foundation (Mexico, D.F.), 1930–46; vis. prof., U. of Minn., 1947–48; asst. prof., Southwestern at Memphis, 1948–49; chmn., Limestone

Coll., 1949–50; chmn., High Point Coll., 1950–53; instr., Cheshire Academy, 1953–55; vis. prof., Highlands U., Summers 1953, 1956; asst. prof., U. of Miss., 1955–59; vis. prof., National Defense Education Act Institute, U. of Miss., Summer 1959; CHMN., MODERN FOREIGN LANGUAGES, PENSACOLA JUNIOR COLL., 1959– . Membership: American Association of Teachers of Spanish and Portuguese; American Association of University Professors. Research: history of literature; Latin American culture and civilization. Author: Challenge to American Youth (1963); The Three H's: Humanity, Humor, Humility (Kentucky Foreign Language Quarterly, Apr. 1956); Breaking the Language Barrier (Mississippi Education Advance, Jan. 1958). Language: Spanish 5,5,5,5; Portuguese 2,1,–,–; French 4,4,3,3. Office: Dept. of Modern Foreign Languages, Pensacola Junior Coll., 1000 College Blvd., Pensacola, Fla. 32504.

ANGUIZOLA, GUSTAVE A., b. Panama, Feb. 28, 1922. HISTORY. B.A., Evansville Coll., 1947; M.A., Ind. U., 1949; M.S., Mich. State U., 1953; Ph. D., Ind. U., 1954. Special asst., public relations, City of Chicago, 1959; prof., chmn., Morris College, 1960–61; vis. prof., State U. of N.Y., Coll. at Geneseo, Summers 1961, 1962; prof., acting chmn., Elizabeth City State Teachers Coll., 1961–62; supervisor-teacher, Board of Education, Raleigh, N.C., 1962; ASST. PROF., HISTORY, PURDUE U., 1962– . U.S. Dept. of State fellow, 1953. Membership: American Academy of Political Science; American Historical Association; Bolivarian Society of the United States; Conference on Latin American History; Mississippi Valley Historical Association. Research: United States policies in the Caribbean, especially with Panama and Costa Rica. Author: The unratified Treaty of 1926 (Panama Ministry of Education Bulletin, 1953); Socialistic Enterprises in the Panama Canal Zone (Panama Chamber of Commerce Bulletin, Dec. 1954); The United States and the Latin American Republics (U.S. Senate Subcommittee on Latin America, 1958). Language: Spanish 5,5,5,5; Portuguese 5,5,5,5; French 5,4,3,3. Home: 704 Wentworth Ave., Calumet City, Ill. Office: Box 23, Purdue U., Calumet Campus, Ind.

ANGULO, MANUEL R., b. New York, N.Y., Sept. 5, 1917. LAW. B.A., Yale Coll., 1939; LL.B., Harvard Law School, 1942. Assoc., Davis, Polk, Wardwell, & Sunderland Law Firm, 1942–46; attaché and economic analyst, Embassy (Santo Domingo), U.S. Dept. of State, 1943–44; staff, Office of Strategic Services (London), 1944; attaché, Embassy (Lisbon), U.S. Dept. of State, 1944–46; general solicitor, Creole Petroleum Corporation (Caracas), 1948–54; lawyer (Venezuela), 1954–61; PARTNER, CURTIS, MALLET-PREVOST, COLT & MOSLE, 1961– . Membership: American Bar Association; American Foreign Law Association; Inter-American Bar Association; International Bar Association; New York State Bar Association; New York County Lawyers Association; Sigma Xi; Société de Législation Comparée. Research: international comparative law; oil and gas laws. Author: La corporación anglo-sajona (Revista Jurídica Caracas, 1952); Comments on the Status of Foreign Corporations Under the Commercial Laws of Argentina and Venezuela (Inter-American Law Review, July-Dec. 1962); Comments on the Mexican Decree of December 28, 1962, Permitting the Issuance and Sale of Convertible Debentures (Fordham Law Review, May 1964). Language: Spanish 5,5,5,5; Portuguese 3,3,3,3; French 4,4,4,4. Home: 20 East 76th St., New York, 21, N.Y. Office: Curtis, Mallet-Prevost, Colt & Mosle, 63 Wall St., New York 5, N.Y.

ANTTILA, EARL, b. Copemich, Mich., Sept. 11, 1914. EDUCATION. B. Sc., Ohio State U., 1936; M.A., U. of Tex., 1948; Ph. D., 1953. English field supervisor, Dept of Education, Government of P.R., 1938–41; dir., U.S. Cultural Center (Medellín, Colombia), 1948–50; dir., district school, U.S. Trust Territory (Majuro, Marshall Islands), 1950–52; prof., Escuela Normal Rural Interamericana, Pan American Union Project (Rubio, Venezuela), 1953–55; ASSOC. PROF., EDUCATION, U. OF P.R., 1955– . Membership: Phi Delta Kappa. Research: United States educational policy in the Caribbean; English as a second language; junior college development. Author: Teaching of English as a Foreign Language (Educación, Apr. 1955); Vernacular and Education in Mexico of the 16th Century (Revista de Estudios Generales, U. of P.R., 1963). Language: Spanish 5,5,5,5; Portuguese 3,–,–,–; French 4,4,3,3; Finnish 5,5,5,5. Home: P.O. Box 21706, U. of P.R., Río Piedras, P.R. Office: School of Education, U. of P.R., Río Piedras.

APONTE, BARBARA BOCKUS, b. Philadelphia, Pa., July 6, 1936. SPANISH AMERICAN LITERATURE. B.A., Vassar Coll., 1957; M.A., Universidad Nacional de México, 1959; Ph. D., U. of Tex., 1964. INSTR., SPANISH, TEMPLE U., 1964– . Helen Dwight Reed Foundation fellow (Mexico), 1957; Buenos Aires Convention fellow (Mexico), 1957–58. Membership: American Association of Teachers of Spanish and Portuguese. Research: contemporary Mexican literature; Alfonso Reyes. Author: El diálogo entre Ramón y Alfonso Reyes (Insula, Apr. 1964). Language: Spanish 5,5,5,5; Portuguese 3,2,1,1; French 3,2,2,2; Italian 4,3,3,3. Home: Apt. 1803, Hopkinson House, Washington Sq. South, Philadelphia, Pa., 19106. Office: Dept. of Foreign Languages, Temple U., Philadelphia, 19102.

APTER, DAVID E., b. New York, N.Y., Dec. 18, 1924. POLITICAL SCIENCE. B.A., Antioch Coll., 1950; M.A., Princeton U., 1952; Ph. D., 1954. Asst. prof., Northwestern U., 1954–57; asst. prof., U. of Chicago, 1957–58; assoc. prof., 1958–61; PROF., POLITICAL SCIENCE, U. OF CALIF., BERKELEY, 1961– ; ACTING DIR., INSTITUTE OF INTERNATIONAL STUDIES, 1962– ; PRINCIPAL INVESTIGATOR, POLITICS OF MODERNIZATION PROJECT, 1964– . Princeton U. scholar in politics, 1950–51; Class of 1883 fellow, Princeton U., 1951–52; Social Science Research Council area research fellow, 1952–53; Center for International Studies fellow, Princeton U., 1953–54; Ford Foundation research fellow, 1955–56; Center for Advanced Studies in the Behavioral Sciences fellow, 1958–59; recipient, Social Science Research Council Auxiliary Research Award, 1959. Membership: African Studies Association; American Political Science Association; International Social Science Council. Research: comparative politics; international relations; analysis of the relevance of political forms to the problems of modernization with particular emphasis on Latin America. Author: The Gold Coast in Transition (1955); Nationalism, Government and Economic Growth (Economic Development and Cultural Change, Jan. 1959). Editor: Ideology and Discontent (1964). Home: 552 Wildcat Canyon Rd., Berkeley 4, Calif. Office: Dept. of Political Science, U. of Calif., Berkeley.

ARELLANO, RICHARD GIBBS, b. Mexico, D.F., Nov. 5, 1934. ECONOMICS. B.A., U. of Tex., 1956; M.A., 1962; Ph. D., 1965. Accountant, Venezuela Gulf Refining Company (Puerto La Cruz, Venezuela), 1957–60; research asst., U. of Tex., 1960–61; lectr., U. of Tex., 1961–63; ASST. PROF., FINANCE AND INTERNATIONAL BUSINESS, FLA. STATE U., 1964– . Fulbright-Hayes prof., Instituto Tecnológico y de Estudios Superiores de Monterrey (Mexico), 1963–64; consultant, Latin American Research Corporation (Austin, Tex.). Membership: American Association of University Professors; American Economic Association; American Finance Association; American Statistical Association. Research: international business; relationship between finance, business development, and economic development; statistics. Language: Spanish 5,5,5,5; Portuguese 3,2,2,1; French 3,2,1,1. Home: 309 Waverly Rd., Tallahassee, Fla. Office: School of Business, Fla. State U., Tallahassee, 32306.

ARENA, CARMELO RICHARD, b. Atlantic City, N.J., May 8, 1925. HISTORY. Universidad Nacional Autónoma de México, Summer 1947; A.B., Temple U., 1951; M.A., Tulane U., 1954; Ph. D., U. of Pa., 1959. Historian, National Park Service, U.S. Dept. of Interior, 1953–58; instr., U. of. P.R., 1955–56; instr., Temple U., 1956–60; principal, Columbia Institute-Taylor School (Philadelphia), 1959–60; AST. PROF., HISTORY, ST. JOSEPH'S COLL., 1960– . Tulane U. fellow (Guatemala), Summer 1951; St. Joseph's Coll. fellow (Mexico), Summer 1963. Membership: Historical Society of Pennsylvania; Phi Alpha Theta; Philadelphia Catholic Historical Society. Research: Spanish Louisiana; Latin American land tenure system; Latin American-United States trade, 1789–1803. Author: Landholding and Political Power in Spanish Louisiana (Louisiana Historical Quarterly, Oct. 1955); Philadelphia-Spanish New Orleans Trade in the 1790's (Louisiana History, Fall 1961); Philadelphia-Mississippi Valley Trade and the Deposit Closure (Pennsylvania History, Jan. 1963). Language: Spanish 4,4,4,4; Portuguese 2,1,1,1; French 3,2,2,2. Home: 5604 Woodcrest Ave., Philadelphia, Pa., 19131. Office: Dept. of History, St. Joseph's Coll., Philadelphia, 19131.

ARIAS LARRETA, ABRAHAM, b. Trujillo, Peru, May 21, 1916. SPANISH AMERICAN LITERATURE AND LANGUAGE. Professor, Instituto Pedagógico (Lima), 1937; Lit. D., Universidad de la Libertad (Peru), 1940; Ph. D., 1942. Prof., Universidad de Trujillo, 1940–47; vis. prof., Universities of Panama, Costa Rica, Guatemala, and Mexico, 1948–49; vis. prof., U. of Calif., Los Angeles, 1949–51; prof., Occidental Coll., 1951–53; dir., Spanish Language Academy (Los Angeles), 1954–57; prof., Defense Language Institute (Monterey, Calif.), 1957–62; ASSOC. PROF., FOREIGN LANGUAGES, MISS. STATE U., 1962– . Membership: American Association of Teachers of Spanish and Portuguese; American Association of University Professors. Research: pre-Columbian literature; ancient civilization of America; teaching of foreign languages; Spanish linguistics. Author: Radiografía de la literatura peruana (1947); Literaturas aborígenes (1951, 1962); This is Latin America (1959). Language: Spanish 5,5,5,5; Portuguese, 3,3,3,3; French 2,2,2,2; Nahuatl 3,3,3,3; Quechua 4,4,4,4; Quiché 3,3,3,3. Linguistic studies: Spanish. Office: Dept. of Foreign Languages, Miss. State U., State College.

ARMILLAS, PEDRO, b. San Sebastian, Spain, Sept. 9, 1914. ANTHROPOLOGY. B.S., U. of Barcelona, 1932; National School of Anthropology (Mexico). Docent, Instituto Nacional de Antropología (Mexico), 1941–55; archeologist, 1942–52; technical asst., Inter American Indian Institute (Mexico), 1955; vis. lectr., Bowdoin Coll., 1955–56; expert in archeology, government consultant, UNESCO mission (Ecuador), 1956–59; vis. curator, vis. lectr., U. of Mich., 1959–60; CURATOR, MUSEUM, ASSOC. PROF., ANTHROPOLOGY, SOUTHERN ILL. U., 1960– . Guggenheim fellow, 1946; Viking Fund grant-in-aid, 1948; advisory editor on Mexico, Encyclopedia Americana, 1952–53; coordinator, Native Period, Program of the History of America, Pan American Institute of Geography and History and Rockefeller Foundation, 1954–56; National Science Foundation research grant, 1961; consultant, Centro Misional Investigaciones Científicas (Quito, Ecuador). Membership: American Anthropological Association; International Congress of Americanists; Society for American Archaeology. Research: archeology; cultural anthropology; aboriginal land use; New World prehistory. Author: The Native Period in the History of the New World (1962); Cronología y periodificación de la historia de la América precolombina (Journal of World History, 1956); Land Use in Pre-Columbian America (in A History of Land Use in Arid Regions, 1961). Language: Spanish 5,5,5,5; Portuguese 3,3,–,–; French 4,3,2,3; Italian 4,4,2,3. Home: Apt. 4, 311½ West Main, Carbondale, Ill. 62903. Office: Museum, Southern Ill. U., Carbondale.

ARMITAGE, RICHARD H., b. Ravenna, Ohio, Apr. 15, 1918. LANGUAGE. B.A., Oberlin Coll., 1939; Ph. D., Ohio State U., 1945. ASSOC. PROF., ROMANCE LANGUAGES, OHIO STATE U., 1941– ; DEAN, GRADUATE SCHOOL, 1962– . Ford fellow, U. of Tex., 1951–52; National Planning and Advisory Committee, College Language Manual Project, Modern Language Association. Membership: American Association of Teachers of Spanish and Portuguese; Modern Language Association. Research: Spanish American fiction; language teaching. Author: Beginning Spanish (1952). Language: Spanish 5,5,5,4; Portuguese 3,2,2,1; French 5,3,3,2. Home: 259 Lenappe Dr., Columbus 14, Ohio. Office: Dept. of Romance Languages, Ohio State U., 164 West 18th Ave., Columbus 10.

ARNADE, CHARLES W., b. Görlitz, Germany, May 11, 1927. HISTORY. A.B., U. of Mich., 1950; M.A., 1952; Ph. D., U. of Fla., 1955. Instr., Universidad de San Francisco Xavier (Bolivia), 1953; instr., U. of Fla., 1953-55; asst. prof., U. of Tampa, 1955-56; asst. prof., Fla. State U., 1956-58; asst. prof.-assoc. prof., U. of Fla., 1958-60; PROF., HISTORY, DIR. OF INTERNATIONAL STUDIES, U. OF SOUTH FLA., 1960- . Doherty fellow (Bolivia), 1952-53; consultant, U.S. Peace Corps, 1961- ; book review editor, Hispanic American Historical Review, 1961-65. Membership: Conference on Latin American History. Research: Bolivia; Spanish Florida. Author: The Emergence of the Republic of Bolivia (1957); The Trial of Florida, 1593-1602 (1959). Co-author: El problema del humanista Tadeo Haenke (1960). Language: Spanish 5,5,5,5; Portuguese 3,3,3,3; French 2,2,2,2; German 5,5,5,5; Italian 2,2,2,2; Quechua 2,2,2,2. Home: Box 238, San Antonio, Fla. 33576. Office: Dept. of History, U. of South Fla., Tampa.

ARORA, SHIRLEY LEASE, b. Youngstown, Ohio, June 3, 1930. SPANISH AMERICAN AND BRAZILIAN LITERATURE. B.A., Stanford U., 1950; M.A., 1951; Ph. D., U. of Calif., Los Angeles, 1962. Instr., U. of Calif., Los Angeles, 1962-63; acting asst. prof., 1963-64; ASST. PROF., SPANISH AND PORTUGUESE, U. OF CALIF., LOS ANGELES, 1964- . National Defense Education Act fellow in Portuguese, U. of Calif., Los Angeles, 1960-62. Membership: American Folklore Society; California Folklore Society. Research: folk speech; folklore; proverbial speech elements of Peru and Mexico. Author: Some Spanish Proverbial Comparisons from California (Western Folklore, Oct. 1961). Language: Spanish 5,5,5,5; Portuguese 4,4,4,4; French 4,3,3,3; German 3,3,2, -; Hindi 2,2,2,1. Home: 720 Magnolia Ave., Pasadena, Calif. 91106. Office: Dept. of Spanish and Portuguese, U. of Calif., Los Angeles, 90024.

ARROM, JOSÉ JUAN, b. Holguín, Cuba, Feb. 28, 1910. SPANISH AMERICAN LITERATURE. B.A., Yale U., 1937; M.A., 1940; Ph. D., 1941. Instr.-PROF., SPANISH, YALE U., 1938-; lectr., Havana U., Summer 1947. Sterling fellow, Yale U., 1944-45; Guggenheim fellow, 1948-49; lectr., Organization of American States (Colombia), 1960; Ford Foundation grant (Mexico), 1963; National Committee on Selections, Fulbright Fellowships to Latin America, 1963, 1964. Membership: Academia Cubana de la Lengua; American Association of Teachers of Spanish and Portuguese; Connecticut Academy of Arts and Sciences; Instituto Internacional de Literatura Iberoamericana; Modern Language Association. Research: Latin American culture; Spanish American drama. Author: Estudios de literatura hispanoamericana (1950); El teatro de Hispanoamérica en la época colonial (1956); Certidumbre de América (1959). Language: Spanish 5,5,5,5; Portuguese 4,4,3,3; French 4,4,4,3; Italian 4,4,4,3. Linguistic studies: French; Italian; Portuguese; Spanish; Taíno. Home: 70 High Lane, Hamden, Conn. 06517. Office: Dept. of Spanish, Yale U., New Haven, Conn.

ASCHMANN, (HAROLD) HOMER, b. San Francisco, Calif., May 5, 1920. GEOGRAPHY. A.B., U. of Calif., Los Angeles, 1940; M.A., 1942; Ph. D., U. of Calif., Berkeley, 1954. Instr.-asst. prof., San Diego State Coll., 1946-48; instr., U. of Nebr., 1950-51; asst. prof., Los Angeles State Col., 1951-54; asst. prof.-ASSOC. PROF., GEOGRAPHY, U. OF CALIF., RIVERSIDE, 1954-. Office of Naval Research grants (Colombia), 1954-55, (Spain, Portugal), 1960; Advisory Committee on Geography to Office of Naval Research, and Committee on Foreign Field Research Program, National Academy of Science-National Research Council. Membership: American Anthropological Association; American Geographic Society; Association of American Geographers; Pacific Coast Council on Latin American Studies; Southwestern Anthropological Association. Research: ethnography; Mexico; Guajira Peninsula of Colombia; Canal Zone. Author: The Central Desert of Baja California, Demography and Ecology (1959); The Subsistence Pattern in Meso-American History (1960); Indian Pastoralists of the Guajira Peninsula (Annals, Association of American Geographers, 1960). Language: Spanish 4,4,4,3; Portuguese 3,2,2,2; French 3,2,2,2; German 4,4,4,3. Home: 4757 Kansas Ave., Riverside, Calif. Office: Dept. of Geography, U. of Calif., Riverside.

ASHBY, JOE C., b. Gatesville, Tex., Aug. 27, 1922. ECONOMICS AND HISTORY. B.S., North Tex. State U., 1943; M.A., U. of Tex., 1950; Ph. D., 1956. Instr.-asst. prof., Tex. Wesleyan Coll., 1947-54; assoc. prof., Lamar State Coll. of Technology, 1954-59; assoc. prof., East Tex. State Coll., 1959-60; PROF., ECONOMICS, ARLINGTON STATE COLL., 1960- . General Education Board fellow, 1952-53. Membership: American Economic Association; Economic History Association; Southern Economic Association; Southwestern Social Science Association. Research: economic development and organized labor of Argentina and Mexico. Author: Labor and the Philosophy of the Argentine Revolution (Inter-American Economic Affairs, Summer 1951); Our Cuban Policy: A Pattern for Latin American Relations? (Ball State Teachers Coll. Forum, Spring 1961); Labor and the Theory of the Mexican Revolution under Lázaro Cárdenas (The Americas, Oct. 1963). Language: Spanish 3,3,2,1; French 2,2,1,1. Home: 1105 West Lovers Lane, Arlington, Tex. Office: Dept. of Economics, Arlington State Coll., Arlington.

ASHTON, JON R., b. Coeur D'Alene, Idaho, Nov. 6, 1914. LIBRARY SCIENCE. B.A., Wash. State Coll., 1936; M.A., 1937; Ph. D., U. of Wis., 1944; M.A.L.S., 1951. Instr.-asst. prof., Spanish, U. of Fla., 1940-45; assoc. prof., U. of Wichita, 1945-48; assoc. prof., Coe Coll., 1948-50; chief, Humanities Div., Library, Wash. State Coll., 1951-52; asst. prof., Library School, U. of Wis., 1952-54; head librarian, U. of N. Dak., 1954-60; acting dir., Biblioteca General, U. of P.R., 1960-62; vis. lectr., School of Library Service, Columbia U., 1962-63; dean, Library School, U. of R.I., 1963-64; PROF., LIBRARY SCIENCE, QUEENS COLL., 1964- . Albert Markham fellow, U. of Wis., 1944; Committee on Relationship with Latin American Librarians, American Library Association. Membership: American Association for the Advancement of Science;

American Library Association; New England Library Association. Research: cataloging and classification; library administration; bibliography of the humanities. Author: Putative Heroides Codex AX as a Source of Alphonsine Literature (Romance Philology, May 1950). Co-author: Adaptations of the Dewey Classification to a Divisional Library (Journal of Cataloging and Classification, Apr. 1954); University of North Dakota in the Days of Maxwell Anderson (North Dakota Quarterly, 1957). Language: Spanish 5,5,5,4; Portuguese 3,3,3,2; French 5,4,3,3. Office: Library School, Queens Coll., Flushing 67, Long Island, N.Y.

ASKINS, ARTHUR LEE-FRANCIS, b. Clarksville, Ark., Aug. 9, 1934. SPANISH AMERICAN AND BRAZILIAN LITERATURE. B.A., U. of Calif., Los Angeles, 1956; M.A., 1958; Ph. D., U. of Calif., Berkeley, 1963. ASST. PROF., SPANISH, U. OF CALIF., BERKELEY, 1963– . National Defense Education Act fellow in Portuguese 1959–61; special consultant, California State Library. Membership: Modern Language Association; Sociedad de Bibliófilos Españoles. Research: lyric and epic poetry of the 16th and 18th centuries; literature of Spain, Portugal, Mexico, and Brazil. Language: Spanish 5,5,4,5; Portuguese 5,5,4,5; French 4,4,2,3; Italian 4,4,3,3. Office: Dept. of Spanish, U. of Calif., Berkeley, 94720.

ASTUTO, PHILIP L(OUIS), b. New York, N.Y., Jan. 5, 1923. SPANISH AMERICAN LITERATURE. B.A., St. John's U. (N.Y.), 1943; M.A., Columbia U., 1947; Ph. D., 1956. Prof., St. John's U. (N.Y.), 1947–57; dir., Latin American Studies, 1957–60; CHMN., MODERN FOREIGN LANGUAGES, ST. JOHN'S U., 1960– . Membership: American Association of Teachers of Spanish and Portuguese; American Historical Association; Modern Language Association. Research: enlightenment period in the Hispanic world; Spanish American colonial literature; Spanish American essay and novel. Author: Eugenio Espejo: Quiteño de la Ilustración (1960); Eugenio Espejo: A Man of the Enlightenment in Ecuador (Revista de Historia de América, Dec. 1957); Scientific Expeditions and Colonial Hispanic America (in Thought Patterns, 1958). Language: Spanish 5,5,5,5; Portuguese 3,3,1,1; French 3,3,3,3; Italian 5,5,3,3; Linguistic studies: French; Italian; Spanish. Home: 11 Steuben Dr., Jericho, N.Y. Office: Dept. of Modern Foreign Languages, St. John's U., Jamaica 32, N.Y.

ATWOOD, ROLLIN SALISBURY, b. Chicago, Ill., June 19, 1903. GEOGRAPHY. B.S., U. of Chicago, 1924; M.A., Clark U., 1925; Ph. D., 1928. Prof., dir. of Inter-American Affairs, U. of Fla., 1928–42; member, Latin American Affairs Div., U.S. Dept. of State, 1942–62; dir., Latin American Operations, International Cooperation Administration, 1955–61; dir., coordinator, Social Development Div., Inter-American Development Bank, 1961–62; PROF., GEOGRAPHY, SCHOOL OF INTERNATIONAL SERVICE, AMERICAN U., 1963– . Cervantes Medal of Instituto de las Españas. Membership: American Geographical Society; Association of American Geographers; Swedish Anthropological and Geographical Society. Research: economic geography; technical cooperation programs; development programs in Latin America. Language: Spanish 4,4,4,3; Portuguese 2,2,2,1; French 3,2,2,1; German 3,2,2,1. Home: 11750 Glen Rd., Rockville, Md. Office: School of International Service, American U., Washington, D.C. 20016.

AUGELLI, JOHN P., b. Celenza, Italy, Jan. 30, 1921. GEOGRAPHY. B.A., Clark U., 1943; M.A., Harvard U., 1949; Ph. D., 1951. Teaching and research, U. of P.R., 1948–52; prof., U. of Md., 1952–61; PROF., GEOGRAPHY, DIR., CENTER OF LATIN AMERICAN STUDIES, U. OF KANS., 1961– . Teaching fellow, Harvard U., 1947–48; consultant, U.S. Dept. of State and Puerto Rico Planning Board; National Research Council Advisory Committee on Geography, National Academy of Science; contributing editor, Handbook of Latin American Studies. Membership: American Association for the Advancement of Science; Association of American Geographers; International Geographic Union; Mid-West Council of the Association for Latin American Studies; Pan American Institute of Geography and History. Research: cultural, economic, and political geography of Latin America; land use and agricultural settlement. Author: Cultural and Economic Adjustments of Bastos: a Japanese Colony on Brazil's Paulista Frontier, (Annals, Association of American Geographers, 1958); The Rimland-Mainland Concept of Culture Areas in Middle America (Annals, Association of American Geographers, 1962); The Controversial Image of Latin America: A Geographer's View (Journal of Geography, Mar. 1963). Language: Spanish 5,5,4,3; Portuguese 4,4,2,2; French 4,2,2,2; Italian 4,4,3,2. Home: 1131 West Hills Parkway, Lawrence, Kans. Office: Center of Latin American Studies, U. of Kans., Lawrence.

AUSTIN, RUBEN VARGAS, b. San Antonio, Tex., July 28, 1915. ECONOMICS. B.A., U. of Dubuque, 1936; M.A., State U. of Iowa, 1940; Ph. D., 1958. Instr., Iowa Public Schools, 1936–42; prof., chmn., U. of Dubuque, 1946–53; instr., State U. of Iowa, 1953–55; asst. dean, Mich. State U., 1955–61; DEAN, SCHOOL OF BUSINESS AND ECONOMICS, U. OF DEL., 1961– . Membership: American Economic Association. Research: population and economic growth; Mexican economic policy; business administration education in Brazil. Language: Spanish 5,5,5,5; Portuguese 3,2,1,1. Home: 241 Cheltenham Rd., Newark, Del. Office: School of Business and Economics, U. of Del., Newark.

AVERITT, ROBERT TABOR, b. Kaufman, Tex., July 12, 1931. ECONOMICS. B.A., North Tex. State U., 1951; M.A., U. of Tex., 1957; Ph. D., 1961. ASST. PROF., ECONOMICS, SMITH COLL., 1961– . National Science Foundation fellow; Southern Fellowship Fund fellow; National Defense Foreign Language fellow in Portuguese, U. of Tex., Summer 1961. Membership: American Economic Association. Research: economic growth in underdeveloped countries; regional economic development. Language: Portuguese 2,2,2,2. Home: 17 Henshaw Ave., Northampton, Mass. 01060. Office: Dept. of Economics, Smith Coll., Northampton, 01060.

AVERY, ROBERT STERLING, b. Pittsfield, Ohio, Dec. 25, 1917. POLITICAL SCIENCE. A.B., Baldwin-Wallace Coll., 1939; M.A., Northwestern U., 1940; Ph. D., 1951.

PROF., POLITICAL SCIENCE, U. OF TENN., 1952– ; chief, Div. of Industry, Government and Technical Services, U.S. Operations Mission (Panama), 1952–54; chief, U. of Tenn. Mission to Bolivia and Panama, 1955–60 ; ASST. ACADEMIC VICE PRESIDENT, U. OF TENN., 1963– . Assoc. editor, The Journal of Politics, 1954–56; public administration consultant, U.S. Operations Mission (Guatemala), 1958; Evaluation Team in Ecuador, International Cooperation Administration, Summer 1961; public administration consultant, U.S. Agency for International Development (Nicaragua), Summer 1962; consultant, Organization of American States, 1963. Membership: American Society for Public Administration; Midwest Council of the Association for Latin American Studies; Panamanian Society for Public Administration; Southern Political Science Association. Research: personnel management; comparative administration of Latin America. Author: Experiment in Management (1954) ; Public Administration (in Ecuador's Participation in the Alliance for Progress, 1961). Co-author: Government in Tennessee (1962). Language: Spanish 5,4,4,4 ; French 2,-,-,-. Home: 4216 Valencia Rd., Knoxville, Tenn. Office: 218 Administration Bldg., U. of Tenn., Knoxville.

AVRETT, ROBERT, b. Rockdale, Tex., Dec. 1, 1901. SPANISH AMERICAN LITERATURE. B.A., U. of Tex., 1927 ; M.A., 1928 ; U. of Pa., 1936–37. Instr., Edinburg Coll. (Tex.), Summer 1928 ; asst. prof., Tex. Coll. of Mines and Metallurgy, 1928–45 ; dir., Instituto Cultural Argentino-Norteamericano (Buenos Aires), 1945–47 ; ASSOC. PROF., ROMANCE LANGUAGES AND LITERATURES, U. OF TENN., 1947– . Harrison fellow in Romanics, U. of Pa., 1936–37 ; editor, Entre Nosotros, 1951–52 ; asst. managing editor, The Modern Language Journal, 1951–56 ; editor, The Lyric, 1957–58 ; Henry H., Bellamann Foundation award, 1960 ; former consultant on Latin American articles, Publications of the Modern Language Association. Membership : American Association of Teachers of Spanish and Portuguese ; American Association of University Professors ; International Institute of Arts and Letters ; Modern Language Association ; National Federation of Modern Language Teachers Associations ; Poetry Society of America ; South Atlantic Modern Language Association. Research : Spanish and comparative literature ; the poetry of Enrique González Martínez. Author: Outline Spanish Review Grammar (1940) ; Spanish in Review (1959) ; Against the Dark (1961). Language: Spanish 5,5,5,5 ; Portuguese 3,3,1,1 ; French 4,2,1,1 ; German 1,1,1,1. Linguistic studies: French; Spanish. Home: 718 Wells Ave., NE., Knoxville, Tenn. 37917. Office : Dept. of Romance Languages and Literatures, U. of Tenn., Knoxville, 37916.

AXFORD, ROGER, b. Grand Island, Nebr. July 22, 1920. EDUCATION. B.A., Nebr. Wesleyan U., 1942 ; M.A., U. of Chicago, 1949 ; Ph. D., 1961. Dean of faculty, Bacone Coll., 1949–50 ; asst. to vice president, Roosevelt U., 1951–54 ; vice president, Shimer Coll., 1955–56 ; ASST. DIR., UNIVERSITY CENTER, U. OF WIS. (RACINE), 1956- ; asst. prof., assoc. dir., University Extension Div., 1961–62 ; dir., Latin American Project, 1962–63 ; ASST. PROF., EDUCATION, ASSOC. DIR., U. OF WIS., EXTENSION DIV., 1963– . Fund for Adult Education fellow, U. of Chicago, 1954–55 ; consultant, U. of P.R., Summer 1964. Membership : Adult Education Association ; International Congress of Adult Education ; Midwest Council of the Association for Latin American Studies. Research : adult education ; community planning ; secondary and higher education in Venezuela. Author: Venezuela's Quiet War Against Ignorance (The Milwaukee Journal, Aug. 25, 1963) ; Latin American Project, U. of Wis.-Milwaukee: Director's Report (U. of Wis., Sept. 1963) ; Venezuela's War on Ignorance (Calif. Crossroads, Jan. 1964). Language: Spanish 3,4,3,2. Home : 3285 North Maryland, Milwaukee, Wis. 53211. Office : School of Education, U. of Wis., 600 West Kilbourn, Milwaukee.

B

BACARISSE, CHARLES ALBERT, b. Houston, Tex., Aug. 29, 1925. HISTORY. B.S., U. of Houston, 1948 ; M.A., 1949 ; Ph. D., U. of Tex., 1955. Asst. prof., U. of Houston, 1955–58 ; assoc. prof., 1958–64 ; vis. prof., U. of Tex., Spring 1962 ; vis. prof., U. of Wis., Spring 1964 ; PROF., HISTORY, U. OF HOUSTON, 1964– . National Defense Foreign Language fellow, 1962. Membership : American Historical Association ; Conference on Latin American History. Research : early national history of Mexico ; Brazilian historiography and nationalism ; United States-Latin American policy. Author: Baron de Bastrop (Southwestern Historical Quarterly, Jan. 1955) ; The Union of Coahuila and Texas (Southwestern Social Science Quarterly, June 1959). Language: Spanish 3,3,3,2 ; Portuguese 3,3,3,2 ; French 1,1,1,1. Home : 4436 Wheeler St., Houston, Tex. 77004. Office : Dept. of History, U. of Houston, Houston.

BACHMURA, FRANK THOMAS, b. Newark, N.J., May 27, 1922. ECONOMICS. B.S., N.Y.U., 1948 ; A.M., U. of Chicago, 1951 ; Ph. D., 1953. Asst. prof., U. of Wyo., 1952–53 ; asst. prof., Denison U., 1953–54 ; asst. prof., Vanderbilt U., 1954–59 ; research consultant, Instituto de Economía (Chile), 1959–60 ; Fulbright prof., U. of Chile, 1959–60 ; research leader, Economic Research Service, U.S. Dept. of Agriculture, 1960–63 ; ASSOC. PROF., ECONOMICS, IND. U., 1963– . Fulbright lectr., U. of Buenos Aires, U. of La Plata, 1959 ; Fulbright lectr., Universidad Comunal del Centro del Peru, U. of Colombia, Universidad del Valle, U. of Medellín, 1960. Membership : American Economic Association ; American Farm Economic Association ; International Conference of Agricultural Economists ; Southern Economic Association. Research : interrelationship of the agricultural and non-agricultural sectors in the process of economic and political development ; agricultural economics in Latin America ; land reform. Author: Man-Land Equalization Through Migration (American Economic Review, Dec. 1959) ; Rural Area Development in a Growing Economy (Journal of Farm Economics, Dec. 1960) ; Manpower Development and Training Act of 1962—Its Significance for Rural Areas (Journal of

Farm Economics, Feb. 1963). Language: Spanish 5,5,5,5; Portuguese 4,4,4,4; French 2,2,2,1. Home: 601 Park Ave. South, Bloomington, Ind. Office: Dept. of Economics, Ind. U., Bloomington, 47405.

BAER, WERNER, b. Offenbach, Germany, Dec. 14, 1931. ECONOMICS. B.A., Queens Coll., 1953; M.A., Harvard U., 1955; Ph. D., 1958. Instr., Harvard U., 1958–61; ASST. PROF., ECONOMICS, YALE U., 1961– . Membership: American Economic Association. Research: economic growth in Brazil; Puerto Rico. Author: The Puerto Rican Economy and United States Economic Fluctuations (1962); Brazil: Inflation and Economic Efficiency (Economic Development and Cultural Change, July 1963); American Capital and Brazilian Nationalism (The Yale Review, Winter 1964). Language: Spanish 2,3,4,5; Portuguese 1,1,1,2; French 1,1,1,2; German 1,1,1,2. Home: 634 George St., New Haven, Conn. Office: Dept. of Economics, Yale U., 52 Hillhouse Ave., New Haven.

BAERREIS, DAVID A., b. New York, N.Y., Nov. 2, 1916. ANTHROPOLOGY. B.A., U. of Okla., 1941; M.A., 1943; Ph. D., Columbia U., 1949. Instr.-PROF., ANTHROPOLOGY, U. OF WIS., 1947– . Member, Div. of Psychology and Anthropology, National Research Council, 1958–60; National Defense grant (Brazil), 1961; consultant on land claims cases, U.S. Dept. of Justice. Membership: American Anthropological Association; American Association for the Advancement of Science; Royal Anthropological Institute; Society for American Archaeology. Research: prehistory and ethnohistory of the New World; archeology. Author: Preceramic Horizons of Northeastern Oklahoma (Anthropological Papers, U. of Mich., 1951). Co-author: A Report on a Bluff Shelter in Northeast Oklahoma (Archives Archaeology, 1959); Archaeological Investigation near Mobridge, South Dakota (Archives Archaeology, 1961). Language: Spanish 3,2,–,–; Portuguese 3,2,–,–,; French 3,1,–,–. Home: 1233 Sweet Briar Rd., Madison 5, Wis. Office: Dept. of Anthropology, U. of Wis., Madison 6.

BAILEY, HELEN MILLER, b. Modesto, Calif., Mar. 13, 1909. HISTORY. B.A., U. of Calif., Berkeley, 1929; M.A., 1930; Ph. D., U. of Southern Calif., 1934. Teacher, Los Angeles Schools, 1932–46; CHMN., HISTORY, EAST LOS ANGELES COLL., 1946– . Membership: Phi Beta Kappa. Author: Santa Cruz of the Etla Hills (1958). Co-author: Our Latin American Neighbors (1952); Latin America, the Development of Its Civilization (1960). Language: Spanish 2,3,3,2; French 3,2,1,1. Home: 5229 Palm Dr., La Cañada, Calif. Office: Dept. of Social Sciences, East Los Angeles Coll., Los Angeles 22, Calif.

BAILY, SAMUEL L., b. Philadelphia, Pa., May 9, 1936. HISTORY. A.B.. Harvard Coll., 1958; M.A., Columbia U., 1963; Ph. D., U. of Pa., 1964. ASST. PROF., HISTORY, RUTGERS U., 1964– . Rockefeller grant (Argentina), Argentine Nationalism Project, U. of Pa., 1961–64; chmn., Latin American Committee, American Friends Service. Membership: American Historical Association. Research: nationalism and labor movement in Argentina. Language: Spanish 4,3,3,2; Portuguese 2,1,1,1; French 3,2,1,2. Home: 7057 Cresheim Rd., Philadelphia 19, Pa. Office: Dept. of History, Rutgers U., New Brunswick, N.J.

BAIRD, JOSEPH ARMSTRONG, JR., b. Pittsburgh, Pa., Nov. 22, 1922. ART AND ARCHITECTURE. B.A., Oberlin Coll., 1944; M.A., Harvard U., 1947; Ph. D., 1951. Instr., U. of Toronto, 1949–53; ASSOC. PROF., ART, U. OF CALIF., DAVIS, 1953 –; vis. prof., U. of Mexico, 1957. Contributing editor, Handbook of Latin American Studies, 1960, 1961; art curator, California Historical Society, 1962–63. Membership: College Art Association; Pacific Coast Council of Latin American Studies; Society of Architectural Historians. Research: Mexican Baroque architecture; art of the United States and Mexico. Author: Time's Wondrous Changes: San Francisco Architecture of 1776–1915 (1962); The Churches of Mexico (1962). Language: Spanish 3,3,2,2; French 3,3,3,2. Home: 114 Toyon Dr., Fairfax, Calif. Office: Dept. of Art, U. of Calif., Davis.

BAKALANOFF, ERIC NICOLAS, b. Graz, Austria, Dec. 9, 1925. ECONOMICS. B.A., Ohio State U., 1949; M.A., 1950; Ph. D., 1958. Foreign management trainee, Chase Manhattan Bank, 1950–54; instr., Ohio State U., 1957–58; assoc. prof., La. State U., 1958–62; ASSOC. PROF., ECONOMICS, DIR., GRADUATE CENTER FOR LATIN AMERICAN STUDIES, VANDERBILT U., 1962– . Fulbright fellow, U. of Chile, 1957; Ford fellow, Harvard Case Study Seminar, Summer 1959; National Defense Foreign Language fellow in Portuguese, U. of Tex., Summer 1962; Vanderbilt U. grant (Brazil), Summer 1963. Membership: American Council for Luso-Brazilian Studies; Southeastern Conference on Latin American Studies; Southern Economic Association. Research: economic development; international economic relations, comparative systems; relationship between foreign capital and economic development in Brazil; economy of Chile. Author: Model for Economic Stagnation: The Chilean Experience with Multiple Exchange Rates (Inter-American Economic Affairs, Summer 1959); Taxation of U.S. Copper Companies in Chile: Economic Myopia vs. Long-Run Self-Interest (National Tax Journal, Mar. 1961); Resource Allocation, Balance of Payments, and Economic Development: Argentina, Chile, and Mexico (in Foreign Trade and Human Capital, 1962). Language: Spanish 4,4,4,3; Portuguese 3,3,3,1; German 3,3,3,3. Home: 4731 Benton Smith Rd., Nashville, Tenn. Office: Graduate Center for Latin American Studies. Box 1806, Vanderbilt U., Nashville, 37203.

BAKER, GEORGE WILLIAM, JR., b. Frederick, Md., Apr. 10, 1931. HISTORY. B.S., Towson State Coll., 1953; M.A., U. of Colo., 1958; Ph. D., 1961. Instr., Mt. Union Coll., 1961; asst. prof., East Carolina Coll., 1961–64; ASST. PROF., HISTORY, RENSSELAER POLYTECHNIC INSTITUTE, 1964– . Conference on Latin American History Prize, 1964. Membership: American Historical Association; Mississippi Valley Historical Association; Southern Historical Association. Research: U.S. relations toward Latin America, especially the Wilson, Harding, and Coolidge eras. Author: The Wilson Administration and Cuba (Mid-America, Jan. 1964); Ideals and Realities in the Wilson Administration Relations With

Honduras (The Americas, July 1964); Benjamin Harrison and Hawaiian Annexation (Pacific Historical Review, Aug. 1964). Language: Spanish 3,-,-,-; French 3,-,-,-; German 2,-,-,-. Home: 1004 Peoples Ave., Troy, N.Y., 12181. Office: Dept. of History, Rensselaer Polytechnic Institute, Troy, 12181.

BAKER, MAURY DAVISON, b. Waukegan, Ill., July 19, 1912. HISTORY. B.A., U. of Miami, 1939; M.A., Duke U., 1943; Ph. D., 1946. Instr., Duke U., 1943–44; asst. prof., Kent State U., 1947–48; assoc. prof., 1948–55; PROF., HISTORY, CHMN., LATIN AMERICAN AREA STUDIES, KENT STATE U., 1955– . U.S. Dept. of State research grant (Chile), 1948–49. Membership: American Association of University Professors; Conference on Latin American History; Phi Alpha Theta; Phi Beta Kappa. Research: the relationship of highway planning and development to national planning; the history of the Pan American Highway. Author: The Perry Expedition up the Orinoco, 1819 (Hispanic American Historical Review, Nov. 1950); Spanish War Scare of 1816 (Mid-America, Apr. 1963); DamYankeeism in Latin America (Social Science, Oct. 1963). Language: Spanish 4,4,4,2; Portuguese 2,1,2,1; French 3,2,2,1; German 2,2,1,1. Home: 1315 Lake Martin Dr., Kent, Ohio. Office: Dept. of History, Kent State U., Kent.

BAKER, PAUL T., b. Burlington, Iowa, Feb. 28, 1927. ANTHROPOLOGY. B.A., U. of N. Mex., 1951; Ph. D., Harvard U., 1956. Physical anthropologist, Climatic Research Laboratory (Lawrence, Mass.), 1952–54; Quartermaster Research and Development Center (Natick, Mass.), 1954–57; ASSOC. PROF., ANTHROPOLOGY, PA. STATE U., 1957– . Fulbright scholar (Peru), 1962; vis. lectr. (Brazil), 1962; dir., Andean Bio-Cultural Studies Project (Peru), 1964– . Membership: American Association of Anthropology; American Association of Physical Anthropologists. Research: physical anthropology; adaptation in man to environmental stresses; Peru. Author: American Negro-White Differences in Heat Tolerance (Quartermaster Research and Engineering Commission Technical Report, June 1958); Climate, Culture and Evolution (Human Biology, Feb. 1960); Ecological and Physiological Adaptation in Indigenous South Americans (Wenner-Gren Foundation Memoir, May 1964). Language: Spanish 4,4,3,3; Portuguese 2,1,1,1; French 3,1,1,1; Italian 3,2,1,1. Home: Box 16E, R.F.D. 1, Bellefonte, Pa. Office: Dept. of Anthropology, Pa. State U., University Park, 16802.

BAKER, RICHARD D(ON), b. Corbin, Ky., Feb. 12, 1925. POLITICAL SCIENCE. B.A., U. of Ky., 1946; M.A., School of Advanced International Studies, Johns Hopkins U., 1947; Ph. D., U. of N.C., 1963. Industrial relations, Mene Grande Oil Company (Venezuela), 1947–50; U.S. Government, 1952–54 (Ecuador, 1953–54); ASST. PROF., GOVERNMENT, U. OF OKLA., 1959– ; prof., adviser, Public Administration and Political Science, U. of Panama, U. of Tenn. Unit, 1962–64. Southern Fellowships Fund grant (Mexico), 1957–58; consultant, U.S. Peace Corps, U. of Okla. Membership: American Political Science Association. Research: the judicial control of constitutionality in Mexico; international relations and theory; comparative government; budget and fiscal administration. Language: Spanish 5,4,4,4; Portuguese 3,1,1,1; French 3,1,1,1. Home: 826½ College Ave., Norman, Okla. Office: Dept. of Government, U. of Okla., Norman.

BALL, JOHN M., b. Highland Park, Mich., Jan. 7, 1923. GEOGRAPHY. A.B., Central Mich. U., 1948; M.S., U. of Chicago, 1952; Ph. D., Mich State U., 1961. Instr., Central Mich. U., 1957–61; PROF., CHMN., GEOGRAPHY, SLIPPERY ROCK STATE COLL., 1961– . International Geographical Union fellow, 1952; Rollin D. Salisbury fellow, U. of Chicago, 1953, 1954, 1958; National Defense fellow in Spanish, U. of Calif., Los Angeles, Summer 1963. Membership: American Association of University Professors; American Geographical Society; Association for Latin American Studies; Association of American Geographers; National Council for Geographic Education; Sigma Xi. Research: regional development; urban geography of Tepic, Nayarit, Mexico. Author: Some Comments on Mexico's Population (Journal of Geography, Oct. 1962). Language: Spanish 3,3,3,1. Home: 346 Franklin St., Slippery Rock, Pa., 16057. Office: Dept. of Geography, Slippery Rock State Coll., Slippery Rock, 16057.

BALL, MARY MARGARET, b. Los Angeles, Calif., Aug. 29, 1909. POLITICAL SCIENCE. B.A., Stanford U., 1931; M.A., 1931; Dr. Jur., U. of Cologne (Germany), 1933; Ph. D., Stanford U., 1935. Prof., Wellesley Coll., 1936–63; specialist in international organization, U.S. Dept. of State, 1942–43; DEAN, THE WOMAN'S COLL., DUKE U., 1963– . Carnegie fellow, 1932–33; Social Science Research Council fellow, 1941–42, Summer 1961; North Atlantic Treaty Organization fellow, 1946; Board of Editors, International Organization, 1947–56; Guggenheim fellow, 1956–57. Membership: American Academy of Arts and Sciences; American Association of University Professors; American Association of University Women; American Political Science Association. Research: international relations; Organization of American States. Author: The Problem of Inter-American Organization (1943); NATO and the European Union Movement (1959). Co-author: International Relations (1956). Language: Spanish 3,3,3,3; Portuguese 2,1,1,1; French 3,3,3,3. Home: The Dean's House, Duke U. Woman's Coll., Durham, N.C. Office: 115 East Duke Bldg., Duke U., Durham, 27708.

BALSEIRO, JOSÉ AGUSTÍN, b. Barceloneta, P.R. SPANISH AMERICAN LITERATURE. Litt. D., Inter-American U. (P.R.) 1950; Sc. D., Catholic U. of Chile, 1954; L.H.D., Belmont Abbey, 1962. Prof., U. of Ill., 1930–33, 1936–38; prof., U. of P.R., 1933–36; vis. prof., Northwestern U., Summer 1937; PROF., HISPANIC LITERATURE, U. OF MIAMI, 1946– ; vis. prof., Duke U., Summers 1947, 1949, 1950; lectr., U.S. Dept. of State (Central and South America), Summer 1954 (Spain and England), 1955–56, (Spain), Oct. 1963; vis. prof., Inter-American U. (P.R.), Summers 1957–63; vis. lectr., National U. of Mexico, Summer 1959. President, International Institute of Ibero-American Literature, 1955–57; U.S. Consultative Committee,

UNESCO, 1959; Medal of Honor, Academia Mexicana de Letras; vice president, III Congress, Academies of the Spanish Language (Bogotá, Colombia), 1960, IV Congress (Buenos Aires), 1964. Membership: Academia Colombiana de Letras; Hispanic-American Academy of Science and Arts; Instituto Sarmiento de Sociología e Historia (Buenos Aires). Research: modern and contemporary Spanish American literature; modern Spanish literature. Author: Expresión de Hispanoamérica (vol. 1, 1960; vol. 2, 1963); Novelistas españoles modernos (1963). Language: Spanish 5,5,5,5. Home: 18480 Caribbean Blvd., Miami, Fla. Office: Graduate School, U. of Miami, Coral Gables, Fla.

BANNON, JOHN FRANCIS, S.J., b. St. Joseph, Mo., Apr. 28, 1905. HISTORY. A.B., St. Louis U., 1928; A.M., 1929; Ph. D., U. of Calif., Berkeley, 1939. Instr., St. Louis U., 1939–41; asst. prof., 1941–44; assoc. prof., 1944–49; PROF., HISTORY, ST. LOUIS U., 1942– ; CHMN., 1943– . Membership: American Catholic Historical Association; American Historical Association; Conference on Latin American History; Mississippi Valley Historical Association. Research: the church in Latin America and American Southwest; studies on the Patronato Real. Author: Colonial North America (1946); The Mission Frontier in Sonora (1955); History of the Americas (revised edition, 1963). Co-author: Latin America: An Historical Survey (revised edition, 1963). Language: Spanish 4,4,3,2; Portuguese 3,2,2,1; French 4,4,4,3; German 2,1,1,1. Home and office: Dept. of History, St. Louis U., St. Louis, Mo. 63103.

BAQUERO, JOSÉ ANTONIO, b. Quito, Ecuador, July 23, 1915. ECONOMICS AND LAW. B.S., Universidad Central (Quito), 1937; LL. D., Universidad Central, 1939; M.F.S., U. of Southern Calif., 1941. Prof., Catholic U. of Ecuador, 1948–52; vis. prof., U. of Fla., 1952–53; prof., Catholic U. of Ecuador, 1953–58, 1960–62; PROF., ECONOMICS, MISS. STATE U., 1962– ; DIR., INSTITUTE OF LATIN AMERICAN STUDIES, 1963– . Consul of Ecuador (Los Angeles); Ambassador of Ecuador to the United Nations; Fulbright prof., Miss. State U., 1958–60; consultant on labor problems, Stanford Research Institute; consultant on educational problems, Catholic U. of America. Membership: Academia de Abogados (Ecuador); American Economic Association; Colegio de Abogados; Inter-American Bar Association; Southern Economic Association. Research: labor, development, and international economics; business and labor law; labor organizations and cooperatives. Author: Causas de la depreciación monetaria (1941); Manual de hacienda pública (1953). Co-author: The Role of Co-operation in the Economic Development of Ecuador (1964). Language: Spanish 5,5,5,5; Portuguese 3,3,3,3; French 4,3,3,3; German 3,3,3,3; Italian 3,2,2,2. Home: 408 Glenn St., Starkville, Miss. 39759. Office: Miss. State U., P.O. Box 1151, State Coll., 39762.

BARAGER, JOSEPH RUFUS, b. Prince Albert, Canada, May 30, 1914. HISTORY AND GOVERNMENT. B.A., U. of Rochester, 1950; RESEARCH ANALYST, U.S. GOVERNMENT, 1951– ; vis. lectr., U. of Pa., 1964. Harrison fellow, U. of Pa., 1948–49; Doherty fellow, Princeton U., 1949–50; Penfield scholar, U. of Pa., 1949–50; chmn., Bolton Prize Committee, Conference on Latin American History. Membership: American Historical Association; Conference on Latin American History; Council on Foreign Relations (N.Y.); Phi Alpha Theta; Phi Sigma Iota. Research: United States-Latin American relations; Argentina. Author: Historiography of the Río de la Plata area since 1830 (Hispanic American Historical Review, Nov. 1959). Language: Spanish 4,4,3,3; Portuguese 2,2,1,1; French 2,2,1,1. Home: 1416 South Greenbrier St., Arlington. Va.

BARANSON, JACK, b. New York, N.Y., Dec. 19, 1924. ECONOMICS. B.A., Wis. U., 1951; M.A., Johns Hopkins U., 1956; Ph. D., Ind. U., 1965. Research assoc., Brookings Institution, 1960; staff research member, Committee for Economic Development (Washington, D.C.), 1960–62; RESEARCH ASSOC., INTERNATIONAL DEVELOPMENT RESEARCH CENTER, IND. U., 1962– . Membership: American Economic Association; Society for International Development. Research: economic development in Central America, Venezuela, Colombia; regionalism in Central America; problems of technological transmittal to underdeveloped areas; problems of foreign enterprise in Latin America. Author: Industrialization and Regionalism in Central America (Inter-American Economic Review, Autumn 1962); Foreign Enterprise under the Alianza (Challenge, Dec. 1962); Un programa de tecnología creativa para ayudar al desarrollo económico de los países menos industrializados (El Trimestre Económico, Jan.-Mar. 1963). Language: Spanish 4,4,4,4; French 4,4,4,4; German 4,4,4,4; Russian 2,2,2,2. Home: 1215 Atwater Ave., Bloomington, Ind. Office: International Development Research Center, Ind. U., 703 East Seventh St., Bloomington, 47403.

BARBER, WILLARD FOSTER, b. Mitchell, S. Dak., Mar. 21, 1909. POLITICAL SCIENCE. A.B., Stanford U., 1928; M.A., 1929; Columbia U., 1930–32; Diploma, National War Coll., 1948. Instr., City Coll. (N.Y.), 1930–38; country officer-deputy asst. secretary for Inter-American Affairs, U.S. Dept. of State, 1938–50; embassy counselor, Foreign Service, U.S. Dept. of State (Colombia, Peru), 1950–62; dir., Dept. of Political Affairs, National War Coll., 1958–59; dir., Senior Officer Training, Foreign Service Institute, 1959–61; LECTR., INTERNATIONAL AFFAIRS, U. OF MD., 1962– . Einstein Prize in American Diplomacy, Columbia U., 1933; Latin American Committee, American Political Science Association, 1947–50; Loyalty and Security Board, U.S. Dept. of State, 1947–50. Membership: American Political Science Association; American Society for International Law; American Society for Public Administration; Foreign Service Association; International Political Science Association; Pan American Society of New York; Southern Political Science Association. Research: inter-American relations. Co-author: American Government (1936). Language: Spanish 4,4,4,3; Portuguese 3,2,1,1; French 3,2,1,1; Polish 3,2,1,1. Home: 3718 University Ave., NW., Washington, D.C. 20016. Office: Dept. of Government and Politics, U. of Md., College Park.

BARNES, ALLEN RAY, b. Newport, Nebr., June 12, 1926. LANGUAGE. B.A., Hastings Coll., 1948; M.A., U. of Idaho, 1950; Ph. D., U. of Madrid, 1953. Assoc. prof., head, Foreign Languages, Nebr. State Teachers Coll., 1955–57; executive dir., Iran-America Society, U.S. Information Agency, 1957–59; executive dir., Chilean-North American Institute (Concepción), U.S. Information Agency, 1959–61; vis. prof., U. of Concepción, 1959–61; PROF., HEAD, FOREIGN LANGUAGES, S. DAK. STATE COLL., 1961– . President, South Dakota Modern Language Association. Membership: American Association of Teachers of Spanish and Portuguese; Association of Latin American Studies; Modern Language Association. Research: Latin American history and literature; idiomatic Spanish. Language: Spanish 4,5,4,4; Portuguese 2,2,1,1; French 2,2,2,2; German 2,2,2,2. Linguistic studies: Persian. Home: 703 Fifth St., Brookings, S. Dak. Office: Foreign Languages Dept., East Men's Hall, S. Dak. State Coll., Brookings.

BARNES, WILLIAM SPRAGUE, b. New York, N.Y., Aug. 18, 1919. LAW. B.A., Yale U., 1941; LL.B., Harvard Law School, 1947; Docteur en Droit, U. of Geneva, 1948. Research assoc., U. of Mich. Law School, 1948–50; secretary, International Legal Studies, Harvard Law School, 1950–55; asst. dean and dir., World Tax Series, Harvard Law School, 1955–64; executive dir., International Tax Series Program, Inter-American Development Bank, 1960–61; DIR., INTER-AMERICAN STUDIES, HARVARD U., 1961– ; PROF., LATIN AMERICAN STUDIES, FLETCHER SCHOOL OF LAW & DIPLOMACY, TUFTS U., 1963– . Consultant, United Nations Dept. of Legal Affairs; consultant, Inter-American Development Bank. Membership: American Association for Comparative Study of Law; American Bar Association; American Society of International Law; Inter-American Bar Association. Research: international comparative law; Latin American tax program. Author: Revision of the Bustamente Code (1958); Principes de Coopération en Droit Comparé (1962); Tax Trends Affecting Investment in Latin America (1963). Language: Spanish 4,4,4,3; Portuguese 4,3,3,2; French 4,5,5,4. Home: 121–A Brattle St., Cambridge, Mass. 01238. Office: Latin American Studies, Harvard U., 77 Dunster St., Cambridge, 01238.

BARNHART, DONALD STANFORD, b. St. Louis, Mo., July 18, 1925. HISTORY. A.B., San Diego State Coll., 1949; M.A., U. of Chicago, 1950; Ph. D., 1953. Asst. prof., Simpson Coll., 1953–56; assoc. prof., W. Va. U., 1956–59; lectr., U. of Pa., 1959–60; ASSOC. PROF., INTER-DISCIPLINARY STUDIES, SAN FRANCISCO STATE COLL., 1960– . Rotary Foundation fellow (Colombia), 1950; M. Wolfe fellow, U. of Chicago, 1952–53. Membership: Conference on Latin American History; Pacific Coast Council of Latin American Studies. Research: economic development and social change in modern Latin America. Author: Colombian Transport and the Reforms of 1931 (Hispanic American Historical Review, Feb. 1958). Language: Spanish 4,3,3,2; Portuguese 3,1,1,1; French 3,1,1,1. Home: 2270 Hamilton Ave., San Bruno, Calif. Office: Dept. of Inter-disciplinary Studies, San Francisco State Coll., San Francisco 27, Calif.

BAROCO, JOHN V., b. Pensacola, Fla., Apr. 10, 1928. LIBRARY SCIENCE. B.A., U. of Miami, 1951; M.A., Fla. State U., 1953; U. of Chicago, 1956–60. Dir. of library, U. of the Americas (Mexico), 1954–55; asst. acquisition librarian, U. of Miami, 1956; administrative asst., Library, U. of Chicago, 1956–57; DIR., LIBRARY, CENTRO REGIONAL DE EDUCACIÓN FUNDAMENTAL PARA AMÉRICA LATINA (PÁTZCUARO, MEXICO), UNESCO, 1961– . U. of Chicago research grant (Mexico), 1957–58; Pan American Union fellow (Guatemala, Mexico), 1959. Membership: American Anthropological Association; American Library Association; Asociación Mexicana de Bibliotecarios. Research: community development; library service to developing areas and bi-cultural communities. Language: Spanish 4,4,4,4; Portuguese 2,1,1,1; French 2,2,2,2. Home: 1606 East De Soto St., Pensacola, Fla.

BARRACLOUGH, SOLON LOVETT, b. Beverly, Mass., Aug. 17, 1922. ECONOMICS. B.S., U. of N.H., 1943; M.A., Ph. D., Harvard U., 1950. Research assoc., Harvard U., 1950; economist, U.S. Forest Service, 1950–54; assoc. forester, U. of Tenn., 1954–58; agricultural economics adviser, U.S. Foreign Service (Lebanon), 1958–59; land economics expert, United Nations Food and Agriculture Organization (Chile), 1959–61; regional land tenure officer, 1961; prof., Cornell U., 1962–63; PROJECT MANAGER, AGRARIAN REFORM TRAINING RESEARCH INSTITUTE (CHILE), 1964– ; vis. prof., U. of Chile, 1964. Membership: American Economic Association. Research: land economics; land tenure relationships with economic development; Chilean rural conditions. Author: Economic Analysis of Farm Forest Operating Units (Harvard Forest Bulletin, 1955); Lo que implica una reforma agraria (Panorama Económico, 1962); Land Tenure and Development in Latin America (Interamerican Committee for Agricultural Development, 1964). Language: Spanish 5,5,4,4; Portuguese 3,3,1,1; French 4,4,3,2. Home: Pepe Vila and Manuel Casanova, Parcela 373, Santiago, Chile. Office: Agrarian Reform Training and Research Institute, c/o FAO-United Nations, Cano y Aponte 995, Casilla 10095, Santiago.

BARRETT, LINTON LOMAS, b. Lanett, Ala., Sept. 1, 1904. BRAZILIAN LITERATURE. B.A., Mercer U., 1928; Ph. D., U. of N.C., 1938. Instr., Mercer U., 1928–30; instr. U. of Ala., 1931–33; asst. prof., Furman U., 1934–35; instr., U. of N.C., 1935–39; instr. Princeton U., 1939–41; asst. prof.-assoc prof., U. of Kans., 1941–48; PROF. ROMANCE LANGUAGES, WASHINGTON AND LEE U., 1948– ; HEAD, 1960– public affairs officer, Embassy (Ecuador) U.S. Dept. of State, 1951–53. DuPont fellow U. of Va., 1930–31; assoc. editor, Hispania 1950– ; Committee of Spanish Examiners College Entrance Examination Board; consultant, U.S. Dept. of State examinations Bibliography Committee, Portuguese

Modern Language Association. Membership: American Association of Teachers of Spanish and Portuguese; International Colloquium on Luso-Brazilian Studies; Modern Language Association; Southeastern Round Table on Latin American Studies. Research: translations of Brazilian literature and scholarly works; Spanish literature. Author: Two Notes on Enrique Amorim, Uruguayan Cuentista and Novelist (in Romance Studies in Honor of William Morton Dey, 1950); Érico Veríssimo e sua idéia do romance: teoria e prática (in Iberoamérica, 1962). Translator: Bandeirantes and Pioneers, by Vianna Moog (1964). Language: Spanish 5,5,5,5; Portuguese 5,4, 3,4; French 4,3,3,3; Italian 4,3,2,3. Home: Box 741, Lexington, Va. 24450. Office: Dept. of Romance Languages, Washington and Lee U., Lexington, 24450.

BARRETT, WARD JUDSON, b. Jersey City, N.J., Aug. 11, 1927. GEOGRAPHY. B.A., Columbia Coll., 1948; M.A., Columbia U., 1949; Ph. D., U. of Calif., Berkeley, 1959. ASST. PROF., GEOGRAPHY, U. OF MINN., 1959– . Latin American Studies Committee, U. of Minn. Research: marine terraces in the Dominican Republic; historical geography of the sugar industry in Mexico; historical geography of a sugar mill in Cuernavaca, 1530–1830. Author: Marine and Stream Terraces of Southeast Coastal Plain of the Dominican Republic (Revista Geográfica, 1961). Language: Spanish 4,4,4,4; Portuguese 3,2,2,1.; French 4,2, 2,2. Home: 234 North Mississippi River Blvd., St. Paul, Minn. 55104. Office: Dept. of Geography, U. of Minn., Minneapolis, 55415.

BARTELL, GILBERT DUKE, b. Chicago, Ill., Jan. 24, 1929. ANTHROPOLOGY. B.S., U. of Ill., 1954; M.A., Ohio State U., 1959; Ph. D., U. of Ariz., 1964. Instr., U. of Ariz., 1960; field investigator, National Institute of Mental Health (Ariz.), 1961; ASST. PROF., ANTHROPOLOGY, IOWA STATE U., 1963– . Standard Oil fellow, 1957; Comins research fellow (Mexico), 1962. Membership: Alpha Kappa Delta; American Anthropological Association; Royal Anthropological Association. Research: social anthropology; Yaqui and Mayo Indians of Sonora, Mexico. Language: Spanish 4,4,4,3; French 3,3,3,2. Home: 322 North Russell, Ames, Iowa. Office: Dept. of Economics and Sociology, Iowa State U., Ames.

BARTON, ROBERT DURRIE, b. London, England, Aug. 29, 1920. EDUCATION. A.B., Bowdoin Coll., 1941. Asst. public affairs officer (Montevideo, Uruguay), U.S. Information Service, 1946–49; public affairs officer (Rosario, Argentina), 1949–52; acting cultural attaché and asst. cultural attaché, Embassy (Madrid), U.S. Dept. of State, 1953–57; dir., Inter-American Dept., Institute of International Education, 1957–61; ASSOC. DIR., INTERNATIONAL FELLOWS PROGRAM AND DIR., EAST CAMPUS DEVELOPMENT, COLUMBIA U., 1961– . Dir., Spanish Institute and Tinker Foundation; Advisory Council, Institute of Inter-American Studies, Miss. Southern Coll. Membership: Pan American Society; Southern Cross Club. Research: university systems; educational exchange with Latin America. Author: Student Exchange in the Caribbean: Problems and Potentials (in The Caribbean: Contemporary Education, 1960); University Students in Latin American Politics (The Nation, Aug. 12, 1961); Arriba España— Slowly (Columbia U. Forum, Dec. 1963). Language: Spanish 4,4,4,3; Portuguese 2,2,1,1; French 3,3,3,1. Home: 32 Park Ave., Bronxville, N.Y. Office: International Fellows Program, Box 18, Columbia U. Law School, New York, N.Y. 10027.

BARWICK, STEVEN, b. Lincoln, Nebr., Mar. 2, 1921. MUSIC. B.A., B. Mus., Coe Coll., 1942; M. Mus., Eastman School of Music, 1943; Ph. D., Harvard U., 1950. Prof., Blue Mountain Coll., 1948–49; asst. prof., U. of Pittsburgh, 1949–51; assoc. prof., Western Ky. State Coll., 1951–55; PROF., MUSIC, SOUTHERN ILL. U., 1955– . John Knowles Paine traveling fellow (Mexico, Central America), 1945–47. Membership: American Association of University Professors; American Musicological Society; Music Teachers National Association. Research: musicology; piano; Mexican church music of the Renaissance and Baroque periods. Author: Choral Series: Motets from Mexican Archives (1957); The Franco Codex of the Cathedral of Mexico (1964); Puebla's Requiem Choirbook (in Essays on Music, 1955). Language: Spanish 4,4,4,3; Portuguese 1,1,1,1; French 4,4,4,3; German 3,3,2,1; Italian 3,2,2,2. Home: 709 West Elm St., Carbondale, Ill. 62901. Office: Dept. of Music, Southern Ill. U., Carbondale.

BASCOM, WILLIAM (RUSSELL), b. Princeton, Ill., May 23, 1912. ANTHROPOLOGY. B.A., U. of Wis., 1933; M.A., 1936; Ph. D., Northwestern U., 1939. Special representative to West Africa, Foreign Economic Administration, 1943–46; economist, U.S. Commercial Company (Ponape, Caroline Islands), 1946; asst. prof., Northwestern U., 1946–47; assoc. prof., 1949–54; prof., 1954– 57; PROF., ANTHROPOLOGY, DIR., LOWIE MUSEUM OF ANTHROPOLGY, U. OF CALIF., BERKELEY, 1957– . Social Science Research Council fellow (Nigeria), 1937–38; Fulbright grant (Nigeria), 1950– 51; National Science Foundation fellow (England), 1958. Membership: American Anthropological Association; American Association of Museums; American Folklore Society. Research: cultural anthropology; Africa and the acculturation of Africans in the New World. Author: The Focus of Cuban Santeria (Southwestern Journal of Anthropology, Spring 1950); Two Forms of Afro-Cuban Divination (Proceedings, XXIX International Congress of Americanists, 1952); Yoruba Acculturation in Cuba (Memoires de L'institut Français d'Afrique Noire, 1953). Language: Spanish 3,3,2,1; French 3,3,2,1; German 2,2,1,1; Yoruba 2,2,1,1. Home: 624 Beloit Ave., Berkeley 8, Calif. Office: Lowie Museum of Anthropology, U. of Calif., Berkeley 4.

BASILE, DAVID GIOVANNI, b. Youngstown, Ohio, Sept. 2, 1914. GEOGRAPHY. A.B., Washington & Lee U., 1936; M.A., Columbia U., 1938. Instr., Columbia U., 1937–41; procurement specialist, U.S. Defense Supplies Corporation, 1943–44; chmn., Coordination Committee for Ecuador, 1945; acting public affairs officer, U.S. Information Service (Ecuador), 1946–48; ASST. PROF.,

GEOGRAPHY, U. OF N.C., 1949– . Social Science Research Council fellow, 1941–43; Southern Fellowships Fund fellow, 1958. Membership: Association of American Geographers. Research: economic geography; rural land use in the Quito Basin of the Ecuadorian highlands. Author: Algunos factores económicos y geográficos que afectan al campesino rural de la provincia de Pichincha, Ecuador (1953); Agricultural Sicily (Economic Geography, Apr. 1941). Language: Spanish 4,4,3,3. Home: Mason Farm Road, Chapel Hill, N.C. Office: Dept. of Geography, U. of N.C., Chapel Hill.

BASTERT, RUSSELL HENRY, b. Quincy, Ill., Oct. 1, 1920. HISTORY. B.A., Knox Coll., 1941; M.A., Yale U., 1943; Ph. D., 1952. Instr.-ASSOC. PROF., HISTORY, WILLIAMS COLL., 1948– . Ford Foundation international relations fellow, U. of Calif., Berkeley, 1957–58; Social Science Research Council grant (Argentina, Chile), 1962–63. Membership: American Historical Association; Conference on Latin American History; Mississippi Valley Historical Association. Research: American diplomatic history; inter-American diplomacy. Author: Diplomatic Reversal: Frelinghuysen's Opposition to Blaine's Pan American Policy (Mississippi Valley Historical Review, Mar. 1956); A New Approach to the Origins of Blaine's Pan American Policy (Hispanic American Historical Review, Aug. 1958); The Two American Diplomacies (Yale Review, Summer 1960). Language: Spanish 4,3,3,2; German 4,1,1,2. Home: Grace Ct., Williamstown, Mass. Office: Dept. of History, Williams Coll., Williamstown.

BATCHELDER, ROBERT BRUCE, b. Seattle, Wash., Nov. 25, 1923. GEOGRAPHY AND CLIMATOLOGY. B.A., U. of Wash., 1947; M.A., Northwestern U., 1949; Ph. D., 1951. Research chief, Puerto Rico Departamento de Agricultura, 1950–51; asst. prof., Stephen F. Austin State Coll., 1951–53; ASSOC. PROF., GEOGRAPHY, BOSTON U., 1953– . Membership: American Geographical Society; American Meteorological Society; Association of American Geographers; International Oceanographic Foundation; Sigma Xi. Research: physical climatology; rural land use; agricultural resource development; regional geography of Caribbean and South America; incidence of fire from natural and cultural causes in the tropical humid world. Author: The Subhumid Plain of Northwestern Puerto Rico: A Study in Rural Land Utilization (in Northwestern Studies in Geography, 1952); The Evaluation of Cuban Land Tenure and Its Relation to Certain Agro-Economic Problems (Southwestern Social Science Quarterly, Dec. 1952); Land Use Problems in the Minor Commercial Agricultural Region of the Hinterland of Isabela (Symposium on the Geography of Puerto Rico, 1955). Language: Spanish 3,3,2,1; Portuguese 2,1,1,1; French 3,2,1,1. Home: 87 Thornton Rd., Needham, Mass. 02192. Office: Dept. of Geography, Boston U., 700 Commonwealth Ave., Boston, Mass., 02115.

BATCHELOR, MALCOLM, C., b. Newark, N.J., Oct. 14, 1914. BRAZILIAN LITERATURE AND LANGUAGE. B.A., Rutgers U., 1937; M.A., Yale U., 1940; Ph. D., 1945. Instr. Rutgers U., 1937–38; asst. instr., Yale U., 1940–46; instr., 1946–50; dir., Undergraduate Studies, 1948–53; asst. prof., 1950–60; dir., Undergraduate Courses in Spanish, 1957–62; dir., Graduate Studies, Spring 1958; ASSOC. PROF., SPANISH AND PORTUGUESE, YALE U., 1960– . President, Connecticut Chapter, American Association of Teachers of Spanish and Portuguese, 1957–61; president, New England Modern Language Association, 1959–61. Membership: American Association of Teachers of Spanish and Portuguese; Modern Language Association. Research: Luso-Brazilian language and literature. Author: Stories and Storytellers of Brazil (1953); Horizontes latinoamericanos (1955); A tí, doña Marina. The Poetry of Diego Hurtado de Mendoza (1959). Language: Spanish 5,5,5,4; Portuguese 5,5,5,5; French 4,4,4,4; Italian 3,3,3,2. Linguistic studies: Portuguese. Home: Box 1, Orchard Hill Rd., Branford, Conn. Office: Dept. of Spanish and Italian, Yale U., 493 College St., New Haven, Conn.

BATES, MARGARET (JANE), b. New York, N.Y., Jan. 27, 1918. SPANISH AMERICAN LITERATURE. B.A., Hunter Coll., 1938; B.L.S., Columbia U., 1940; Ph. D., Catholic U. of America, 1945. Asst. curator, Hispanic Collection, Library of Congress, 1940–41; library consultant, Coordinator of Latin American Affairs, U.S. Dept. of State (Brazil), 1941–42; instr., U. of Md., 1942–44; library consultant, Library of Congress and U.S. Dept. of State (Peru), 1944; ASSOC. PROF., SPANISH AND PORTUGUESE, DIR., INSTITUTE OF IBERO-AMERICAN STUDIES, DIR., LANGUAGE LABORATORY, CATHOLIC U. OF AMERICA, 1944– . Ford Foundation faculty fellow, 1953. Membership: American Association of Teachers of Spanish and Portuguese; American Association of University Professors; Modern Language Association. Research: modern literary criticism of Spanish and Portuguese literature; descriptive linguistics; prosodic analysis; Brazilian literature. Author: Las poesías de Gabriela Mistral (1958, 1962). Language: Spanish 5,5,4,4; Portuguese 5,5,4,3; French 5,-,-,-; German 3,-,-,-; Italian 3,-,-,-; Latin 3,-,-,-. Linguistic studies: Portuguese; Spanish. Home: 5914 Carlton Lane, Washington, D.C., 20016. Office: Box 6, Catholic U. of America, Washington, D.C., 20017.

BATIZA, RODOLFO, b. México, D.F., Mar. 18, 1917. LAW. B.S.S., National U. Preparatory School (Mexico), 1935; LL.B., National U. of Mexico, 1941; School of Law, Columbia U., 1948, 1952. Attorney, Petroleos Mexicanos, 1942–47; attorney, Curtis, Mallet Prevost, Colt & Mosle (N.Y.), 1948–52; vice president in charge of Trust Dept., Banco del Atlántico, S.A. (México, D.F.), 1952–57; asst. manager, International Relations, Banco Nacional, S.A. (México, D.F.), 1957–58; assoc. prof., School of Law, Tulane U., 1958–63; ASSOC. DIR., INSTITUTE OF COMPARATIVE LAW, SCHOOL OF LAW, TULANE U., 1958– : PROF. LATIN AMERICAN LEGAL STUDIES, 1963– . Chmn., Committee on Commercial Law, Inter-American Bar Association, 1959–62; summer grant to General Archives at Seville, Spain. Membership: Association of American Law Schools; Barra Mexicana, Colegio de Abogados; Inter-American Bar Association. Research:

comparative law; commercial law; legal regime of foreign investments in Latin America; Latin American legal history; legal system of Mexico; legal history of Louisiana; Mexico and the Caribbean area. Author: Tres estudios sobre el fideicomiso (1954); El fideicomiso: Teoría y práctica (1958); Estudios jurídicos sobre el Quijote (1964). Language: Spanish 5,5,5,5; Portuguese 3,3,3,3; French 3,3,3,3. Home: 6324 South Robertson, New Orleans, La. 70118. Office: School of Law, Tulane U., New Orleans, 70118.

BAUR, JOHN EDWARD, b. Chicago, Ill., Feb. 19, 1922. HISTORY. A.B., U. of Calif., Los Angeles, 1945; A.M., 1947; Ph. D., 1951. Editorial asst., Pacific Historical Review, 1949-53; instr., U. of Calif., Los Angeles, Spring 1954; INSTR., HISTORY, EDUCATION DIV., LOS ANGELES COUNTY MUSEUM, 1954– : instr., U. of Calif., Los Angeles, Winter 1959-60; instr., Extension Div., 1957– . F. Bancroft Award, 1947; Huntington Library grant-in-aid, 1954. Membership: American Historical Association; California Historical Society; Conference on Latin American History. Research: republican period of Mexico, Haiti, and LaPlata areas, 1825-1870; Caribbean history. Author: The Presidency of Nicolas Geffrard of Haiti (The Americas, Apr. 1951); The Welsh in Patagonia, an Example of Nationalistic Migration (Hispanic American Historical Review, Nov. 1954); A Mexican Foreign Trade Policy, 1821-1828 (The Americas, Jan. 1963). Language: Spanish 3,3,2,3; French 3,2,2,2; German 2,1,1,2. Home: 7616 Lexington Ave., Los Angeles 46, Calif. Office: Education Div., Los Angeles County Museum, 900 Exposition Blvd., Los Angeles 7.

BAUSUM, HENRY S., b. Annapolis, Md., Feb. 19, 1924. HISTORY. B.A., U. of Md., 1949; M.A., Boston U., 1951; Ph. D., U. of Chicago, 1963. ASSOC. PROF., HISTORY, CARSON-NEWMAN COLL., 1956– . Membership: American Historical Association; Phi Alpha Theta. Research: economic development and ideological structure of Latin America, especially Brazil; expansion of Europe in the Western world. Language: Spanish 3,2,2,1; German 4,3,2,1. Home: 904 George St., Jefferson City, Tenn. Office: Dept. of History, Carson-Newman Coll., Jefferson City.

BAYITCH, STOYAN ALBERT, b. Postojna, Austria, Nov. 18. 1901. LAW. J.U.D., U. of Ljubljana, 1924; J.D., U. of Chicago, 1951. Attaché, International Labor Office (Geneva), 1939-40; docent-prof., State U. (Ljubljana), 1934-42; research asst., Comparative Law Center, U. of Chicago, 1949-52; PROF., LAW, FOREIGN LAW LIBRARIAN, SCHOOL OF LAW, U. OF MIAMI, 1952– . Editorial Board, American Journal of International Law. Membership: American Association of International Law. Research: international comparative law; conflict law. Author: Guide to Interamerican Legal Studies (1957); Aircraft-Mortgage in the Americas (1960); Latin America: A Bibliographical Guide (1961). Language: Spanish 5,5,3,1; French 5,4,5,4; German 5,5,5,5; Serbian 5,5,5,5; Slovenian 5,5,5,5. Home: 41 Veragua Ave., Coral Gables 34, Fla. Office: School of Law, U. of Miami, Coral Gables 46.

BEALS, CARLETON, b. Medicine Lodge, Kans., Nov. 13, 1893. HISTORY. B.A., U. of Calif., 1916; M.A., Columbia U., 1917. Dir., English Preparatory Institute (Mexico, D.F.), 1919; principal, American High School (México, D.F.), 1919-20: instr., personal staff of President Carranza (Mexico), 1920; newspaper correspondent in Latin America, 1923-61 (intermittently); lectr., N.Y. Board of Education, 1924; assoc. editor, Mexican Folkways, 1925-37; assoc. editor, Latin American Press Syndicate, 1933-34; lectr., Latin American universities, 1962; RETIRED–. Bonheim Award, 1916, 1917; Bryce History Prize, 1917; Guggenheim fellow, 1931-32; contributing editor, Common Sense, 1933-41; Modern Monthly, 1935-37, Current History, 1939; president, Editorial Board, Latin American Digest, 1934-36; Advisory Board, Better Understanding Foundation; Board of Governors, Academy of Foreign Relations. Membership: American Geographical Society; Foreign Press Club (Mexico); Pi Gamma Mu; Society of American Historians. Research: international affairs. Author: The Long Land: Chile (1948); Latin America: World in Revolution (1963); Eagles of the Andes (1963). Language: Spanish 5,5,5,5; Portuguese 3,2, 2,2; French 2,2,2,2; German 3,3,3,2; Italian 4,4,4,2; Nahuatl 2,2,2,1. Home: R.F.D. 2, Box 25, Killingworth, Conn.

BEALS, RALPH L(EON), b. Pasadena, Calif., July 19, 1901. ANTHROPOLOGY. A.B., U. of Calif., Berkeley, 1926; Ph. D., 1930. Instr., U. of Calif., Los Angeles, 1936-38; asst. prof., 1938-41; assoc. prof., 1941-47; chmn., 1941-42, 1944-48; dir., Latin American Ethnic Studies, Smithsonian Institution, 1942-43; PROF., ANTHROPOLOGY, U. OF CALIF., LOS ANGELES, 1947– ; prof., U. of Buenos Aires, 1961-62. National Research Council fellow, 1930-32; Southwest Society fellow, 1932-33; Social Science Research Council grant (South America), 1947-48; Wenner-Gren Foundation Award, 1947-48; White House Conference on Improvement of Teaching of Anthropology in Latin America, 1961. Membership: American Anthropological Association; American Association for the Advancement of Science; American Ethnological Society; American Sociological Association; Phi Beta Kappa; Sociedad Mexicana de Antropología; Society for American Archaeology; Society for Applied Anthropology; Southwest Anthropological Society. Research: acculturation of Indians in contemporary Mexico; ethnology of Mexico and Ecuador; Middle American Indians. Author: Cherán: A Sierra Tarascan Village (1946); Kinship Terminology and Social Structure (in Alfred L. Kroeber: A Memorial, 1961). Co-author: An introduction to Anthropology (1953, 1959; Spanish edition, 1963). Language: Spanish 4,4,4,3; Portuguese 3,2,2,1; French 3,2,2,1; Italian 3,2,2,1. Home: 16016 Anoka Dr., Pacific Palisades, Calif. Office: Haines Hall 360, U. of Calif., 405 Hilgard Ave., Los Angeles 24.

BEAR, DONALD VAN TWISK, b. New York, N.Y., May 28, 1932. ECONOMICS. A.B., Princeton U., 1954; B. Phil., Oxford U., 1956; M.S., Stanford U., 1961; Ph. D., 1963. Acting instr., Stanford U., 1956-61; ASST.

PROF., ECONOMICS, U. OF CHICAGO, 1961– ; vis. prof., Centro de Investigaciones Económicas, Universidad National de Cuyo (Mendoza, Argentina), 1963. Consultant, RAND Corporation, 1958–60; Ford Foundation faculty research fellow, 1964–65; National Science Foundation research grant, 1964–65. Membership: American Economic Association; Econometric Society; Royal Economic Society. Research: mathematical economics and economic theory. Author: Saving and the Rate of Interest (Review of Economics and Statistics, Feb. 1961); Multisector Growth Model (Review of Economics and Statistics, May 1961); The Matrix Multiplier and Distributed Lags (Econométrica, July 1963). Language: Spanish 3,3,3,3; Portuguese 1,1,1,1; French 1,1,1,1. Home: Apt. 1023, 1451 East 55th St., Chicago, Ill. 60615. Office: Dept. of Economics, U. of Chicago, Chicago, 60637.

BEATTY, W. DONALD, b. South Bend, Wash., Aug. 10, 1907. HISTORY. B.A., U. of Wash., 1933; Ph. D., U. of Minn., 1947. Instr.-asst. prof., U. of Minn., 1946–50; assoc. prof., 1950–60; ASST. CHMN., HISTORY, U. OF MINN., 1960– . Chmn., Latin American Area Committee, U. of Minn.; Doherty fellow (Chile), 1949–50. Membership: American Association of University Professors; American Historical Association; Conference on Latin American History; Hispanic American Historical Association; Mississippi Valley Historical Association. Research: Latin American and United States diplomatic history; recent economic and social history of Chile. Coauthor: An Introduction to Hispanic American history (1950). Language: Spanish 4,3,3,1; French 3,2,2,2. Home: 2162 South Rosewood Lane, St. Paul, Minn. Office: Dept. of History, 614–B, Social Science Bldg., West Campus, U. of Minn., Minneapolis.

BECK, VERA F., b. Prague, Czechoslovakia, Apr. 2, 1905. SPANISH AMERICAN AND BRAZILIAN LITERATURES. B.A., Rockford Coll., 1927; Ph. D., Charles IV U., 1932. Instr., Rockford Coll., 1939–41; instr., Lake Erie Coll., 1941–43; instr., Abbot Academy, 1943–45; asst. prof., Western Coll., 1945–47; asst. prof., Wilson Coll., 1947–49; editor, translator, scriptwriter, Radio Free Europe (N.Y.), 1951–57; LECTR., SPANISH LANGUAGE AND LITERATURE, QUEENS COLL., 1958– ; asst. prof., Harvard U., Summer 1962. Research fellow, Radcliffe Coll., 1944. Membership: American Association for Comparative Litterature; American Association of Teachers of Spanish and Portuguese; Instituto Internacional de Literatura Iberoamericana; Modern Language Association; Spanish Translators and Copywriters. Research: theatrical and literary movements of Brazil; Latin American civilization reflected in literature. Author: Observaciones sobre el teatro argentino contemporáneo (Revista Iberoamericana, Jan. 1952); La Revista Nosotros (Cuadernos Hispanoamericanos, 1952); La fuerza matriz en la obra dramática de Rodolfo Usigli (Revista Iberoamericana, Sept. 1953). Language: Spanish 5,5,5,5; Portuguese 5,5,5,5; French 5,5,5,5; German 5,5,5,5; Italian 4,4,4,4; Russian 3,3,3,3. Home: 42–10 82nd St., Elmhurst 73, N.Y. Office: Queens Coll., Flushing 54, N.Y.

BECK, WARREN ALBERT, b. Minneapolis, Minn., Dec. 9, 1918. HISTORY. A.B., Wayne U., 1947; M.A., 1948; Ph. D., Ohio State U., 1954. Instr., Augustana Coll., 1948–50; prof., chmn., Santa Ana Coll., 1958–61; ASSOC. PROF., HISTORY, ORANGE STATE COLL., 1961– . Membership: American Historical Association; Conference on Latin American History; Mississippi Valley Historical Association; Pacific Coast Council on Latin American Studies. Research: United States policy in Guatemala. Author: A History of New Mexico (1962); Lincoln and Negro Colonization in Central America (Lincoln Quarterly, Sept. 1950). Language: Spanish 4,3,3,2. Home: 1307 West Santa Clara, Santa Ana, Calif. Office: Dept. of History, Orange State Coll., Fullerton, Calif.

BEHRMAN, JACK NEWTON, b. Waco, Tex., Mar. 5, 1922. ECONOMICS. B.A., Davidson Coll., 1943; M.A., U. of N.C., 1945; Ph. D., Princeton U., 1952. Asst. prof., Davidson Coll., 1946–48; instr., research asst., Princeton U., 1948–52; assoc. prof., Washington & Lee U., 1952–57; prof., U. of Del., 1957–61; asst. secretary, U.S. Dept. of Commerce, 1961–64; PROF., ECONOMICS, U. OF N.C., 1964– . Consultant, Pan American Union. Research: international business; economic development; international finance; foreign economic policy. Author: Financing Trade with the Sino-Soviet Bloc (1957); International Economics (1957); U.S. Government and Private Investment Abroad (1961). Language: Spanish 3,3,3,3; French 3,3,3,3. Home: 4 The Glen, Chapel Hill, N.C. Office: Dept. of Economics, U. of N.C., Chapel Hill.

BEILHARZ, EDWIN ALANSON, b. Philippsburg, Kans., June 18, 1907. HISTORY. A.B., Creighton U., 1931; M.A., U. of Nebr., 1934; Ph. D., U. of Calif., 1951. PROF., CHMN., HISTORY, U. OF SANTA CLARA, 1936– . University fellow, U. of Calif.; Heller Memorial scholar, U. of Calif.; sabbatical grant (Spain), 1961–62. Membership: American Historical Association; American Catholic Historical Association. Research: the Spanish frontier in North America; archival research. Author: Communism and History (The Catholic Mind, Nov. 1954); The New Frontier and the Old (U.S. Chamber of Commerce, 1962). Language: Spanish 4,3,2,3; French 4,1,2,1; German 4,2,2,1. Home: 16021 Wood Acres Rd., Los Gatos, Calif. Office: Dept. of History, U. of Santa Clara, Santa Clara, Calif.

BEISHLAG, GEORGE A., b. Syracuse, N.Y., Mar. 4, 1907. GEOGRAPHY. B.A., Wayne U., 1930; M.A., Clark U., 1937; Ph. D., U. of Md., 1953. Research analyst, U.S. Government, 1942–49; geographer, mapper, Dept. of Agriculture and Commerce, Government of P.R., 1951; vis. prof., U. of Manitoba, Summer 1964; PROF., GEOGRAPHY, TOWSON STATE COLL., 1954– . Consultant, Naval Post Graduate Intelligence School, 1946, Secretariat of the United Nations, 1946, and Baltimore County Office of Planning and Office of Recreation, 1958. Membership: American Association of University Professors; American Geographical Society; Association of American Geographers; International Geographical

Union; Maryland State Teachers Association; National Council for Geographic Education. Research: land use mapping. Author: Trends in Land Use in Southeast Puerto Rico (in Symposium on the Geography of Puerto Rico, 1955). Contributor: Our United States in a World of Neighbors (1958). Language: Spanish 4,3,3,2; Portuguese 2,1,1,1; French 3,3,3,2; German 3,3,3,2. Home: 1530 Taylor Ave., Baltimore, Md., 21234. Office: Dept. of Social Science, Towson State Coll., Baltimore, 21204.

BELITT, BEN, b. New York, N.Y., b. 1911. SPANISH AMERICAN LITERATURE. B.A., U. of Va., 1932; M.A., 1934. Asst. editor, The Nation Magazine, 1937-38; PROF., COMPARATIVE LITERATURE, BENNINGTON COLL., 1938– . Guggenheim fellow in poetry, 1946; Brandeis Creative Arts Award in Poetry, 1962. Membership: Phi Beta Kappa. Research: poetry; translations of contemporary Spanish and Spanish American poetry. Editor and translator: F. García Lorca's Poet in New York (1955); Selected Poems of Pablo Neruda (1961); Juan de Mairena: Antonio Machado (1963). Language: Spanish 4,4,3,2; Portuguese 1,1,1,1; French 4,3,2,1; Russian 2,2,1,1. Office: Bennington Coll., Bennington, Vt., 05201.

BELL, BETTY BONITA, b. Los Angeles, Calif., Mar. 31, 1918. ANTHROPOLOGY. B.A., U. of Calif., Los Angeles, 1955; Ph. D., 1961. Specialist, Dept. of Social Affairs, Pan American Union, 1961-64; RESEARCH ASSOC., ANTHROPOLOGY, LATIN AMERICAN CENTER, U. OF CALIF., LOS ANGELES, 1964– . Membership: American Anthropological Association; American Association for the Advancement of Science; Archaeological Institute of America; Association for Latin American Studies; Sigma Xi; Society for American Archaeology; Southwestern Anthropological Association. Research: Mesoamerican archeology; social planning and development of Latin America under the Alliance for Progress. Author: Archaeology of Nayarit, Colima and Jalisco (in Handbook of Middle American Indians). Contributor: The Ancient Maya (1956). Language: Spanish 4,3,3,3; Portuguese 2,1,1,1; French 2,1,1,1; German 3,-,-,-. Home: 2641 Kelton Ave., Los Angeles 64, Calif. Office: Latin American Center, U. of Calif., Los Angeles.

BELL, JOHN FRED, b. Cambridge, Ohio, Feb. 21, 1898. ECONOMICS. A.B., Muskingum Coll., 1923; A.M., U. of Ill., 1924; Ph. D., 1928; LL.D., Muskingum Coll., 1957. Instr., U. of Ill., 1924-27; asst. prof., Syracuse U., 1928-29; assoc. prof., Western Reserve U., 1929-31; prof., chmn., Temple U., 1931-41; PROF., ECONOMICS, U. of ILL., 1941– ; chmn., 1957-63. Consultant, U. of the Andes (Colombia); consultant, U.S. Agency for International Development (Brazil), 1959. Membership: American Economic Association; Royal Economic Society. Research: history of economic thought; international economics; economic growth; graduate curriculum planning for economics and business administration. Author: A History of Economic Thought (1953). Contributor: Intellectual and Cultural History of the Western World (1941); The Economics of War (1943). Language: Spanish 1,1,1,1;

French 2,3,3,3: German 2,3,3,3. Home: 605 West Delaware Ave., Urbana, Ill. 61801. Office: Dept. of Economics, U. of Ill., Urbana.

BELL, ROBERT E., b. Marion, Ohio, June 16, 1914. ANTHROPOLOGY. B.A., U. of N. Mex., 1940; M.A., U of Chicago, 1943; Ph. D., 1947. PROF., ANTHROPOLOGY, U. OF OKLA., 1947– . National Science Foundation grants (Ecuador). Membership: American Anthropological Association; Society for American Archaeology. Research: early man in the New World; archeological field work in Ecuador. Author: Survey of Oklahoma Archaeology (1951); Projectile Point Guides (1958). Language: Spanish 3,3,2,1; French 3,2,2,2. Home: 1625 South Berry Rd., Norman, Okla. Office: Dept. of Anthropology, U. of Okla., Norman.

BELSHAW, MICHAEL, b., New Zealand, June 23, 1928. ECONOMICS. A.B., Columbia Coll., 1951; Ph. D., Columbia U., 1956. Instr., Adelphi Coll., 1953-54; instr., Barnard Coll., 1954-58; asst. prof., Douglass Coll., 1957-60; ASST. PROF., HUNTER COLL., 1960– . Social Science Research Council grant (Mexico), Summer 1962. Membership: American Academy of Political and Social Science; American Economic Association; National Planning Association; Royal Economic Society; Society for Applied Anthropology. Research: rural welfare; economic and social conditions of a Mexican Tarascan village; allocation criteria in the ecomonic development plans of underdeveloped countries. Author: Operational Capital Allocation Criteria for Development Planning (Economic Development and Cultural Change, Apr. 1958); Aspects of the Theory of Discounting (Engineering Economist, Spring 1961); Aspects of Community Development in Rural Mexico (Inter-American Economic Affairs, Spring 1962). Language: Spanish 4,3,3,3; Portuguese 1,1,1,1; French 2,2,1,1. Home: Box 268A, R.F.D. 1, New Milford, Conn. Office: Dept. of Economics, Hunter Coll., 695 Park Ave., New York 21, N.Y.

BEMIS, SAMUEL FLAGG, b. Worcester, Mass., Oct. 20, 1891. HISTORY. A.B., Clark U., 1912; A.M., 1913; A.M., Harvard U., 1915; Ph. D., 1916. STERLING PROF. EMERITUS, DIPLOMATIC HISTORY AND INTER-AMERICAN RELATIONS, YALE U., 1960– . Pulitzer Award, 1927, 1950; dir., European Mission, Library of Congress, 1927-29; Carnegie vis. prof. (Latin America), 1937-38. Membership: Academia de la Historia (Cuba); American Historical Association; American Antiquarian Society; Sociedad de Geografía e Historia (Mexico). Author: Early Diplomatic Missions from Buenos Aires to the United States, 1811-1824 (1940); The Latin American Policy of the United States, an Historical Interpretation (1943); the United States as a World Power; a Diplomatic History, 1900-1955 (1955). Home: 120 Ogden St., New Haven, Conn. Office: 241 Hall of Graduate Studies, Yale U., New Haven.

BENEKE, RAYMOND R., b. Laurens, Iowa. ECONOMICS. B.S., Iowa State U., 1940; M.S., 1946; Ph. D., U. of Minn., 1949. Instr., U. of Minn., 1946-48; asst. prof.— PROF., AGRICULTURAL ECONOMICS, IOWA STATE U., 1964– . Iowa Mission- U.S. Agency for International Development

(Lima, Peru), Summer 1964. Research: agricultural economics; farm planning; farm management. Author: Managing the Farm Business (1955); Managing the Tenant Operated Farm (1957). Language: Spanish 3,3,3,2; French 1,-,-,-. Office: Dept. of Agricultural Economics, Iowa State U., Ames.

BENNETT, CHARLES FRANKLIN, JR., b. Oakland, Calif., Apr. 10, 1926. GEOGRAPHY. B.A., U. of Calif., Los Angeles, 1955; Ph. D., 1960. Associate in Tropical Biogeography, U. of Calif., Berkeley (Panama), 1957–58; ASST. PROF., GEOGRAPHY, U. OF CALIF., LOS ANGELES, 1959– . Office of Naval Research grant (Panama), 1963. Membership: American Anthropological Association; American Association for the Advancement of Science; American Association of Mammalogists; Association of American Geographers; Ecological Society of America; New York Academy of Sciences; Sigma Xi; Society for Study of Evolution. Research: tropical human geography; biogeography of Panama, Mexico, and Costa Rica. Author: The Bayano Cuna Indians, Panama: An Ecological Study of Livelihood and Diet (Annals, Association of American Geographers, 1962); A Phytophysiognomic Reconnaissance of Barro Colorado Island, Canal Zone (1963); Stingless Beekeeping in Western Mexico (Geographical Review, Jan. 1964). Language: Spanish 4,3,3,3; Portuguese 3,2,2,1; French 3,1,1,1; German 3,2,2,1. Home: Apt. 12, 11665 Kiowa Ave., Los Angeles, Calif., 90049. Office: Dept. of Geography, U. of Calif., Los Angeles, 90024.

BENNETT, ROBERT L., b. Medicine Lodge, Kans., Mar. 3, 1931. ECONOMICS. B.A., U. of Tex., 1951; M.A., 1955; Ph. D., 1963. Instr., West Tex. State Coll., 1955–56; asst. prof., Tex. Western Coll., 1956–59; research assoc., U. of Wis., 1962–63; ASST. PROF., ECONOMICS, U. OF MD., 1963– . Ford Foundation fellow, 1961–62; Rockefeller Foundation fellow, 1962–63. Membership: American Economic Association; Society for International Development. Research: financial structure and economic development in Latin America; financial intermediaries in Mexican economic development, 1944–60; financial institutions of Chile, Colombia, Ecuador, Peru, and Venezuela. Author: Financial Innovation and Structural Change in the Early Stages of Industrialization: Mexico, 1945–59 (Journal of Finance, Dec. 1963). Language: Spanish 4,3,3,4; French 3,2,2,3. Home: 7308 New Hampshire Ave., Takoma Park, Md., 20012. Office: Dept. of Economics, U. of Md., College Park, 20742.

BENNINGER, LAWRENCE J., b. New York, N.Y., Dec. 9, 1912. ECONOMICS AND ACCOUNTING. B.A., State U. of Iowa, 1937; M.A. 1940; Ph. D., U. of Mo., 1949. Instr., U. of Tulsa, 1940–42; instr., Miami U. (Ohio), 1942–44; teacher, High School (Ariz.), 1944–45; assoc. prof., chmn., Accounting, Bowling Green State U., 1945–47; assoc. prof., U. of Ala., 1955–56; prof., U. of Mo., 1947–55; PROF., ACCOUNTING, U. OF FLA., 1956– ; adviser, prof., U. of P.R., Summers 1961, 1962. Consultant, U.S. Agency for International Development (Nicaragua), 1962. Membership: American Accounting Association; American Association of University Professors; National Association of Accountants. Research: cost concepts and standards; graduate program of business administration. Author: Cost Accounting (1963). Language: Spanish 2,2,2,2; French 3,2,2,3. Home: 1022 NE. 20th Ave., Gainesville, Fla. Office: Dept. of Accounting, Matherly Hall, U. of Fla., Gainesville.

BENSON, NETTIE LEE, b. Arcadia, Tex., Jan. 15, 1905. HISTORY AND BIBLIOGRAPHY. B.A., U. of Tex., 1929; M.A., 1935; Ph. D., 1949. Teacher, Instituto Inglés-Español (Monterrey, Mexico), 1925–27; teacher, Ingleside High School (Tex.), 1932–41; LECTR., HISTORY, LIBRARIAN, U. OF TEX., 1942–60, 1962– ; acquisitions, New York Public Library, 1960–62. Membership: American Historical Association; American Library Association; Conference on Latin American History. Research: bibliographical and institutional acquisition of library materials in Latin America. Author: La diputación provincial y el federalismo mexicano (1955). Translator: Report of Ramos Arizpe to the Cortes (1950); The United States versus Porfirio Diáz, by Cosío Villegas (1963). Language: Spanish 5,5,4,4; Portuguese 4,3,2,3; French 3,2,2,3. Home: 2834 Shoal Crest, Austin 5, Tex. Office: Latin American Collection, U. of Tex. Library, Austin 12.

BENTON, GABRIELE VON MUNK, b. Vienna, Austria, May 5, 1903. SPANISH AMERICAN LITERATURE. Ph. D., U. of Vienna (Austria), 1928. Assoc. prof., Western Coll. (Ohio), 1941–42; assoc. prof., Rockford Coll., 1942–47; asst. prof., U. of Southern Calif., Los Angeles, 1947–50; PROF., FOREIGN LANGUAGES AND LATIN AMERICAN AFFAIRS, OCCIDENTAL COLL., 1952– . Rockefeller Foundation grants (Mexico), 1954, 1955, 1957; Fulbright prof. (Innsbruck, Austria), 1956. Membership: American Association of Teachers of Spanish and Portuguese; Instituto de Literatura Iberoamericana; Modern Language Association; Pacific Coast Council on Latin American Studies. Research: modern period; literature of Mexico and Argentina. Author: The Poetry of Octavio Paz (Revista Iberoamericana, Sept. 1955); Women Writers of Mexico (Books Abroad, Winter 1959); El español visto por unos cuentistas de hoy (Cuadernos, 1963). Language: Spanish 5,5,5,5; Portuguese 2,2,1,1; French 5,5,5,5; German 5,5,5,5; Italian 5,5,3,2. Office: Dept. of Foreign Languages, Occidental Coll., Los Angeles 41, Calif.

BERBUSSE, EDWARD JOSEPH, S.J., b. Port Chester, N.Y., Nov. 30, 1912. HISTORY AND INTERNATIONAL LAW. B.A., Loyola U. (Chicago), 1938; M.A., Fordham U., 1948; Ph. D., Georgetown U., 1952. Asst. prof., Canisius Coll., 1952–54; asst. prof., Fordham U., 1954–59; rector, Colegio San Ignacio (P.R.), 1959–62; DIR, INSTITUTO IGNACIANO, 1962– . Research: political and cultural history of Puerto Rico. Author: Neutrality Diplomacy of U.S.-Mexico, 1910–11 (The Americas, Jan. 1956); Origins of the McLane-Ocampo Treaty of 1859 (The Americas, Jan. 1958); Aspects in Church-State Relations in Puerto Rico, 1898–1900 (The Americas, Jan. 1963). Language: Spanish 4,4,4,4; French 2,-,-,-; Latin 4,-,-,-. Home and office: Instituto Ignaciano, 398 Francisco Sein, Hato Rey, P.R.

BERG, SHERWOOD OLMAN, b. Hendrum, Minn., May 17, 1919. ECONOMICS. B.S., S. Dak. State Coll., 1947; M.S., Cornell U., 1948; Ph. D., U. of Minn., 1951. Agricultural attaché, U.S. Dept. of State (Yugoslavia), 1951–54; agricultural attaché, U.S. Dept. of State (Denmark, Norway), 1954–57; prof., head, Agricultural Economics Dept., U. of Minn., 1957–63; DEAN, INSTITUTE OF AGRICULTURE, U. OF MINN., 1963– . Danforth Foundation fellow, 1942; Caleb Dorr research fellow, 1948–49; Greater University Fund graduate fellow, 1949–50; Kellogg Foundation traveling fellow (Far East), 1958; consultant, U.S. Agency for International Development, 1958– ; consultant, U.S. Dept. of Agriculture, 1960– ; Minnesota Governor's Committee on Agriculture, 1961– ; consultant, Ford Foundation (Latin America), 1963. Membership: Agricultural History Society; American Association of University Professors; American Economic Association; American Farm Economic Association; International Association of Agricultural Economists. Research: agricultural economics; developmental economics; agricultural economics of Chile and Mexico. Author: International Opportunities for American Land-Grant Universities (Journal of Farm Economics, Dec. 1961); Evaluation of Land-Grant University International Research Activities (in Food—One Tool of International Economic Development, 1962); Appraisal: Policies to Maximize Agricultural Exports (CAEA Report, 1962). Language: German 2,2,2,2; Danish 4,4,4,4; Norwegian 4,4,4,4; Serbo-Croatian 2,2,3,3. Home: 2009 North Aldine St., St. Paul, Minn. 55113. Office: Institute of Agriculture, U. of Minn., St. Paul, 55101.

BERGER, EVELYN MILLER, b. Hanford, Calif., Nov. 7, 1896. EDUCATION AND PSYCHOLOGY. M.A., Stanford U., 1930; Ph. D., Columbia U., 1932. Teacher, Methodist Church (Panama, Chile), 1917–19, (Argentina), 1921–23; teacher, San Jose High School (Calif.), 1921–30; dir., Spanish House, Coll. of the Pacific, Summers 1929–30; dean of women, Allegheny Coll., 1932–36; dean of women, U. of Idaho, 1936–37; dean of women, San Diego State Coll., 1937–39; ADMINISTRATIVE DIR., EAST BAY PSYCHOLOGICAL CENTER, 1941– . Membership: American Psychological Association; International Council of Psychologists; National Association of Marriage Counselors; National Family Relations Council; National Vocational Guidance Association. Research: social problems in education; special factors in learning; counseling. Author: La joven (1923); Extracurricular Activities for the Spanish Department (1927). Language: Spanish 5,4,4,3. Home: 34 La Salle Ave., Piedmont, Calif. Office: East Bay Psychological Center, 315 14th St., Oakland 12, Calif.

BERGMANN, JOHN FRANCIS, b. Los Angeles, Calif., Oct. 8, 1928. GEOGRAPHY. A.B., U. of Calif., Los Angeles, 1950; M.A., U. of Tex., 1952; Ph. D., U. of Calif., Los Angeles, 1959. Asst. prof., Southern Methodist U., 1957–60; ASSOC. PROF., GEOGRAPHY, U. OF ALBERTA, 1960– . U. of Tex. scholar, 1952; Doherty fellow (Central America), 1954–55. Membership: American Geographical Society; Association of American Geographers; Canadian Association of Geographers; Sigma Xi. Research: historical and economic geography; Central America; Jamaica. Author: Cacao and Its Production in Central America (Tijdschrift voor Economische en Sociale Geografie, Feb. 1957). Language: Spanish 4,3,3,3; Portuguese 3,2,2,2; French 1,1,1,1. Home: Apt. 10E, 9820 104th St., Edmonton, Alberta, Canada. Office: Dept. of Geography, U. of Alberta, Edmonton.

BERLE, ADOLF AUGUSTUS, b. Boston, Mass., Jan. 29, 1895. LAW AND ECONOMICS. A.B., Harvard U., 1913; A.M., 1914; LL.B., 1916. PROF., LAW, COLUMBIA U., 1927– ; asst. secretary of state, U.S. Dept. of State, 1938–44; U.S. ambassador to Brazil, 1945–46. Delegate of U.S. Government, Inter-American Conference for Maintenance of Peace (Buenos Aires), 1936–37; delegate, 8th Pan American Conference (Lima), 1938; delegate, Pan American Conference (Havana), 1940; chmn., Task Force on Latin America, 1961; consultant to Secretary of State, U.S. Dept. of State, 1961– . Membership: Phi Beta Kappa. Research: international law; United States-Latin American diplomacy. Author: Latin America-Diplomacy and Reality (1962); The American Economic Republic (1963). Co-author: The Modern Corporation and Private Property (1932). Language: Spanish 4,4,4,3; Portuguese 4,4,4,3; French 4,4,4,3. Home: 70 Pine St., New York, N.Y. Office: School of Law, Columbia U., Morningside Heights, New York.

BERMAN, BARBARA R., b. New York, N.Y., 1927. ECONOMICS AND STATISTICS. B.A., Cornell U., 1948; M.A., Radcliffe Coll., 1955; Ph. D., Harvard U., 1959. Senior research asso., Harvard Economic Research Project, 1954–58; economist, New York Metropolitan Region Study, 1957–61; instr., Harvard U., 1958–61; senior staff economist, Council of Economic Advisers, Executive Office of the President, 1961–62; ASSOC. PROF., ECONOMICS, BRANDEIS U., 1962– ; SENIOR STAFF MEMBER, THE BROOKINGS INSTITUTION, 1963– . Membership: American Economic Association; Regional Science Association. Research: statistics; money and banking; business cycles; economic theory; structural unemployment; development of lowlands in Bolivia. Author: Transportation in the Strategy of Bolivian Development: The Cochabamba-Santa Cruz Highway (1964). Co-author: Projection of a Metropolis (1961). Language: Spanish 3,2,1,1; French 3,3,3,2. Home: 1911 S St., NW., Washington, D.C. Office: The Brookings Institution, 1775 Massachusetts Ave., NW., Washington, D.C. 20036.

BERNARD, JUDITH ANN, b. Madison, Wis., Aug. 23, 1936. SPANISH AMERICAN LITERATURE. B.A., U. of Wis., 1958; M.A., 1959; Ph. D., 1964. Asst. prof., U. of Mo., 1963–64; ASST. PROF., SPANISH AND PORTUGESE, U. OF WASH., 1964– . Fulbright fellow (Chile), 1961–62. Membership: American Association of Teachers of Spanish and Portuguese; Modern Language Association. Research: poetry of Octavio Paz. Language: Spanish 5,4,4,4; Portuguese 4,4,3,4; French 3,2,2,1. Office: Dept. of Romance Languages and Literature, U. of Wash., Seattle.

BERNDTSON, C. ARTHUR E., b. Chicago, Ill., Jan. 31, 1913. PHILOSOPHY. A.B.,

U. of Chicago, 1935; Ph. D., 1940. Instr., U. of Mo., 1945–46; asst. prof., 1946–51; assoc. prof., 1951–59; PROF., PHILOSOPHY, U. OF MO., 1959– ; CHMN., PHILOSOPHY, 1962– . Ford Foundation fellow, 1951–52. Membership: American Association of University Professors; American Philosophical Association; American Society for Aesthetics. Research: recent history of philosophy; aesthetics; metaphysics; philosophy of Argentina, Mexico, and Uruguay. Author: Mexican Philosophy: The Aesthetics of Antonio Caso (Journal of Aesthetics, June 1951); Teaching Latin American Philosophy (The Americas, Jan. 1953). Editor and translator: Readings in Latin American Philosophy (1949). Language: Spanish 4,3,3,3; French 3,2,1,2; German 4,3,3,3; Swedish 3,3,3,3. Home: 1107 West Rollins Rd., Columbia, Mo. 65201. Office: Dept. of Philosophy, U. of Mo., Columbia, 65202.

BERNSTEIN, EDWARD MORRIS, b. Bayonne, N.J., Dec. 16, 1904. ECONOMICS. Ph. B., U. of Chicago, 1927; A.M., Harvard U., 1928; Ph. D., 1931. Assoc. prof.-prof., U. of N.C., 1930–40; economist, U.S. Treasury Dept., 1940–46; dir. of research, International Monetary Fund, 1946–58; PRESIDENT, EMB (LTD.) RESEARCH ECONOMISTS, 1958– . Consultant, Organization of American States; chmn., U.S. Review Committee on Balance of Payments Statistics. Membership: American Economic Association; Council on Foreign Relations; Society for International Development; Washington Institute of Foreign Affairs. Research: Colombian monetary policy; inflation in Brazil; Ecuador. Author: The Price of Coffee and Monetary Policy (Trimestre Económico, July-Sept. 1950); Inflation and Development (International Monetary Fund Staff Papers, Nov. 1952); Strategic Factors in Balance of Payments Adjustment (International Monetary Fund Staff Papers, June 1956). Language: Spanish 4,3,2,2; French 5,4,3,3. Home: 1821 23d St. NW., Washington, D.C., 20008. Office: EMB (Ltd.) Research Economists, 1329 18th St., NW., Washington, 20036.

BERNSTEIN, HARRY, b. New York, N.Y., Oct. 13, 1909. HISTORY. B.A., City Coll. (N.Y.), 1933; M.A., Columbia U., 1934; Ph. D., 1945. PROF., HISTORY, BROOKLYN COLL., 1945– ; vis. prof., N.Y.U., 1960– ; vis. prof., U. of Rochester, Summer 1961; vis. prof., U. of Calif., Berkeley, 1962. Social Science Research Council fellow, 1943–44; Ford Foundation grant, 1953–54; American Philosophical Society grants; consultant, Ford Foundation–N.Y. State Dept. of Education, Summer 1963; consultant, Brazil-Venezuela studies, Special Operations Research Office, American U. Membership: American Historical Association; Conference on Latin American History; Hispanic Society of America; International Congress of Americanists. Research: South America. Author: Making an Inter-American Mind (1961); Emerging Brazil (1964); History of Latin America; Readings on Latin America (1964). Language: Spanish 4,4,4,4; Portuguese 4,4,3,2; French 4,3,3,2; German 4,3,3,3; Italian 4,3,3,3. Home: 191 Lexington Ave., Freeport, Long Island, N.Y. Office: Dept. of History, Brooklyn Coll., Brooklyn, N.Y.

BERNSTEIN, MARVIN DAVID, b. Newark, N.J., Oct. 22, 1923. HISTORY. B.S.S., City Coll. (N.Y.), 1944; M.A., U. of Mich., 1944; Ph. D., U. of Tex., 1951. Instr., City Coll. (N.Y.), 1946–51; historian, U.S. Dept. of Defense, 1951–53; instr., Mass. State Coll., Worcester, 1954–57; lectr., Clark U., Summers 1955, 1956; vis. prof., U. of Panama, Central U. (Ecuador), 1957–58; vis. asst. prof., U. of Nebr., 1958–59; ASSOC. PROF., SOCIAL STUDIES, STATE U. OF N.Y., COLL. AT FREDONIA, 1959– . Consultant, U.S. Dept. of Justice, 1956–62; Smith-Mundt Act fellow (Panama, Ecuador), 1957–58; State U. of N.Y. grant-in-aid, 1962–64; State U. of N.Y. faculty research fellow, 1964; Bolton Prize Committee, Conference on Latin American History, 1964. Membership: American Association of University Professors; American Historical Association; Bolivarian Society; Conference on Latin American History. Research: Mexican economic structure and development, specifically in the mining industry and mining law. Author: Economic Organization of the Mexican Coal Industry (Inter-American Economic Affairs, Spring 1952); The OAS: Guardian of Peace or Pawn of Power Politics? (Social Education, Apr. 1961); Colonial Latin America and Revolutionary Movements (in Encyclopaedia Britannica, 1962). Language: Spanish 5,4,4,2; Portuguese 2,1,1,1; French 3,2,1,1. Home: 42 Carol Ave., Fredonia, N.Y. 14063. Office: Dept. of Social Studies, State U. of N.Y., Coll. at Fredonia, Fredonia, 14063.

BERRY, R. ALBERT, b. Stratford, Ontario, Canada, Jan. 26, 1937. ECONOMICS. B.A., U. of Western Ontario, 1959; Ph. D., Princeton U., 1963. ECONOMIST, RESEARCH STAFF, ECONOMIC GROWTH CENTER, YALE U., 1962– . Membership: American Economic Association; Society for International Development. Research: economic development; international trade; economic structure and growth of Colombia. Language: Spanish 4,4,4,3; French 2,1,1,1. Office: Economic Growth Center, 52 Hillhouse Ave., Yale U., New Haven, Conn.

BEYER, ROBERT CARLYLE, b. St. Paul, Minn., Dec. 7, 1915. HISTORY. B.A., Hamline U., 1937; B.A., Oxford U., 1939; M.A., 1943; Ph. D., U. of Minn., 1947. Research, U.S. Bureau of Foreign and Domestic Commerce, 1942; U.S. Naval Reserve (Brazil, 1944), 1942–46; research (Colombia), U.S. Dept. of State, 1946–47; asst. prof., U. of Miami, 1948–50; U.S. Naval Reserve, 1950–52; prof., U. of Miami, 1952–55; economist, Klein & Saks Economic and Financial Mission to Chile, 1955–56; PROF., HISTORY, U. OF MIAMI, 1956– . Rhodes scholarship, 1937; coordinator, Hispanic American Studies, U. of Miami. Membership: American Association of University Professors; American Historical Association; Association of American Rhodes Scholars; Phi Alpha Theta; Southeast Conference on Latin American Studies. Research: economic history, development; coffee industry in Colombia. Author: Transportation and the Coffee Industry in Colombia (Inter-American Economic Affairs, Winter 1948); Point Four and Latin America (Miami Law Quarterly, June 1950); Land Distribution and Tenure in Colombia

(Journal of Inter-American Studies, Apr. 1961). Language. Spanish 4,4,4,3; Portuguese 3,2,2,3; French 3,3,3,3; German 2,-,-,-. Home: 12540 SW. 80th Ave., Miami, Fla. Office: Dept. of History, U. of Miami, Coral Gables, Fla.

BIDWELL, ROBERT LELAND, b. Prairie Grove, Ark., Nov. 30, 1920. HISTORY. A.B., Austin Coll., 1942; A.M., William and Mary Coll., 1948; Ph. D., U. of Va., 1960. Principal, Texas-Mexican Industrial Institute, 1948–54; instr.-asst. prof., Mexico City Coll., 1956–60; asst. prof., East Tex. State Coll., 1960–62; DEAN, U. OF THE AMERICAS (MEXICO), 1962– . Research: National Archives of Mexico; Archives of the Dept. of Defense, Mexico. Language: Spanish 4,5,4,4. Home and office: U. of the Americas, Km. 16, Carretera México-Toluca, México 10, D.F.

BIERCK, HAROLD ALFRED, b. Philadelphia, Pa., Jan. 20, 1916. History. B.A. U. of Calif., Los Angeles, 1938; M.A., 1940; Ph. D., 1944. Instr., U.S. Navy (Bainbridge Md.), 1945–46; asst. prof., Carnegie Institute of Technology, 1946–48; lectr., U. of Pittsburgh, 1947–48; PROF., HISTORY, U. OF N.C., 1948– . Rockefeller Foundation research fellow, 1950–51; Ford Foundation fellow, 1955–56; history consultant, Banco de Venezuela. Membership: American Historical Association; Conference on Latin American History; Pan-American Institute of Geography and History; Southeastern Conference on Latin American Studies; Southern Historical Association. Research: inter-American trade, commerce. Author: Vida pública de don Pedro Gual (1947); Selected Writings of Bolívar (1951); First Instance of U.S. Foreign Aid (Inter-American Economic Affairs Quarterly, Summer 1955). Language: Spanish 4,3,3,3; Portuguese 2,-,-,-; French 2,-,-,-. Home: 1019 Highland Woods, Chapel Hill, N.C. Office: Dept. of History, U. of N.C., Chapel Hill.

BIESANZ, JOHN BERRY, b. Winona, Minn., Aug. 14, 1913. SOCIOLOGY AND ANTHROPOLOGY. B.A., U. of Chicago, 1936; London School of Economics, 1939; Ph. D., U. of Iowa, 1941. Instr., Winona State Coll., 1940–42; exchange prof., U. of Costa Rica, 1942–43; vis. prof., U. of Panama, 1946–47; assoc. prof., U. of Pittsburgh, 1947–48; assoc. prof., Tulane U., 1948–50; PROF., SOCIOLOGY AND ANTHROPOLOGY, DIR., SOCIAL SCIENCE PROGRAM, WAYNE STATE U., 1950– ; community development expert (Paraguay), United Nations, 1964–65. Carnegie Foundation grants-in-aid (Panama, Central America), Summers 1948, 1949; Smith-Mundt prof., U. of San Carlos (Guatemala), 1956; Fulbright prof. (Germany), 1958–59. Membership: American Anthropological Association; American Sociological Association. Research: analysis of society and culture in Costa Rica, Panama, Caribbean, and Guatemala; community development in Paraguay. Author: Costa Rican Life (1944); The People of Panama (1955); Modern Society, An Introduction to Social Science (1954, 1959, 1964). Language: Spanish 5,4,4,3; Portuguese 2,2,1,-; French 3,3,3,1; German 3,4,3,2. Home: 8405 Marygrove, Detroit 21, Mich. Office: Dept of Sociology, Wayne State U., Detroit 2.

BIGGS, ARTHUR PERRY, b. Detroit, Mich., May 5, 1910. GEOGRAPHY. B.A., U. of Calif., Los Angeles, 1933; 1933–35. Teacher, Methodist Board of Foreign Missions (La Paz), 1936–39 (Cochabamba, Bolivia), 1940–41; acting chief, Latin American Map Div., Office of Strategic Services, 1943–45; acting chief, Latin American Map Div., U.S. Dept. of State, 1945–47; geographic attaché, Foreign Service, U.S. Dept. of State (Bogotá), 1947–48, (Buenos Aires), 1948–51, (Caracas), 1951–53, (Buenos Aires), 1956–60; asst. geographer, Office of the Geographer, U.S. Dept. of State, 1962–64; GEOGRAPHIC ATTACHÉ, EMBASSY (PARIS), U.S. DEPT. OF STATE, 1964– . Advisory Committee on Geography to Dept. of State, National Academy of Science-National Research Council, 1962–64. Membership: Academia Argentina de Geografía; American Geographical Society; Association of American Geographers; Association of Pacific Coast Geographers; Sociedade Brasileira de Cartografia; Pan American Institute of Geography and History, 1962–64. Research: geography and maps of Latin America. Language: Spanish 4,4,4,4; Portuguese 3,3,3,1. Home: 4056 Golf Dr., San Jose, Calif. Office: c/o American Embassy, APO 230, New York, N.Y.

BILLINGSLEY, EDWARD BAXTER, b. Melbourne, Ark., June 18, 1910. HISTORY. B.S., U.S. Naval Academy, 1932; M.A., Northwestern U., 1947; Ph. D., U. of N.C., 1964. Jr. officer-rear admiral, U.S. Navy, 1932–59; ASST. PROF., HISTORY, METHODIST COLL., 1964– . Membership: American Historical Association; Hispanic American Society; Naval Historical Foundation; Southeastern Conference on Latin American Studies; Southern Historical Association. Research: U.S. Navy and Latin American independence in Chile and Peru, 1817–1825. Language: Spanish 3,3,3,3; Portuguese 2,1,1,1; French 1,1,1,1; German 3,3,3,3. Home: 1808 Martindale Dr., Fayetteville, N.C. 28304. Office: Dept of History, Methodist Coll., Fayetteville, 28301.

BILLMAN, CALVIN JAMES, b. Charles City, Iowa, Apr. 21, 1921. HISTORY. A.B., State Coll. of Iowa, 1949; M.A., Tulane U., 1953; Ph. D., 1954. Instr., U. Coll., Tulane U., Summers 1950, 1951, 1952; ASST. PROF., HISTORY, FLA. STATE U., 1954–): vis prof., St. Mary's Coll. (Minn.), Summer 1956; dir., Fla. State U. Armed Forces Program (C.Z.), 1957–58. Teaching fellow, Sophie Newcomb Coll., Tulane U., 1951–53; Rockefeller Foundation fellow, 1953. Membership: Conference on Latin American History; Southeastern Committee on Latin American Studies; Southern Historical Association. Research: United States-Latin American diplomatic relations. Language: Spanish 5,3,3,2; Portuguese 2,2,1,1; French 3,3,2,1. Home: 2112 Gibbs Dr., Tallahassee, Fla. Office: Dept. of History, Fla. State U., Tallahassee.

BIRCH, JACK W., b. Glassport, Pa., Nov. 27, 1915. PSYCHOLOGY AND EDUCATION. B.S., Calif. State Coll., 1937; M. Ed., Pa. State U., 1941; Ph. D., U. of Pittsburgh, 1951. Supervisor of special education (Somerset, Pa.), 1941–48; dir., Special Education and Educational Clinic, Board of Education (Pittsburgh, Pa.), 1948–58; chmn., Program in Special Education and Rehabilitation, U. of Pittsburgh, 1958–

63; prof., U. of Pittsburgh faculty in Ecuador, 1963; PROF., ASSOC. DEAN, SCHOOL OF EDUCATION, U. OF PITTSBURGH, 1963– . Consultant, U.S. Agency for International Development (Quito, Ecuador), 1963; Fulbright Commission for selection of students from Ecuador to receive Fulbright grants to the United States, 1963; consultant, National Society for the Prevention of Blindness. Membership: American Association of University Professors; American Association on Mental Deficiency; American Psychological Association; American Speech and Hearing Association; Association for Gifted Children; Council on Exceptional Children; National Education Association. Research: school psychology; education and rehabilitation of exceptional children and youth; educational system and teacher education in Ecuador. Author: The Non-professional Worker in Special Education and Rehabilitation: A Review of the Literature (Rehabilitation Literature, Mar. 1963); Social Maturity and Reading Readiness (in Getting Ready for Functional Basic Reading: A Guide for Teachers, 1963). Co-author: Early Admission of Able Children to School (School Life, June 1964). Language: Spanish 2,2,2,2; French 2,1,1,2. Home: University Square 1, Apt. 206, 4625 Fifth Ave., Pittsburgh, Pa. 15213. Office: School of Education, U. of Pittsburgh, Pittsburgh, 15213.

BIRD, JUNIUS BOUTON, b. Rye, N.Y., Sept. 21, 1907. ANTHROPOLOGY. Columbia U., 1926–29, 1930–33; D.S. (honorary), Wesleyan U., 1958. Field asst., American Museum of Natural History, 1931–37; asst. curator, 1937–47; assoc. curator, 1947–57; CURATOR OF SOUTH AMERICAN ARCHAEOLOGY, AMERICAN MUSEUM OF NATURAL HISTORY, 1957– . Advisory Committee for Pre-Columbian Art, Dumbarton Oaks Research Library and Collection; consultant, Primitive Art Museum (New York); trustee, Textile Museum (Washington, D.C.). Membership: American Archaeological Association; Archaeological Institute of America; New York Academy of Science; Society for American Archaeology. Research: archeology of South America; prehistory of Bolivia, Chile, and Peru. Author: Excavations in Northern Chile (American Museum of Natural History, Anthropological Papers, 1943). Co-author: Andean Culture History (1949, 1960); Paracas Fabrics and Nazca Needlework (1954). Home: 2735 Palisade Ave., Bronx, N.Y. 10063. Office: American Museum of Natural History, Central Park West and 79th St., New York, 10024.

BISHKO, CHARLES JULIAN, b. New York, N.Y., Oct. 6, 1906. HISTORY. B.A., Syracuse U., 1929; M.A., 1930; M.A., Harvard U., 1931; Ph. D., 1937. Asst. prof., U. of Va., 1945–48; assoc. prof., 1948–55; PROF., HISTORY, U. OF VA., 1955– . Francis Parkman fellow, Harvard U., 1932–33; Sheldon traveling fellow (Spain), 1933–34; Board of Editors, Hispanic American Historical Review; bibliographical editor, American Historical Review; consulting editor, Anuario de estudios medievales; Editorial Board, Studia Monástica. Membership: American Historical Association; Conference on Latin American History; Economic History Society; Medieval Academy of America; Sociedad de Estudios Monásticos. Research: colonial Latin America; Luso-Hispanic backgrounds of Latin America. Author: Peninsular Background of Latin American Cattle Ranching (Hispanic American Historical Review, Nov. 1952); Iberian Background of Latin American History (Hispanic American Historical Review, Feb. 1956); Castilian as Plainsman (in The New World Looks at Its History, 1963). Language: Spanish 4,3,3,3; Portuguese 4,2,3,3; French 4,2,3,3; German 4,2,–,–. Home: "Querencia", 9 Orchard Rd., Charlottesville, Va. Office: Dept. of History, U. of Va., Charlottesville.

BLAIR, CALVIN PATTON, b. Orange, Tex., Nov. 25, 1924. ECONOMICS AND BUSINESS ADMINISTRATION. B.A., U. of Tex., 1949; M.A., 1953; Ph. D., 1957. Instr., U. of Tex., 1953–56; asst. prof.-PROF., MARKETING, U. OF TEX., 1956– ; Smith-Mundt vis. prof., Universidad de Nuevo León (Monterrey, Mexico), 1959–60; vis. prof., Instituto Tecnológico (Monterrey, Mexico), Summer 1963; vis. prof., Harvard Business School, 1964–65. E. D. Farmer fellow, Universidad Nacional Autónoma de México, 1950; consultant, Arthur D. Little, Inc. (Mexico), 1963– . Membership: American Economic Association. Research: Mexican public development bank; business and economic development in Central America; border city growth; population and industrial growth of small areas. Author: Fluctuations in United States Imports from Brazil, Colombia, Chile, and Mexico, 1919–1954 (1959); Economic Growth Projections for the Dallas, Fort Worth, and Houston Trading Areas (1961); Nacional Financiera: Entrepreneurship in a Mixed Economy (in Public and Private Enterprise in Mexico, 1964). Language: Spanish 5,5,5,4; Portuguese 2,2,1,1; French 2,2,1,1. Home: 2115 West 12th, Austin, Tex. 78703. Office: B.E.O.B. 710, U. of Tex., Austin, 78712.

BLAIR, ROBERT WALLACE, b. Santa Barbara, Calif., Sept. 25, 1930. LINGUISTICS. B.A., Brigham Young U., 1955; M.A., 1957; Ph. D., Ind. U., 1964. INSTR., LINGUISTICS, BRIGHAM YOUNG U., 1959– . National Defense Foreign Language fellow in Quechua, 1962–64; Brigham Young U. faculty research fellow for study of Kekchi in Guatemala; U. of Chicago research fellow, 1964–65. Membership: Linguistic Society of America. Research: language and culture of Yucatec Maya. Author: Spoken Yucatec (1965). Language: Spanish 3,4,3,3; Portuguese 1,1,1,1; French 2,1,1,2; Finnish 3,4,3,3; Quechua –,2,2,–; Russian 2,2,2,3. Linguistic studies: Kekchi; Maya; Quechua; Twi. Home: 980 Cedar Ave., Provo, Utah.

BLAISDELL, LOWELL LAWRENCE, b. Chicago, Ill., Nov. 13, 1919. HISTORY. B.A., Elmhurst Coll., 1941; M.A., Rochester U., 1944; Ph. D., U. of Wis. 1949. Asst. prof., Elmira College, 1948–49; asst. prof., N. Mex. A. & M. Coll., 1949–53; asst. prof., Ark. Polytechnic Coll., 1954–56; vis. asst. prof., U. of Okla., 1956–57; assist prof.-PROF., HISTORY, TEX. TECHNOLOGICAL COLL., 1957– . Chmn., History Program Committee, Southwestern Social Science Association, 1962. Membership: American Association of University Professors; American Historical Association; Southwestern Social Science Association.

Research: revolutionary history, especially in Mexico. Author: The Desert Revolution (1962); Was It Revolution or Filibustering (Pacific Historical Review, May, 1954); Henry Lane Wilson and the Overthrow of Madero (Southwestern Social Science Quarterly, Sept. 1962). Language: Spanish 4,3,3,2; Portuguese 2,-,-,-; French 3,2,2,1. Home: 2515 24th St., Lubbock, Tex. Office: Dept. of History, Tex. Technological Coll., Lubbock.

BLANCO, RICHARD LIDIO, b. New York, N.Y., May 12, 1926. HISTORY. B.S., U. of Md., 1950; M.A., Western Reserve U., 1956; Ph. D., 1960. Teacher, Cleveland Public Schools, 1954–57; instr., State U. of N.Y., Coll. of Geneseo, 1957–58; instr., Western Reserve U., 1958–59; instr., Duquesne U., 1959–60; asst. prof.-ASSOC. PROF., HISTORY, MARIETTA COLL., 1960– . Membership: American Association of University Professors; American Historical Association; Hispanic American Association. Research: United States-Caribbean diplomatic relations; contemporary Central America. Language: Spanish 4,4,4,3. Home: 203 Coventry Rd., Marietta, Ohio. Office: Dept. of History, Marietta Coll., Marietta.

BLANKSTEN, GEORGE I(RVING), b. Chicago, Ill., Sept. 19, 1917. POLITICAL SCIENCE. B.A., U. of Chicago, 1939; A.M., 1940; Ph. D., U. of Calif., Los Angeles, 1949. Instr., Chicago Public Junior Colleges, 1940–42; political analyst, U.S. Dept. of State, 1942–46; instr., Northwestern U., 1947–50; asst. prof., 1950–52; assoc. prof., 1952–57; PROF., POLITICAL SCIENCE, NORTHWESTERN U., 1957– ; vis. prof., U. of Calif., Los Angeles, 1951, U. of Chicago, 1953–55, 1958, Ohio State U., 1957, Universidad Nacional Autónoma de México, 1959. Social Science Research Council fellow (Argentina), 1950–51; Ford Foundation fellow (Peru, Paraguay), 1959–60; Citizens Advisory Committee on Alliance for Progress, 1962– . Membership: American Academy of International Law; American Political Science Association; Midwest Conference of Political Scientists. Research: political problems; Ecuadorian constitutional problems. Author: Ecuador: Constitutions and Caudillos (1951); Perón's Argentina (1953). Contributor: Politics of Developing Areas (1960). Language: Spanish 4,4,3,3; Portuguese 2,2,1,1; French 3,2,1,2. Home: 725 Lavergne Ave., Wilmette, Ill., 60091. Office: Dept. of Political Science, Northwestern U., Evanston, Ill.

BLASIER, COLE, b. Jackson, Mich., Mar. 16, 1925. POLITICAL SCIENCE. A.B., U. of Ill., 1947; M.A., Columbia U., 1950; Certificate, The Russian Institute, 1950; Ph. D., Columbia U., 1955. Foreign Service Officer, Embassy (Yugoslavia, Germany, Russia), U.S. Dept. of State, 1951–60; executive asst. to the president and secretary of the board, Colgate U., 1960–63; vis. prof., Universidad del Valle (Cali, Colombia), 1963–64; DIR., CENTER FOR LATIN AMERICAN STUDIES, U. OF PITTSBURGH, 1964– . Rotary International fellow (Santiago, Chile), 1947–48; Rockefeller Foundation grant, Universidad del Valle, 1963–64. Membership: American Political Science Association; Phi Beta Kappa. Research: international relations; comparative politics; Latin American communism, especially in Cuba and Chile; Yugoslav, German and Soviet political and related problems. Author: The Cuban and Chilean Communist Parties as Instruments of Soviet Policy, 1935–1948 (1955): Deutsch-Amerikanische Zusammenarbeit in West Berlin (1957); Chile: A Communist Battleground (Political Science Quarterly, Sept. 1950). Language: Spanish 4,4,4,4; Portuguese 2,2,1,1; French, 3,2,-,-; German 3,3,3,2; Russian 4,4,3,3; Serbo-Croatian 3,3,3,2. Home: 5306 Westminster Pl., Pittsburgh 32, Pa. Office: Center for Latin American Studies, U. of Pittsburgh, Pittsburgh, 15213.

BLICK, JAMES DONALD, b. Santa Monica, Calif., July 19, 1922. GEOGRAPHY. A.B., U. of Calif., Los Angeles, 1947; M.A., 1950; Ph. D., 1956. Part-time asst. prof., Los Angeles State Coll., 1950–51, 1952–53; asst. prof., U. of Md. (Heidelberg, Germany), 1956–57; instr., U. of Idaho, 1957–58; teacher, Fullerton Jr. Coll., 1958–60; ASSOC. PROF., GEOGRAPHY, U. OF THE PACIFIC, 1960– . Membership: American Geographical Society; Association of American Geographers; Association of Pacific Coast Geographers; California Council of Geography Teachers; Sigma Xi. Research: physical and cultural geography of Mexico. Author: California Mission Agriculture (Pacific Historian, 1964). Language: Spanish 4,3,4,4; Portuguese 1,1,1,1; French 3,2,2,2; German 3,3,3,3. Home: 2036 Bishop St., Stockton, Calif., 95205. Office: Dept. of Geography, U. of the Pacific, Stockton, 95204.

BLITZ, RUDOLPH C., b. Vienna, Austria, Jan. 23, 1919. ECONOMICS. B.A., Earlham Coll., 1940; M.A., U. of Calif., Berkeley, 1948; Ph. D., 1956. Instr.-asst. prof., Northwestern U., 1952–58; asst. prof., Vanderbilt U., 1958–60; ASSOC. PROF., ECONOMICS, VANDERBILT U., 1960– . Fund for the Advancement of Education research grant, 1951–52; Ford Foundation research grants, Summers 1957–60; Rockefeller overseas prof., U. of Chile, 1961–62. Membership: American Association of University Professors; American Economic Association; Economic History Association; Southern Economic Association. Research: economic development; economics of education; manpower in Chile; Chilean educational system in relation to economic growth. Author: Capital Longevity and Economic Development (American Economic Review, June 1958); The Nation's Educational Outlay and A Calculation of Income Foregone by Students (in Economics of Higher Education, 1962); High Level Manpower Problems in Chile (in High Level Manpower for Economic Development, 1964). Language: Spanish 4,3,3,2; German 4,5,5,5. Home: 303 Fairfax Ave., Nashville, Tenn. Office: Dept. of Economics, Vanderbilt U., Nashville, 37203.

BLOSSOM, THOMAS, b. Dedham, Mass., Feb. 15, 1912. HISTORY. A.B., Amherst Coll., 1934; M.A. Columbia U., 1935; Ph. D., Duke U., 1956. Teacher, Western Carolina Coll., 1941–43; teacher, Indian Service, U.S. Dept. of the Interior, 1941, 1943–44; assoc. prof., The Citadel, 1946–56; assoc. prof., chmn., Southern State Coll. (Ark.), 1956–58; ASST. PROF., HUMANITIES, U. OF FLA., 1958– . Southern Fellowships grant, Summers 1955, 1958; co-editor, Journal of Latin American Studies, 1960–61; Pan American travel and study grant and U. of Fla. Graduate Council grant (Colombia), 1962. Membership: Caribbean Conferences, 1958–63; Phi Alpha Theta; Southern Historical Association. Research: Colombian independence. Author: New Mexico (in Columbia Encyclopedia, 1940); Antonio Nariño, Precursor of Colombian Independence (South Carolina Historical Association Proceedings, 1952); The Library of a Revolutionary Leader, Antonio Nariño, Precursor of Colombian Independence (Arkansas Academy of Science Proceedings, 1958). Language: Spanish 4,3,-3,2; French 4,2,2,3; German 2,2,2,2; Italian 3,2,2,1. Home: 1020 NW. 36th Ave., Gainesville, Fla. Office: Dept. of Humanities, U. of Fla., Gainesville.

BLUMER, HERBERT G., b. St. Louis, Mo., Mar. 7, 1900. SOCIOLOGY. A.B., U. of Mo., 1921; A.M., 1922; Ph. D., U. of Chicago, 1929. Prof., U. of Chicago, 1927–52; vis. prof., U. of Mich., 1936-37; chmn., board of arbitration, U.S. Steel Corporation, 1945-47; vis. prof., U. of Hawaii, 1950–51; PROF., SOCIOLOGY, U. OF CALIF., BERKELEY, 1952- ; guest lectr., U. Coll. of the West Indies (Jamaica), 1954. Social Science Research Council fellow (France), 1932; consultant on race relations, Rhodes-Livingston Institute (Northern Rhodesia); resident expert, Latin American Center for Research in the Social Sciences (Brazil), 1958–59. Membership: American Sociological Association; International Sociological Association; Society for the Study of Social Problems; Sociological Research Association. Research: methods of research in social psychology; social effects of industrialization in Brazil; race relations and urban community development in Latin America. Author: Early Industrialization and the Laboring Class (Sociological Quarterly, Jan. 1960); Industrialization and the Traditional Order (Sociology and Social Research, Jan. 1964). Language: Spanish 5,2,2,2; Portuguese 5,2,2,2; French 4,2,2,2; German 3,1,1,1; Italian 3,1,1,1. Home: 134 Crest View Dr., Orinda, Calif., 94563. Office: Dept. of Sociology, U. of Calif., Berkeley, 94720.

BOARD, JOSEPH BRECKINRIDGE, b. Princeton, Ind., Mar. 5, 1931. POLITICAL SCIENCE. A.B., Ind. U., 1953; B.A., Oxford U., 1955; J.D., Ind. U., 1958; M.A., Oxford U., 1961; Ph. D., Ind. U., 1962. Lectr., Ind. U., 1958–59; asst. prof., Elmira Coll., 1959–61; assoc. prof.-PROF., CHMN., POLITICAL SCIENCE, CORNELL COLL., 1961- . Rhodes scholar; Associated Colleges of the Midwest, Central American fellow (Costa Rica), Summer 1962; National Defense fellow, U. of Tex., Summer 1963. Membership: American Association of University Professors; American Political Science Association; Iowa Political Science Association; Midwest Political Science Association. Research: Latin American legal and political theory; Brazil. Language: Spanish 4,4,4,3; Portuguese 4,4,4,3; French 4,4,4,3; German 3,3,3,3; Italian 3,3,3,3; Russian 2,2,2,2; Swedish 4,4,4,3. Home: 508 Third Ave. South, Mt. Vernon, Iowa, 52314. Office: Dept. of Political Science, Cornell Coll., Mt. Vernon, 52314.

BOBB, BERNARD EARL, b. Mitchell, S. Dak., Oct. 21, 1917. HISTORY. B.A., U. of Calif., Los Angeles, 1939; M.A., 1941; Ph. D., 1949. Instr.-PROF., HISTORY, WASH. STATE U., 1949- . History fellow, 1948–49. Membership: Conference on Latin American History; Pacific Coast Council on Latin American Studies. Research: 18th century; Mexico. Author: The Viceregency of Antonio María Bucareli in New Spain, 1771–1779 (1962); Pedro Sarmiento de Gamboa and the Strait of Magellan (Pacific Historical Review, Aug. 1948); Historiografía Mexicanista: Estados Unidos, 1959–60 (Historia Mexicana, Oct.–Dec. 1961). Language: Spanish 3,2,2,3. Home: 412 Grant St., Pullman, Wash. Office: Dept. of History, Wash. State U., Pullman.

BOEHRER, GEORGE C. A., b. New York, N.Y., June 20, 1921. HISTORY. A.B., Boston Coll., 1942; M.A., Catholic U. of America, 1943; Ph. D., 1951. Instr., Marquette U., 1949–51; lectr., Mexico City Coll., Summer 1950; asst. prof., Marquette U., 1951–55; assoc. prof., Georgetown U., 1955–62; vis. prof, U. of Wis. (Brazil), Summer 1962; CULTURAL ATTACHÉ (BRAZIL), U.S. INFORMATION AGENCY, 1962- . U.S. Dept. of State grant (Brazil), 1947; Penfield traveling fellow (Portugal), 1948; Georgetown U. Alumni grant (Portugal), 1957; Social Science Research Council-American Council of Learned Societies grant (Brazil), 1960–61. Membership: American Association of University Professors; American Historical Association; Catholic Historical Association; Conference on Latin American History. Research: 19th century history of Brazil. Author: Da monarquia à república história do Partido Republicano do Brasil, 1870–1889 (1954); The Flight of the Brazilian Deputies from the Côrtes Gerais of Lisbon, 1822 (Hispanic American Historical Review, Nov. 1960). Translator: Fátima in the Light of History, by J. I. F. de Costa Brochado (1955). Language: Spanish 4,4,3,2; Portuguese 5,5,4,3; French 4,3,2,1; German 3,1,1,1; Italian 3,2,1,1. Home and Office: American Embassy (USIS), APO 676, New York, N.Y.

BOGGS, RALPH STEELE, b. Terre Haute, Ind., Nov. 17, 1901. SPANISH AMERICAN LITERATURE AND LANGUAGE. Ph. D., U. of Chicago, 1930. Instr., U. of P.R., 1926–28; prof., U. of N.C., 1929–48; PROF., SPANISH, U. OF MIAMI, 1948- ; vis. prof., U. of Santo Domingo, Summer 1944; vis. prof., National U. of Mexico, 1945–46; vis. prof. of N. Mex., Summer 1948; vis. lectr., Ministry of Education, Republic of Honduras, Aug. 1961; vis. prof., U. of Calif., Los Angeles, Summer 1963. U.S. collaborator, Volkskundlische Bibliographie, 1925–34; editor, Folklore Section, Handbook of Latin American Studies, 1936–45; bibliographer, Southern Folklore Quarterly, 1937–58; dir. and editor, Folklore de las Américas. Membership: Academia de Cultura Guaraní; American Folklore Society; Asociación Folklórica Argentina; Sociedad Folklórica de Bolivia; Sociedad Folklórica de México; Sociedad Venezolana de Folklore. Research: Pan-American folklore; Spanish linguistics; medieval Spanish literature; English as a foreign language. Author: Bibliography of Latin American Folklore (1940); Spanish Pronunciation Exercises (1954); El folklore en los Estados Unidos (1954). Language: Spanish 4,4,4,4; Portuguese 3,2,1,1; French 3,2,1,1; German 3,2,1,1. Linguistic studies: English; Spanish. Home: 536 Altara Ave., Coral Gables 46, Fla.

BOGGS, STANLEY HARDING, b. Warsaw, Ind,. Aug. 8, 1914. ANTHROPOLOGY: ARCHEOLOGY. A.B., Northwestern U., 1935; M.A., U. of Ariz., 1936; Harvard U., 1937-39. Archeologist, Harvard-Columbus Expedition (North Haiti), 1939; archeologist, Copan Project, Carnegie Institution of Washington, 1939; archeologist, El Salvador Project, Institute of Andean Research, 1942; asesor técnico, Museo Nacional de El Salvador, 1942-46; archeologist, Zaculeu Project, United Fruit Company (Huehuetenango, Guatemala), 1946-47; chief, Dept. of Archeological Excavations, Ministry of Culture (El Salvador), 1947-54; farming (Ind.), 1955-61; PROF., UNIVERSIDAD DE EL SALVADOR, 1963- . American Philosophical Society and American Academy of Arts and Sciences grants, Peabody Museum, Harvard U., 1961-63; technical adviser, Salvador National Museum; Salvadoran Commission for Preservation of Cultural Heritage. Membership: American Anthropological Association; American Oriental Society; Society for American Archaeology. Research: exploration, restoration and construction of regional museums for four national prehistoric parks in Central America. Language: Spanish 5,5,4,4; Portuguese 3,2,1,2; French 4,3,2,2; German 3,2,1,2. Home: Apartado 1600, San Salvador, El Salvador. Office: Facultad de Humanidades, Universidad de El Salvador, San Salvador.

BOHAN, MERWIN L(EE), b. Chicago, Ill., Jan. 21, 1899. ECONOMICS. Foreign trade and publicity manager, Dallas Chamber of Commerce, 1921-27; commercial attaché, U.S. Dept. of Commerce (Cuba), 1927-28, (Guatemala, El Salvador, Honduras), 1928-31, (Ecuador, Peru), 1931-33, (Chile), 1933-39; commercial attaché, U.S. Dept. of State (Chile), 1939-40; (Colombia), 1940-41; chief, U.S. Economic Mission to Bolivia, 1941-42; economic counselor, U.S. Dept. of State (Argentina), 1942-44, (Mexico), 1945-49; prof., American Institute for Foreign Trade (Phoenix), 1949-50; officer, Foreign Service, U.S. Dept. of State, 1950-55; LATIN AMERICAN CONSULTANT (DALLAS, TEX.), 1955- . Chmn., American Section, Joint Brazil-U.S. Development Commission, 1951-53; acting U.S. representative, United Nations Economic Commission for Latin America (Mexico), 1951, (Brazil), 1953; U.S. representative, Inter-American Economic and Social Council, 1951-55; delegate, Tenth Inter-American Conference (Caracas), 1954; head, U.S. Agency for International Development Mission (Brazil), 1961; head, Inter-American Development Bank Mission (Guatemala), 1962; consultant, Pan American Union; dir., Dallas Council on World Affairs; dir., United Nations Association of Dallas. Membership: American Foreign Service Association; Diplomatic and Consular Officers Retired. Research: economic development and structure of Latin America; Argentine economy. Author: Investment in Cuba (1956); Investment in Chile (1960). Language: Spanish 5,5,4,4; Portuguese 3,4,3,1. Home and office: 6902 Westlake Ave., Dallas, Tex. 75214.

BOLINGER, DWIGHT LeMERTON, b. Topeka, Kans., Aug. 18, 1907. LINGUISTICS AND LANGUAGE. B.A., Washburn Coll., 1930; M.A., U. of Kans., 1932; Ph. D., U. of Wis., 1936. Instr., Spanish, Junior Coll. of Kansas City, 1937; assoc. prof., Washburn U., 1937-44; exchange prof., Colegio San Luis Gonzaga (Cartago, Costa Rica), 1941; asst. prof.-prof., U. of Southern Calif., 1944-60; prof., U. of Colo., 1960-63; PROF., ROMANCE LANGUAGES AND LITERATURES, HARVARD U., 1963- . Sterling fellow in linguistics, Yale U., 1943-44; Haskins Laboratories fellow, 1956-57. Membership: American Association of Teachers of Spanish and Portuguese; American Association of University Professors; American Dialect Society; Asociación de Lingüística y Filología de América Latina; Hispanic American Society; Linguistic Circle of New York; Linguistic Society of American; Modern Language Association; Phonetic Society of Japan. Research: Spanish and English linguistics; syntax and prosody; language teaching methods. Author: Algo más que entrenamiento (Hispania, Mar. 1961); Secondary Stress in Spanish (Romance Philology, Feb. 1962). Co-author: Modern Spanish (1960). Language: Spanish 4,4,4,4; Portuguese 3,1,1,1; French 2,1,1,1. Linguistic studies: English; Spanish. Home: 52 Scott Rd., Belmont, Mass. 02178. Office: Dept. of Romance Languages and Literatures, 206 Boylston Hall, Harvard U., Cambridge, Mass. 02138.

BORAH, WOODROW (WILSON), b. Utica, Miss., Dec. 22, 1912. HISTORY. A.B., U. of Calif., Los Angeles, 1935; M.A., 1936; Ph. D., U. of Calif., Berkeley, 1940. Instr., Princeton U., 1941-42; analyst, U.S. Office of Strategic Services and U.S. Dept. of State, 1942-47; asst. prof.-prof., U. of Calif., Berkeley, 1948-62; PROF., HISTORY, U. OF CALIF., BERKELEY, 1962- . Guggenheim fellow, 1951-52, 1958-59; Bolton Prize Committee, Conference on Latin American History, 1961. Membership: American Historical Association; Conference on Latin American History; Sociedad Mexicana de Antropología. Research: demographic history; colonial Mexico; socioeconomic history of Latin America. Author: New Spain's Century of Depression (1951); Early Colonial Trade and Navigation between Mexico and Peru (1954); The Aboriginal Population of Central Mexico on the Eve of the Spanish Conquest (1963). Language: Spanish 5,4,4,4; Portuguese 4,3,3,2; French 5,4,3,4; German 4,4,3,3; Italian 4,3,3,2. Home: 451 Vincente Ave., Berkeley 4, Calif. Office: Dept. of History, U. of Calif., Berkeley 4.

BORHEGYI, STEPHAN FRANCIS de, b. Budapest, Hungary, Oct. 17, 1921. ANTHROPOLOGY. Ph. D., Peter Pazmany U. (Hungary), 1946. Asst. lectr., Peter Pazmany U., 1945-48; asst. curator, Hungarian National Museum, 1945-48; field researcher, Carnegie Institute of Washington, 1949-51; chief analyst, Human Relations Area Files, Yale U., 1951-52; assoc. prof., U. of Okla., 1954-59; dir., Stovall Museum, U. of Okla., 1954-59; ASSOC. PROF., ANTHROPOLOGY, U. OF WIS., 1959- |; DIR. MILWAUKEE PUBLIC MUSEUM, 1959- . Wenner-Gren Foundation fellow (Central America), 1948-50; Bollingen

Foundation fellow, 1952–54; National Science Foundation fellow, 1961–64; dir., UNESCO's Latin American Museum Seminar, 1962. Membership: American Anthropological Association; American Association of Museums; Central States Anthropological Association; Instituto de Antropología e Historia de Guatemala; Midwest Museums Conference; Royal Anthropological Society; Society for American Archaeology; Wisconson Archaeological Survey. Research: Middle and South America archaeology and ethnology. Author: Cultura folk y cultura compleja en el area Maya meridional (Ciencias Sociales, Apr. 1954); Underwater Archaeology in the Maya Highlands (Scientific American, Mar. 1959); Ball Game Handstones and Ball Game Gloves (in Essays in Pre-Columbian Art and Archaeology, 1961). Language: Spanish 4,4,5,4; Portuguese 2, 2,1,1; French 4,4,4,3; German 5,5,5,5; Hungarian 5,5,5,5. Home: 2515 North Terrace Ave., Milwaukee, Wis. 53211. Office: Milwaukee Public Museum, 800 West Wells St., Milwaukee, 53211.

BORK, ALBERT WILLIAM, b. Prescott, Ariz., August 12, 1906. HISTORY AND SPANISH AMERICAN LITERATURE. B.A., U. of Ariz., 1935; M.A., 1938; Litt. D., Universidad Nacional Autónoma de México, 1944. Asst. prof., State Coll. of Wash., 1944–46; catedrático, Universidad Nacional de México, 1946; asst. prof., U. of Ariz., 1946–50; assoc. prof., dean of undergraduate studies, Mexico City Coll., 1950–53; dir., asst. to vice president, Personnel and Industrial Relations, General Electric, S.A. de C.V. (Mexico), 1953–57; PROF., SPANISH, DIR., LATIN AMERICAN INSTITUTE, SOUTHERN ILL. U., 1958– . Roosevelt scholarship, Institute of International Education (Mexico), 1942–44; American Council of Learned Societies grant, 1943–44; Fulbright lectr., Universidad Nacional Mayor de San Marcos (Peru), 1959–60. Membership: American Association of Teachers of Spanish and Portuguese; American Historical Association; Modern Language Association; Phi Kappa Phi; Sigma Delta Pi; Sociedad Folklórica de México. Research: political and social conditions in Mexico; Mexican literature. Author: Nuevos aspectos del comercio entre Nuevo México y Misuri, 1822–1846 (1944); Doña Inés de Castro y otros motivos del Romancero General (Anuario de la Sociedad Folklórica de México, 1944); Mexico—1960 (Arizona Quarterly, Winter 1960). Language: Spanish 5,5,5,5; Portuguese 4,4,4,4; French 3,2,2,2; Catalán 3,2,-2,2; German 3,2,2,2. Home: Route 1, Carbondale, Ill. 62901. Office: Latin American Institute, Southern Ill. U., Carbondale, 62903.

BORMAN, MARLYTTE BUBS, b. St. Charles, Ill., May 2, 1926. LINGUISTICS. B.A., Columbia Bible Coll., 1949; Summer Institute of Linguistics-U. of Okla., 1949, 1950, 1959. Pilot, Summer Institute of Linguistics (Peru), 1949–53; TRANSLATOR, LINGUIST, SUMMER INSTITUTE OF LINGUISTICS, 1953– . Research: descriptive linguistics and translation; culture and language of the Cofan Indian tribe of Ecuador. Author: Cofan Phonemes (Summer Institute of Linguistics, 1962). Language: Spanish 3,3,3,3; Cofan 4,3,3,4. Linguistic studies: Cofan. Home and office: Summer Institute of Linguistics, Box 1960, Santa Ana, Calif.

BORTON, RAYMOND EUGENE, b. Lansing, Mich., Sept. 11, 1931. ECONOMICS. B.S., Cornell U., 1954; M.S., Mich. State U., 1957; Ph. D., Mont. State U., 1964. Technician, International Voluntary Services (South Vietnam), 1958–61; research asst., Mont. State Coll., 1961–64; lectr. and discussion leader, U.S. Peace Corps Training Program for Ecuador, Mont. State Coll., Summers 1962, 1963, 1964; lectr., U.S. Peace Corps Training Program for Ecuador, U. of Wis.-Milwaukee, Sept. 1963; SPECIALIST, AGRICULTURAL DEVELOPMENT COUNCIL (N.Y.), 1964– . International Cooperation Center fellow, Mont. State Coll. (Mexico), 1962; consultant, U.S. Peace Corps Training Programs for Ecuador. Membership: American Farm Economic Association; International Association of Agricultural Economists. Research: agricultural economics; agricultural development of emerging nations; consumption economics; economic development in Ecuador; resource development and land reform programs. Author: Consumer Use of Mass Media for Food Information (1957); Tzintzuntzan: Place of the Hummingbird (1962); Irrigation on the Crow Reservation (1964). Language: Spanish 3,3,3,3. Home: Apt. 11 R, 400 Central Park West, New York, N.Y. 10025. Office: Agricultural Development Council, 630 Fifth Ave., New York, 10020.

BOTHWELL, LYMAN DUTTON, b. San Juan, P.R., June 5, 1904. ECONOMICS. A.B., U. of Ariz., 1933; M.A., U. of Mich., 1934; Ph. D., George Washington U., 1964. Instr., Whitman Coll., 1937–41; U.S. Army, 1941–59; asst. prof., George Washington U., 1959–63: PROF., ECONOMICS, U. OF NUEVO LEÓN (MONTERREY, MEXICO), 1964– . Lectr., International Center (Washington, D.C.) and Airlie House (Warrenton, Va.). Membership: American Economic Association; Puerto Rican Economic Association. Research: economic theory and development; capital accumulation in Puerto Rico, 1950–1960. Author: Puerto Rico Population Problem (1936); American Consumption Problems (Proceedings, Pacific Economic Association, 1940). Language: Spanish 5,5,5,5; French 3,3,3,3. Home: 102 Amazonas Ote., Monterrey, Mexico. Office: Dept. of Economics, U. of Nuevo León, Monterrey.

BOUQUET, SUSANA, b. Tlalpujahua, Mexico, Sept. 19, 1919. SOCIOLOGY. B.S., Columbia U., 1955; M.S., 1956; Ph. D., 1961. Translator, editor, Psychiatric Institute, School of Medicine of Rio de Janeiro (Brazil), 1951–52; bi-lingual interviewer, National Opinion Research Center (N.Y.), 1956–57; language instr., The First National City Bank of New York, 1957–60; instr., Brooklyn Coll., 1961–62; ASST. PROF., SOCIAL SCIENCES, QUEENSBOROUGH COMMUNITY COLL., 1962– ; ASSOC. PROF., ROMANCE LANGUAGES, COLUMBIA U., 1963– . Membership: American Psychological Association; American Sociological Association; Interamerican Society of Psychology; New York State Psychology Association; Society for the Psychological Studies of Social Issues. Research: acculturation of Puerto Rican children in New York; the sociopyschological impact of the Peace Corps volunteers upon some communities in Brazil. Author: Taquick (1945). Language: Spanish 5,5,5,5; Portuguese 5,5,5,5; French 5,5,5,5; Italian 4,5,5,3. Home: 370 Riverside Dr., New York, N.Y. 10025. Office: Dept. of Social Sciences, Queensborough Community Coll., Springfield Blvd. and Long Island Expressway, Bayside 64, N.Y.

BOURGEOIS, LOUIS CLARENCE, b. Opelousas, La., May 27, 1927. SPANISH AMERICAN LITERATURE. B.A., La. State U., 1949; M.A., U. of Calif., Los Angeles, 1954; Ph. D., 1964. Instr., Wayne State U., 1957–59; John Carroll U., 1958–61; instr.-asst. prof., U. of Pittsburgh, 1962–64; ASST. PROF., MODERN LANGUAGES, FLA. STATE U., 1964– . Book reviewer, Revista Iberoamericana, 1964– . Membership: American Association of Teachers of Spanish and Portuguese; American Association of University Professors; Midwest Council of the Association for Latin American Studies; Modern Language Association. Research: literature of Argentina, Brazil, Chile, Mexico, and Venezuela; works of Augusto D'Halmar. Author: The Tolstoy Colony, A Chilean Utopian-Artistic Experiment (Hispania, Sept. 1963). Language: Spanish 5,5,5,5; Portuguese 5,4,4,4; French 5,3,3,2; German 2,1,1,1; Japanese 1,2,2,1. Linguistic studies: Spanish. Office: Dept. of Modern Languages, Fla. State U., Tallahassee.

BOURGUIGNON, ERIKA EICHHORN, b. Vienna, Austria, Feb. 18, 1924. ANTHROPOLOGY. B.A., Queens Coll., 1945; Ph. D., Northwestern U., 1951. Instr., Ohio State U., 1949–56; asst. prof., 1956–60; ASSOC. PROF., ANTHROPOLOGY, OHIO STATE U., 1960– ; lectr., U.S. Peace Corps Training Program, 1961; lectr., Columbus State Hospital, 1962. Carnegie fellow (Haiti), 1947–48; dir., Cross-Cultural Study of Dissociational States, Institute of Mental Health grant, 1964– . Membership: American Anthropological Association; American Ethnological Society; Central States Anthropological Society. Research: cultural anthropology; cultural and social change; ethnolinguistics of Haitian Creole; Haiti. Author: Rorschachs of Seventy-five Haitian Children, Aged 7–15, and Forty-two Haitian Adults (in Microcard Publications of Primary Records in Culture & Personality, 1956); The Persistence of Folk Belief: Some Notes on Cannibalism and Zombis in Haiti (Journal of American Folklore, 1959); Voodoo (in Collier's Encyclopedia, 1960). Language: Spanish 4,4,3,3; Portuguese 3,2,2,1; French 5,5,5,5; German 5,5,5,5; Haitian Creole –,5,5,5. Linguistic studies: Haitian Creole. Home: 1555 Belmont Ave., Columbus 19, Ohio. Office: Dept. of Sociology and Anthropology, Ohio Stat U., 1775 South College Rd., Columbus 10.

BOWEN, J(EAN) DONALD, b. Malad City, Idaho, Mar. 19, 1922. LANGUAGE. A.B., Brigham Young U., 1944; M.A., Columbia U., 1949; Ph. D., U. of N. Mex., 1952. Instr., Duke U., 1952–53; assoc. prof., Foreign Service Institute, U.S. Dept. of State, 1953–58; co-dir., Philippine Center for Language Study, U. of Calif., Los Angeles (Manila), 1958–63; ASSOC. PROF., ENGLISH, U. OF CALIF., LOS ANGELES, 1963– . English Teaching Advisory Panel, U.S. Information Service, 1964–67; California State Foreign Language Committee, 1965– . Membership: American Association of Teachers of Spanish and Portuguese; Linguistic Society of America; Modern Language Association; National Association of Foreign Student Affairs. Research: linguistics; English as a second language. Author: Modern Spanish (1960); Patterns of Spanish Pronunciation (1960); Spanish Juncture and Intonation (Language, 1956). Language: Spanish 4,4,4,4; Portuguese 2,2,1,1; French 3,2,2,1. Linguistic studies: Spanish; Tagalog. Home: 3055 Corda Dr., Los Angeles, Calif. 90049. Office: Dept. of English, U. of Calif., Los Angeles, 90024.

BOYD, MAURICE, b. Guthrie, Ky., Apr. 3, 1921. HISTORY. B.A., U. of Mo., 1943; M.A., U. of Mich., 1948; Ph. D., 1951. Assoc. prof., Bradley U., 1950–56; vis. prof., Universidad de Michoacán (Mexico), Summer 1953; prof., U. of Fla., 1956–64; vis. prof., Vanderbilt U., Summer 1962; PROF., HISTORY, TEX. CHRISTIAN U., 1964– . Membership: American Historical Association; Association for General and Liberal Education; Mississippi Valley Historical Association; Southern Historical Association. Research: Mexico. Author: Cardinal Quiroga: Inquisitor General of Spain (1954); Eight Tarascan Legends (1958); American Civilization (1964). Language: Spanish 4,4,4,4; French 4,–,–,3; Latin 4,–,–,3. Office: Dept. of Hist., Tex. Christian U., Ft. Worth, Tex.

BOYD, WILLIS D., b. Santa Monica, Calif., Apr. 30, 1924. HISTORY. B.A., U. of Calif., Los Angeles, 1945; M.A., 1947; Ph. D., 1954. Instr., El Camino Coll., 1951–54; ASSOC. PROF., HISTORY, VALPARAISO U., 1954– . Valparaiso U. grant (Mexico), 1963–64. Membership: American Historical Association; Midwest Latin American Council; Phi Beta Kappa. Research: race relations in the Americas; Latin America in the 20th century. Author: James Redpath and American Negro Colonization in Haiti, 1860–62 (The Americas, Oct. 1955); Negro Colonization in the Reconstruction Era, 1865–1870 (Georgia Historical Quarterly, Dec. 1956); The American Colonial Society and the Slave Recaptives of 1860–61 (Journal of Negro History, Apr. 1962). Language: Spanish 4,–,–,–; Portuguese 1,1,1,1; French 4,4,4,4; German 2,2,2,2. Home: 904 Chicago St., Valparaiso, Ind. Office: Dept. of History, Valparaiso U., Valparaiso.

BOYD-BOWMAN, PETER MUSCHAMP, b. Matsue, Japan, Oct. 29, 1924. LANGUAGE AND LINGUISTICS. B.A., U. of Toronto, 1944; M.A., 1947; M.A., Harvard U., 1948; Ph. D., 1950. Instr., Harvard U., 1949–52; lectr., Mexico City Coll., Summer 1952; asst. prof., Yale U., 1952–55; PROF., SPANISH AND LINGUISTICS, HEAD, FOREIGN LANGUAGES, KALAMAZOO COLL., 1955– ; vis prof., El Colegio de México, Fall 1963. Guggenheim fellow (Spain), 1956–57; Fulbright prof. (Bogotá), 1959–60; special U.S. observer, III Congreso de la Lengua Española (Bogotá), July–Aug. 1960; dir., National Defense Education Act Summer Spanish Institute, 1962, 1963; dir., National Defense Neglected Language Project, Kalamazoo Coll., 1963–65. Membership: American Association of University Professors; Modern Language Association. Research:

early colonial history of Latin America; Spanish America dialectology; historical and descriptive linguistics. Author: El habla de Guanajuato (1960); Índice geobiográfico de 40,000 pobladores españoles de América en el siglo XVI (vol. 1, 1963); Regional Origins of the Earliest Spanish Colonists of America (Publications of the Modern Language Association, Dec. 1956). Language: Spanish 5,5,5,5; Portuguese 3,2,1,1; French 5,4,4,3; German 5,5,4,3; Italian 3,2,1,1. Linguistic studies: English; French; Spanish; Tukano. Home: 2404 South Westnedge Ave., Kalamazoo, Mich. Office: Dept. of Foreign Languages, Kalamazoo Coll., Kalamazoo.

BOYER, MILDRED VINSON, b. Newport, Tenn., June 1, 1926. SPANISH AMERICAN LITERATURE. B.A., Baylor U., 1947; M.A., 1949; Ph. D., U. of Tex., 1956. Instr., U. of P.R., Summer 1950; U. of Tex., 1953–54; U. of Ill., 1955–58; asst. prof., U. of Ark., 1958–59; U. of Tex., 1959–62; ASSOC. PROF., SPANISH, U. OF TEX., 1962– . National Advisory Committee, Foreign Language Program, Modern Language Association, 1962–65; assoc. dir., Language and Area Center for Latin American Studies, U. of Tex., 1963–64; consultant, U.S. Office of Education. Membership: American Association of Teachers of Italian; American Association of Teachers of Spanish and Portuguese; American Association of University Professors; National Education Association. Research: 18th century Spanish literature; bilingualism. Author: A Note on 18th Century Aristocratic Education (Hispania, Mar. 1959); Texas Squanders Non-English Resources (Texas Foreign Language Association Bulletin, Oct. 1963). Co-translator: Dreamtigers, by J. L. Borges (1964). Language: Spanish 4,4,4,4; Portuguese 3,2,1,1; French 3,2,2,1. Home: 902 Lund,, Austin, Tex., 78704. Office: Dept. of Spanish, U. of Tex., Austin, 78712.

BRADLEY, CHARLES HENRY, b. Baltimore, Md., Dec. 26, 1930. ANTHROPOLOGY: LINGUISTICS. B.A., Wheaton Coll., 1953; M.A., 1956; Cornell U. FIELD WORKER CONSULTANT, SUMMER INSTITUTE OF LINGUISTICS (MEXICO), 1955– . National Defense Foreign Language fellow in Mixteco, 1962–63. Membership: American Anthropological Association; Linguistic Circle of New York; Linguistic Society of America. Research: cultural anthropology; measurement of dialect differentiation and mutual intelligibility; semantic analysis of Mixteco; comparative study of Mixtec languages; proto-Mixteco kinship system. Author; the Syllable in Jicaltepec Mixteco (in Memoria Volume of Linguistics Section of Mesa Redonda, 1957). Language: Spanish 4,4,4,4; Portuguese 2,3,1,1; Mixteco 4,4, 4,4. Linguistic studies: Mixteco. Home: 3504 Belvedere Ave., Baltimore, Md., 21215. Office: Instituto Lingüístico de Verano, Apartado 22067, México 22, D.F.

BRADSHER, JULIAN HILL, b. Florence, S.C., Nov. 12, 1913. ECONOMICS. A.B., U. of S.C., 1935; M.A., U. of Colo., 1939; Ph. D., U. of Calif., Berkeley, 1959. Instr., Mills Coll., 1946–47; asst. prof., Okla. State U., 1948–59; ASSOC. PROF., ECONOMICS, OKLA. STATE U., 1959– . Membership: American Economic Association; Southern Economic Association. Research: Mexican agrarian reform; economic development and recent changes in Mexican agriculture. Language: Spanish 3,3,3,–; French 2,2,2,–. Home: 2814 North Monroe St., Stillwater, Okla. Office: Dept. of Economics, Okla. State U., Stillwater.

BRADY, HELENA REAL, b. Havana, Cuba, Aug. 18, 1932. POLITICAL SCIENCE. B.S., Fordham U., 1952; M.A., 1954; Ph. D., U. of Pa., 1963. Asst. prof., Rosemont Coll., 1954–55, 1956–57; ASSOC. PROF., MARYMOUNT COLL., 1960– ; adjunct assoc. prof., Fordham U., Summer 1963, Good Counsel Coll., 1963–64. U. of Pa. fellow, 1957–58; Joseph M. Bennett fellow, U. of Pa., 1958–60. Membership: American Association of University Professors; American Historical Association; American Political Science Association. Research: international relations; constitutions of Cuba; Orthodox Church in Russia, before and after the Communist revolution. Language: Spanish 5,5,5,5; Portuguese 4,3,2,1; French 4,2,2,1. Home: Scarsborough Rd., Scarsborough, N.Y. Office: Dept. of Political Science, Marymount Coll., Tarrytown, N.Y.

BRAM, JOSEPH, b. Ekaterinburg, Russia, July 17, 1904. ANTHROPOLOGY. Licencié ès-Lettres, U. of Paris, 1930; Ph. D., Columbia U., 1941. Instr.-asst. prof., Queens Coll., 1940–48; assoc. prof.-PROF., ANTHROPOLOGY, GRADUATE SCHOOL OF ARTS AND SCIENCE, N.Y.U., 1948– . Membership: American Anthropological Association; American Ethnological Society; American Sociological Association; American Society for the Scientific Study of Religion; New York Academy of Sciences. Research: contemporary religious movements; intercultural relations and ethnic-cultural ideologies; Inca militarism. Author: An Analysis of Inca Militarism (1941); Language and Society (1955). Language: Spanish 4,4,3,2; Portuguese 4,3,2,1; French 5,5,5,4; German 5,5,4,4; Russian 5,5,5,5. Home: 4 Prospect St., Baldwin, Long Island, N.Y. Office: Graduate School of Arts and Science, N.Y.U., New York, 10003.

BRANDENBURG, FRANK R., b. Faribault, Minn., July 8, 1926. POLITICAL SCIENCE AND ECONOMICS. B.A., U. of Calif., 1950; M.A., U. of Pa., 1951; Ph. D., 1955. Instr., U. of Pa., 1951–56; asst. prof., Mich. State U., 1956–57; prof., Universidad Nacional Autónoma de México, 1957–62; chmn., Economics, U. of the Americas (Mexico), 1958–62; staff member, International Studies, National Planning Association, 1962– ; PROF., SCHOOL OF INTERNATIONAL SERVICE, AMERICAN U., 1964– ; STAFF MEMBER, COMMITTEE FOR ECONOMIC DEVELOPMENT 1964– . Consultant to business in Latin America, 1951–64; Doherty fellow and Penfield Committee fellow (Mexico), 1953–54; Ford Foundation fellow, 1955; Social Science Research Council grant, 1957–58. Membership: American Economic Association; American Political Science Association; Conference on Latin American History; Delta Phi Epsilon; Delta Sigma Pi; Phi Alpha Theta; Pi Sigma Alpha. Research: public and business policy; politics in Mexico. Author: The Making of Modern Mexico (1964); The Development of Latin American Private Enterprise (1964). Contributor: Government and Politics in Latin America (1958). Language: Spanish 5,5,5,4; Portuguese

5,4,4,3; French 3,3,3,2; Italian 3,3,3,1. Home: 5001 Battery Lane, Bethesda, Md. Office: Committee for Economic Development, 1000 Connecticut Ave., NW., Washington, D.C., 20006.

BRANSON, ROBERT EARL, b. Dallas, Tex., Dec. 3, 1918. ECONOMICS. B.S., Southern Methodist U., 1941; M.P.A., Harvard U., 1948; M.A. 1949; Ph. D., 1954. Economist, U.S. Dept. of Agriculture, 1941–48, 1950–54; economist, Office of Research and Intelligence, U.S. Dept. of State, 1946; assoc. project dir., Marketing Research, U. of P.R., 1949–50; assoc. prof.-PROF., ECONOMICS, CHMN., CONSUMER ECONOMICS, TEX. A. & M. U., 1955– . Membership: American Economic Association; American Farm Economic Association; American Marketing Association. Research: agricultural economics; food markets in Puerto Rico; beef export market in Argentina. Co-author: Marketing Efficiency in Puerto Rico (1955); A Program for Stabilizing Argentine Beef Exports (1962). Language: Spanish 3,2,2,2. Home: 4008 Culpepper Dr., Bryan, Tex. Office: Dept. of Agricultural Economics and Sociology, Tex. A. & M. U., College Station.

BRASCHI, WILFREDO, b. New York, N.Y., July 28, 1918. JOURNALISM AND PUBLIC RELATIONS. B.A., U. of P.R., 1950; M.A., 1952; Ph. D., U. of Madrid, 1954; London School of Economics, 1957–58. Editorial writer, La Democracia, 1940–47; dir. of public relations, P.R. Dept. of Agriculture, 1954–56; editorial writer, El Mundo (San Juan), 1958–59; dir. of public relations, P.R. Dept. of Education, 1959–60; dir. Educational Radio Station WIPR, P.R. Dept. of Education, 1960–61; PROF., PUBLIC RELATIONS, SCHOOL OF PUBLIC ADMINISTRATION, U. of P.R., 1961– . Reid Foundation fellow, N.Y. Herald Tribune, 1957. Membership: Academia de Artes y Ciencias de Puerto Rico; American Academy of Political and Social Sciences; American Society for Public Administration; Instituto de Cultura Puertorriqueña; Sociedad Puertorriqueña de Periodistas y Escritores; Unión Federalista Mundial de Puerto Rico. Research: public relations. Author: Cuatro Caminos (1963). Language: Spanish 5,5,5,5; French 2,-,-,-. Home: Los Mirtos St., Hyde Park, Río Piedras, P.R. Office: Box 21853, U. of P.R., Río Piedras, 00931.

BREATHETT, GEORGE, b. Nov. 11, 1925. HISTORY. B.S., Tenn. State U., 1948; A.M., U. of Mich., 1949; Ph. D., U. of Iowa, 1954. PROF., HISTORY, BENNETT COLL., 1953– . Research asst., U. of Iowa, 1951–53; coordinator of summer programs at Tuskegee Institute under auspices of International Paper Company Foundation, 1958– . Membership: American Association of University Professors; American Historical Association; Association of Social Science Teachers; Southern Historical Association. Research: Haiti and French Caribbean, with emphasis on church and state relations in the colonial period. Author: The Socio-Economic Problem of Haitian Representation in the French National Assembly, 1789–1790 (Journal of Social Science Teachers, Aug. 1959); Catholic Missionary Activity and the Negro Slave in Haiti (Phylon, Fall 1962); The Jesuits in Colonial Haiti (The Historian, Feb. 1962). Language; Spanish 3,1,1,3; French 4,4,4,3. Home: 1901 Finley St., Greensboro, N.C. 27406. Office: Dept. of History, Bennett College, Greensboro, 27402.

BREND, RUTH MARGARET, b. Winnipeg, Canada, Jan. 8, 1927. LINGUISTICS. A.B., U. of Manitoba, 1946; A.M., U. of Mich., 1960; Ph. D., 1964. Field worker, Summer Institute of Linguistics (Mexico), 1953–57; instr., Summer Institute of Linguistics, U. of Okla., Summers 1954– ; ASST., SUMMER INSTITUTE OF LINGUISTICS, 1957– . U. of Mich. fellow. Membership: Linguistic Society of America. Research: descriptive linguistics; analysis of indigenous languages; phonemic and grammatical theory; tagmemic analysis of Mexican Spanish clauses. Co-author: Cayapa Phonology (1962). Language: Spanish 4,4,4,4; French 3,3,2,2; German 2,2,1,1. Linguistic studies: Popoloca; Spanish. Home: 1030 Oakland, Ann Arbor, Mich. 48104. Office: Summer Institute of Linguistics, Box 1960, Santa Ana, Calif.

BREYMAN, WALTER NORMAN, b. Freeport, Ill., Apr. 29, 1919. HISTORY. B.S., U. of Ill., 1941; M.A., 1947; Ph. D., 1950. Teacher, Drummer Township High School (Ill.), 1941–42; prof., chmn., Southern State Coll. (Ark.), 1950–56; PROF. CHMN., HISTORY, DRAKE U., 1956– . Membership: American Association of University Professors; American Historical Association; Conference on Latin American History; Instituto Panamericano de Geografía e Historia; Midwest Association for Latin American Studies; Society for the History of Discoveries. Research: Mexican Revolution of 1910; Mexican positivism in the Díaz era; development of rail transport in Mexico; the Amazon Valley in the age of exploration and colonial period. Author: The Cientificos, Critics of the Díaz Regime, 1892–1903 (Arkansas Academy of Science Proceedings, 1954); The Cientificos and the Collapse of the Díaz Regime, 1903–1911 (Arkansas Academy of Science Proceedings, 1955). Language: Spanish 3,3,3,3; Portuguese 3,1,1,1. Home: 4512 Beaver Crest Dr., Des Moines 10, Iowa. Office: Dept. of History, Drake U., Des Moines.

BRIGHT, WILLIAM O., b. Oxnard, Calif., Aug. 13, 1928. LINGUISTICS. B.A., U of Cailf., Berkeley, 1949; Ph. D., 1955. Scientific linguist, Foreign Service Institute, U.S. Dept. of State, 1957–58; asst. prof., U of Cailf., Berkeley, 1958–59; asst. prof.-ASSOC. PROF., ANTHROPOLOGY, U OF CALIF., LOS ANGELES, 1959– . Junior linguistics fellow, Deccan Coll. (India), 1955–57; American Council of Learned Societies fellow, 1964–65; editor, Abstracts and Translations and Notes and Reviews sections, International Journal of American Linguistics; contributing editor, Handbook of Latin American Studies. Membership: American Anthropological Association; Linguistic Society of America. Research: relations between language and culture; Mexican aboriginal languages and cultures, especially Aztec. Author: The Karok Language (1957); An Outline of Colloquial Kannada (Deccan College Monograph, 1958). Language: Spanish 4,3,3,3; Portuguese 4,2,2,2; French 4,2,2,2; German 3,2,2,2. Linguistic studies: Aztec; Cahuilla; Hindi; Kanarese; Darok; Lushai; Tamil; Tulu. Home: 2724 North Beverly Glen Blvd., Los Angeles, Calif. 90024. Office:

Dept. of Anthropology, U. of Calif., Los Angeles, 90024.

BRISTOL, WILLIAM BAKER, b. Philadelphia, Pa., Apr. 13, 1915. HISTORY. B.A., Gettysburg Coll., 1936; M.A., U of Pa., 1938; Ph. D., 1947. Exchange instr., U. of P.R., 1939–40; instr., Princeton U., 1947–48; asst. prof., Union Coll. (N.Y.), 1948–55; assoc. prof., 1955–62; PROF., HISTORY, UNION COLL. (N.Y.), 1962– . Harrison fellow, U. of Pa., 1940–41; Social Science Research Council fellow, 1941–42; Penfield scholar, U. of Pa., 1946–47; consultant, Choice: Books for College Libraries, 1964. Membership: American Association of University Professors; American Historical Association; Conference on Latin American History; Phi Beta Kappa. Research: Protestant-Catholic relations in Colombia in the 19th and 20th centuries, especially 1948–58; Latin America in the national period. Author: Hispanidad in South America, 1936–1945 (1951); Let's Talk About Cuba; Historical Background: Cuba and the United States (1963); Hispanidad in South America (Foreign Affairs, Jan. 1943). Language: Spanish 4,3,3,3; Portuguese 2,–,–,–; French 2,–,–,–. Home: 135 Rosa Rd., Schenectady, N.Y. 12308. Office: Div. of Social Studies, Union Coll., Schenectady, 12308.

BROADBENT, SYLVIA MARGUERITE, b. London, England, Feb. 26, 1932. ANTHROPOLOGY. A.B., U. of Calif., Berkeley, 1952; Ph. D., 1960. Instr., Northwestern U., 1961; ASST. PROF., ANTHROPOLOGY, BARNARD COLL., 1961– . Doherty fellow (Colombia), 1960; Columbia U. grant (Colombia), 1963; area studies coordinator, U.S. Peace Corps Training Center, 1963. Membership: American Anthropological Association; Society for American Archaeology. Research: American Indians; Colombia; the Chibcha. Author: Excavaciones en Tunjuelito (Revista Colombiana de Antropología, 1962). Language: Spanish 4,4,4,4; Portuguese 2,1,1,1; French 3,3,3,2; German 2,2,2,1. Linguistic studies: Rumsen; Southern Sierra Miwok; Tagalog. Home: Apt. 52, 79 Morningside Dr., New York 27, N.Y. Office: Dept. of Anthropology, Barnard Coll., New York 27.

BROOKS, PHILIP COOLIDGE, b. Washington, D.C., Jan. 14, 1906. HISTORY AND ARCHIVAL MANAGEMENT. B.A., U. of Mich., 1928; M.A., U. of Calif., Berkeley, 1930; Ph. D., 1933. Bibliographical asst., American Historical Association, 1933–35; examiner and staff officer, U.S. National Archives, 1935–48; records officer, U.S. National Security Resources Board, 1948–50; archivist, branch chief, U.S. National Archives and Records Service, 1950–57; chief, Federal Records Center (Calif.), 1953–57; DIR., HARRY S. TRUMAN LIBRARY, U.S. NATIONAL ARCHIVES AND RECORDS SERVICE, 1957–. Native Sons of the Golden West fellow, 1932–33; archives and records management adviser, State of Texas, 1950. Membership: American Historical Association; International Council on Archives; Society of American Archivists. Research: United States-Spanish-Latin American diplomatic relations in the early 19th century; evaluation and research use of archives and historical manuscripts; Truman career and administration. Author: Diplomacy and the Borderlands: The Adams-Onís Treaty of 1819 (1939); Public Records Management (1949; Spanish edition, 1952); El manejo de archivos y documentos (1955). Language: Spanish 3,3,3,3; Portuguese 1,–,–,–; French 2,2,–,–. Home: 701 Bellevista Dr., Independence, Mo. 64050. Office: Harry S. Truman Library, Independence.

BROTHERS, DWIGHT STANLEY, b. Sterling, Kans., May 3, 1929. ECONOMICS. B.A., Colo. Coll., 1951; M.A., Princeton U., 1954; Ph. D., 1957. Instr., Princeton U., 1954–56; ASSOC. PROF., ACTING CHMN., ECONOMICS, RICE U., 1956– ; vis. prof., Brookings Institution, 1961–62; vis. scholar, Centro de Estudios Monetarios Latinamericanos (Mexico), 1962. Fulbright fellow, U. of Bristol (England), 1951–52; Junior fellow, Cuyler fellow, Princeton U., 1952–54; Social Science Research Council grant (Mexico), Summer 1963. Membership: American Association of University Professors; American Economic Association. Research: monetary theory and policy; Latin American economic development; Mexican financial development. Author: Specialization or Diversification? A Basic Policy Decision Confronting Economically Underdeveloped Countries (Rice Pamphlet, Jan. 1959); Nexos entre la estabilidad monetaria y el desarrollo económico en América Latina: Un escrito doctrinal y de política (El Trimestre Económico, Oct.–Dec. 1962); The Financing of Capital Formation in Mexico (Comercio, Dec. 1963). Language: Spanish 4,3,2,1; French 3,1,1,1; German 3,1,1,1. Home: 1736 Milford, Houston 6, Tex. Office: Dept. of Economics, Rice U., Houston, 77001.

BROUSSARD, RAY F., b. Lafayette, La., Apr. 22, 1926. HISTORY. B.A., U. of Southwest La., 1949; M.A., U. of Tex., 1952; Ph. D., 1959. Instr., Howard County Jr. Coll. (Tex.), 1955–57; dir., Bi-National Cultural Center (Cartagena, Colombia), U.S. Information Agency, 1959–61; ASST. PROF., HISTORY, MISS. STATE U., 1961–. Specialist on Colombia, Special Operations Research Office, American U., 1962–63; National Defense Foreign Language postdoctoral fellow in Portuguese, 1963; American Philosophical Society research grant (Mexico), 1963. Research: Mexican reform period; filibustering expeditions to Latin America from Mississippi. Author: Correspondence of Ignacio Comonfort with his daughters (Library Journal of the University of Texas, Spring 1959); Las mocedades de Comonfort (Historia Mexicana, Jan. 1964). Language: Spanish 5,4,4,3; Portuguese 4,3,3,2; French 4,2,3,2. Home: P.O. Box 203, State College, Miss., 39762. Office: Dept. of History, Miss. State U., State College, 39762.

BROWN, GERARDO CASTILLO, b. Havana, Cuba, Oct. 3, 1916. SOCIOLOGY. Ph. D., U. of Havana, 1944; El Colegio de México, 1944–45; Mich. State U., 1955–56. Prof., Escuela Nacional de Antropología e Historia (Mexico), 1948–52, 1956–57; planning economist, Banco Nacional de Crédito Ejidal (Mexico), 1956–57; adviser in social sciences, Junta Nacional de Planificación (Havana), 1957–58; counselor, Cuban State Dept. (Havana), 1959–60; prof., National Defense Education Act Summer Institute, Hofstra Coll., 1961; teacher, Plainview Junior High School, 1961–62; prof., National Defense Education Act Summer Institute, Iona Coll., 1962; assoc. prof., Hartwick Coll., 1962–64; ASSOC. PROF., SPANISH, ST. LAWRENCE COLL., 1964– . Delegate, Instituto de Investigación Sociales de la Universidad Autónoma de México al II Congreso Mexicano de Ciencias Sociales, 1945; adviser, Tribunal de Cuentas (Havana), 1952–55; organizer, I Seminario Nacional de Ciencias Sociales, U. of Havana, 1955; adviser, Junta Nacional de Planificación, 1957–58. Membership: American Association of Teachers of Spanish and Portuguese; Sociedad Cubana de Ciencias Sociales, Políticas y Económicas; Sociedad Mexicana de Estudios Históricos. Research: social problems of Latin America; economic planning in relation to social problems; capital formation and investment in agriculture in Mexico. Author: Estudios sobre Abad y Queypo (1947); Cuba colonial. Ensayo histórico social de la integración de la sociedad cubana (1952). Language: Spanish 5,5,5,5; Portuguese 3,1,3,1; French 3,2,2,1. Home: 248 Chestnut St., Oneonta, N.Y. 13820.

BROWN, JOSEPH ROBERT, b. St. Louis, Mo., June 25, 1926. HISTORY. A.B., Tex. Western Coll., 1948; M.A., U. of Chicago, 1949; Ph. D., La. State U., 1954; Universidad Nacional Autónoma de México, 1959. Bibliographer-researcher, Library of Congress, 1952; instr., Nicholls State Coll., 1952–53; PROF., HISTORY, NORTHEAST LA. STATE COLL., 1953– . Research supervisor, consultant, Louisiana Historical Committee for the Tidelands Project, 1955; sabbatical grant (Mexico), 1959; American Philosophical Society research grant, 1961; Publications Committee, Louisiana History Journal; Board of Directors, Louisiana Historical Association. Membership: Louisiana Historical Association; Louisiana Teachers Association; Southern Historical Association. Research: foreign enterprise in Latin America; United States foreign relations. Author: The Chilean Nitrate Railways Controversy (Hispanic American Historical Review, Nov. 1958); Nitrate Crises, Combinations, and the Chilean Government in the Nitrate Age (Hispanic American Historical Review, May 1963); The Frustration of Chile's Nitrate Imperialism (Pacific Historical Review, Nov. 1963). Language: Spanish 4,2,2,3. Home: 3708 Lafayette St., Monroe, La. Office: Dept. of History, Northeast La. State Coll., Monroe.

BROWN, LYLE CLARENCE, b. Hume, N.Y., Aug. 7, 1926. POLITICAL SCIENCE AND HISTORY. B.A., U. of Okla., 1948; M.A., 1952; Ph. D., U. of Tex., 1964. Instr., Mexico City Coll., Summer 1958; asst. prof., Tex. Coll. of Arts & Industries, 1958–62; asst. prof., Wayland Baptist Coll., 1962–63; ASST. PROF., POLITICAL SCIENCE, BAYLOR U., 1963– . U. of Tex. teaching fellow; Instituto Tecnológico de Monterrey scholar, Summer 1952; Board of Editors, A Journal of Church and State. Membership: Academy of Political Science; American Academy of Political and Social Science; American Association of University Professors; American Historical Association; American Political Science Association; American Studies Association; Mississippi Valley Historical Association; Southwestern Social Science Association. Research: General Lázaro Cárdenas and Mexican presidential politics 1933–1940; Russian and Latin American government and politics. Author: The Mexican Liberals and Their Struggle against the Díaz Dictatorship, 1900–1906 (in Antología MCC, 1956); Comments on the Closed Ice Box of East Siberia (U.S. Naval Institute Proceedings, Nov. 1961); Party and State in the U.S.S.R. (Social Studies, Feb. 1962). Language: Spanish 5,5,4,4; Portuguese 2,1,1,1; French 5,2,2,2. Home: 1814 South 5th St., Waco, Tex. Office: Dept. of Political Science, Baylor U., Waco.

BROWN, STANLEY B., b. Royal Oak, Mich., Jan. 8, 1919. EDUCATION. Ed. D., Stanford U., 1951. ASSOC. PROF., EDUCATION, HEAD, SCIENCE EDUCATION, IND. U., 1963– . Science education specialist, International Cooperation Administration (Brazil), 1959–61. Research: science education at elementary, secondary and teacher education levels. Language: Portuguese 3,3,3,3. Office: Dept. of Education, Ind. U., Bloomington, 47405.

BROWN, TIMOTHY, JR., b. Madison, Wis., Sept. 4, 1922. BRAZILIAN LITERATURE. B.A., U. of Wis., 1947; M.A., 1948; Ph. D., 1956. Instr., U. of Ariz., 1952–57; asst. prof., 1957–61; faculty, U. of Ariz. Summer Session (Guadalajara, Mexico), 1959, 1960, 1962; ASSOC. PROF., ROMANCE LANGUAGES, U. OF ARIZ., 1961– . Sabbatical (Brazil), 1961. Membership: American Association of Teachers of Spanish and Portuguese; Arizona College Association; Arizona Foreign Language Association; Modern Language Association; Philological Association of the Pacific Coast. Research: works of Monteiro Lobato. Author: Small Language Classes for Adults (Arizona Foreign Language Teachers' Forum, Oct. 1956); Carnival in Rio (Arizona Foreign Language Teachers' Forum, May 1961); Portuguese at Arizona (Hispania, Sept. 1962). Language: Spanish 4,4,4,4; Portuguese 4,4,4,4. Linguistic studies: Portuguese; Spanish. Home: 2532 East Drachman St., Tucson, Ariz., 85716. Office: Dept. of Romance Languages, U. of Ariz., Tucson.

BROWN, WILLIAM FRANCIS, b. Seattle, Wash., Mar. 14, 1911. ECONOMICS: MARKETING. B.A., U. of Calif., Los Angeles, 1933; M.S., 1934; Ph. D., Northwestern U., 1941. Lectr.-asst. prof., U. of Calif., Los Angeles, 1936–46; assoc. prof., Northwestern U., 1946–48; asst. prof.-PROF., MARKETING, U. OF CALIF., LOS ANGELES, 1948– ; instr., Instituto Chileno de Administración Racional de Empresas, Council for International Progress in Management, Summers 1959, 1960, 1961. Fulbright letr., U. of Aix-Marseille (France), 1961–62. Membership: American Association for Public Opinion Research; American Economic Association; American Marketing Association; Regional Science Association. Research: consumer behavior; legal aspects of marketing; marketing institutions; retail methods and structure; Chile. Author: Guild Pricing in the Service Trades (Quarterly Journal of Economics, Feb. 1947); The Federal Trade Commission and False Advertising (Journal of Marketing, July 1947); The Determination of Factors Influencing Brand Choice (Journal of Marketing, Apr. 1950). Language: Spanish 2,2,2,1; Portuguese 1,1,1,1; French 3,3,3,3. Hon : 14018 Ostego St., Sherman Oaks, Calif Office:

Graduate School of Business Administration, U. of Calif., Los Angeles, 90024.

BROWNING, HARLEY L., b. Akron, Ohio, Apr. 28, 1927. SOCIOLOGY. Ph. D., U. of Calif., 1962. ASST. PROF., SOCIOLOGY, ASSOC. DIR., POPULATION RESEARCH CENTER, U. OF TEX., 1962– . Membership: American Sociological Association; Population Association. Research: demography and urbanization in Mexico and Central America. Author: Recent Trends in Latin American Urbanization (Annals of the American Academy of Political and Social Sciences, Mar. 1958); Methods for the Study of Age and Sex Structure (in Urban Research Methods, 1961). Language: Spanish 4,4,4,2; Portuguese 3,2,1,1; French 3,2,1,1. Office: Population Research Center, U. of Tex., 217 Archway, Austin, 78705.

BROWNLEE, OSWALD HARVEY, b. Moccasin, Mont., Apr. 14, 1917. ECONOMICS. B.S., Mont. State Coll., 1938; M.A., U. of Wis., 1939; Ph. D., Iowa State Coll., 1945. Research assoc., asst. prof., Iowa State U., 1943–47; asst. prof., Carnegie Institute of Technology, 1947–48; asst. prof., U. of Chicago, 1948–50; prof., U. of Minn., 1950–56; economist, International Cooperation Administration Mission (Chile), 1956–57; PROF., ECONOMICS, U. OF MINN., 1957– ; vis. prof., Universidad Nacional de Cuyo (Argentina), Summers 1963, 1964; vis. prof., Universidad de Los Andes (Bogotá), 1963–64. Farm Foundation fellow. Membership: American Economic Association; Econometric Society. Research: monetary theory; public finance; economic theory; Chilean economic structure. Author: Economics of Public Finance (1954); Taxation and Price Level in Short Run (Journal of Political Economy, Feb. 1954). Co-author: Utility, Liquidity, and Debt Management (Econometrica, July 1963). Language: Spanish 4,4,4,4; Portuguese 3,2,1,1; French 3,1,1,1. Home: 1943 East River Rd., Minneapolis, Minn. 55414. Office: Dept. of Economics, U. of Minn., Minneapolis, 55455.

BRUBAKER, GEORGE A., b. Excello, Ohio, Sept. 25, 1928. HISTORY. B.A., U. of Ariz., 1951; M.A., 1952; Ph. D., U. of Tex., 1960. Asst. administrative secretary, U.S. Senator Carl Hayden, 1951–52; instr., Tex. A. & M. Coll., 1955–56; vis. lectr., U. of Ariz., Summer 1959; dir., Bi-National Center (Antofagasta, Chile), U.S. Information Agency, 1959–61; ASST. PROF., HISTORY, STATE U. OF. N.Y., COLL. AT BUFFALO, 1961– . Buenos Aires Convention fellow, (Colombia), 1956–57; University fellow, U. of Tex., 1958; Fulbright grant (Colombia), 1964–65. Membership: American Historical Association; Conference on Latin American History. Research: politics in Colombia. Language: Spanish 5,5,4,4; Portuguese 3,2,2,1; French 2,1,1,1. Home: Apt. 4, 43 Newell Ave., Tonawanda, N.Y. Office: Dept. of History, State U. of N.Y., Coll. at Buffalo, Buffalo 14.

BRUMAN, HENRY J(OHN), b. Berlin, Germany, Mar. 25, 1913. GEOGRAPHY. A.B., U. of Calif., Los Angeles, 1935; Ph. D., U. of Calif., Berkeley, 1940. Instr.-asst. prof., Pa. State Coll., 1940–44; cultural geographer, Institute of Social Anthropology, Smithsonian Institution, 1944–45; asst. prof.-PROF., GEOGRAPHY, U. OF CALIF., LOS ANGELES, 1945– ; acting dir., Center of Latin American Studies, 1962–63, assoc. dir., 1963–; dir., National Defense Education Act Program in Latin American Studies, 1963– . Advisory Committee on Geography, Pan American Institute of Geography and History, 1961–63; Foreign Area Fellowship Committee on Faculty Exchange with Latin America, 1962–64; Fulbright fellow (Portugal), 1964. Membership: American Association for the Advancement of Science; American Geographical Society; Association of American Geographers; Association of Pacific Coast Geographers; International Geographical Union; Sigma Xi; Sociedad Colombiana de Geógrafos. Research: historical and cultural geography; economic and domestic plants; agricultural colonization in South America since World War II; pre- and post-Columbian transoceanic plant migration; post-war colonization in Brazil. Author: Early Coconut Culture in Western Mexico (Hispanic American Historical Review, May 1945); The Caribbean and the Panama Canal (in the Changing World, 1956). Language: Spanish 4,4,3,3; Portuguese 4,3,3,3; French 4,2,2,3. Home: 10729 Weyburn Ave., Los Angeles, Calif., 90024. Office: Dept. of Geography, U. of Calif., Los Angeles, 90024.

BRUNDAGE, BURR C., b. Buffalo, N.Y., Dec. 15, 1912. HISTORY. A.B., Amherst Coll., 1936; Ph. D., U. of Chicago, 1939. Desk officer, Office of the Coordinator of Inter-American Affairs, U.S. Dept. of State, 1943–44; Peru and Chile desk officer, U.S. Dept. of State, 1944–47; prof., Cedar Crest Coll., 1947–62; PROF., HISTORY, FLA. PRESBYTERIAN COLL., 1962– . Membership: Conference on Latin American History. Research: Incas in the greater Cuzco area of Peru; Oriental history. Author: The Juniper Palace (1951); Empire of the Inca (1963). Language: Spanish 1,3,3,2; French 1,2,2,2; Quechua 4,–,5,–. Home: 4411 Cortez Way St., St. Petersburg, Fla. Office: Dept. of History, Fla. Presbyterian Coll., St. Petersburg.

BRUSHWOOD, JOHN STUBBS, b. Glenns, Va., Jan. 23, 1920. SPANISH AMERICAN LITERATURE. B.A., R a n d o l p h-Macon Coll., 1940; M.A., U. of Va., 1942; Ph. D., Columbia U., 1950. Instr., Va. Polytechnic Institute, 1942–44; instr., U. of Mo., 1946–50; asst. prof., 1950–52; assoc. prof., 1952–56; chmn., Romance Languages, 1953–59; PROF., SPANISH, U. OF MO., 1957– ; dir., National Defense Education Act Summer Language Institute, 1959–60. U. of Mo. research fellow (Mexico), 1953, 1958, 1961; American Philosophical Society g r a n t (Mexico), 1957; American Council of Learned Societies grant (Mexico), 1961. Membership: A m e r i c a n Association of Teachers of Spanish and Portuguese; Central States Modern Language Teachers' Association; Instituto Internacional de Literatura Iberoamericana; Modern Language Association. Research: the Mexican novel. Author: An Introductory Essay on Modernism (in Swan, Cygnets, Owl, 1956); La novela mexicana frente al porfirismo (Historia Mexicana, Jan.–Mar. 1958). Co-author: B r e v e historia de la novela mexicana (Historia M e x i c a n a, 1958). Language: Spanish 5,4,4,4; Portuguese 3,2,1,1; French 4,1,1,1; Italian 2,1,1,1.

Home: 1108 West Stewart Rd., Columbia, Mo. Office: Arts and Sciences 23, U. of Mo., Columbia.

BRYAN, ALAN LYLE, b. Friday Harbor, Wash., June 21, 1928. ANTHROPOLOGY. B.A., U. of Wash., 1951; M.A., 1955; Ph. D., Harvard U., 1962. ASST. PROF., ANTHROPOLOGY, U. OF ALBERTA, 1963- . Organization of American States fellow and Doherty fellow (Brazil), 1960. Membership: American Anthropological Association; Arctic Institute; Polynesian Society; Society for American Archaeology. Research: Brazilian anthropology and archeology. Author: Excavation of a Brazilian Shell Mound (Science of Man, Aug. 1961); An Archaeological Survey of Northern Puget Sound (1963); Paleo-American Prehistory (1964). Language: Spanish 4,3,3,1; Portuguese 4,3,3,1. Home: 10515 53rd Ave., Edmonton, Alberta, Canada. Office: Dept. of Sociology and Anthropology, U. of Alberta, Edmonton.

BULLARD, WILLIAM R., JR., b. Springfield, Mass., June 4, 1926. ANTHROPOLOGY. B.A., Harvard U., 1950; M.A., 1955; Ph. D., 1960. Lectr., Harvard U., 1960-61; field dir. (British Honduras), U. of Toronto, 1961-63; ASST. DIR., PEABODY MUSEUM OF ARCHAEOLOGY AND ETHNOLOGY, HARVARD U., 1963- . Membership: American Anthropological Association; Society for American Archaeology. Research: Middle American archeology, especially Maya archeology. Author: Maya Settlement Pattern in Northeastern Peten, Guatemala (American Antiquity, Jan. 1960); The Cerro Colorado Site and Pithouse Architecture in the Southwest United States prior to A.D 900 (Papers of the Peabody Museum, Harvard U., 1963). Language: Spanish 4,3,3,3; French 2,1,1,1. Home: 12 Robinson St., Cambridge 38, Mass. Office: Peabody Museum of Archaeology and Ethnology, Harvard U., Cambridge 38.

BULLEN, RIPLEY PIERCE, b. Winthrop, Mass., Sept. 21, 1902. ANTHROPOLOGY. ME., Cornell U., 1925; Harvard U., 1940-46. Engineer, General Electric Company, 1925-40; staff member, R. S. Peabody Foundation for Archaeology, 1940-48; asst. archeologist, Fla. Park Service, 1948-52; CURATOR, FLA. STATE MUSEUM, 1952- . Harvard U. fellow, 1945-46. Membership: American Anthropological Association; Florida Anthropological Society; Florida Historical Society; International Congress of Americanists; International Congress of Anthropological and Ethnological Sciences; Society for American Archaeology. Research: archeology and prehistory; Florida and the Caribbean area; Honduras. Author: Ceramic Periods of St. Thomas and St. John's Islands (1962); Preceramic Archaic Sites in the Highlands of Honduras (American Antiquity, 1963); Archaeology of Grenada, West Indies (1964). Language: French 3,2,2,3. Home: 2720 SW. 8th Dr., Gainesville, Fla. Office: Fla. State Museum, Seagle Bldg., Gainesville, 32601.

BUMGARTNER, LOUIS E., b. Chaleroi, Pa., Oct. 26, 1924. HISTORY. B.S., Kent State U., 1949; M.A., 1951; Ph. D., Duke U., 1956. Asst. prof.-assoc. prof., Birmingham-Southern Coll., 1956-62; assoc. prof., U. of Denver, 1962-63; ASSOC. PROF., HISTORY, U. OF GA., 1963- . Buenos Aires Convention fellow (Guatemala), 1954-55; Birmingham-Southern Coll. grant (Guatemala), 1958; Southern Fellowships Fund grant, Summer 1960; American Philosophical Society-Social Science Research Council grant, Summer 1963. Membership: American Historical Association. Research: the colonial period, and the period of the republics in Central America. Author: Documentos de la independencia de Guatemala (1961); José del Valle of Central America (1963). Language: Spanish 5,4,4,4. Home: 2080 Gaines School Rd., Athens, Ga. Office: Dept. of History, U. of Ga., Athens.

BUNTING, BAINBRIDGE, b. Kansas City, Mo., Nov. 23, 1913. ARCHITECTURE AND ART. B.S., U. of Ill., 1937; Ph. D., Harvard U., 1953. ASSOC. PROF., ART AND ARCHITECTURE, U. OF N. MEX., 1948- . Editor, New Mexico Architect, 1950- ; Fund for Advancement of Education fellow (Mexico), 1953-54. Membership: American Institute of Architects; College Art Association; Society of Architectural Historians. Research: art and architecture of the colonial period and the 19th century; architectural preservation in urban renewal. Author: Domestic Architecture of Taos, New Mexico (1963); The Plan of Back Bay Area in Boston (Journal, Society of Architectural Historians, May 1954). Language: Spanish 3,3,3,2; Portuguese 1,1,1,1; French 2,2,2,2; German 2,2,2,2; Italian 2,2,2,2. Home: 5021 Guadalupe Trail, Albuquerque, N. Mex. Office: Dept. of Art, U. of N. Mex., Albuquerque.

BURKS, DAVID DONALD, b. Duluth, Minn., Feb. 1, 1924. HISTORY. B.A., Earlham Coll., 1945; Ph. D., U. of Chicago, 1952. Asst. prof., Muskingum Coll., 1949-52; asst. prof., Otterbein Coll., 1952-54; assoc. prof., 1955-57; intelligence research specialist, Bureau of Intelligence and Research, U.S. Dept. of State, 1957-60; assoc. prof.-PROF., HISTORY, U. OF MICH., DEARBORN CENTER, 1960- . Council on Foreign Relations research fellow (Mexico, Venezuela, El Salvador, Dominican Republic, Brazil), 1962-63; consultant, U.S. Dept. of State; contributing editor, Handbook of Latin American Studies. Membership: American Association of University Professors; American Historical Association; Conference on Latin American History. Research: Cuba; influence of the Cuban Revolution on other countries. Author: The United States and the Geneva Protocol of 1924: A New Holy Alliance? (American Historical Review, July 1959); Cuba under Castro (Foreign Policy Association Headline Series, June 1964). Co-author: Evolution or Chaos: Dynamics of Latin American Government and Politics (1963). Language: Spanish 5,5,4,3; Portuguese 4,3,2,1; French 4,2,1,1. Home: 627 North Rosevere St., Dearborn, Mich. Office: Dept. of History, U. of Mich., Dearborn Center.

BURNETT, BEN GEORGE, b. Seattle, Wash., May 20, 1924. POLITICAL SCIENCE. A.B., U. of Calif., Los Angeles, 1948; Ph. D., 1955. Instr., Kent State. U., 1951-53; ASSOC. PROF., POLITICAL SCIENCE, DIR., EVENING CLASSES, WHITTIER COLL., 1951- ; prof., dir., Whittier Coll. in Copenhagen, 1961-62; vis. prof., U. of

Calif., Los Angeles, 1962–63. Danforth fellow; Ford research assoc.; Haynes fellow, 1945, 1958, 1959, 1962; Social Science Research Council fellow (Chile), 1963–64. Membership: American Political Science Association; Pacific Coast Council on Latin American Studies; Southern California Political Science Association; Southern Political Science Association; Western Political Science Association. Research: comparative governments and politics; labor movement in Latin America; the Colombian party system; Mexico; and Chile. Author: Latin American Labor Law: A Synthesis (Inter-American Economic Affairs, Autumn 1958); Communist Strategy in the Latin American Labor Movement (Social Science, Apr. 1960). Co-author: The Rise of the Latin American Labor Movement (1960). Language: Spanish 4,4,4,4; French 3,2,2,2; Norwegian 2,2,2,1; Russian 1,1,1,1. Home: 9831 South Cullman Ave., Whittier, Calif. Office: Dept. of Political Science, Whittier Coll., Whittier, Calif.

BURNIGHT, ROBERT GALEN, b. Lancaster, Pa., Aug. 6, 1918. SOCIOLOGY. A.B., Franklin and Marshall Coll., 1940; M.A., U. of Pa., 1947; Ph. D., 1952. Instr., U. of Pa., 1947–49; asst. prof.-prof., U. of Conn., 1949–61; PROF., SOCIOLOGY, BROWN U., 1961– . Guggenheim fellow (Mexico), 1959; Brown U. Committee on Latin America. Membership: American Sociological Association; American Statistical Association; Committee on Population Statistics; International Union for Scientific Study of Population; Population Association of America. Research: demography; social research methods; Mexican population. Author: Estimates of Net Migration, Mexico, 1930–1950 (1963). Co-author: Differential Rural-Urban Fertility in Mexico (American Sociological Review, Feb. 1956); Internal Migration in Mexico (Rural Sociology, June 1956). Language: Spanish 3,1,1,1; French 3,1,1,1. Home. 226 Waterman St., Providence, R.I. 02906. Office: Dept. of Sociology, Brown U., Providence, 02912.

BURNS, DONALD H., b. Sacramento, Calif., July 15, 1925. LINGUISTICS. Bachiller, Universidad Nacional Mayor de San Marcos, 1952; Doctor en Letras, 1959. Field linguist, Summer Institute of Linguistics (Peru), 1948–54; field dir. (Ecuador), 1954–58; prof., Universidad Nacional Mayor de San Marcos (Peru), 1958–59; regional secretary (U.S.), 1959–61; asst. to dir., Hispanic Studies, Stanford U., 1960; research asst., Cornell U., 1960–61; LINGUIST, SUMMER INSTITUTE OF LINGUISTICS (PERU), 1961– ; PROF., LINGUISTICS, UNIVERSIDAD NACIONAL DE SAN CRISTÓBAL DE HUAMANGA, 1961– . Area coordinator, Committee of Indigenous Languages, Inter-American Program of Linguistics and Language Teaching. Membership: Asociación de Lingüística y Filología en América Latina. Research: applied linguistics; tribal ethnology; literacy and fundamental education; educational institutions, language and culture in Peru, Ecuador, Guatemala, and Bolivia. Author: Quechua Hablado (1964). Contributor: Latin American Report (Summer, 1960). Language: Spanish 5,5,5,5; Portuguese 3,3,3,1; Quechua 2,2,2,2. Linguistic studies: English; Kiowa; Quechua; Spanish. Home: 2500 54th St., Sacramento, Calif.

Office: Summer Institute of Linguistics, Box 1960, Santa Ana, Calif.

BURNS, E. BRADFORD, b. Muscatine, Iowa, Aug. 28, 1932. HISTORY. Universidad de San Carlos (Guatemala), 1953; B.A., State U. of Iowa, 1954; M.A., Tulane U., 1955; U. of Lisbon, 1955–56; Ph. D., Columbia U., 1963. Instr., Rutgers U., 1961–62; guest lectr., United States-Brazilian Cultural Institute (Brazil), 1962; guest lectr., U. of Paraná (Brazil), 1963; ASST. PROF., HISTORY, STATE U. OF N.Y., COLL. AT BUFFALO, 1963– . Venezuelan Government Pan-American award, Universidad Central de Caracas, 1959–60; Mexican Government award; Andrew Carnegie fellow; Rotary Foundation fellow; Lydia C. Roberts fellow; National Defense Education Act fellow; Cordell Hull grant; Doherty fellow. Membership: American Association of University Professors; Conference on Latin American History; Phi Beta Kappa; Phi Sigma Iota; Society for the History of Discoveries. Research: Brazilian history; United States-Brazilian diplomatic relations. Author: The Sixteenth Century Jesuit Letters of Brazil (Mid-America, July 1962); Introduction to The Brazilian Jesuit Letters (Mid-America, July 1962); Rio-Branco visto pelos seus contemporáneos norteamericanos (Jornal de Comércio, Aug. 1963). Language: Spanish 5,4,4,4; Portuguese 5,5,5,4; French 2,1,1,1. Home: 215 Mary Pl., Muscatine, Iowa. Office: Dept. of History, State U. of N.Y., Coll. at Buffalo, Buffalo, N.Y. 14214.

BURNS, HOBERT W., b. Los Angeles, Calif., Oct. 13, 1925. EDUCATION. A.B., Stanford, U., 1950; A.M., 1951; Ed. D., 1957. Instr., Stanford U., 1950–57; prof., Rutgers U., 1957–60; area chmn. and prof., Syracuse U., 1960–63; DEAN OF EDUCATION, HOFSTRA U., 1963– . Fulbright prof., Universidad de Chile, 1959; Institute of International Education grant; consultant, U.S. Agency for International Development (Bolivia), 1963; UNESCO grant (Chile, Argentina, Peru); consultant on experimental education, Government of Guatemala; Conference Board, Associated Research Councils. Membership: American Association for the Advancement of Science; American Association of University Professors; American Philosophical Association; American Sociological Association. Research: use of education as an instrument in national economic and social development in the underdeveloped nations; educational systems of Argentina, Bolivia, Chile, and Guatemala. Author: Pragmatism and the Science of Behavior (Philosophy of Science, Jan. 1960); The Logic of the Educational Implication (Educational Theory, Jan. 1962); Influence of Social Class on Education in Latin America (Comparative Education Review, June 1963). Language: Spanish 3,3,3,3; Portuguese 1,1,1,1; French 2,1,1,1. Home: 381 Smith Ave., Islip, N.Y. Office: School of Education, Hofstra U., Hempstead, N.Y.

BURR, ROBERT N., b. Rochester, N.Y., Oct. 15, 1916. HISTORY AND INTERNATIONAL RELATIONS. B.A., U. of Rochester, 1939; Ph. D., U. of Pa., 1948. Instr., Rutgers U., 1946–48; asst. prof.-PROF., HISTORY, U. OF CALIF., LOS

ANGELES, 1948– . Penfield fellow (Colombia), 1942–43; Social Science Research Council grant, 1947–48; Doherty fellow (Chile), 1951–52; Eisenhower exchange fellow (South America), 1957; Rockefeller Foundation grant, 1961–62; chmn., Joint Committee on Latin American Studies, American Council of Learned Societies-Social Science Research Council, 1959– ; consultant, Foreign Area Fellowship Program, 1961– . Membership: American Historical Association; Conference on Latin American History; Pacific Coast Council on Latin American Studies; Pan American Institute of Geography and History. Research: history and international relations of South American nations. Author: The Stillborn Panama Congress: Power Politics and Chilean-Colombian Relations During the War of the Pacific (1962). Co-author: Documents on Inter-American Cooperation, 1810–1948 (1955). Language: Spanish 4,4,3,3; Portugese 3,1,1,1; French 4,1,1,1. Home: 10856 Wellworth Ave., Los Angeles 24, Calif. Office: Dept. of History, U. of Calif., Los Angeles 24.

BURRUS, ERNEST JOSEPH, S.J., b. El Paso, Tex., Apr. 20, 1907. HISTORY. A.B., Gonzaga U. (Wash.), 1931; M.A., 1932; Loyola U. (La.), 1933; Litt. D. (honoris causa), U. of St. Louis, 1960. Instr., Loyola U. (La.), 1932–35, 1939–50; dean, 1947–50; staff member, Jesuit Historical Institute (Rome), 1950– ; DIR., HISTORY, JESUIT HISTORICAL INSTITUTE (U.S.), 1960– . Carnegie grant-in-aid (Mexico), 1945–50; Guggenheim fellow (Italy), 1957–59; American Council of Learned Societies grant, 1961–62. Membership: American Jesuit Historians; Instituto Panamericano. Research: New Spain; archival research in Mexico; research in Italian archives on Hispanic American sources. Editor: Historia de México (1949). Translator: Kino Reports to Headquarters, by E. F. Kino (1954); Historia de la Provincia de la Compañía de Jesús de Nueva España, 1556–1767 (1956–60). Language: Spanish 5,5,5,5; Portuguese 5,2,2,2; French 5,5,5,5; German 5,5,5,5; Italian 5,5,5,5; Latin 5,–,–,5. Home and office: Via dei Penitenzieri 20, Rome 6, Italy; in U.S., Dept. of History, St. Louis U., St. Louis 3, Mo.

BUSEY, JAMES L(YNN), b. Seattle, Wash., Feb. 4, 1916. POLITICAL SCIENCE. B.A., U. of Puget Sound, 1940; M.A., Ohio State U., 1947; Ph. D., 1952. Asst. prof., U. of Wyo., 1949–52; vis. instr., N. Mex. Highlands U., Summer 1951; PROF., POLITICAL SCIENCE, U. OF COLO., 1952– ; vis. instr., N. Mex. Western Coll., Summers 1954, 1957, U. of New Brunswick, Summer 1960, U. of Hawaii, Summer 1961. National Defense Education Act fellow in Portuguese, U. of Tex., Summer 1962; Fulbright lectr., Escola de Sociologia e Política (Brazil), 1963. Membership: Academy of Political Science; American Association of University Professors; American Political Science Association; Rocky Mountain Council for Latin American Studies; Western Political Science Association. Research: international relations; Central America; Brazilian political movements. Author: Latin American Political Guide (1957–); Notes on Costa Rican Democracy (1962); Latin America: Political Institutions and Processes (1964). Language: Spanish 5,5,4,4; Portuguese 4,4,3,3; French 3,2,1,1; Norwegian 2,2,1,2. Home: 2100 Baseline Rd., Boulder, Colo. 80302. Office: Dept. of Political Science, U. of Colo., Boulder, 80304.

BUSH, ROBERT NELSON, b. Colo., Feb. 1, 1914. EDUCATION. B.A., Colo. State Coll. 1935; M.A., 1937; Ed. D., Stanford U., 1941. Teacher, counselor, and administrator, public and private schools (Colo., Calif., Kans.), 1935–43; dean of faculty, Kans. State Teachers Coll., 1943–45; PROF., EDUCATION, STANFORD U., 1945– . Editor, Journal of Secondary Education, 1951–64; consultant, Latin American Div., Ford Foundation (Colombia, Venezuela), 1962–64; Fulbright senior research scholar (Australia, New Zealand); chmn., Pacific Regional Conference, UNESCO. Membership: American Association of Colleges for Teacher Education; National Education Association. Research: teacher education; secondary education. Author: The Teacher-Pupil Relationship (1954); A New Design for High School Education (1964). Language: Spanish 2,1,1,1; French 2,2,1,1. Office: Dept. of Education, Stanford U., Stanford, Calif.

BUSHNELL, CLYDE GILBERT, b. Sioux City, Iowa, June 6, 1912. HISTORY. B.A., Union Coll. (Nebr.), 1933; M.A., Universidad Nacional de México, 1948; Ph. D., U. of Tex., 1958. President, Training Coll. (Colombia), 1948–49; high school principal and supervisor of education, Seventh-Day Adventist Church (P.R.), 1949–52; CHMN., COMMUNICATIONS DIV., SOUTHERN MISSIONARY COLL., 1952– . Southern Fellowship grant, U. of Tex. Membership: American Association of Teachers of Spanish and Portuguese; Southeastern Latin Americanists. Research: social conditions in Mexico prior to Santa Ana's overthrow in 1855. Language: Spanish 4,4,4,4; Portuguese 2,2,2,1; French 3,2,2,2; German 3,3,3, 3; Italian 3,2,2,2. Home: Collegedale, Hamilton County, Tenn. Office: Communications Div., Southern Missionary Coll., Collegedale.

BUSHNELL, DAVID, b. Philadelphia, Pa., May 14, 1923. HISTORY. A.B., Harvard U., 1943; A.M., 1948; Ph. D., 1951. Research analyst, Latin American Div., U.S. Office of Strategic Services, 1944–45; research analyst, U.S. Dept. of State, 1944–46; instr.-asst. prof., U. of Del., 1949–56; historian, U.S. Air Force Missile Development Center (N. Mex.), 1956–61; chief, Historical Div., Office of Aerospace Research, 1961–63; ASSOC. PROF., HISTORY, U. OF FLA., 1963– . Sheldon traveling fellow, 1943; Social Science Research Council fellow, 1948–49; contributing editor, Handbook of Latin American Studies, 1955– . Bolton Prize Committee, Conference on Latin American History, 1962. Membership: American Historical Association; Conference on Latin American History. Research: independence period of Spanish South America; 19th and 20th century Colombia; development of scientific research in Latin America. Author: The Santander Regime in Gran Colombia (1954); Two Stages in Colombian Tariff Policy: The Radical Era and the Return to Protection (Inter-American Economic Affairs, Spring 1956). Co-author: Space Biology (1960; 1962). Language: Spanish 5,4,4,4; Portuguese 4,2,2,3; French 4,2,2,3; German

3,2,2,1. Home: 2314 NE. 12th St., Gainesville, Fla. Office: Dept. of History, U. of Fla., Gainesville.

BUSHNELL, JOHN HEMPSTEAD, b. Minneapolis, Minn., May 3, 1922. ANTHROPOLOGY. A.B., U. of Calif., Berkeley, 1948; Ph. D., 1955. Instr., Vassar Coll., 1954–55; research assoc., Mellon Foundation, Vassar Coll., 1955–59; DIR., DIV. OF RESEARCH, NEW YORK STATE COMMISSION FOR HUMAN RIGHTS, 1959– . U. of Calif., Berkeley, grant-in-aid, 1950–51. Membership: American Anthropological Association; American Ethnological Society; Society for Applied Anthropology; Society for the Study of Social Problems. Research: Mesoamerican ethnology; culture and personality. Author: La Virgen de Guadalupe as Surrogate Mother in San Juan Atzingo (American Anthropologist, Apr. 1958); Student Culture at Vassar (in The American College, 1962); Student Values: A Summary of Research and Future Problems (in The Larger Learning: Teaching Values to College Students, 1960). Language: Spanish 3,-,-,-; Portuguese 1,-,-,-; French 1,-,-,-. Home: 5 Jones St., New York 14, N.Y. Office: New York State Commission for Human Rights, 270 Broadway, New York 7.

BUSHONG, ALLEN DAVID, b. West Palm Beach, Fla., Mar. 25, 1931. GEOGRAPHY. B.A., U. of Miami, 1952; M.A., U. of Fla., 1954; Ph. D., 1961. Map researcher, Library of Congress, 1954–56; ASST. PROF., GEOGRAPHY, BOWLING GREEN STATE U., 1961– . Pan American Foundation grant (British Honduras), Summer 1959; National Science Foundation grant (British Honduras), 1964. Membership: Association of American Geographers; International Geographical Union. Research: cultural and historical geography of the Caribbean; population, colonization, and settlement; agricultural settlement in British Honduras. Co-author: Theses on Pan American Topics Prepared by Candidates for Doctoral Degrees in Universities and Colleges in the United States and Canada (1962). Language: Spanish 3,2,2,2; Portuguese 1,1,1,1; French 1,1,1,1. Home: Apt. C–2, Colony Terrace, State St., Bowling Green, Ohio, 43402. Office: Dept. of Geography, Bowling Green State U. Bowling Green, 43402.

BUTLER, GEORGE NORWOOD, b. Pernambuco, Brazil, Nov. 26, 1912. EDUCATION. B.S., Wilson Teachers Coll., 1936; U. of Md. Teacher, public schools (Washington, D.C.), 1936–39; Portuguese language script writer and announcer, General Electric Company (N.Y.), 1939; specialist, inter-American educational relations, U.S. Office of Education, 1939–41; motion picture translator and narrator, U.S. Dept. of the Interior, 1941; liaison officer, Office of Coordinator of Inter-American Affairs, 1941–42; vice president, International Training Administration, 1942–44; executive secretary, Inter-American Commercial Arbitration Commission, 1944; dir., international arbitration, American Arbitration Association, 1944–47; executive asst. to president, Georgetown U., 1947–52; dir., Technical Cooperation, U.S. Dept. of State (El Salvador), 1952-54; chief, country public affairs officer, attaché, U.S. Information Agency (Venezuela), 1954–57, (Chile), 1957–58; chief, Latin American Div., Voice of America, 1958–59; deputy dir. of international television service, 1959–61; CHIEF, COUNTRY PUBLIC AFFAIRS OFFICER, ATTACHÉ, U.S. INFORMATION AGENCY (GUATEMALA), 1961–. Membership: Biological Society; International Education Honor Society; Kappa Delta Pi. Research: public relations; educational television. Author: The Progress of Education in Brazil (School and Society, May 1941); Foreign Trainees Acquire U.S. Technical Know-How (Foreign Commerce Weekly, Sept. 1946); Arbitrations Tested Techniques Smooth World Trade Paths (Foreign Commerce Weekly, June 1948). Language: Spanish 5,5,4,4; Portuguese 5,5,5,5; French 2,2,2,2. Office: c/o U.S. Information Agency, U.S. Dept. of State, Washington, D.C. 20521.

BUTLER, RUTH LAPHAM, b. Chicago, Ill., Dec. 19, 1896. HISTORY AND BIBLIOGRAPHY. AB., Northwestern U., 1918; M.S., 1919; Ph. D., 1925; LL.D., Loyola U. (Ill.), 1962. Asst., Bibliography and Book Selection Dept., Newberry Library, 1920–22; research dir., William Smith Mason Franklin Collection, 1922–25; prof., Hillsdale Coll., 1925–26; curator, E. E. Ayer Collection, Newberry Library, 1927–62; HONORARY CONSULTANT, LIBRARY, KALAMAZOO COLL., 1962–. History fellow, Northwestern U., 1919–20. Membership: American Historical Association; Conference on Latin American History. Research: bibliographical history; colonial Latin American history. Author: Dr. Franklin, Postmaster General (1932); A Check List of Manuscripts in the Edward E. Ayer Collection (1937); Guide to the Hispanic American Historical Review (1950). Language: Spanish 3,3,3,1; Portuguese 3,3,1,1; French 3,3,1,1; German 2,1,1,1; Italian 3,1,1,1. Home: 806 East Michigan, Paw Paw, Mich. Office: Library, Kalamazoo Coll., Kalamazoo, Mich.

BUTTE, WOODFIN LEE, b. Muskogee, Okla., Nov. 1, 1908. LAW. B.A., U. of Tex., 1927; LL. B., Yale U. School of Law, 1931; Dr. en Ciencias, Universidad Central de Venezuela, 1939. Law clerk, Schuster and Feuille (Caracas), 1931–32; secretary to Governor of P.R., 1932–33; attorney (P.R.), 1933–35; resident partner, Schuster and Feuille (Caracas), 1935–39; legal executive, Standard Oil Company (N.J.), 1940–56; dir., Creole Petroleum Corporation (Caracas), 1956–58; deputy, Middle East rep. (London), Standard Oil Company (N.J.), 1958–61: MIDDLE EAST REPRESENTATIVE (LONDON), STANDARD OIL COMPANY (N.J.), 1961–. Membership: American Bar Association; American Geographical Society; American Society for International Law; Colegio de Abogados (Caracas); Pan-American Society; Phi Alpha Delta. Research: foreign law, especially Latin American law; petroleum law. Language: Spanish 4,4,4,4; Portuguese 3,3,3,2; French 4,4,3,3; Italian 3,2,2,1. Home: 25 Wilton Pl., London S.W. 1, England. Office: Standard Oil Company (New Jersey), 30 Rockefeller Plaza, New York 20, N.Y.

BYERS, DOUGLAS SWAIN, b. Newton, Mass., Jan. 15, 1903. ANTHROPOLOGY. A.B., Harvard Coll., 1925; M.A., Harvard U., 1928. Asst. dean, Harvard Coll., 1929–31;

asst. to dir., Peabody Museum, Harvard U., 1931–33; asst. dir., R. S. Peabody Foundation, 1933–38; DIR., R. S. PEABODY FOUNDATION, 1938–. Editor, American Antiquity, 1939–46; administrator, National Science Foundation grant, Tehuacán Project (Puebla, Mexico), 1961–63; editor in chief, Technical Papers, Tehuacán project. Membership: American Anthropological Association; Society for American Archaeology. Research: archeology; Guatemala; Mexico. Author: Bull Brook—A Fluted Point Site in Ipswich, Massachusetts (American Antiquity, Apr. 1954); The Eastern Archaic: Some Problems and Hypotheses (American Antiquity, Jan. 1959); New England and the Arctic (in Technical Paper 11, Arctic Institute of North America, 1962). Language: Spanish 3,3,3,3; French 3,2,1,2. Home: Phillips St., Andover, Mass. Office: R. S. Peabody Foundation, Box 71, Andover, Mass.

C

CADENHEAD, IVIE EDWARD, JR., b. Montgomery, Ala., Nov. 23, 1923. HISTORY. B.S., Auburn U., 1946; M.S., 1947; Ph. D., U. of Mo., 1950. Asst. instr., U. of Mo., 1948–50; PROF., HISTORY, U. OF TULSA, 1950– . Membership: American Studies Association; Conference on Latin American History; Mid-Continent American Studies; Southern Historical Association. Research: 19th century Mexican history. Author: González Ortega and the Presidency of Mexico (Hispanic American Historical Review, Aug. 1952); American Socialists and Mexican Revolution (Southwestern Social Science Quarterly, Sept. 1962); Flores Magón y el periódico "The Appeal to Reason" (Historia Mexicana, Sept. 1963). Language: Spanish 3,2,1,1; German 2,1,1,1. Office: Dept. of History, U. of Tulsa, Tulsa 4, Okla.
CALBICK, GLADYS STANLEY, b. Kalispell, Mont., June 24, 1901. SPANISH AMERICAN LITERATURE. B.S., U. of Minn., 1923; M.A., 1936; Ph. D., U. of Chicago, 1944. Instr.-PROF., SPANISH, MILWAUKEE-DOWNER COLL., 1936– . Membership; American Association of Teachers of Spanish and Portuguese; Modern Language Association; Wisconsin Modern Language Teachers Association. Research: Spanish American civilization and social thought. Language: Spanish 5,4,4,4; French 4,3,3,3. Home: 129 Fourth Ave., East Kalispell, Mont. Office: Dept. of Spanish, Milwaukee-Downer, Coll., 2512 East Hartford, Milwaukee 11, Wis.
CALDWELL, HELEN F., b. Omaha, Nebr., July 9, 1904. BRAZILIAN LITERATURE. A.B., U. of Calif., Los Angeles, 1925; M.A., 1939. LECTR., CLASSICS, U. OF CALIF., LOS ANGELES, 1942– . Officer, Order of the Southern Cross (Brazil), 1959; Shirley Farr fellow, 1959–60; Machado de Assis Medal, Academia Brasileira de Letras, 1963. Membership: American Association of Teachers of Spanish and Portuguese; American Philological Association; Modern Language Association. Research: Greek and Roman drama; fiction of Machado de Assis. Author: The Brazilian Othello of Machado de Assis (1960). Translator: Dom Casmurro (1953, 1960); The Psychiatrist and Other Stories (1963). Language: Portuguese 4,4,4,3; French 4,4,4,3. Home: 11639 Kiowa Ave., Los Angeles, Calif. 90049.
Office: Dept. of Classics, U. of Calif., Los Angeles, 90024.
CALKIN, CARLETON IVERS, b. Grand Rapids, Mich., July 27, 1914. ART AND ANTHROPOLOGY. B.F.A., U. of S. Dak., 1935; M.A., Ohio U., 1941; Ph. D., U. of Calif., Berkeley, 1953. Instr., Ohio U., 1940–42; asst. prof., 1946–50; lectr., U. of Calif., Berkeley, 1950–53; assoc. prof., Tex. Christian U., 1953–55; PROF., ART HISTORY, PURDUE U., 1955– . Lectr. on contemporary Latin American art, Foreign Language Institute, Purdue U.; lectr., Latin American art, Inter-American Fine Arts Festival, Tex. Christian U.; lectr. on Peruvian Indian art, College Art Association Convention, 1958. Membership: International Congress of Americanists; Society for American Archaeology; Society of Architectural Historians. Research: primitive art history; Latin American art and architecture. Author: Moche Figure-Painted Pottery (1957); Latin American Sculpture (in Encyclopaedia Britannica, 1963); Latin American Indian Creation Legends (Proceedings, International Congress of Americanists, Summer 1964). Language: Spanish 3,3,3,3; French 2,1,1,1; German 1,1,1,1. Home: 228 DeHart St., West Lafayette, Ind. Office: Dept. of Art, Purdue U., West Lafayette.
CALLAGHAN, MARY CONSUELA, I.H.M., b. Philadelphia, Pa., June 19, 1908. HISTORY. B.S., U. of Pa., 1932; M.A., 1934; Ph. D., 1951. Teacher, Philadelphia School District, 1932–37; McDevitt High School (Pa.), 1938–40; instr., Immaculata Coll., 1940–42; head, Social Studies, J. W. Hallahan High School (Pa.), 1942–53; dir., Teacher Education, Immaculata Coll., 1954–59; CHMN., HISTORY, IMMACULATA COLL. (PA.), 1959– . Corporation grant (Peru), 1962; U.S. coordinator for Villa Maria Coll. (Peru). Membership: American Historical Association; Catholic Historical Association; Conference on Latin American History; National Council for the Social Studies. Research: social situations in Peru. Author: The Sisters of the Immaculate Heart in Peru (Catholic Historical Bulletin, 1964). Language: Spanish 5,4,4,3. Home and office: Dept. of History, Immaculata Coll., Immaculata, Pa.
CALLCOTT, WILFRID HARDY, b. Guadalupe County, Tex., Nov. 12, 1895. HISTORY. A.B., Southwestern U., 1919; M.A., Columbia U., 1920; Ph D., 1926. Assoc. prof., U. of S.C., 1923–28; PROF., HISTORY, U. OF S.C., 1928– ; vis. prof, U. of Tex., 1961–62. Fulbright lectr., Oxford U., 1963–64; lecture tour (Yugoslavia, Italy), 1964; lectr., Miami U. and George Washington U. Membership: American Historical Association; Deans of Southern Graduate Schools; South Carolina Historical Association; Southern Historical Association. Research: hemisphere policy of the United States; Mexican history and relations. Author: Santa Anna, An Enigma that Once Was Mexico (1926, 1964); Liberalism in Mexico, 1857–1929 (1931); Caribbean Policy of the United States, 1890–1920 (1942). Language: Spanish 5,4,3,3; French 4,3,2,–. Home: 1718 College St., Columbia, S.C. 29208. Office: Dept. of History, U. of S.C., Columbia, 29208.
CALNEK, EDWARD EUGENE, b. Canandaigua, N.Y., Apr. 13, 1930. ANTHROPOL-

OGY. B.A., Mexico City Coll., 1954; M.A., U. of Chicago, 1960; Ph. D., 1962. ASST. PROF., ANTHROPOLOGY, U. of ROCHESTER, 1964– . Organization of American States fellow, 1961; National Science Foundation fellow, 1961–64. Research: archeology; development of urban civilization in Mesoamerica; highland Chiapas before the Spanish conquest. Language: Spanish 4,4,4,4; Portuguese 2,1,1,1; French 3,1,1,1; German 3,1,1,1. Home: 77 Mountbatten St., Rochester, N.Y. 14623. Office: Dept of Anthropology, U. of Rochester, Rochester. 14627.

CAMERON, RONDO, b. Linden, Tex., Feb. 20, 1925. ECONOMICS. A.B., Yale U., 1948; A.M., 1949; Ph. D., U. of Chicago, 1952. Instr., Yale U., 1951–52; asst. prof., U. of Wis., 1952–56; vis. prof., U. of Chicago, 1956–57; PROF., ECONOMICS AND HISTORY, U. of WIS., 1957– . Fulbright awards, 1950–51, 1962–63; Guggenheim fellow, 1954–55; Center for Advanced Study in the Behavioral Sciences fellow, 1958–59; Economic History Association trustee, 1958–62; Council for Research in Economic History trustee, 1958– , vice-chmn., 1963– . Membership: American Economic Association; American Historical Association; Economic History Association; Economic History Society (Great Britain); Scandinavian Economic History Association. Research: role of financial institutions in the early stages of industrialization, especially in Latin America; financial institutions and economic development in Brazil. Author: France and the Economic Development of Europe, 1800–1914 (1961); Banking in the Early Stages of Industrialization (1965); Comparative Economic Progress (Comparative Studies, Jan. 1961). Language: Spanish 3,2,2,2; Portuguese 3,3,3,3; French 4,4,4,4; Dutch 2,2,2,2; German 2,2,2,2; Italian 3,2.2,2. Home: 3736 Nakoma Rd., Madison, Wis. 53711. Office: 350 Social Science, U. of Wis., Madison, 53706.

CAMPA, ARTHUR LEON, b. Guaymas, Mexico, Feb. 20, 1905. SPANISH AMERICAN LITERATURE. B.A., U. of N. Mex., 1928; M.A., 1930; Ph. D. Columbia U., 1940. Instr.-prof., U. of N. Mex., 1929–46; CHMN., MODERN LANGUAGES, U. OF DENVER, 1946– . Guggenheim grant (Mexico); Rockefeller grant. Membership: American Council on Education; Argentine Folklore Society; Brazilian Folklore Society; Mexican Folklore Society; Peruvian Folklore Society; Rocky Mountain Council for Latin American Studies. Research: Latin American culture and Southwestern folklore. Author: Spanish Folk Poetry in New Mexico (1946); The Treasure of Sangre de Cristo (1963). Language: Spanish 5,5,5,5; German 3,3,3,3; Italian 4,4,4,4. Home: 2031 South Madison, Denver, Colo. 80210. Office: Dept. of Modern Languages, U. of Denver, Denver, 80210.

CAMPA, DAVID L., b. El Paso, Tex., Oct. 8, 1903. HISTORY. M.A., U. of N. Mex., 1930; Universidad Nacional de México, 1930–32; Ph. D., U. of Calif., Berkeley, 1940. Teacher, American High School (Mexico, D.F.), 1930–33; teacher, Santa Fe Public Schools, 1933–36; asst. prof., N. Mex. State U., 1939–42; LATIN AMERICAN POLITICAL RESEARCH, U.S. GOVERNMENT, 1942– ; dir., Education Program for Latin American Educators, U.S. Government, 1944–47. U. of Calif. teaching fellow, 1936–39; adviser and liaison officer, U.S. Delegation, Inter-American Economic Conference (Brazil), 1954 (Argentina), 1957. Membership: American Association of University Professors; Instituto Internacional de Literatura Iberoamericana; Inter-American Bibliographical and Library Association; Phi Alpha Theta. Research: Mexican history and literature; political and sociological research on Latin America. Language: Spanish 5,5,5,5; Portuguese 4,4,3,–; French 4,3,2,–. Home: 7708 Granada Dr., Bethesda, Md. 20034.

CAMPBELL, MARGARET VIRGINIA, b. Ft. Pierce, Fla., Dec. 18, 1901. SPANISH AMERICAN LITERATURE. B.A., Fla. State Coll. for Women, 1922; M.A., 1935; Ph. D., U. of N.C., 1946. Instr.-ASSOC. PROF., MODERN LANGUAGES, FLA. STATE U., 1936– . Institute of International Education, Women's Club of Florida, U.S. Dept. of State grants (Chile), 1941. Membership: American Association of Teachers of Spanish and Portuguese; Modern Language Association. Research: Chilean literature; Spanish American theater. Author: Development of the National Theatre in Chile to 1842 (1958); Don Juan en el Nuevo Mundo (Hispanófila, May 1961). Language: Spanish 4,4,4,4; French 4,3,2,2. Home: 718 West Pensacola St., Tallahassee, Fla. Office: Dept. of Modern Languages, Fla. State U., Tallahassee.

CANCIAN, FRANCESCA MICAELA, b. New York, N.Y., Oct. 31, 1937. SOCIOLOGY. B.A., Reed Coll., 1958; Ph. D., Harvard U., 1963. LECTR., SOCIAL RELATIONS, HARVARD U., 1963– . National Institute of Mental Health fellow, 1959–63, (Mexico) 1960–62. Membership: American Sociological Association; Eastern Sociological Association. Research: interaction patterns of ten Maya Indian families in Mexico. Author: Functional Analysis of Change (American Sociological Review, Dec. 1960). Language: Spanish 3,3,3,1; Portuguese 1,1,1,1; French 4,3,2,2; German 2,3,2,1; Tzotzil 5,4,4,4. Home: 3400 Guerneville Rd., Santa Rosa, Calif. Office: Dept. of Social Relations, 9 Bow St., Harvard U., Cambridge 38, Mass.

CANCIAN, FRANK A., b. Stafford Springs, Conn., Aug. 14, 1934. ANTHROPOLOGY. B.A., Wesleyan U., 1956; Ph. D., Harvard U., 1963. Instr., Harvard U., 1963–64; ASST. PROF., ANTHROPOLOGY, STANFORD U., 1964– . National Institute of Mental Health research grants (Mexico), 1960–62. Membership: American Anthropological Association. Research: social anthropology; native economic systems in Mexico. Author: Informant Error and Native Prestige Ranking in Zinacantan (American Anthropologist, Oct. 1963); Political and Religious Organizations (in Handbook of Middle American Indians). Language: Spanish 3,4,3,2; Italian 2,3,2,1; Tzotzil (Maya) –,2,1,–. Office: Dept. of Anthropology, Stanford U., Stanford, Calif.

CANEDO, LINO GÓMEZ, O.F.M., b. Laracha, Spain, June 24, 1908. HISTORY. Diploma on Paleography and Archives, State Archives (Rome), 1937; Diploma of Librarian, Vatican Library, 1937; Ph. D., Gregorian U., 1938. Editor, Archivo Ibero-Americano (Madrid), 1940–47; RESIDENT

MEMBER, ACADEMY OF AMERICAN FRANCISCAN HISTORY, ASST., EDITOR, THE AMERICAS, 1952– . Junta de Relaciones Culturales, Spanish Foreign Office research grant (archives and libraries of America), 1947–49; Creole Foundation and Organization of American States fellow (Venezuela), 1958–59; research of Puerto Rican historical archives for U. of P.R., 1960. Membership: Academia Colombiana de Historia; Junta Mexicana de Estudios Históricos; Real Academia de la Historia (Madrid). Research: sources and archives in Latin America; historiography. Author: Los estudios hispánicos en los Estados Unidos (1947); Crónica Franciscana de las Provincias del Perú (1957); Los archivos de la historia de América (1961). Language: Spanish 5,5,5,5; Portuguese 4,4,4,3; French 4,3,3,3; German 2,–,1,1; Italian 4,–,4,3. Home: Convento San Francisco, Santiago de Compostela, Spain. Office: Academy of American Franciscan History, Box 5966, Washington, D.C., 20014.

CANET, GERARDO ÁLVAREZ, b. Holguín, Cuba, Nov. 23, 1911. GEOGRAPHY AND ECONOMICS. B.A., Havana U., 1939; M.A., Harvard U., 1944; Ph. D., Havana U., 1948. Prof., Víbora High School (Havana), 1946–50; head, Natural Resources Office, Cuban Bank for the Development of Industry and Agriculture, 1950–58; prof., Havana, U., 1958–60; vice president, Cuban Bank for the Development of Industry and Agriculture, 1958–60; economic consultant, Arthur D. Little, Inc. (Latin America), 1960–62; coordinator, Technical Assistance, Pan American Union (Ecuador), 1962–63; EXECUTIVE SECRETARY, PANEL OF EXPERTS, ORGANIZATION OF AMERICAN STATES, 1963– . Guggenheim fellow, Harvard U.; representative of Cuba, Pan American Institute of Geography and History; consultant, Development Board of Tacna, Peru. Membership: Association of American Geographers; Sociedad Económica de los Amigos del País; Sociedad Geográfica de Cuba. Research: human, economic, and regional geography of Latin America; resource inventory and distribution; natural resources of Cuba; industrial development; economic development of Peru and Ecuador. Author: Atlas of Cuba (1949). Editor: Revista Geográfica de Cuba (vols. 1–4, 1960). Language: Spanish 5,5,5,5; Portuguese 3,3,1,1; French 2,2,1,1; Italian 3,2,1,1. Home: 5528 Westbard Ave., Bethesda, Md. Office: Panel of Experts, Alliance for Progress, Pan American Union, 1725 Eye St. NW., Washington, D.C.

CANFIELD, (DELOS) LINCOLN, b. Cleveland, Ohio, Dec. 13, 1903. LANGUAGE. A.B., U. of Tex., 1926; M.A., Columbia U., 1927; Ph. D., 1934. Instr., Spanish, U. of Rochester, 1927–31; instr., Columbia U., 1932–34; asst. prof.-assoc. prof., U. of Rochester, 1934–46; chmn., Modern Languages, Fla. State U., 1946–52; vis. prof., linguistics, U. of Guatemala, Summer 1949; researcher, U. of San Salvador (El Salvador), Summer 1952; PROF., CHMN., LANGUAGE AND LINGUISTICS, U. OF ROCHESTER, 1952– ; vis. prof., U. of Ill., Spring 1963. Consultant, U.S. Dept. of State (Mexico), U.S. Office of Education, 1945; Fulbright lectr., Instituto Caro y Cuervo (Bogotá), 1960; assoc. editor, Hispania; National Defense Education Act Summer Language Institutes prof., 1961–63; consultant, College Entrance Examination Board, Oxford U. Press, Pathescope Educational Films. Membership: American Association of Teachers of Spanish and Portuguese; American Association of Teachers of French; American Association of University Professors; Modern Language Association; Sigma Delta Pi. Research: Hispanic dialectology, especially pronunciation; history of the Spanish language. Author: Spanish Literature in Mexican Languages as a Source for the Study of Spanish Pronunciation (1934); La pronunciación del español en América: ensayo histórico-descriptivo (1963); Observaciones sobre el español salvadoreño (Filología, VI, 1962). Language: Spanish 5,5,5,5; Portuguese 4,3,1,1; French 4,3,3,3; German 3,2,2,1; Italian 4,3,3,2. Linguistic studies: English; Nahuatl; Spanish. Home: 88 Normandy Ave., Rochester 19, N.Y. Office: Dept. of Languages and Linguistics, U. of Rochester, Rochester 27.

CANTER, JACOB, b. Newton, Mass., July 13, 1911. EDUCATION. A.B., Harvard U., 1932; A.M., 1933; Ph. D., 1940. Asst. prof., U.S. Naval Academy, 1941–46; public affairs officer, Embassy (Nicaragua), U.S. Dept. of State, 1946–47; cultural affairs officer, Embassy (Bogotá), 1947–49; public affairs officer, Embassy (Caracas), 1949; public affairs officer, Embassy (Havana), 1950–54; cultural affairs adviser, U.S. Information Agency, 1954–57; cultural affairs officer, Embassy (Mexico), U.S. Dept. of State, 1957–58, (Madrid), 1959–62; DIR., OFFICE OF INTER-AMERICAN PROGRAMS, U.S. DEPT. OF STATE, 1962– . Sheldon traveling fellow, Harvard U. Membership: Foreign Service Association. Research: educational institutions, culture, and history of Colombia, Cuba, Mexico, Nicaragua, and Venezuela. Author: Cuentos norteamericanos (1956). Language: Spanish 5,5,5,5; Portuguese 3,2,2,2; French 5,5,4,4; Italian 3,3,2,2. Home: 5209 38th St., NW., Washington, D.C. 20015. Office: Office of Inter-American Programs, Bureau of Educational and Cultural Affairs, U.S. Dept. of State, Washington, D.C.

CANYES, MANUEL, b. Barcelona, Spain, Oct. 12, 1903. LAW. B.S.F.S., Georgetown U., 1931; LL.B., Columbus Law School, 1940. Research asst., Inter-American High Commission, 1926–33; staff, Pan American Union, 1934–47; DEPUTY DIR., DEPT. OF LEGAL AFFAIRS, PAN AMERICAN UNION, 1947– ; adjunct prof., School of International Service, American U.; UNESCO Committee of Specialists on Copyright, 1951; delegate, UNESCO Intergovernmental Conference on Copyright (Geneva), 1952; International Law Commission of the United Nations, 1956; delegate, United Nations Conference on the Law of the Sea, 1958. Membership: American Bar Association; American Society of International Law; Inter-American Bar Association. Research: international law; copyright; treaties; Latin American political and juridical affairs. Author: The Codification of International Law (1958); The Meetings of Consultation of Ministers of Foreign Affairs (1962); The Organization of American States and the United Nations (1963). Language: Spanish 5,5,5,5; Portuguese 2,2,2,–; French 2,2,2–. Home: Apt. 15, 3??? 39th

St., NW., Washington, D.C. 20016. Office: General Secretariat, Pan American Union, Organization of American States, Washington, D.C.

CARDENAS, LEONARD, JR., b. Del Rio, Tex., July 1, 1930. POLITICAL SCIENCE AND ECONOMICS. B.S., St. Louis U., 1951; M.A., 1953; Ph. D., U. of Tex., 1964. Asst. attaché, Embassy (Bolivia), U.S. Dept. of State, 1957–59; ASST. PROF., GOVERNMENT, TEX. WESTERN COLL., 1962– . Organization of American States research grant, 1961; Fulbright prof., Universidad Mayor de San Andrés (La Paz, Bolivia), 1964–65; consultant, Braddock, Dunn and McDonald, Inc. (El Paso, Tex.). Membership: American Political Science Association; Rocky Mountain Council for Latin American Studies. Research: municipal administration in Mexican border states; Latin American local and state government; the Andean countries. Author: The Municipality in Northern Mexico (1963). Language: Spanish 5,5,5,5; Portuguese 3,3,3,3; French 2,2,2,2. Home: 513 Ridgemont Dr., El Paso, Tex. 79912. Office: Dept. of Government, Tex. Western Coll., El Paso, 79902.

CARDOZO, MANOEL, b. Ribeiras, Pico, Azores, Dec. 24, 1911. HISTORY. A.B., Stanford U., 1931; A.M., 1934; Ph. D., 1939. CURATOR, OLIVEIRA LIMA LIBRARY, CATHOLIC U. OF AMERICA, 1940– ; lectr., Catholic U. of America, 1940–44; asst. prof., 1944–47; assoc. prof., 1947–54; PROF., HISTORY, CATHOLIC U. OF AMERICA, 1954– ; HEAD, 1961– . Social Science Research Council grant, 1941; consultant, Library of Congress, 1950–51; American Philosophical Society grant, 1953; Smith-Mundt lectr. (Portugal), 1958; Organization of American States fellow, 1963; Advisory Committee, Who's Who in Latin America; Cavaleiro, Ordem Nacional do Cruzeiro do Sul (Brazil); Rio Branco Medal (Brazil). Membership: Academy of American Franciscan History; American Association of University Professors; American Catholic Historical Association; Conference on Latin American History; Council for Basic Education; Institute of Ibero-American Studies; Instituto do Ceará; Instituto Histórico da Terceira (Azores); Instituto Histórico e Geográfico (São Paulo); Instituto Histórico e Geográfico do Maranhão; Inter-American Council; Phi Alpha Theta; Sigma Delta Pi; Sociedad Peruana de Historia; Sociedade de Geografía (Lisbon). Research: church-state relations in Brazil; 18th century Brazil; biography of Oliveira Lima. Author: The Holy See and the Question of the Bishop-Elect of Río, 1833–1839 (The Americas, July 1953); The Idea of History in the Portuguese Chroniclers of the Age of Discovery (Catholic Historical Review, Apr. 1963). Editor: Impressões da América Espanhola, by Oliveira Lima (1953). Language: Spanish 5,5,5,5; Portuguese 5,5, 5,5; French 3,3,3,3; Italian 3,3,3,3. Home: 325 Franklin St. NE., Washington, D.C. 20002. Office: Dept. of History, Catholic U. of America, Washington, 20017.

CAREY, JAMES CHARLES, b. Bancroft, Nebr., Apr. 1, 1915. HISTORY. A.B., Nebr. State Teachers Coll., 1937; M.A, U. of Colo., 1940; Universidad de San Marcos (Peru), 1942; Ph. D., U. of Colo., 1948. Dir., Colegio Americano (Peru), 1941–45; instr., U. of Colo., 1947–48; PROF., HISTORY, KANS. STATE U., 1948– ; vis. prof., Colegio Pan Americano (Mexico), 1953–54. U. of Colo. fellow; dir., Biblioteca Pública del Callao (Peru); consultant for U.S. Senator Gale McGee. Membership: American Association of University Professors; American Historical Association; Mississippi Valley Historical Association; Phi Alpha Theta. Research: United States diplomacy in Latin America; Peru. Author: United States Policy in Peru, 1919–1930 (Bulletin : U. of Colo. Studies, 1951); Mexico's Hands-Off Policy (The Midwest Quarterly, Spring 1962); Lord Cochrane: Critic of San Martin's Campaign (The Americas, Apr. 1962). Language: Spanish 4,4,4,4; Portuguese 2,1,1,1; French 3,2,1,1. Home: 332 North 15th St., Manhattan, Kans. Office: Dept. of History, Kans. State U., Manhattan.

CARLISLE, DOUGLAS HILTON, b. Jackson, Miss., July 27, 1920. POLITICAL SCIENCE. M.A., U. OF N.C., 1942; Ph. D., 1951. Asst. prof., U. of S.C., 1946–51; assoc. prof., 1951–57; PROF., POLITICAL SCIENCE, U. of S.C., 1958– ; vis. prof., U.S. Naval War Coll., 1957–58. Consultant, U.S. Army, 1951–52, U.S. Secretary of Defense, 1963– , Office of External Research, U.S. Dept. of State, 1964. Membership: American Political Science Association; International Law Association; Southern Political Science Association. Research: Latin American international relations and law; Venezuelan foreign affairs, 1905–35; Panama. Author: International Regional Organizations and Defense Arrangements (1958); Party Loyalty (1963). Language: Spanish 3,3,3,3; Portuguese 3,-3,3,3; French 3,3,3,3. Home: 1100 Gregg St., Columbia, S.C. Office: Dept. of Political Science, U. of S.C., Columbia.

CARLSON, FRED A., b. Pittsfield, Mass., Oct. 24, 1892. GEOGRAPHY. B.S., U. of Mass., 1918; Ph. D., Cornell U., 1922. Instr., Cornell U., 1920–22; asst. prof., U. of Calif., Berkeley, 1922–23; asst. prof., Ohio State U., 1923–26; prof., 1926–63; PROF. EMERITUS, GEOGRAPHY, OHIO STATE U., 1963– . Membership: American Geographical Society; Association of American Geographers; National Council for Geographic Education. Research: physiography; soil technology. Author: Geography of Latin America (1952). Language: Spanish 3,3,3,3; Swedish 3,3,3,1. Home: Apt. 261C, 30 West Kelso Rd., Columbus, Ohio 43202. Office: Dept. of Geography, Ohio State U., 1775 South College Rd., Columbus, 43201.

CARMIN, ROBERT LEIGHTON, b. Muncie, Ind., Nov. 28, 1918. GEOGRAPHY. B.S., Ohio U., 1940; M.A., U. of Nebr., 1942; Ph. D., U. of Chicago, 1953. Instr.-asst. prof., Mich. State U., 1942–50; cartographer, Cartography Unit, Office of Strategic Services, 1944–45; asst. prof.-prof., U. of Ill., 1951–62; dir., Center for Latin American Studies, 1959–62; head, Latin American Studies Section, U.S. Office of Education, 1962; PROF., GEOGRAPHY, DEAN, DIV. OF SCIENCES AND HUMANITIES, BALL STATE TEACHERS COLL., 1962– . Salisbury fellow in Geography, U. of Chicago, 1946–47; Pan American

World Airways Travel fellow (Brazil), 1948; U.S. Office of Education maintenance grant (Brazil), 1948–49; consultant on cartography and Latin America, Spencer Press, Inc., 1954–61; travel and maintenance research grant, U.S. Office of Quartermaster General (Brazil), 1956; Fulbright scholar, Universidad de Cuyo (Argentina), 1958; U.S. delegate, VI General Assembly, Pan American Institute of Geography and History (Buenos Aires), 1961; U. of Ill. Research Board grant (Brazil), 1961; American Association of Colleges for Teacher Education study grant (Ecuador, Peru, Brazil), 1963; consultant, Language Development Branch, U.S. Office of Education, 1963–64. Membership: Associação dos Geógrafos Brasileiros (Rio de Janeiro); Association for Latin American Studies; Association of American Geographers; Illinois Academy of Sciences; Illinois Geographical Society; Indiana Academy of Social Sciences; National Council for Geographic Education. Research: economic and regional geography; Latin American cartography; frontier settlement in Latin America. Author: Anápolis, Brazil: Regional Capital of an Agricultural Frontier (1953); Land Use Map from Census Data—Paraná, Brazil as an Example (Transactions, Illinois Academy of Sciences, 1957); Itapací, Brazil: Rapid Growth of a Frontier Town (Transactions, Illinois Academy of Sciences, 1960). Language: Spanish 4,3,3,2; Portuguese 4,4,4,2; French 3,1,1,1. Home: 2505 Johnson Rd., Muncie, Ind. Office: Dept. of Geography, Ball State Teachers Coll., Muncie.

CARNEIRO, ROBERT L(EONARD), b. New York, N.Y., June 4, 1927. ANTHROPOLOGY. B.A., U. of Mich., 1949; M.A., 1952; Ph. D., 1957. Instr., U. of Wis., 1956–57; ASSOC. CURATOR, SOUTH AMERICAN ETHNOLOGY, AMERICAN MUSEUM OF NATURAL HISTORY, 1957– . Doherty fellow (Brazil), 1953–54. Membership: American Anthropological Association; American Association for the Advancement of Science; Society for American Archaeology. Research: South American ethnology; Kuikuru Indians of central Brazil; Amahuaca Indians of eastern Peru. Author: Slash-and-Burn Agriculture and Its Implications for Settlement Patterns (Proceedings, International Congress of Americanists, 1960); Slash-and-Burn Cultivation Among the Kuikuru and Its Implications in the Cultural Development in the Amazon Basin (Antropológica, Caracas, Sept. 1961); Scale Analysis as an Instrument for the Study of Cultural Evolution (Southwestern Journal of Anthropology, Summer 1962). Language: Spanish 5,5,3,4; Portuguese 4,3,2,1; French 2,1,1,1. Linguistic studies: Amahuaca; Kuikuru. Home: 4499 Henry Hudson Parkway, New York 71, N.Y. Office: American Museum of Natural History, Central Park West and 79th St., New York 24.

CARNES, HUGH BYRON, b. Belle Center, Ohio, Jan. 23, 1904. ECONOMICS. A.B., U. of Mich., 1926; M.A., 1938; Litt. D., Universidad Nacional de México, 1941. Instr.-assoc. prof., Tulane U., 1926–39; PROF., FOREIGN TRADE, TULANE U., 1939– ; lectr., Specialists' Div., U.S. Dept. of State, 1955–56. Membership: American Economic Association. Research: Latin American economics and foreign trade; Spanish-American literature. Author: Manual de correspondencia comercial española (1929); Facundo y su obra (1941); Notes on Argentina's Bilateral Compensatory Trade Agreements (1949). Language: Spanish 5,5,5,5; Portuguese 2,2,1,1; French 3,3,3,3. Linguistic studies: Algonquin; Maya. Home: 8240 Panols St., New Orleans, La., 70118. Office: School of Business Administration, Tulane U., 6823 St. Charles Ave., New Orleans, 70118.

CARR, ROBERT FRANKLIN, II, b. Pittsburgh, Pa., May 7, 1931. ARCHITECTURE AND ARCHEOLOGY. B.A.E., Pa. State U., 1954. Draftsman, D. H. Drayer-Architect (Washington, D.C.), 1958–59, 1960–62; surveyor, Tikal Project, Museum, U. of Pa. (Guatemala), 1959–60; architect, Keyes, Lethbridge and Condon, 1962–63; ARCHITECT, VICTOR SMOLEN (WASHINGTON, D.C.), 1963– . Research: geography, archeology, and ecology of El Petén, Guatemala. Cartographer: Map of the ruins of Tikal, El Petén, Guatemala (in Tikal Report No. 11, 1961). Language: Spanish 4,4,3,3; Portuguese 2,1,1,1; Russian 3,2,2,2. Home: 5122 11th St. South, Arlington, Va. 22204. Office: Victor Smolen, 805 15th St. NW., Washington, D.C.

CARRASCO, PEDRO, b. Madrid, Spain, Sept. 20, 1921. ANTHROPOLOGY. Maestro en ciencias antropológicas, Universidad Nacional de México, 1945; Ph. D., Columbia U., 1953. Ethnologist, Museo Nacional (Mexico), 1950–51; acting asst. prof. and research anthropologist, U. of Wash., 1951–53; research assoc., Yale U., 1954–56; vis. asst. prof., U. of Calif., Berkeley, 1956–57; asst. prof.-ASSOC. PROF., ANTHROPOLOGY, U. of CALIF., LOS ANGELES, 1957– . Guggenheim fellow, 1953–54; Pan American Union grant, 1960; American Council of Learned Societies research grant, 1963–64. Membership: American Anthropological Association; American Ethnological Society; Sociedad Mexicana de Antropología. Research: ethnohistory; folk cultures in Mexico. Author: Los Otomíes (1950); Tarascan Folk Religion (1953); The Civil-Religious Hierarchy (American Anthropologist, June 1961). Language: Spanish 5,5,5,5; Portuguese 4,3,3,1; French 4,4,3,3; German 3,1,1,1; Italian 4,3,1,1. Linguistic studies: Nahuatl. Home: 1050 Fiske St., Pacific Palisades, Calif. Office: Dept. of Anthropology, U. of Calif., Los Angeles 24.

CARRÉ, SHIRLEY DESHON, b. Rochester, N.Y., Oct. 31, 1924. ANTHROPOLOGY. B.A., Smith Coll., 1946; U. of Ariz., 1952–54; Ph. D., Yale U., 1959. Instr., U. of Md., 1959–61; asst. prof., St. Lawrence U., 1962–63. Membership: American Anthropological Association. Research: cultural anthropology; Middle America; Southwest United States; local and regional economic structure of henequen production; Mexico. Author: Compadrazgo on a Henequen Hacienda in Yucatan: A Structural Reevaluation (American Anthropologist, June 1963). Language: Spanish 4,4,3,3; French 5,5,4,4; German 3,1,1,2. Home: La Joie, Sark, Channel Islands, Great Britain.

CARRINO, FRANK G., b. Lima, Ohio, Feb. 15, 1922. LANGUAGE. B.A., Baldwin Wallace Coll., 1946; M.A., U. of Wis., 1947; Ph. D., U. of Mich., 1956. Instr., Spanish,

Muhlenberg Coll., 1947–48; prof., State U. of N.Y. (Albany), 1948–59; dir., Bi-National Center, U.S. Information Service, 1959–61; asst. to president, State U. of N.Y. (Albany), 1961–62; DIR., CENTER FOR INTER-AMERICAN STUDIES, STATE U. OF N.Y., 1962– ; American specialist, Bureau of Education and Cultural Affairs, U.S. Dept. of State (Dominican Republic), 1963. Consultant, Ministry of Education, Government of Paraguay, 1960–61; consultant, U.S. Information Service (Dominican Republic), 1962–63. Membership: American Association of Teachers of Spanish and Portuguese; National Association of Foreign Student Advisers. Research: English as a foreign language; Spanish language textbooks. Author: Let's Speak English, Book II (1960); Let's Speak English, Book III (1961). Language: Spanish 5,5,5,4; Italian 3,4,3,1. Home: 34 Loudon Parkway, Loudonville, N.Y. 12211. Office: Center for Inter-American Studies, State U. of N.Y., 135 Western Ave., Albany, 12203.

CARTER, BOYD GEORGE, b. Duffield, Va., May 8, 1908. SPANISH AMERICAN LITERATURE. M.A., U. of Ill., 1933; Ph. D., 1937. Instr., U. of Idaho, 1937–38; asst. prof., U. of Wyo., 1938–39; prof., chmn., Foreign Languages, Coe Coll., 1939–45; instr., Army Specialized Training Program, U. of Ill., 1943–44; asst. prof.-prof., U. of Nebr., 1945–49; chmn., Romance Languages, 1950–56; PROF., ROMANCE LANGUAGES, SOUTHERN ILL. U., 1959– . Research: literary periodicals of Mexico. Author: Las revistas literarias de Hispanoamérica (1959); En torno a Gutiérrez Nájera y las letras mexicanas del siglo XIX (1960); Backflash on the Centennial of Manuel Gutiérrez Nájera (Hispania, Dec. 1961). Language: Spanish 5,5,5,4; Portuguese 3,2,1,1; French 5,5,5,4; German 4,4,3,2. Home: 206 Pine Lane, Carbondale, Ill. Office: Dept. of Foreign Languages, Southern Ill. U., Carbondale.

CARTER, GEORGE FRANCIS, b. San Diego, Calif., Apr. 6, 1912. GEOGRAPHY. A.B., U. of Calif., Berkeley, 1934; Ph. D., 1942. Assoc. research analyst, U.S. Office of Strategic Services, 1941–42; PROF., GEOGRAPHY, JOHNS HOPKINS U., 1942– . Guggenheim fellow. Membership: American Anthropological Association; American Association for the Advancement of Science; American Geographical Society; Association of American Geographers; Instituto Interamericano; Society for American Antiquity. Research: economic botany; plant geography. Author: Plant Geography and Culture History in the American Southwest (1945); Cultural Geography (1964); Movement of People and Ideas Across the Pacific (in Plants and Migrations of Pacific Peoples, 1963). Language: Spanish 2,–,–,–; French 2,–,–,–; German 2,–,–,–. Home: 6417 Pinehurst Rd., Baltimore 12, Md. Office; Isaiah Bowman School of Geography, Johns Hopkins U., Baltimore 18.

CARTER, HENRY HARE, b. Staten Island, N.Y., June 28, 1905. BRAZILIAN LITERATURE. B.S., U. of Pa., 1928; U. of Madrid, 1931; A.M., U. of Pa., 1933; Sorbonne, 1933; Ph.D., U. of Pa., 1937; Instituto Inter-Universitario (Rome), 1937; Universidade de Coimbra, 1939. Instr., Lehigh U., 1928–32; prof., Cedar Crest Coll., 1932–37; asst. prof., Northwestern U., 1937–42; U.S. Naval liaison officer with Brazilian Navy, 1942–45; instr., U.S. Naval Academy, 1945–46; cultural attaché, U.S. Dept. of State (São Paulo), 1946–47; asst. prof., U. of Pa., 1947–51; assoc. prof., De Paul U., 1951–52; prof., head, Foreign Languages, Colo. Coll., 1952–56; prof., U. of Recife (Brazil), 1956; PROF., MODERN LANGUAGES, U. OF NOTRE DAME, 1956– . Participant, Luso-Brazilian Colloquium (Washington, D.C.), 1950; Smith-Mundt traveling lectr. (Spain, Portugal), 1955. Membership: American Association of Teachers of Spanish and Portuguese; Modern Language Association; Sociedade Filológica (São Paulo). Research: Romance philology; paleography; Portuguese and Spanish literature. Author: Paleographical Edition and Study of the Language of a Portion of Codex Alcobacensis 200 (1938); Cancioneiro da Ajuda, Diplomatic Edition (1941); Latin-Old Portuguese Verb Dictionary (Romance Philology, 1953). Language: Spanish 5,5,5,5; Portuguese 5,5,5,5; French 5,5,5,5; Italian 5,5,4,5. Home: 3722 North Lilac Rd., South Bend, Ind. Office: Dept. of Modern Languages, U. of Notre Dame, Notre Dame, Ind.

CARTER, PHYLLIS G., b. Elsinore, Mo., Aug. 13, 1915. STATISTICS AND LIBRARY SCIENCE: BIBLIOGRAPHY. A.B., U. of Chicago, 1936. Chief, Card Dept., Library, U. of Chicago, 1937–42; librarian, Editorial Dept., Encyclopaedia Britannica, 1942–44; researcher, reference librarian, Inter American Statistical Institute, 1944–51; chief, Census Library Project, Library of Congress, 1951–55; asst. editor, Handbook of Latin American Studies, Library of Congress, 1955–58; chief, Foreign Research Office, U.S. Bureau of the Census, 1958–60; CHIEF, TECHNICAL REPORTS BRANCH, U.S. BUREAU OF THE CENSUS, 1960– . Membership: American Statistical Association; Population Association of America. Research: demography; organization of statistical information centers and libraries in Latin America. Editor: Bibliography of Selected Statistical Sources of the American Nations (1947); Statistical Yearbooks, an Annotated Bibliography of the General Statistical Yearbooks of Major Political Subdivisions of the World (1954); Procedural Report on the 1960 Censuses of Population and Housing (1963). Language: Spanish 5,4,4,3; Portuguese 4,2,2,–; French 3,1,1,1. Home: Apt. 514, 1200 South Courthouse Rd., Arlington, Va., 22204. Office: U.S. Bureau of the Census, Washington, D.C., 20233.

CARTER, ROY ERNEST, JR., b. Ulysses, Kans., Apr. 7, 1922. JOURNALISM, SOCIOLOGY, AND COMMUNICATION. B.A., Fort Hays Kans. State Coll., 1948; M.A., U. of Minn., 1951; Ph. D., Stanford U., 1954. Reporter, managing editor, Boise Statesman, 1944–49; assoc. prof., chmn., Ohio Wesleyan U., 1951–52; acting assoc. prof., Stanford U., 1952–54; research prof., U. of N.C., 1954–58; PROF., JOURNALISM, SOCIOLOGY, INTERNATIONAL RELATIONS; DIR., COMMUNICATIONS RESEARCH DIV., U. OF MINN.. 1958– . Kellogg Foundation fellow, Stanford U., 1952–53; U.S. Dept. of State lectr. (Chile), Fall 1961; Fulbright prof. and Social Science Research Council grant, Universidad de Chile, 1962–63; consultant, Sociology Program, U. of Concepción (Chile), and School of Journalism, U. of Chile; U.S. Dept. of State lectr. (Venezuela), Mar. 1963. Membership: American Association for Public Opinion Research; American Marketing Association; American Sociological Association; American Statistical Association; Association for Education in Journalism; International Association for Mass Communication Research; Midwest Sociological Society. Research: public opinion and survey research; social psychology and social structure; mass communications. Author: Newspaper Gatekeepers and the Sources of News (Public Opinion Quarterly, Fall 1958); Communications Research and the Social Sciences (American Behavioral Scientist, Dec. 1960); Field Methods in Communication Research (in Introduction to Mass Communications Research, 1963). Language: Spanish 5,5,4,4; Portuguese 4,2,2,1; French 3,1,1,1. Home: 2230 Quebec Ave. South, Minneapolis 26, Minn. Office: School of Journalism, U. of Minn., Minneapolis 14.

CARTER, THOMAS PELHAM, b. Pasadena, Calif., June 19, 1927. EDUCATION. B.A., U. of Calif., 1950; B.A.F.T., American Institute of Foreign Trade, 1951; Ph. D., U. of Tex., 1964. Trainee, junior officer, National City Bank of N.Y. (P.R.), 1951–53; teacher and administrator, Indio School District (Indio, Calif.), 1956–61; dir., Bi-National Center, U.S. Information Agency (Arequipa, Peru), 1961–63; asst. dir., Center for International Education, U. of Tex., 1963–64; ASST. PROF., EDUCATION, U. OF CALIF., RIVERSIDE, 1964– . Research: education in Peru. Language: Spanish 4,4,4,3; Portuguese 2,2,2,1. Home: 1992 Prince Albert Dr., Riverside, Calif. Office: Dept. of Education, U. of Calif., Riverside.

CARTER, WILLIAM EARL, b. Dayton, Ohio, Apr. 29, 1927. ANTHROPOLOGY. B.A., Muskingum Coll., 1949; S.T.B., Boston U., 1955; Ph. D., Columbia U., 1963. Teacher, youth dir., Board of Foreign Missions, The Methodist Church (Uruguay, Bolivia), 1950–54; administrative dir., Passaic Valley Methodist Parish, 1955–59; lectr., Brooklyn Coll., 1962; research assoc., Bureau of Applied Social Research, Columbia U., 1962–63; ASST. PROF., ANTHROPOLOGY, U. OF FLA., 1962– . Columbia U. fellow, 1959; Doherty fellow, 1960; National Institute of Mental Health fellow (Bolivia), 1960–62. Membership: American Anthropological Association; Society for Applied Anthropology. Research: cultural anthropology; land reform in highland Bolivia; southern South America. Author: The First Book of South America (1961); The First Book of Bolivia (1963). Language: Spanish 5,5,5,4; Portuguese 4,2,2,1; French 2,2,2,1; Aymará 2,1,2,2; Greek 2,1,1,1. Linguistic studies: Aymará. Home: 900 Boulevard, Gainesville, Fla. Office: Dept. of Anthropology, U. of Fla., Gainesville.

CASAD, ROBERT CLAIR, b. Council Grove, Kans., Dec. 8, 1929. LAW. A.B., U. of Kans., 1950; M.A., 1952; J.D., U. of Mich., 1957. Instr., School of Law, U. of Mich., 1957–58; lawyer (Winona, Minn.), 1958–59; ASSOC. PROF., LAW, SCHOOL OF LAW, U. OF KANS., 1959– . Asst. dir., Fourth Seminar on Higher Education in the Americas, Jan.–Mar. 1963; Kans. U.–Costa Rica Faculty Exchange, Summers 1962, 1963. Membership: American Association of University Professors; American Bar Association; Association of American Law Schools; Kansas Bar Association; Minnesota Bar Association. Research: judicial remedies and administration; court systems and land tenure in Costa Rica. Author: Kansas Notary Register (1963); Street and Sidewalk Safety: The Scope of the Municipal Duty (Minnesota Law Review, Jan. 1961); The Establishment Clause and the Ecumenical Movement (Michigan Law Review, Jan. 1964). Language: Spanish 4,3,3,4; French 1,1,–,–; German 2,2,2,1. Home: 1611 Learnard St., Lawrence, Kans. Office: School of Law, U. of Kans., Lawrence.

CASAGRANDE, JOSEPH BARTHOLOMEW, b. Cincinnati, Ohio, Feb. 14, 1915. ANTHROPOLOGY. A.B., U. of Wis., 1938; Ph. D., Columbia U., 1951. Instr., U. of Rochester, 1959–60; staff member, Social Science Research Council, 1950–60; PROF., CHMN., ANTHROPOLOGY, U. OF ILL., 1960– . Social Science Research Council fellow, 1946–47, 1948–49; Board of Directors, Columbia, Cornell, Harvard, Illinois Universities Program of Summer Field Training in Social Anthropology in Latin America; 1960– ; Advisory Panel in Anthropology, National Science Foundation, 1962– ; president, American Ethnological Society, 1963–64; dir., Social Science Research Council, 1963– . Membership: American Anthropological Association; American Ethnological Society; Linguistic Circle of New York; Linguistic Society of America; Royal Anthropological Society of Great Britain and Ireland; Society for Applied Anthropology. Research: ethnolinguistics; cultural change; Ecuador. Author: Comanche Linguistic Acculturation (International Journal of Linguistics, Jan. 1955); Colonization as a Research Frontier; The Ecuadorean Case (1964). Editor: In the Company of Man: Twenty Portraits by Anthropologists (1960, 1964). Language: Spanish 4,3,2,2; French 4,2,2,2; German 3,3,2,2. Home: 302 West Florida Ave., Urbana, Ill. Office: Dept. of Anthropology, U. of Ill., Urbana, 61803.

CASE, THOMAS EDWARD, b. Minneapolis, Minn., Feb. 27, 1934. SPANISH AMERICAN LITERATURE. B.A., St. Thomas Coll., 1956; M.A., State U. of Iowa, 1958; Ph. D., 1962. ASST. PROF., SPANISH, SAN DIEGO STATE COLL., 1961– . Fulbright prof. (Bogotá, Colombia), 1965; contributing editor, Handbook of Latin American Studies. Membership: American Association of Teachers of Spanish and Portuguese; Pacific Coast Council on Latin American Studies; Pacific Coast Philological Association. Research: applied linguistics; Paraguayan novel. Language: Spanish 5,5,5,4; Portuguese 3,2,2,2; French 4,4,4,4; German 3,2,2,2. Office: Dept. of Spanish, San Diego State Coll., San Diego, Calif., 92115.

CASTAÑEDA, JULIO R., b. Camagüey, Cuba, Sept. 25, 1907. SPANISH AMERICAN LITERATURE. B.S., U. of San Francisco 1952; M.A., Stanford U., 1953; Ph. D., U. of Madrid, 1958. Asst., U. of Calif., Berkeley, 1953–57; lectr., Oberlin Coll., 1957–58; ASST. PROF., SPANISH, COLL. OF ST.

CATHERINE, 1959– . Membership: American Association of Teachers of Spanish and Portuguese; American Association of University Professors: Instituto de Cultura Hispánica; Midwest Council of the Association for Latin American Studies. Research: contemporary Spanish theater; Mexican literature. Language: Spanish 5,5,5,5; Portuguese 3,3,1,1; French 3,2,–,1; Italian 3,4,3,2. Linguistic studies: Spanish. Home: Capri Hotel, 7th and Wabasha, St. Paul, Minn. Office: Dept. of Spanish, The Coll. of St. Catherine, St. Paul, 55116.

CASTEDO, LEOPOLDO H. DE P., b. Madrid, Spain, Feb. 27, 1915. ART. Bachiller, Instituto Escuela (Madrid), 1930; Licenciatura, Universities of Madrid and Barcelona, 1936. Writer, 1941–64; prof., Fine Arts and Education, U. of Chile, 1957–61; dir., Audiovisual Aids, U. of Chile, 1959–61; INFORMATION STAFF, INTER-AMERICAN DEVELOPMENT BANK, 1961– ; PROF., SPANISH, GEORGE WASHINGTON U., 1964– . Fulbright lectr., U. of Calif., 1960. Research: Latin American colonial art; Latin American civilization and culture. Author: Arte colonial iberoamericana (1960); The Baroque Prevalence in Brazilian Art (1964). Editor: Resumen de la historia de Chile (1954). Language: Spanish 5,5,5,5; Portuguese 5,5,4,3; French 4,4,3,2. Home: 1656 Foxhall Rd., NW., Washington, D.C. Office: Inter-American Development Bank, 808 17th St., NW., Washington, D.C.

CASTILLO, HOMERO, b. Valparaiso, Chile, Dec. 7, 1918. SPANISH AMERICAN LITERATURE. B.A., U. of Chile, 1938; Licenciado, 1944; M.A., St. Louis U., 1947; Ph. D., U. of Chicago, 1953. Instr., Chilean Public Schools, 1940–44; instr., St. Louis U., 1944–49; assoc. prof., Northwestern U., 1949–61; prof. and dir., Chilean Project, U.S. Peace Corps., 1961; PROF., ROMANCE LANGUAGES, STATE U. OF IOWA, 1963– . Institute of International Education fellow, St. Louis U., 1944; American Philosophical Society grants (Argentina, Peru, Uruguay), 1955, 1958, 1962; Executive Council, Midwest Modern Language Association, 1961–62; consultant, Encyclopaedia Britannica; assoc. editor, Duquesne Hispanic Review. Membership: American Association of Teachers of Spanish and Portuguese; Instituto Internacional de Literatura Iberoamericana; Modern Language Association; Phi Sigma Iota. Research: Spanish American culture, civilization, literature, and language; Chilean literature. Author: Historia bibliográfica de la novela chilena (1961); El criollismo en la novelística chilena (1962); La literatura chilena en los Estados Unidos (1963). Language: Spanish 5,5,5,5; Portuguese 3,3,–,–; French 3,3,1,1; German 1,1,1,1; Italian 4,4,1,1. Home: 223 Melrose Ave., Iowa City, Iowa. Office: Dept. of Romance Languages, State U. of Iowa, Iowa City.

CATALYNE, ALICE RAY, b. Bakersfield, Calif., June 30, 1914. MUSIC. B.A., Occidental Coll., 1935; M.A., 1942; Ph. D., U. of Southern Calif., 1953. Teacher, Los Angeles City Schools, 1936–38, 1940–44; instr.-asst. prof., School of Music, U. of Southern Calif., 1951–59; lectr., Graduate School, U. of Calif., Los Angeles, 1959–63; ASSOC. PROF., MUSIC, LOS ANGELES VALLEY COLL., 1960– . Consultant on Mexico, Institute of Ethnomusicology, U. of Calif., Los Angeles. Membership: American Musicological Society; Music Educators National Conference; Society for Ethnomusicology. Research: musicology; piano; liturgical music in colonial Mexico in the 17th and 18th centuries; the Baroque Villancico in Mexico. Language: Spanish 3,3,2,2; French 4,4,4,3. Home: 2006 North Hobart Blvd., Los Angeles, Calif., 90027. Office: Dept. of Music, Los Angeles Valley Coll., 5800 Fulton Ave., Van Nuys, Calif., 91401.

CAUGHEY, JOHN W., b. Wichita, Kans., July 3, 1902. HISTORY. B.A., U. of Tex., 1923; M.A., U. of Calif., 1926; Ph. D., 1928. Asst. prof., U. of Calif., Los Angeles, 1930–47; PROF., HISTORY, U. OF CALIF., LOS ANGELES, 1947– . Native Sons of the Golden West fellow; Rockefeller Foundation fellow; American Council of Learned Societies fellow; Shreve fellow, Princeton U.; consultant, Dept. of Justice, State of Calif.; consultant, Dept. of Water and Power, City of Los Angeles. Membership: American Association of University Professors; American Historical Association; American Civil Liberties Union; California Historical Society; Mississippi Valley Historical Association. Research: western America. Author: History of the Pacific Coast (1933); Bernardo de Gálvez in Louisiana, 1776–1783 (1934). Editor: The Indians of Southern California in 1852 (1952). Language: Spanish 3,3,1,–; Portuguese 2,–,–,–; French 3,2,1,–. Home: 1897 Mango Way, Los Angeles 49, Calif. Office: Dept. of History, U. of Calif., Los Angeles, 90024.

CHAMBERLAIN, ROBERT S., b. Canton, Ohio, Oct. 19, 1903. HISTORY. A.B., Stanford U., 1925; B. Sc. in Ed., Ohio State U., 1927; Ph. D., Harvard U., 1936. Staff member, Historical Research Div., Carnegie Institution of Washington, 1936–48; cultural relations officer (Guatemala), U.S. Dept. of State, 1941–45; assoc. prof., U. of Miami, 1947–48; U.S. GOVERNMENT, 1948– . Woodbury Lowery fellow (Spain), 1932–34. Membership: Academy of American Franciscan History; American Historical Association; Conference on Latin American History; Hakluyt Society (England); Pan American Institute of Geography and History; Sociedad de Geografía e Historia (Guatemala); Sociedad de Geografía e Historia (Honduras). Research: Hispanic colonial history. Author: The Castilian Backgrounds of the Repartimiento Encomienda (1939); The Governorship of the Adelantado Francisco de Montejo in Chiapas, 1539–1544 (1947); The Conquest and Colonization of Yucatan, 1517–1550 (1948); The Conquest and Colonization of Honduras, 1502–1550 (1953). Language: Spanish 5,4,4,4; Portuguese 4,3,2,1; French 4,2,1,1; German 3,–,–,1. Home: 804 Grand View Dr., Alexandria, Va.

CHAMBERLIN, EUGENE KEITH, b. Gustine, Calif., Feb. 15, 1916. HISTORY. B.A., U. of Calif., Berkeley, 1939; M.A., 1940; Ph. D., 1949. Teacher, Calif. Public Schools, 1941–45; prof., Mont. State U., 1948–54; PROF., HISTORY, SAN DIEGO CITY COLL., 1954– . Rockefeller-Huntington Library grant, Summer 1952; chmn. Baja California Historical Materials Committee, Library, U. of Calif., San Diego. Membership: American Association of University Professors; Conference on Latin American History; American Historical Association; Pacific Coast Council on Latin American Studies; Phi Alpha Theta. Research: Mexican northwest area and Baja California; United States-Mexican relations. Author: Mexican Colonization versus American Interests in Baja California (Pacific Historical Review, Feb. 1951); Baja California after Walker: the Zerman Enterprise (Hispanic American Historical Review, May 1954); Nicholas Trist and Baja California (Pacific Historical Review, Feb. 1963). Language: Spanish 3,3,3,3; Portuguese 1,1,1,1; French 2,1,1,1; German 2,1,1,1. Home: 3033 Dale St., San Diego, Calif., 92104. Office: Dept. of History, San Diego City Coll., 1425 Russ Blvd., San Diego, 92101.

CHAMPION, J. RENE, b. Paris, France, Feb. 27, 1921. ANTHROPOLOGY. B.S., City Coll. (N.Y.), 1950; Ph. D., Columbia U., 1962. Instr., City Coll. (N.Y.), 1951–56; SOCIAL SCIENTIST, SYSTEM DEVELOPMENT CORPORATION, 1956– . Membership: American Anthropological Association; American Ethnological Society; American Sociological Association; Phi Beta Kappa. Research: ethnology; culture change; northern Mexico; operational analysis; information processing science. Author: A Study of Culture Persistence: The Tarahumaras of Northwest Mexico (1962); Acculturation among the Tarahumara of Northwest Mexico since 1890 (Transactions, N.Y. Academy of Sciences, 1955). Language: Spanish 5,5,4,4; Portuguese 3,2,1,1; French 5,5,5,5; German 3,2,2,1; Italian 3,2,2,1. Home: 100 Hartwell Rd., Bedford, Mass. Office: System Development Corporation, 45 Hartwell Ave., Lexington 73, Mass.

CHANG-RODRÍGUEZ, EUGENIO, b. Trujillo, Peru, Nov. 15, 1924. SPANISH AMERICAN LITERATURE. Ph. B., San Marcos U. (Peru), 1946; B.A., William Penn Coll., 1949; M.A., U. of Ariz., 1950; M.A., U. of Wash., 1953; Ph. D., 1956. Instr., U. of Wash., 1952–56; asst. prof., U. of Pa., 1956–61; asst. prof., Temple U., Summer 1960; asst. prof., U. of Southern Calif., Summers 1961, 1962; ASST. PROF., ROMANCE LANGUAGES, QUEENS COLL., 1961– . San Marcos U. scholar; William Penn Coll. merit scholar; U. of Ariz. graduate scholar; assoc. editor, Hispania; Modern Language Association Advisory Committee on Spanish Textbooks; Board of Directors, International League for the Rights of Man; president, Northwest Chapter, American Association of Teachers of Spanish and Portuguese. Membership: American Association of University Professors; Hispanic Institute of the United States; Instituto Internacional de Literatura Iberoamericana; Linguistic Circle of New York; Phi Sigma Iota; Sigma Delta Pi. Research: linguistics, social sciences, and civilization of Spanish America. Author: La literatura política de Prado, Mariátegui y Haya (1957). Co-author: La América Latina de hoy (1961). Co-editor: The Hemisphere's Present Crisis (1963). Language: Spanish 5,5,5,5; Portuguese 4,4,4,4; French 3,3,3,3; Italian 3,3,3,3. Linguistic studies: Chinese; French; Italian; Portuguese; Rumanian;

Spanish. Home: Box 33, Queens Coll., Flushing 67, N.Y. Office: Dept. of Romance Languages, Queens Coll., Flushing 67.

CHAPLIN, DAVID, b. Yonkers, N.Y., Nov. 30, 1930. SOCIOLOGY. B.A., Amherst Coll., 1953; M.A., Princeton U., 1958; Ph. D., 1963. Instr., Bucknell U., 1960–64; ASST. PROF., SOCIOLOGY, U. OF WIS., 1964– . Junior fellow, Princeton U., 1957; Pan American Union fellow (Peru), 1958–59; National Science Foundation grant. Membership: American Sociological Association; Population Association of America. Research: social history of Peru, 1896–1940; Peruvian industrial relations; distribution of wealth and the pattern of land-holding in Peru. Language: Spanish 4,3,3,3; Portuguese 1,1,1,1; French 3,2,1,1. Home: 1716 Hoyt St., Madison, Wis. Office: Dept. of Sociology, U. of Wis., Madison.

CHAPMAN, G. ARNOLD, b. Fresno, Calif., June 26, 1917. SPANISH AMERICAN LITERATURE. A.B., Fresno State Coll., 1939; M.A., U. of Wis., 1941; Ph. D., 1946. Instr., Sophie Newcomb Coll., 1942; instr., Oberlin Coll., 1945–46; instr.-ASSOC. PROF., SPANISH AND PORTUGUESE, U. OF CALIF., BERKELEY, 1946– . Editorial Board, Revista Iberoamericana; contributing editor, Handbook of Latin American Studies. Membership: American Association of Teachers of Spanish and Portuguese; Instituto Internacional de Literatura Iberoamericana; Modern Language Association. Research: literature of Chile and Argentina; contemporary novel; United States-Spanish American literary relations. Author: Sherwood Anderson and Eduardo Mallea (Publications of the Modern Language Association, Mar. 1954); Pampas and Big Woods (Comparative Literature, Winter 1959); Waldo Frank in the Hispanic World (Hispania, Dec. 1961). Language: Spanish 5,4,4,4; Portuguese 3,2,2,1; French 4,3,2,2. Home: 231 Yale Ave., Berkeley 8, Calif. Office: Dept. of Spanish and Portuguese, U. of Calif., Berkeley 4.

CHAPMAN, MARY P., b. Los Angeles, Calif., Aug. 20, 1917. HISTORY. B.A., Stanford U., 1939; M.A., 1942; Ph. D., 1950. Analyst, Hoover Library, Stanford U., 1948–49; research asst., Prof. Hubert Herring, Claremont Graduate School, 1950–52; research analyst, U.S. Dept. of State, 1955–59; DIPLOMATIC HISTORIAN, HISTORICAL OFFICE, U.S. DEPT. OF STATE, 1959– . Membership: American Historical Association; Conference on Latin American History; Phi Alpha Theta. Research: past and current United States-Latin American relations. Author: The Mission of Elisha O. Crosby to Guatemala, 1861–1864 (Pacific Historical Review, Aug. 1955); The Mission of Lansing Bond Mizner to Central America (The Historian, Aug. 1957). Language: Spanish 4,4,4,3; French 2,1,1,1. Home: 2117 E St. NW., Apt. 816, Washington, D.C. 20037. Office: Historical Office, U.S. Dept. of State, Washington 25, D.C.

CHARDON, ROLAND E., b. Boston, Mass., Apr. 15, 1929. GEOGRAPHY. B.A., U. of Minn., 1951; M.S., Fla. State U., 1954; Ph. D., U. of Minn., 1961. Instr., State U. of Iowa, 1956–58; field research contractor, National Academy of Science-National Research Council (Yucatan), 1958–59; vis. prof., U. of Minn., Summer 1961; asst. prof., Ohio State U., 1959–63; ASST.

PROF., GEOGRAPHY, VANDERBILT U., 1963– . National Defense fellow in Portuguese, U. of Tex., Summer 1962; Vanderbilt U. Graduate Center for Latin American Studies fellow (Brazil), Summers 1963, 1964. Membership: American Geographical Society; Association of American Geographers; National Geographic Society; Regional Science Association; Southeastern Conference on Latin American Studies. Research: cultural geography; plantation agriculture; Mexico; Brazil. Author: Geographic Aspects of Plantation Agriculture in Yucatan (1961). Language: Spanish 4,4,4,3; Portuguese 4,4,4,3; French 5,5,5,3. Home: Apt. F–4, Hillsboro Garden, Nashville 12, Tenn. Office: Graduate Center for Latin American Studies, Vanderbilt U., Nashville, 37203.

CHARMATZ, JAN PAUL, b. Czechoslovakia, Mar. 30, 1909. LAW. J.U.D., U. of Prague, 1933; LL.M., Yale U., 1952; LL.B., U. of Miss., 1955. Assoc. prosecutor, U.S. Office of Chief of Counsel for War Crimes (Nuremberg), 1945–48; prof., U. of P.R., 1949–51; lectr., Yale U., 1952–53; assoc. prof., La. State U., 1953–55; prof., U. of Miss., 1955–57; vis. prof., Tulane U., 1957–58; prof., International U. of Comparative Science (Luxembourg), Summers 1958, 1959, 1962, 1964; PROF., LAW, SCHOOL OF LAW, SOUTHERN METHODIST U., 1958– . Faculty editor, Revista Jurídica de la Universidad de Puerto Rico, 1949–51; Sterling fellow, Yale Law School, 1951–52; faculty editor, Louisiana Law Review, 1953–55; faculty adviser, Tulane Law Review, 1957–58; Board of Editors, American Journal of Comparative Law, 1958– ; Committee on International Interchange of Jurists, American Bar Association, 1958– . Membership: American Bar Association; American Society of International Law; Foreign Law Association; Mississippi State Bar; Texas Bar Association. Research: international and comparative law; law in Mexico and Spain. Author: Comparative Studies in Community Property Law (1955). Co-author: La nueva constitución de Puerto Rico, informes a la Convención Constituyente (1954); Repatriation of Prisoners of War and the 1949 Geneva Convention (Yale Law Journal, Feb. 1953). Language: Spanish 5,5,4,4; Portuguese 1,1,1,1; French 5,5,4,4; German 5,5,4,5. Home: P.O. Box 8245, Dallas 5, Tex. Office: School of Law, Southern Methodist U., Dallas 5.

CHASE, GILBERT, b. Havana, Cuba, Sept. 4, 1906. MUSIC. B.A., U. of N.C., 1950; D. Litt. (honorary), U. of Miami, 1955. Music critic, Continental Daily Mail (Paris), 1929–35; assoc. editor, International Cyclopedia of Music and Musicians, 1936–38; editor, G. Schirmer, Inc., 1939–40; Latin American specialist, Music Div., Library of Congress, 1940–43; music supervisor, NBC U. of the Air, 1943–48; manager, Education Dept., RCA Victor, 1948–49; cultural attaché, Embassy (Lima), U.S. Dept. of State, 1951–53; cultural attaché, Embassy (Buenos Aires), 1953–55; dir., School of Music, U. of Okla., 1955–56; acting dean, Coll. of Fine Arts, 1956–57; 1st vice president, Inter-American Music Center, 1956–57; cultural attaché, Embassy (Brussels, Belgium), U.S. Dept. of State, 1958–60; PROF., LATIN AMERICAN STUDIES, TULANE U., 1960– ; DIR., INTER-AMERICAN INSTITUTE FOR MUSICAL RESEARCH, 1961– . Advisory Committee on Music, U.S. Dept. of State, 1943–45; music consultant, Pan American Union, 1943–45; U.S. Advisory Committee on Cultural Information, 1957– ; president, Inter-American Music Council, 1960– . Membership: American Musicological Society; Instituto Español de Musicología; Music Library Association; Société Française de Musicologie; Society for Ethnomusicology. Research: Iberian and Latin American music. Author: The Music of Spain (1941, 1959); A Guide to Latin American Music (1945, 1962). Editor: Recordings of Latin American Songs and Dances; an Annotated Selective List of Popular and Folk-Popular Music (1950). Language: Spanish 5,5,5,5; Portuguese 4,4,3,3; French 5,5,5,5; Italian 5,3,3,2; Catalán 3,1,1,1. Office Inter-American Institute for Musical Research, Tulane U., New Orleans 18, La.

CHATELAIN, VERNE ELMO, b. Waco, Nebr., July 22, 1895. HISTORY. B.A., Nebr. State Coll., 1917; M.A., U. of Chicago, 1925; Ph. D., U. of Minn., 1943. Prof., chmn., Nebr. State Coll., 1925–31; chief historian, Branch of Historic Sites and Buildings, U.S. National Park Service, 1931–36; research asst., dir., St. Augustine Program (Fla.), Carnegie Institution of Washington, 1936–42; liaison administrative officer, U.S. Government, 1942–45; PROF. HISTORY, U. OF MD., 1945– . U. of Minn. fellow, 1928–29; consultant on St. Augustine Program, State of Florida; National Advisory Committee on the Program for Spanish Florida, Carnegie Institution; Committee for National Parks and Monuments, U.S. Dept. of Interior. Membership: American Bar Association; American Historical Association; Mississippi Valley Historical Association; Pan American Institute of Geography and History. Research: Spanish Florida. Author: The Defenses of Spanish Florida, 1565–1763 (1941); The St. Augustine Historical Restoration (1958); Spanish Contributions to American Culture (Florida Historical Quarterly, Jan. 1941). Language: Spanish 4,3,2,4; French –,2,2,3. Home: 1206 Noyes Dr., Silver Spring, Md. Office: Dept. of History, U. of Md., College Park.

CHIAPPETTA, MICHAEL, b. Tacoma, Wash., May 23, 1921. EDUCATION. A.B., U. of Mich., 1942; M.A., 1947; Ph. D., 1950. Vis. prof., U. of Colo., Summer 1950; assoc. prof., Ariz. State U., 1950–52; vis. prof., U. of Mich., Summer 1951; asst. prof., U. of Calif., Berkeley, 1952–53; vis. prof., U. of Ill., Summer 1953; assoc. prof., Pa. State U., 1953–59; lectr., National U. of Mexico and U. of Guadalajara, Summer 1956; educational adviser, U.S. Agency for International Development (Lima, Peru), 1960–63; EDUCATIONAL ADVISER, LATIN AMERICAN BUREAU, U.S. AGENCY FOR INTERNATIONAL DEVELOPMENT, 1963– . Fulbright lectr., Ministry of Education (Lima), 1959–60. Membership: Comparative Education Society; National Society of College Teachers of Education; Phi Delta Kappa. Research: social foundations of education; philosophy of education; education planning; human resource development; Andean countries. Author: History of Education in Training of Teachers (National Society of College Teachers of Education, 1954); Comparative Education and Training of Teachers (National Education Association Journal, 1958); Philosophy of Education in Latin America (Phi Delta Kappan, Jan. 1964). Language: Spanish 5,5,5,4; French 3,2,2,1; Italian 3,3,2,1. Home: 5406 Wilson Lane, Bethesda, Md. Office: Latin American Bureau, U.S. Agency for International Development, Washington, D.C.

CHILCOTE, RONALD HODELL, b. Cleveland, Ohio, Feb. 20, 1935. POLITICAL SCIENCE. A.B., Dartmouth Coll., 1957; M.B.A,. Stanford U., 1959; M.A., 1963; Ph. D., 1965. Asst. editor, Hispanic American Report, 1961–63; asst. to dir., Institute of Hispanic American and Luso-Brazilian Studies, Stanford U., 1961–63; ASST. PROF., POLITICAL SCIENCE, COORDINATOR, LATIN AMERICAN RESEARCH PROGRAM, U. OF CALIF., RIVERSIDE, 1963– . Membership: American Academy of Political and Social Sciences; American Geographical Society; American Political Science Association; Hispanic American Society; Pacific Coast Council on Latin American Studies. Research: comparative politics; developing areas; industry in Chile and Guatemala; political, social, and economic development in northeast Brazil. Author: The Press in Latin America, Spain, and Portugal (1963). Language: Spanish 4,4,4,4; Portuguese 4,4,4,4; French 4,3,3,3. Home: Apt. 4, 1812 11th St., Riverside, Calif. Office: Dept. of Political Science, U. of Calif., Riverside, 92502.

CHIPMAN, DONALD EUGENE, b. Hill City, Kans., Nov. 19, 1928. HISTORY. B.A., Fort Hays Kans. State Coll., 1955; M.S., 1958; Ph. D., U. of N. Mex., 1962. Vis. prof, U. of Wash., Summer 1962; ASST. PROF., HISTORY, FORT HAYS KANS. STATE COLL., 1962– . University fellow, U. of N. Mex., 1960–61; American Council of Learned Societies grant-in-aid (Spain), Summer 1963. Membership: American Historical Association; Conference on Latin American History. Research: paleography; Spanish archival research; Mexican history. Author: New Light on the Career of Nuño de Guzmán (The Americas, Apr. 1963). Language: Spanish 4,3,3,2; French 2,1, 1,1. Home: 408 East 6th, Hays, Kans. Office: Dept. of History, Fort Hays Kans. State Coll., Hays.

CHOWNING, ANN, b. Little Rock, Ark., Apr. 18, 1929. ANTHROPOLOGY. B.A., Bryn Mawr Coll., 1950; M.A., U. of Pa., 1952; Ph. D., 1958. Archeologist, Carnegie Institution of Washington (Yucatán, Mexico), Summer 1955; instr., Barnard Coll., 1958–60; archeologist, Tikal Project (Guatemala), U. of Pa. Museum, 1959; ASST. PROF., ANTHROPOLOGY, BARNARD COLL., 1960– ; CHMN., 1961– . Membership: American Anthropological Association; American Ethnological Society; American Folklore Society; Royal Anthropological Institute; Society for American Archaeology. Research: ethnography, archeology, folklore, and comparative linguistics; anthropology of Oceania; Maya archeology; Melanesian languages. Language: Spanish 4,4,4,3; Portuguese 2,1,1,1; French 3,2,2,2; Melanesian Pidgin 5,5,4,5. Home: 2110 Country Club Lane, Little Rock, Ark. Office: Dept. of Anthropology, Barnard Coll., Columbia U., New York, N.Y. 10027.

CHRISTIANSEN, PAIGE W., b. Miles City, Mont., July 7, 1923. HISTORY. B.A., Mich. State U., 1949; M.A., U. of N. Mex., 1954; Ph. D., U. of Calif., Berkeley, 1959. Instr., U. of Calif., Berkeley, 1949; ASST. PROF., HISTORY, N. MEX. INSTITUTE OF MINING AND TECHNOLOGY, 1959– . Advisory Council, New Mexico State Archives and Records Center. Membership: American Association of University Professors; Phi Alpha Theta. Research: Mexico; inter-American affairs. Author: Pascual Orozco: Chihuahua Rebel (New Mexico Historical Review, Apr. 1961); A Brief History of Socorro County (New Mexico Geological Society, Oct. 1963); Hugo Oconor's Inspection of Nueva Vizcaya and Coahuila, 1773 (Louisiana Studies, Fall 1963). Language: Spanish 5,3,3,4. Home: 8 North Dr., Socorro, N. Mex. Office: Dept. of Humanities, N. Mex. Institute of Mining and Technology, Socorro.

CHRISTOPHER, HENRY ANTHONY, b. Boston, Mass., Dec. 7, 1923. POLITICAL SCIENCE. B.A., Boston U., 1951; Ph. D., Northwestern U., 1964. Political analyst, U.S. Dept. of Defense, 1951–55; political officer, Embassy (Madrid), U.S. Dept. of State, 1955–57; instr., Kent State U., 1962–64; ASST. PROF., POLITICAL SCIENCE, KENT STATE U., 1964– . Membership: American Academy of Political and Social Science; American Association of University Professors; American Political Science Association. Research: militarism in Latin America; economic development in Latin America; regionalism in Latin America. Language: Spanish 4,4,4,3; French 2,1,1,1; Italian 2,3,2,1. Home: 3747 Northview, Stow, Ohio. Office: Dept. of Political Science, Kent State U., Kent, Ohio.

CICOUREL, AARON VICTOR, b. Atlanta, Ga., Aug. 29, 1928. SOCIOLOGY. B.A., U. of Calif., Los Angeles, 1951; M.A., 1955; Ph. D., Cornell U., 1957. Asst. prof., Northwestern U., 1958–60; ASST. PROF., SOCIOLOGY, U. OF CALIF., RIVERSIDE, 1960– . Russell Sage fellow, 1957–58; Social Science Research Council grant (Argentina), 1963–64. Membership: American Association of University Professors; American Sociological Association; Pacific Sociological Society. Research: fertility and family organization in Argentina; political orientation, union organization, and leisure time of textile union workers in Argentina. Author: The Educational Decision-Makers (1963); Method and Measurement in Sociology (1964). Language: Spanish 4,4,4,4; Portuguese 2,2,2,1; French 3,3,3,2. Home: 147 West Broadbent Dr., Riverside, Calif. Office: Dept. of Sociology, U. of Calif., Riverside.

CIRUTI, JOAN E(STELLE), b. Ponchatoula, La., Aug. 8, 1930. SPANISH AMERICAN LITERATURE. B.A., Southeastern La. Coll., 1950; National U. of Mexico, Summer 1952; M.A., U. of Okla., 1954; Ph. D., Tulane U., 1959. Instr.-asst. prof., U. of Okla., 1957–63; research asst., Language Development Program, U.S. Office of Education, 1959–60; ASST. PROF., SPANISH,

MOUNT HOLYOKE COLL., 1963– . Consultant, U.S. Office of Education, 1960–61; collaborator on poetry section, Handbook of Latin American Studies, 1963– . Membership: American Association of Teachers of Spanish and Portuguese; Modern Language Association. Research: Spanish American poetry; Guatemalan novel. Author: Humor in the Cancionero Apócrifo of Antonio Machado (Modern Language Forum, Dec. 1957); Cervantes and the Words He Says Are Arabic (Hispania, Mar. 1957). Language: Spanish 5,5,5,5; Portuguese 2,1,1,1; French 3,3,2,3; German 2,1,1,1. Home: 19 Woodbridge St., South Hadley, Mass. 01075. Office: Dept. of Spanish, Mount Holyoke Coll., South Hadley, 01075.

CLAGETT, HELEN L., b. San Juan, P.R., Nov. 12, 1905. LAW. A.B., U. of P.R., 1928; LL.B., Law School, George Washington U., 1941. Latin American law librarian, Los Angeles County Law Library, 1941–43; CHIEF, HISPANIC LAW DIV., LIBRARY OF CONGRESS, 1943– . Membership: American Bar Association, Section of International and Comparative Law; Inter-American Bar Association; Washington Foreign Law Society. Research: international and comparative law; acquisition and classification of materials; indexing and bibliographical work of legislation and source materials. Author: Administration of Justice in Latin America (1952). Editor: Guide to the Law and Legal Literature of Argentina, 1917–1946, Bolivia, Chile, 1917–1946, Ecuador, the Mexican States, Paraguay, Peru, Uruguay, Venezuela (9 vols., 1947–48). Language: Spanish 5,5,5,5; Portuguese 4,3,3,–; French 4,3,3,–; Italian 3,1,–,–. Home: 2801 Quebec St., NW., Washington, D.C. 20008. Office: Hispanic Law Div., Library of Congress, Washington, D.C. 20540.

CLARK, RONALD JAMES, b. Tucson, Ariz., Aug. 13, 1935. ECONOMICS. B.S., U. of Calif., 1957; M.B.A., Ind. U., 1958; Ph. D., 1963. ASST. PROF., AGRICULTURAL ECONOMICS, LAND TENURE CENTER, U. OF WIS., 1962– . Membership: American Economic Association. Research: agricultural development; international economics; Latin American economic relations with the Soviet bloc, 1954–61; Central American economic development in agriculture via the Common Market; land reform in Bolivia and Peru. Language: Spanish 3,3,3,3; Portuguese 1,1,1,1; French 1,1,1,1. Home: 3-D University Houses, Madison, Wis. Office: Dept. of Agricultural Economics, U. of Wis., Madison.

CLARK, WESLEY CLARKE, b. Cleveland, Ohio, Sept. 17, 1907. JOURNALISM. A.B., Marietta Coll., 1930; M.A., U. of Pa., 1937; Ph. D., 1942. Reporter, Philadelphia Evening Bulletin, 1930–41; asst. prof., Syracuse U., 1941–43; asst. to secretary, U.S. Dept. of Interior, 1943–47; PROF., JOURNALISM, SYRACUSE U., 1947– ; DEAN, SCHOOL OF JOURNALISM, 1952– . Consultant, Caribbean Commission, 1951; lectr., U.S. Dept. of State (Mexico, Ecuador), 1961. Research: journalism education; public relations; freedom of the press. Author: Journalism Tomorrow (1959); El derecho de la información (1962); Public Administration and Public Interest (Annals of the American Academy, Mar. 1952). Language: Spanish 4,3,3,3; French 4,3,3,3; German 2,2,2,2. Home: 18 North St., Marcellus, N.Y. Office: School of Journalism, Syracuse U., Syracuse 10, N.Y.

CLARKE, BERTA LOU, b. Grand Junction, Colo., Feb. 11, 1935. LIBRARY SCIENCE. B.A., Colo. Coll., 1957; M.A., U. of Denver, 1963. English teacher, North American–Chilean Cultural Institute (Santiago), 1959–61; teacher, Littleton High School (Colo.), 1961–62; CATALOGER, LATIN AMERICAN LIBRARY, TULANE U., 1963– . Buenos Aires Cultural Convention scholar (Chile), 1959–60. Membership: American Library Association; Louisiana Library Association. Research: Latin American history; Popular Front and Pedro Aguirre Cerda in Chile. Language: Spanish 4,3,3,3; Portuguese 2,1,1,1; French 4,2,2,2; German 2,2,1,1. Home: 2231½ Wirth Pl., New Orleans, La. 70115. Office: Latin American Library, Tulane U., New Orleans, 70118.

CLEAR, VAL B., b. Jan. 31, 1915. SOCIOLOGY. A.B., Anderson Coll., 1941; Universidad Nacional Mayor de San Marcos (Lima), 1941–44; Ph. D., U. of Chicago, 1953. Asst. principal, Colegio San Andrés (Lima), 1941–44; researcher, Church Federation of Greater Chicago, 1944–47; PROF., CHMN., SOCIOLOGY AND SOCIAL WORK, ANDERSON COLL., 1947– ; vis. prof., Seminario Evangélico de P.R., 1960–61. Consultant on church planning (P.R.), National Council of Churches, 1960–61; research consultant, Indiana Legislature, 1962–63; staff member, Institute on Church Planning in P.R., Lilly Endowment, 1963. Membership: Christian Welfare Associates; Council of Social Work Education; Indiana Association of Family Service; Indiana State Conference on Social Work; Religious Research Association. Research: social work: religious institutions in changing communities; culture and religion in Cuba and Puerto Rico; exotic aviculture. Author: The Urbanization of a Holiness Body (in Cities and Churches, 1962); Reflections of a Post-sectarian (Christian Century, Jan. 1963); Puerto Rican Breakthrough (Christian Century, Oct. 1963). Language: Spanish 4,4,4,4. Home: 303 Cottage Ave., Anderson, Ind., 46012. Office: Dept. of Sociology, Anderson Coll., Anderson, 46012.

CLEGERN, WAYNE M., b. Edmond, Okla., Nov. 28, 1929. HISTORY. A.B., U. of Okla., 1951; M.A., 1954; Ph. D., U. of Calif., Berkeley, 1959. Asst. prof., La. State U., 1959–62; asst. prof., acting chmn., 1962–63; ASSOC. PROF., CHMN., HISTORY, LA. STATE U., NEW ORLEANS, 1963– . Doherty fellow (Central America), 1958–59. Membership: American Historical Association; Conference on Latin American History; Louisiana Historical Association. Research: international disputes; British Honduras. Author: Maudslay's Central America (1962); New Light on the Belize Dispute (American Journal of International Law, Apr. 1958); A Guatemalan Defense of the British Honduras Boundary of 1859 (Hispanic American Historical Review, Nov. 1960). Language: Spanish 3,–,–,–; Portuguese 2,–,–,–; German 2,–,–,–. Home: 4653 Kendall Dr., New Orleans 26, La. Office: Dept. of History, La. State U., New Orleans 22.

CLEMENT, MEREDITH OWEN, b. Colusa,

Calif., June 7, 1926. ECONOMICS. B.S., U. of Calif., Berkeley, 1950; Ph. D., 1958. Research economist, Central Intelligence Agency, 1954–56; ASSOC. PROF., ECONOMICS, DARTMOUTH COLL., 1956– ; vis. prof., U. of Calif., Berkeley, 1961–62; RESEARCH PROF., BROOKINGS INSTITUTION, 1964– . Dartmouth Coll. Comparative Studies Center grant, Summer 1964. Membership: American Economic Association; Econometric Society; Royal Economic Society. Research: international economics; economic development; macroeconomics in its policy aspects; role of international trade in Latin American development programs. Author: The Impact of Federal Grants-in-Aid on New England (1961); The Quantitative Impact of Automatic Stabilizers (Review of Economics and Statistics, Feb. 1960). Language: Spanish 3,2,2,1; French 3,2,1,1; German 3,2,1,1; Rumanian 3,1,1,1. Office: Dept. of Economics, Dartmouth Coll., Hanover, N.H. 03755.

CLENDENEN, CLARENCE C., b. Colorado Springs, Colo., June 8, 1899. HISTORY. B.S., U.S. Military Academy, 1920; M.A., Mich. State U., 1953; Ph. D., Stanford U., 1959. Second lieutenant-colonel, U.S. Army, 1918–1954; instr., Stanford U., 1959–60; instr., Menlo Coll., 1960–63; RESEARCH ASST. AND MILITARY CURATOR, HOOVER INSTITUTION ON WAR, REVOLUTION AND PEACE, STANFORD U., 1963– . Membership: American Historical Association: American Military Institute; Naval Historical Foundation. Research: revolutionary history of Mexico. Author: The United States and Pancho Villa (1961); Dan Showalter—California Secessionist (California Historical Society Quarterly, Dec. 1961); A Confederate Spy in California (Southern California Quarterly, Sept. 1963). Language: Spanish 4,4,3,4; German 2,1,1,2. Home: 1587 Dennis Lane, Mountain View, Calif. Office: Hoover Institution on War, Revolution and Peace, Stanford U., Stanford, Calif.

CLIFFORD, KATHLEEN EMMONS, b. Las Animas, Colo., Sept. 27, 1908. LIBRARY SCIENCE. Certificate, U. of Grenoble (France), 1927; A.B., U. of Mich., 1931; B.S. in L.S., U. of Wash., 1932. Reference librarian, Library, U of Wash., 1932–33; dir. of American School, U.S. Naval Government of Guam, 1933–36; librarian and teacher, Arlington Hall Junior Coll. for Girls, 1936–38; descriptive cataloger, Library of Congress, 1938–52; asst. in reorganization, cataloging and classification, National Library (Rio de Janeiro), 1945–46; dir., U.S. Information Library (Lisbon), 1948–49; SENIOR SUBJECT CATALOGER AND CLASSIFIER, LIBRARY OF CONGRESS, 1952– . Membership: American Library Association; District of Columbia Library Association. Research: cataloging and classification of Latin American materials. Language: Spanish 3,3,1,1; Portuguese 4,4,4,3; French 4,4,4,3; German 2,1,1,1; Italian 3,2,1,1; Latin 2,1,1,1. Home: 2204 South Knoll Rd., Arlington, Va. 22202. Office: Descriptive Cataloging Div., Library of Congress, Washington, D.C. 20540.

CLIFFORD, ROY ARTHUR, b. Knowles, Okla., Jan. 18, 1923. SOCIOLOGY. M.A.,

U. of Okla., 1947; U. of Tex., 1947–49; U. of Fla. Asst. prof., Vanderbilt U., 1949–51; sociologist, Inter-American Institute of Agricultural Sciences (Montevideo, Uruguay), 1951–52; asst. prof., Mich. State U., 1952–57; SOCIOLOGIST, INTER-AMERICAN INSTITUTE OF AGRICULTURAL SCIENCES (SAN JOSÉ, COSTA RICA), 1954– ; asst. dir., Latin American Language and Area Program, U. of Fla., 1964–65. Consultant, U.S. Agency for International Development (Dominican Republic, Colombia, Honduras, Guatemala); consultant, United Nations Food and Agriculture Organization (Lima, Peru). Membership: American Sociological Association; International Development Society; Rural Sociological Society. Research: Latin American public institutions; rural leadership in Latin America; decline and growth of rural population centers of Mexico. Author: The Rio Grande Flood: A Comparative Study of Border Communities in Disaster (1956). Co-author: Turrialba: Social Systems and the Introduction of Change (1953); La sociología rural (1960). Language: Spanish 5,5,4,4; Portuguese 4,4,3,3; French 4,2,1,1; German 3,1,1,1. Home: 325 Hampton Lane, Key Biscayne, Miami, Fla. Office: Inter-American Institute of Agricultural Sciences, Apartado 4359, San José, Costa Rica.

CLINE, HOWARD FRANCIS, b. Detroit, Mich., June 12, 1915. HISTORY, ANTHROPOLOGY, AND GEOGRAPHY. S.B., Harvard Coll., 1939; A.M., Harvard U., 1942; Ph. D., 1947. Asst. dean, Harvard Coll., 1943–46; instr., Harvard U., 1946–47; instr., Yale U., 1947–49; asst. prof., Northwestern U., 1949–52; DIR., HISPANIC FOUNDATION, LIBRARY OF CONGRESS, 1952– . Sheldon Prize fellow, 1939; Social Science Research Council fellow, 1942–43; Woodbury Lowery fellow, 1947; Social Science Research Council grant-in-aid, 1951, 1955; chmn., Conference on Latin American History, 1964. Membership: American Anthropological Association; American Historical Association; Conference on Latin American History; Phi Beta Kappa. Research: Mexico; Middle American ethnohistory; Mexico pictorial documents. Author: The United States and Mexico (1953); Mexico: Revolution to Evolution, 1940–1960 (1962); Colonial Lienzos and Communities of the Mazatec Indians, Oaxaca, Mexico (in Ancient Oaxaca, by J. Paddock, 1966). Language: Spanish 4,4,4,2; Portuguese 4,3,3,1; French 4,2,2,1; German 4,3,3,1; Italian 3,2,2,1; Maya 2,2,1,1. Linguistic studies: Chinantec. Home: 1701 North Patrick Henry Dr., Arlington, Va. Office: Hispanic Foundation, Library of Congress, Washington, D.C. 20540.

COBB, CARL WESLEY, b. Yazoo City, Miss., Aug. 11, 1926. SPANISH AMERICAN LITERATURE. B.A., Peabody Coll., 1950; M.A., 1952; Ph. D., Tulane U., 1961. Teacher, Centro Colombo-Americano (Bogotá), 1958; asst. prof., Middle Tenn. State Coll., 1961–62; ASSOC. PROF., SPANISH, FURMAN U., 1962– . Buenos Aires Convention fellow (Colombia), 1957–58; Southern fellow, Tulane U., 1960–61. Membership: American Association of Teachers of Spanish and Portuguese; American Association of University Professors; Modern Language Association. Research: modern Spanish literature; Spanish translations of English and American poetry; Colombian literature. Author: J. A. Silva and Oscar Wilde (Hispania, Dec. 1962); Milton and Blank Verse in Spain (Philological Quarterly, Apr. 1963); A New Translation of the Romance Sonámbulo (Furman Studies, May 1964). Language: Spanish 5,5,5,5; Portuguese 1,1,1,1; French 2,2,1,1. Home: 31 Nera Dr., Greenville, S.C. Office: Dept. of Spanish, Furman U., Greenville.

COBB, H. LOGAN, b. Aurora, Mo., May 17, 1906. SPANISH AMERICAN LITERATURE. B.S., U. of Mo., 1930; A.M., 1937; Ph. D., 1947. Teacher, Balboa High School (C.Z.), 1941–42; instr., U. of Mo., 1946–47; asst. prof., Mary Washington Coll., 1947–50; assoc. prof., Millikin U., 1950–55; teacher, Junior High School (Decatur, Ill.), 1955–57; head, Foreign Languages, High School (Decatur), 1957–63; ASSOC. PROF., FOREIGN LANGUAGES, EASTERN ILL. U., 1963– . Membership: American Association of Teachers of Spanish and Portuguese; American Association of University Professors; Instituto Internacional de Literatura Iberoamericana; Midwest Council of Association of Latin American Studies; Modern Language Association; National Education Association. Research: life and works of Juan de Dios Peza. Language: Spanish 4,4,4,4; French 3,2,2,3. Home: 2209 University Dr., Charleston, Ill., 61920. Office: Dept. of Foreign Languages, Eastern Ill. U., Charleston, 61920.

COCHRANE, JAMES DAVID, b. Cherokee, Iowa, Sept. 4, 1938. POLITICAL SCIENCE AND ECONOMICS. B.A., Morningside Coll., 1960; M.A., State U. of Iowa, 1961; Ph. D., 1964. Legislative asst. to Member, U.S. House of Representatives, 1961–62; RESEARCH FELLOW, BROOKINGS INSTITUTION, 1964– . National Defense Education Act fellow in Latin American Studies; State U. of Iowa graduate fellow, 1962–64. Membership: American Political Science Association; District of Columbia Political Science Association; Southern Political Science Association. Research: Latin American politics; Central American economic integration; Latin American foreign policies. Author: Partisan Aspects of Congressional Committee Staffing (Western Political Quarterly, Sept. 1964). Language: Spanish 3,2,2,3; French 4,3,3,3. Home: 19 5th St. SE., Washington, D.C. Office: Brookings Institution, 1775 Massachusetts Ave. NW., Washington, D.C.

COE, MICHAEL DOUGLAS, b. New York, N.Y., May 14, 1929. ANTHROPOLOGY. A.B., Harvard Coll., 1950; Ph. D., Harvard U., 1959. Asst. prof., U. of Tenn., 1958–60; instr.-ASSOC. PROF., ANTHROPOLOGY, YALE U., 1960– . Adviser, Bliss Collection of Pre-Columbian Art, Dumbarton Oaks, Harvard U.; editor, Yale U. Publications in Anthropology; consultant, Educational Services, Inc. Membership: American Anthropological Association; Sociedad Mexicana de Antropología; Society for American Archaeology. Research: archeology of Mesoamerica. Author: La Victoria: An Early Site on the Pacific Coast of Guatemala (1961); Mexico (1962); Costa Rican Archaeology and Mesoamerica (Southwestern Journal of Anthropology, Summer 1962). Language: Spanish 4,4,4,3; Portuguese 2,2,1,1; French 4,3,2,2; German 2,2,2,1; Italian 2,2,2,1. Home: 376 Saint Ronan St., New Haven, Conn. Office: Dept. of Anthropology, Yale U., New Haven.

COHEN, ALVIN, b. Washington, D.C., June 30, 1931. ECONOMICS. B.A., George Washington U., 1953; M.B.A., Columbia U., 1955; Ph. D., U. of Fla., 1962. Instr., U. of Fla., 1958–61; Fulbright vis. prof., San Marcos U. (Peru), 1961–62; lectr., National U. of El Salvador, Aug. 1962; ASST. PROF., ECONOMICS, LEHIGH U., 1962– . Fulbright scholar (Chile), 1957–58. Membership: American Economic Association; Hispanic American Society. Research: economic theory and development; cultural obstacles to the growth process; Chilean economy; Peruvian economic development. Author: Economic Change in Chile, 1929–1959 (1960); Definición alternativa para el desarrollo económico (Economía Salvadoreña, 1961); Societal Structure, Agrarian Reform, and Economic Development in Peru (Inter-American Economic Affairs, Summer 1964). Language: Spanish 5,4,4,4. Home: Apt. 4D, William Penn Ct., Easton, Pa. Office: Dept. of Economics, Lehigh U., Bethlehem, Pa.

COHEN, SAUL B., b. Malden, Mass., July 28, 1925. GEOGRAPHY. A.B., Harvard Coll., 1947; A.M., Harvard U., 1949; Ph. D., 1954. Prof., Boston U., 1952–64; vis. prof., Yale U., 1955–56; vis. prof., U.S. Naval War Coll., 1956–57; EXECUTIVE OFFICER, ASSOCIATION OF AMERICAN GEOGRAPHERS, 1964– . National Academy of Science-National Research Council Committee on Geography; delegate, Association of American Geographers to American Council of Learned Societies. Membership: Association of American Geographers. Research: political and economic geography; economic base, resource use, and urban functions of small Venezuelan cities. Author: Store Location Research for the Food Industry (1961); Geography and Politics in a World Divided (1963); Dynamics of Store Trading Areas and Market Equilibrium (Annals, Association of American Geographers, 1961). Language: Spanish 2,2,–,–; French 3,3,2,2; Hebrew 5,5,4,4. Home: 8510 16th St., Silver Spring, Md. Office: Association of American Geographers, 1146 16th St., NW., Washington, D.C.

COLBERG, SEVERO E., b. Cabo Rojo, P.R., Sept. 16, 1924. POLITICAL SCIENCE: PUBLIC ADMINISTRATION. B.A., U. of P.R., 1950; M.P.A., Harvard U., 1954. Administrative asst. to Dean of Social Sciences, U. of P.R., 1952–53; ASST. PROF., PUBLIC ADMINISTRATION, U. OF P.R., 1952– ; asst. dir., Graduate School of Public Administration, 1954–56; asst. to the chancellor, 1956–59; executive asst., 1959–61; dir., Graduate School of Public Administration, 1961–63. Consultant in administrative problems, Dept. of Commerce (P.R.); Academic Senate, U. of P.R.; weekly columnist for El Imparcial (San Juan), 1963– . Membership: Puerto Rican Association of Political Science; Puerto Rican Society of Public Administration. Research: educational programs in public administration. Language: Spanish 5,5,5,5. Home: Ox-5 Faculty Residences, U. of

P.R., Río Piedras, P.R. Office: Dept. of Public Administration, U. of P.R., Río Piedras.

COLBY, BENJAMIN N., b. Evanston, Ill., Sept. 14, 1931. ANTHROPOLOGY. B.A., Princeton U., 1953; Ph. D., Harvard U., 1960. Instr., Harvard U., 1961-63; ASSOC. CURATOR, MUSEUM OF N. MEX., 1963- . National Institutes of Health grants; field dir., Harvard-Columbia Field Institute in Anthropology. Membership: American Anthropological Association. Research: social anthropology of indigenous and modern Latin America; ethnic relations in Mexico and Guatemala. Author: Ethnic Relations in Southeastern Mexico (American Anthropologist, Aug. 1961); Mesoamerican Psychological Orientations (in Handbook of Middle American Indians). Language: Spanish 4,4,4,4; Portuguese 3,3,2,2; French 1,1,1,1; German 2,2,2,2. Linguistic studies: Ixil; Tzotzil. Home: Fort Union Dr., Santa Fe, N. Mex. Office: Laboratory of Anthropology, Box 1727, Santa Fe.

COLE, WILLIAM EDWARD, b. Mineola, Tex., Feb. 5, 1931. ECONOMICS. B.A., U. of Tex., 1952; Ph. D., 1965. Auditor, Procter and Gamble (Cincinnati and P.R.), 1955-61; TEACHING ASST., ECONOMICS, U. OF TEX., 1961- . National Defense Education Act fellow, 1962-64; U. of Tex. fellow. Membership: Cincinnati Council of World Affairs. Research: Mexican iron and steel industry; Central American Common Market; role of government monopoly and mixed enterprise in the development of Mexico's economy. Language: Spanish 3,3,3,3. Home: 903 Newsom St., Mineola, Tex. Office: Dept. of Economics, U. of Tex., Austin.

COLEMAN, WILLIAM JACKSON, M.M., b. Shelby, Ohio, Mar. 29, 1911. HISTORY. Maryknoll Seminary (N.Y.), 1935-39; M.A., Catholic U. of America, 1942; Ph. D., 1950. Prof., Maryknoll Coll., 1947-50; dir., Colegio Gonzalo Correa (Chile), 1950-56; prof., Maryknoll Seminary (N.Y.), 1956-61; PROF., HISTORY, MARYKNOLL SEMINARY (ILL.), 1961- . Catholic Foreign Mission Society research fellow, Vatican Archives, 1945-47. Membership: American Historical Association; Catholic Historical Association; Interamerican Conference. Research: Latin American church and mission history, especially the early national period. Author: The First Apostolic Delegation in Rio de Janeiro and Its Influence in Spanish America (1950); La restauración del episcopado chileno en 1828 según fuentes vaticanas (1954); Latin American Catholicism (1958). Language: Spanish 4,-,-,-; Portuguese 3,-,-,-; French 3,-,-,-; Italian 3,-,-,-. Home and office: Maryknoll Seminary, Glen Ellyn, Ill. 60137.

COLFORD, WILLIAM EDWARD, b. Brooklyn, N.Y., May 9, 1908. EDUCATION AND LANGUAGE. B.A., City Coll. (N.Y.), 1929; M.A., Columbia U., 1933; Ph. D., 1942; Teachers' Coll., Columbia U., 1945-55. Instr.-prof., City Coll. (N.Y.), 1929-50; chmn., Romance Languages, 1950-52; asst. dir., Summer Session, 1952-57; ASST. DEAN, CITY COLL. (N.Y.), 1957- . Chmn., Fulbright Committee, City Coll. (N.Y.). Membership: Mexican Institute of Linguistic Investigation; Phi Beta Kappa; Sigma Delta Pi. Research: college administration; guidance and curriculum planning; English as a foreign language; education in Argentina, Brazil, Chile, Peru, and Uruguay. Author: Juan Meléndez Valdes. A Study in the Transition from Neoclassicism to Romanticism in Spanish Poetry (1942); New York: Gateway to the U.S.A., A Conversational Reader for Students of English (1963); Classic Tales from Latin America (1963). Language: Spanish 5,5,5,5; Portuguese 5,5,5,5; French 4,4,4,4; German 2,2,2,2; Italian 3,3,3,3; Latin 3,-,-,-. Linguistic studies: Nahuatl. Home: 539 Chilton St., Elizabeth 3, N.J. Office: Asst. Dean, City Coll. of N.Y., New York 31, N.Y.

COLLADO, EMILIO GABRIEL, b. Cranford, N.J., Dec. 20, 1910. ECONOMICS. S.B., Mass. Institute of Technology, 1931; A.M., Harvard U., 1934; Ph. D., 1936. Economic analyst, U.S. Treasury Dept., 1934-36; economist, Federal Reserve Bank (N.Y.), 1936-38; asst. chief, Div. of American Republics, U.S. Dept. of State, 1938-46; executive dir., International Bank for Reconstruction and Development, 1946-47; financial analyst, Standard Oil Company, 1947-49; asst. treasurer, 1949-54; treasurer, 1954-60; dir., Standard Oil Company, 1960-62; VICE PRESIDENT-FINANCE, STANDARD OIL COMPANY, 1962- . Trustee, Committee for Economic Development. Membership: American Economic Association; U.S. Council of International Chamber of Commerce. Research: economic development. Author: Private Investment and Economic Development (Foreign Affairs, July 1957); Economic Development through Private Enterprise (Foreign Affairs, July 1963). Language: Spanish 5,4,4,4; Portuguese 4,3,2,2; French 5,4,3,2. Home: 501 Old Westbury Rd., Roslyn Heights, N.Y. Office: Standard Oil Company, 30 Rockefeller Plaza, New York, N.Y., 10020.

COLLIER, DONALD, b. Sparkill, N.Y., May 1, 1911. ANTHROPOLOGY. A.B., U. of Calif., Berkeley, 1933; Ph. D., U. of Chicago, 1954. CURATOR, SOUTH AMERICAN ARCHEOLOGY AND ETHNOLOGY, CHICAGO NATURAL HISTORY MUSEUM, 1941- ; LECTR., ANTHROPOLOGY, U. OF CHICAGO, 1949- . Review editor, American Antiquity, 1958-62. Membership: American Anthropological Association; Institute for Andean Research; Society for American Archaeology. Research: archeology; culture history of the Americas; rise of civilization in Mesoamerica and Peru. Author: Survey and Excavations in Southern Ecuador (1943); Cultural Chronology and Change in Viru Valley, Peru (1955). Co-author: Indians before Columbus (1947). Language: Spanish 4,4,3,2; French 3,2,1,1. Home: 5632 Kimbark Ave., Chicago 37, Ill. Office: Chicago Natural History Museum, Roosevelt Rd. and Lake Shore Dr., Chicago.

COLLVER, O. ANDREW, b. Eugene, Oreg., May 12, 1929. SOCIOLOGY. B.A., U. of Oreg., 1955; M.A., U. of Calif., Berkeley, 1958; Ph. D., 1964. RESEARCH SOCIOLOGIST, INTERNATIONAL POPULATION AND URBAN RESEARCH, U. OF CALIF., BERKELEY, 1960- ; supplementary faculty, Latin American Summer Program, U. of Calif., Berkeley, Summer 1964. Membership: American Sociological Association; Population Association of America.

Research: historical trends of fertility in Latin America; urban community; population; ecology. Author: The Family Cycle in India and the United States (American Sociological Review, Feb. 1963). Co-author: Economic Classification of Cities and Metropolitan Areas (in The Municipal Year Book, 1959); The Female Labor Force in Metropolitan Areas (Economic Development and Cultural Change, July 1962). Language: Spanish 2,1,1,2; Portuguese 2,1,1,1; French 3,2,2,3; German 2,1,1,1. Home: 1547 Sacramento St., Berkeley, Calif., 94702. Office: International Population and Urban Research, U. of Calif., Berkeley, 94720.

COMITAS, LAMBROS, b. New York, N.Y., Sept. 29, 1927. ANTHROPOLOGY. A.B., Columbia U., 1948; Ph. D., 1962. Dir., Caribbean Program, Research Institute for the Study of Man, 1959-61; field dir., Brandeis U. (Barbados, British West Indies), 1960; project coordinator, U.S. Peace Corps Training Unit for Jamaica, West Indies, 1962; ASSOC. DIR., RESEARCH INSTITUTE FOR THE STUDY OF MAN, 1962-; ASST. PROF., ANTHROPOLOGY, COLUMBIA U., 1962- . Fulbright scholar (Jamaica), 1957-58; consultant, U.S. Peace Corps, 1961-63; chmn., Caribbean Seminar, Institute for Latin American Studies, Columbia U. Membership: American Anthropological Association; American Ethnological Society; Society for Applied Anthropology. Research: cultural and social anthropology; studies of fishing villages; surveys of rural cooperatives; Barbados; Jamaica. Author: Metropolitan Influences in the Caribbean: The West Indies (Annals of the New York Academy of Sciences, Jan. 1960); Occupational Multiplicity in Rural Jamaica (Proceedings of the American Ethnological Society, 1964). Co-author: Emigration and Depopulation: Some Neglected Aspects of Population Geography (The Geographical Review, Apr. 1962). Language: Spanish 3,3,2,3; French 2,2,2,2; Greek 5,5,5,5. Home: 41-42 Elbertson St., Elmhurst, N.Y. Office: Dept. of Anthropology, Columbia U., New York, N.Y., 10027.

COMPTON, CARL BENTON, b. Estherville, Iowa, Dec. 10, 1905. ANTHROPOLOGY AND ART. B.A., Notre Dame U., 1929; B.F.A., Art Institute of Chicago, 1935; Maestro de Bellas Artes, Escuela Universitaria de Bellas Artes (Mexico), 1943. Head, Dept. of Art and History, Southwestern U. (Tex.), 1936-43; instr., La. State U., 1943-44; ASSOC. PROF., ART, NORTH TEX. STATE U., 1944- ; DIR., INSTITUTO INTERAMERICANO. Dir., Summer School, U. de Guanajuato-North Tex. State Coll. (Mexico), 1945, 1946; collaborator in anthropology, Western Speleological Institute. Membership: Academia Romana de Scienzi de Arti; Centro Cultural México-Colombiano; Centro de Investigaciones Antropológicos de México; Pennsylvania Institute of Archaeology; Royal Anthropological Institute; Society for American Archaeology; Sigma Xi; Texas Archaeological Society. Research: cultural anthropology; the arts of West Mexico from the earliest record through the colonial period. Author: The Cult of the Female among the Tarascans (Magazine of Art, Feb. 1953); Preliminary Study of the Distribution of the Bird-Form Vessel (Bulletin, Texas Archeological Society, 1956); The Long-Nosed God—a Distributional Study (Tennessee Archaeological Society Miscellaneous Paper, 1957). Language: Spanish 4,4,4,4; Portuguese 3,2,1,1; French 3,2,2,1; Catalán 3,2,1,1; Italian 3,2,1,1; Rumanian 3,2,1,1. Home: R.F.D. 1, Denton, Tex. 76203. Office: Instituto Interamericano, 5133 North Tex. U. Station, Denton, 76203.

COMPTON, MERLIN DAVID, b. Ogden, Utah, July 22, 1924. SPANISH AMERICAN LITERATURE. B.A., Brigham Young U., 1952; M.A., 1954; Ph. D., U. of Calif., Los Angeles, 1959. Asst. coordinator, Madrid School Project, U. of Calif., Los Angeles, 1957; asst. prof., Adams State Coll., 1959-63; ASSOC. PROF., FOREIGN LANGUAGES, WEBER STATE COLL., 1963- . Membership: American Association of Teachers of Spanish and Portuguese; National Federation of Modern Language Teachers Associations; Utah Educational Association. Research: Spanish honor in the Tradiciones Peruanas of Richardo Palma; honor in Lope de Vega's plays. Language: Spanish 5,4,4,5; Portuguese 3,2,3,3; French 3,1,1,1. Home: 2208 West 5025 South Roy, Utah. Office: Dept. of Foreign Languages, Weber State Coll., Ogden, Utah.

CONNALLY, ERNEST ALLEN, b. Groesbeck, Tex., Nov. 15, 1921. ARCHITECTURE. B. Arch., U. of Tex., 1950; M.A., Harvard U., 1952, Ph. D., 1955. Asst. prof., Miami U., 1952-55; assoc. prof., Washington U., 1955-57; U. of Ill., 1957-61; PROF., ARCHITECTURE, U. OF ILL., 1961- ; vis. prof., Washington U., 1962. American Philosophical Society grant (Mexico), Summer 1957; Fulbright lectr., U. of Melbourne, 1963. Membership: College Art Association; National Trust for Historic Preservation; Society of Architectural Historians. Research: history of architecture in the Spanish province of Texas; city planning in the Spanish colonies. Language: Spanish 3,2,2,2; Portuguese 1,-,-,-; French 4,4,4,3; German 3,2,2,1; Italian 3,2,2,2. Home: 503 Eliot Dr., Urbana, Ill. 61801. Office: Dept. of Architecture, U. of Ill., Urbana.

CONNOLLY, BRENDAN, S.J., b. Boston, Mass., Feb. 10, 1913. LIBRARY SCIENCE. A.M., Boston Coll., 1938; S.T.L., Weston Coll., 1944; Ph. D., U. of Chicago, 1955. Instr., Boston Coll., 1938-40; instr., Catholic U. of America, 1950-51; librarian and asst. prof., Weston Coll., 1951-59; DIR. OF LIBRARIES, BOSTON COLL., 1959- . Consultant, Library, St. George's Coll. (Jamaica), 1962. Membership: American Association of University Professors; American Library Association; Catholic Library Association; Conference of Jesuit Libraries. Research: library development in Jesuit institutions in Venezuela. Author: Jesuit Library Beginnings (The Library Quarterly, Oct. 1960); The Catholic Library World: A Report and a Projected Discussion (The Catholic Library World, Apr. 1961). Language: Spanish 2,1,1,1; Portuguese 2,1,1,1; French 3,2,1,1; Italian 2,2,2,1; Latin 5,5,4,4. Home and office: Dir. of Libraries, Boston Coll., Chestnut Hill, Mass., 02167.

CONRAD, DAVID E., b. Marietta, Okla., Aug. 22, 1928. HISTORY. B.A., U. of Okla., 1952; M.A., 1957; Ph. D., 1962. ASSOC. PROF., HISTORY, SOUTHWEST TEX. STATE COLL., 1957- . Southern Fellowships Fund grant-in-aid, 1959, fellow, 1961. Membership: Agricultural History Association; Mississippi Valley Historical Association. Research: Mexican-American border area. Author: The Whipple Expedition on the Great Plains (Great Plains Journal, Spring 1963). Language: Spanish 3,3,2,2; French 3,2,2,2. Home: R.F.D. 2, Box 474-A, San Marcos, Tex. Office: Dept. of History, Southwest Tex. State Coll., San Marcos.

CONSTANTINE, MILDRED, b. Brooklyn, N.Y., June 28, 1914. ART. B.A., N.Y.U., 1933. Editorial asst., Parnassus, asst. secretary, Traveling Exhibitions and Lecture Program, College Art Association, 1929–37; dir. of education, National Committee for Art Appreciation, 1937–39; dir. of promotion, National Art Society, 1939–40; asst. keeper, Archive of Hispanic Culture, Hispanic Foundation, Library of Congress, 1942–44; ASSOC. CURATOR, MUSEUM OF MODERN ART (N.Y.), 1949– . Consultant, Div. of Education, Coordinator of Inter-American Affairs, 1941–42; consultant, Associated American Artists, Inc., 1946–47. Membership: American Institute of Graphic Arts; College Art Association; International Design Conference. Research: history of graphic design. Author: Sign Language (1961); Afiches (Norte, Nov. 1941). Editor: Preliminary Guide to Institutions and Individuals in the Fields of Art, Architecture, Archeology and Ethnology in Latin America (1942). Language: Spanish 4,4,4,3; Portuguese 3,3,3,2; French 4,4,3,3; German 2,2,2,–; Italian 2,2,2,–. Home: 60 Saw Mill Rd., New City, N.Y. Office: Museum of Modern Art, 11 West 53d St., New York 19, N.Y.

COOK, ARTHUR J. D., b. Quillota, Chile, Dec. 15, 1918. ECONOMICS. B.A., U. of Kans., 1942; M.A., 1947; Ph. D., 1957. Asst. in industrial relations, Raymond-Hegeman Company (Caracas), 1948–49; statistician, Middlewest Motor Freight Bureau, 1952–54; instr., Ohio U., 1953–55; asst. prof., Kansas City U., 1955–57; training dir., Latin American Paper Division, W. R. Grace and Company, 1957–60; assoc. prof., Fairleigh Dickinson U., 1960–62; ASSOC. PROF., MANAGEMENT, TEMPLE U., 1962– . Membership: American Economic Association. Research: industrial relations and international development and management, especially in Cuba, Peru, Puerto Rico, and Venezuela. Author: Economic Growth and the Alliance for Progress (Economic and Business Bulletin, Temple U., June 1963); The Case for Private International Investment (Economic and Business Bulletin, Temple U., June 1964). Language: Spanish 4,4,3,3. Home: 301 Midland Ave., Wayne, Pa. Office: School of Business Administration, Temple U., Philadelphia 22, Pa.

COOK, HUGH LINCOLN, b. Prattville, Ala., Dec. 6, 1911. ECONOMICS. A.B., Piedmont Coll., 1935; B.S., Auburn U., 1940; M.S., 1942; Ph. D., U. of Wis., 1950. Agricultural economist, U.S. Dept. of Agriculture, 1943–49; PROF., AGRICULTURAL ECONOMICS, U. OF WIS., 1949– ; agricultural economist, U.S. Agency for International Development (Philippines), 1957–58. Consultant, Consejo de Bienestar Rural (Venezuela), 1960; consultant, World Bank (Latin America). Membership: American Economic Association; American Farm Economics Association; International Association of Agricultural Economists. Research: agricultural economics and marketing; economic development; marketing aspects of agrarian reform. Author: Land Reform and Development in the Philippines (1961); Observations on Market Structures and National Economic Development in the Philippines (Journal of Farm Economics, Aug. 1959); The New Agrarian Reform Law and Economic Development in Venezuela (Land Economics, Feb. 1961). Language: Spanish 3,2,2,2; French 3,2,1,2; German 2,2,1,2. Home: 2051 Allen Blvd., Middleton, Wis. Office: Dept. of Agricultural Economics, U. of Wis., Madison.

COOK, ROSEMOND F., b. Valley City, N. Dak., June 16, 1909. LIBRARY SCIENCE. B.A., U. of Calif., Los Angeles, 1930; B.S. L.S., School of Library Service, Columbia U, 1933. Asst. librarian, State Teachers Coll. (Valley City, N. Dak.), 1931–34; N.Y. State Teachers Coll. (Potsdam), 1935–41; N.Y. State Teachers Coll. (Brockport), 1941–49; catalog librarian, Biblioteca Benjamin Franklin (Mexico, D.F.), 1949–51; asst. librarian, Centro Regional de Educación Fundamental para la América Latina (Pátzcuaro, Mexico), UNESCO, 1951–53; CATALOG LIBRARIAN, SAN DIEGO COUNTY DEPT. OF EDUCATION, 1953– . Membership: American Library Association; United States National Commission for UNESCO. Research: librarianship in educational institutions. Language: Spanish 3,3,3,3; Portuguese 2,1,1,1; French 3,2,2,2; German 2,2,1,1; Italian 2,2,1,1. Home: 5517 Bellevue, La Jolla, Calif. 92037. Office: San Diego County Dept. of Education, 6401 Linda Vista Rd., San Diego, Calif.

COOK, SHERBURNE F., b. Springfield, Mass., Dec. 31, 1896. HISTORY, DEMOGRAPHY, AND ECOLOGY. A.B., Harvard U., 1919; M.A., 1923; Ph. D., 1925. PROF, PHYSIOLOGY, U. OF CALIF., BERKELEY, 1928– . Guggenheim fellow, 1939, 1946. Research: Mexican archeology, soils and ethnography. Author: Soil Erosion and Population in Central Mexico (1949). Co-author: Population of Central Mexico in the 16th Century (1948); The Aboriginal Population in Central Mexico on the Eve of the Spanish Conquest (1962). Language: Spanish 4,3,3,3; French 4,2,2,2; German 4,3,3,4. Home: 105 Grand Ave., Pacific Grove, Calif. Office: Dept. of Physiology, U. of Calif., Berkeley.

COOK, WARREN L., b. Spokane, Wash., July 29, 1925. HISTORY AND ANTHROPOLOGY. Bach. Human., Universidad de San Marcos (Peru), 1950; Litt. D., 1955; M.A., Yale U., 1957; Ph. D., 1960. Bibliographical research, Universidad de San Marcos, 1950–52; instr., 1953; asst. prof., Castleton State Coll., 1960–63; ASSOC. PROF., SOCIAL SCIENCE, CASTLETON STATE COLL., 1963– . Membership: American Anthropological Association; American Association of University Professors; American Historical Association; Conference on Latin American History; Northern New England Historian's Conference. Research: Andean history; Spanish period of the American West; Mexico. Author: Fray Buenaventura de Salinas y Córdova, su vida y su obra (Revista del Museo Nacional, Lima, 1955; revised edition, in Memorial de las Historias del Nuevo Mundo Perú, 1957). Language: Spanish 5,5,5,4; Portuguese 4,3,3,2; French 4,3,2,2; German 3,3,3,2. Box 195, Castleton, Vt. Office: Dept. of Social Science, Castleton State Coll., Castleton.

COONS, DIX SCOTT, b. Mesa, Ariz., July 11, 1930. SPANISH AMERICAN LITERATURE. B.A., Brigham Young U., 1956; M.A., 1957; Ph. D., U. of Tex., 1964. Missionary, Church of Latter Day Saints (Argentina), 1950–53; instr., St. Stephen's Episcopal School (Austin, Tex.), 1957–63; ASST. PROF., SPANISH, BROWN U., 1963– . Research: modern novel and short story in Latin America; Horacio Quiroga. Language: Spanish 4,4,4,4; Portuguese 1,1,1,1; French 3,2,2,2. Home: 30 Viceroy Rd., Warwick, R.I., 02886. Office: Dept. of Spanish, Brown U., Providence, R.I., 02912.

COOPER, DONALD BOLON, b. Columbus, Ohio, Aug. 20, 1931. HISTORY. B.A., Ohio State U., 1957; M.A., 1958; Ph. D., U. of Tex., 1963. Asst. prof., Okla. State U., 1961–63; ASST. PROF., HISTORY, TULANE U., 1963– . Woodrow Wilson fellow, 1957–58; University fellowships, U. of Tex., 1958–60, 1961; Doherty fellow (Mexico), 1960; U.S. Public Health Service fellow, 1962; National Defense Foreign Language post-doctoral fellow in Portuguese, Summer 1963. Membership: American Association of University Professors; Phi Alpha Theta; Phi Beta Kappa; Pi Sigma Alpha. Research: history of Brazil, particularly social, municipal, and medical history; Mexico. Author: A Cycle of Sickness: The Fight Against Epidemics in Mexico City, 1761–1813 (1964); A Selective List of the Colonial Manuscripts in the Department of Health and Welfare, Mexico City, 1564–1800 (Hispanic American Historical Review, Aug. 1962); The Withdrawal of the United States from Haiti, 1928–1934 (Journal of Inter-American Studies, Jan. 1963). Language: Spanish 3,3,3,2; Portuguese 3,2,2,1; French 2,1,–,–. Home: 595 Gordon Ave., New Orleans 23, La. Office: Dept. of History, Newcomb Coll., Tulane U., New Orleans, 70118.

COOPER, WILLIAM FRAZIER, b. Louisville, Ky., Feb. 14, 1932. PHILOSOPHY. B.D., Baptist Theological Seminary, 1958; M.A., Baylor U., 1959; Ph. D., Ind. U., 1965. ASST. PROF., PHILOSOPHY, LYCOMING COLL., 1964– . Fulbright research scholar (Argentina), 1962–63; Ind. U. Dissertation Year fellow, 1963–64. Research: philosophical basis for development in Latin America; Argentine philosophical thought. Author: Bibliografía de Francisco Romero (1964). Translator: Theory of Man, by Francisco Romero (1964). Language: Spanish 5,5,5,5; Portuguese 4,4,3,3; French 4,4,3,3; German 3,3,2,2. Home: 1200 Pearl St., Montoursville, Pa. Office: Dept. of Philosophy, Lycoming Coll., Williamsport, Pa., 17704.

COPE, ORVILLE G., b. New York, N.Y., Aug. 30, 1932. POLITICAL SCIENCE. B.A., Whittier Coll., 1955; M.A., Claremont Graduate School, 1958; Ph. D., 1964. Instr., Chadwick School, 1958–59; Claremont Men's Coll., 1962–63; ASST. PROF., U. of WIS.-MILWAUKEE, 1963– . Parker Honor fellow, Whittier Coll., 1954–55; General In-Residence fellow, Claremont Graduate School, 1957–58; 1960–61; Relm Foundation fellow, 1961–62. Membership: American Political Science Association; Midwest Political Science Association; Pi Sigma Alpha; Western Political Science Association. Research: public administration; political parties and election procedures in Chile; problems of administration in Latin America. Language: Spanish 4,3,3,3; French 4,2,2,2. Home: Apt. 6, 2120 East Locust St., Milwaukee 11, Wis. Office: Dept. of Political Science, U. of Wis., Milwaukee, Milwaukee 11.

CORBETT, JOHN MAXWELL, b. New York, N.Y., July 4, 1913. ANTHROPOLOGY. A.B., U. of Southern Calif., 1937; M.A., 1939; Ph. D., Columbia U., 1950. Field archeologist, N. Mex. State Museum, 1939–40; field archeologist, Institute of Andean Research (Peru), 1941–42; laboratory archeologist, U.S. National Park Service (Miss.), 1947–48; archeologist-CHIEF ARCHEOLOGIST, U.S. NATIONAL PARK SERVICE, 1948– . School of American Research fellow (Ecuador), 1940–41. Research: archeology; Andean South America; salvage archeology. Co-author: Excavations at Pachacamac, Peru (1943); Excavations at Bynum Mounds, Mississippi (1950); Excavations at Ancón and Supe, Peru (1954). Language: Spanish 3,2,2,2. Home: 4311 Americana Dr., Annandale, Va. Office: National Park Service, U.S. Dept. of the Interior, Washington, D.C., 20240.

CORBITT, DUVON CLOUGH, b. Atkinson County, Ga., July 4, 1901. HISTORY. A.B., Asbury Coll., 1923; M.A., Emory U., 1926; Ph. D., U. of N.C., 1938. Dept. head, Candler Coll. (Cuba), 1927–29, 1931–43, 1945–46; chmn., History, Columbia Coll. (S.C.), 1943–45; vis. prof., Fla. State U., Summer 1944, Ohio State U., Summer 1944, U. of Omaha, Summer 1945; CHMN., DIV. OF SOCIAL STUDIES, ASBURY COLL., 1946– ; lectr., National Defense Education Act Language Institute, Vanderbilt U., 1963. Membership: Academia de la Historia de la Medicina; Southern Historical Society. Research: history of Cuba and the Caribbean; archival research in Cuba; documents from Spanish archives concerned with the Southwest of the United States. Author: The Chinese in Cuba (Research Bureau for Post-War Economics, 1944); Historical Publications of the Martí Centennial (Hispanic American Historical Review, Aug. 1954); Cuban Revisionist Interpretations of Cuba's Struggle for Independence (Hispanic American Historical Review, Aug. 1963). Language: Spanish 5,4,4,3; Portuguese 3,3,3,1; French 4,3,2,1. Home: 205 East Morrison Ave., Wilmore, Ky. Office: Div. of Social Studies, Asbury Coll., Wilmore.

CORBITT, ROBERTA DAY, b. Blue Mound, Kans., Oct. 20, 1902. SPANISH AMERICAN LITERATURE. B.A., U. of Chicago, 1941; M.A., 1941; Ph. D., U. of Ky., 1955. Teacher, Candler Coll. (Marianao, Cuba), 1937–43, 1945–46; instr., History, Columbia Coll. (S.C.), 1943–45; PROF., SPANISH, CHMN., LANGUAGES, ASBURY COLL., 1946– . Membership: American Association of Teachers of Spanish and Portuguese; Midwest Council of the Association of Latin American Studies. Research: Cuban, Spanish, and English literature. Author: Costumbrismo in Cuba (Hispania, Feb. 1950). Co-author: Papers from the Spanish Archives Relating to Tennessee and the Old Southwest, 1783–1800 (East Tennessee Historical Society Publications, 1937–63). Language: Spanish 5,5,5,5; French 3,–,–,–. Linguistic studies: Spanish. Home: 205 East Morrison St., Wilmore, Ky. Office: Dept. of Languages, Asbury Coll., Wilmore.

CORD, WILLIAM OWEN, b. St. Louis, Mo., May 1, 1921. SPANISH AMERICAN LITERATURE. B.S., Mo. State Coll., 1943; M.A., Washington U., 1948; Ph. D., U. of Colo., 1960. Instr., St. Louis U., 1943–51; chmn., Foreign Languages, Glenbrook High School (Ill.), 1953–56; instr., U. of Colo., 1956–58; asst. prof., Fresno State Coll., 1958–63; ASSOC. PROF., SPANISH, SONOMA STATE COLL., 1963– . Membership: American Association of Teachers of Spanish and Portuguese; American Association of University Professors; Foreign Language Association of Northern California; Pacific Council for Latin American Studies. Research: Mexican literature. Author: José Rubén Romero: Poemas y cuentos inéditos (1963); Romero's Image of Mexico (Hispania, 1962); El escritor visto por sí mismo (Iberoamérica, 1962). Language: Spanish 5,5,5,5; Portuguese 4,3,3,2; French 5,4,3,2. Linguistic studies: English; French; Spanish. Home: 431 Bruce, Rohnert Park, Calif. Office: Dept. of Spanish, Sonoma State Coll., Rohnert Park.

CÓRDOVA, EFRÉN CÓRDOVES, b. Havana, Cuba, Sept. 5, 1923. POLITICAL SCIENCE AND LAW. LL.D., U. of Havana, 1944. Cuban Delegate, International Labor Organization (Geneva), 1950–57, 1959; asst. prof., Law School, U. of Havana, 1953–60; technical adviser, Labor Ministry (Cuba), 1959; ASST. PROF., PUBLIC ADMINISTRATION, U. OF P.R., 1960– . Research: administration of labor law; municipal government. Author: Cuban Labor Law (1957); On Minimum Wages (1958). Language: Spanish 5,5,5,5; Portuguese 2,2,1,1; French 2,1,1,1. Home: Faculty Residence D–6, U. of P.R., Río Piedras, P.R. Office: School of Public Administration, U. of P.R., Apartado W, University Station, San Juan, 00931.

CORNEHLS, JAMES VERNON, b. Dallas, Tex., Nov. 16, 1936. ECONOMICS. B.A., U. of the Americas, 1961; Ph. D., U. of Tex., 1965. ASST. PROF., COLUMBIA TEACHERS COLL. TEAM, PERU PROGRAM (PERU), 1964– . National Defense graduate fellow, U. of Tex., 1961–64. Membership: American Economic Association; Omicron Chi Epsilon; Southern Economic Association. Research: Mexican agriculture, especially agrarian reform and economic development. Language: Spanish 4,4,4,4. Home: 1146 North Windomere, Dallas, Tex. Office: c/o American Embassy, Lima, Peru.

CORVALÁN, OCTAVIO E., b. Santiago del Estero, Argentina, Mar. 2, 1923. SPANISH AMERICAN LITERATURE. Profesor, Universidad de Tucumán (Argentina), 1944. Prof., U. of Tucumán, 1946–58; assoc. prof., Colby Coll., 1959; instr., Rutgers U., 1959–61; lectr., Queen's U. (Canada), 1961–63; ASST. PROF., SPANISH, IND. U., 1963– . International Institute of Education fellow, U. of Wash., 1952; Fulbright lectr., Colby Coll., 1958; research assoc., Queen's U., Summer 1962. Membership: American Association of Teachers of Spanish and Portuguese; Instituto Internacional de Literatura Iberoamericana; Modern Language Association. Research: Latin American literature and civilization. Author: El Postmodernismo (1961); Diacronías culturales en América Latina (Nueva Era, 1958); América, ¿Tertisferio? (Estaciones, Spring 1960). Language: Spanish 5,5,5,5; Portuguese 4,3,2,2; French 3,3,2,2; Italian 4,4,3,2. Home: 1105 Atwater Ave., Bloomington, Ind. Office: Dept. of Spanish, Ind. U., Bloomington.

CORWIN, ARTHUR F., b. Raton, New Mex., Nov. 10, 1924. HISTORY. B.A., Trinity Coll. (Dublin), 1950; M.A., Mexico City Coll., 1952; Ph. D., U. of Chicago, 1958. Conferencista, U. of P.R., 1956; catedrático, Universidad de Nuevo León (Mexico), 1958–62; vis. prof., U. of Texas, 1962–63; ASST. PROF., HISTORY, U. OF KY., 1963– . U. of Chicago-U. of Madrid exchange fellow, 1954–55; consultant, General Education Program, Universidad del Valle (Colombia), Apr. 1961. Membership: Hispanic American Society. Research: economic history of Latin America. Author: Contemporary Mexican Attitudes Toward Poverty and Population (1963); The Spanish Abolition Law of 1870 (Revista de Ciencias Sociales, U. of P.R., Mar. 1960). Co-editor: Evolución de la civilización contemporánea (U. of Nuevo León, Sept. 1963). Language: Spanish 5,5,5,5; Portuguese 3,3,2,2; French 3,3,2,3. Home: 1917 Oxford Circle No. 5, Lexington, Ky. Office: Dept. of History, U. of Ky., Lexington.

COSTANZO, G. A., b. Birmingham, Ala., Nov. 20, 1916. ECONOMICS: BANKING. A.B., Birmingham-Southern Coll., 1937; M.A., U. of Va., 1940; Ph. D., 1941. Asst. prof., U. of Md., 1941–42; Japanese language officer, U.S. Navy, 1943–46; economist, U.S. Dept. of State, 1946–48; economist, U.S. Treasury Dept., 1948–51; member, Currency Board, Bank of Greece (Athens), 1951–55; deputy-dir., Western Hemisphere Dept., International Monetary Fund, 1955–61; VICE PRESIDENT, SOUTH AMERICAN DISTRICT, FIRST NATIONAL CITY BANK, 1961– . Research: central and commercial banking in Latin America. Author: Stabilization Programs in Latin America (1958); The International Monetary Fund and American Business (1962). Co-author: Nazi Europe and World Trade (1942). Language: Spanish 5,5,4,3; Portuguese 3,3,2,1; Italian 5,5,4,3. Home: Toby's Lane, New Canaan, Conn. Office: 399 Park Ave., New York, N.Y.

COTNER, THOMAS EWING, b. Dallas, Tex., Oct. 26, 1916. HISTORY AND EDUCATION. A.B., Baylor U., 1937; A.M., U. of Tex., 1939; Ph. D., 1947. Teacher, Brownwood High School (Tex.), 1937–39; dir., History Div., Tex. Memorial Museum, 1939–40; instr., U. of Tex., Summer 1940; instr., Tulane U., 1940–41; specialist, American Republics Section, U.S. Office of Education, 1942–43; DIR., TECHNICAL ASSISTANCE AND EXCHANGE PROGRAM, DIV. OF INTERNATIONAL EDUCATION, U.S. OFFICE OF EDUCATION, 1946– ; lectr., George Washington U., 1948–53. Graduate fellow, U. of Tex., 1939–40, 1941–42; Superior Service Award from the Secretary of U.S. Dept. of Health, Education, and Welfare, 1961. Membership: Academy of Political Science; Alpha Chi; American Historical Association; National Education Association; Phi Kappa Sigma; Texas Historical Society. Research: history of Mexico; international exchange of students, teachers, and professors. Author: The Military and Political Career of President José Joaquín de Herrera, 1792–1854 (1946); International Educational Exchange: A Selected Bibliography (1961). Editor: Essays in Mexican History (1958). Language: Spanish 4,4,3,3; Portuguese 2,-,-,-; French 2,-,-,-; Italian 2,-,-,-. Home: 228 Buxton Rd., Falls Church, Va. Office: Div. of International Education, U.S. Office of Education, Washington, D.C., 20202.

COUMES, GEORGE RAOUL, b. New Orleans, La., Feb. 22, 1925. LAW. B.S., Loyola U. of the South, 1947; LL.B., 1952. Accountant, Standard Oil Company of Calif. (Maracaibo, Venezuela), 1947–50, 1952–53; administrative asst., 1953–56; attorney, 1956–58; asst. manager (Cochabamba, Bolivia), 1958–61; asst. to vice president (San Francisco, Calif.), 1961–62; DEPUTY DIR. OF MISSION, U.S. AGENCY FOR INTERNATIONAL DEVELOPMENT (COSTA RICA), 1962– . Membership: Alpha Sigma Nu; Blue Key. Research: industrial relations; government relations; budget and cost control. Language: Spanish 4,4,4,3. Home and office: U.S. Agency for International Development, American Embassy, San José, Costa Rica.

COURTNEY, DALE ELLIOTT, b. Ashton, Idaho, Mar. 3, 1918. GEOGRAPHY. B.A., U. of Wash., 1947; M.A., 1950; Ph. D., 1959. Team chief, Rural Land Use Mapping Project, Dept. of Agriculture and Commerce (P.R.), 1950–51; instr., Bowling Green State U., 1952–56; ASSOC. PROF., GEOGRAPHY, PORTLAND STATE COLL., 1956– . National Defense fellow in Spanish, U. of Calif., Los Angeles, Summer 1963. Membership: Association of American Geographers; Association of Pacific Coast Geographers; National Council for Geographic Education. Research: land use analysis and projection; rural economy of the west coast of Mexico. Author: Land Use Trends in San Sebastian and Moca, Puerto Rico (Association of Pacific Coast Geographers Yearbook, 1959). Language: Spanish 3,3,-3,3; French 3,2,2,1. Home: 3105 SW. Sherwood Pl., Portland, Oreg. 97201. Office: Dept. of Geography, Portland State Coll., Portland, 97201.

COWGILL, GEORGE LEWIS, b. Grangeville, Idaho, Dec. 19, 1929. ANTHROPOLOGY. B.A., Stanford U., 1952; M.S., Iowa State Coll., 1954; M.A., U. of Chicago, 1956; Ph. D., Harvard U., 1963. Instr.-ASST. PROF., ANTHROPOLOGY, BRANDEIS U., 1960– . National Science Foundation fellow, 1955–56, 1959–60; Doherty fellow (Guatemala), 1958–59; Committee for Latin American Studies; Brandeis U. Membership: American Anthropological Association; Seminario de Cultura Maya (Mexico); Society for American Archaeology. Research: Middle American archeology, ethnohistory, and cultural anthropology, especially in the Maya area. Author: The End of Classic Maya Culture (Southwestern Journal of Anthropology, Summer 1964). Language: Spanish 4,3,3,3; Portuguese 2,2,1,1; French 2,2,1,1; German 3,2,2,2. Office: Dept. of Anthropology, Brandeis U., Waltham 54, Mass.

CRAIN, CLARK N., b. Ft. Collins, Colo., Apr. 3, 1914. GEOGRAPHY. B.A., U. of Colo., 1938; M.A., 1939; Ph. D., Clark U., 1951. PROF., CHMN., GEOGRAPHY, U. OF DENVER, 1945– ; operations analyst, U.S. Air Force, 1955– ; vis. prof., U. of Ga., 1956–57; principal investigator, Advanced Research Projects Agency, 1963– . Delegate, Pan American Institute of Geography and History Meeting, 1955; consultant on development problems, R. J. Tipton & Co. (Colombia), 1958. Membership: Association of American Geographers. Research: land use and planning; development and terrain in Chihuahua, Mexico. Author: The Geographer and the Analysis of Development Problems of the Smaller Community (Proceedings, XVII Congress, International Geographical Union, 1953); A Geographic Classification of Mass Wasting (Annals, Association of American Geographers, Sept. 1957); Some Comments on the Statistical Method (American Scientist, Sept. 1959). Language: Spanish 3,2,2,3; French 2,-,-,2. Home: 5075 East Vassar Lane, Denver 22, Colo. Office: Dept. of Geography, U. of Denver, Denver 10.

CRAMPTON, C. GREGORY, b. Kankakee, Ill., Mar. 22, 1911. HISTORY. A.B., U. of Calif., Berkeley, 1935; M.A., 1936; Ph. D., 1941. Special agent, Federal Bureau of Investigation, U.S. Dept. of Justice, 1943–45; historian, Calif. Quartermaster Depot, U.S. War Dept., 1944–45; PROF., HISTORY, U. OF UTAH, 1945– ; vis. asst. prof., Northwestern U., Summer 1946; vis. prof., U. of Panama, 1955; prof., Overseas Program (Europe), U. of Md., 1956–57; vis. lectr., Eastern Mont. Coll. of Education, Summer 1961. Rockefeller Foundation traveling fellow (Latin America), 1941–42; Rockefeller Foundation fellow, 1948–49. Membership: American Historical Association; Mississippi Valley Historical Association; Phi Alpha Theta. Research: Mexico and Central America; western United States. Author: Historical Sites in Glen Canyon, Mouth of San Juan River to Lee's Ferry (1960); Historical Sites in Glen Canyon, Mouth of Hansen Creek to Mouth of San Juan River (1962). Editor: The Mariposa Indian War, Diaries of Robert Eccleston: The California Gold Rush, Yosemite and the High Sierra (1957). Language: Spanish 4,4,4,2; Portuguese 3,3,3,1; French 2,2,2,1. Home: 322 South 12th East, Salt Lake City, Utah. Office: Dept. of History, U. of Utah, Salt Lake City, 84112.

CRAVEN, J. HOWARD, b. Eureka, Utah, Feb. 7, 1921. ECONOMICS. A.B., Brigham Young U., 1942; M.P.A., Harvard U., 1946; M.A., 1947; Ph. D., 1951. Economist, Office of Strategic Services, 1942–45; economist, U.S. Dept. of State, 1945–46; asst. prof., U. of Wyo., 1947–50; economist, U.S. Dept. of Interior, 1951–52; program officer, Institute of Interamerican Affairs (Bolivia), 1952–53; assoc. economist, Bank of America, 1954–60; CHIEF ECONOMIST, BANK OF AMERICA, 1960– ; VICE PRESIDENT, 1963– . Littauer fellow, 1946–47; Social Science Research Council grant,

1946–47. Membership: American Economic Association; American Statistical Association; National Association of Business Economists; Western Economic Association; World Affairs Council of Northern California. Research: banking. Author: The Feasibility of Compensations for Losses Due to Abolition of Tariffs (Proceedings, Western Farm Economics Association, 1954); The Differential Impact of Money-Tightening Processes on Alternative Paths of Inflation (Proceedings, Western Farm Economics Association, 1957); The Challenge of the Alliance for Progress (in New Look at Latin America, 1962). Language: Spanish 4,4,4,4; French 2,2,2,2; German 2,2,2,2; Russian 1,1,1,1. Home: 3839 Dixon Pl. Palo Alto, Calif., 94306. Office: Bank of America, 300 Montgomery St., San Francisco, Calif.

CRAWFORD, JOHN CHAPMAN, b. Iron Mountain, Mich., July 5, 1926. LINGUISTICS. Ph. D., U. of Mich., 1960. LINGUIST, SUMMER INSTITUTE OF LINGUISTICS (MEXICO), 1951– . Research: descriptive linguistics; dialect distance; mutual intelligibility between related dialects; Mixe tribe of Mexico. Author: Totontepec Mixe Phonotagmemics (1963). Language: Spanish 3,4,4,3; French 3,1,1,1. Linguistic studies: Mixe. Home: Lyons, Mich. Office: Instituto Lingüístico de Verano, Apartado 22067, México 22, D.F.

CRAWFORD, WILLIAM REX, b. Beaver, Pa., May 13, 1898. SOCIOLOGY. B.A., U. of Pa., 1919; M.A., 1922; Ph. D., 1926. Instr., U. of Pa., 1919–22; PROF., SOCIOLOGY, U. OF PA., 1922– ; cultural attaché (Brazil), U.S. Dept. of State, 1943–45. Social Science Research Council fellow (Europe), 1933–34; exchange prof., U. of Chile, 1941; U.S. Dept. of State lectr. (South America), Summer 1952; dir., Salzburg Seminar in American Studies (Austria), 1953–54; dir., U. of Pa. Institute of Humanistic Studies for Executives, 1954–60; Fulbright lectr. (Portugal), 1963–64; Advanced Committee on American Studies; Joint Committee on American Studies. Membership: American Sociological Association; Eastern Sociological Society. Research: social thought of Latin America. Author: A Century of Latin American Thought (1944; 1961); Panorama da Cultura Americana (1944). Translator: A Mexican Ulysses (1963). Language: Spanish 4,4,4,4; Portuguese 4,4, 4,4; French 4,4,4,4; German 4,4,4,4; Italian 4,4,4,4; Russian 3,3,3,3; Swedish 3,3,3,3. Home: 51 East Penn St., Philadelphia 44, Pa. Office: Dept. of Sociology, U. of Pa., Philadelphia 3.

CRIM, ED FRANKLIN, JR., b. Okmulgee, Okla., Aug. 18, 1923. ECONOMICS. B.S., U. of Okla., 1943; M.S., U. of Ill., 1953; Ph. D., 1960. Chemist, Tropical Oil Company (Colombia), 1944; chemist, Stanolind Oil & Gas Company (Okla.), 1947–50; ASSOC. PROF., ECONOMICS, U. OF OKLA., 1955– ; instr., U. of Okla. at U. of Honduras (Tegucigalpa), 1963–64. Membership: American Economic Association; American Statistical Association; Econometric Society. Research: statistics; econometrics; aggregate theory. Author: Oklahoma State Expenditures (1957). Language: Spanish 4,3,4,4; French 3,3,3,3. Home: 811 Chautauqua, Norman, Okla., 73069. Office: Dept. of Economics, U. of Okla., Norman, 73069.

CRISCENTI, JOSEPH THOMAS, b. Detroit, Mich., Aug. 7, 1920. HISTORY. Ph, B., U. of Detroit, 1942; A.M., Harvard U., 1947: Ph. D., 1956. ASSOC. PROF., HISTORY, BOSTON COLL., 1955– . Pan American World Airways traveling fellow (Argentina and Uruguay), 1950–52; Robertson Prize, 1961; American Philosophical Society grant (Argentina and Uruguay), 1963. Membership: American Historical Association; Conference on Latin American History. Research: 19th century developments in the Río de la Plata area—Argentina, Uruguay, Brazil; economic, political and international factors contributing to the formation of the Argentine state, 1810–1880. Author: The Campaign Against Rosas: Minutes of Conferences on Military Plans, June 1851 (Hispanic American Historical Review, Feb. 1954); Argentine Constitutional History, 1810–1852: A Re-examination (Hispanic American Historical Review, Aug. 1961). Language: Spanish 5,5,5,4; Portuguese 3,4,3,2; French 4,3,2,2; Italian 4,4,3,2. Home: 28 Richard Rd., Needham, Mass. Office: Dept. of History, Boston Coll., Chestnut Hill 67, Mass.

CRIST, RAYMOND E., b. Seven Mile, Ohio, Oct. 11, 1904. GEOGRAPHY. B.A., U. of Cincinnati, 1925; Litt. D., Université de Grenoble, 1937. Field geologist, El Águila, Sinclair, and Atlantic Refining Companies (Mexico, Venezuela), 1926–27, 1928–31; instr.-assoc. prof., U. of Ill., 1936–42; instr., Northwestern U., Summers 1936, 1938; assoc. prof., U. of P.R., 1942–47; prof., U. of Md., 1947–51; RESEARCH PROF., GEOGRAPHY, U. OF FLA., 1951– . American Field Service fellow, 1932–33; Guggenheim fellow, 1940–41; Smithsonian Institution grant (Colombia), 1949; Rockefeller Foundation grant (Near East), 1951–52; Social Science Research Council grant-in-aid (Cuba), Summer 1951; Guggenheim research grant, 1954; Creole Petroleum Corporation grant (Colombia, Venezuela), 1957–58; Fulbright research prof. (France), 1959. Membership: American Geographical Society; Association of American Geographers; Sigma Xi. Research: land tenure systems and human migration in Andean South America; Indians of the Goajira Peninsula; Caribbean area. Author: The Cauca Valley, Colombia—Land Tenure and Land Use (1952); Venezuela, Around the World Program (1959); Learning About Latin America (1961). Language: Spanish 5,5,5,5; Portuguese 4,4,–,–; French 5,5,5,5; German 5,5,5,5. Office: Dept. of Geography, U. of Fla., Gainesville.

CROCKER, WILLIAM HENRY, b. San Francisco Calif., Aug. 20, 1924. ANTHROPOLOGY. B.A., Yale Coll., 1950; M.A., Stanford U., 1953; Ph. D., U. of Wis., 1962. ASSOC. CURATOR FOR SOUTH AMERICA, DIV. OF ETHNOLOGY, SMITHSONIAN INSTITUTION, 1962– . Contributing editor, Handbook of Latin American Studies, 1962– . Membership: American Anthropological Association; Associação Brasileira de Antropologia. Research: cultural anthropology; ethnology; Brazil. Author: Os índios canelas de hoje: Nota prévia (Boletim do Museu Paraense, July 1958); The Canelas Since Nimuendaju: A Preliminary Report on

Cultural Change (Anthropological Quarterly, Apr. 1961); Conservatism among the Canela: An Analysis of Contributing Factors (35th International Congress of Americanists, 1962). Language: Spanish 3,3,3,2; Portuguese 4,4,4,3; French 3,2,2,2. Linguistic studies: Gê. Home: 1549 33rd St., NW., Washington, D.C. 20007. Office: Div. of Ethnology, Smithsonian Institution, Washington 25, D.C.

CROFT, KENNETH, b. Ripley, Tex., June 10, 1917. LINGUISTICS. B.A., U. of Okla., 1939; M.A., U. of Mich., 1942; Summer Institute of Linguistics, 1947; Ph. D., Ind. U., 1953. English teacher, Mexican-American Cultural Institution (México, D.F.), 1943–44, 1945–46, 1949–50; English specialist, U.S. Information Agency, 1951–53, 1955–56; deputy dir., American U. Language Center, 1953–55, 1956–61; ASSOC. DIR., AMERICAN LANGUAGE INSTITUTE, GEORGETOWN U., 1961– . American Philosophical Society research grants, Summers 1948, 1949; Rockefeller Foundation research grant (Mexico), Fall 1949. Membership: American Anthropological Association; Linguistic Society of America; National Association of Foreign Student Advisors; Washington Linguistic Club. Research: anthropological linguistics; English as a foreign language. Author: Reading and Word Study: For Students of English as a Second Language (1960); Six Decades of Nahuatl: A Bibliographical Contribution (International Journal of American Linguistics, Jan. 1953); Matlapa Nahuatl II: Affix List and Morphophonemics (International Journal of American Linguistics, Oct. 1953). Language: Spanish 4,4,4,4; French 2,2,2,2. Linguistic studies: Cheyenne; Nahuatl. Home: 3915 Military Rd NW., Washington, D.C. 20015. Office: American Language Institute, Georgetown U., 3605 O St. NW., Washington, D.C. 20007.

CROMWELL, FREDERICK N., b. Prescott, Ariz., Feb. 23, 1909. LIBRARY SCIENCE. B.A., U. of Ariz., 1935; M.A., Stanford U., 1937; certificate in librarianship, U. of Calif., 1938. Asst. dir., Library, Eastern Wash. State Coll., 1938–39; asst. dir., Libraries, U. of Ariz., 1939–41; dir., 1942–52; dir., International Relations Office, American Library Association, 1947–48; dir., Library and Book Programs, U.S. Information Agency (Madrid), 1952–56; branch public affairs officer (Seville), 1956–57; cultural affairs officer, Embassy (Bogotá), U.S. Information Agency, 1957–60; CHIEF, SPECIAL ACTIVITIES BRANCH, BUREAU OF EDUCATIONAL AND CULTURAL AFFAIRS, U.S. DEPT. OF STATE, 1960– . Editor, Arizona Quarterly, 1945–47; Library School fellow, U. of Chicago, 1946; American Library Association observer, UNESCO Conference (Mexico), 1947; chmn., Commission for Educational Exchange between the United States of America and Colombia, 1957–58. Membership: American Library Association; Arizona Library Association; National Citizens Committee for United Nations Day; Phi Beta Kappa; Southwestern Library Association. Research: educational and cultural exchange programs. Language: Spanish 4,4,4,3; Portuguese 1,1,1,1; French 3,2,1,1. Home: Apt. 300, 913 North Van Dorn St., Alexandria, Va. Office: Bureau of Educational and Cultural Affairs, U.S. Dept. of State, Washington, D.C.

CRONON, E(DMUND) DAVID, b. Minneapolis, Minn., Mar. 11, 1924. HISTORY. B.A., Oberlin Coll., 1948; M.A., U. of Wis., 1949; Ph. D., 1953. Instr.-asst. prof., Yale U., 1953–59; assoc. prof.-prof., U. of Nebr., 1959–62; PROF., HISTORY, U. OF WIS., 1962– . Fulbright fellow, U. of Manchester (England), 1950–51; Henry L. Stimson grant (Mexico), Summer 1955, fellow, Yale U., 1958–59. Membership: American Historical Association; Mississippi Valley Historical Association. Research: United States contemporary history and foreign relations. Author: Black Moses: The Story of Marcus Garvey and the Universal Negro Improvement Association (1955); Josephus Daniels in Mexico (1960); The Cabinet Diaries of Josephus Daniels (1963). Language: Spanish 2,2,1,1; French 2,2,2,2; German 2,2,2,2. Home: 5601 Varsity Hill, Madison 5, Wis. Office: Dept. of History, U. of Wis., Madison 6.

CROW, JOHN ARMSTRONG, b. Wilmington, N.C., Dec. 18, 1906. SPANISH AMERICAN LITERATURE. A.B., U. of N.C., 1927; M.A., Columbia U., 1930; Ph. D., Universidad Central de Madrid, 1933. Instr., Davidson Coll., 1927–28; asst. prof., N.Y.U., 1928–37; PROF., SPANISH, U. OF CALIF., LOS ANGELES, 1937– . Consultant and contributing editor, Handbook of Latin American Studies, Encyclopaedia Britannica, Encyclopedia Americana, Collier's Encyclopedia, World Book Encyclopedia. Membership: American Association of Teachers of Spanish and Portuguese; Modern Language Association; Phi Beta Kappa. Research: history and culture of Latin America. Author: The Epic of Latin America (1946); Mexico Today (1957); Spain: The Root and the Flower (1963). Language: Spanish 5,4,4,4; French 3,3,3,2. Home: 218 North Bundy Dr., Los Angeles 49, Calif. Office: Dept. of Spanish and Portuguese, U. of Calif., Los Angeles 24.

CROWLEY, FLORENCE JOSEPH, b. New York, N.Y., June 12, 1937. HISTORY. B.A., Brooklyn Coll., 1959; M.A., 1960; Ph. D., U. of Fla., 1963. U.S. ARMY, 1963–1965. Research: intellectual history of Mexico; Argentina; Brazil. Language: Spanish 4,4,4,4; Portuguese 2,2,2,2; French 2,2,2,2. Home: 1933 Batchelder St., Brooklyn 29, N.Y.

CULBERT, JAMES I., b. Breitung Township, Minn., Mar. 25, 1902. GEOGRAPHY. A.B., U. of Minn., 1923; M.A., Clark U., 1938; Ph. D., 1939. Assayer, Minas Metales de Matahambre (Cuba), 1928–30; principal, N. Mex. Public Schools, 1930–36; Coach, 1940–42; assoc. prof., West Liberty State Coll., 1942–43; prof., N. Mex. State U., 1943–45; petroleum engineer, Stanolind Oil and Gas Company, 1945–46; assoc. prof., Ariz. State U., 1946–47; PROF., EARTH SCIENCE, N. MEX. STATE U., 1947– . Membership: American Association of Petroleum Geologists; Association of American Geographers; American Geographical Society. Research: economic geography; geomorphology; cartography. Language: Spanish 3,3,3,2; Portuguese 2,2,2,2. Home: 201 West Greening Ave., Las

Cruces, N. Mex. Office: Box 216, N. Mex. State U., University Park.

CULBERT, T. PATRICK, b. Minneapolis, Minn.. June 13, 1930. ANTHROPOLOGY. B.A., U. of Minn., 1951; M.A., U. of Chicago, 1957; Ph. D., 1962. Acting asst. prof., U. of Miss., 1960–61; archeologist, Tikal Project, U. of Pa. (Guatemala), 1961–62; vis. prof., U. of San Carlos (Guatemala), 1962; ASST. PROF., SOCIAL SCIENCES, SOUTHERN ILL. U., EDWARDSVILLE CAMPUS, 1962– . National Science Foundation fellow (Mexico), 1958–59, 1959–60; Explorers' Club of New York fellow, 1963. Membership: American Anthropological Association; Seminario de Cultura Maya (Mexico); Society for American Archaeology. Research: archeology of Mesoamerica; the ceramic sequence of the Central Highlands of Chiapas, Mexico. Language: Spanish 4,4,3,2; French 3,1,1,1; German 3,1,1,1. Home: 457 Cass Ave., Edwardsville, Ill. Office: Dept. of Social Sciences, Southern Ill. U., East St. Louis.

CULVER, JOHN WILLIAM, b. Mountain Home, Idaho, Nov. 12, 1906. HISTORY. B.A., U. of Wis., 1932; Ph. D., 1938. Instr., U. of Wis., 1937–41; dir., União Cultural Brasil–E.E.U.U. (São Paulo, Brazil), 1942–45; dir., Instituto Chileno-Norteamericano de Cultura (Santiago), 1945–48; vis. prof., U. of Chile, 1947; assoc. prof., Western Reserve U., 1948–51; ASSOC. PROF., HISTORY, CASE INSTITUTE OF TECHNOLOGY, 1951– ; vis. prof., U. of P.R., Summer 1956; dir., Jr. Year in Brazil Program, N.Y.U., 1960–61. Regents' fellowship, teaching fellow, U. of Wis.; consultant, Champion Paper Co., 1958. Membership: American Historical Association; Conference on Latin American History; Pen International; Phi Delta Kappa. Research: Brazil. Language: Spanish 5,5,4,3; Portuguese 5,5,5,3; French 4,3,3,2; German 3,2,2,1; Italian 3,2,2,1. Home: 1838 Wymore, East Cleveland, Ohio. Office: Dept. of History, Case Institute of Technology, Cleveland 6.

CUMBERLAND, CHARLES CURTIS, b. Kingsville, Tex., May 6, 1914. HISTORY. B.A., Tex. Coll. of Arts & Industries, 1936; M.A., 1938; Ph. D., U. of Tex., 1949. Asst. prof., Princeton U., 1946–48; asst. prof., Rutgers U., 1948–55; PROF., HISTORY, MICH. STATE U., 1955– . Doherty fellow (Mexico); Social Science Research Council grant-in-aid; Fulbright lectr. (Spain). Membership: American Historical Association; Conference on Latin American History; Texas Historical Association. Research: 20th century Latin American revolutions; modern Mexican history and United States-Mexican relations. Author: Mexican Revolution: Genesis under Madero (1952); Twentieth Century Revolutions in Latin America (Centennial Review, Fall 1962). Co-author: U.S. University Cooperation in Latin America (1960). Language: Spanish 4,4,4,4; Portuguese 3,2,1,1; French 3,1,1,1. Home: 2216 Iroquois Rd., Okemos, Mich. Office: Dept. of History, Mich. State U., East Lansing.

CUMMINS, LEJEUNE, b. San Diego, Calif., Nov. 18, 1924. HISTORY AND INTERNATIONAL RELATIONS. A.B., U. of Calif., Berkeley, 1950; M.A., 1951; Ph. D., 1964. Instr., Imperial Valley Coll., 1951–52; instr.,

Berkeley Unified School District, 1953–59; ASST. PROF., HISTORY, CALIF. STATE COLL., HAYWARD, 1963– . Woodrow Wilson traveling grant, 1962. Membership: American Historical Association; Hispanic American Society, Mississippi Valley Historical Association; Phi Alpha Theta; Phi Beta Kappa. Research: Pan Americanism; United States diplomatic history. Author: Quijote on a Burro, Sandino and the Marines, a Study in the Formulation of Foreign Policy (1958); Antonelli, the Younger, First Engineer of the Indies (Mid-America, Jan. 1956). Language: Spanish 4,4,3,3; Portuguese 2,1,1,1; French 2,1,1,1. Home: 3505 Isla Vista, San Diego 5, Calif. Office: Dept. of History, Calif. State Coll., Hayward, 94542.

CUNNINGHAM, JAMES STEWART, JR., b. San Francisco, Calif., Apr. 25, 1911. HISTORY. A.B., U. of Calif., Berkeley, 1934; M.A., 1936; Ph. D., 1946. Asst.-assoc. prof., Goucher Coll., 1946–51; research specialist and acting chief, American Republics Div., U.S. Dept. of State, 1951–57; prof., Foreign Service Institute, U.S. Dept. of State, 1953; second-first secretary, Embassy (Tegucigalpa, Honduras), U.S. Dept. of State, 1958–60; first secretary, chief, Political Section, Embassy (Asunción, Paraguay), U.S. Dept. of State, 1961–63; FIRST SECRETARY AND CHIEF, POLITICAL SECTION, EMBASSY (MONTEVIDEO, URUGUAY), U.S. DEPT. OF STATE, 1963– . Editor, Latin American Section, American Historical Review, 1946–51; Seminar on Latin American Studies, Social Security Research Council, Stanford U., 1963. Research: United States policy and diplomacy in Latin America; political and social change in modern Latin America. Author: Spanish Colonization in Patagonia, 1778–1783 (in Greater America, Essays in Honor of Herbert Eugene Bolton, 1945). Co-author: Brazil (in Britannica Book of the Year, 1939, 1940, 1941); Colombia (in Britannica Book of the Year, 1939). Language: Spanish 4,3,3,3. Office: American Embassy, Montevideo, Uruguay.

CUTTER, DONALD COLGETT, b. Chico, Calif., Jan. 9, 1922. HISTORY. A.B., U. of Calif., Berkeley, 1943; M.A., 1947; Ph. D., 1950. Instr., San Diego State Coll., 1950–51; asst. prof.-prof., U. of Southern Calif., 1951–61; PROF., HISTORY, U. OF N. MEX., 1962– . Native Sons of the Golden West fellow, 1947–48; U. of Calif. teaching fellow, 1948–49; Social Science Research Council fellow (Mexico), 1949–50; Del Amo fellow (Spain), 1953; Social Science Research Council faculty research fellow, 1956–59; Fulbright scholar (Spain), 1961–62; chief historical research consultant, Council of California Indians, 1953–56; Board of Editors, The Americas, The American West, Arizona and the West, Journal of the West. Membership: American Historical Association; Pacific Coast Council of Latin American Studies; Phi Alpha Theta; Sigma Delta Pi; Western History Association. Research: Spanish colonial history in California and American West; explorations; Spanish naval history. Author: The Diary of Ensign Gabriel Moraga's Expedition of Discovery in the Sacramento Valley, 1808 (1957); Malaspina in California (1960); Documentos para la historia de Sonora (1964). Language:

Spanish 4,4,4,4; Portuguese 3,3,2,2; French 3,3,2,3; German 2,2,1,2; Italian 2,2,2,2. Home: 2508 Harold Pl., Albuquerque, N. Mex. Office: Dept. of History, U. of N. Mex., Albuquerque.

D

DABASI-SCHWENG, LORAND, b. Beszterce- banya, Hungary, Aug. 18, 1905. ECONOM- ICS. B.S., Palatine Joseph U. (Hungary), 1927; M.S., 1928; Ph. D., 1940. Economist, chief of economic research dept,. National Bank of Hungary, 1940–48; Under Secre- tary, Ministry of Finance, Government of Hungary, 1945; consultant, National Plan- ning Association (Washington, D.C.), 1949; research assoc., Mid-European Stud- ies Center, National Committee for a Free Europe (N.Y.-Washington, D.C.), 1950; technical assistance expert, Food and Agri- culture Organization (Jordan and Rome), 1951–53; consultant, International Bank for Reconstruction and Development (El Salvador, Mexico, Panama, Haiti, and Guatemala), 1953–55; chief of community development project (Bolivia), Interna- tional Labor Office, 1955–56; economic ad- viser, Klein and Saks (Guatemala), 1956– 57; statistical adviser, Surveys and Resea rch Corporation (Korea), 1958–60; researcch assoc., Guayana Project Joint Center for Urban Studies of Mass. Institute of Technology and Harvard U. (Venezuela), 1961–63; consultant, Tippetts-Abbett-Mc- Carthy-Stratton (Colombia, Peru), 1964; AGRICULTURAL ECONOMIST, HARZA ENGINEERING COMPANY (PAKISTAN), 1965– . Membership: American Economic Association; Society for International De- velopment. Research: agricultural econom- ics and rural development; transportation; social and economic problems of the less- developed countries with special reference to agriculture and education. Author: La producción del maíz en Guatemala (1959); Food and the Industrial Development of the Guayana (1962); Improving Small Family Farms (in International Handbook of Man- agement, 1964). Language: Spanish 4,4,4, 3; French 4,4,4,3; German 5,5,5,5; Hun- garian 5,5,5,5. Home: c/o Mr. F. J. Weyl, 3025 Macomb St., NW., Washington, D.C.

DABBS, JACK AUTREY, b. Mercury, Tex., Jan. 31, 1914. HISTORY AND LINGUIS- TICS. B.A., U. of Tex., 1935; M.A., 1936; Ph. D., 1950. Teacher, Tex. Wesleyan Academy, 1936–37; teacher, Lockhart High School (Tex.), 1937–38; instr., St. Ed- ward's U., 1938–40, 1948–50; dir., Amer- ican Language Institute (Iraq), 1957–58; PROF., MODERN LANGUAGES, TEX. A. & M. U., 1950– . Institute of Latin Amer- ican Studies, U. of Tex., summer research grants, 1956, 1959, 1961, 1962, 1963; Ford Foundation grant (East Pakistan), 1960. Membership: American Name Society; Lin- guistic Society of America; Modern Lan- guage Association. Research: anthropol- ogy; literature; Mexican history and docu- ments; namelore. Author: Catalog of the Manuscripts in the Manuel E. Gondra Man- uscript Collection (1953); Independent Mexico in Documents (1955); The French Army in Mexico, 1861–1867 (1963). Co- author: Guide to Latin American Manu- scripts in the University of Texas Library (1940). Language: Spanish 5,4,4,4; Por- tuguese 3,3,2,2; French 5,4,3,4; Bengali 2, 2,2,2; German 3,3,3,3; Russian 2,2,2,2. Home: 1011 Edgewood, Bryan, Tex. Office: Dept. of Modern Languages, Tex. A. & M. U., College Station.

DA CAL, ERNESTO GUERRA, b. El Ferrol, Spain, Dec. 19, 1911. SPANISH AMER- ICAN AND BRAZILIAN LITERATURES. B.S., U. of Madrid, 1928; M.A., 1936; Ph. D., Columbia U., 1950; doutor honoris causa, U. of Bahia (Brazil), 1959. Instr., Brooklyn Coll., 1939–41; Columbia U., Summers 1940–45; instr.-prof., N.Y.U., 1941–64, chmn., Spanish and Portuguese, Wash. Sq. Coll., 1953–60; PROF., SPAN- ISH AND PORTUGUESE, QUEENS COLL., 1964– . Writer and broadcaster, Voice of America, U.S. Information Agency, 1952– ; supervisor, N.Y.U. Junior Year in Spain, U. of Madrid, 1955–62; Guggenheim fellow, 1958–59; Order of Merit, Cruzeiro do Sul (Brazil), 1959; organizer, N.Y.U. Junior Year in Brazil, 1959; National Selecting Committee for Fulbright Awards to Latin America, 1959–62; trustee, Hispanic So- ciety of America, 1961– ; consultant, Dicio- nário das Literaturas Portuguêsa, Galega e Brasileira; Editorial Board, Revista His- pánica Moderna. Membership: American Association of Teachers of Spanish and Portuguese; Modern Language Association; Phi Beta Kappa; Sigma Delta Pi. Re- search: Spanish, Portuguese and Galician literatures; stylistics. Author: Don Se- gundo Sombra, teoría y símbolo del gaucho (Cuadernos Americanos, Sept.-Oct. 1945). Co-author: A Grammar of Everyday Span- ish (1950); Literatura del Siglo XX: An- tología selecta (1955). Language: Spanish 5,5,5,5; Portuguese 5,5,5,5; French 5,5,3,2; Catalán 5,5,4,2. Home: 299 Riverside Dr., New York, N.Y., 10025. Office: Dept. of Romance Languages, Queens Coll., Flushing, N.Y.

DAHL, VICTOR CHARLES, b. Dickinson, N. Dak., Dec. 11, 1928. HISTORY. B.A., Mont. State U., 1950; M.A., 1951; Ph. D., U. of Calif., 1959. Asst. prof., Portland State Coll., 1959–61; ADMINISTRATIVE ASST., PRESIDENTS OFFICE, PORTLAND STATE COLL., 1961– . Membership: American Historical Association; Montana Historical Society; Pacific Coast Council on Latin American Studies. Research: Mexico; Uruguay. Author: Alien Labor on the Gulf Coast of Mexico, 1880–1900 (The Americas, July 1960); Business Influence in the Anglo-Mexican Reconciliation of 1884 (Latin American Economic Affairs, Aug. 1961). Language: Spanish 4,3,3,3; Portu- guese 3,2,1,1; German 3,2,2,1. Home: 13138 SW. 63rd Pl., Portland 19, Oreg. Office: P.O. Box 751, Portland State Coll., Portland.

DALE, GEORGE A., b. Denver, Colo., Feb. 17, 1900. EDUCATION. B.A., U. of Denver, 1922; M.A., State U. of Iowa, 1932; Ph. D., 1938. Dir. of education, Bureau of In- dian Affairs, U.S. Dept. of Interior (Alaska), 1935–50; education specialist, Bureau of In- dian Affairs, U.S. Dept. of Interior, 1950– 54; community education adviser, U.S. In- ternational Cooperation Administration (Haiti), 1954–59; education adviser, U.S. Agency for International Development (Honduras), 1959–63; CHIEF EDUCATION ADVISER, U.S. AGENCY FOR INTERNA- TIONAL DEVELOPMENT (PARAGUAY), 1963– . Consultant on school constrution programs, U.S. Operation Mission (Nicaragua), 1960; consultant, Board of Education, Escuela Americana de Honduras, 1961. Membership: Arctic Institute of North America; Kappa Delta Pi; Phi Delta Kappa; Phi Sigma. Research: analysis, planning, and development of educational programs in developing countries; Central America. Author: Education for Better Living (1954); Education in the Republic of Haiti (1959). Co-author: Alaska: The Land and the People (1957). Language: Spanish 3,3,3,2; French 2,1,1,1; Home: c/o Mrs. R. D. Butler, Forest St., Dover-Foxcraft, Maine. Office: U.S. Agency for International Development, c/o American Embassy, Asunción, Paraguay.

DAMBAUGH, LUELLA N., b. DuBois, Pa., July 14, 1908. GEOGRAPHY. B.S., State Teachers Coll. (Indiana, Pa.), 1930; M.S., U. of Chicago, 1937; Ph. D., U. of Md., 1947. PROF., GEOGRAPHY, U. OF MIAMI, 1947– ; vis. prof., Pa. State U., Summer 1962. Chmn., Conservation Section, Florida Academy of Sciences. Membership: American Geographical Society; Association of American Geographers; Florida Academy of Sciences; National Council for Geographic Education; National Geographic Society; Sigma Xi. Research: world regional and economic geography; food and population resources; conservation of resources; demography in Mexico, Central America, and Brazil. Author: Industralization in Argentina (1947); The Coffee Frontier in Brazil (1959). Contributor: The Caribbean: Contemporary International Relations (1957). Language: Spanish 3,2,2,2; French 1,1,1,1. Home: 6116 SW. 45th St., Miami, Fla. 33155. Office: Dept. of Geography, U. of Miami, Coral Gables, Fla.

DANCO, LÉON ANTOINE, b. New York, N.Y., May 30, 1923. E C O N O M I C S. A.B., Harvard U., 1943; M.B.A., 1947; Ph. D., Western Reserve U., 1963. Sales promotion manager, Risdon Manufacturing Company (Conn.), 1951–55; consultant, L. A. Danco & Company (Conn.), 1955–56; assoc. dir. of management development, Case Institute of Technology, 1956–57; C O N S U L T I N G ECONOMIST, L. A. DANCO & COMPANY (CLEVELAND), 1958– ; DIR., MANAGEMENT CONFERENCES, SCHOOL OF BUSINESS, JOHN CARROLL U., 1960– . Research: economics of industrial growth. Author: Economic Development of Paraguay, 1946–1960 (1963). L a n g u a g e : Spanish 3,3,3,2; Portuguese 2,2,1,1; French 4,5,4,3. Home: 28230 Cedar Rd., Pepper Pike, Cleveland, Ohio 44124. Office: School of Business, John Carroll U., Cleveland, 44118.

DANIELS, MARION GORDON, b. Gordon, Nebr., Apr. 17, 1920. ECONOMICS. A.B., Doane Coll., 1947; M.A., U. of Tex., 1949. Prof., Universidad Autónoma de El Salvador, 1951–52; research asst., Institute of Latin American Studies, U. of Tex., 1952–53; asst. prof., Tex. A. & M. U., 1953–61; ECONOMIC OFFICER, EMBASSY (COLOMBIA, CHILE), U.S. DEPT. OF STATE, 1961– . Teaching fellow, U. of Tex., 1950–51; Fulbright lectr., Central U. (Quito), 1959–60. Membership: American Economic Association. Research: Latin American economics and history; Colombia; Chile. Language: Spanish 5,4,4,4; French 3,3,2,3; Bengali –,2,2,–; German 3,3,2,2. Home: 3902 Oaklawn St., Bryan, Tex. Office: U.S. Dept. of State, Washington, D.C. 20521.

D'ANTONIO, WILLIAM VINCENT, b. New Haven, Conn., Feb. 7, 1926. SOCIOLOGY. B.A., Yale U., 1949; M.A., U. of Wis., 1953; Ph. D., Mich. State U., 1958. Instr., Mich. State U., 1957–59; ASSOC. PROF., SOCIOLOGY, U. OF NOTRE DAME, 1959– . Carnegie Foundation, U.S. Public Health Service grants (Mexico), 1954–55, 1958; Social Science Research Council grant (Mexico), 1962; consultant, U.S. Civil Rights Commission, 1962. Membership: American Association of University Professors; American Sociological Association; Midwest Council of Latin Americanists; Ohio Valley Sociological Association. Research: political parties and community social structures; religion and social change in Latin America; local elections in Mexico. Author: Power and Democracy in America (1961). Co-author: Influentials in Decision-Making: A Study of Two Border Cities (1964). Language: Spanish 5,4,5,4; Italian 3,2,3,2. Home: 1444 South Bend Ave., South Bend 17, Ind. Office: Dept. of Sociology, Notre Dame U., Notre Dame, Ind.

DASILVA, JOSÉ FABIO BARBOSA, b. São Paulo, Brazil, Sept. 1, 1934. SOCIOLOGY. B.A., U. of São Paulo, 1957; M.A., Fundação da Escola de Sociologia e Política de São Paulo, 1959; M.A., U. of São Paulo, 1960; Ph. D., U. of Fla., 1963. Research asst.-assoc., Center for Research in Education, U. of São Paulo, 1957–60; ASST. PROF., SOCIOLOGY, TEX. WESTERN U., 1964– . U. of Fla. fellow, 1960–63. Membership: American Sociological Association; Brazilian Sociological Association; Population Association of America. Research: demography; rural problems; internal migration in Brazil; rural problems of Paraguay. Author: Marginality Among Male Adolescents in São Paulo (1963); Sources of Errors in Official Educational Statistics (Educação e Pesquisa, 1958); Organização social do juázeiro e tensões entre litoral e interior (Sociología, Sept. 1962). Language: Spanish 5,5,4,4; Portuguese 5,5,5,5; French 5,4,3,3. Home: 607 Coffin Ave., El Paso, Tex. Office: Dept. of Sociology, Tex. Western Coll., El Paso.

DAUSTER, FRANK NICHOLAS, b. Irvington, N.J., Feb. 5, 1925. SPANISH AMERICAN LITERATURE. B.A., Rutgers U., 1949; M.A., 1950; Ph. D., Yale U., 1953. Instr., Wesleyan U., 1950–54; asst. prof., 1954–55; asst. prof., Rutgers U., 1955–58; assoc. prof., 1958–61; PROF., ROMANCE LANGUAGES, RUTGERS U., 1961– . Social Science Research Council grant (Mexico, P.R.), Summer 1961; Cady Prize, Yale U. Membership: American Association of Teachers of Spanish and Portuguese; American Association of University Professors; Instituto Internacional de Literatura Iberoamericana; Modern Language Association; Phi Beta Kappa; Sigma Delta Pi. Research: contemporary theater and history of the theater of Latin America; Mexican poetry. Author: Breve historia de la poesía mexicana (1956); Ensayos sobre poesía mexicana (1963). Language: Spanish 5,5,5,5; Portuguese 4,3,2,1. Home: 40 Lake Park Dr., Route 44, New Brunswick, N.J. 08904. Office: Box 533, Rutgers U., New Brunswick, 08903.

DAVIS, ETHELYN CLARA, b. St. Joseph, Mo., Oct. 9, 1915. SOCIOLOGY. B.A., Southern Methodist U., 1935; M.A., 1936; Ph. D., U. of Mo., 1942. Teacher, Brownsville High School (Tex.), 1936-37; Grandfalls High School (Tex.), 1937-40; PROF., SOCIOLOGY, TEX. WOMAN'S U., 1942- ; DIR., 1953- . Membership: American Sociological Association; Southwestern Social Science Association; Southwestern Sociological Association. Research: American colony in Mexico City. Language: Spanish 4,5,3,3. Home: 415 Woodland St., Denton, Tex. Office: Dept. of Sociology, Tex. Woman's U., Denton.

DAVIS, HAROLD EUGENE, b. Girard, Ohio, Dec. 3, 1902. HISTORY AND POLITICAL SCIENCE. B.A., Hiram Coll., 1924; M.A., U. of Chicago, 1927; Ph. D., Western Reserve U., 1933. Prof., Hiram Coll., 1927-44; dean, 1944-47; dir., Div. of Educational & Teacher Aids, Office of the Coordinator of Inter-American Affairs, U.S. Govt., 1943-46; instr., U.S. Army U. (France), 1945-46; prof., chmn., Div. of Social Sciences, American U., 1947-52; dir., American Language Center, 1952-53; dean, Arts & Sciences, 1953-58; PROF., CHMN., LATIN AMERICAN AREA STUDIES, SCHOOL OF INTERNATIONAL SERVICE, AMERICAN U., 1958- . Washington Evening Star Research Award, 1958; Fulbright prof., U. of Chile, 1958-59; Survey of U. of Asunción (Paraguay) for U.S. Dept. of State, 1959; consultant for reviews of books for U.S. Information Agency, Operations & Policy Research, Inc.; consultant in general education, Calif. State Coll. (Pa.). Membership: American Historical Association; American Political Science Association; American Society of International Law; Instituto de la Historia del Derecho (Buenos Aires); Instituto Interamericano Indigenista; Inter-American Council (Washington, D.C.). Research: history of Latin American social thought; the presidency in Latin America; inter-American relations. Author: The Americas in History (1953); Latin American Social Thought (1961). Co-author: Government and Politics in Latin America (1958). Language: Spanish 4,4,4,4; Portuguese 4,3,3,2; French 4,3,3,2. Home: 4842 Langdrum Lane, Chevy Chase, Md. 20015. Office: School of International Service, The American U., Washington, D.C. 20016.

DAVIS, IRVINE ELWIN, b. Modesto, Calif., Sept. 26, 1922. LINGUISTICS. B.S., U. of Calif., Berkeley, 1943; M.A., U. of N. Mex., 1958; Ph. D., 1960. Missionary, Baptist Mid-Missions (Territorio de Roraima, Brazil), 1949-54; linguistic field worker and consultant, North American Branch, Summer Institute of Linguistics, 1954-63; PROF., LINGUISTICS, U. OF BRASILIA (BRAZIL), 1963- ; LINGUISTIC CONSULTANT, SUMMER INSTITUTE OF LINGUISTICS (BRAZIL), 1963- . Membership; Congresso Brasileiro de Antropologia; Linguistic Society of America. Research: anthropological linguistics; American Indian languages; applied linguistics. Author: Phonological Function in Cheyenne (International Journal of American Linguistics, 1961); The Native Languages of America (Phonetica, 1962). Language: Spanish 3,2,2,1; Portuguese 4,4,4,3; French 2,1,1,1; German 3,2,2,1; Keres -,2,2,-. Linguistic studies: Cheyenne; Chin; Keres; Portuguese. Home: Star Route, Box 86, Bernalillo, N. Mex. Office: Summer Institute of Linguistics, P.O. Box 1960, Santa Ana, Calif.

DAVIS, JACK EMORY, b. Holland, Mich., May 11, 1913. SPANISH AMERICAN LITERATURE AND LANGUAGE. B.A., U. of Ariz., 1947; M.A., Tulane U., 1948; Ph. D., 1956. Instr., Tulane U., 1948-49; instr.-ASSOC. PROF., SPANISH, U. OF ARIZ., 1949- ; assoc. prof., Guadalajara Summer School (Mexico), Summers 1959-63. Membership: American Association of Teachers of Spanish and Portuguese; Arizona Foreign Language Teachers Association; Instituto Internacional de Literatura Ibero-americana. Research: linguistics of New World Spanish; Mexican literature. Author; Teaching Spanish in a Bilingual Area (Hispania, May 1957); Algunos problemas lexicográficos en El Periquillo Sarmiento (Revista Iberoamericana, Jan. 1958). Translator: Aztec Thought and Culture, by Miguel León Portilla (1963). Language: Spanish 5,5,5,5; Portuguese 4,3,2,1; French 3,-,2,2. Linguistic studies: English; Spanish. Home: 408 East Calle del Arizona, Tucson, Ariz. Office: Dept. of Spanish, U. of Ariz., Tucson.

DAVIS, JOE EDWARD, JR., b. Sterling City, Tex., Oct. 27, 1915. LANGUAGE. B.S., U. of Tex., 1938; M.A., 1949; Ph. D., 1951. PROF., SPANISH, JUDSON COLL., 1951- . E. D. Farmer International scholar, National U. of Mexico, 1947-48. Membership: American Association of Teachers of Spanish and Portuguese; Modern Language Association; Phi Delta Kappa; Sigma Delta Pi. Research: life, education, and literature of Spanish America. Language: Spanish 5,4,4,4; Portuguese 1,1,1,1; French 3,2,2,2; Italian 2,3,3,2. Home: 203 LaFayette, Marion, Ala. Office: Dept. of Spanish, Judson Coll., Marion.

DAVIS, KINGSLEY, b. Tuxedo, Tex., Aug. 20, 1908. SOCIOLOGY. A.B., U. of Tex., 1930, M.A., 1932; M.A., Harvard U., 1933; Ph. D., 1936. Assoc. prof., Princeton U., 1942-48; prof., Columbia U., 1948-55; PROF., SOCIOLOGY, U. OF CALIF., BERKELEY, 1955- ; CHMN., INTERNATIONAL POPULATION & URBAN RESEARCH, 1957- ; chmn., Sociology, 1961-63. Social Science Research Council fellow, 1940-41; U.S. representative, Population Commission of the United Nations, 1955-61; Center for Advanced Study in the Behavioral Sciences fellow, 1956-57; National Science Foundation senior post graduate fellow for Latin American research, 1963-64; chmn., Div. of Behavioral Sciences, National Research Council, 1964-65. Membership: American Association for the Advancement of Science; American Sociological Association; Population Association of America. Research: demography; urbanization; family structure; comparative studies of population and social structure in Latin America. Co-author: Urbanization in Latin America (1946); The World's Metropolitan Areas (1959). Editor: A Crowding Hemisphere: Population Change in the Americas (1958). Language: Spanish 4,4,3,2; Portuguese 2,1,1,1; French 4,4,3,2. Home: 199 Hillcrest Rd., Berkeley, Calif. 94705. Office: Dept. of Sociology, U. of Calif., Berkeley 5.

DAVIS, RUSSELL GERARD, b. Hopkinton, Mass., Oct. 29, 1922. STATISTICS AND EDUCATION. A.B., Coll. of the Holy Cross, 1943; M.A., Harvard U., 1952; Ed. M., 1953; Ed. D., 1955. Dir., Center for Case Collection, Harvard U., 1953-55; researcher, U.S. International Cooperation Administration-Okla. State U., 1955-57; dir., Office of Research, Boston Coll., 1957-60; adviser, U.S. Agency for International Development and Alliance for Progress (Nicaragua), 1960-62; LECTR. AND RESEARCH ASSOC., CENTER FOR STUDIES IN EDUCATION AND DEVEOPMENT, HARVARD U., 1962- . Consultant on Venezuela and Central America, Harvard U., 1957-60; consultant, Human Resource Planning in Dominican Republic, Ford Foundation, 1962-63; consultant, U.S. Agency for International Development (Guatemala), 1963-64; consultant, Study of Higher Technical Education in Mexico, Ford Foundation, 1963-64; contrib. ed., Handbook of Latin American Studies; Central American Regional Task Force. Membership: American Association for the Advancement of Science; American Association of School Administrators; American Educational Research Association; American Statistical Association; Linguistic Society of America; Society for International Development. Research: application of statistics to social and educational planning; influence of historical and social development on education in Latin America; higher education in Latin America. Author: Strangers in Africa (1963); West Africa: Land in the Sun (1963); Programación lineal; Los modelos, los métodos de los cálculos y las matemáticas básicas (1963). Language: Spanish 5,5,4,3; Portuguese 4,3,2,2; French 4,2,1,2. Office: Center for Studies in Education and Development, Harvard U., 38 Kirkland St., Cambridge, Mass.

DAVIS, THOMAS BRABSON, JR., b. Hillsboro, Tex., Aug. 3, 1905. HISTORY. B.A., North Tex. State Teachers Coll., 1925; M.A., U. of Tex., 1928; Ph. D., Yale U., 1942. PROF., HISTORY, HUNTER COLL., 1942- . U.S. Dept. of State travel grant (Argentina), 1941. Membership: American Association of University Professors; American Historical Association; Conference on Latin American History. Research: early diplomatic relations between Argentina and the United States. Author: Carlos de Alvear, Man of Revolution (1955); James Monroe and Carlos de Alvear (Hispanic American Historical Review, Dec. 1942). Language: Spanish 4,4,4,4. Home: 22 Francis Lane, Port Chester, N.Y. Office: Dept. of History, Hunter Coll., 695 Park Ave., New York 21, N.Y.

DAVIS, TOM EDWARD, b. Akron, Ohio, June 11, 1929. ECONOMICS. A.B., Tufts U., 1950; M.A., Johns Hopkins U.; Ph. D., 1956. Asst. prof., U. of Chicago, 1956-58; assoc. prof., 1958-62; ASSOC. PROF., ECONOMICS, ACTING DIR., LATIN AMERICAN PROGRAM, CORNELL U., 1962- . Consultant, U.S. Agency for International Development; research assoc., School of Hygiene and Public Health, Johns Hopkins U., 1962- ; research assoc., Catholic U. of Chile. Membership: American Economic Association. Research: monetary and fiscal policy; evolution of the Chilean economy. Author: The Growth of Output, Employment, Capital Stock, and Real Wages in Basic Sectors of the Chilean Economy (in Hearings on Economic Developments in Latin America, 1962); Eight Decades of Inflation in the Chilean Economy: 1879-1959, A Political Interpretation (Journal of Political Economy, Aug. 1963); Dualism, Stagnation and Welfare (Industrial and Labor Relations Review, Apr. 1964). Language: Spanish 4,4,4,4; Portuguese 2,-,-,-; French 2,-,-,-; German 2,-,-,-. Home: 211 North Triphammer Rd., Ithaca, N.Y. 14850. Office: Dept. of Economics, Cornell U., Ithaca, 14850.

DAVIS, WILLIAM CARLTON, b. New York, N.Y., Aug. 1, 1907. ECONOMICS. A.B., U. of Nev., 1939; M.A., 1940; Ph. D., Yale U., 1949. Administrative asst., City Coll. (N.Y.), 1941-50; manager of marketing research, General Electric Company, 1950-52; vice president, Fuller & Smith & Ross, Inc., 1952-59; PROF., HEAD, MARKETING, U. of ARIZ., 1959- . Lectr., U.S. Agency for International Development (Central America, Colombia, Dominican Republic, Mexico), 1960-62, 1964; consultant, U.S. Agency for International Development, 1964. Membership: American Economic Association; American Management Association; American Marketing Association; American Statistical Association. Research: marketing; marketing research; economics and industrial development. Language: Spanish 3,3,3,3; French 3,3,3,3; German 3,3,3,3. Home: 3504 East Third St., Tucson, Ariz. Office: Dept. of Marketing, Coll. of Business & Public Administration, U. of Ariz., Tucson.

DAVIS, WILLIAM COLUMBUS, b. Birmingham, Ala., Aug. 28, 1910. HISTORY AND POLITICAL SCIENCE. A.B., U. of Ala., 1931; M.A., 1932; M.A., Harvard U., 1943; Ph. D., 1948. Instr., U. of Ala., 1931-32; asst. prof., U. of Ga., 1948-51; research analyst, U.S. Central Intelligence Agency, 1951-52; PROF., LATIN AMERICAN HISTORY, DIR., LATIN AMERICAN STUDIES, GEORGE WASHINGTON U., 1951- ; prof., Political Affairs, The National War College, 1963- . Research: recent political and economic developments in Latin America. Author: The Last Conquistadores (1950). Co-author: Soviet Bloc Latin American Activities and Their Implications for United States Foreign Policy (1960). Editor: Index to the Writings on American History, 1902-1940 (1956); The American Historical Association Guide to Historical Literature (1960). Language: Spanish 4,4,4,4; Portuguese 4,-,-,-; French 4,-,-,-. Home: 5100 Darnall Dr., McLean, Va. Office: Dept. of History and Political Science, George Washington U., Washington 6, D.C.

DAVISON, NED J., b. Salt Lake City, Utah, Oct. 3, 1926. SPANISH AMERICAN LITERATURE. B.A., U. of Utah, 1949; M.A., U. of Calif., Los Angeles, 1952; Ph. D., 1957. Instr., Coll. of Idaho, 1954; asst. prof., U. of Oreg., 1954-63; ASSOC. PROF., SPANISH, U. OF. N. MEX., 1963- . Membership: American Association of Teachers of Spanish and Portuguese; American Association of University Professors; Instituto Internacional de Literatura Iberoamericana; Modern Language Association; Rocky Mountain Council of Latin American Studies. Research: Spanish American poetry. Author: Sobre el arte de Barrios (Atenea, Jan.–Mar. 1961); El frío como símbolo en Los Pozos de Amado Nervo (Revista Iberoamericana, Jan.–July 1961): The One-page Novels of Bernard Teyssèdre (Northwest Review, Fall 1962). Language: Spanish 4,4,4,4; Portuguese 3,3,2,1; French 4,4,–,–; Italian 2,3,1,1. Home: 939 Manzano NE., Albuquerque, N. Mex. 87110. Office: Dept. of Modern and Classical Languages, U. of N. Mex., Albuquerque.

DAY, LOWELL CURTIS, b. Richmond, Ind., May 28, 1932. POLITICAL SCIENCE. B.A., Earlham Coll., 1955; M.A., U. of Pittsburgh, 1957; Ph. D., 1965. Asst. prof., Baldwin-Wallace Coll., 1960–62; part-time asst. prof., Western Reserve U., 1961–62; CAMPUS COORDINATOR, ECUADOR PROJECT, U.S. AGENCY FOR INTERNATIONAL DEVELOPMENT– U. OF PITTSBURGH CONTRACT, 1963– . Doherty fellow (Latin America), Princeton U., 1962–63. Membership: American Association of University Professors; American Political Science Association; Association for Latin American Studies; International Political Science Association. Research: government and politics of Chile; U.S. policy toward Pan Americanism, 1949–1959. Language: Spanish 3,3,3,3; French 2,2,2,2. Home: 4251 Minnesota St., Pittsburgh 17, Pa. Office: Campus Coordinator, Ecuador Project Office, U. of Pittsburgh, Pittsburgh 13.

DEAL, CARL WANAMAKER, b. Hickory, N.C., Sept. 15, 1930. LIBRARY SCIENCE. B.A., Kans. State Teachers Coll., 1952; M.A., Mexico City Coll., 1956; M.S., Kans. State Teachers Coll., 1959. Archivist and library cataloger, Kans. State Historical Society, 1956–58; administrative aide, Wichita City Library, 1959–61; asst. head, Acquisitions Dept., Library, U. of Kans., 1961–64; dir., U. of Kans. Junior Year at U. of Costa Rica, 1963; LATIN AMERICAN BIBLIOGRAPHER, LIBRARY, U. OF KANS., 1964– . Asst. dir., 5th Seminar on Higher Education in the Americas, 1964. Membership: American Library Association; Kansas Library Association; Midwest Association for Latin American Studies. Research: library resources and research collections in Central America; development of library resources and facilities in Latin America. Language: Spanish 4,–,–,–; Portuguese 2,–,–,–. Home: 2203 Massachusetts, Lawrence, Kans. Office: Library, U. of Kans., Lawrence.

DEAN, WARREN KEMPTON, b. Passaic, N.J., Oct. 17, 1932. HISTORY. B.A., U. of Miami, 1953; M.A., U. of Fla., 1961; Ph. D., 1964. Translator, Instituto de Estudos Sociais e Econômicos (São Paulo), 1962; POST-DOCTORAL FELLOW, U. OF TEX., 1964–65. Foreign Area training fellow, 1962–64; Interamerican U. Foundation, Brazilian Student Seminars, Harvard U., 1964. Membership: American Historical Association. Research: economic development; Brazilian entrepreneurship and economic nationalism; Cuba; international economic relationships, 1870– . Language: Spanish 4,4,3,3; Portuguese 5,5,4,4; French 3,2,2,1. Home: 4619–B Bull Creek Rd., Austin, Tex., 78731. Office: Graduate School, U. of Tex., Austin, 78712.

DE ARMOND, LOUIS CUSHMAN, b. Orland, Calif., June 2, 1918. HISTORY. A.B., U. of Calif., Berkeley, 1940; M.A., 1947; Ph. D., 1950. Foreign Service (Chile), U.S. Dept. of State, 1942–44; PROF., HISTORY, DIR., INSTITUTE OF LATIN AMERICAN STUDIES, LOS ANGELES STATE COLL., 1950– . Ford Foundation Fund for the Advancement of Education grant (South America), 1954–55. Membership: American Historical Association; Conference on Latin American History; Pacific Coast Council on Latin American Studies. Research: colonial history and contemporary problems of Latin America; the activities of some United States groups in Latin America, such as the San Domingo Improvement Company. Author: Justo Sierra O'Reilly and Yucatecan-United States Relations, 1847–1848 (Hispanic American Historical Review, Aug. 1951); Frontier Warfare in Colonial Chile (Pacific Historical Review, May 1954). Language: Spanish 4,4,4,4; Portuguese 3,3,2,1; French 2,1,1,1; Japanese 1,2,–,–. Home: 436 East Benwood, Covina, Calif. Office: Institute of Latin American Studies, Los Angeles State Coll., 5151 State College Dr., Los Angeles 32, Calif.

DEARTH, JOHN A(RTHUR), b. Framingham, Mass., Mar. 5, 1907. HISTORY. A.B., Dartmouth Coll., 1929; M.A., Clark U., 1932; Ph. D., U. of Colo., 1954. Instr., Santiago Coll. (Chile), 1940–42; lectr., Chile-American Cultural Institute, 1942; instr., Drake U., 1946–49; asst. prof., Mission House Coll., 1955–56; assoc. prof., Cottey Coll., 1956–58; assoc. prof., Nebr. State Teachers Coll., Peru, 1958–61; PROF., SOCIAL SCIENCES, SLIPPERY ROCK STATE COLL., 1961– . Membership: American Association of University Professors; American Historical Association; National Education Association. Research: colonial Hispanic American history; Mexico. Language: Spanish 3,3,3,3; Portuguese 1,–,–,–; French 3,3,3,3. Home: 363 Franklin St., Slippery Rock, Pa. Office: Dept. of Social Sciences, Slippery Rock State Coll., Slippery Rock.

DE BEERS, JOHN STERLING, b. Evanston, Ill., July 7, 1914. ECONOMICS. B.A., Cornell U., 1937; M.A., American U., 1939; Ph. D., U. of Chicago, 1951. Junior-asst. economist, U.S. Tariff Commission, 1937–40; asst.-assoc. economist, Div. of Monetary Research, U.S. Treasury Dept., 1941–43, 1946–47; chief, Latin American Div., Office of International Finance, 1947–55; dir., Economic Research Dept., Government Development Bank for Puerto Rico, 1955–58; consultant, EMB, Ltd., 1958–60; professorial lectr., U. of Md., 1958–60; ECONOMIST, INTER-AMERICAN DEVELOPMENT BANK, 1960– . Brookings fellow, 1940–41. Membership: American Economic Association; Society for International Development. Research: international finance and trade; economic development; money and banking; Alliance for Progress; Mexican balance of payments, public finance, and development planning. Author: El peso mexicano, 1941–1949 (Problemas Agrícolas e Industriales de México, Jan.–Mar. 1953); A Study of Puerto Rico's Banking System

(1960). Language: Spanish 4,4,4,3; Portuguese 2,2,1,1; French 2,2,2,1. Home: 5135 Newport Ave., NW., Washington, D.C., 20016. Office: Inter-American Development Bank, Washington, D.C., 20577.

DEBICKI, ANDREW PETER, b. Warsaw, Poland, June 28, 1934. SPANISH AMERICAN LITERATURE. B.A., Yale U., 1955; Ph. D., 1960. Instr., Trinity Coll., 1957–60; asst. prof., Grinnell Coll., 1960–62; ASSOC. PROF., SPANISH, GRINNELL COLL., 1962– . Yale College fellow, 1955–57; Danforth Foundation grant (Mexico), Summer 1959. Membership: American Association of Teachers of Spanish and Portuguese; American Association of University Professors; Instituto Internacional de Literatura Iberoamericana; Modern Language Association. Research: contemporary Spanish and Spanish American poetry; Mexican poetry and literature. Author: La poesía de José Gorostiza (1962); Sobre la poética y la crítica literaria de José Gorostiza (Revista Iberoamericana, Jan.–June 1961); La función de la naturaleza en Canciones para cantar en las barcas (Revista Iberoamericana, Jan.–June 1962). Language: Spanish 5,5,5,4; Portuguese 3,2,2,1; French 3,3,3,3; Polish 5,5,5,4. Home: 1517 Elm St. Grinnell, Iowa. Office: Dept. of Spanish, Grinnell Coll., Grinnell.

DE CAPRILES, MIGUEL (ANGEL), b. Mexico, D.F., Mexico, Nov. 30, 1906. LAW AND ECONOMICS. B.S., N.Y.U., 1927; M.A., 1931; J.D., 1935. Instr., N.Y.U., 1928–35; asst. prof., 1935–42; special asst. to U.S. Attorney General, War Div., U.S. Dept. of Justice, 1942–47; assoc. prof., School of Law, N.Y.U., 1945–47; PROF., LAW, SCHOOL OF LAW, N.Y.U., 1947– ; assoc. dean, 1948–63; VICE DEAN, 1963– . Counsel to Board of Trustees, Hofstra Coll., 1936–38; dir. Inter-American Law Institute, N.Y.U., 1947–57; consultant, New York State Leigslature on revision of corporation laws, 1959–64; consultant, Ford Foundation on Higher Education in Latin America, 1963. Membership: American Association for Comparative Study of Law; Inter-American Bar Association. Research: corporation and comparative law; legal education; organization, and administration of higher education; business organization, finance, and accounting. Author: Modern Financial Accounting (1963). Co-author: The New York University Self-Study (1956). Language: Spanish 5,5,4,4; Portuguese 2,2,1,1; French 4,4,4,4; Italian 2,2,1,1. Home: 37 Washington Sq. West, New York, N.Y. 10011. Office: School of Law, N.Y.U., Washington Sq., New York, N.Y. 10003.

DE CONDE, ALEXANDER, b. Utica, N.Y., Nov. 13, 1920. HISTORY. B.A., San Francisco State Coll., 1943; M.A., Stanford U., 1947; Ph. D., 1949. Instr., Stanford U., 1947–48; asst. prof.-assoc. prof., Whittier Coll., 1948–52; asst. prof., Duke U., 1952–57; assoc. prof., U. of Mich., 1957–61; assoc. prof., Stanford U., Summer 1960; PROF., HISTORY, U. OF CALIF., SANTA BARBARA, 1961– ; CHMN., 1964– . Social Science Research Council grants, 1950, 1956; Guggenheim fellow, 1959–60; American Philosophical Society grant, 1963. Membership: American Association for the United Nations; American Association of University Professors; American Historical Association; Mississippi Valley Historical Association. Research: history and development of United States foreign policy. Author: Herbert Hoover's Latin American Policy (1951); Entangling Alliance: Politics and Diplomacy under George Washington (1957) History of American Foreign Policy (1963). Home: 1105 North Ontare Rd., Santa Barbara, Calif. Office: Dept. of History, U. of Calif., Santa Barbara.

DeFOREST, JOHN DUANE, b. Peabody, Kans., Jan. 13, 1930. Economics. B.S., Kans. State U., 1955; M.S., 1957; Ph. D., State U. of Iowa, 1961. Instr., State U. of Iowa, 1957–58; asst. prof., Denison U., 1959–62; program economist, U.S. Agency for International Development mission (Colombia), 1962–64; PROF., ECONOMICS, PARSONS COLL., 1965– . Cordell Hull fellow, Vanderbilt U., 1956–57; State U. of Iowa graduate fellow, 1958–59; Chase Manhattan Bank fellow, Summer 1961; U. of Mich. post-doctoral fellow, 1964–65. Membership: Alpha Kappa Psi; American Association for the Advancement of Science; American Economic Association; Midwest Economic Association; Phi Kappa Phi; Society for International Development; Southern Economic Association. Research: economic development and history; economy of Colombia. Author: Low Levels of Technology and Economic Development Prospects (Social Science, June 1963). Language: Spanish 3,3,3,2. Home: 600 West Carpenter, Fairfield, Iowa, 52556. Office: Dept. of Economics, Parsons Coll., Fairfield.

DE GRUMMOND, JANE LUCAS, b. Bellefonte, Pa., Dec. 27, 1905. HISTORY. A.B., American U., 1929; M.A., La. State U., 1943; Ph. D., 1946. Teacher, Colegio Robinson (P.R.), 1925–28; teacher, Tyrone High School (Pa.), 1929–42; PROF., HISTORY, LA. STATE U., 1942– . Membership: Conference on Latin American History; Historical Society of Pennsylvania. Research: influence of sea power in Latin America's wars for independence; Bolivar and his admirals. Author: Envoy to Caracas (1951); Caracas Diary (1954); Baratarians and the Battle of New Orleans (1961). Language: Spanish 5,5,3,3; French 3,-,-,-. Home: 354 Albert Hart Dr., Baton Rouge 8, La. Office: Dept. of History, La. State U., Baton Rouge.

DEINHARD, HANNA, b. Osnabrueck, Germany, Sept. 29, 1912. ART. Diplôme d'Études Superieures, Sorbonne, 1934; Ph. D., 1936. Ministério de Educação e Saude, Diretoria do Patrimônio Histórico e Artístico Nacional, 1937–47; PROF., THE NEW SCHOOL, 1948– ; instr. Duchesne Residence School, Convent of the Sacred Heart (N.Y.), 1950–60; instr., People's Coll. (N.Y.), 1950–61; vis. prof., Dept. of Architecture, Technion (Israel), 1957; instr., Bronxville Adult School, 1958–59; ASSOC. PROF., ART, BARD COLL., 1961– . Contributing editor, Handbook of Latin American Studies, 1947–48. Membership: American Association of University Professors; American Society for Aesthetics; College Art Association. Research: painting and sculpture; modern art; sociology of art; history of Brazilian art. Author: Problemas en torno de la historia de arte Brasileño (Cuadernos Americanos, Sept. 1947); Modern Tile Murals in Brazil (Craft Horizons,

Spring 1950). Language: Spanish 3,2,2,–; Portuguese 5,5,5,5: French 5,5,5,5: German 5,5,5,5; Italian 4,3,3,1. Home: Apt. 11–D, 102 West 85th St., New York, N.Y., 10024. Office: The New School, 66 West 12th St., New York 11.

DE JONG, GERRIT, JR., b. Amsterdam, Holland, Mar. 20, 1892. BRAZILIAN LITERATURE. A.B., U. of Utah, 1920; M.A., 1925; Ph. D., Stanford U., 1933. Instr., Murdock Academy, 1916–18; prof., Latter-day Saint U., 1919–25; dean, Coll. of Fine Arts, Brigham Young U., 1925–59; PROF., MODERN LANGUAGES, BRIGHAM YOUNG U., 1925– ; dir., Centro Cultural Brasil-Estados Unidos (Santos, Brazil), 1947–48. Stanford U. fellow, 1931–32. Membership: American Association for Latin American Studies; American Association of Teachers of Spanish and Portuguese; American Guild of Organists; Modern Language Association of America; Utah Academy of Sciences, Arts and Letters. Research: phonetics; Brazilian music; fine arts. Author: Two Brazilian Poems (1962); Villa-Lobos of Brazil (1962); Music in Brazil (Music Journal, Sept. 1963). Language: Spanish 5,5,5,5; Portuguese 5,5,5,5; French 5,4,4,5; Dutch 5,5,5,5; German 5,5,5,5. Linguistic studies: Dutch; French; German; Portuguese; Spanish. Home: 640 North University Ave., Provo, Utah 84601. Office: Dept. of Modern Languages, Brigham Young U., Provo, 84601.

DE LA GARZA, PETER J., b. San Antonio, Tex., May 12, 1926. LIBRARY SCIENCE. B.A., U. of Wash., 1950; M.L.S., 1959. Manager, Trade Book Dept., University Book Store (Seattle), 1954–58; head, Order Preparation Section, Order Div., Library of Congress, 1959–60; HEAD OF ACQUISITIONS, COLUMBUS MEMORIAL LIBRARY, PAN AMERICAN UNION, 1960– . Acquisitions Committee and rapporteur general, Seminars on the Acquisition of Latin American Library Materials. Membership: American Library Association; District of Columbia Library Association. Research: acquisitions, gift and exchange, government publications, and current bibliography of Latin America. Author: Commercial Bibliography in Latin America (1961); Acquisitions of Research Materials from Brazil and Their Selection (1963). Contributor: UNESCO International Guide to Education Documentation (1963). Language: Spanish 5,5,4,4; Portuguese 4,2,1,2; French 3,1,1,2; German 2,1,1,1; Italian 2,1,1,1. Home: 122 10th St., SE., Washington, D.C. 20003. Office: Columbus Memorial Library, Pan American Union, Washington, D.C. 20006.

DELANEY, ROBERT FINLEY, b. Fall River, Mass., Aug. 2, 1925. SOCIOLOGY AND INTERNATIONAL RELATIONS. B.N.S., Holy Cross Coll., 1946; A.M., Boston U., 1948; B.L.S., Ph. D., Catholic U. of America, 1950. Intelligence officer, U.S. Navy, 1949–50; Foreign Service officer, U.S. Dept. of State, 1950–63; LATIN AMERICAN PUBLIC RELATIONS ADVISER, INTERNATIONAL PETROLEUM COMPANY, LTD., 1963– . Membership: American Catholic Sociological Society; American Foreign Service Association; American Library Association; American Sociological Society. Research: public relations media and communication development in the Caribbean and Central America; El Salvador. Author: Your Future in Foreign Service (1960); The Literature of Communism in America (1962); Studies in Guerrilla Warfare (1963). Language: Spanish 3,4,4,3; French 2,1,2,1; German 2,2,1,1; Italian 2,3,2,1. Home: 6235 SW. 114th St., Miami, Fla. Office: International Petroleum Company, Ltd. (ESSO), 396 Alhambra Circle, Coral Gables 34, Fla.

DELANEY, ROBERT W., b. Macon County, Mo., Oct. 5, 1918. HISTORY. A.B., B.S., Northeast Mo. State Teachers Coll., 1948; M.A., U. of N. Mex., 1950; Ph. D., 1955. Assoc. prof., Nebr. State Teachers Coll., 1955–57; CHMN., DIV. OF HUMANITIES, FORT LEWIS A. & M. COLL., 1957– . Consultant, U.S. Peace Corps Peruvian Projects, U. of Denver, 1963. Membership: American Association of University Professors; American Historical Association; Conference on Latin American History; Conference of Western Historians. Research: colonial and national periods in Latin America. Author: Matamoros, Port for Texas during the Civil War (Southwestern Historical Quarterly, Apr. 1955); General Miller and the Confederación Perú-Boliviana (The Americas, Jan. 1962). Language: Spanish 4,3,3,3; French 3,2,2,2. Home: 1549 West Third Ave., Durango, Colo. Office: Div. of Humanities, Fort Lewis A. & M. Coll., Durango.

DELAPLANE, WALTER, HAROLD, b. Toledo, Ohio, Feb. 2, 1907. ECONOMICS. A.B., Oberlin Coll., 1929; A.M., 1931; Ph. D., Duke U., 1934. Instr., Duke U., 1934–40; asst. to Dean, Graduate School, 1937–43; asst. prof., 1940–43; principal economist, head, Iberian Section, Blockade Div., Foreign Economic Administration, 1943–45; vis. prof., National U. of Paraguay, 1945–46; head, Economics and Business Administration, St. Lawrence U., 1946–48; chmn., Economics, Tex. A. & M. U., 1948–53; dean, 1953–58; dean, Southern Methodist U., 1958–62; VICE PRESIDENT FOR ACADEMIC AFFAIRS, U. OF ARIZ., 1962– . Duke U. grant-in-aid (Colombia), Summer 1941; Rockefeller Foundation grant, Summer 1941; lectr., Colegio Libre (Buenos Aires), 1946; lectr., Escuela Nacional de Economía, National U. of México, 1950. Membership: American Association of Univerity Professors; American Economic Association; Economic History Association. Research: Latin American economics; Mexico. Author: The War and an Agricultural Economy: The Case of Colombia (Southern Economic Journal, July 1942); Some Problems of Economic Development of Latin America (Texas Journal of Science, Dec. 1949); La economía nacional y la internacional (Investigación Económica, Jan. 1950). Language: Spanish 4,4,4,4; Portuguese 1,1,1,1; French 2,1,1,1. Home: R.F.D. 4, Box 167–H, Tucson, Ariz. 85704. Office: Office of the Vice President for Academic Affairs, Tucson, 85721.

DE LAUBENFELS, DAVID JOHN, b. Pasadena, Calif., Dec. 5, 1925. GEOGRAPHY. A.B., Colgate U., 1949; A.M., U. of Ill., 1950; Ph. D., 1953. Asst.-assoc. prof., U. of Ga., 1953–59; ASSOC. PROF., GEOGRAPHY, SYRACUSE U., 1959– . U. of Ill. fellow (Chile), 1952; Johns Hopkins U. fellow, 1955–56. Membership: American Association of University Professors; American Geographical Society; Association of

American Geographers; Botanical Society of America; Ecological Society of America; International Society of Plant Morphology; National Council of Geography Teachers; Sigma Xi. Research: urban development in Latin America; the vegetation of Latin America; West coast of South America; urban development in South America. Author: The Temuco Region, A Geographic Study in South Central Chile (1953); Urban Centers of South Central Chile (Annals, Association of American Geographers, 1957). Map: Vegetation of Latin America (1963). Language: Spanish 4,3,4,3; Portuguese 3,3,3,2; French 4,3,3,3; German 3,2,2,2. Home: 201 Butternut Dr., De Witt, N.Y. 13214. Office: Dept. of Geography, Syracuse U., Syracuse, 13210.

DE LA VEGA, AURELIO, b. Havana, Cuba, Nov. 28, 1925. MUSIC. B.A., De La Salle Coll. (Cuba), 1944; M.A., U. of Havana, 1945; Ph. D., 1946; Ph. D., Ada Iglesias Music Institute, 1956. Prof., Central U. (Cuba), Summer 1954; music critic, Alerta (Havana newspaper), 1950–56; prof., dean, School of Music, U. of Oriente, 1952–59; ASSOC. PROF., MUSIC, SAN FERNANDO VALLEY STATE COLL., 1959– . Guest lectr., U. of Southern Calif., Summer 1959; Andrew Mellon fellow, U. of Pittsburgh, 1963; dir., Festival of the Arts, San Fernando Valley State Coll., 1963, 1964. Membership: International Society for Contemporary Music; National Association for American Composers and Conductors; Pacific Coast Council on Latin American Studies. Research: composition; criticism; history of Latin American music; Latin American literature; Argentine contemporary music. Author: The Negative Emotion (1950); Arnold Schönberg and the Atonalists (1952). Language: Spanish 5,5,5,5; Portuguese 2,2,1,1; French 4,3,2,2. Home: Apt. 203, 19119 Nordhoff St., Northridge, Calif. Office: Dept. of Music, San Fernando Valley State Coll., Northridge.

DELLA CAVA, RALPH S., b. Yonkers, N.Y., Sept. 11, 1934. HISTORY. B.S.S., Fordham U., 1956; Ph. D., Columbia U., 1965. Latin American representative, U.S. National Student Association, 1956–58; asst. secretary general, Latin American Area, World Assembly of Youth (Belgium), 1958–60. International Fellows Program, Columbia U., 1960–61; National Defense Foreign Language grant, 1961–62, 1962–63, 1963–64; Foreign Area Fellowship Program grant (Brazil), 1963–64; Board of Directors, Commission for International Development. Membership: Conference on Latin American History. Research: student movements, labor, and politics in Latin America; reform movements in the Brazilian Northeast, 1889–1930. Language: Spanish 5,5,5,4; Portuguese 5,5,4,4; French 5,5,5,4; Italian 5,5,4,4; Russian 3,3,3,2. Home: 4634 Garden Pl., New York 70, N.Y.

DELLEPIANE, ANGELA BLANCA. b. Río Cuarto, Argentina, May 13, 1926. SPANISH AMERICAN LITERATURE. M.A., Universidad de Buenos Aires, 1949; Ph. D., 1952. Prof., Teachers School (Buenos Aires), 1949–57; dir. of Seminar, U. of Buenos Aires, 1949–57; asst. prof., Fordham U., 1961–63; ASST. PROF., ROMANCE LANGUAGES, CITY COLL. (N.Y.), 1963– . Membership: American Association of Teachers of Spanish and Portuguese; Modern Language Association. Research: Spanish American novel; literature of the gaucho; Spanish phonetics; novels of Ernesto Sábato. Author: Ficción e historia en la trilogía de los Pizarros de Tirso (Filología, Jan.-Dec. 1952–53). Language: Spanish 5,5,5,5; Portuguese 5,3,2,1; French 4,4,4,3; Italian 4,4,3,2. Linguistic studies: Spanish. Home: 510 East 86th St., New York 28, N.Y. Office: Dept. of Romance Languages, City Coll., 133rd St. at Convent Ave., New York 31.

DEL RÍO, FERNANDO, b. Añasco, P.R., May 30, 1916. EDUCATION. B.S.A., U. of P.R., 1939; M.A., Cornell U., 1954; Ph. D., 1958. Teacher, Dept. of Education (San Juan, P.R.), 1939–46; instr., U. of P.R., 1946–47; assoc. educationist, Institute of Inter-American Affairs (Guatemala), 1947–49; asst. prof., U. of P.R., 1949–50; agricultural extensionist, Inter-American Institute of Agricultural Sciences (Costa Rica), Organization of American States. 1950–63; AGRICULTURAL PROGRAM PLANNER, CONSEJO AGRÍCOLA, DEPT. OF AGRICULTURE (P.R.), 1963– . Ford Foundation fellow; Rockefeller Foundation fellow. Membership: Colegio de Agrónomos de Puerto Rico; Gamma Sigma Delta; Sociedad Puertorriqueña de Administración Pública. Research: Latin American agricultural education programs; agricultural problems of Puerto Rico. Author: Limitaciones de extensión agrícola en América Latina como instrumento de desarrollo integral (1959); Agricultural Education in Latin America and Its Promises for the Future (1964). Language: Spanish 5,5,5,5; Portuguese 2,1,1,1; French 2,1,1,1. Home: San Ignacio 1435, Altamesa, Río Piedras, P.R. Office: Consejo Agrícola de Puerto Rico, Departamento de Agricultura, Santurce.

DEL ROSARIO, RUBEN, b. Yauco, P.R., June 13, 1907. LANGUAGE AND LINGUISTICS. B.A., U. of P.R., 1929; Ph. D., Universidad Central y Centro de Estudios Históricos de Madrid, 1931. Instr., U. of P.R., 1931–36; asst. prof., 1936–40; assoc. prof., 1940–43; PROF., LINGUISTICS, U. OF P.R., 1943– ; dir., National Defense Language Institute for Secondary School Teachers of Spanish, U. of P.R., Summer 1961. Consultant in linguistics, Dept. of Education of P.R., 1936– ; consultant in linguistics, Superior Educational Council, U. of P.R., 1946– ; coordinator of Caribbean Region, First and Second Inter-American Symposia in Linguistics and Language Teaching (Colombia and U.S.), 1963, 1964. Research: Spanish linguistics; the Spanish of Puerto Rico. Author: El endecasílabo español (1944); La lengua de Puerto Rico (1955); Consideraciones sobre la lengua de Puerto Rico (1958). Language: Spanish 5,5,5,5; Portuguese 5,5,3,5; French 5,5,5,5; German 4,3,3,3; Italian 4,4,3,3. Linguistic studies: Spanish. Home: 862 Estéban González–6B, Río Piedras, P.R. Office: Dept. of Linguistics, U. of P.R., Río Piedras, 00931.

DELWART, LOUIS OLIVER, b. Tournay, Belgium, Sept. 14, 1924. ECONOMICS. M.A., Georgetown U., 1952. Economist, International Monetary Fund, 1947–50; consultant, Klein and Saks, 1956–58; research dir., Inter-American Committee, National Planning Association, 1958–61; chief, Planning and Programming Div., Organization of American States, 1961–63; DEPUTY DIR., EUROPEAN OFFICE, ORGANIZATION OF AMERICAN STATES, 1963– . Membership: American Economic Association. Research: international trade policy; development planning; international finance. Author: Latin American Exports to the United States: 1965 and 1970 (1960). Co-author: Regional Account Projections in the Context of National Projections (in The Design of Regional Accounts, 1962). Language: Spanish 5,5,5,5; Portuguese 5,4,–,–; French 5,5,5,5; Dutch 4,4,4,4; German 4,4,4,4; Italian 4,4,4,4. Home: 3333 P St. NW., Washington 7, D.C. Office: European Office, Organization of American States, 1725 Eye St. NW., Washington.

DEMBITZ, LEWIS N., b. Washington, D.C., Sept. 1, 1910. ECONOMICS: FINANCE. A.B., George Washington U., 1930; M.B.A., Harvard, 1932. Economist, Federal Reserve Board, 1934–43; economist, U.S. Board of Economic Warfare, 1943–45; asst. dir., Div. of International Finance, Federal Reserve Board, 1945–56; lectr., Centro de Estudios Monetarios Latinoamericanos (México, D.F.), 1954, 1960; ASSOC. ADVISER, DIV. OF RESEARCH AND STATISTICS, FEDERAL RESERVE BOARD, 1956– . Adviser on development bank financing, U.S. Agency for International Development (Rio de Janeiro), 1963. Membership: American Economic Association; American Statistical Association. Research: investments and security markets; commercial banking and bank regulation; foreign exchange problems; development banks as a channel for the financing of economic development and effects of inflation on capital markets and savings in Brazil. Language: Spanish 3,2,3,3; Portuguese 3,1,2,1. Home: 3414 Garfield St., NW., Washington, D.C., 20007. Office: Federal Reserve Board, Washington, D.C. 20551.

DEMERATH, NICHOLAS JAY, b. Kewanee, Ill., Nov. 15, 1913. SOCIOLOGY. A.B., DePauw U., 1936; Ph. D., Harvard U., 1942. Prof., U. of N.C., 1946–56; vis. prof., U. of Birmingham (England), 1948, Harvard U., 1952; PROF., SOCIOLOGY, DIR., SOCIAL SCIENCE INSTITUTE, WASHINGTON U., 1956– ; Ford Foundation vis. prof., Ind. U., 1960–61. Consultant, Ford Foundation, National Institutes of Health, U.S. Air Force, Standard Oil Company of N.J., United Nations World Health Organization, American Society for Public Administration, Commission on Race and Housing, Federal Aviation Agency, U.S. Civil Service Commission and U.S. Treasury Dept; consultant on public health administration, Pan American Health Organization (Latin America), 1958–59; management and regional planning consultant, Sonora State Government (Mexico), 1962. Membership: Academy of Management; American Association of University Professors; American Institute of Planners; American Public Health Association; American Sociological Association; Society for Applied Anthropology. Research: management and organization; regional planning; housing; public health; community development. Author: Power, Presidents, and Professors (1964). Co-editor: The Urban South (1954). Language: Spanish 4,3,3,1.

Home: 506 South Meramec, Clayton 5, Mo. Office: Dept. of Sociology and Anthropology, Washington U., St. Louis 30, Mo.

DE MORELOS, LEONARDO CALDERON, b. Puruándiro, México, June 7, 1905. SPANISH AMERICAN LITERATURE. B.A., U. of Calif., Los Angeles, 1934; M.A., U. of Calif., Berkeley, 1935; Ph. D., Columbia U., 1954. ASSOC. PROF., SPANISH, COLUMBIA U., 1945– . U.S. Peace Corps Language Coordinator, Columbia U.; assoc. dir., Hispanic Institute. Membership: American Association of Teachers of Spanish and Portuguese; American Association of University Professors; Modern Language Association. Research: Mexican literature. Author: Luís González Obregón, Mexican Chronicler (1956). Language: Spanish 5,5,5,5; Portuguese 5,5,4,4; French 5,5,4,4; German 5,4,4,4; Italian 5,5,4,4. Linguistic studies: French; Italian; Portuguese; Spanish. Home: 438 West 116th St., New York, N.Y. 10027. Office: Dept. of Spanish, 102 Hamilton Hall, Columbia U., New York, 10027.

DENEMARK, GEORGE WILLIAM, b. Chicago, Ill., Nov. 13, 1921. EDUCATION. A.B., U. of Chicago, 1943; A.M., 1948; Ed. M., U. of Ill., 1949; Ed. D., 1956. Executive secretary and editor, Educational Leadership, Association for Supervision and Curriculum Development, 1952–56; asst. dean, Coll. of Education, U. of Md., 1956–58; PROF., DEAN, SCHOOL OF EDUCATION, U. OF WIS.-MILWAUKEE, 1958– . Consultant on curriculum, Commissioner of Education (Virgin Islands), Summer 1955; consultant on teacher education, U. of P.R., 1959; consultant, American Association of Colleges for Teacher Education-U.S. Dept. of State grant (Colombia), 1963; consultant, Johnson Foundation School (Fortaleza, Brazil), 1963; Advisory Board, Cyclo-Teacher Learning Aid; Editorial Board, Education; Study Committee, National Commission on Teacher Education and Professional Standards. Membership: American Association of Colleges for Teacher Education; Association for Supervision and Curriculum Development; John Dewey Society; Midwest Council of the Association for Latin American Studies; National Education Association; National Society for the Study of Education. Research: planning and organization connected with successful national conferences on education; teacher education; planning of high school and vocational education programs. Author: Criteria for Curriculum Decisions in Teacher Education (1963). Co-author: The Good Citizen as an Expert in Human Relations (in Education for Democratic Citizenship, 1952); Area, State, Regional and National In-Service Education Programs (in In-Service Education, 1957). Language: Spanish 2,2,1,1; Portuguese 2,1,1,1. Office: School of Education, U. of Wis.-Milwaukee, Milwaukee 53211.

DENEVAN, WILLIAM M., b. San Diego, Calif., Oct. 16, 1931. GEOGRAPHY. B.A., U. of Calif., 1953; M.A., 1958; Ph. D., 1963. Writer, Peruvian Times magazine (Lima), 1956; air photo field classifier, Inter-American Geodetic Survey (Nicaragua), Spring 1957; draftsman, U. of Calif., Berkeley, 1957–58; geographer, Central Intelligence Agency, 1958–59; instr., U. of Manitoba, Summer 1960; geographer-ecologist, U.S. Agency for International

Development (Brazil), 1962–63; ASST. PROF., GEOGRAPHY, U. OF WIS., 1963– . Fulbright fellow (Nicaragua), 1957; Woodrow Wilson fellow, U. of Calif.; National Academy of Sciences fellow (Bolivia), 1961–62; Ibero-American Area Studies Committee, U. of Wis.; consultant, U.S. Agency for International Development (Brazil). Membership: American Geographical Society; Association of American Geographers; Association of Pacific Coast Geographers. Research: physical and cultural geography; tropical America, especially the Amazon Basin and the savanna lands. Author: The Upland Pine Forests of Nicaragua (1961); The Physical Geography of the Planalto Central of Brazil (in Survey of the Agricultural Potential of the Central Plateau of Brazil, 1963). Language: Spanish 4,3,3,3; Portuguese 2,2,2,1; French 3, 1,1,1; German 2,1,1,1. Home: 4637 Bonner Lane Madison 4, Wis. Office: Dept of Geography, Science Hall, U. of Wis., Madison 6.

DENT, CHARLES H., b. Georgetown, Tex., Nov. 14, 1911. EDUCATION. B.A., Souththern Methodist U., 1931; M.A., 1941; Ed. D., N.Y.U., 1951. Assoc. prof., U. of Tex., 1951–61; elementary curriculum materials adviser, U.S. Agency for International Development (Brazil), 1961–63; ASSOC. PROF., ELEMENTARY CURRICULUM, U. OF TEX., 1963– ; elementary education consultant, American Community School (Buenos Aires), 1964–65. Representative for South America, International Center for Education of the U. of Tex., 1964. Membership: Association for Childhood Education International; Association for Supervision and Curriculum Development; Phi Delta Kappa. Research: child study; elementary and secondary curriculum development; preparation of educational materials in Brazil; curriculum improvement in Buenos Aires. Author: Inter-professional Communication (1963); Rationale for Teacher Certification (1963); Education is a Dynamic Process (The Bulletin Board, June 1964). Language: Spanish 4,3,3,4; Portuguese 5,3,4,4. Home: 3505 Mount Barker Dr., Austin, Tex. Office: Coll. of Education, U. of Tex., Austin.

DE ONÍS, FEDERICO, b. Salamanca, Spain, Dec. 20, 1885. SPANISH AMERICAN LITERATURE. Ph. D., U. of Madrid, 1908. Catedrático, U. of Oviedo, 1911–15; catedrático, U. of Salamanca, 1915–16; prof., Columbia U., 1916–54; PROF., HISPANIC STUDIES, U. OF P.R., 1954– . Dir., Hispanic Institute in the U.S. Membership: Hispanic Society of America. Author: Ensayos sobre el mundo de la cultura española (1932); Antología de la poesía española e hispano-americana (1934); España en América (1955). Language: Spanish 5,5,5,5; Portuguese 5,5,5,5; French 5, 5,5,–; German 5,1,–,–; Italian 5,2,–,–. Office: Seminario de Estudios Hispánicos, U. of P.R., Río Piedras.

DE ONÍS, JOSÉ, b. Oviedo, Spain, Jan. 28, 1911. SPANISH AMERICAN LITERATURE. B.A., U. of Ala., 1937; M.A., Columbia U., 1937; Ph. D., 1948. Instr., Manhattan Coll., 1938–40; instr., Vassar Coll., 1940–42; asst. prof., Lawrence Coll., 1942–43; asst. prof., Conn. Coll., 1946–49; assoc. prof., U. of Colo., 1949–55; PROF., ROMANCE LANGUAGES, U. OF COLO., 1955– ; chmn., Latin American Studies, 1959–61; CHMN., SPANISH, ITALIAN, AND PORTUGUESE, 1964– . Columbia U. fellow; Guggenheim fellow, 1955; chmn., Rocky Mountain Council for Latin American Studies, 1959; U. of Colo. faculty fellow, 1960. Membership: Modern Language Association; Rocky Mountain Council for Latin American Studies. Research: literary relations between the United States and the Hispanic world. Author: The United States as Seen by Spanish American Writers, 1776–1890 (1952, 1956); Las misiones españolas en los Estados Unidos (1959); Pan-Hispanismo (Inter-American Review of Bibliography, Oct. 1963). Language: Spanish 5,5,5,5; Portuguese 3,3,3,–; French 5, 5,4,3; German 5,4,4,3. Home: 2824 4th St., Boulder, Colo. Office: Main 107, Dept of Spanish, Italian, and Portuguese, U. of Colo., Boulder, 80304.

DE ONÍS, JUAN, b. New York, N.Y., Oct. 22, 1927. JOURNALISM. B.A., Williams Coll., 1948; M.S., Columbia U., 1951. Correspondent and editor, United Press, 1953–57; CORRESPONDENT (SOUTH AMERICA), THE NEW YORK TIMES, 1957– . Author: The America of José Martí (1953). Language: Spanish 5,5,5,4; Portuguese 5,5,5,4. Home: Avenida Rio Branco 25,12° andar, Rio de Janeiro, Brazil. Office: The New York Times, 229 West 43rd St., New York 36, N.Y.

DE ROSSO, ALPHONSE, b. Montreal, Canada, Feb. 18, 1921. ECONOMICS. B.A., Sir George Williams U., 1943; McGill U., 1943–44; M.A., Johns Hopkins U., 1945; Columbia U., 1949. Executive asst., The Texas Company (Panama), 1945–46; economic affairs officer, United Nations, 1946–57; general manager and secretary, Corporación Financiera Continental (Caracas), 1957–60; PUBLIC AFFAIRS ASST., REGIONAL COORDINATOR FOR LATIN AMERICA, STANDARD OIL COMPANY, 1960– . Research: Latin American political, economic and social affairs; investment in Venezuela; public finances of Brazil; economic development of El Salvador. Language: Spanish 5,5,5,3; Portuguese 5,5,2,1; French 5,5,5,4; Italian 5,5,4,3. Home: 10 Mimosa Dr., Cos Cob, Conn. Office: Standard Oil Company of New Jersey, 30 Rockefeller Plaza, New York, N.Y. 10020.

DEUEL, PAULINE BRANDT, b. San Luis Obispo, Calif., Nov. 13, 1921. SPANISH AMERICAN LITERATURE. B.A., Stanford U., 1942; M.A., 1943; Ph. D., 1951. Instr., Pomona Coll., 1947–48; instr.-assoc. prof., U. of Redlands, 1951–63; teacher, Guadalajara Summer School (Mexico), 1961; vis. assoc. prof., Stanford U., Summer 1962; ASST. PROF., SPANISH, U. OF SOUTHERN CALIF., 1963– . Del Amo fellow (Spain), 1953–54. Membership: American Association of Teachers of Spanish and Portuguese; Historical Society of California; Instituto Internacional de Literatura Iberoamericana; Modern Language Association; Pacific Coast Council on Latin American Studies. Research: Latin American culture; Mexican folklore; imagery in the works of Manuel Gutiérrez Nájera. Author: Mexican Serenade: The Story of the Mexican Players and the Padua Hills Theatre (1961). Language: Spanish 5,5,5,5; Portuguese 4,4,3,3; French 4,4,2,3.

Home: 631 Orange Grove Ave., South Pasadena, Calif. 91030. Office: Dept. of Spanish, U. of Southern Calif., Los Angeles 90007.

DE VORE, BLANCHE BLUE, b. May 19, 1912. HISTORY. B.S., Appalachian State Teachers Coll., 1939; Ph. D., U. of Southern Calif., 1963. Teacher, Blowing Rock High School (N.C.), 1941–43; teacher, San Diego County Public Schools (Calif.), 1943–48; teacher, Los Angeles County Public Schools (Calif.), 1953–63; INSTR., HISTORY, RIO HONDO JUNIOR COLL., 1963– . Membership: Phi Alpha Theta. Research: the Mexican Revolution; international relations. Language: Spanish 3,2,2,2; Portuguese 1,1,1,1; French 3,2,2,1; German 3,2,2,2. Home: 14711 Valeda Dr., La Mirado, Calif. Office: Dept. of History, Rio Hondo Junior Coll., Whittier, Calif.

DE VRIES, HENRY PETER, b. Curaçao, Netherlands Antilles, Dec. 21, 1911. LAW. A.B., Columbia U., 1934; LL.B., 1937. Assoc., Sullivan and Cromwell, 1937–48; PROF., LAW, COLUMBIA U., 1948– ; law practice (Colombia), 1949–52; law practice (Brazil), 1954–55. Consultant, legal adviser, U.S. Dept. of State, 1962–63; Executive Committee, Institute for Latin American Studies, Columbia U. Membership: American Bar Association; American Foreign Law Association; American Society of International Law; Association of the Bar of the City of New York; Council on Foreign Relations. Research: comparative law; international law. Author: Counseling in International Transactions (1948); The French Legal System (1958); Inter-American Legal Systems (1963). Language: Spanish 5,5,5,5; Portuguese 4,4,4,4; French 5,5,5,5; German 3,4,3,3; Italian 4,4,3,3. Home: 125 East 81st St., New York 28, N.Y. Office: School of Law, Columbia U., New York.

DIAZ, ALBERT JAMES, b. Philadelphia, Pa., Oct. 17, 1931. LIBRARY SCIENCE. B.A., Swarthmore Coll., 1952; M.S. in L.S., U. of N.C., 1956. Special collections librarian, U. of N. Mex., 1956–58; sales and promotion manager, Microcard Foundation, 1958–59; EXECUTIVE DIR., MICROCARD EDITIONS INC., 1960– . Membership: American Documentation Institute; American Historical Association; American Library Association; National Microfilm Association. Research: microreproduction; history of the Latin American collection at the University of North Carolina. Author: Manuscripts and Records in the University of New Mexico Library (1957); A Bibliography of Bibliographies Relating to the History and Literature of Arizona and New Mexico (Arizona Quarterly, Autumn 1958); Guide to Microforms in Print (in National Microfilm Association Proceedings of the Tenth Annual Meeting and Convention, 1961). Language: Spanish 3,3,3,3; French 2,1,1,1. Home: 1703 Mark Lane, Rockville, Md. Office: Microcard Editions Inc., 901 26th St., NW., Washington, D.C. 20037.

DIAZ, MAY NORDQUIST, b. Nederkalix, Sweden, May 2, 1921. ANTHROPOLOGY. A.B., U. of Calif., Berkeley, 1946; Ph. D., 1963. Lectr., U. of Calif., Berkeley, 1961–63; ACTING ASST. PROF., ANTHROPOLOGY, U. OF CALIF., BERKELEY, 1963– . National Science Foundation grant (Mexico), 1959–60. Membership: American Anthropological Association. Research: socialization; Latin American social structure; Mexico. Author: Alliance and Opposition in a Mexican Town (Ethnology, Apr. 1963). Co-author: Conflict in the Modern Teotihuacan Irrigation System (Comparative Studies in Society and History, July 1962). Language: Spanish 5,5,4,4; German 3,2,1,2; Swedish 5,5,4,4. Home: 1475 Olympus Ave., Berkeley 8, Calif. Office: Dept. of Anthropology, U. of Calif., Berkeley 2.

DIAZ-ROJAS, ARMANDO, b. P.R., Feb. 18, 1918. ECONOMICS. B.B.A., U. of P.R., 1952; M.S., U. of Wis., 1954; Ph. D., N.Y.U., 1963. Accounting, management, Dept. of Public Works, Dept. of Agriculture, Government of P.R., 1945–50; dir. of tax research, Dept. of Finance of P.R., 1950–54; instr.-ASST. PROF., ECONOMICS AND ACCOUNTING, U. OF P.R., 1954– . Consultant, Government of P.R.; financial editor, El Mundo (San Juan, P.R.) Membership: American Economic Association; National Tax Association; Puerto Rican Economic Association. Research: accounting; public finance; fiscal policy; economic development in P.R. Co-author: A Tax Program for Puerto Rico. Language: Spanish 5,5,5,5. Office: Dept. of Economics and Accounting, U. of P.R., Río Piedras.

DÍAZ-SOLER, LUIS M., b. San Juan, P.R., Nov. 12, 1916. HISTORY. B.A., U. of P.R., 1939; M.A., La. State U., 1947; Ph. D., 1950. Clerk, U.S. Engineer Office, 1940–41; head, District Div., U.S. Censorship Office, 1941–43; PROF., HISTORY, U. OF P.R., 1943– . Vice president, IV Reunión de Consulta, Instituto Pan Americano de Geografía e Historia, 1959. Membership: Institute International de Civilisations Differents (Belgium). Research: history of Puerto Rico and the Caribbean. Author: Historia de la Esclavitud Negra en Puerto Rico (1953); Rosendo Matienzo Cintrón (1960). Language: Spanish 5,5,5,5; Portuguese 1,1,–,–; French 1, –,–,–. Home: 110 Janer St., Río Piedras, P.R. Office: Box 22133, University, San Juan, P.R. 00931.

DIBBLE, CHARLES ELLIOT, b. Layton, Utah, Aug. 18, 1909. ANTHROPOLOGY. B.A., U. of Utah, 1936; M.A., Universidad Nacional Autónoma de México, 1938; Ph. D., 1942. PROF., CHMN., ANTHROPOLOGY, U. OF UTAH, 1941– ; vis. prof., U. of Minn., 1957, 1959. Roosevelt fellow, 1942; National Science Foundation grant, 1957, 1962. Membership: Sociedad Mexicana de Antropología. Research: cultural anthropology; Mexico; Nahuatl linguistics. Author; El Códice Xolotl (1951); Historia de la nación mexicana (1963). Co-editor and translator: Florentine Codex (1950–1963). Language: Spanish 5,4,4,4; Portuguese 3,3,3,1; French 3,3,3,1; German 4,4,4,3; Russian 2,2,2,2. Linguistic studies: Nahuatl. Home: P.O. Box 216, North Salt Lake, Utah. Office: Dept. of Anthropology, U. of Utah, Salt Lake City.

DICKEN, SAMUEL NEWTON, b. Fleming County, Ky., Jan. 26, 1901. GEOGRAPHY. A.B., Marietta Coll., 1924; Ph. D., U. of Calif., Berkeley, 1931. Instr., Carleton Coll., 1928–29; instr.-prof., U. of Minn., 1929–47; PROF., GEOGRAPHY, U. OF OREG., 1947– . Chmn., 1947–63. Consultant, Army Air Force, 1941–43; consultant, Office of Strategic Services, 1943; U. of Minn. Graduate Research Funds grants, 1931, 1933, 1936, 1937, 1939; U. of Oreg. grant, 1953–54; Office of Naval Research grant, 1960–61; Carnegie grant (Mexico), Summer 1964. Membership: American Geographical Society; Association of American Geographers; Association of Pacific Coast Geographers; National Council of Geography Teachers; Oregon Council of Geography Teachers. Research: economic geography; geomorphology; land use; coastal features; geography of the Colima, Mexico, coast. Author: Regional Economic Geography (1949); Economic Geography (1955). Co-author: Introduction to Human Geography (1963). Language: Spanish 4,3,3,3; French 4,2,2,2. Home: 2385 Madrona Dr., Eugene, Oreg. Office: Dept. of Geography, U. of Oreg., Eugene, 97403.

DIEBOLD, ALBERT RICHARD, JR., b. New York, N.Y., Jan. 20, 1934. ANTHROPOLOGY: LINGUISTICS. A.B.,Yale U., 1956; Ph. D., 1961. Instr., Harvard U., 1961–62; ASST. PROF., ANTHROPOLOGY, HARVARD U., 1962– . National Institute of Mental Health research grant, 1964; National Defense Education Act research grant, 1964. Membership: American Anthropological Association; Linguistic Society of America; New York Linguistic Circle. Research: social anthropology; bilingualism and biculturalism in a Huave community; Mexico. Author: Incipient Bilingualism (Language, Jan.–Mar. 1961); A Laboratory for Language Contact (Anthro-Linguistics, Jan. 1962); A Survey of Psycho-linguistics (Language, July–Sept. 1964). Language: Spanish 5,4,4,4; Portuguese 3,1,-,-; French 4,3,2,2; Cantonese 1,3,3,1; German 4,4,3,3; Italian 3,3,2,2. Linguistic studies: Huave; Modern Greek; Spanish; Tarascan. Home: 12 Arnold Circle, Cambridge, Mass. 02139. Office: Dept. of Social Relations, Harvard U., Cambridge, 02138.

DIFFIE, BAILEY, W., b. Detroit, Tex., June 27, 1902. HISTORY. A.B., Southeastern Teachers Coll., 1923; M.A., Tex. Christian U., 1926; Ph. D., Central U. (Spain), 1929. Instr., Tex Christian U., 1926–27; instr., City Coll. (N.Y.), 1930–36; asst. prof., 1936–46; vis., lectr., Cornell U., 1943; economic analyst, Foreign Economics Administration, 1943–44; assoc. prof., City Coll. (N.Y.), 1946–47; vis. lectr., Yale U., 1946–47; PROF., HISTORY, CITY COLL. (N.Y.), 1951– ; vis. prof., N.Y.U., 1962; vis. prof., Columbia U., 1963–64. Rotary Club grant (Spain), 1926–27; American Fund for Public Service grant, 1929–30; Editorial Board, Hispanic American Historical Review, 1946– ; grants from Social Science Research Council and American Philosophical Society, 1948–49, 1952, 1958–59, 1960, 1962. Membership: American Historical Association; Amigos de España; Conference on Latin America History. Research: history of Portugal and Brazil to 1808. Author: Porto Rico: A Broken Pledge (1931); Latin American Civilization: Colonial Period (1945); Prelude to Empire: Portugal Overseas before Henry the Navigator (1960). Language: Spanish 4,-,4,4; Portuguese 4,-,4,4; French 4,-,3,3; Italian 3,-,2,-. Home: 181–41 Kruger Rd., Jamaica, N.Y. Office: Dept. of History, City Coll., Convent Ave. at 139th, New York 31, N.Y.

DI FRANCO, JOSEPH, b. Cleveland, Ohio, Apr. 11, 1917. EDUCATION. M.S., Ohio State U., 1940; M.A., Columbia U., 1955; Ed. D., 1958. Extension specialist, International Cooperation Administration (Rome), 1952–55; prof., graduate school, Cornell U., 1955–58; CHMN., ECONOMICS AND SOCIAL SCIENCES, INSTITUTO INTERAMERICANO DE CIENCIAS AGRÍCOLAS (TURRIALBA, COSTA RICA), 1958– . Columbia U. fellow; extension specialist for Latin America, U.S. Agency for International Development. Membership: International Development Association. Research: agricultural extension education in Latin America. Author: Analytical Studies of Extension Services (1960–63); An Analytical Study of the Extension Service of Honduras (1962); Some Aspects of Extension Work (1963–64). Language: Spanish 4,4,3,2; Portuguese 2,2,-,-; French 2,-,-,-; Italian 4,5,4,2. Home and office: Instituto Inter-Americano de Ciencias Agrícolas, Turrialba, Costa Rica.

DIGGS, IRENE, b. Monmouth, Ill., Apr. 13, 1906. ANTHROPOLOGY AND SOCIOLOGY. A.B., U. of Minn., 1928; A.M., Atlanta U., 1933; Ph. D., U. of Havana, 1945. ANTHROPOLOGIST, SOCIOLOGY, MORGAN STATE COLL., 1947– . Guest prof., Bard Coll., Brooklyn Coll., Lincoln U.; cofounder, Phylon, The Atlantic University Review of Race and Culture; U.S. Dept. of State exchange scholar (Montevideo, Uruguay), 1946–47; Roosevelt fellow, Institute of International Education, U. of Havana. Membership: American Anthropological Association; American Association for the Advancement of Science. Research: race relations in South America; African influence in Latin America, especially Cuba. Author: Singing and Dancing in Afro-Cuba (Crisis, Dec. 1951); Negro Painters in Uruguay (Crisis, May 1952); Color in Colonial Spanish America (Journal of Negro History, Oct. 1953). Language: Spanish 4,4,4,4; French 3,3,3,3. Home: 2207 Southern Ave., Baltimore, Md. 21214. Office: Dept. of Sociology, Morgan State Coll., Baltimore, 21212.

DILLON, DOROTHY, R., b. New York, N.Y., Apr. 10, 1917. HISTORY. A.B., Hunter Coll., 1939; A.M., Columbia U., 1940; Ph. D., 1947. Instr., Sweet Briar Coll., 1942–44; instr., Rutgers U., 1944–48; dir., Latin American Bibliographical Project for the United Nations, Library of Congress, 1948–49; Latin American intelligence officer, U.S. Government, 1949–51; Latin American research officer, U.S. Dept. of State, 1951–54; chief, Latin American Research Bureau, deputy chief, Worldwide Research Div., U.S. Information Agency, 1954–61; planning staff, Bureau of Educational and Cultural Affairs, U.S. Dept. of State, 1961–63; CULTURAL ATTACHÉ (GUATEMALA), U.S. INFORMATION AGENCY, 1963– . Rutgers U. Faculty Research Council fellow (Uruguay), 1947. Membership: American Association of University Women; American Historical Association; Conference on Latin American History. Research: politics, education, and culture in Latin America. Author: The New York Triumvirate (1949); Latin America: A Selected Bibliography (1950); International Communism and Latin America (1962). Language: Spanish 4,4,3,3,; Portuguese 3,2,1,1; French 4,3,1,1. Home: 5809 MacArthur Blvd., NW., Washington,

D.C. 20016. Office: Guatemala, U.S. Dept. of State, Washington, D.C., 20521.

DIMMICK, RALPH EDWARD, b. Cincinnati, Ohio, Oct. 19, 1916. BRAZILIAN LITERATURE. B.A., Pa. State U., 1937; A.M., Harvard U., 1938; Ph. D., 1941. Asst. dir. of courses, União Cultural Brasil-Estados Unidos (São Paulo), 1943–46; instr., Harvard U., 1946–49; instr., Northwestern U., 1949–51; asst. to dir., Dept. of Cultural Affairs, Pan American Union, 1952–58; SPECIAL ASST. TO THE SECRETARY GENERAL, PAN AMERICAN UNION, ORGANIZATION OF AMERICAN STATES, 1958– . Sheldon traveling fellow (Argentina, Bolivia, Brazil, Chile, Peru, Uruguay), 1942–43; contributing editor, Handbook of Latin American Studies, 1949– . Membership: American Association of Teachers of Spanish and Portuguese. Research: culture of Brazil. Author: The Brazilian Literary Generation of 1930 (Hispania, May 1951). Translator: Brief History of Brazilian Literature, by M. Bandeira (1958). Language: Spanish 5,5,5,5; Portuguese 5, 5,5,5; French 5,5,4,4; German 4,4,3,3; Italian 4,4,4,3; Russian 2,2,2,2. Linguistic studies: French; Italian; Portuguese; Rumanian; Spanish. Home: Apt. 4, 4400 North Henderson Rd., Arlington, Va. 22203. Office: Office of the Secretary General, Pan American Union, Washington, D.C. 20006.

DI PESO, CHARLES CORRADINO, b. St. Louis, Mo., Oct. 20, 1920. ANTHROPOLOGY. B.F.T., American Institute of Foreign Trade, 1947; M.A., U. of Ariz., 1950; Ph. D., 1953. City archeologist, Phoenix, Ariz., 1946–47; instr., American Institute of Foreign Trade, 1947–48; DIR., THE AMERIND FOUNDATION, INC., 1948– ; dir., Joint Casas Grandes expedition (Mexico), 1958–61. Consultant on archeological research, Republic of Mexico; Alfred Vincent Kidder Award, 1959; member of board, Foundation for Anthropological Research in Latin America. Membership: Phi Kappa Psi; Sigma Xi. Research: archeology; cultural anthropology; Mexico. Author: The Sobaipuri Indians of the Upper San Pedro River Valley, Southeastern Arizona (1953); The Upper Pima of San Cayetano del Tumacacori (1956); Cultural Developments in Northern Mexico (1963). Language: Spanish 3,3,3,3. Home: F F Ranch, Dragoon, Ariz. Office: The Amerind Foundation, Inc., Dragoon.

DIX, ROBERT HELLER, b. Elizabeth, N.J., Aug. 18, 1930. POLITICAL SCIENCE. B.A., Harvard U., 1951; M.A., 1953; Ph. D., 1962. Foreign Service officer (Colombia), U.S. Dept. of State, 1957–60; ASST. PROF., POLITICAL SCIENCE, YALE, U., 1962– . Harvard U. teaching fellow, 1961–62. Membership: American Political Science Association. Research: two-party system in Colombia; Latin American politics. Language: Spanish, 4,4,4,4; French 2,1,1,1. Home: 854 Edgewood Ave., New Haven, Conn. Office: Dept. of Political Science, Yale U., New Haven.

DIXON, KEITH ALAN, b. San Francisco, Calif., Sept. 23, 1929. ANTHROPOLOGY. B.A., U. of Ariz., 1950; M.A., 1952; Ph. D., U. of Calif., Los Angeles, 1956. Archeologist, asst. field dir., New World Archeological Foundation (Mexico), 1956–58; ASSOC. PROF., ANTHROPOLOGY, LONG BEACH STATE COLL., 1958– ; archeologist, Museum, U. of Pa. (Guatemala), Summers 1959, 1960. Research assoc. in anthropology, Los Angeles County Museum; Board of Directors, Long Beach Institute of Folklore and Mythology. Membership; American Anthropological Association; Centro de Investigaciones Antropológicas de México; Sociedad Mexicana de Antropología; Society for American Archaeology; Sigma Xi; Southwestern Anthropological Association. Research: archeology; Mexico; Guatemala. Author: Hidden House, A Cliff Ruin in Sycamore Canyon, Central Arizona (Bulletin 29, Museum of Northern Arizona, 1956); Ceramics from Two Preclassic Periods, at Chiapa de Corzo, Chiapas, Mexico (Papers, New World Archaeological Foundation, 1959); The Interamerican Diffusion of a Cooking Technique: The Culinary Shoe-Pot (American Anthropologist, June 1963). Language: Spanish 4,4,4,3; French 1,–,–,–; German 1,–,–,–. Home: 2902 Angler Lane, Los Alamitos, Calif. Office: Dept. of Anthropology, Long Beach State Coll., Long Beach 4, Calif.

DOBYNS, HENRY FARMER, b. Tucson, Ariz., July 3, 1925. ANTHROPOLOGY. B.A., U. of Ariz., 1949; M.A., 1956; Ph. D., Cornell U., 1960. Research assoc., Ariz. State Museum, 1958–59; research coordinator, Cornell-Peru Project, Cornell U., 1959–63; LECTR. AND SENIOR RESEARCH ASSOC., ANTHROPOLOGY, CORNELL U., 1963– . National Science Foundation fellow (Mexico), 1957–58; area studies lectr., U.S. Peace Corps Training Programs, 1962, 1964. Membership: American Anthropological Association; Arizona Archaeological and Historical Society; Arizona Pioneers' Historical Society; Society for Applied Anthropology. Research: ethnohistory and applied social science; Peru; Indian affairs in Ecuador and Bolivia; folk religion in Mexico. Author: Hepah, California! The Journal of Cave J. Couts from Monterrey, Mexico to Los Angeles, California, 1848–1849 (1961); Experiment in Conservatism (in Human Problems in Technological Change, 1952; Spanish edition, 1963). Co-editor: Migración e integración en el Perú (1963). Language: Spanish 5,4,4,4; Portuguese 2,3,1,1; French 3,1, 1,1. Linguistic studies: Northeastern Pai; Papago. Home: 442 North Aurora St., Ithaca, N.Y. 14850. Office: Dept. of Anthropology, Cornell U., Ithaca.

DOCKSTADER, FREDERICK J., b. Los Angeles, Calif., Feb. 3, 1919. ANTHROPOLOGY. B.A., Ariz. State Coll., 1940; M.A., 1941; Ph. D., Western Reserve U., 1951. Teacher, Cranbrook School (Mich.), 1941–50; staff ethnologist, Cranbrook Institute of Science, 1950–52; instr., curator of anthropology, Museum, Dartmouth Coll., 1952–55; asst. dir., Museum, Heye Foundation, 1955–61; DIR., MUSEUM, HEYE FOUNDATION, 1961– ; ADJUNCT PROF., ART HISTORY AND ARCHAEOLOGY, COLUMBIA U., 1962– . Chmn., Indian Arts and Crafts Board, U.S. Dept. of Interior; Columbia U. Advisory Council. Membership: American Anthropological Association; American Association for the Advancement of Science; American Ethnological Society; American Museums Association; International Congress of Americanists; Rochester Society of Arts and Science; Society for American Archeology. Research:

ethnology; use of material culture; Indian culture, arts, and crafts. Author: The American Indian in Graduate Studies (1954); Indian Art in America (1962); Indian Art in Middle America (1963). Language: Spanish 5,4,4,4; Portuguese 3,3,3,3; French 4,3,3,3. Home: 790 Riverside Dr., New York, N.Y. 10032. Office: Museum of the American Indian, Broadway at 155th St., New York, 10032.

DOERR, ARTHUR HARRY, b. Johnston City, Ill., Aug. 28, 1924. GEOGRAPHY. B.A., Southern Ill. U., 1947; M.A., Ind. U., 1948; Ph. D., Northwestern U., 1951. Field team chief and cartographer, Dept. of Agriculture and Commerce of P.R., Summer 1950; asst. prof.-PROF., GEOGRAPHY, U. of OKLA., 1951– ; DEAN, GRADUATE COLL., 1961– ; summer vis. prof., Eastern Ill. State Coll., 1951, Central Wash. Coll., 1952, George Peabody Coll., 1953, Wis. State Coll., 1955, Western Wash. Coll., 1957, Northwestern U. 1960. U. of Okla. Teaching Award, 1955; intelligence expert, U.S. Dept. of the Army, Summer 1956. Membership: American Association for Advancement of Science; Association of American Geographers; Oklahoma Academy of Science; Sigma Xi; Southwestern Social Science Association. Research: physical and economic geography; tropical land use; Puerto Rico and the Caribbean area. Author: Programa de clasificación de terrenos rurales, mapa de utilización de terrenos rurales (1950–51); Cultural Relationships to Coastline Forms on Caribbean Islands (Proceedings, Oklahoma Academy of Science, 1961). Co-author: Population Distribution in Mexico—1950 (Journal of Geography, May 1956). Language: Spanish 2,2,1,2; French 2,1,1,1; German 1,1,1,1. Home: 1213 Leslie Lane, Norman, Okla. Office: Graduate Coll., U. of Okla., Norman, 73069.

DOLE, GERTRUDE EVELYN, b. Cavendish, Vt., Oct. 10, 1915. ANTHROPOLOGY. A.B., Middlebury Coll., 1937; M.A., U. of N.C., 1949; Ph. D., U. of Mich., 1957. Lectr., New School for Social Research, Summer 1958; lectr., Columbia U., 1958–60; ethnographer, American Museum of Natural History, 1960–61; lectr., Columbia U., 1961–62; LECTR., ANTHROPOLOGY, N.Y.U., 1961– . Doherty fellow (Brazil), 1953–54. Membership: American Anthropological Association; American Association for the Advancement of Science; American Ethnological Society. Research: ethnology; Indians of South America; social organization; Brazil; Peru. Author: Ownership and Exchange among the Kuikuru Indians of Mato Grosso (Revista do Museu Paulista, 1959); Techniques of Preparing Manioc Flour as a Key to Culture History in Tropical America (Proceedings, Fifth International Congress of Anthropological and Ethnological Sciences, 1960). Co-editor: Essays in the Science of Culture (1960). Language: Spanish 4,3,3,2; Portuguese 4,3,3,2; French 4,3,3,3. Linguistic studies: Keresan Pueblo Indian; Kuikuru. Home: 4499 Henry Hudson Parkway, New York 71, N.Y. Office: Dept. of Sociology and Anthropology, N.Y.U., New York 3.

DOMIKE, ARTHUR L., JR., b. Santa Monica, Calif., Jan. 19, 1926. ECONOMICS. B.A., U. of Calif., Los Angeles, 1948; M.S., U. of Wis., 1953; Ph. D., 1961. Research assoc., U. of Minn. and U.S. Dept. of Agriculture, 1953–55; assoc. prof., U. of R.I., 1955–61; economist, Economic Research Service, U.S. Dept. of Agriculture, 1961–62; economist, Organization of American States (Argentina), 1962–64; REGIONAL OFFICER, FOOD AND AGRICULTURE ORGANIZATION, UNITED NATIONS (SANTIAGO, CHILE), 1964– . Consultant, Ford Foundation (Argentina), 1964. Membership: American Economic Association; American Farm Economic Association; International Association of Agricultural Economists. Research: land tenure and agrarian reform problems in Latin America; integration of reform projects with overall economic development; administration of reform projects. Author: Tenencia de la tierra; Aspectos de la estructura agropecuaria en el desarrollo argentino (1963); Land Tenure and Agricultural Development in Argentina (1964). Co-author: Agriculture and Economic Growth (1963). Language: Spanish 4,4,4,4; Portuguese 3,3,2,1; French 3,3,2,2; German 3,2,2,2. Home and office: Food and Agriculture Organization, United Nations Latin American Regional Office, Casilla 10095, Santiago, Chile.

DONAHUE, FRANCIS JAMES, b. Chicago, Ill., Nov. 21, 1917. LANGUAGE. B.A., U. of Omaha, 1941; M.A., U of Wis., 1942; Ph. D., U. of Southern Calif., 1965. Specialist, U.S. Naval Intelligence (Chicago; Washington, D.C.), 1942–46; asst. prof., U.S. Merchant Marine Academy, 1948–54; cultural attaché, U.S. Information Agency (Havana; Caracas), 1954–60; ASST. PROF., FOREIGN LANGUAGES, CALIF. STATE COLL., 1960– . National Defense Education Act foreign language fellow, 1963–65. Membership: Academia Cubana de la Lengua; American Association of Teachers of Spanish and Portuguese; Foreign Policy Association. Research: Cuban history and culture; Central America; the Caribbean. Author: Washington Irving (1958); Truth's Story Teller (The Pan American Magazine, Feb. 1947); Impresos cubanos editados en los Estados Unidos de Norteamerica (Revista de la Biblioteca Nacional, Apr.–June 1956). Language: Spanish 5,5,5,5; Portuguese 5,4,3,2; French 4,3,3,2. Home: 6692 Marietta Ave., Garden Grove, Calif. Office: Dept. of Foreign Languages, Calif. State Coll., Long Beach.

DONALD, CARR LOWE, b. Cedar Rapids, Iowa, Aug. 7, 1929. POLITICAL SCIENCE. B.A., U. of Iowa, 1951; M.I.A., Columbia U., 1955; Ph. D., U. of Tex., 1959. Instr., U. of Wis., 1958–60; INSTR., U. OF VA., NORTHERN VA. CENTER, 1960– ; program specialist, Pan American Union, 1960–62; intelligence research specialist, U.S. Dept. of State, 1962–63; PROGRAMS OFFICER, PAN AMERICAN UNION, 1963– . Doherty fellow (Brazil), 1957–58; Social Science Research Council fellow; National Defense fellow; consultant, U.S. Peace Corps Training Center, U. of Wis., Milwaukee, 1964– . Membership: American Political Science Association. Research: Brazilian and Peruvian politics and government; Central American university integration; the Organization of American States. Author: Brazilian Local Self-Government (Western Political Quarterly, Dec. 1959); The Problem of Brazilian Local Government Finance (Inter-American Economic Affairs, Summer 1959). Language:

Spanish 4,5,5,4; Portuguese 4,4,4,3; French 3,1,1,1. Home: 6112 Xavier Ct., McLean, Va. Office: Pan American Union, Washington, D.C. 20006.

DONOHUE, JOHN AUGUSTINE, S. J., b. San Francisco, Calif., Aug. 28, 1916. HISTORY. M.A., Gonzaga U. (Wash.), 1941; S.T.L., Alma Coll., 1948; Ph. D., U. of Calif., Berkeley,. 1957. Teacher, librarian, St. Ignatius High School (San Francisco), 1941–43; instr., U. of San Francisco, 1943–44; asst. pastor, Roman Catholic Church (México, D.F.), 1953–54; ASSOC. PROF., HISTORY, LOYOLA U. OF LOS ANGELES, 1955– . Research: history of Mexico; archival research. Author: Unlucky Jesuit Mission of Bac (Arizona and the West, Summer 1960). Language: Spanish 3,3,3,3; French 3,1,1,1; Latin 4,3,3,3. Home and office: Dept. of History, Loyola U., 7101 West 80th St., Los Angeles 45, Calif.

DORAN, EDWIN, JR., b. Baton Rouge, La., Jan. 11, 1918. GEOGRAPHY. B.A., La. State U., 1938; M.S., 1947; Ph. D., U. of Calif., Berkeley, 1953. Instr., U. of Tex., 1950–55; asst. prof., La State U., 1955–56; assoc. prof., U. of S.C., 1956–58; geographer consultant, Pacific Missile Range, 1958–60; ASSOC. PROF., GEOGRAPHY, TEX. A. & M. U., 1960– . Symposium convener, 10th Pacific Science Congress (Honolulu), 1961. Membership: American Geographical Society; Association of American Geographers; Phi Kappa Phi; Sigma Xi. Research: tropical areas; West Indies. Author: Informe detallado sobre la geografía del valle del río Huallaga (in Informe Sobre el Huallaga, 1950); Cayman Islands-A Sketch (The Caribbean, Sept. 1956); This Caicos Confusion (The Professional Geographer, July 1961). Language: Spanish 2,1,2,1; French 3,1,1,1; German 3,1,2,2. Home: 1114 Langford St., College Station, Tex. Office: Dept. of Geography, Tex. A. & M. U., College Station.

DORNER, PETER PAUL, b. Luxemburg, Wis., Jan. 13, 1925. ECONOMICS. B.S., U. of Wis., 1951; M.S., U. of Tenn., 1953; Ph. D., Harvard U., 1959. Asst. prof., U. of Wis., 1954–56; research assoc., Fund for the Republic, 1958–59; PROF., AGRICULTURAL ECONOMICS, U. OF WIS., 1959– ; prof., Instituto de Economía (Santiago, Chile), 1963–65. Membership: American Economic Association; American Farm Economic Association. Research: agricultural economics; agricultural and development policy; land economics; land reform; Chilean agricultural economics. Author: Resource Adjustments, Income Growth, and Tenure (University of Wisconsin Research Bulletin 242, May 1963); Land Tenure, Income Distribution, and Productivity Interactions (Journal of Land Economics, Aug. 1964). Co-author: Relevant Research Programs to be Conducted in Developing Countries (Journal of Farm Economics, Dec. 1964). Language: Spanish 4,3,3,3; Portuguese 2,1,1,1; French 1,1,1,1; German 2,2,2,1. Home: 541 Woodside Ter., Madison, Wis. Office: Dept. of Agricultural Economics, U. of Wis., Madison.

DOTSON, FLOYD WHITNEY, b. Joseph, Oreg., Oct. 2, 1917. SOCIOLOGY. B.A., Reed Coll., 1942; Ph. D., Yale U., 1950. Instr., U. of Mass., 1949–50; asst. prof.-ASSOC. PROF., SOCIOLOGY, U. OF CONN., 1950– . U. of Conn. research fellow (Mexico), 1958–59; Fulbright research fellow, Rhodes-Livingstone Institute for Social Research (British Central Africa), 1959–61. Membership: American Association of University Professors; American Sociological Society; Asociación Mexicana de Sociología; Eastern Sociological Society. Research: comparative urban research; associations of urban workers, urban ecology and leadership in urban communities in Mexico; Indian population of British Central Africa. Author: A Note on Participation in Voluntary Associations in a Mexican City (American Sociological Review, Aug. 1953). Co-author: Urban Centralization and Decentralization in Mexico (Rural Sociology, Mar. 1956); The Ecological Structure of Mexican Cities (Revista Mexicana de Sociología, Jan.–Apr. 1957). Language: Spanish 4,3,3,3; French 2,1,1,1. Home: Hunting Lodge Rd., Storrs, Conn. 06268. Office: Dept. of Sociology and Anthropology, U. of Conn., Storrs, 06268.

DOUDNA, QUINCY V., b. Poynette, Wis., Jan. 16, 1907. EDUCATION. B.A., Carroll Coll., 1927; M.A., U. of Wis., 1930; Ph. D., 1948. Dean of administration, Wis. State Coll., 1945–56; specialist in teacher education, Institute of Inter-American Affairs and U.S. International Cooperation Administration (Peru) 1950–51, (Venezuela) 1954; PRESIDENT, EASTERN ILL. U., 1956– . Membership: American Association of Colleges for Teacher Education; Association for Higher Education; Illinois Education Association; National Education Association. Research: teacher education and university administration. Language: Spanish 4,3,4,3. Home: 933 Eleventh St., Charleston, Ill. Office: Eastern Ill. U., Charleston.

DOUGHTY, PAUL L., b. Beacon, N.Y., Feb. 27, 1930. ANTHROPOLOGY. B.A., Ursinus Coll., 1952; U. of Pa., 1955–57; Ph. D., Cornell U., 1963. Dir., Community Service Units (Mexico, El Salvador), American Friends Service Committee, 1953–55; 1957; research asst., Cornell U. (Peru), 1959–62; instr., Summer Studies Program, Columbia U. (Peru), 1960, 1961; area studies coordinator, Peru Training Program, U.S. Peace Corps, 1962; research assoc., Cornell-Peru Project (Peru), 1962–64; ASST. PROF., ANTHROPOLOGY, IND., U., 1964–. Membership: American Anthropological Association; American Ethnological Society; Rural Sociological Society; Society for Applied Anthropology. Research: cultural and social change in present-day Latin America; migration; community development; peasant societies. Author: Huaylas: Un distrito en la perspectiva nacional (in Migración y integración en el Perú, 1963). Language: Spanish 5,5,4,4; French 1,–,–,–. Home: 3960 Walnut Leas Rd., Bloomington, Ind. Office: Dept. of Anthropology, Ind. U., Bloomington.

DOZER, DONALD MARQUAND, b. Zanesville, Ohio, June 7, 1905. HISTORY. B.A., Wooster Coll., 1927; M.A., Harvard U., 1930; Ph. D., 1936. Instr., U. of Md., 1937–41; research analyst, Latin American Div., U.S. Office of Strategic Services, 1941–43; liaison officer, U.S. Government research analyst, asst. chief, Div. of American Republics, U.S. Dept. of State., 1944–46; asst. chief, assoc. chief, acting chief, Div. of Research for American Republics, 1946–51; asst. to chief, Historical Div., 1951–56;

lectr., American U. and U. of Md., 1956–59; assoc. prof.-PROF., HISTORY, U. OF CALIF., SANTA BARBARA, 1959– . Consultant on Latin America, Brookings Institution, 1950–51; Latin American fellow, Relm Foundation, 1963. Membership: American Historical Association; Conference on Latin American History; Delta Sigma Rho; Omicron Delta Kappa; Pacific Coast Council on Latin American Studies; Phi Beta Kappa. Research: inter-American relations; Latin American policy of the United States; Panama. Author: Are we Good Neighbors (1959); Latin America: An Interpretive History (1962); Roots of Revolution in Latin America (Foreign Affairs, Jan. 1949). Language: Spanish 5,5,4,4; Portuguese 4,3,–,–; French 3,3,3,–. Home: 421 Miramonte Dr., Santa Barbara, Calif. Office: Dept. of History, U. of Calif., Santa Barbara.

DOZIER, CRAIG LANIER, b. Spartanburg, S.C., June 14, 1920. GEOGRAPHY. B.A., U. of Wis., 1947; M.A., U. of Md., 1951; Ph. D., Johns Hopkins U., 1954. Instr., Centro Cultural Brasil-Estados Unidos (Santos, Brazil), 1952; instr., McCoy Coll., Johns Hopkins U., 1953–54; asst. prof., U., of S.C., 1954–56; asst. prof., Rollins Coll., 1957–59; assoc. prof., La. Polytechnic Institute, 1959–60; ASSOC. PROF., GEOGRAPHY, U. of N.C., 1960– . National Research Council-National Academy of Sciences research grant (Central America), 1956–57; consultant, U. of Fla. Press. Membership: American Geographical Society; Association of American Geographers. Research: land development and colonization; structural reform of inadequately-utilized lands; irrigation; conservation; economic and physical geography relationships of Brazil, Mexico, and Central America. Author: North Paraná, Brazil: An Example of Organized Regional Development (Geographical Review, July 1956); Establishing a Framework for Development in Sardinia: The Campidana (Geographical Review, Oct. 1957); Mexico's Transformed Northwest: The Yaqui, Mayo, and Fuerte Examples (Geographical Review, Oct. 1963). Language: Spanish 3,3,3,3; Portuguese 2, 2,2,2; French 2,2,2,2. Home: 1614 North College Park Dr., Greensboro, N.C. Office: Dept. of Geography, U. of N.C., Greensboro.

DREIER, JOHN CASPAR, b. Brooklyn, N.Y., Dec. 27, 1906. POLITICAL SCIENCE AND HISTORY. A.B., Harvard Coll., 1928. Latin American Bureau, U.S. Dept. of State, 1941–50; U.S. Ambassador to Organization of American States, 1950–60; VIS. PROF., INTERNATIONAL RELATIONS, DIR., INTER-AMERICAN CENTER, SCHOOL FOR ADVANCED INTERNATIONAL STUDIES, JOHNS HOPKINS U., 1961– . Consultant, U.S. Dept. of State, 1963; political science panel member, Seminar on Latin American Studies, American Council of Learned Societies-Social Science Research Council, 1963. Membership: American Political Science Association; Inter-American Council. Research: the inter-American system; U.S. policy in Latin America; Mexico, Central America, Colombia, and Chile. Author: The Organization of American States and the Hemisphere Crisis (1962); The OAS and U.S. Policy (1963). Editor: The Alliance for Progress (1962). Language: Spanish 4,4,4,3; Portuguese 3,2,1,1; French 3,2,1,1; German 3,3,2,1. Home: 3511 Lowell St., NW., Washington, D.C. 20016. Office: School of Advanced International Studies, 1740 Massachusetts Ave., NW., Washington, D. C. 20036.

DREWES, WOLFRAM U., b. Frankfurt, Germany, Jan. 9, 1929. GEOGRAPHY. B.A., U. of Colo., 1951; M.A., Syracuse U., 1952; Ph. D., 1957. CHIEF, NATURAL RESOURCES UNIT, PAN AMERICAN UNION, 1963– . International Geographical Congress, 1952, 1956, 1960; International Road Federation, 1958; U.S. delegate, Pan American Institute of Geography and History, 1959; consultant, Organization of American States, 1963. Membership: American Geographical Society; Association of American Geographers; Geographic Society of Lima; Indian Geographical Society; Sigma Xi; Society for International Development. Research: natural resources evaluation and development; regional planning; transportation economics; terrain and resources of Bolivia, Brazil, Chile, Colombia, Ecuador, Guatemala and Peru. Author: Climate and Related Phenomena of the Eastern Andean Slopes of Central Peru (1957); Los transportes: Plan regional para el desarrollo del sur del Perú (1959); Evaluación de recursos naturales: Programa de colonización; zona Río Apurimac (1961). Language: Spanish 4,4,4,3; Portuguese 2,3,2,1; French 1,1,1,1; German 4,5, 4,3. Home: 6821 Algonquin Ave., Bethesda, Md. 20034. Office: Organization of American States, Room 1115, 1725 I St., NW., Washington, D.C. 20006.

DRIVER, HAROLD EDSON, b. Berkeley, Calif., Nov. 17, 1907. ANTHROPOLOGY. B.A., U. of Calif., Berkeley, 1930; M.A., 1934; Ph. D., 1936. Research assoc., U. of Calif., Berkeley, 1948–49; asst. prof., Ind. U., 1949–53; assoc. prof., 1953–58; PROF., ANTHROPOLOGY, IND. U., 1958– . Research fellow, U. of Calif., Berkeley, 1936–37; Social Science Research Council fellow, 1937–38. Membership: American Anthropological Association; American Association of University Professors; American Ethnological Society; American Indian Ethnohistorical Conference; Central States Anthropological Society; Indiana Academy of Science; Sigma Xi. Research: comparative ethnology of North America; Indians of Mexico; cross-cultural research. Author: Indians of North America (1961); Ethnography and Acculturation of the Chi-Chimeca-Jonaz of Northeast Mexico (1963); Comparative Studies of North American Indians (Transactions, American Philosophical Society, 1957). Language: Spanish 3,2,2,3; Portuguese 2,2,2,2; French 2,2,2,2; German 2,2,2,2. Home: 1824 East Hunter Ave., Bloomington, Ind. 47404. Office: Dept. of Anthropology, Ind. U., Bloomington, 47405.

DUBOIS, JULES, b. New York, N.Y., Mar. 31, 1910. JOURNALISM. Correspondent (Panama), 1929–40; U.S. Army, 1940–46; asst. to president, The Star and Herald, La Estrella de Panamá (Panama), 1946–47); LATIN AMERICAN CORRESPONDENT, THE CHICAGO TRIBUNE, 1947– . Chmn., Committee on Freedom of the Press, 1950– , Board of Directors, 1950–64, Executive Committee, 1959– , Advisory Council, 1964– , Inter-American Press Association. Membership: Inter-American Press Association; National Press Club; Overseas Press Club; Sigma Delta Chi. Research: law and history of Latin America. Author: Fidel Castro, Rebel, Liberator or Dictator? (1959); Freedom Is My Beat (1959); Danger over Panama (1964). Language: Spanish 5,5,5,5; Portuguese 4,4,4,4; French 3,3,3,3. Home: 423 Palermo Ave., Coral Gables, Fla. 33134. Office: The Chicago Tribune, Chicago, 60611.

DUKES, JAMES HENDERSON, b. Charleston, S.C., Apr. 30, 1919. ECONOMICS. B.S., Ga. Institute of Technology, 1940; M.A., Emory U., 1953; U. of Fla. Asst. to manager, Texaco (P.R.), construction engineer, Texaco (Cuba), 1940–42; asst. security officer, U.S. Naval Base (Curaçao), 1943–44; Latin American sales representative, Tennessee Eastman Corporation (Tenn.), 1947–48; representative in charge of foreign sales, Tennessee Eastman Corporation (N.Y.), 1948–50; asst. contract coordinator, Education Div., Foreign Operations Administration, 1955; program analyst, Embassy (Rio de Janeiro), U.S. Dept. of State, 1955–57; instr., U. of Fla., 1960–63; asst. prof., Jacksonville U., 1963–64; ASST. PROF., ECONOMICS, U.S. NAVAL ACADEMY, 1964– . Membership: American Economic Association; Society for International Development; Southeastern Conference on Latin American Studies; Southern Economic Association. Research: international trade; public finance; money and banking; Latin American development; monetary and fiscal policy of Brazil, 1953–62. Language: Spanish 4,4,4,4; Portuguese 4,4,4,4; French 3,2,1,1. Office: Dept. of Naval Science, Luce Hall, U.S. Naval Academy, Annapolis, Md. 21402.

DULLES, JOHN WATSON FOSTER, b. Auburn, N.Y., May 20, 1913. HISTORY AND ENGINEERING. A.B., Princeton U., 1935; M.B.A., Harvard Business School, 1937; B.S. Met. E., U. of Ariz., 1943; M. Met. Eng., 1951. Engineer, asst. general manager, executive vice president, Cia. Minera de Peñoles, S.A. (Mexico), 1943–59; vice president, Cia. de Mineração Novalimense (Brazil), The Hanna Mining Company (Cleveland), 1959–62; PROF., LATIN AMERICAN STUDIES, HUMANITIES RESEARCH CENTER, U. of TEX., 1962– . Organization of American States grant (Brazil), Summer 1963. Research: political history; Brazil; Mexico. Author: Yesterday in Mexico (1961). Language: Spanish 5,4,3,3; Portuguese 5,4,3,3. Home: 1904 Hill Oaks Ct., Austin, Tex. Office: Box 7934, University Station, U. of Tex., Austin 12.

DULSEY, BERNARD MARTIN, b. Chicago, Ill., Feb. 27, 1914. SPANISH AMERICAN LITERATURE. A.B., U. of Chicago, 1936; A.M., 1939; Ph. D., U. of Ill., 1950. Instr., De Pauw U., 1941–42; instr., Purdue U., 1946–51; PROF., FOREIGN LANGUAGES, U. OF MO. AT KANSAS CITY, 1951– ; acting dept. head, Foreign Languages, vis. prof., N. Mex. Highlands U., Summer 1952; assoc. prof., Kans. U., Summer 1960. Contributing editor, Handbook of Latin American Studies; assoc. editor, U. of Kans. City Review. Membership: American Association of Teachers of Spanish and Portuguese; American Association of University Professors; Modern Language Association; Modern Language Teachers Association. Research: Spanish American culture; popular music and dances of Mexico and the Caribbean; Mexican novel of the revolution. Author: José Rubén Romero—1890–1952 (Modern Language Journal, Nov. 1953); Literary Highlights of a South American Trip (American Book Collector, Nov. 1959). Translator: Villagers (Huasipungo), by Jorge Icaza (1964). Language: Spanish 5,5,5,5; Portuguese 3,2,2,2; French 4,4,3,3; German 3,3,2,2; Italian 3,3,2,2. Home: 2226 West 71st Ter., Prairie Village, Kans. Office: Dept. of Foreign Languages, U. of Mo., 5100 Rockhill Rd., Kansas City, 10.

DUMOND, DON EDWARD, b. Childress, Tex., Mar. 23, 1929. ANTHROPOLOGY. B.A., U. of N. Mex., 1949; M.A., Mexico City Coll., 1957; Ph. D., U. of Oreg., 1962. ASST. PROF., ANTHROPOLOGY, U. OF OREG., 1962– . Social Science Research Council fellow, 1961–62; National Science Foundation research grant, 1963–65. Membership: American Anthropological Association; Northwest Anthropological Conference; Sigma Xi; Society for American Archaeology. Research: cultural change; Latin American prehistory; Mexican and Guatemalan ethnology. Author: Swidden Agriculture and the Rise of Maya Civilization (Southwest Journal of Anthropology, Winter 1961); Two Early Phases from the Naknek Drainage (Arctic Anthropology, 1963). Language: Spanish 3,3,3,2; German 2,1,1,1. Home: 1744 Moss St., Eugene, Oreg. Office: Dept. of Anthropology, U. of Oreg., Eugene.

DuMOULIN, ROCKWELL KING, b. Chicago, Ill., Jan. 31, 1906. ARCHITECTURE. A.B., Columbia U., 1928; B. Arch., 1932. ARCHITECT, PRIVATE PRACTICE, 1936– ; architect, Institute of Inter American Affairs, 1943–44; United Nations Relief and Rehabilitation Administration, 1944–47; consultant, Institute of Inter American Affairs, 1949–54; head, Architecture, Rhode Island School of Design, 1958–62; Pan American program dir., American Institute of Architects, 1963. Charles Follen McKim fellow, Columbia U.; U.S. delegate, 7th and 8th Pan American Congress of Architects (Havana; México, D.F.), 1950, 1952; American Institute of Architects Committee for Pan American Congress, 1961–62; Committee on Relations with Foreign Schools of Architecture, Association of Collegiate Schools of Architecture, 1963–64. Membership: American Institute of Architects; Association of Collegiate Schools of Architecture. Research: housing in Latin America; administration of architectural education. Author: Modern Architecture (1940); Rammed Earth Construction (Consumers' Research, 1939). Language: Spanish 4,4,4,2; Portuguese 2,1,–,1; French 4,4, 4,2; German 2,2,2,1; Greek 1,1,1,1; Italian 2,2,2,–; Serbo-Croatian 1,1,1,1; Swedish 1, 1,1,1. Home: 3001 Cambridge Pl., NW., Washington, D.C. 20007.

DUNCAN, ROLAND E., b. Detroit, Mich., Oct. 31, 1922. HISTORY. B.A., Wayne State U., 1944; M.A., U. of Calif., Berkeley, 1949; Ph. D., 1960. Dir., Foreign Microfilm Project in Great Britain, Bancroft Library, U. of Calif., Berkeley, 1951–53; dir., German Foreign Ministry Archives Microfilm Project,

General Library, 1953 ; assoc. in history, U. of Calif., Davis, 1957–59 ; vis. asst. prof., Ind. U., 1961–62 ; ASST. PROF., HISTORY, U. OF TENN., 1960– ; vis. asst. prof., dir., Junior Year in Peru Program, Ind. U., 1964. Robertson Prize Committee, Conference on Latin American History, 1963. Membership: American Association of University Professors ; American Historical Association ; Phi Alpha Theta. Research : biography of William Wheelwright. Author : William Wheelwright : Early Plans and Projects for Pacific Steam Navigation, 1820–35 (Atlantic and Pacific Breezes, Spring, Summer 1960) ; Batista and Castro in Cuba (Indiana Alumni Magazine, Jan. 1962) ; Latin America : Past and Present (Indiana Review, Nov. 1962). Language : Spanish 4,3,3,3 ; Portuguese 2,1,1,1 : French 2,1,1,1. Home : 6411 Kingston Pike, Knoxville 19, Tenn. Office : Dept. of History, U. of Tenn., Knoxville.

DUNHAM, LOWELL, b. Wellston, Okla., Oct. 14, 1910. SPANISH AMERICAN LITERATURE. B.A., U. of Okla., 1932 ; M.A., 1935 ; Ph. D., U. of Calif., Los Angeles, 1955. Prof., Central State Coll. (Okla.), 1936–40 ; special agent, Federal Bureau of Investigation, 1940–46 ; asst. agent in charge, Federal Bureau of Investigation (San Juan, Puerto Rico), 1942–46 ; PROF., SPANISH, U. OF OKLA., 1946– ; CHMN., MODERN LANGUAGES, 1957– : Andrés Bello Award, Acad. Venezolana de la Lengua, 1948 ; Miles M. Sherover Foundation Award, 1958 ; dir., National Placement Bureau, American Association of Teachers of Spanish and Portuguese. Membership : Modern Language Association ; Phi Beta Kappa. Research : Venezuelan literature. Author : Vida y obra : M. Díaz Rodríguez (1957) ; Rómulo Gallegos : Vida y obra (1957). Co-translator and co-editor : The Latin American Mind (1963). Language : Spanish 5,5,5,5 ; Portuguese 2,3,4,3 ; French 2,3,3,3. Home : 439 Chautauqua, Norman, Okla. Office : Dept. of Modern Languages, U. of Okla., Norman.

DURLAND, ROBERT EDWIN, b. Oak Park, Ill., Dec. 8, 1927. GEOGRAPHY. B.A., U. of Wis., 1949 ; M.A., 1951 ; Ph. D., Northwestern U., 1963. Teacher, Wis. State Coll., 1951–52 ; instr., U. of Buffalo, 1953–54 ; instr., Ohio State U., 1956–58 ; geographer, U.S. Bureau of the Census, 1958–60 ; computer programmer, 1960–62 ; SOCIAL SCIENCE ANALYST, FOREIGN DEMOGRAPHIC ANALYSIS DIV., U.S. BUREAU OF THE CENSUS, 1962– . Population Council, Inc., fellow (Chile), 1955–56. Membership : American Geographical Society ; Association for Computing Machinery ; Association of American Geographers ; National Council for Geographic Education ; Population Association of America. Research : population research ; digital computer applications and programming ; census map preparation ; farm size and land use in the Plan Chillan area of Chile ; urban settlement in Santiago, Chile ; population geography of Mexico, Central America, West Indies and Chile. Language : Spanish 3,2,3,3. Home : 4316 Fort Dr., Suitland, Md. 20023. Office : Foreign Demographic Analysis Div., U.S. Bureau of the Census, Washington, D.C.

DUSENBERRY, WILLIAM HOWARD, b. Carmichaels, Pa., June 6, 1908. HISTORY. A.B., Waynesburg Coll., 1932 ; M.A., U. of Mich., 1936 ; Ph. D., 1941. Teacher, Pa. Public Schools, 1930–38 ; instr., Fresno State Coll., Spring 1942 ; instr., U. of Calif., Los Angeles, 1946–48 ; assoc. prof., U. of Pittsburgh, 1948–61 ; CHMN., SOCIAL SCIENCES, WAYNESBURG COLL., 1962–. U. of Pittsburgh grant (Mexico), 1949, 1952. Membership : Agricultural History Society ; American Association of University Professors ; American Historical Association. Research : the role of the vaquero in the development of Mexican society. Author : The Mexican Mesta : The Administration of Ranching in Colonial Mexico (1963) ; Foot-and-Mouth Disease in Mexico, 1946–1951 (Agricultural History, Apr. 1955) ; Juan Manuel de Rosas as Viewed by American Diplomats (Hispanic American Historical Review, Nov. 1961). Language : Spanish –,–,3,– ; French 3,–,–,–. Home : 53 South Morris St., Waynesburg, Pa. Office : Dept. of Social Sciences, Waynesburg Coll., Waynesburg.

DUTTON, BERTHA P(AULINE), b. Algona, Iowa, Mar. 29, 1903. ANTHROPOLOGY. B.A., U. of N. Mex., 1935 ; M.A., 1937 ; Ph. D., Columbia U., 1952. Asst. to dir., Museum of N. Mex., 1936–40 ; CURATOR, MUSEUM OF N. MEX., 1938– . School of American Research scholar (Mexico, Peru), 1935, 1936 ; School of American Research grant (Mexico), 1950 ; American Association of University Women fellow (Guatemala, Mexico), 1953–54 ; Wenner-Gren fellow, 1962 ; National Science Foundation research grant, 1962–63. Membership : Arizona Society of Archaeology and History ; International Congress of Americanists ; New Mexico Archaeological Society ; New Mexico Historical Society ; Northern Arizona Society of Science and Art ; Sociedad Mexicana de Antropología ; Southwestern American Anthropological Association. Research : archeology and ethnology in Mesoamerica and the American Southwest. Author : Sun Father's Way (1963) ; Indians of the Southwest (1963). Co-author : Excavations at Tajumulco, Guatemala (1943). Language : Spanish 3,3,3,3. Office : Museum of N. Mex., P.O. Box 2087, Santa Fe, 87501.

DYE, HOWARD SPENCER, b. Firth, Idaho, Apr. 9, 1920. ECONOMICS. A.B., Cornell U., 1941 ; M.A., 1942 ; Ph. D., 1949. Assoc. prof., U. of Tex., 1948–51 ; PROF., ECONOMICS, DIR., GRADUATE STUDIES, U. OF TENN., 1951– . Fulbright prof. (Ireland), 1959–60. Membership : American Economic Association ; Southern Economic Association. Research : managerial economics ; capital budgeting ; international development problems. Author : Certain Questions Raised by Hick's Theory of the Trade Cycle (Southern Economic Journal, Oct. 1952) ; Development of the Banco Central in Argentina's Economy (Southern Economic Journal, Jan. 1955). Co-author : Economics (1962). Language : French 3,2,3,3 ; German 3,2,2,3. Home : 4824 Tomache Dr., Knoxville 19, Tenn. Office : Dept. of Economics, U. of Tenn., Knoxville.

DYER, DONALD RAY, b. Mesa, Colo., Sept. 29, 1918. GEOGRAPHY. A.B., Stanford U., 1947 ; M.S., Northwestern U., 1948 ; Ph. D., 1950. Asst.-assoc. prof., U. of Fla., 1950–62 ; GEOGRAPHIC SPECIALIST, EMBASSY (RIO DE JANEIRO), U.S. DEPT. OF STATE, 1962– . University fellow, Northwestern U. ; Smith-Mundt vis. prof., Universidad de la Habana (Cuba), Summer

1953; Fulbright lectr., Universidad Nacional de San Marcos (Peru), 1958–60; Land Classification and Land Use Committee, Pan American Institute of Geography and History. Membership: American Geographical Society; Asociación de Geógrafos de Perú; Association of American Geographers; International Geographic Union; National Council for Geographic Education; Sociedade Brasileira de Cartografía; Sociedad Geográfica del Perú. Research: economic and human geography of Latin America; urbanism; map and geographical publications procurement. Author: Lesser Antilles (1959). Co-author: Symposium on the Geography of Puerto Rico (1955); Global Geography (1957). Language: Spanish 5,4,4,3; Portuguese 5,4,4,3; French 2,2,1,1. Office: American Embassy, Avenida Presidente Wilson 147, Rio de Janeiro, Brazil.

DYER, JOHN MARTIN, b. St. Louis, Mo., Feb. 27, 1920. ECONOMICS: MARKETING. A.B., St. Louis U., 1941; LL.B., U. of Miami, 1951; M.B.A., U. of Pa., 1953. ASSOC. PROF., MARKETING, U. OF MIAMI, 1950– . Adviser, Latin American Dept., Fla. Development Commission; lectr., National U. of Nicaragua at León; foreign trade consultant, U.S. Dept. of Commerce, June 1960; foreign trade consultant, Fla. Electric Motors Company, Inc., Apr. 1961; staff dir., Sub-committee for Latin America, U.S. Senate Interstate and Foreign Commerce Committee; special consultant for international affairs to President, Fla. Atlantic U., 1963– ; honorary vice-consul of Guatemala. Membership: Alpha Kappa Psi; American Bar Association; American Foreign Law Association; American Marketing Association; Florida Bar Association; Phi Alpha Delta; Southern Economic Association. Research: foreign trade and commerce; advertising problems in Mexico; Latin American market; international trade; economic study of Central America. Author: United States-Latin American Trade and Financial Relations (1961); Export Financing (1963); The Latin American Market: A Review (International Trade Review, Aug. 1963). Home: 7701 SW. 52nd Ct., Miami 43, Fla. Office: Dept. of Marketing, U. of Miami, Coral Gables, Fla.

E

EALY, LAWRENCE ORR, b. Ocean City, N.J., Sept. 17, 1915. HISTORY AND POLITICAL SCIENCE. A.B., Temple U., 1934; LL.B., U. of Pa., 1937; A.M., 1947; Ph. D., 1951. Asst. prof., Temple U., 1947–54; lectr., Rutgers U., 1954–55; assoc. prof., Temple U., 1955–58; prof., U.S. Naval War Coll., 1958–59; provost, prof., Hobart Coll., 1959–62; DEAN, PROF., HISTORY, RIDER COLL., 1962– . Consultant, Area Handbook for Panama for U.S. Dept. of Defense, Special Operations Research Office, American University, 1962. Membership: American Academy of Political and Social Science; American Bar Association; American Conference of Academic Deans; American Historical Association; Conference on Latin American History; World Affairs Council. Research: international relations and law. Author: The Republic of Panama in World Affairs (1951); The Development of an Anglo-American System of Law in the Panama Canal Zone (American Journal of Legal History, Oct. 1958); The Monroe Doctrine and International Law (Social Science, Jan. 1963). Language: Spanish 4,3,3,4; French 2,2,2,2. Home: 25 Vander Veer Dr., University Park, Trenton, N.J. 08638. Office: Dept. of History, Rider Coll., Trenton.

EARLE, PETER G., b. Yonkers, N.Y., May 31, 1923. SPANISH AMERICAN LITERATURE. B.A., Mexico City Coll., 1949; M.A., 1951; Ph. D., U. of Kans., 1959. Instr., Princeton U., 1956–59; asst. prof., Wesleyan U., 1959–63; ASSOC. PROF., ROMANCE LANGUAGES, U. OF PA., 1963– . Danforth Foundation grant (Mexico), Summer 1960; assoc. editor, Hispanic Review, 1963– . Membership: American Association of Teachers of Spanish and Portuguese; Modern Language Association. Research: Latin American cultural history; modern and contemporary literature of Latin America and Spain; Mexican and Argentine literature. Author: El sentido poético de Don Segundo Sombra (Revista Hispanica Moderna, July–Oct. 1960); Espacio y soledad en la literatura argentina (Sur, Nov.–Dec. 1962). Translator: Profile of Man and Culture in Mexico, by S. Ramos (1962). Language: Spanish 5,5,5,5; Portuguese 4,2,2,2; French 5,2,2,2; Italian 3,1,1,1. Home: 543 Hampshire Rd., Drexel Hill, Pa. Office: Dept. of Romance Languages, U. of Pa., Philadelphia.

EASBY, DUDLEY T., JR., b. Lock Haven, Pa., Dec. 3, 1905. ANTHROPOLOGY AND LAW. B.S., Princeton U., 1928; LL.B., U. of Pa., 1931. Lawyer (Philadelphia, Pa.), 1931–39; senior attorney, U.S. Dept. of Treasury, 1939–40; asst. general counsel, Office of Inter-American Affairs, 1940–43; chief counsel, Pan American Branch, Foreign Economic Administration, 1943–45; SECRETARY OF THE CORPORATION, METROPOLITAN MUSEUM OF ART, 1945– . Vice President, Institute of Andean Research, Inc.; trustee and legal advisor, Archaeological Institute of America; consulting fellow, U. of Pa. Museum; commander, Orden al Mérito (Peru). Membership: Colegio de Abogados de Buenos Aires; Pan American Society; Pennsylvania Bar Association; New York Bar Association; Sociedad Mexicana de Antropología. Research: pre-Columbian metallurgy and metalworking. Author: Metalwork (in Andean Culture History, 1960); Fine Metalwork in Pre-Conquest Mexico (in Essays in Pre-Columbian Art and Archaeology, 1961); Two South American Metal Techniques Found Recently in Western Mexico (American Antiquity, Jan. 1962). Language: Spanish 5,4,4,5; Portuguese 4,4,4,5. Home: 110 East End Ave., New York, N.Y. 10028. Office: The Metropolitan Museum of Art, New York, 10028.

EASTLACK, CHARLES LEONARD, b. Ridgewood, N.J., Dec. 9, 1933. LINGUISTICS AND LANGUAGE. A.B., Harvard Coll., 1955; M.A., U. of Tex., 1958; Ph. D., 1964. Editorial asst., Hispanic American Historical Review, 1958–59; instr., U. of Tex., 1961–64; instr., Harvard U., Summer 1964; ASST. PROF., LINGUISTICS, CORNELL U., 1964– . Fulbright scholar (Brazil), 1959–60; U. of Tex. fellow, 1960–61; National Defense Education Act fellow, 1963–64. Membership: Linguistic Society of America. Research: Brazilian Portuguese; Amerindian linguistic structures; Spanish linguistics; teaching materials for Portuguese. Language: Spanish 4,4,4,4; Portuguese 4,4,4,4. Linguistic studies: Arabic; German; Japanese; Portuguese; Spanish. Home: R.F.D. 2, Dillsburg, Pa. Office: Div. of Modern Languages, Coll. of Arts and Sciences, Cornell U., Ithaca, N.Y.

EBEL, ROLAND HINKLEY, b. Oak Park, Ill., Oct. 11, 1928. POLITICAL SCIENCE. A.B., Wheaton Coll., 1950; M.A., Northwestern U., 1952; Ph. D., Mich. State U., 1960. Teacher, Academia Bautista (P.R.), 1950–51; instr., Wheaton Coll., 1952–54; research asst., Republican State Central Committee (Mich.), 1956; asst. publicity dir., Republican State Central Committee (Mich.), 1958; asst. instr., Mich. State U., 1958–60; ASST. PROF., POLITICAL SCIENCE, WESTERN MICH. U., 1960– . Falk fellow, Mich. State U., 1955–58; Carnegie Foundation and Western Mich. U. research grant (Guatemala), 1962; National Defense Foreign Language fellow in Spanish, U. of Calif., Los Angeles, Summer 1963. Membership: American Political Science Association; Midwest Council of the Association for Latin American Studies. Research: political modernization in underdeveloped countries; Guatemalan Indian community political systems. Author: The Political Professionals (1960); Political Change in Guatemalan Indian Communities: Two Transitional Cases (Journal of Inter-American Studies, Jan. 1964). Language: Spanish 3,3,3,3; Portuguese 1,1,1,1; French 2,1,1,1. Home: 709 Darby Lane, Kalamazoo, Mich. Office: Dept. of Political Science, Western Mich. U., Kalamazoo.

EDBERG, GEORGE JOHN, b. Philadelphia, Pa., Oct. 6, 1924. SPANISH AMERICAN LITERATURE. B.S., Temple U., 1949; A.M., Universidad de la Habana, 1951; Ph. D., U. of Kans., 1959. Instr., Universidad de la Habana, 1950; instr., Instituto Cultural Cubano-Norteamericano (Cuba), 1950–51; asst. instr., U. of Kans., 1953–57; instr., U. of Va., 1957–59; asst. prof., Purdue U., 1959–60; asst. prof., National Defense Education Act Summer Language Institute, Purdue U., 1960; asst. prof., Dickinson Coll., 1961–64; asst. prof., National Defense Education Act Summer Language Institute, U. of Fla., 1963; ASST. PROF., SPANISH, NATIONAL DEFENSE EDUCATION ACT SUMMER LANGUAGE INSTITUTE, U. OF PITTSBURGH, 1964– . Andrew Mellon fellow, U. of Pittsburgh, 1964–65; consultant, Modern Language Association. Membership: American Association of Teachers of Spanish and Portuguese; Association of Modern Language Teachers; Instituto Internacional de Literatura Iberoamericana; Modern Language Association. Research: Central American literature; the Cuadro form in literature. Author: The Guatemalan Cuadros of José Milla (1965); The Guatemalan José Milla and His Cuadros (Hispania, Dec. 1961); Un estudio de don Manuel del Pez, una creación literaria galdosiana (Humanitas, 1961). Language: Spanish 5,5,5,5; Portuguese 4,4,3,3; French 4,4,3,3; German 3,3,2,2; Swedish 4,5,3,3. Office: Dept. of Romance Languages and Literatures, 1617–D Cathedral of Learning, U. of Pittsburgh, Pittsburgh, Pa. 15213.

EDDS, JOHN R., JR., b. Newark, N.J., July 31, 1925. LAW AND ECONOMICS: BANKING. A.B., N.Y.U., 1950; LL.B., Cornell U., 1953. Attorney, Federal Reserve Bank of New York, 1953–59; junior officer, First National City Bank (New York), 1957–59; asst. manager (Buenos Aires), 1959–62; asst. manager (Bogotá), 1962–64; MANAGER, FIRST NATIONAL CITY BANK (QUITO), 1964– . Research: banking; commerce and industry of Argentina, Colombia, and Ecuador. Language: Spanish 4,4,4,3. Office: First National City Bank, Apartado 1393, Quito, Ecuador.

EDER, GEORGE JACKSON, b. New York, N.Y., Sept. 5, 1900. LAW AND ECONOMICS: FINANCE. A.B., National U. (Washington, D.C.), 1928; LL.B., 1928. Research asst., Inter-American High Commission, 1925–26; chief, Latin American section, U.S. Bureau of Foreign and Domestic Commerce, 1926–32; manager Foreign Securities Div., Standard Statistics Company (N.Y.), 1932–37; manager, Pan American Management Corporation (Buenos Aires), 1937–39; asst. general attorney, International Telephone and Telegraph Corporation (Buenos Aires; N.Y.), 1939–61; research assoc., Harvard Law School, 1961–63; VIS. LECTR., RESEARCH ASSOC., GRADUATE SCHOOL OF BUSINESS ADMINISTRATION, U. OF MICH., 1963– . Executive dir., Monetary Stabilization Council and economic adviser to President of Bolivia, 1956–57; chmn., Committee on Land Utilization, United States Inter-American Council, 1960. Membership: American Bar Association; American Economic Association; American Foreign Law Association; Inter-American Bar Association; Pan American Society of the United States. Research: Latin American legal aspects of finance and investments; Argentine administrative law; inflation in Latin America. Author: Taxation in Colombia (1964). Co-author: International Competition in the Trade of Argentina (1931). Language: Spanish 5,5,5,5; Portuguese 4,3,3,1; French 5,4,4,3. Home: 2631 Devonshire Rd., Ann Arbor, Mich. 48104. Office: Graduate School of Business Administration, U. of Mich., Ann Arbor, 48104.

EDER, HERBERT MICHAEL, b. Los Angeles, Calif., Jan. 8, 1936. GEOGRAPHY. A.B., U. of Calif., Los Angeles, 1958; M.A., 1960; Ph. D., 1963. ASST. PROF., GEOGRAPHY, U. OF CALIF., BERKELEY, 1963– . Recipient, Office of Naval Research contract (Colombia), Summer 1961. Membership: American Geographical Society; Association of American Geographers; Pacific Coast Association of Geographers; Pi Gamma Mu; Sigma Xi. Research: cultural geography; agricultural societies and systems in the tropics; primitive man and his ecology; tropical lowlands and Indians of Chocó, Colombia. Author: El Río y El Monte: A Preliminary Geographical Reconnaissance of the Río Siguirisua Valley, Chocó, Colombia (1963). Language: Spanish 3,3,3,3; French 3,3,3,3; German 3,3,3,3. Home: 6540 Waldo St., El Cerrito, Calif. Office: Dept. of Geography, U. of Calif., Berkeley 4.

EDMINSTER, ROBERT REGAN, b. Valley City, N. Dak., Apr. 5, 1916. ECONOMICS. B.A., U. of Wash., 1948; Ph. D., U. of Calif., 1959. Asst. prof., U. of Wash., 1951–52;

asst. prof., Humboldt State Coll., 1952–53; ASSOC. PROF., ECONOMICS, U. OF UTAH, 1953– ; economic adviser, U.S. Agency for International Development (Bolivia), 1963–65. Fulbright lectr., U. of Guayaquil (Ecuador), 1960. Membership: American Economic Association; Western Economic Association. Research: international trade; economic development; modern economic history of Mexico. Author: Mexico (in Economic Development: Analysis and Case Studies, 1961). Language: Spanish 4,4,4,4. Home: 1395 Michigan Ave., Salt Lake City, Utah. Office: Dept. of Economics, U. of Utah, Salt Lake City.

EDMONSON, MUNRO STERLING, b. Nogales, Ariz., May 18, 1924. ANTHROPOLOGY. B.A., Harvard U., 1945; M.A., 1948; Ph. D., 1952. Instr., Washington U., 1951; PROF., ANTHROPOLOGY, TULANE U., 1951– ; prof., Universidad de San Carlos (Guatemala), 1960–61. Membership: American Anthropological Association; American Association for the Advancement of Science; American Ethnological Society. Research: social anthropology; folklore; cultural psychology; Middle America; Maya culture. Author: Los Manitos (1957); Status Terminology and Social Structure of North American Indians (1958). Co-editor: The Eighth Generation (1960). Language: Spanish 5,5,5,5; Portuguese 4,1,1,1; French 5,4,3,3; German 3,2,2,1; Russian 3,2,2,1. Linguistic studies: Quiche. Home: 1123 Pine St., New Orleans 18, La. Office: Dept. of Sociology and Anthropology, Tulane U., New Orleans 18.

EDWARDS, CLINTON RALPH, b. Washington, D.C., Apr. 17, 1926. GEOGRAPHY. A.B., U. of Calif., Berkeley, 1954; M.A., 1957; Ph. D., 1962. Assoc.-instr., U. of Calif., Berkeley, 1961–62; ASST. PROF., GEOGRAPHY, U. OF VA., 1962– . Field technician, Office of Naval Research grant (Mexico), Summer 1954; National Academy of Sciences-National Research Council grant (Panama, Colombia, Ecuador, Peru, Chile), 1957–58. Membership: American Association for the Advancement of Science; American Geographical Society; Association of American Geographers; Society for Nautical Research (England); Society for the History of Discoveries. Research primitive water-craft; subsistence and commercial fishing, small scale river and maritime transport; resource utilization. Author: Quintana Roo; Mexico's Empty Quarter (Office of Naval Research Technical Report, 1957); Sailing Rafts of Sechura: History and Problems of Origin (Southwestern Journal of Anthropology, Autumn 1960). Language: Spanish 4,4,4,3; Portuguese 3,2,1,1; French 3,2,1,1; German 3,2,1,1. Home: 109 Mimosa Dr., Charlottesville, Va. Office: Dept. of Geography, Cabell Hall, U. of Va., Charlottesville.

EIDT, ROBERT C., b. Mt. Pleasant, Mich., Jan. 20, 1923. GEOGRAPHY. A.B., U. of Calif., Los Angeles, 1947; M.A., 1951; Ph. D., 1954. Instr., U. of Minn., 1954–56; asst. prof., Los Angeles State Coll., 1956–60; assoc. prof., 1961–64; PROF., GEOGRAPHY, CALIF. STATE COLL. AT LOS ANGELES, 1964– . Contributing editor, Handbook of Latin American Studies, 1949– ; Buenos Aires Convention grant (Colombia), Summer 1955, participant, U.S. Dept. of State Exchange Program (Colombia), 1958, 1959; Fulbright lectr., Universidad Nacional de San Cristóbal de Huamanga (Peru), 1960; consultant on Latin American projects, Mammoth Mountain Inn Corporation and Lockheed Aircraft International, 1962, 1963; U.S. Peace Corps lectr., 1963. Membership: American Association for the Advancement of Science; American Meteorological Society; American Radio Relay League; Association of American Geographers; California Council of Geography Teachers; Pacific Coast Council of Geographers; Sigma Xi. Research: meteorology; pioneer settlement and colonization in Latin America; agricultural work and settlement studies in Colombia and Argentina. Author: La estación meteorológica de Ayacucho (Boletín informativo, no. 18, 1960); Pioneer Settlement in Eastern Peru (Annals, Association of American Geographers, 1962); Comparative Problems and Techniques in Pioneer Settlement: Colombia, Peru, and Argentina (Yearbook of the Association of Pacific Coast Geographers, 1963). Language: Spanish 4,4,4,4; Portuguese 2,2,2,2; German 3,3,3,3. Home: 1394 Kempton Ave., Monterey Park, Calif. Office: Dept. of Geography, Calif. State Coll. at Los Angeles, 5151 State Coll. Dr., Los Angeles 32.

EISELEN, ELIZABETH, b. Evanston, Ill., Aug. 22, 1910. GEOGRAPHY. B.A., Northwestern U., 1931; M.A., Columbia U., 1933; Ph. D., U. of Chicago, 1943. Instr., Dean of Women, Union Coll., 1934–37; instr., Western Mich. U., Summer 1946; PROF., GEOGRAPHY, WELLESLEY COLL., 1942– . Membership: Association of American Geographers; National Council for Geographic Education; Society of Women Geographers. Research: economic geography; Peru. Author: A Tourist Geographer Visits Iquitos, Peru (Journal of Geography, Apr. 1956); Quinoa, A Potentially Important Food Crop of the Andes (Journal of Geography, Oct. 1956); Impressions of Belem, Manaus, and Iquitos, Amazonia's Largest Cities (Journal of Geography, Feb. 1957). Language: Spanish, 1,–,–,–; Portuguese 1,–,–,–; French 1,–,–,–. Home: 11 Strathmore Rd., Wellesley, Mass. 02181. Office: Dept. of Geography, Wellesley Coll., Wellesley, 02181.

EKHOLM, GORDON, F., b. St. Paul, Minn., Nov. 25, 1909. ANTHROPOLOGY. B.A., U. of Minn., 1933; Ph. D., Harvard U., 1941. Field asst., American Museum of Natural History, 1937–41; asst. curator, 1942–50; lectr., Columbia U., 1943–62; assoc. curator, American Museum of Natural History, 1950–57; CURATOR, ANTHROPOLOGY, AMERICAN MUSEUM OF NATURAL HISTORY, 1957– . Consultant on Middle American art, Museum of Primitive Art (N.Y.); secretary-treasurer, Institute of Andean Research, 1943– . Membership: American Anthropological Association; Sociedad Mexicana de Antropología; Society for American Archaeology. Research: archeology; Mexico; Central America. Author: Excavations at Guasave, Sinaloa, Mexico (Anthropological Papers, American Museum of Natural History, 1942); Excavations at Tampico and Panuco in the Huasteca, Mexico (Anthropological Papers, American Museum of Natural History, 1944); A Possible Focus of Asiatic Influence in the Late Classic Cultures of Mesoamerica (American Antiquity, Jan. 1953). Language: Spanish 4,4,4,3. Home: 369 Old Sleepy Hollow Rd., Pleasantville, N.Y. Office: American Museum of Natural History, New York 27.

ELLENBOGEN, BERT L., b. New York, N.Y., July 5, 1917. SOCIOLOGY. B.A., U. of Wis., 1948; M.A., 1950; Ph. D., 1959. Rural sociologist, Consejo Bienestar Rural (Venezuela), U. of Wis. Andean Survey, 1952–53; ASSOC. PROF., RURAL SOCIOLOGY, CORNELL U., 1955– ; vis. prof., U. of Calif., Berkeley, 1962–64. Rural Medical Service Committee, N.Y. Medical Society, 1956– ; managing editor, Rural Sociology, 1959–60; consultant, U.S. International Cooperation Administration mission in Brazil, 1961. Membership: American Sociological Society; Hispanic American Society; Rural Sociological Society. Research: rural sociology; social changes; adoption of health practices; social organization of a plantation community in southeast Venezuela; Brazil; changing role of Brazilian women. Author: Comparability of Responses to a Socially Concordant Question: Open-end and Closed (Journal of Health and Human Behavior, Summer 1962). Co-author: Social Status and the Measured Intelligence of Small City and Rural Children (American Sociological Review, Oct. 1952); Social and Economic Problems of the Venezuelan Andes (vol. I, 1955; vol. II, 1956). Language: Spanish 3,3,3,2; Portuguese 3,3,3,2. Home: 710 Mitchell St., Ithaca, N.Y. Office: Dept. of Rural Sociology, 322 Warren Hall, Cornell U., Ithaca.

ELLIS, HOWARD S., b. Denver, Colo., July 2, 1898. ECONOMICS. A.B., U. of Iowa, 1920; A.M., U. of Mich., 1922; U. of Heidelberg (Germany), 1924–25; Ph. D., Harvard U., 1929; LL.D., U. of Mich., 1951. Instr.-prof., U. of Mich., 1920–22, 1924–38; prof., U. of Calif., Berkeley, 1938–43; economic analyst, Federal Reserve System, 1943–44; asst. dir. of research and statistics, Board of Governors of the Federal Reserve System, 1944–45; vis. prof., Columbia U., 1944–45, 1949–50; FLOOD PROF. OF ECONOMICS, U. OF CALIF., BERKELEY, 1946– ; vis. prof., U. of Tokyo, Summer 1951; vis. prof., U. of Bombay, 1958–59; vis. prof., Center of Economic Research (Athens), 1963. Ricardo Prize fellow, 1923; Sheldon traveling fellow, 1924–25; David A. Wells Award, Harvard U., 1930; Social Science Research Council fellow, U. of Vienna, 1933–35; American Academy of Arts and Sciences fellow, 1942–46; consultant, U.S. House of Representatives Committee on Postwar Planning, 1944–45; consultant, Economic Policy Committee, U.S. Chamber of Commerce, 1945–46; dir., Marshall Aid Research Project, Council on Foreign Relations, 1949–50; co-editor, Kyklos, International Journal of the Social Sciences, 1950– ; head, Joint UNESCO-Economic Commission for Latin American-Organization of American States Mission on Economic Education in Latin America, 1960. Membership: American Economic Association; International Economic Association; Phi Beta Kappa; Royal Economic Society. Research: economic development; money and banking; international finance. Co-author: Economic Development and International Trade (1959); The Teaching of Economics in Latin America (1961). Editor: El desarrollo económico y América Latina (1960). Language: Spanish 4,3,2,2; Portuguese 1,1,1,1; French 2,3,2,3; German 5,5,5,5. Home: 936 Cragmont Ave., Berkeley, Calif. 94708. Office: Dept. of Economics, U. of Calif., Berkeley.

ELLIS, JOSEPH ALBERT, b. Springfield, Pa., Aug. 28, 1930. HISTORY. B.S., Temple U., 1952; A.M., Columbia U., 1953; Universidad Nacional Autónoma de México, 1956–57; Ph. D., Columbia U., 1961. ASST. PROF., HISTORY, DIR., LATIN AMERICAN STUDIES PROGRAM, ST. FRANCIS COLL. (N.Y.), 1957– ; lectr., Brooklyn Coll., 1959–60; lectr., Iona Coll., 1962–63. Mexican Government grant, 1955–56; group leader, Experiment in International Living (Mexico and Central America), 1962; St. Francis Coll. research grant (Chile), Summer 1963; consultant, University Work Projects (Mexico and Peru), 1962, 1963. Membership: American Catholic Historical Association; American Historical Association; Association of International Clubs; Bolivarian Society; Conference on Latin American History. Research: the national period, institutional structure, and contemporary trends. Author: Toward Progress and Unity in Latin America (Proceedings, Association of International Relations Clubs, 1962). Language: Spanish 4,4,4,4; Portuguese 3,3,3,2,1; French 2,2,1,1. Home: 215 Willoughby Ave., No. 1208, Brooklyn 5, N.Y. Office: Latin American Studies Program, St. Francis Coll., Remsen St., Brooklyn 31.

ELLISON, FRED PITTMAN, b. Denton, Tex., Jan. 11, 1922. BRAZILIAN AND SPANISH AMERICAN LITERATURE; LANGUAGE. B.A., U. of Tex., 1941; M.A., U. of Calif., Berkeley, 1948; Ph. D., 1952. Translator and special agent, Federal Bureau of Investigation, U.S. Dept. of Justice, 1941–44; assoc. prof., U. of Ill., 1952–61; PROF., ROMANCE LANGUAGES, DIR., LATIN AMERICAN LANGUAGE AND AREA CENTER, U. OF TEX., 1961– . Latin American Joint Committee, Social Science Research Council-American Council of Learned Societies, 1960– ; National Defense grant, 1959–61; consultant, Latin American Unit, Language Development Branch, U.S. Office of Education, 1961–62; Organization of American States research fellow (Brazil), 1962. Membership: Instituto Internacional de Catedráticos de Literatura Iberoamericana; Modern Language Association; National Education Association. Research: Brazilian Portuguese; foreign language teaching methodology; Brazilian literature. Author: Brazil's New Novel (1954); University of Illinois Experiment in Foreign Languages for Elementary Schools (Hispania, Sept. 1961); La conferencia de Rubén Darío sobre Joaquim Nabuco: Introducción y texto (Revista Iberoamericana, July-Dec. 1961). Language: Spanish 5,4,4,4; Portuguese 4,4,4,4; French 4,3,2,3. Home: 2907 Townes Lane, Austin, Tex. Office: Dept. of Romance Languages, Batts Hall 108, U. of Tex., Austin.

ELLSWORTH, PAUL THEODORE, b. Rutland, Vt., Nov. 20, 1897. ECONOMICS. B.A., U. of Wash., 1920; B.A., Oxford U., 1924; Ph.D., Harvard U., 1932. Instr., Harvard U., 1928–32; assoc. prof., U. of Cincinnati, 1932–41; chief, Board of Economic

Warfare, 1943–44; economic adviser, U.S. Dept. of State, 1943–44; PROF. ECONOMICS, U. OF WIS., 1944– ; chief economist of mission, International Bank for Reconstruction and Development (Ceylon), 1951–52; chief of mission, International Bank for Reconstruction and Development (Thailand), 1957–58; vis. prof., U. of Hawaii, 1963–64. Guggenheim fellow (Chile), 1941–42; adviser, Corporación de Fomento (Caracas), 1952. Membership: American Economic Association; Royal Economic Society. Research: international economics; economic development; Chile; Venezuela. Author: International Economics (1938); Chile: An Economy in Transition (1945); The International Economy (1950, 1957, 1964). Language: Spanish 4,4,4,4; French 3,3,3,3; German 3,3,3,3. Home: 1709 Jefferson St., Madison 11, Wis. Office: Dept. of Economics, Social Science Bldg. 365, U. of Wis., Madison 6.

ELSASSER, EDWARD ORR, b. Oak Park, Ill., Feb. 16, 1918. HISTORY. B.A., Bethany Coll., 1942; M.A., Clark U., 1948; Ph. D., U. of Chicago, 1954. Lectr., Roosevelt U., 1954–55; asst. prof., Western Mich. U., 1955–59; ASSOC. PROF., HISTORY, WESTERN MICH. U., 1959– . Fulbright research grant (Argentina), 1963. Membership: American Association of University Professors; American Historical Association; Midwest Council, Association for Latin American Studies; Conference on Latin American History; Mississippi Valley Historical Association. Research: Argentine history; United States-Latin American relations. Author: Argentina and the Export-Import Bank, 1934–1945 (Inter-American Economic Affairs, Spring 1955). Language: Spanish 3,4,2,2. Home: 301 Edgemoor, Kalamazoo, Mich. Office: Dept. of History, Western Mich. U., Kalamazoo.

ELSON, BENJAMIN F., JR., b. Burbank, Calif., Dec. 8, 1921. LINGUISTICS. A.B., Seattle Pacific Coll., 1950; M.A., Cornell U., 1954; Ph. D., 1956. FIELD WORKER, SUMMER INSTITUTE OF LINGUISTICS (MEXICO), 1942– : FIELD DIR., 1957– ; assoc. prof., Linguistics, U. of Wash., Summers 1958– . Membership: Linguistic Society of America. Research: indigenous languages in Mexico. Author: Gramática del popoluca de la sierra (1960); Sierra Popoluca Morphology (International Journal of American Linguistics, July 1960). Co-author: An Introduction to Morphology and Syntax (1962). Language: Spanish 4,4,4,3. Linguistic studies: Sierra Popoluca. Home: Box 1960, Santa Ana, Calif. Office: Summer Institute of Linguistics, Apartado 2975, México, D.F.

ELY, DONALD PAUL, b. Buffalo, N.Y., Sept. 3, 1930. COMMUNICATION AND EDUCATION. B.A., State U. of N.Y., Albany, 1951; M.A., Syracuse U., 1953; Ph. D., 1961. Dir., Audiovisual Center, asst. prof., State U. Coll., New Paltz, N.Y., 1952–55; dir., Audiovisual Center, Hicksville Public Schools (N.Y.), 1955–56; PROF., DIR. AUDIOVISUAL CENTER, SYRACUSE U., 1956– ; vis. lectr., U. of Colo., Summer 1962. Fulbright lectr., Universidad de Chile, 1963; principal investigator, audiovisual media research in Latin America, U.S. Office of Education; consultant, Education Policies Commission, National Education Association. Membership: National Education Association; National Society for the Study of Communications. Research: audiovisual media for the communication of ideas; educational institutions in Chile. Author: The Changing Role of the Audiovisual Process in Education: A Definition and Glossary of Related Terms (1963). Language: Spanish 3,3,3,2; Portuguese 1,1,1,1; French 2,2,2,1. Home: 121 Butternut Dr., Dewitt, N.Y., 13214. Office: Audiovisual Center, Syracuse U., 121 College Pl., Syracuse, 13210.

ELY, ROLAND TAYLOR, b. Philadelphia, Pa., Sept. 27, 1924. HISTORY AND ECONOMICS. A.B., Princeton U., 1947; A.M., Harvard U., 1949; Universidad Nacional de México, Summer 1949; Ph. D., Harvard U., 1959. Instr., Rutgers U., 1957–59; master, Lawrenceville School (N.J.), 1958–59; asst. prof., Rutgers U., 1959–63; vis. asst. prof., Stanford U., Summer 1963; ASST. PROF., HISTORY, RUTGERS U., 1963– . 12th Annual Global Strategy Discussions, Naval War College, Newport, 1960; Congreso de Instituciones Hispánicas, Sección Económica, Madrid, 1963; officer, Orden Nacional al Mérito (Ecuador), Orden de Mayo al Mérito (Argentina), Ordem Nacional do Cruzeiro do Sul (Brazil). Membership: Academy of Political and Social Sciences; Academy of Political Science; American Association of University Professors; American Brazilian Association; American Economic Association; American Historical Association; Conference on Latin American History; Newcomen Society; Pan American Society. Research: economic development and contemporary problems in Latin America. Author: La economía cubana entre las dos Isabelas, 1492–1832 (1960); Economic Integration in Latin America (Financial Analysts Journal, July-Aug. 1962). Language: Spanish 4,4,4,4; French 3,3,2,2. Office: Dept. of History, NCAS, Rutgers U., 42 James St., Newark 2, N.J.

ENGELKIRK, JOHN E(UGENE), b. New York, N.Y., Sept. 24, 1905. SPANISH AMERICAN AND BRAZILIAN LITERATURES. B.A., Bard Coll., 1926; M.A., Northwestern U., 1928; Ph. D., Columbia U., 1934. Instr.-assoc. prof., U. of N. Mex., 1928–39; assoc. prof.-prof., Tulane U., 1939–58; chmn., Spanish and Portuguese, 1939–58; principal publications officer, Office of Inter-American Affairs, 1942–44; special representative to Brazil, Inter-American Educational Foundation, 1945–46; PROF., SPANISH AND PORTUGUESE, U. OF CALIF., LOS ANGELES, 1958– ; chmn., Spanish and Portuguese, 1959–62. Institute of International Education fellow (Chile), 1933; U. of Calif., Los Angeles, and Tulane U. grants (Mexico), 1940, (Venezuela and Colombia), 1947, (Caribbean), 1954; American Council of Learned Societies grants (Mexico), 1942 (Uruguay and Brazil), 1959. Membership: American Association of Teachers of Spanish and Portuguese; American Association of University Professors; Instituto Internacional de Literatura Iberoamericana; Modern Language Association. Research: inter-American literary relations; Hispanic folk theater; culture, customs and folkways of Central America; culture and educational institutions of Brazil. Author: Poe in Hispanic Literature (1934); Obras norteamericanas en traducción española (1944); A literatura norteamericana no Brasil (Revista Iberoamericana, 1952). Language: Spanish 5,5,5,5; Portuguese 5,5,4,4; French 5,4,4,4; German 3,3,2,1; Italian 3,4,2,1. Home: 11164 Ophir Dr., Los Angeles 24, Calif. Office: Dept. of Spanish and Portuguese, U. of Calif., Los Angeles 24.

ENGLISH, VAN H., b. Miami, Fla., July 18, 1914. GEOGRAPHY. A.B., Colo. State Coll., 1936; Ph. D., Clark U., 1942. Cartographer, Office of Strategic Services, 1942–46; PROF., GEOGRAPHY, DARTMOUTH COLL., 1946– . Libbey fellow, Clark U., 1941–42; Cartography Committee, Exhibit of International Geographical Union (Portugal), 1952. Membership: American Association for the Advancement of Science; American Geographical Society; Association of American Geographers; National Council of Geography Teachers. Research: physical geography; cartography; terrain and resources of Peru and Chile. Author: Landforms of European Union of Soviet Socialist Republics (1950). Co-author: Introductory Economic Geography (1956). Maps: Dartmouth Bible (1950). Language: Spanish 2,2,2,1; French 3,2,1,1. Home: Norwich, Vt. Office: Dept. of Geography, Dartmouth Coll., Hanover, N.H.

ENGUÍDANOS, MIGUEL, b. Valencia, Spain, Jan. 8, 1924. SPANISH AMERICAN LITERATURE. M.A., Universidad de Valencia, 1946; Ph. D., Universidad de Madrid, 1949. Professor ayudante, Universidad de Valencia, 1946; professor ayudante, Universidad de Madrid, 1947–51; asst. prof., Universidad de Puerto Rico, 1951–56; vis. prof., Long Island U., Summer 1956; asst. prof., U. of Houston, 1956–58; asst. prof.-prof., U. of Tex., 1958–64; vis. prof., U. of Wis., Summer 1962; PROF., SPANISH, IND. U., 1964– . Guggenheim fellow (Spain), 1965. Membership: Modern Language Association. Research: Spanish American civilization; modern Spanish literature; life and works of Rubén Darío. Author: La poesía de Luis Palés Matos (1961); Azorín en busca del tiempo divinal (Papeles de Son Armadans, Oct. 1959); Introduction (in Dreamtigers, by Jorge Luis Borges, 1964). Language: Spanish 5,5,5,5; Portuguese 2,2,1,1; French 4,3,3,3. Home: 501 North Park, Bloomington, Ind. Office: Dept. of Spanish and Portuguese, Ind. U., Bloomington.

ENTRIKIN, ISABELLE WEBB, b. Chew's, N.J., Jan. 7, 1906. LIBRARY SCIENCE. B.S. in L.S., Drexel Institute, 1931; A.M., U. of Pa., 1937; Ph. D., 1943. Deputy chief, Index Catalogue, Army Medical Library, 1945–52; dir., Library Service (Santiago, Chile), U.S. Information Service, 1952–55; asst. cultural attaché officer (Buenos Aires), 1955–59; exchange program officer, Latin American area, U.S. Dept. of State, 1959–62; ASST. CULTURAL ATTACHÉ, U.S. INFORMATION SERVICE (MADRID), 1962– . Membership: American Library Association; Society of Woman Geographers. Research: Latin American history and literature. Language: Spanish 4,4,4,3; Portuguese 3,2,1,–; French 4,3,2,–. Home: R.F.D. 2, Box 380A, Blackwood, N.J. Office: U.S. Information Agency, 1776 Pennsylvania Ave., NW., Washington, D.C.

EPSTEIN, JEREMIAH F., b. New York, N.Y., Feb. 14, 1924. ANTHROPOLOGY. B.S., U. of Ill., 1949; M.A., 1951; Ph. D., U. of Pa., 1959. Research scientist, Dept. of Anthropology, U. of Tex., 1958–60; ASST. PROF., ANTHROPOLOGY, U. OF TEX., 1960– . Wenner-Gren Foundation grant (France), 1961; National Science Foundation grant (Mexico), 1963; Fulbright-Hays research grant (Mexico), 1964. Membership: Sociedad Mexicana de Antropología e Historia; Society for American Archaeology. Research: archeology and culture of northeastern Honduras, northeastern Mexico and the highlands of Chiapas, Mexico. Author: Dating the Ulua Polychrome Complex (American Antiquity, July 1959); The San Isidro and Puntita Negra Sites (in Homenaje a Don Pablo Martínez del Río, 1961); Burin-faceted Projectile Point (American Antiquity, 1963). Language: Spanish 4,3,3,3; French 2,2,2,2; German 2,2,2,2. Home: 5909 Highland Hills Ter., Austin, Tex. Office: Dept. of Anthropology, U. of Tex., Austin, 78712.

ERASMUS, CHARLES JOHN, b. Pittsburgh, Pa., Sept. 23, 1921. ANTHROPOLOGY. B.A., U. of Calif., Los Angeles, 1942; M.A., U. of Calif., Berkeley, 1950; Ph. D., 1955. Field anthropologist, Smithsonian Institute (Colombia), 1950–52; anthropologist, Point Four Program (Colombia, Ecuador, Haiti, Chile), 1952–54; research assoc., Culture Change Project (Mexico), U. of Ill., 1955–59; vis. asst. prof., Yale U., 1959–60; assoc. prof., U. of N.C., 1960–62; research assoc. prof., Land Tenure Center, U of Wis. (Bolivia), Summer 1963; consultant, U.S. Agency for International Development (Caracas, Venezuela), 1963–64; ASSOC. PROF., ANTHROPOLOGY, U. OF CALIF., SANTA BARBARA, 1962– . Membership: American Anthropological Association; American Sociological Association. Research: social anthropology; Mexican economic development and cultural change; technical assistance programs and local reaction in Colombia; technical assistance programs in Haiti, Ecuador, and Chile; agrarian reform in Bolivia and Venezuela. Author: Las dimensiones de la cultura (1953); Man Takes Control: Cultural Development and American Aid (1961); An Anthropologist Views Technical Assistance (Scientific Monthly, Mar. 1954). Language: Spanish 4,4,4,3. Home: 6190 Barrington Dr., Goleta, Calif. Office: Dept. of Anthropology, U. of Calif., Santa Barbara, 93018.

ERICKSEN, (EPHRAIM) GORDON, b. Salt Lake City, Utah, Sept. 7, 1917. SOCIOLOGY. B.S., U. of Utah, 1938; M.S., 1939; Ph. S., U. of Chicago, 1947. Lectr., U. of Ind., 1946–47; instr., U. of Calif., Los Angeles, 1947–49; asst. prof.-prof., U. of Kans., 1949–64; HEAD, SOCIOLOGY, U. OF TENN., 1965– . Consultant, International Cooperation Administration, Caribbean Commission, Organization of American States (British West Indies, Colombia, Eastern Caribbean), 1954–56; Carneigie grant (Costa Rica), Summers 1963, 1964. Membership: American Sociological Association; Midwest Sociological Society; Population Association of America. Research: demography and urban sociology of underdeveloped countries; population problem in British West Indies; fertility of the middle classes in Costa Rica. Author: Urban Behavior (1954); The West Indies Population Problem (1963); Africa Company Town (1964). Language: Spanish 3,3,3,3; French 2,-,-,2. Office: Dept. of Sociology, U. of Tenn., Knoxville.

ERICKSON, MARTIN ELMER, b. Duluth, Minn., Feb. 22, 1900. SPANISH AMERICAN LITERATURE. B.A., U. of Oreg., 1928; M.A., 1930; Ph. D., U. of Wash., 1940. Instr., U. of Wash., 1937–41; asst. prof., U. of Tex., 1941–42; asst. prof., Northwestern U., 1942–44; PROF., FOREIGN LANGUAGES, LA. STATE U., 1944– . Membership: American Association of Teachers of Spanish and Portuguese; Modern Language Association. Research: Central American literature; Mexican literature. Author: Escritores modernistas de Guatemala (Revista Iberoamericana, May 1943); History as a Source of Drama (Hispania, Feb. 1953); A Review of Scholarship on Love's Cure (Studies in Comparative Literature, 1962). Language: Spanish 5,5,5,5; Portuguese 3,3,3,3; French 4,4,4,4; Italian 4,4,4,4; Swedish 3,3,3,3. Linguistic studies: English; Italian; Spanish. Home: 675 Delgado Dr., Baton Rouge 8, La. Office: Dept. of Foreign Languages, La. State U., Baton Rouge.

ERICSON, ANNA-STINA LOUISE, b. Swissvale, Pa., Jan. 12, 1926. ECONOMICS AND LAW. A.B., Bryn Mawr Coll., 1948; M.A., U. of Pittsburgh, 1954. International labor economist, Bureau of Labor Statistics, U.S. Dept. of Labor, 1960–61: international relations officer, Bureau of International Labor Affairs, 1961–62; CHIEF, LATIN AMERICAN SECTION, DIV. FOR LABOR CONDITIONS, U.S. DEPT. OF LABOR, 1962– . Research: foreign economic problems; labor conditions in Latin America. Author: Labor Law and Practice in Honduras (1961); Labor Law and Practice in Venezuela (1961); Labor Law and Practice in Bolivia (1962). Language: Spanish 4,2,2,1; Danish 3,1,1,1; Norwegian 3,1,1,1; Swedish 3,2,1,1. Home: 4109 W St. NW., Washington 7, D.C. Office: Div. of Foreign Labor Conditions, Bureau of Labor Statistics, U.S. Dept. of Labor, Washington, D.C.

ERVIN, DWAIN T., b. Craig, Colo., Feb. 14, 1918. HISTORY. B.A., U. of Colo., 1942; M.A., 1945; Ph. D., 1953. Instr., Boise Junior Coll., 1946–47; asst. prof., N. Dak. State U., 1947–57; PROF., HISTORY, CHMN., SOCIAL SCIENCE, CENTRAL METHODIST COLL., 1957– . U. of Colo. research fellow, 1950–51; Doherty fellow (Argentina), 1954–55. Membership: American Historical Association; Conference on Latin American History; Hispanic American Society; Midwest Council, Association for Latin American Studies; Mississippi Valley Historical Association. Research: Argentine history, particularly the period of the wars of independence, 1810–1820. Language: Spanish 4,3,3,3; Portuguese 2,1,1,1; French 3,2,2,–. Home: 1103 West Davis St., Fayette, Mo. Office: Dept. of History, Central Methodist Coll., Fayette. 65248.

ERVIN, ROGER EDWARD, b. Danbury, Nebr., Oct. 9, 1921. GEOGRAPHY. A.B., U. of Wash., 1947; M.A., 1949; Ph. D., U. of Fla., 1954. Intelligence staff, Aeronautical Chart and Information Center, U.S. Air Force, 1954–55; instr., U. of Del., 1955–57; ASSOC. PROF., GEOGRAPHY, FRESNO STATE COLL., 1957– . Institute of International Education fellow (Chile), 1951–52; U. of Fla. fellow, 1953–54. Membership: American Association for the Advancement of Science; American Association of University Professors; American Geographical Society; Association of American Geographers; Association of Pacific Coast Geographers; California Council of Geography Teachers; International Geographic Union; Pacific Coast Council on Latin American Studies. Research: economic geography; land use in southern middle Chile. Author: Industry in the Concepción Area of Chile (American Journal of Economics and Sociology, Apr. 1955). Language: Spanish 3,2,3,2; German 2,1,1,1. Home: 4455 East Sierra Madre St., Fresno, Calif. 93726. Office: Dept. of Geography, Fresno State Coll., Fresno, 93726.

ESPINOSA, JOSÉ MANUEL, b. Chicago, Ill., Feb. 2, 1909. HISTORY AND EDUCATION. B.A., Stanford U., 1930; M.A., 1931; Ph. D., U. of Calif., Berkeley, 1934. Instr.-asst. prof., St. Louis U., 1934–39; assoc. prof., Loyola U. (Ill.), 1939–44; DEPUTY DIR., OFFICE OF INTER-AMERICAN PROGRAMS, BUREAU OF EDUCATIONAL AND CULTURAL AFFAIRS, U.S. DEPT. OF STATE, 1944– . American Folklore Society research grant, 1951; advisory editor, The Americas and Mid-America. Membership: Royal Spanish Academy of History. Research: Spanish borderlands of the United States; international education exchange programs. Author: First expedition of Vargas into New Mexico (1939); Spanish Folktales from New Mexico (1937); Crusaders of the Rio Grande (1942). Language: Spanish 5,5,4,4; Portuguese 3,4,–,–; French 3,4,–,–. Home: 13 Vassar Circle, Glen Echo, Md.

ESQUENAZI-MAYO, ROBERTO, b. Havana, Cuba, Apr. 22, 1920. SPANISH AMERICAN LITERATURE AND HISTORY. Litt. D., U. of Havana, 1941; Columbia U. Foreign correspondent at United Nations for El Mundo (Havana), and El Tiempo (Bogotá), 1946–48; instr., Sweet Briar Coll., 1948–49; editor, Americas, Pan American Union, 1949–52; Board of Editors, Time-Life International, 1952–59; asst. prof., Columbia U., 1960–61; DIR., LATIN AMERICAN AREA STUDIES, ASST. PROF., ROMANCE LANGUAGES, U. OF NEBR., 1961– . Cuban National Prize for Literature, 1951; Latin American Committee, Overseas Press Club; Board, Instituto de las Españas; contributing editor, Handbook of Latin American Studies; Board of Editors, Revista Iberoamericana de Literatura and Cuadernos. Membership: American Association of Teachers of Spanish and Portuguese; American Association of University Professors; Instituto Internacional de Literatura Iberoamericana; International Association of Hispanists; Modern Language Association. Research: the essay; origin of the Latin American novel; cultural development of Latin America; parallel literary movements in Latin America and the United States. Author: Memorias de un estudiante soldado (1951); Ensayos y apuntes (1954); Historiografía de la guerra entre México y los Estados Unidos (Duquesne Hispanic Review, Autumn-Winter

1962). Language: Spanish 5,5,5,5; Portuguese 4,4,4,4; French 4,4,4,4; Italian 3,3,3,3. Home: 1212 South 20th, Lincoln, 2, Nebr. Office: Dept, of Romance Languages, U. of Nebr., Lincoln 8.

ESSA, ROBERT NEWYIA, b. Urmia, Iran, Mar. 17, 1910. LANGUAGE. Ph. D., Inter-American U., 1958. Instr., Ceres High School (Calif.), 1949-55; CHMN., FOREIGN LANGUAGE, DIR., LANGUAGE LABORATORY, SIERRA COLL., 1955– . Post doctoral fellow, U. of Texas., Summer 1963; consultant, Calif. State Dept. of Education. Membership: Foreign Language Association of Northern California; Modern Language Association. Research: Brazilian Portuguese; Mexico. Language: Spanish 5,5,5,5; Portuguese 3,3,3,3; French 4,4,4,4; Italian 4,3,3,3. Home: 150 Awali Ave., Auburn, Calif. 95603. Office: P.O. Box 789, Sierra Coll., Rocklin, Calif.

ESTEP, RAYMOND, b. Purcell, Okla., July 23, 1910. HISTORY. B.S., East Central State Coll., 1937; M.A., Okla. A. & M. Coll., 1938; Ph. D., U. of Tex., 1942; U. of Mexico, Summer 1946; instr., historian, Intelligence Div., Army Air Force, 1942-46; asst. prof. Okla. A. & M. Coll., 1946; PROF., LATIN AMERICAN HISTORY, AEROSPACE STUDIES INSTITUTE, AIR U., 1946– ; instr., U. of Ala., Montgomery Center, 1950-51; 1962-63. Fellowship, U. of Tex., 1940-41, advanced fellowship, 1941-42. Membership: Hispanic American Society; Southeastern Conference on Latin American Studies; Southern Historical Association; Texas State Historical Association. Research: archival research in Mexico. Author: Lorenzo de Zavala: profeta del liberalismo mexicano (1952); The Military and Diplomatic Services of Alexander Le Grand for the Republic of Texas, 1836-1837 (Southwestern Historical Quarterly, Oct. 1950). Editor: The Removal of the Texas Indians and the Founding of Fort Cobb: Lieutenant William E. Burnet Letters (1961). Language: Spanish 4,4,3,3; Portuguese 2,2,1,1; French 2,1,1,1. Home: 3420 Cleveland Ave., Montgomery, Ala. 36105. Office: Air U., Aerospace Studies Institute, Maxwell Air Force Base, Montgomery.

EVANS, ALONA E., b. Providence, R.I., Feb. 27, 1917. POLITICAL SCIENCE. INTERNATIONAL LAW. A.B., Duke U., 1940; Ph. D., 1945. Instr., Westminster Coll., 1945; instr., Wellesley Coll., 1945-48; asst. prof., 1948-52; assoc. prof., 1952-58; PROF., POLITICAL SCIENCE, WELLESLEY COLL., 1958– . Social Science Research Council research fellow (Chile, Mexico), 1948-49; Harbison Award, Wellesley Coll., 1954-55; assoc. editor, Background on World Politics, 1958-61; Liberal Arts fellow, Harvard Law School, 1961-62. Membership: American Association of University Women; American Political Science Association; American Society of International Law; Association for Asian Studies; Indian Society of International Law; International Law Association. Research: international law in Chile and Mexico; comparative treaty law; political asylum; international rendition of fugitive offenders. Author: Self Executing Treaties in the United States of America (in British Year Book of International Law, 1953); Treaty Enforcement in Chile, Argentina and Mexico (Proceedings of the American Society of International Law, 1959); Reflections upon the Political Offense in International Practice (American Journal of International Law, Jan. 1963). Language: Spanish 4,3,3,3; Portuguese 3,1,1,1; French 4,3,3,3; German 3,2,2,1. Home: 22 Fiske House, Wellesley 81, Mass. Office: Dept. of Political Science, Wellesley Coll., Wellesley 81.

EVANS, CLIFFORD, b. Dallas, Tex., June 13, 1920. ANTHROPOLOGY. A.B., U. of Southern Calif., 1941; Ph. D., Columbia U., 1950. Assoc. curator, archeologist, Smithsonian Institution, 1950-63; CURATOR, SUPERVISORY ARCHEOLOGIST, SMITHSONIAN INSTITUTION, 1963– . Membership: American Anthropological Association; Anthropological Society of Washington; Society for American Archaeology. Research: archeology in Peru, Brazil, British Guiana, Venezuela, and Ecuador. Co-author: Archeological Investigations at the Mouth of the Amazon (1957); Archeological Investigations in British Guiana (1960). Editor: Aboriginal Cultural Development in Latin America: An Interpretative Review (1963). Language: Spanish 4,4,4,3; Portuguese 4,4,4,3; German 3,-,-,-. Home: 1227 30th St., NW., Washington 7, D.C. Office: Div. of Archeology, U.S. National Museum, Smithsonian Institution, Washington 25, D.C.

EWALD, ROBERT HAROLD, b. Stephenson, Mich., June 4, 1922. ANTHROPOLOGY. A.B., U. of Mich., 1950; M.A., 1951; Ph. D., 1954. Lectr., U. of Mich., 1954-55; research asst., Human Relations Area Files, Inc. (New Haven, Conn.), 1955-57; PROF., ANTHROPOLOGY, CALIF. STATE COLL., LOS ANGELES, 1957– . Social Science Research Council area research fellow (Guatemala), 1952-53; National Science Foundation research fellow (Panama), Summer 1960; Fulbright lectr. (Arequipa, Peru), 1962; asst. dir., U.S. Peace Corps Training Programs for Latin America, Calif. State Coll., Los Angeles, 1964. Membership: American Anthropological Association; American Ethnological Society; Sociedad Mexicana de Antropología; Southwestern Anthropological Association. Research: cultural anthropology; Latin American social systems; culture change among Indians in Guatemala; Chocó Indians of Panama; urban slums of Peru. Author: Bibliografía anotada de antropología social en Guatemala, 1900-1955 (1956); Culture Change in a Guatemalan Indian Community (Social Forces, Dec. 1957); Central America (in Encyclopaedia Britannica, 1963). Language: Spanish 3,3,3,2. Home: 600 Cecil St., Monterey Park, Calif. 91754. Office: Dept. of Anthropology, Calif. State Coll., Los Angeles, 5151 State College Dr., Los Angeles, 90032.

EWING, FLOYD FORD, JR., b. Lockney, Tex., Sept. 21, 1915. HISTORY. B.S., West Tex. State Coll., 1936; M.A., U. of Tex., 1950; Ph. D., 1952. Teacher, principal, Cameron County Public Schools (Tex.), 1936-49; PROF., CHMN., HISTORY, GRADUATE DEAN, MIDWWESTERN U., 1952– ; vis. prof., U. of Mo., Summer 1960. Membership: American Historical Association; Great Plains Historical Association; Hispanic American Society; Rocky Mountain Council for Latin American Studies; Southwestern Social Science Association; Texas State Historical Association; West

Texas Historical Association. Research: history of the American Southwest and Mexico; United States-Latin American relations. Language: Spanish 3,2,2,2; French 2,1,1,1. Home: 3507 Sheridan, Wichita Falls, Tex. Office: Dept. of History, Midwestern U., Wichita Falls.

EWING, RUSSELL CHARLES, b. Manhattan, Kans., Feb. 16, 1906. HISTORY. B.A., U. of Calif., Berkeley, 1929; M.A., 1931; Ph. D., 1934. Regional historian, National Park Service, U.S. Dept. of the Interior, 1935–37; asst. prof.-PROF., CHMN., HISTORY, U. OF ARIZ., 1937– ; lectr., U. of Andes (Colombia), 1956–57. Smith-Mundt fellow (Colombia), 1956–57; participant, American Assembly on Latin America, 1959. Membership: American Historical Association; Rocky Mountain Council of Latin American Studies. Research: history of Mexico and the Spanish borderlands, 1513–1848. Author: The Pima Outbreak in November, 1751 (New Mexico Historical Review, Oct. 1938); The First Histories and Historians of the Southwest (Arizona Quarterly, Winter 1946); The Spanish Past (in Arizona, Its People and Resources, 1960). Language: Spanish 5,5, 4,2; Portuguese 4,2,2,1; French 5,3,2,1; German 2,2,1,1. Home: 2804 East 9th St., Tucson, Ariz. Office: Dept. of History, U. of Ariz., Tucson.

EZELL, PAUL HOWARD, b. Saratoga, Wyo., Aug. 12, 1913. ANTHROPOLOGY. B.A., U. of Ariz., 1937; M.A., 1939; Ph. D., 1956. Archeologist, El Paso Natural Gas Company (Ariz.), 1950; teacher, Ariz. State Coll., 1956; INSTR., ANTHROPOLOGY, SAN DIEGO STATE COLL., 1956– . Holiday fellow, U. of Ariz., 1953; anthropological consultant, Gila River Pima-Maricopa Indian Community, 1951– . Membership: American Anthropological Association; American Ethnological Society; Society for American Archaeology; Southwestern Anthropological Association. Research: archeology and ethnohistory of the trans-Colorado area; culture change. Author: The Hispanic Acculturation of the Gila River Pimas (American Anthropologist, Memoir Series, 1961). Co-author: Thematic Changes in Yuman Warfare (Proceedings, American Ethnological Society, 1957); Death of a Society (Ethnohistory, Spring 1963). Language: Spanish 3,3,3,3; German 2,2,2,2. Home: 4965 Emelene, San Diego, Calif. 92109. Office: Dept. of Anthropology, San Diego State Coll., San Diego, 92115.

F

FABILLI, JOSEPHINE CAROLINE, b. Pacentro, Italy. LIBRARY SCIENCE. A.B., U. of Calif., Berkeley, 1932; certificate in librarianship, 1933. Asst. to head librarian, Marysville Public Library (Calif.), 1934–37; cataloger, Notre Dame High School (San Francisco), 1937–38; cataloger, Libraries, Stanford U., 1938–43; executive asst., library consultant, Hispanic Foundation, Library of Congress, 1943–45; chief library consultant in South America, Foreign Affairs Office, U.S. Dept. of State, 1945–53; acting chief reference librarian, Columbus Memorial Library, Pan American Union, 1955–56; head, Adult Dept., Free Public Library (Worcester, Mass.), 1956–59; supervising social science librarian, Library, Los Angeles State Coll., 1959–62; ASST. LIBRARIAN, PUBLIC SERVICES, UNIVERSITY LIBRARY, U. OF SOUTHERN CALIF., 1962– . Book reviewer, Revista Interamericana de Bibliografía, 1956– . Membership: American Library Association; American Association of University Professors; California Library Association; Pacific Coast Council on Latin American Studies. Research: Latin American bibliography and library science education. Author: Major Latin American Collections in U.S. Libraries (1956). Co-editor: Repertorio de publicaciones periódicas actuales latinoamericanas (1958). Language: Spanish 5,5,5,5; Portuguese 4,4,3,3; French 5,5,5,5; German 2,2,2,2; Italian 5,5,5,5. Home: 3789 Menlo Ave., Los Angeles, Calif. 90007. Office: University Library, U. of Southern Calif., Los Angeles, 90007.

FAGEN, RICHARD REES, b. Chicago, Ill., Mar. 1, 1933. POLITICAL SCIENCE. B.A., Yale U., 1954; M.A., Stanford U., 1959; Ph. D., 1962. Editor, U.S. Army (P.R.), 1955–57; research asst. and study dir., Institute for Communications Research, Stanford U., 1961–62; ASST. PROF., POLITICAL SCIENCE, STANFORD U., 1962– . Social Science Research Council and American Council of Learned Societies joint grant, 1964. Membership: American Association for Public Opinion Research; American Association of University Professors; American Political Science Association; Society for the Study of Social Problems. Research: political development and change in Latin America; Cuban revolution; charismatic authority and the leadership of Fidel Castro. Author: Calculation and Emotion in Foreign Policy: The Cuban Case (Journal of Conflict Resolution, Sept. 1962); Cubans in Exile: A Demographic Analysis (Social Problems, Spring 1964). Language: Spanish 4,3,3,3. Home: 754 Holly Oak Dr., Palo Alto, Calif. Office: Dept. of Political Science, Stanford U., Stanford, Calif.

FAGG, JOHN EDWIN, b. San Saba, Tex., Nov. 21, 1916. HISTORY. B.A., U. of Tex., 1938; M.A. U. of Chicago, 1939; Ph. D., 1942. PROF., CHMN., HISTORY, DIR., PORTUGUESE LANGUAGE AND AREA CENTER, WASHINGTON SQUARE COLL., N.Y.U., 1946– ; asst. dean, Graduate School of Arts & Sciences, 1950–56. Special consultant, U.S. Air Force, 1946–51, 1956–57; Latin American consultant, Crowell-Collier Publications; National Woodrow Wilson Fellowship Committee. Membership: American Historical Association. Research: colonial Latin America. Author: The Republican Movement in Spain (1944); Introduction to Letters of Christopher Columbus (1961); Latin America: A General History (1963). Language: Spanish 5,4,4,3; Portuguese 2,2,2,2; French 2,2,2,2. Home: 40 Washington St., East Orange, N.J. Office: Dept. of History, N.Y.U., New York 3.

FAHS, NED C., b. Omaha, Nebr., Oct. 1, 1910. EDUCATION. B.A., U. of Calif., Berkeley, 1932; M.A., 1933; Ph. D., 1938. Instr., Mesa Coll., 1934–35; Instr., U. of Del., 1938–39; liaison officer (U.S. and Brazil), U.S. Navy, 1939–45; cultural officer (Brazil, Chile, Colombia), U.S. Dept. of State, 1946–55; DIR., LATIN AMERICAN DIV., KELLOGG FOUNDATION, 1955–. Research:

development of educational institutions in Latin America. Language: Spanish 5,5,5,4; Portuguese 5,5,5,4; French 5,5,5,4; German 3,3,3,3; Italian 3,3,3,3. Home: 43 Merwood Dr., Battle Creek, Mich. 49017. Office: Kellogg Foundation, 250 Champion St., Battle Creek, 49014.

FALCONIERI, JOHN V., b. New York, N.Y., Feb. 17, 1920. SPANISH AMERICAN LITERATURE. B.A., U. of Mich., 1941; M.A., 1948; Ph. D., 1950. Instr., U. of Mich., 1950–52; asst. prof., Bowling Green State U., 1952–58; ASSOC. PROF., SPANISH, WESTERN RESERVE U., 1958– ; vis. prof., Oberlin Coll., 1962–63. Library fellow, The Newberry Library; Fulbright research fellow (Spain), 1961–62; editor, Theatre Annual. Membership: American Association of Teachers of Italian; American Association of Teachers of Spanish and Portuguese. Research: fantastic literature, especially the short story and novel. Author: La Commedia de l'Arte en España (1958). Language: Spanish 5,5,5,5; Portuguese 2,2,2,1; French 4,3,2,2; Italian 5,5,4,3. Office: Dept. of Languages, Western Reserve U., Cleveland 6, Ohio.

FARMAN, CARL HUGO, b. Napa, Calif., Dec. 10, 1901. SOCIAL WELFARE. A.B., U. of Southern Calif., 1923; A.M., Harvard U., 1929; Ph. D., U. of Southern Calif., 1931. SOCIAL SCIENCE ANALYST, U.S. DEPT. OF HEALTH, EDUCATION, AND WELFARE, 1936–. Membership: American Academy of Political and Social Science; American Statistical Association; Maryland Historical Association. Research: social security in Chile and Mexico; government welfare programs. Author: Old-Age, Survivors, and Invalidity Programs Throughout the World (1954). Co-author: Social Security Legislation Throughout the World (1949, 1964). Language: Spanish 5,2,3,3; Portuguese 3,1,1,1; French 5,2,3,3; German 3,2,3,2. Home: 1601 Jonquil St. NW., Washington, D.C. 20012. Office: International Social Security Branch, Social Security Administration, U.S. Dept. of Health, Education, and Welfare, Washington, D.C.

FARON, LOUIS, C., b. Brooklyn, N.Y., July 16, 1923. ANTHROPOLOGY. A.B., Columbia Coll., 1949; Ph. D., Columbia U., 1954. Research assoc., U. of Ill., 1955–59; asst. prof., Calif. State Coll., Los Angeles, 1959–62; ASSOC. PROF., ANTHROPOLOGY, U. OF PITTSBURGH, 1962– . Doherty fellow (Chile); National Science Foundation fellow (Panama), 1960 (Mexico), 1963–64; assoc. editor, Ethnology. Membership: American Anthropological Association; American Association for the Advancement of Science. Research: social and cultural anthropology with emphasis on social structure; economic and political structures in coastal Peru; the Otomí of Mexico; Chocó Indians of Panama; Araucanian Indians of Chile. Author: Mapuche Social Structure (1961); Hawks of the Sun (1964). Co-author: Native Peoples of South America (1959). Language: Spanish 5,4,4,4; Portuguese 3,1,1,1; French 4,2,2,1; German 2,1,1,1. Home: 6700 Beacon St., Pittsburgh 17, Pa. Office: Dept. of Anthropology, U. of Pittsburgh, Pittsburgh 13.

FARRAH, ADELAIDE GEORGIANA, b. Boston, Mass., Feb. 25, 1931. EDUCATION. B.S., Boston State Coll., 1952; Ed. M., Harvard U., 1954; Ed. D., 1961. Teacher. George Washington School (Cartagena, Colombia), 1956–57; adviser, Naval Academy (Cartagena), 1956–57; teacher, Orinoco Mining Company (Puerto Ordaz, Venezuela), 1959; program specialist, Div. of Regional Development-Div. of Education, Organization of American States, 1960–62; PROGRAM SPECIALIST, REGIONAL TRAINING, ORGANIZATION OF AMERICAN STATES, 1962– . Membership: Comparative Education Society. Research: development of human resources; role of education and training in economic and social development; vocational education and technical training in Central America; development and evaluation of university programs in Latin America; primary school supervision in Latin America. Author: Annotated Bibliography on the Role of Education in Economic and Social Development (1962); Technical Cooperation Activities in the Americas (1963). Language: Spanish 4,4,4,4; Portuguese 3,2,1,1; French 2,2,1,1; Arabic 2,3,3,2. Home 2020 F St., N.W., Washington 6, D.C. Office: Organization of American States, Washington, D.C. 20006.

FAUST, AUGUSTUS FINLINSON, b. Delta, Utah, July 5, 1918. EDUCATION. B.A., U. of Utah, 1943; M.A., 1947; Ph. D., 1950. Missionary (Brazil), 1938–41; assoc. prof., U. of Utah, 1949–57; prof., 1957–63; ASST. DEAN, PROF., EDUCATIONAL ADMINISTRATION, U. OF UTAH, 1963– . U. of Utah research fellow, 1947–49; travel fellow, U.S. Office of Education (Argentina), 1948–49; consultant, U.S. Office of Education (Brazil), 1957; Utah State Foreign Language Curriculum Committee; Latin American Area Committee, U. of Utah. Membership: American Association of University Professors; Comparative Education Society; Phi Delta Kappa; Sigma Kappa Phi; Utah Education Association. Research: comparative education in Latin America, Asia and Africa; public school system of Argentina; education system of Brazil; Domingo Faustino Sarmiento. Author: Brazil: Education in an Expanding Economy (1959); United States of Brazil (in Comparative Educational Administration, 1962); A Yanqui Looks at Argentine Education (History of Education Journal, Spring 1954). Language: Spanish 5,4,4,3; Portuguese 5,4,4,3; French 3,2,1,1; German 5,4,4,4; Italian 3,3,2,1. Home: 3342 Monte Verde Dr., Salt Lake City, Utah 84109. Office: Dept. of Educational Administration, U. of Utah, Salt Lake City, 84112.

FAVELL, THOMAS ROYDEN, b. Rice Lake, Wis., Jan. 23, 1919. ECONOMICS. B.A., U. of Wis., 1941; M.A., Fletcher School of Law & Diplomacy, 1947; Ph. D., 1950. Third secretary, Embassy (Colombia), U.S. Dept. of State, 1947–50; second secretary, Embassy (Spain), 1950–53; second secretary, Embassy (Cuba), 1953–56; international economist, Bureau of Economic Affairs (Washington, D.C.), 1956–60; ECONOMIC COUNSELOR, EMBASSY (CHILE), U.S. DEPT. OF STATE, 1960– . Research: international economic relations. Language: Spanish 4,4,4,3; Portuguese 2,2,2,1; French 2,2,2,1. Home: Rice Lake, Wis. Office: American Embassy, Santiago, Chile.

FAY, GEORGE EMORY, b. St. Louis, Mo., Dec. 17, 1927. ANTHROPOLOGY. A.B., U. of Mo., 1948; M.A., U. of Mich., 1951;

U. of N. Mex.; Universidad Interamericana (Mexico). Asst. prof., Southern State Coll., 1955–62; ASST. PROF., SOCIOLOGY AND ANTHROPOLOGY, WIS. STATE U., 1962– . American Philosophical Society and Kansas Academy of Science research grants (Mexico), 1953; American Philosophical Society research grant (Mexico), 1955; Explorers Club of New York City grants (Mexico), 1957, 1963; Wenner-Gren Foundation grant (Mexico), 1957; Bollingen Foundation, Inc. grant (Mexico), 1958; Interam Foundation grants, 1960, 1961, 1962, 1963; National Science Foundation grant, 1961–62; Wis. State Coll. Board of Regents research grant (Mexico), 1963, 1964; Museum of the American Indian grant, 1964; editor-publisher, Katunob. Membership: American Anthropological Association; American Association for the Advancement of Science; American Sociological Association; Archaeological Institute of America; Instituto Interamericano; Middle American Research Institute; Royal Anthropological Institute of Great Britain and Ireland; Seminario de Cultura Maya; Society for American Archaeology. Research: archeology of the west coast of Mexico. Author: A Bibliography of Fossil Man (1959, 1964); A Handbook of Pottery Types from Nayarit, Mexico (Instituto Interamericano, Oct. 1959); Arts and Crafts of Mexico (Katunob, Feb. 1962). Language: Spanish 3,3,3,3; French 2,1,1,1. Home: Ravenswood Apts., 644 Otter St., Oshkosh, Wis., 54091. Office: Dept. of Sociology and Anthropology, Wis. State U., Algoma Blvd., Oshkosh, 54902.

FEDER, ERNEST, b. Berlin, Germany, Aug. 23, 1913. ECONOMICS. Ph. D., U. of Geneva, 1938; M.S., U. of Calif., Berkeley, 1948. Assoc. prof., U. of Nebr., 1954–61; vis. prof., Universidad del Valle (Colombia), 1961–62; agricultural economics adviser, U.S. Agency for International Development (Bogotá, Colombia), 1961–62; consultant, Committee of Nine, Organization of American States, 1962; consultant, United Nations Economic Commission for Latin America (Rio de Janeiro), 1962–63; CHIEF, AGRICULTURAL ECONOMICS UNIT, ORGANIZATION OF AMERICAN STATES, 1963– . Fulbright prof., U. of Chile, 1958. Membership: American Economic Association; American Farm Economic Association; Mexican Sociology Congress. Research: agricultural economics and law; agricultural reform and development; land tenure and agricultural development in Brazil. Author: Dairy dilemma (1956); El crédito agrícola en Chile (1960); Some Reflections on the Common Market in Latin America (American Journal of Economics and Sociology, June 1961). Language: Spanish 5,5,5,5; French 5,5,5,5; German 5,5,5,5. Home: 1545 18th St., NW., Washington, D.C. Office: Agricultural Economics Unit, Organization of American States, Washington, D.C.

FEIN, JOHN MORTON, b. Chicago, Ill., Dec. 23, 1922. SPANISH AMERICAN LITERATURE. B.A., Harvard U., 1944; M.A., 1944; Ph. D., 1950. Vis prof., Universidad Menéndez y Pelayo (Santander, Colombia), Summer 1948; instr., Harvard U., 1949–50; asst. prof., Duke U., 1950–56; assoc. prof., 1956–63; PROF., ROMANCE LANGUAGES, DUKE U., 1963– . Sheldon traveling fellow, 1948, Fulbright lectr. (Santiago), 1957–58; Executive Council, American Association of Teachers of Spanish and Portuguese, 1963–65. Membership: Instituto Internacional de Literatura Iberoamericana; Modern Language Association. Research: Chilean literature. Author: Modernismo in Chilean Literature: The second Period (1964); The Mirror as Image and Theme in the Poetry of Octavio Paz (Symposium, Fall 1956); Eugenio de Castro and the Introduction of Modernismo to Spain (Publications of the Modern Language Association, Dec. 1958). Language: Spanish 5,5,5,5; Portuguese 5,4,3,4. Home: 2742 Circle Dr., Durham, N.C. Office: Dept. of Romance Languages, Duke U., Durham.

FELDMAN, ARNOLD SANFORD, b. Hartford, Conn., Mar. 1, 1926. SOCIOLOGY. A.B., Wayne U., 1949; Ph. D., Northwestern U., 1956. Asst. project dir., Social Science Research Center, U. of P.R., 1953–56; asst. prof., U. of Del., 1956–62; research assoc., Center of International Studies, Princeton U., 1960–61; ASSOC. PROF., SOCIOLOGY, NORTHWESTERN U., 1962– . Ad hoc group on social change, Social Science Research Council; Social Science Research Council grant-in-aid. Membership: American Sociological Association; Mid-West Sociological Society. Research: social stratification; economic development; social change; Puerto Rico. Author: Social Class and Social Change in Puerto Rico (1961); Labor Commitment and Social Change in Newly Developing Societies (1961). Language: Spanish 3,4,3,2. Home: 1032 Maple Ave., Evanston, Ill. Office: Dept. of Sociology, Northwestern U., Evanston.

FELDMAN, DAVID M., b. Los Angeles, Calif., Oct. 30, 1937. LANGUAGE AND LINGUISTICS, A.B., U. of Southern Calif. 1958; A.M., Cornell U., 1960; Ph. D., 1962. Instr., Cornell U., 1958–61; instr., Princeton U., 1961–62; vis. prof., U. of Colo., Summers 1961, 1962; DIR. PROGRAM IN GENERAL LINGUISTICS, DIR., MODERN LANGUAGE INSTITUTE, ASST. PROF., LINGUISTICS, U. OF COLO., 1962– . Committee for the Development of Portuguese Studies. Membership: American Association of Teachers of German; American Association of Teachers of Spanish and Portuguese; American Association of University Professors; Asociación de Lingüística y de Filología de América Latina; Linguistic Society of America; Modern Language Association. Research: Spanish and Portuguese philology; applied linguistics; Portuguese. Author: The Modern Teaching of Spanish (1963); A Survey of Portuguese Studies in the United States (Hispania, Dec. 1963); Some Structural Characteristics of the Modal Verb Phrase in Spanish (Boletín de Filología, 1964). Language: Spanish 5,5,5,5; Portuguese 5,5,5,5; French 5,5,4,4; German 5,5,5,5; Italian 5,5,3,4. Linguistic studies: Spanish; Portuguese. Home: 2519 East Floyd Ave., Englewood, Colo., 80110. Office: Modern Language Institute, U. of Colo., Boulder, 80304.

FELIX, DAVID, b. New York, N.Y., June 10, 1918. ECONOMICS. B.A., U. of Calif., Berkeley, 1942; M.A., 1947; Ph. D., 1955. Acting asst. prof., U. of Wash., 1950–52; assoc., U. of Calif., Berkeley, 1952–54;

PROF., ECONOMICS, WAYNE STATE U., 1954– ; vis. asst. prof., U. of Calif., Berkeley, 1956; research assoc., Research Center in Economic Development and Cultural Change, U. of Chicago, 1957–58, 1959. Rockefeller fellow (Chile), 1957–58; vis. lectr., National U. of Chile, 1958; Rockefeller travel grant (Colombia), 1961; Ford fellow (Great Britain), 1962–63; Yale U. travel grant (Brazil), 1963; contributing editor, Handbook of Latin American Studies. Membership: American Economic Association; Economic History Association. Research: inflation and growth; import-substituting industrialization; trade and economic development; Argentine industrialization; inflation in Chile. Author: Inflation and Industrial Growth: The Historic Record and Contemporary Analogies (Quarterly Journal of Economics, Aug. 1956); U.S. Business and Labor in Latin America (1960); Chile (in Economic Development: Analysis and Case Studies, 1961). Language: Spanish 3,3,3,3; Portuguese 2,2,1,1; French 3,2,2,2. Home: 16190 Roselawn, Detroit, Mich., 48221. Office: Dept. of Economics, Wayne State U., Detroit 2.

FELT, JEREMY POLLARD, b. Miami, Fla., Dec. 26, 1930. HISTORY. A.B., Duke U., 1951; M.A., 1956; Ph. D., Syracuse U., 1959. ASST. PROF., HISTORY, U. OF VT., 1959– . University fellow in history, Syracuse U., 1956–57. Membership: American Historical Association; Conference on Latin American History; Mississippi Valley Historical Association; Northern New England Historians Conference; Phi Beta Kappa. Research: United States-Latin American relations. Author: Lucius B. Northrop: The Confederacy's Subsistence Department (Virginia Magazine of History & Geography, Apr. 1961). Language: Spanish 3,3,3,3; Portuguese 1,1,1,1; French 2,2,2,2. Home: Star Route, Essex Junction, Vt. Office: Dept. of History, U. of Vt., Burlington.

FENWICK, CHARLES G., b. Baltimore, Md., May 26, 1880. LAW AND POLITICAL SCIENCE. Ph. D., Johns Hopkins U., 1913. Prof., Bryn Mawr Coll., 1914–40; U.S. representative, Inter-American Jurdical Committee (Brazil), 1940–48; dir., Dept. of Legal Affairs, Pan American Union, 1948–62; LEGAL CONSULTANT, DEPT. OF LEGAL AFFAIRS, PAN AMERICAN UNION, 1962– . Assoc. editor, American Political Science Review and American Journal of International Law, consultant, Inter-American Institute for International Studies (Costa Rica), 1963. Membership: American Society of International Law; Inter-American Bar Association. Research: international law. Author: International Law (1924, 1934, 1948); Cases on International Law (1935, 1951); Organization of American States (1963). Language: Spanish 4,4,3,4; Portuguese 4,4,3,4; French 4,4,3,4; German 3,3,2,3. Home: 2653 Woodley Rd., Washington, D.C. 20008. Office: Pan American Union, Washington, D.C. 20006.

FERDON, EDWIN NELSON, JR., b. St. Paul, Minn., June 14, 1913. ANTHROPOLOGY AND GEOGRAPHY. B.A., U. of N. Mex., 1937; M.A., U. of Southern Calif., 1942. Curator, Branch Museums, Museum of N. Mex., 1937–38; curator, Middle American Archaeology, 1938–40; research assoc., Hispanic Studies, 1940–45; procurement specialist, U.S. Cinchona Mission (Ecuador), 1944–45; research assoc., Hispanic Studies and State Monuments, Museum of N. Mex., 1945–57; assoc. dir., Museum of International Folk Art, 1957–60; coordinator of interpretation, Div. of Anthropology, 1960–61; ASSOC. DIR., ARIZ. STATE MUSEUM, 1961– . Assoc. dir., Summer Institute in Anthropology for Museum Personnel, American Association of Museums—National Science Foundation. Membership: Sigma Xi; Society for American Archaeology. Research: archeology; human geography; prehistory and geography of Polynesia with special concern for Easter Island as an administrative unit of Chile. Author: Studies in Ecuadorian Geography (1950); Tonala, Mexico: An Archaeological Survey (1953); Agricultural Potential and the Development of Cultures (Southwestern Journal of Anthropology, Spring 1959). Language: Spanish 3,3,3,2. Home: 2141 East Juanita St., Tucson, Ariz. 85719. Office: Arizona State Museum, U. of Ariz., Tucson, 85721.

FERGUSON, THOMAS STUART, b. Pocatello, Idaho, May 21, 1915. ANTHROPOLOGY. A.B., U. of Calif., Berkeley, 1937; LL.B., 1942. Federal Bureau of Investigation agent, 1941–45; attorney at law (Oakland, Calif.), 1946–64; PRESIDENT AND SECRETARY, NEW WORLD ARCHAEOLOGICAL FOUNDATION, 1952– . Membership: American Anthropological Association; California Bar Association; Society for American Archaeology. Research: archeology; origins of the early high civilizations of Mexico and Central America. Author: One Fold and One Shepherd (1962); Ancient America and the Book of Mormon (1964). Language: Spanish 2,2,2,2. Home: 1 Irving Lane, Orinda, Calif. Office: New World Archaeological Foundation, c/o Librarian, Brigham Young U., Provo, Utah.

FERNANDEZ, CHARLES J., b. Tampa, Fla., Oct. 14, 1919. JOURNALISM. A.B., U. of Miami, 1947. Reporter, Tampa Times (Fla.), 1936–42; reporter and foreign correspondent (Latin America), Miami Herald and Chicago Daily News, 1946–54; CO-OWNER, NEWS AND PROGRAM DIR., RADIO STATION WKXY (SARASOTA, FLA.) 1954– . Membership: Florida Associated Press Broadcasters; Florida Association of Broadcasters; National Association of Broadcasters. Language: Spanish 4,4,4,4. Home: 3139 Bay Shore Rd., Sarasota, Fla. Office: WKXY RADIO, 2500 10th St., P.O. Box 2431, Sarasota.

FERNÁNDEZ, JUAN RAMÓN, b. San Juan, P.R., Aug. 9, 1936. POLITICAL SCIENCE: PUBLIC ADMINISTRATION. B.S., U. of P.R., 1957; M.B.A., 1963. Asst. to the dir., School of Public Administration, U. of P.R., 1961–62; DIR., OFFICE OF SPECIAL PROGRAMS, SCHOOL OF PUBLIC ADMINISTRATION, 1962– . Membership: Sociedad Puertorriqueña de Administración Pública. Research: use of autonomous entities by Latin American governments; administrative structure of the Venezuelan government; collective baragaining in the public corporation of the government of Puerto Rico. Author: Is Law 142 of 1961 Constitutional? (Revista de Administración

Pública, Dec. 1963). Language: Spanish 5,5,5,5; Portuguese 3,2,1,1; French 2,1,1,1. Home: 1664 Dakota St., Urb. San Gerardo, Río Piedras, P.R. Office: School of Public Administration, U. of P.R., Río Piedras.

FERNANDEZ, OSCAR, b. St. Louis, Mo., Mar. 22, 1916. BRAZILIAN LITERATURE AND LANGUAGE. A.B., Wash. U., 1937; M.A., 1940; Ph. D., U. of Wis., 1953. Instr., Wash. U., 1940–41; U.S. Naval Intelligence officer, Spanish and French Combined Communications Teams (U.S. and North Africa), 1942–46; prof., U.S. Naval Academy, 1945–62; vis. prof., N.Y.U., 1961–62; PROF., DIR., PORTUGUESE PROGRAM, N.Y.U., 1962– . Portuguese Materials Committee, chmn. of Portuguese section, 1962–63, chmn. of Research and Bibliography Committee on the Language and Literature of Brazil, Portugal, and Galicia, 1958– . Modern Language Association. Membership: American Association of Teachers of Spanish and Portuguese; Modern Language Association; Omicron Delta Kappa; Phi Beta Kappa; Phi Eta Sigma; Phi Sigma Iota. Research: Brazilian theatre; translation of Brazilian plays. Author: De qué hablamos? (1952); The Teaching of Spanish and Portuguese at the U.S. Naval Academy (Modern Language Journal, Dec. 1954); The Contemporary Theatre in Rio de Janeiro and in São Paulo, 1953–1955 (Hispania, Dec. 1956). Language: Spanish 5,5,5,5; Portuguese 5,5,5,5; French 4,4,4,4; Italian 3,3,3,3. Home: 52 Somerstown Rd., Ossining, N.Y., 10562. Office: Dept. of Romance and Slavic Languages and Literatures, N.Y.U., New York, 10003.

FERNÁNDEZ-MÉNDEZ, EUGENIO, b. July 11, 1924. ANTHROPOLOGY. B.A., U. of P.R., 1947; Columbia U. ASSOC. PROF., ANTHROPOLOGY, U. OF P.R., 1949– ; dir., Dept of Sociology, U. of P.R., 1953–57; president, P.R. Institute of Culture. 1955– ; dir., U. of P.R. press, 1959– . Research: ethnology; Mesoamerican archeology; social and economic history of the Caribbean; Mexico; pre-Colombian cultures; colonial hacienda system. Author: Identidad y la cultura (1956); Crónicas de Puerto Rico 1493–1956 (1957); Ensayos de antropología popular (1961). Language: Spanish 5,5,5, 5; Portuguese 5,3,3,–; French 4,3,–,–. Home: 187 Los Mirtos St., Hyde Park, Río Piedras, P.R.

FERRATER-MORA, JOSÉ, b. Barcelona, Spain, Oct. 30, 1912. PHILOSOPHY. Licenciado en Filosofía, U. of Barcelona, 1936. Prof., U. of Chile, 1943–47; assoc. prof., Bryn Mawr Coll., 1949–56; PROF., BRYN MAWR COLL., 1956– ; vis. prof., Princeton U., 1956–57. Guggenheim fellow, 1947–49; American Philosophical Society grant, Summer 1962; American Council of Learned Societies grant, 1963–64. Membership; American Philosophical, Association; Association for Symbolic Logic; Brazilian Society of Philosophy. Research: history of philosophy. Author: El hombre en la encrucijada (1948); Diccionario de filosofía (1958); El ser y la muerte (1962). Language: Spanish 5,5,5,5; Portuguese 5,5,3,2; French 5,5,5,5; German 5,4,4,4; Italian 5,4,4,4. Home: 915 Wyndon Ave., Bryn Mawr, Pa. 19010. Office: Dept. of Philosophy, Bryn Mawr Coll., Bryn Mawr, 19010.

FERRER-CANALES, JOSÉ, b. Santurce, P.R., Sept. 18, 1913. SPANISH AMERICAN LITERATURE. A.B., U. of P.R., 1937; M.A., 1944; Doctor, Universidad Nacional Autónoma de México, 1952. Instr., U. of P.R., 1944, 1946–48; Hunter Coll., 1945–46; Hostos Coll. (P.R.), 1948–49; Dillard U., 1949–51; asst. prof., 1953–56; assoc. prof., Tex. Southern U., 1956–57; ASSOC. PROF., SPANISH, HOWARD U., 1957– . John Hay Whitney fellow; U. of P.R. fellow; Howard U. research grant. Membership: American Association of Teachers of Spanish and Portuguese; American Association of University Professors; Ateneo Americano de Washington; College Language Association; Instituto Internacional de Literatura Iberoamericana; Inter-American Council; Modern Language Association. Research: the essay in Spanish American literature; the Golden Age and 20th century Spanish literature. Author: Imagen de Varona (1964); Martí y Puerto Rico (Cuadernos Americanos, Mar.-Apr. 1955); Hora de Puerto Rico (Cuadernos Americanos, Jan.–Feb. 1962). Language: Spanish 5,5,5,5. Home: Box 841, Howard U., Washington 1, D.C. Office: Dept. of Spanish, Howard U., Washington 1.

FETTER, FRANK WHITSON, b. San Francisco, Calif., May 22, 1899. ECONOMICS. A.B., Swarthmore, 1920; A.M., Princeton U., 1922; A.M., Harvard U., 1924; Ph. D., 1926. Asst. prof.-prof., Princeton U., 1927–34; asoc. prof.-prof., Haverford Coll., 1934–48; economist, Office of Lend Lease Administration and U.S. Dept. of State, 1943–46; PROF., ECONOMICS, NORTHWESTERN U., 1948– . Guggenheim fellow, 1937–38; economic adviser, Export-Import Bank (Ecuador), Summer 1939, Central Bank of Ecuador, Summer 1940; economic consultant, International Bank for Reconstruction and Development, Summer 1950; dir., National Bureau of Economic Research, 1950– ; adviser on German economic affairs, U.S. Dept. of State, Summer 1951. Membership: American Economic Association; Midwest Economic Association. Research: central banking and international economic relations. Author: Monetary Inflation in Chile (1932). Co-author: The Irish Pound (1955). Language: Spanish 4,4,4,3; Portuguese 4,3,2,2; French 4,4,3,3; German 4,4,4,3; Italian 4,4,3,2. Home: 580 Orchard Lane, Winnetka, Ill. Office: Dept. of Economics, Northwestern U., Evanston, Ill.

FEUERLEIN, WILLY J., b. Zurich, Switzerland, May 8, 1911. ECONOMICS. A.B., M.A., George Washington U., 1935; Ph. D., Yale U., 1939. Statistician, Federal Reserve Bank of New York, 1938–42; economist, Foreign Economic Administration, 1942–44; foreign trade specialist and accountant, DuPont de Nemours & Company, 1944–50; lectr., Temple U., U. of Del., 1946–49; consultant, International Monetary Fund, 1950–51; head of mission, Technical Assistance Administration, United Nations (San Salvador), 1952–53; technical adviser, prof., and consultant, Government of El Salvador, 1953–56; vis. prof., U. of Fla., 1956–57; liaison officer, U.S. Agency for International Development (Pakistan),

1957–62; ASST. DIR. FOR DEVELOPMENT, OFFICE OF BRAZIL AFFAIRS, CHIEF, BRAZIL LENDING DIV., U.S. AGENCY FOR INTERNATIONAL DEVELOPMENT, 1962– . Yale/Brookings fellow 1937–38; Rockefeller fellow, 1938–39; Economic and Financial Mission to Peru, 1949. Membership: American Association for Advancement of Science; American Economic Association; Society for International Development. Research: international economics; economic development of underdeveloped Latin American countries. Author: Dollars in Latin America (1940); Dólares en América Latina (1944); Proposals for the Further Economic Development of El Salvador (1953, 1954). Language: Spanish 4,4,3,3; Portuguese 2,2,1,1; French 4,4,3,3. Home: The Towers, Apt. 1020W, 4201 Cathedral Ave., NW., Washington, D.C. 20016. Office: Agency for International Development, U.S. Dept. of State, Washington, 20025.

FINAN, JOHN JOSEPH, b. St. Louis, Mo., Sept. 1, 1925. HISTORY. A.B., Washington U., 1945; M.A., 1947; Ph. D., Harvard U., 1956. Latin American specialist, Manuscripts Div., Library of Congress, 1953–55; political officer, Embassy (Colombia), U.S. Dept. of State, 1958–61; ASSOC. PROF. OF LATIN AMERICAN STUDIES, SCHOOL OF INTERNATIONAL SERVICE, AMERICAN U., 1961– . University scholar, Harvard U., 1949–50; Buenos Aires Convention fellow (Mexico), 1951–52; Brown University President's Fellow in Argentina, 1956–58. Membership: American Historical Association; Conference on Latin American History. Research: rural history in colonial Mexico and 19th century Argentina; contemporary agrarian problems of Latin America. Author: Maize in the Great Herbals (1951). Language: Spanish 4,4,4,4; Portuguese 3,3,2,1; French 4,3,2,3. Home: Apt. 1033, 4201 South 31st St., Arlington, Va. Office: School of International Service, American U., Washington, D.C. 20016.

FINCH, WILLIAM A., JR., b. Smithfield, N.C., July 31, 1927. GEOGRAPHY. B.A., East Carolina Coll., 1952; M.A., U. of Okla., 1954; Ph. D., U. of Ill., 1965. Field representative, Prentice-Hall, Inc., 1954–56; instr., Northeast Mo. Teachers Coll., Summers 1957, 1958, 1959, 1961; ASST. PROF., GEOGRAPHY, SAN DIEGO STATE COLL., 1961– ; geographer, Wilson, Nuttal, Raimond, Inc., Summer 1962. National Science Foundation-National Academy of Sciences research grant (Mexico). Membership: Association of American Geographers; Sigma Xi. Research: Physical geography; regional geography of Latin America; landform analysis; geomorphology; tropical environments; Karst landscape of Yucatan, Mexico. Language: Spanish 2,2,2,2; French 2,1,1,1; German 2,1,1,1. Home: 7130 Waite Dr., Lemon Grove, Calif. Office: Dept. of Geography, San Diego State Coll., San Diego, Calif. 92115.

FIRESTONE, HOMER LEON, b. Fargo, Okla., Dec. 10, 1921. ANTHROPOLOGY: LINGUISTICS. A.B., U. of Kansas City, 1946; M.A., U. of Chicago, 1955; Ph. D., U. of N. Mex., 1963. Missionary, Church of God (Bolivia), 1946–63; MISSIONARY, WORLD-WIDE MISSIONS (BOLIVIA), 1963– . Membership: American Anthropological Association; Linguistic Society of America. Research: linguistics and culture; personality; Bolivia; a description and classification of Sirionó. Author: Chama Phonology (International Journal of American Linguistics, Jan. 1955). Language: Spanish 5,5,5,4; French 3,2,2,2. Linguistic studies: Aymará; Guaraní; Guarayo; Navajo; Quechua; Sirionó. Home: 107 East Pine, El Dorado Springs, Mo. Office: World-Wide Missions, Casilla 758, Cochabamba, Bolivia; or Box 27, Altadena, Calif.

FISCHMAN, JEROME, b. New York, N.Y., Aug. 2, 1928. HISTORY. B.S.S., City Coll. (N.Y.), 1951; M.A., 1952; Ph. D., N.Y.U., 1962. Instr., U. of P.R., 1955–58; instr., Hofstra U., 1958–62; lectr., Universidad de Caracas, Summer 1962; ASST. PROF., HISTORY, LEHIGH U., 1962– . Membership: American Historical Association. Research: Caribbean area; political parties in Puerto Rico; the church in politics in Puerto Rico. Language: Spanish 5,5,5,5; Portuguese 4,4,4,4; French 3,3,3,3. Home: 1910 Aripine Ave., Bethlehem, Pa. Office: Dept. of History, Lehigh U., Bethlehem.

FITCHETT, DELBERT ARTHUR, b. Merced, Calif., Nov. 6, 1936. ECONOMICS. B.A., Pomona Coll., 1958; M.A., Yale U., 1959; Ph. D., U. of Calif., Berkeley, 1963. RESEARCH ECONOMIST, RAND CORPORATION, 1964– . Union Carbide Corporation scholar, Pomona Coll., 1954–58; Rabinowitz fellow, Yale U., 1958–59; Fulbright grant (Peru), 1961–62. Membership: American Economic Association; American Economic History Association; International Association of Agricultural Economists; Phi Beta Kappa. Research: agrarian and land reform; economic and agrarian conditions on the coast of Peru and in the Andes. Author: Population Patterns on the Northern Coast of Peru (Estadística, Dec. 1963); Cadastral Systems on the Northern Coast of Peru: Some Problems and Proposals (Journal of Inter-American Studies, Oct. 1964); Land Use and Land Control on the Northern Coast of Peru (Land Economics, Nov. 1964). Language: Spanish 5,4,4,4; Portuguese 3,2,2,2; French 3,3,2,2. Office: Logistics Dept., RAND Corporation, 1700 Main St., Santa Monica, Calif.

FITZGIBBON, RUSSELL H., b. Columbus, Ind., June 29, 1902. POLITICAL SCIENCE. A.B., Hanover Coll., 1924; M.A., Ind. U., 1928; Ph. D., U. of Wis., 1933; LI.D., Hanover Coll., 1952. Prof., Hanover Coll., 1924–36; prof., U. of Calif., Los Angeles, 1936–64; senior political analyst, Office of Inter-American Affairs, 1944–45; PROF., POLITICAL SCIENCE, U. OF CALIF., SANTA BARBARA, 1964– . Del Amo Foundation fellow (Colombia), 1943–44, (Spain), 1959; Doherty fellow and Social Science Research Council fellow (Uruguay, Argentina), 1951; Fulbright research grant (Italy), 1958–59; Organization of American States team of observers, Dominican Republic presidential election, Dec. 1962. Membership: American Political Science Association; Association for Latin American Studies; Western Political Science Association. Research: international relations; political organization of Uruguay, Argentina, Colombia and Cuba. Author: Cuba and the United States, 1900–1935 (1935); Uruguay: Portrait of a Democracy (1954). Editor: The Constitutions of the Americas (1948). Language: Spanish 4,4,4,4; Portuguese 3,2,2,2; French 3,2,–,–. Home: 1201 North Ontare Rd., Santa Barbara, Calif. 93105. Office: Dept. of Political Science, U. of Calif., Santa Barbara, 93018.

FLACCUS, ELMER WILLIAM, b. Pittsburgh, Pa., Apr. 12, 1909. HISTORY. A.B., Washington & Jefferson Coll., 1932; M.A., 1933; Ph. D., U. of Tex., 1951. PROF., HISTORY, AUSTIN COLL., 1951–; chmn., 1958–63. Danforth Summer Fellowship, 1959; Southern Association Fellowship, 1960; Austin Coll. sabbatical (England), 1963–64. Membership: Conference on Latin American History; East Texas Historical Society; Hispanic American Historical Association; Southwestern Social Science Association. Research: Mexico in the 1820's. Author: Commodore David Porter and the Mexican Navy (Hispanic American Historical Review, Aug. 1954). Language: Spanish 3,–,–,–; Portuguese 1,–,–,–; French 2,–,–,–. Home: 1102 West College St., Sherman, Tex. Office: Dept. of History, Austin Coll., Sherman.

FLAMMANG, ROBERT ARTHUR., b. Orleans, Nebr., Sept. 29, 1934. ECONOMICS. B.S., U. of Nebr., 1956; M.A., U. of Iowa, 1959; Ph. D., 1962. Instr., U. of Iowa, 1957–62; ASST. PROF., ECONOMICS, LA. STATE U., 1962– . Pan American Union fellow (Chile), Summer 1963. Membership: American Economic Association; Mississippi Valley Council on World Trade; Southeastern Conference on Latin American Studies; Southern Economic Association; Southwestern Social Science Association; Western Economic Association. Research: economic development; international economics; economic integration in Latin America; Latin American Free Trade Association. Author: The Common Market Movement (Iowa Business Digest, Fall 1961). Language: Spanish 3,3,3,3; Portuguese 1,1,1,1; French 1,1,1,1. Home: 740 West Chimes, Baton Rouge, La. 70802. Office: Dept. of Economics, La. State U., Baton Rouge, 70803.

FLIEGEL, FREDERICK CHRISTIAN, b. Edmonton, Canada, Apr. 3, 1925. SOCIOLOGY. B.A., U. of Wis., 1949; M.A., 1952; Ph. D., 1955. ASSOC. PROF., RURAL SOCIOLOGY, PA. STATE U., 1955– . Consultant, Organization of American States (Brazil), 1962–63; Fulbright lectr., Universidade do Rio Grande do Sul (Brazil), 1962–63. Membership: American Association for the Advancement of Science; American Sociological Association; Pennsylvania Sociological Society; Rural Sociological Society. Research: rural sociology; rural development in southern Brazil; diffusion of innovations and value orientations of peasant farmers. Author: Aspirations of Low-Income Farmers and Their Performance and Potential for Change (Rural Sociology, Sept. 1959); Farm Practice Attributes and Adoption Rates (Social Forces, May 1962); Receptividade de idéias novas e êxodo rural numa área colonial (Estudos e Trabalhos, 1963). Language: Spanish 2,2,2,1; Portuguese 4,3,3,3; German 5,5,4,3. Home: 178 West Hamilton Ave., State College, Pa.

Office: Dept. of Sociology, Pa. State U., University Park.

FLORES, ÁNGEL, b. Barceloneta, P.R., Oct. 2, 1900. SPANISH AMERICAN LITERATURE. A.B., N.Y.U., 1923; M.A., Lafayette Coll., 1924; Ph. D., Cornell U., 1947. Instr., Union Coll., 1924–25; Rutgers U., 1925–29; Cornell U., 1930–33; editorial asst., Div. of International Cooperation, Pan American Union, 1939–45; PROF., ROMANCE LANGUAGES AND COMPARATIVE LITERATURE, QUEENS COLL., 1945– ; chmn., Latin American Area Studies. Contributing editor, Handbook of Latin American Studies; Translation Committee, Instituto Internacional de Literatura Iberoamericana; Comité de Historia de Ideas en América, Instituto Panamericano de Geografía e Historia. Membership: Ateneo de Washington; Instituto Internacional de Literatura Iberoamericana; Modern Language Association. Research: comparative literature; translations of Spanish classics and foremost Latin American writers. Author: Great Spanish Stories 1956); Historia y antología del cuento y la novela Hispanoamérica (1959); Anthology of Spanish Poetry (1961). Language: Spanish 5,5,5,5; Portuguese 5,5,4,–; French 5,5,4,4; Catalán 5,4,1,1; Italian 5,5,3,–. Linguistic studies: French; Italian; Portuguese; Spanish. Home: 217–47 51st Ave., Bayside 67, N.Y. Office: Dept. of Modern Languages, Queens Coll., Flushing 67, N.Y.

FLORIPE, RODOLFO OROZCO, b. Estelí, Nicaragua, Sept. 6, 1909. SPANISH AMERICAN LITERATURE. B.A., U. of Toledo, 1940; M.A., U. of Wis., 1942; Ph. D., 1950. ASSOC. PROF., ROMANCE LANGUAGES, U. OF MINN., 1948– ; assoc. prof., Guadalajara Summer School Institute, Summer 1960. Contributing editor, Handbook of Latin American Studies, 1961–62; Committee on U.S.-Latin American Faculty Exchange, U. of Minn. Membership: American Association of Teachers of Spanish and Portuguese; Hispanic Institute in the United States; Instituto Internacional de Literatura Iberoamericana; Midwest Council of the Association for Latin American Studies; Modern Language Association. Research: Spanish American novelists and poets, especially Mexican, Venezuelan, Uruguayan, Argentine, and Chilean; post Civil War Spanish novelists and playwrights. Author: Rubén Darío y Jules Lemaître; una fuente secundaria de Azul (Revista Iberoamericana, Jan. 1952). Language: Spanish 5,5,5,5; Portuguese 4,4,4,4; French 4,4,4,4; Italian 3,3,3,3. Home: 415 5th Ave., SE., Minneapolis, Minn. 55414. Office: Dept. of Romance Languages, U. of Minn., Minneapolis, 55455.

FLORIT, EUGENIO, b. Madrid, Spain, Oct. 15, 1903. SPANISH AMERICAN LITERATURE. Doctor of Law, Universidad de la Habana, 1926. PROF., SPANISH, MIDDLEBURY COLL., SUMMERS 1944– ; PROF., SPANISH, BARNARD COLL., GRADUATE SCHOOL OF COLUMBIA U., 1945– . Membership: American Association of Teachers of Spanish and Portuguese; Hispanic Society of America; International Association of Hispanists; Modern Language Association. Research: Spanish American and Spanish poetry. Co-author:

Literatura hispanoamericana; antología e introducción histórica (1960); Retratos de Hispanoamérica (1962). Translator and editor: Antología de la poesía norteamericana contemporánea (1955). Language: Spanish 5,5,5,5; French 3,-,3,2; Italian 2,2,2,1. Home: Apt. 64, 440 Riverside Dr., New York, N.Y., 10027. Office: Dept. of Spanish, Barnard Coll., New York, 10027.

FLOYD, TROY SMITH, b. Rampart, Alaska, Jan. 31, 1920. HISTORY. B.J., U. of Mo., 1948; A.M., 1949; Ph. D., U. of Calif., Berkeley, 1959. ASST. PROF., HISTORY, U. OF N. MEX., 1959- . American Philosophical Society grant (Guatemala), 1962. Membership: Conference on Latin American History. Research: colonial Central America. Author: The Guatemala Merchants, the Government, and the Provincianos, 1750–1800 (Hispanic American Historical Review, Feb. 1961); Bourbon Palliatives and the Central American Mining Industry, 1765–1800 (The Americas, Oct. 1961). Language: Spanish 4,4,4,3; Portuguese 4,2,2,2,; French 1,1,1,1; German 1,1,1,1. Home: 10124 Propps Dr., NE., Albuquerque, N. Mex. Office: Dept. of History, U. of N. Mex., Albuquerque.

FLUMIANI, CARLO, M., b. Trieste, Italy, Aug. 15, 1911. ECONOMICS. London School of Economics, 1934–35; Ph. D., U. of Milan, 1938. Asst. prof., U. of Santa Clara, 1946–53; prof., Coll. of St. Joseph on the Rio Grande, 1953–56; ASSOC. PROF., ECONOMICS, BOSTON COLL., 1956- . Scholarships, U. of Paris, London School of Economics, Harvard U.; consultant, Latin America Advisory Service, Institute for Economic and Financial Research. Membership: American Economic Association; American Finance Association. Research: international finance; foreign corporate financing; exports and imports. Author: The Cylinder Theory (1962); The Warning Signals (1963); The Technical Wall Street Encyclopedia (1964). Language: Spanish 5,5,4,4; French 5,5,4,4; German 4,4,3,3; Italian 5,5,5,5. Home: P.O. Box 58, Gloucester, Mass. Office: Dept. of Economics, Boston Coll., Chestnut Hill 67, Mass.

FORBES, JACK DOUGLAS, b. Long Beach, Calif., Jan. 7, 1934. HISTORY AND ANTHROPOLOGY. A.B., U. of Southern Calif., 1955; M.A., 1956; Ph. D., 1959. Lectr., U. of Southern Calif., 1958–59; instr., Citrus Coll., 1959–60; ASST. PROF., HISTORY, SAN FERNANDO VALLEY STATE COLL., 1960- . Social Science Research Council research fellow (Spain), 1957–58; Social Science Research Council grant-in-aid, 1961–62; Guggenheim fellow, 1963–64; Board of Editors, Journal of the West, 1962- . Membership: American Indian Ethnohistoric Conference; Pacific Coast Council on Latin American Studies; Phi Beta Kappa; Western History Association. Research: ethnohistory; Indian-European contact studies; the Indians of Chihuahua, 1560–1750; the chumash of California. Author: Apache, Navaho and Spaniard (1960); The Quechans: Warriors of the Colorado (1964); Melchior Díaz and the Discovery of Alta California (Pacific Historical Review, Fall 1958). Language: Spanish 3,3,3,3; German 2,2,1,1. Home: 1461 Vaquero Dr., Simi, Calif. Office: Dept. of History, San Fernando Valley State College, Northridge, Calif.

FORD, EDWIN D., JR., b. La Crosse, Wis., Nov. 7, 1899. LAW. B.A., Whitman Coll., 1921; B.A. Juris., Oxford U., 1923; B.C.L., 1924; M.A., 1937. Assoc. lawyer, Kingman, Cross, Morley & Company (Minn.), 1925–30; PARTNER, REID & PRIEST (N.Y.), 1930- . Membership: American Bar Association; Interamerican Bar Association; International Bar Association; New York City Bar Association; New York State Bar Association; Phi Beta Kappa. Research: international law; corporate law. Language: Spanish 4,4,4,4; Portuguese 4,-,-,-. Home: Apt. 11, 20 East 79th St., New York 21, N.Y. Office: Reid & Priest, 2 Rector St., New York 6.

FORD, THOMAS R., b. Lake Charles, La., June 24, 1923. SOCIOLOGY. B.S., La. State U., 1946; M.A., 1948; Ph. D., Vanderbilt U., 1951. Instr., La. State U., 1948–49; asst. prof., U. of Ala., 1950–56; demographic statistician, U.S. Air Force, 1953–56; PROF., SOCIOLOGY, U. OF KY., 1956- . Cordell Hull fellow (Peru), 1948–49; Guggenheim fellow (Peru), 1962–63. Membership: American Association for the Advancement of Science; American Sociological Association; Ohio Valley Sociological Society; Population Association of America; Rural Sociological Society; Southern Sociological Society. Research: social change; demography; land distribution, land tenure, and social change in Peru. Author: Man and Land in Peru (1955); Health and Demography in Kentucky (1964). Editor: The Southern Appalachian Region: A Survey (1962). Language: Spanish 4,4,4,3; Portuguese 2,2,1,1; French 3,2,2,1. Home: 1107 Eldemere Rd., Lexington, Ky. 40506. Office: Dept. of Sociology, U. of Ky., Lexington, 40506.

FORREST, FREDERICK AUGUST, b. Buenos Aires, Argentina, Dec. 27, 1914. LIBRARY SCIENCE AND HISTORY. B.A., San Jose State Coll., 1947; M.A., Stanford U., 1948; Ph. D., 1951; B.L.S., U. of Calif., Berkeley, 1955. Cataloger, Long Beach State Coll., 1955–58; head librarian, asst. prof., History, Southern Ill. U., 1958–60; dean of libraries and communication arts, Inter American U. (P.R.), 1960–64; CURATOR, LATIN AMERICAN COLLECTION, STERLING LIBRARY, YALE U., 1964- . Institute of International Education travel fellow (Argentina), 1952–53; Argentine Congress research fellow. Research: Latin American archives; Argentine history. Language: Spanish 5,5,5,5; Portuguese 5,4,4,4; French 4,3,3,3; Italian 4,4,4,4. Office: Sterling Library Yale U., New Haven, Conn.

FORSTER, MERLIN HENRY, b. Delta, Utah, Feb. 24, 1928. SPANISH AMERICAN LITERATURE. B.A., Brigham Young U., 1956; M.A., U. of Ill., 1957; Ph. D., 1960. Instr., U. of Tex., 1960–61; asst. prof., 1961–62; ASST. PROF., SPANISH AND PORTUGUESE, U. OF ILL., 1962- . Membership: American Association of Teachers of Spanish and Portuguese; Instituto Internacional de Literatura Iberoamericana; Modern Language Association. Research: Hispanic American poetry and drama; contemporary Mexican literature; Brazilian and Portuguese literature. Author: Los Contemporáneos: 1920–1932. Perfil de un experimento vanguardista (1964); Structure and Meaning in Erico Veríssimo's Noite (Hispania, Dec. 1962); La revista Contemporáneos. ¿Hacia una mexicanidad universal? (Hispanófila, Jan. 1963). Language: Spanish 5,5,5,5; Portuguese 4,4,4,3; French 3,3,3,2; German 2,2,1,1; Russian 2,2,1,1. Home: 310 West Illinois, Urbana, Ill. 61801. Office: Dept. of Spanish and Portuguese, U. of Ill., Urbana, 61803.

FORTIER-ORTIZ, ADOLFO, b. Ponce, P.R., Oct. 4, 1923. POLITICAL SCIENCE. B.A., U. of P.R., 1945; M.P.A., Maxwell School at Syracuse U, 1946. Asst. prof., U. of P.R., 1953–56; lectr., Getulio Vargas Foundation, 1953; dir., School of Public Administration, dean, Faculty of Social Science, U. of P.R., 1956–59; resident dir., John Diebold & Associates (Venezuela), 1959–62; REGIONAL DIR., COLLEGE ENTRANCE EXAMINATION BOARD (PUERTO RICO), 1963– . Technical consultant, Commission for the Reorganization of the Executive Branch in P.R., 1949; technical consultant, Constitutional Convention of P.R., 1950–51; field trip consultant, John Diebold & Associates, Summer 1959; field trip consultant, College Entrance Examination Board, 1962. Membership: American Society of Public Administration; Puerto Rico Association of Public Administration; Puerto Rico Teachers Association. Research: public administration; reorganization of the executive branch in Puerto Rico; political organization of Brazil and Venezuela. Author: Admission Problems in Latin American Universities (1963). Co-author: La Nueva Constitución (1953). Language: Spanish 5,5,5,5; Portuguese 4,4,4,4. Home: Faculty Residence DX–1, U. of P.R., Río Piedras. Office: College Entrance Examination Board, 1101 Muñoz Rivera Ave., Río Piedras, P.R.

FOSCUE, EDWIN JAY, b. Camden, Ark., Aug. 26, 1899. GEOGRAPHY. B.A., Southern Methodist U., 1922; M.S., U. of Chicago, 1925; Ph. D., Clark U., 1931. PROF., GEOGRAPHY, SOUTHERN METHODIST U., 1923– ; vis. prof., U. of Nebr., Western Reserve U., U. of Colo., U. of Wash., U. of Va., Columbia U., Stanford U., Summers 1937–42, 1946, 1948, 1950–51; asst. dir., Board on Geographic Names, U.S. Dept. of the Interior, 1943–44. Clark U. fellow; delegate, International Geographical Congresses, 1949, 1952, 1956, 1960; Advisory Committee on Geography to U.S. Dept. of State for Pan American Institute of Geography and History, 1952–60. Membership: Association of American Geographers. Research: regional geography of Latin America. Co-author: Regional Geography of Anglo-America (1943; 2nd edition, 1954; 3rd edition, 1964; Spanish edition, 1961). Language: Spanish 3,3,2,2. Home: 3225 Hanover, Dallas 25, Tex. Office: Dept. of Geography, Southern Methodist U., Dallas 22.

FOSTER, GEORGE McCLELLAND, JR., b. Sioux Falls, S. Dak., Oct. 9, 1913. ANTHROPOLOGY. Ph. D., U. of Calif., Berkeley, 1941. Head, Mexican Center, Institute of Social Anthropology, Smithsonian Institution, 1944–46; institution dir. (Washington, D.C.), 1946–52; vis. prof., U. of Calif., Berkeley, 1953–55; PROF., ANTHROPOLOGY, U. OF CALIF., BERKELEY, 1955– . Wenner-Gren Foundation grant, 1948; Guggenheim fellow, 1949; consultant, U.S. Agency for International Development, 1955, 1957, 1961, 1962. Research: cultural anthropology; Mexico. Author: Empire's Children, the People of Tzintzuntzan (1948); Culture and Conquest: America's Spanish Heritage (1960); Traditional Cultures and the Impact of Technological Change (1962). Language: Spanish 4,4,4,3; French 3,2,–,–. Home: 790 San Luis Rd., Berkeley 7, Calif. Office: Dept. of Anthropology, U. of Calif., Berkeley 4.

FOX, EUGENE J., b. Drumright, Okla., July 14, 1914. LANGUAGE. B.S., Central State Coll., 1938; M.A., Okla. U., 1944; Litt. D., Universidad Nacional de México, 1951. Asst. prof., Okla. Military Academy, 1944–48; asst. prof., N. Mex. Military Institute, 1948–59; ASSOC. PROF., MODERN LANGUAGES, DIR., LANGUAGE LABORATORY, EASTERN N. MEX. U., 1959– . Fulbright fellow, U. of the Andes (Colombia), 1958; co-chmn., Standards Committee, Rocky Mountain Modern Language Association. Membership: American Association of Teachers of Spanish and Portuguese; American Association of University Professors; Modern Language Association. Author: Storm in the Sacramentos (New Mexico Magazine, Jan. 1959); The Girl Behind the Alamo (High Adventure, 1960); Summer Seminar for Spanish Teachers (Hispania, Mar. 1960). Language: Spanish 5,5,4,5; French 3,3,3,3; German 4,3,3,3; Italian 3,3,3,3. Linguistic studies: English; French; German; Italian; Spanish. Home: 129 New Mexico Dr., Portales, N. Mex. Office: Dept. of Modern Languages, Eastern N. Mex. U., Portales.

FRANCIS, MICHAEL JACKSON, b. Oberlin, Kans., Mar. 24, 1938. POLITICAL SCIENCE. B.A., Fort Hays Kans. State Coll., 1960; Ph. D., U. of Va., 1963. INSTR., GOVERNMENT, TEX. A. & M. U., 1963– . Tex. A. & M. U. Fund for Organized Research grant, Summer 1964. Membership: American Political Science Association; Southwestern Social Science Association. Research: international relations; politics of developing nations; attitudes of U.S. Government toward military cooperation with Latin America. Author: The U.S. Congress and Military Aid to Latin America (Journal of Inter-American Studies, July 1964); The United States and the Act of Chapultepec (Southwestern Social Science Quarterly, Dec. 1964). Language: Spanish 3,2,1,1. Home: 301 Ayrshire, College Station, Tex. Office: Government Dept., Tex. A. & M. U., College Station.

FRANKEL, BENJAMIN ADAM, b. New York, N.Y., Jan. 4, 1918. HISTORY. M.A., U. of Calif., Berkeley, 1948; Ph. D., 1964. Teacher, Academia Milton (Mexico, D.F.), 1938–42; PROF., HISTORY, ST. MARY'S COLL. OF CALIF., 1949– ; prof. San Francisco State Coll., 1953–57. Fundación John Boulton fellow (Caracas, Venezuela); North American Association of Venezuela grant; Woodrow Wilson grant-in-aid. Membership: American Association of University Professors; American Historical Association; Pacific Historical Association. Research: caste relationships in Latin America as a basis for evaluation of the role of socio-economic factors in political developments; United States-Latin American cultural relations; newspaper and radio; Mexico, Venezuela, and Colombia. Author: Bolivar and the Role of the Colored Castes in the Wars of Independence (Academia Nacional de la Historia de Venezuela, 1949); Venezuela y los Estados Unidos: ayuda, alianza, y asociación (Boletín Histórico, Caracas, May 1964). Language: Spanish 5,5,5,5; Portuguese 4,4,3,2; French 4,3,2,2; German 4,4,4,3. Home: 1 Rochdale Way, Berkeley, Calif. 94708. Office: Dept. of History, St. Mary's Coll. of Calif., St. Mary's College, Calif.

FRANKENHOFF, CHARLES ANTHONY, b. Philadelphia, Pa., Aug. 24, 1922. ECONOMICS. B.S., Yale U., 1943; M.A., St. Louis U., 1955; Ph. D., Georgetown U., 1963. Instr., Fordham U., 1955–56; instr., Georgetown U., 1961–62; PROF., ECONOMICS, U. OF P.R., 1962– . Observer, Centro Interamericano de Vivienda y Planeamiento (Colombia), 1963; observer, Comisión Económica Para América Latina (Chile), 1964. Membership: American Economic Association. Research: economics of development; monetary economics; low-cost housing in Latin America; economic role of the construction sector in Puerto Rican growth. Author: The Prebisch Thesis: Theory of Industrialization (Journal of Inter-American Studies, Apr. 1962); Low-Cost Housing in a Latin Economy (Inter-American Economic Affairs, Apr. 1964); La Importación de Fondos Externos en Puerto Rico (Revista de Ciencias Sociales, June 1964). Language: Spanish 4,4,4,4; Portuguese 4,3,3,–; French 3,–,–,–. Home: 398 Francisco Seín, Hato Rey, P.R. 00917. Office: Dept. of Economics, Ciencias Sociales, U. of P.R., Río Piedras.

FRÁNQUIZ, JOSÉ ANTONIO, b. Yauco, P.R., Oct. 15, 1906. PHILOSOPHY AND PSYCHOLOGY. A.B., Colgate U., 1930; S.T.B., Boston U., 1933; Ph. D., 1940. Psychologist, lectr., Dept. of Justice, and Federal Relief Administration, Government of P.R., 1934–36; lectr., Institute of Free Studies of the Atheneum of P.R., 1935–37; asst. prof., chmn., Philosophy, U. of P.R., 1936–46; PROF., CHMN., PHILOSOPHY, W. VA. WESLEYAN COLL., 1946– . Hostos' Interamerican Centenary Committee; cofounder, West Virginia Philosophical Society; consultant and contributor, Runes Dictionary of Philosophy, Luminar, and The Personalist. Membership: American Academy of Religion; American Association for Aesthetics; American Association for the Scientific Study of Religion; American Metaphysical Society; American Philosophical Association; Interamerican Congress of Philisophy; Interamerican Congress of Psychology; International Congress of Philosophy. Research: theology; philosophy of religion. Author: Ideological Essence of Hostos' Thought (in América y Hostos, 1939); Personalism in Latin American Philosophy (The Philosophical Forum, 1954); Psychology and Metaphysics of the Experience of Communion with God (in Wesleyan Studies in Religion, 1960–61). Language: Spanish 5,5,5,5; Portuguese 5,5,4,4; French 5,5,4,5; German 3,3,2,2; Greek 2,2,1,1; Italian 5,5,4,4. Home: 7 Lightburn St., Buckhannon, W. Va. 26201. Office: Chmn., Dept. of Philosophy, W. Va. Wesleyan Coll., Buckhannon, 26201.

FRANTZ, HARRY WARNER, b. Cerro Gordo, Ill., Nov. 5, 1891. JOURNALISM. Stanford U., 1913–19. INTERNATIONAL CORRESPONDENT, 1917– ; STAFF, FOREIGN DEPT., UNITED PRESS INTERNATIONAL, 1920– ; dir. of publicity, Yellowstone National Park, 1923; press dir., Office of Inter-American Affairs, 1941–44; information officer with Asst. Secretary of State for American Republics, 1944–45; information staff, Chapultepec and San Francisco Conferences, 1945. Order of Southern Cross (Brazil); Order of Merit Eloy Colon Alfaro medal (Ecuador); Maria Moors Cabot gold medal for journalism, Columbia U., 1957. Membership: National Geographic Society; American Geophysical Union. Research: writing and adapting news files for publication in foreign countries. Home: 5804 Aberdeen Rd., Bethesda 14, Md. Office: Foreign Dept., United Press International, Bethesda, 20034.

FRAZER, ROBERT WALTER, b. Sacramento, Calif., Dec. 19, 1911. HISTORY. B.A., U. of Calif., Los Angeles, 1936; M.A., 1940; Ph. D., 1941. Asst. prof., Adams State Coll., 1940–42; PROF., CHMN., HISTORY, U. OF WICHITA, 1946– ; vis. prof., U. of Calif., Los Angeles, 1961–62. Membership: American Geographical Society; Conference on Latin American History; Hispanic American Society; Mississippi Valley Historical Association; Western History Association. Research: Mexican history; American West; inter-American relations. Author: Maximilian's Propaganda Activities in the United States, 1865–1866 (Hispanic American Historical Review, Feb. 1944); The Truce of Altmark (The Municipal University of Wichita Bulletin, Aug. 1947); The Role of the Lima Congress, 1864–65, in the Development of Pan-Americanism (Hispanic American Historical Review, Aug. 1949). Language: Spanish 4,4,3,4; Portuguese 3,2,2,3; French 3,2,2,2. Office: Dept. of History, U. of Wichita, Wichita 8, Kans.

FRAZIER, CHARLES EDWARD, JR., b. Pine Bluff, Ark., July 15, 1925. HISTORY. Biarritz American U., 1945; B.A., U. of Tenn., 1949; M.A., N.Y.U., 1949; Ph. D., U. of Tex., 1958. Asst. prof., Tex. A. & M. Coll, 1956–60; asst. prof., U. of Nev., 1960–63; ASSOC. PROF., HISTORY, WIS. STATE COLL., 1963– . Buenos Aires Convention grant (Nicaragua), 1955; U. of Tex. graduate fellow, 1955–56; Membership: Conference on Latin American History; Pacific Coast Council on Latin American Studies. Research: Central America; inter-American agreements and relations. Author: Colonel Henry L. Stimson's Peace Mission to Nicaragua (Journal of the West, Jan. 1963); Augusto César Sandino: Good Devil or Perverse God? (Journal of the West, Jan. 1964). Language: Spanish 4,3,3,3; French 3,2,2,2. Home: 920 North Main, Oshkosh, Wis. 54901. Office: Dept. of History, Wis. State Coll., Oshkosh, 54902.

FREEBAIRN, DONALD K., b. La Salle, Ill., Jan. 30, 1929. ECONOMICS. B.S., U. of Ill., 1950; M.S., 1952; Ph. D., Cornell U., 1956. Asst. agricultural economist, Rockefeller Foundation, 1956–64; ASSOC. PROF., ECONOMICS, CORNELL U., 1964– . Head, Dept. of Agricultural Economics, Mexico Agricultural Research Institute. Membership: American Economic Association; American Farm Economic Association; International Conference of Agricultural Economists. Research: agricultural development economics; Mexico. Author: Metodología de la investigación en economía agrícola (1961); Relative Production Efficiency between Tenure Classes in the Yaqui Valley, Sonora, Mexico (Journal of Farm Economics, Dec. 1963). Co-author: Economía agrícola del noroeste: I. Los ejidatarios individuales (1964). Language: Spanish 5,5,5,4; Portuguese 4,3,3,1; French 3,1,1,1. Home: 710 Handshaw Rd., Ithaca, N.Y. 14850. Office: Dept. of Agricultural Economics, Cornell U., Ithaca, 14850.

FRIED, JACOB, b. Philadelphia, Pa., June 21, 1924. ANTHROPOLOGY. B.A., Temple U., 1947; Ph. D., Yale U., 1952. ASSOC. PROF., ANTHROPOLOGY, McGILL U. (CANADA), 1952– . Research consultant, Hospital Obrero (Lima, Peru), 1956, 1958. Membership: American Anthropological Association. Research: culture change; mental health; mestizaje in Latin America, especially in Sierra Madre Mountains of Chihuahua, Mexico and in urban and Andean mountain communities in Peru. Author: The Indian and Mestizaje in Peru (Human Organization, Spring 1961); An Interpretation of Tarahumara Interpersonal Relations (Anthropological Quarterly, Apr. 1961); Social Organization and Personal Security in a Peruvian Hacienda Community (American Anthropologist, Aug. 1962). Language: Spanish 4,4,4,3; French 3,3,–,2. Home: Apt. 5, 3465 Stanley St., Montreal 2, Quebec, Canada. Office: Dept. of Anthropology, McGill U., Montreal 2.

FRIEDMANN, JOHN R. P., b. Austria, Apr. 16, 1926. CITY AND REGIONAL PLANNING; ECONOMICS. M.A., U. of Chicago, 1951; Ph. D., 1955. Economist, Tennessee Valley Authority, 1952–55; adviser, International Cooperation Administration (Brazil, Korea), 1955–61; ASSOC. PROF., CITY AND REGIONAL PLANNING, MASS. INSTITUTE OF TECHNOLOGY, 1961– . Consultant, Organization of American States (Brazil), 1961; consultant, Mass. Institute of Technology-Harvard U. Joint Center of Urban Studies (Venezuela), 1962–63; consultant, Ford Foundation (Chile), 1964. Membership: American Economic Association; Regional Science Association. Research: economic development planning; Latin American development problems; national economic planning and regional economic development in Venezuela; demographic problems in Brazil. Author: Regional Development and Planning (1964); Regional Policy for Developing Areas (1965). Language: Spanish 4,3,3,2; Portuguese 4,4,4,3; German 5,5,5,5. Office: Dept. of City and Regional Planning, Mass. Institute of Technology, Cambridge 39, Mass.

FRIEDRICH, PAUL W., b. Cambridge, Mass., Oct. 22, 1927. ANTHROPOLOGY: LINGUISTICS. B.A., Harvard U., 1950; M.A., 1951; Ph. D., Yale U., 1957. Instr., U. of Conn., 1956–57; instr., Harvard U., 1957–58; junior linguist, Deccan Coll. (India), 1958–59; asst. prof., U. of Pa., 1959–62; asst. prof., U. of Mich., Summers 1960, 1961; ASSOC. PROF., ANTHROPOLOGY, U. OF CHICAGO, 1962– . Membership: American Anthropological Association; Linguistic Society of America. Research: general ethnology and political anthropology in Mexico; structural linguistics. Author: A Mexican Cacicazgo: Structure and Function (in Society and Cultures of Latin America, 1964); Semantic Structure and Social Structure: An Instance from Russia (in Explorations in Cultural Anthropology, 1964). Language: Spanish 4,4,4,3; French 3,2,2,1; German 4,4,4,3; Italian 3,–,–,–; Russian 4,4,3,3. Linguistic studies: Malayan; Tarascan. Home: 7214 South Shore Dr., Chicago 49, Ill. Office: Dept of Anthropology, U. of Chicago, 1126 East 59th St., Chicago 37.

FRIKART, JOHN M., b. Buenos Aires, Argentina, Apr. 29, 1901. ECONOMICS. B.A., U. of Ariz., 1925; B.F.T., American Institute of Foreign Trade, 1951; M.A., U. of Ariz., 1954; Ph. D., U. of Colo., 1959. Businessman (Peru, Bolivia), 1928–37; asst. prof., American Institute for Foreign Trade, 1946–55; instr., U. of Colo., 1955–56; assoc. prof., U. of Southwestern La., 1956–60; ASST. PROF., ECONOMICS, U. OF ARIZ., 1960– . Membership: American Association of University Professors; American Economic Association; Rocky Mountain Latin American Studies Association; Western Economic Association. Research: economic growth; international economics; foreign trade; import-export banking; economic development of underdeveloped countries; Argentine economy. Language: Spanish 5,5,5,5; Portuguese 3,4,4,3; French 3,4,4,3; German 4,5,5,4; Italian 4,5,5,4. Home: 1919 East Lee St., Tucson, Ariz. 85719. Office: Dept. of Economics, U. of Ariz., Tucson.

FROST, MELVIN JESSE, b. Salt Lake City, Utah, Aug. 14, 1920. GEOGRAPHY. B.S., Ariz. State U., 1959; M.S., Brigham Young U., 1961; Ph. D., U. of Fla., 1964. Missionary, Church of the Latter Day Saints (Argentina), 1952–55; PART-TIME INSTR., GEOGRAPHY, U. OF FLA., 1961– . Pan American Research Foundation, Inc. grant (Guatemala). Aug. 1961; Caribbean Research Foundation grant (Guatemala), Summer 1962. Membership: American Geographical Society; Association of American Geographers; University Archeological Society. Research: physical geography; land settlement and utilization; colonization in Guatemala. Author: A Decimal System of Angular Measurements (Professional Geographer, Nov. 1961). Language: Spanish 4,4,4,3. Home: 208 NW. 36th Ter., Gainesville, Fla. 32601. Office: Dept. of Geography, U. of Fla., Gainesville, 32601.

FULLMER, ROBERT G., b. Germany, May 27, 1927. ECONOMICS. Polytechnic Institute of P.R.; B.A., U. of Idaho, 1952; Dr., U. of Innsbruck (Austria), 1958. Economist, P.R. Economic Development Administration, 1954–60; industrial economist, U.S. Agency for International Development (San José, Costa Rica), 1960–64; FULBRIGHT LECTR., UNIVERSIDAD TÉCNICA DE PIURA (PERU), 1964– . Government of P.R. scholar. Membership: American Foreign Service Association; Inter-American Planning Society; Phi Beta Kappa; Pi Gamma Mu; Society for International Development. Research: industrial promotion; community and area development; economic development theory. Author: Developments in Costa Rican Fisheries Industry (1960). Language: Spanish 5,5,5,4; Portuguese 2,2,2,–. Home: % A.

Higgs, Apartado 1044, San José, Costa Rica; or % Mrs. R. L. Richmond, R.F.D. 1, Surrey, Va.

FUSON, ROBERT HENDERSON, b. Bloomington, Ind., July 7, 1927. GEOGRAPHY AND ANTHROPOLOGY. A.B., Ind. U., 1949; M.A., Fla. State U., 1951; Ph. D., La. State U., 1958. Chief, Latin American Section, U.S. Air Force Aeronautical Chart and Information Service, 1951–53; instr., La. State U. Caribbean Program (C.Z.), 1955–56; instr., La. State U., 1956–57; instr., U. of Miami, 1957–58; asst. prof., La. State U., 1958–60; ASSOC. PROF., CHMN., GEOGRAPHY, U. OF SOUTH FLA., 1960– . Advisory Committee, Trustees of Internal Improvement Fund (Fla.); chmn., International Studies Committee, Latin American Studies Program, U. of South Fla. Membership: American Geographical Society; Association of American Geographers; American Meteorological Society; Florida Society of Geographers; National Council for Geographic Education; Society for the History of Discoveries. Research: tropical geography and climatology; culture of the tropics; tropical forest Indians of Latin America. Author: The Origin and Nature of American Savannas (1963); The Isoxeromene as a Tropical Climatic Boundary (Professional Geographer, May 1963); The House Types of Panama (Annals, Association of American Geographers, June 1964). Language: Spanish 4,3,3,3; Portuguese 3,2,2,2; French 4,2,2,2; German 3,2,2,2; Italian 3,2,2,2. Home: 14805 Daisy Lane, Tampa, Fla. 33612. Office: Dept. of Geography, U. of South Fla., 4202 Fowler Ave., Tampa, 33620.

G

GAARDER, ALFRED BRUCE, b. Des Moines, N. Mex., Nov. 10, 1911. LANGUAGE. M.A., National U. of Mexico, 1936; Ph. D., 1954. Asst. prof., Eastern N. Mex. Coll., 1937–41; asst. prof., Morningside Coll., 1946–47; assoc. prof., La. State U., 1947–59; chief, Language Research Section, U.S. Office of Education, 1959–64; SPECIALIST, FOREIGN LANGUAGES, U.S. OFFICE OF EDUCATION, 1964– . Research: Spanish, foreign language development; psycholinguistics; Mexico; supervision of foreign language instruction. Author: Language Laboratory Techniques: The Teacher and the Language Laboratory (International Journal of American Linguistics, Oct. 1960); The Basic Course in Modern Foreign Languages (in Reports of Surveys and Studies in the Teaching of Modern Foreign Languages, 1961). Language: Spanish 5,5,5,5; French 5,4,4,4. Home: 4225 North 23rd St., Arlington, Va. Office: U.S. Office of Education, Washington, D.C. 20202.

GAGLIANO, JOSEPH ANTHONY, b. Milwaukee, Wis., Apr. 15, 1930. HISTORY. B.S., Marquette U., 1954; M.A., 1956; Ph. D., Georgetown U., 1960. Instr., Aquinas Coll., 1959–62; ASST. PROF., HISTORY, LOYOLA U. (ILL.), 1962– . Membership: American Association of University Professors; American Historical Association; Catholic Historical Association; Hispanic American Historical Association. Research: the Andean republics. Author: The Coca Debate in Colonial Peru (The Americas, July 1963); The Identity of Gerónimo de Vivar (The Newberry Library Bulletin, Mar. 1964). Language: Spanish 3,3,3,3; Portuguese 2,1,1,1; French 3,1,1,1. Home: 1134 Pratt Blvd., Chicago, Ill. 60611. Office: Dept. of History, Loyola U., 820 North Michigan Ave., Chicago, 60626.

GAKENHEIMER, RALPH A., b. Baltimore, Md., Jan. 17, 1935. CITY AND REGIONAL PLANNING. B.E.S., Johns Hopkins U., 1957; M.R.P., Cornell U., 1959; Ph. D., U. of Pa., 1964. ASST. PROF., CITY PLANNING, U. OF N.C., 1962– . Sears-Roebuck Foundation fellow; Samuel S. Fels Fund fellow; George L. Harrison fellow; Fulbright fellow (Peru), 1960–61; consultant, U.S. Agency for International Development, Regional Office for Central America and Panama, Summer 1963. Membership: American Institute of Planners; American Society of Civil Engineers; Inter-American Planning Society. Research: transportation planning; urban structure in the Spanish city of 16th century vice-regal Peru; Central America. Author: Qualifications of Planners (in Planning 1963, 1962); Planning Education in Central America (1963); Planning, Transportation and the Small City (Traffic Quarterly. Apr. 1964). Language: Spanish 5,4,4,4; French 2,2,2,1. Home: 4 Briarbridge Lane, Chapel Hill, N.C. Office: Dept. of City and Regional Planning, U. of N.C., Chapel Hill.

GALE, THOMAS MARTIN, b. Green Bay, Wis., May 16, 1926. HISTORY. B.A., U. of Calif., Berkeley, 1949; M.A., 1950; Ph. D., U. of Pa., 1958. Instr.-asst. prof., U. of Kans., 1954–62; ASSOC. PROF., HISTORY, ASST. DEAN, COLL. OF ARTS & SCIENCES, U. OF KANS., 1963– ; dir., Junior Year Program in Costa Rica, 1961; dir., U.S. Peace Corps Project (Costa Rica), U. of Kans. contract, 1963–64. Social Science Research Council fellow (Peru), 1952–53; Social Science Research Council fellow, 1953–54; Huntington Library summer fellow, 1959; Fulbright fellow (Peru), 1960–61. Membership: American Historical Association; Conference on Latin American History. Research: Latin American urbanism; colonial Lima, Peru; a bibliography of Latin American urban studies. Language: Spanish 5,5,5,4; Portuguese 2,1,1,1. Office: Dept. of History, U. of Kans., Lawrence.

GÁLVEZ, LUIS A., b. Cuenca, Ecuador, Nov. 23, 1909. EDUCATION AND LANGUAGE. Profesor de Literatura, Universidad Central de Ecuador, 1945; M.S., U. of Notre Dame, 1947; Ph. D., 1949. Recording secretary, Congress of Ecuador, 1955–59; prof., Literature, Colegio Benalcázar (Quito), 1955–60; prof., Psychology, Academia Militar Ecuador, 1956–60; instr., Spanish, U. of Notre Dame, Summers 1957, 1959; asst. prof., St. Mary's Coll. (Minn.), 1960–61; ASST. PROF., MODERN LANGUAGES, COLL. OF ST. TERESA, 1961– . Consultant, Catholic Conference on Inter-American Student Problems. Membership: American Association of Teachers of Spanish and Portuguese; American Association of University Professors; Association for Latin American Studies. Research: comparative education; different systems and philosophies of education; Latin American culture and civilization; Alliance for Progress. Author: Lecciones de ética (1955); Preceptiva literaria (1959). Translator: Filosofía de la educación (1956). Language: Spanish 5,5,5,5; Portuguese 3,3,1,1; French 5,5,4,4; Greek 3,3,-,-; Italian 3,3,1,1; Latin 3,3,-,-. Home: 118 West Sarnia, Winona, Minn. 55987. Office: Dept. of Modern Languages, Coll. of St. Teresa, Winona, 55987.

GANS, ALTHA ROBERT, b. Gans, Pa., Nov. 5, 1904. ECONOMICS. B.S., Pa. State U., 1926; M.S., U. of Vt., 1927; Ph. D., Cornell U., 1933. Agricultural economist, U. of Vt., 1926-28; statistician, NV Potash Export, Inc. (N.Y.), 1930-31; senior statistician, Farm Credit Administration (Washington, D.C.), 1934-39; DIR. OF RESEARCH, FARM CREDIT BANKS OF SPRINGFIELD, 1939- ; lectr., Cornell U., 1957. Consultant, U.S. Agency for International Development (Bolivia), 1962-63. Membership: American Farm Economic Association. Research: agricultural economics, especially agricultural credit; organization and operation of agricultural credit programs. Author: Elasticity of Supply of Milk in Vermont (1927); Relation of Quality to Retail Price of Eggs (1934); Risk Problems of Production Credit Associations (1952). Language: Spanish 2,2,2,1. Home: 777 Stony Hill Rd., Wilbraham, Mass. Office: Farm Credit Banks of Springfield, 310 State St., Springfield, Mass.

GARBUNY, SIEGFRIED, b. Berlin, Germany, Mar. 28, 1915. ECONOMICS. M.A., U. of Berlin, 1936; Columbia U., 1939-41; Dr. Econ., U. of Freiburg, 1957. Foreign Service Reserve Officer, U.S. Dept. of State, 1955-60; acting chief, Internal Economics and Finance Div., Organization of American States, 1961-63; PROFESSORIAL LECTR., LATIN AMERICAN ECONOMICS, GEORGETOWN U., 1962- . Contributing editor, Handbook of Latin American Studies, 1956- . Membership: American Association of University Professors; American Economic Association; American Foreign Service Association. Research: Latin American economics. Language: Spanish 5,5,4,4; Portuguese 5,5,4,4; French 5,5,5,5; German 5,5,5,5; Italian 5,4,3,2; Russian 4,3,2,2. Home: 510 21st St., NW., Washington, D.C. Office: Dept. of Economics, Georgetown U., Washington, D.C.

GARCÍA-GIRÓN, EDMUNDO, b. Albuquerque N. Mex., Feb. 19, 1916. SPANISH AMERICAN LITERATURE AND LANGUAGE. A.B., U. of Calif., Berkeley, 1940; M.A., 1947; Ph. D., 1952. Chief, Translation Unit, Coordinator of Inter-American Affairs, 1941-42; instr., Marquette U., 1952-53; asst. prof., U. of Oreg., 1953-56; asst. prof., Western Reserve U., 1956-57; assoc. head, Modern Language Dept., D.C. Heath & Company, 1957-62; DIR., MODERN LANGUAGE DEPT., PRENTICE-HALL, INC., 1962- . Membership: American Association of Teachers of Spanish and Portuguese; American Association of University Professors; Instituto Internacional de Literatura Iberoamericana; Modern Language Association. Research: modern language textbooks. Author: El modernismo como evasión cultural (1957); La azul sonrisa, disquisición sobre la adjetivación modernista (Revista Iberomericana, Mar. 1955); La adjetivación modernista en la poesía de Rubén Darío (Nueva Revista de Filología Hispánica, July-Dec. 1959). Language: Spanish 5,5,5,5; Portuguese 3,2,1,1; French 3,2,2,1; Italian 3,2,2,1. Home: Apt. 12E, 412 East 55th St., New York, N.Y. 10022. Office: Modern Language Dept., Prentice-Hall, Inc., Englewood Cliffs, N.J.

GARCÍA-MORA, MANUEL R., b. Las Tablas, Panama, Mar. 4, 1921. LAW AND POLITICAL SCIENCE. B.S., U. of Panama, 1943; LL.B., 1943; LL.M., Harvard U., 1944; A.M., 1946; J.S.D., Yale U., 1948. Instr., U. of Miami, 1947; instr.-assoc. prof., U. of Detroit, 1948-56; prof., 1956-61; PROF., LAW, SCHOOL OF LAW, FORDHAM U., 1961- . Sterling fellow, Yale Law School, 1947-48; Fulbright lectr., U. of San Marcos (Peru), 1959-60. Membership: Academy of Political Science; American Society of International Law; Inter-American Bar Association. Research: international law; Anglo-American law; United States-Panamanian foreign policy; legal and political organization of Central America and Peru. Author: International Law and Asylum as a Human Right (1956); International Responsibility for Subversive Activities and Hostile Propaganda by Private Persons Against Foreign States (1962); La protección de las inversiones extranjeras (Revista de Derecho de la Pontífica Universidad Católica del Peru, 1962). Language: Spanish 5,5,5,5; Portuguese 4,4,4,4; French 2,2,2,2; Italian 2,2,2,2. Home: 500 Mariomi Rd., New Canaan, Conn. Office: School of Law, Fordham U., Lincoln Sq., New York 23.

GARCÍA-PRADA, CARLOS, b. Málaga, Colombia, Nov. 2, 1898. SPANISH AMERICAN LITERATURE. Ph. B., Colegio del Rosario (Bogotá), 1918; M.A., U. of Mich., 1924; Ph. D., U. of Colombia, 1928. Instr., U. of Mich., U. of Wash., 1921-28; asst. prof., U. of Wash., 1928-35; dir. of universities, Ministry of Education (Colombia), 1935-36; assoc. prof., U. of Wash., 1936-39; prof., 1937-57; summer vis. prof., U. of Southern Calif., 1940, Stanford U., 1941, Duke U., 1942, Mills Coll., 1947, San Diego State Coll., 1953, U. of Colo., 1961: PROF. EMERITUS, SPANISH, U. OF WASH., 1957- . Editor-in-chief, Revista Iberoamericana, 1938-44; assessor, Colombian Section, Dictionary of Latin American Literature, Pan American Union. Membership: American Association of Teachers of Spanish and Portuguese; American Association of University Professors; Ateneo Americano de Washington; Bolivarian Society of Bogotá; Bolivarian Society of Caracas; Centro de Historia de Santander-Bucaramanga; Colombian Academies of Language, of Fine Arts and of Sciences of Education; Instituto Internacional de Literatura Iberoamericana. Research: Latin American poets and writers. Author: Poetas modernistas hispanoamericanos (1956); Teorías estéticas (1962); Letras hispanoamericanas, ensayos de simpatía (1963). Language: Spanish 5,5,5,5; Portuguese 4,3,1,1,; French 3,3,2,2. Home: 9214 SE. 42nd St., Mercer Island, Wash. 98040.

GARDNER, MARY ADELAIDE, b. Kingston, Ohio, July 19, 1920. JOURNALISM. B.A., Ohio State U., 1942; M.A., 1953; Ph. D., U. of Minn., 1960. English instr., Tower of Babel, and Instituto Cultural Peruano-Norteamericano (Lima), 1954–55; program asst., World Affairs Program, Minneapolis Star, 1957–59; copy editor, Minneapolis Star, 1960–61; ASST. PROF., SCHOOL OF JOURNALISM, U. OF TEX., 1961– . Buenos Aires Convention fellow (Peru), 1954; Tozer Foundation scholar; Organization of American States research fellow; American specialist, U.S. Dept. of State (Honduras and Colombia), Summer 1962; U.S. Dept. of State vis. prof., Centro Internacional de Estudios Superiores de Periodismo para América Latina (Quito), Summer 1963. Membership: American Association for Education in Journalism; Kappa Tau Alpha; South Central Modern Language Association; Theta Sigma Phi. Research: the role of Latin American mass media as a social institution; the press of Argentina, Honduras, Peru, and Mexico. Author: The Press Since Peron (Journalism Quarterly, Summer 1960); Escuelas de Periodismo en los Estados Unidos: La Universidad de Texas (Véritas, Oct. 1962); The Press of Honduras: A Portrait of Five Dailies (Journalism Quarterly, Winter 1963). Language: Spanish 4,4,4,2; Portuguese 2,1,1,1; French 2,2,1,1; German 1,2,2,1. Home: 3004 Speedway, Austin, Tex. 78705. Office: School of Journalism, U. of Tex., Austin, 78712.

GARGANIGO, JOHN FRANK, b. Como, Italy, Mar. 17, 1937. SPANISH AMERICAN LITERATURE. B.A., Iona Coll., 1959; M.A., U. of Ill., 1961; Ph. D., 1965. ASST. PROF., SPANISH, WASHINGTON U., 1964– . National Defense Education Act fellow, 1963–64, Summer 1964. Membership: Modern Language Association; Sigma Delta Pi. Research: novels of Argentina and Uruguay; contemporary literary movements in Mexico. Author: Pito Pérez. Héroe o anti héroe? (1963). Language: Spanish 4,4,4,4; French 3,3,3,3; Italian 5,5,5,4. Home: 336 West 56th St., New York 19, N.Y. Office: Dept. of Spanish, Washington U., St. Louis, Mo.

GARLOCH, LORENA A., b. Lake City, Pa., Sept. 28, 1906. LIBRARY SCIENCE. A.B., Westminster Coll., 1927; A.B. in L.S., U. of Mich., 1928; M.A., U. of Pittsburgh, 1943. Cataloger, Oberlin Coll., 1928–29; order librarian, U. of Pittsburgh, 1929–31; order librarian, American Library in Paris, 1930–31; reference librarian, U. of Pittsburgh, 1931–40; dir. of public services, 1940–47; asst. librarian, 1947–52; university librarian, 1952–63; ASSOC. DIR., LIBRARY, U. OF PITTSBURGH, 1963– ; asst. prof., Library Science, Rutgers U., 1964– . President, Tri State Association of College and Research Libraries, 1958–59; president, Pennsylvania Library Association, 1961–62. Membership: Pennsylvania Library Association; Phi Alpha Theta; Pittsburgh Library Club; Sigma Xi; Tri State Association of College and Research Libraries. Research: geography; Laguna cotton region of Mexico. Author: Cotton in the Economy of Mexico (Economic Geography, Jan. 1944); Two B or Not 2b (Library Journal Indexer, Nov. 1958). Editor: Library Trends in Urban Universities (Library Trends, Apr. 1962). Language: Spanish 3,3,2,1; French 3,3,2,1. Home: 1558 Graham Blvd., Pittsburgh 35, Pa. Office: U. of Pittsburgh, Pittsburgh 13.

GARRETT, NAOMI MILLS, b. Columbia, S.C., Aug. 24, 1906. HAITIAN LITERATURE. A.B., Benedict Coll., 1927; M.A., Atlanta U., 1936; Ph. D., Columbia U., 1954. Instr., Kittrell Coll., 1937–40; instr., Booker Washington Junior High School, 1941–42; teacher, U.S. Government English Project (Haiti), 1942–44; PROF., FRENCH, CHMN., ROMANCE LANGUAGES, WEST VA. STATE COLL., 1947– . Rosenwald fellow, 1944–45; Columbia U. fellow, 1946–47; Ford Foundation fellow, Columbia U., 1951–52; Fulbright fellow, 1958–59; consultant, National Screening Committee for Fulbright awards, Institute of International Education, 1964–65. Membership: American Association of Teachers of French; American Association of University Professors; College Language Association; Modern Language Association; Modern Language Teacher's Association; National Association of Foreign Student Advisers. Research: Haiti; American literature and language. Author: The Renaissance of Haitian Poetry (1963); Saint Marc, Haiti (Opportunity, Winter 1947); French Poets of African Descent (College Language Association Journal, Sept. 1961). Language: Spanish 3,3,2,2; Portuguese 1,1,1,1; French 5,5,5,5. Office: Dept. of Romance Languages, West Va. State Coll., Institute, W. Va.

GATELL, FRANK OTTO, b. New York, N.Y., July 28, 1931. HISTORY. B.A., City Coll. (N.Y.), 1956; A.M., Harvard U., 1958; Ph. D., 1960. Vis. lectr., U. of P.R., Summer 1959; ASST. PROF., HISTORY, U. OF MD., 1959– . Membership: American Historical Association; Phi Alpha Theta. Research: Caribbean history, particularly Puerto Rico. Author: Puerto Rico and the Tydings Bill of 1936 (Hispanic American Historical Review, Feb. 1958); Panama Canal Episode in Retrospect (The Americas, July 1960); Muñoz Rivera and the Puerto Rican Jones Bill (The Americas, July 1960). Language: Spanish 5,5,4,4; Portuguese 2,2,1,1; French 3,2,1,1. Home: 8523 Garland Ave., Takoma Park, Md. Office: Dept. of History, U. of Md., College Park.

GATES, EUNICE JOINER, b. Ribeirão Preto, Brazil, Oct. 12, 1898. SPANISH AMERICAN AND BRAZILIAN LITERATURE. B.A., Southwestern U., 1921; M.A., U. of Mich., 1927; Ph. D., U. of Pa., 1933. Instr., Southwestern U., 1922–24; acting head, Romance Languages, Southwest Tex. State Teachers Coll., 1924–25; instr.-assoc. prof., Tex. Technological Coll., 1925–45; prof., Tex. Christian U., 1946–48; prof., Spanish and Portuguese, Tex. Technological Coll., 1948–64; RETIRED, 1964– . Membership: American Association of Teachers of Spanish and Portuguese; Ibero-American Institute; Modern Language Association. Research: works of Luis de Góngora, Calderón de la Barca, and Andrés de Uztarroz. Author: The Imagery of Don Segundo Sombra (Hispanic Review, Jan. 1948); Usigli as Seen in His Prefaces and Epilogues (Hispania, Dec. 1954); Charles Darwin and Benito Lynch's El Inglés de los Güesos (Hispania, May 1961). Langauge: Spanish 5,4,4,4; Portuguese 5,5,4,5; French 3,2,2,2.

Home; 102 Beverly Dr., San Antonio, Tex., 78201.

GAULD, CHARLES ANDERSON, b. Portland, Oreg., Aug. 12, 1911. HISTORY. A.B., Stanford U., 1932; M.A., U. of Wash., 1936; Ph. D., Stanford U., 1964. Instr., Hill Military Academy (Oreg.), 1932–34; junior specialist on Latin American official publications, Library of Congress, 1938–41; editorial writer, Foreign Broadcast Intelligence Service, Federal Communications Commission, 1941–42; writer, Press and Information, Office of Inter-American Affairs, 1942–45; freelance research and writing (Brazil), 1946–54; asst. prof., Inter-American U. (P.R.), 1955–58; LECTR., ASST. EDITOR, HISPANIC AMERICAN REPORT, HISPANIC AMERICAN INSTITUTE, STANFORD U., 1955–58, 1962– . Membership: American Historical Association; American Geographical Society; Conference on Latin American History. Research: industrial and mining history and development; economic history and geography of Brazil and Spanish America. Author: Directory of Americans Interested in Brazil (1950); The Last Titan: Percival Farquhar, American Entrepreneur in Latin America (1964). Language: Spanish 5,5,5,4; Portuguese 5,5,5,4; French 3,2,2,3. Home: c/o Donaugh, 11737 East Evergreen, Vancouver, Wash. 98664. Office: Hispanic American Studies, Stanford U., Stanford, Calif., 94305.

GAUTHIER, HOWARD L., JR., b. Meriden, Conn., Aug. 29, 1935. GEOGRAPHY. B.S., Central Conn. State Coll., 1957; M.A., Northwestern U., 1960; Ph. D., 1964. ASST. PROF., GEOGRAPHY, OHIO STATE U., 1963– . National Academy of Science fellow (Brazil), 1961–62; National Science Foundation fellow. Membership: Association of American Geographers; Regional Science Association. Research: urban and transportation planning; international trade. Language: Spanish 3,3,3,3; Portuguese 4,4,4,4; French 5,5,5,5; German 2,2,-2,2; Italian 2,2,2,2. Home: 919 Faculty Dr., Columbus 2, Ohio. Office: Dept. of Geography, Ohio State U., 1775 South College Rd., Columbus 10.

GAYTON, ANNA HADWICK, b. Santa Cruz, Calif., Sept. 20, 1899. ANTHROPOLOGY. A.B., U. of Calif., Berkeley, 1923; M.A., 1924; Ph. D., 1928. PROF., ANTHROPOLOGY, CURATOR OF TEXTILES, LOWIE MUSEUM OF ANTHROPOLOGY, U. OF CALIF., BERKELEY, 1948– . National Research Council fellow, 1928–30; Guggenheim fellow, 1947. Membership: American Anthropological Association; American Folklore Society; Sigma Xi; Society for American Archaeology. Research: textile and costume history; ethnic and archeological textiles of Middle and South America, especially ancient Peru; Portuguese Espírito Santo Festival. Author: The Cultural Significance of Peruvian Textiles (1961); Textiles and Costumes (in Handbook of Middle American Indians). Co-author: The Uhle Pottery Collections from Nazca (1927). Language: Spanish 3,2,1,1; Portuguese 3,2,1,2; French 3,1,1,1. Home: P.O. Box 880, Santa Cruz, Calif., 95061. Office: Dept. of Decorative Art, U. of Calif., Berkeley, 94720.

GERASSI, JOHN, b. Paris, France, July 12, 1931. JOURNALISM. Bac. ès lettres, Lyceé Français de New York, 1950; B.A., Columbia U., 1952; M.A., 1954. Editor, Latin American Section, Time Magazine, 1957–61; correspondent, New York Times (Latin America), 1961–62; freelance writer, 1962–63; EDITOR, LATIN AMERICA, NEWSWEEK MAGAZINE, 1963– . Research: philosophy; anthropology; political science. Author: The Great Fear (1963); The Meaning of Castroism (The New Republic, 1963); Series on South America (Baltimore Sun, 1962–63). Language: Spanish 5,5,5,4; Portuguese 3,3,3,1; French 5,5,5,5. Home: 789 West End Ave., New York 25, N.Y. Office: Newsweek, 444 Madison Ave., New York 22.

GERASSI, MARYSA, b. Pamplona, Spain, Oct. 12, 1934. HISTORY. B.A., Instituto José Batlle y Ordoñez (Uruguay), 1955; M.A., Columbia U., 1960; Ph. D., 1964. Lectr., Consejo de Enseñanza Secundaria (Uruguay), 1955–58; lectr., Riverdale Country School, 1958–59; lectr., Hunter Coll., 1963–64; lectr., Rutgers U., 1963–64; ASST. PROF., HISTORY, NEWARK STATE COLL., 1964– . Institute of International Education fellow, Douglass Coll., Rutgers U., 1956–57; Organization of American States grant (Argentina), 1961–62; Social Science Research Council grant, 1962–63; consultant, Council of Foreign Relations. Membership: American Historical Association. Research: Argentina. Language: Spanish 5,5,5,5; Portuguese 5,5,4,1; French 5,5,5,5; Italian 5,5,4,1. Home: 789 West End Ave., New York 25, N.Y. Office: Dept. of History, Newark State Coll., Morris Ave., Union, N.J.

GERHARD, PETER, b. Evanston, Ill., Sept. 26, 1920. HISTORY. Accountant, American Smelting & Refining Company (Mexico), 1947–49; industrial relations supervisor, Mene Grande Oil Company (Venezuela), 1949–51, 1953–58, RETIRED, 1958– . Research: ethnohistory and historical geography; Mexico. Author: Lower California Guidebook (1956, 1958, 1962); México en 1742 (1962); El avance español en México y Centroamérica (Historia Mexicana, July–Sept. 1959). Language: Spanish 5,-5,5,4; Portuguese 2,2,1,1; French 4,3,3,1; Nahuatl 1,2,2,1. Linguistic studies: Nahuatl. Home: Torre de Atongo, Tepoztlán, Morelos, México.

GERLACH, ARCH C., b. Tacoma, Wash., May 12, 1911. GEOGRAPHY. B.A., San Diego State Coll., 1933; M.A., U. of Calif., Los Angeles, 1935; Ph. D., U. of Wash., 1943. Instr., Los Angeles City Coll., 1939–42; cartographer, administrator, Office of Strategic Services, 1942–45; chief, Map Div., U.S. Dept. of State, 1945–46; assoc. prof., U. of Wis., 1947–50; CHIEF, MAP DIV., CHAIR OF GEOGRAPHY, LIBRARY OF CONGRESS, 1950– ; vis. prof., U. of Mich., 1957–58; chief, National Atlas Project, U.S. Geological Survey, 1962–64. Map editor, Handbook of Latin American Studies, 1950–61; editor, The Professional Geographer, 1951–54; chmn., U.S. National Section, Pan American Institute of Geography and History. Membership: Association of American Geographers; International Geographical Union; Special Libraries Association. Research: cartography. Author: Geography and Map Cataloging and Classification in Libraries (Special Libraries, May–June 1961); Globes Terrestrial (Encyclopedia of Science and Technology, 1960) ; National Atlas of the United States; American Geography, 1960–1963 (1964). Language : Spanish 3,2,2,1 ; French 2,-,-,-. Home : 5615 Newington Rd., Washington 16, D.C. Office: Map Div., Library of Congress, Washington, D.C. 20540.

GIBBS, BEVERLY JEAN, b. Cadillac, Mich., Dec. 6, 1929. SPANISH AMERICAN LITERATURE. B.A., U. of Mich., 1951 ; M.A., 1952 ; Ph. D., U. of Wis., 1960. Instr., U. of Tex., 1957–61 ; asst. prof., 1961–64; ASSOC. PROF., SPANISH, U. OF TEX., 1964– . U. of Wis. Spanish Departmental fellow, 1955–56. Membership: American Association of Teachers of Spanish and Portuguese ; American Association of University Professors ; Modern Language Association ; Texas Association of College Teachers. Research : contemporary literature and novel of Argentina and Mexico. Author: Impressionism as a Literary Movement (Modern Language Journal, Apr. 1952) ; Spatial Treatment in the Contemporary Psychological Novel of Argentina (Hispania, Sept. 1962). Language : Spanish 5,4,4,4 ; Portuguese 3,2,1,1 ; French 4,2,2,3 ; German 2,1,1,1 ; Italian 3,2,1,1. Home : 3604 Winfield Cove, Austin, Tex. 78704. Office: Dept. of Romance Languages, U. of Tex., Austin, 78712.

GIBSON, CHARLES, b. Buffalo, N.Y., Aug. 12, 1920. HISTORY. B.A., Yale U., 1941 ; M.A., U. of Tex., 1947 ; Ph. D., Yale U., 1950. Asst. prof.-Prof., State U. of Iowa, 1949–1965 ; PROF., HISTORY, U. OF MICH., 1965– . Social Science Research Council fellow, 1948 ; Guggenheim fellow, 1952–53 ; Rockefeller Foundation grant, 1961. Membership: American Historical Association ; Conference on Latin American History. Research : colonial Latin America ; Mexico. Author: Tlaxcala in the Sixteenth Century (1952) ; Guide to Hispanic American Historical Review (1958). Coauthor: The Tovar Calendar (1951). Language : Spanish 4,4,3,3 ; Portuguese 2,-,-,- ; French 4,3,3,3. Linguistic studies: Nahuatl. Home : 2872 Glacier Way, Ann Arbor, Mich. Office: Dept. of History, U. of Mich., Ann Arbor.

GICOVATE, BERNARD, b. Santos, Brazil, Apr. 21, 1922. SPANISH AMERICAN LITERATURE. Dr., U. of Buenos Aires, 1943 ; B.A., Bowdoin Coll., 1945 ; M.A., U. of N.C., 1946 ; Ph. D., Harvard U., 1952. Instr., Randolph Macon Woman's Coll., 1946–47 ; instr., Boston U., 1947–49 ; prof., U. of Oreg., 1949–55 ; vis. prof., U. of Calif., Berkeley, Summer 1954 ; PROF., SPANISH AND PORTUGUESE, DIR., CENTER FOR LATIN AMERICAN STUDIES, TULANE U., 1955– . Ford faculty fellow, 1953–54 ; Tulane Council on Research grant (Paris), 1958–59 ; American Council of Learned Societies grant-in-aid, 1960 ; contributing editor, Handbook of Latin American Studies, 1961– . Membership: American Association of Teachers of Spanish and Portuguese ; Instituto Internacional de Literatura Iberoamericana ; Modern Language Association. Research : comparative literature ; poetry. Author: Julio Herrera y Reissig and the Symbolists (1957) ; La poesía de Juan Ramón Jiménez. Ensayo de exégesis (1959) ; Conceptos fundamentales de literatura comparada (1962). Language : Spanish 5,5,5,5 ; Portuguese 3,2,1,1 ; French 4,4,4,2. Home : 3035 Calhoun St., New Orleans, La. 70118. Office: Center for Latin American Studies, Tulane U., New Orleans, 70118.

GIFFIN, DONALD WARREN, b. Long Beach, Calif., July 7, 1927. HISTORY. B.A., U. of Calif., Santa Barbara, 1950 ; M.A., Vanderbilt U., 1956 ; Ph. D., 1962. Teacher, Kamehameha Schools (Hawaii), 1952–54 ; assoc. dir., Development, Vanderbilt U., 1958–61 ; asst. prof., Ga. State Coll., 1962–63 ; ASST. PROF., ASST. CHMN., HISTORY, U. OF MD., 1963– . Membership: American Historical Association ; Mississippi Valley Historical Association ; Southern Historical Association. Research: Brazil ; Brazil-United States relations. Author : The American Navy at Work on the Brazil Station, 1827–1861 (American Neptune, Oct. 1959). Language : Spanish 3,2,2,1 ; Portuguese 3,2,2,1. Home : Apt. 4, 4605 Calvert Rd., College Park, Md. Office : Dept. of History, U. of Md., College Park.

GIL, FEDERICO GUILLERMO, b. Havana, Cuba, Feb. 10, 1915. POLITICAL SCIENCE. B.A., U. of Havana, 1935 ; LL.D., 1940 ; Ph. D., 1941 ; Licentiate of Diplomatic and Consular Law, 1942. Instr., U. of N.C., 1943–45 ; asst. prof., 1945–49 ; assoc. prof., 1949–55 ; PROF., POLITICAL SCIENCE, U. OF N.C., 1955– ; research prof., Instituto de Ciencias Políticas y Administrativas, U. of Chile, 1956–57 ; DIR., INSTITUTE OF LATIN AMERICAN STUDIES, U. OF N.C., 1959– ; vis. prof., Instituto de Estudios Políticos (San José, Costa Rica), Oct. 1960. Institute of International Education fellow, 1942 ; Rockefeller fellow, 1944–45, 1956–57 ; Ford Foundation fellow, Summer 1958 ; Social Science Research Council grant, 1958 ; consultant, International Training and Research Program, Ford Foundation, 1962–63. Membership: American Association of Latin American Studies ; American Association of University Professors ; American Political Science Association ; Argentine Association of Political Science ; Asociación Latinoamericana de Ciencias Políticas; Asociación Latinoamericana de Sociología ; National Academy of Law and Social Science (Argentina) ; Southeastern Conference of Latin American Studies ; Southern Political Science Association. Research : politics and governments in Latin America ; Chilean politics. Author: Genesis and Modernization of Political Parties in Chile (1962) ; Chile : Society in Transition (in Political Systems of Latin America, 1963). Coauthor: Governments of Latin America (1957). Language : Spanish 5,5,5,5 ; Portuguese 5,5,3,3 ; French 3,2,2,1 ; Italian 4,3,3,1. Home : 5 Mount Bolus, Chapel Hill, N.C. Office: Dept. of Political Science, U. of N.C., Chapel Hill.

GILL, CLARK C., b. Winona County, Minn., Feb. 19, 1915. EDUCATION. B.A., Hamline U., 1935 ; M.A., U. of Minn., 1939 ; Ph. D., 1948. Instr., Macalester Coll., 1947–48 ; teacher, State Coll. (Pa.), 1948–50 ; curriculum dir., U.S. Armed Forces Institute, 1950–52 ; coordinator of course writing, U. of Wis., 1952–54 ; ASSOC. PROF., EDUCATION, U. OF TEX., 1954– . Fulbright prof., U. of San Marcos (Lima), 1960 ; field study of Chilean education, U.S. Office of Education, Summer 1963. Membership: American Association of University Professors; National Council for the Social Studies; National Society for Study of Education; Phi Delta Kappa; Texas Council for Social Studies; Texas State Teachers Association. Research: public education in Mexico; education in Latin America. Author: South American Students Ask about United States Schools (School and Society, Apr. 1963); Peru: One Nation or Two (Social Science, Oct. 1963). Language: Spanish 4,4,4,4. Office: School of Education, U. of Tex., Austin 12.

GILLASPIE, WILLIAM ROSCOE, b. Kansas City, Mo., Feb. 11, 1931. HISTORY. B.A., Westminster Coll., 1952; M.A., U. of Mo., 1954; Ph. D., U. of Fla., 1961. ASSOC. PROF., HISTORY, MEMPHIS STATE U., 1961– . American Philosophical Society grant (Mexico), Summer 1963. Membership: Conference on Latin American History; Mississippi Valley Historical Association. Research: civilian-military relations in Mexico, 1876–1910; inter-American relations. Language: Spanish 4,3,3,4. Home: 3687 Norriswood Ave., Memphis, Tenn. 38111. Office: P.O. Box 653, Memphis State U., Memphis, 38111.

GILLIM, MARION HAMILTON, b. Owensboro, Ky., Apr. 12, 1909. ECONOMICS. A.B., Mount Holyoke Coll., 1930; A.M., Columbia U., 1938; Ph. D., 1944. Instr., N.J. Coll. for Women, Rutgers U., 1941–42; instr., Mount Holyoke Coll., 1942–44; asst. prof., 1944–48; assoc. prof., 1948–49; consultant, U.S. Dept. of Labor (Costa Rica, Ecuador, Uruguay), 1949–52; assoc. prof., Barnard Coll., 1952–62; PROF., ECONOMICS, BARNARD COLL., 1962– ; adviser in public finance, Economic Commission for Latin America (Mexico, D.F.), 1964–65. Brookings Institution research prof., 1958–59. Membership: Academy of Political Science; American Association of University Professors; American Economic Association; American Statistical Association; International Fiscal Association; International Institute of Public Finance; National Tax Association; Phi Beta Kappa. Research: public finance; international economics; fiscal aspects of international economic integration; the taxation of family income; family expenditure studies; consumer price indexes; Latin American Free Trade Association; Central American Common Market. Author: The Incidence of Excess Profits Taxation (1944). Language: Spanish 4,4,4,4; Portuguese 1,1,1,1; French 4,3,3,3. Home: 1505 Griffith Ave., Owensboro, Ky. 42301. Office: Dept. of Economics, Barnard Coll., Columbia U., New York, N.Y. 10027.

GILLIN, JOHN PHILLIP, b. Waterloo, Iowa, Aug. 1, 1907. ANTHROPOLOGY. B.A., U. of Wis., 1927; M.A., 1930; Ph. D., Harvard U., 1934. Staff member, Peabody Museum, Harvard U., 1934–35; asst. prof., U. of Utah, 1935–37; asst. prof., Ohio State U., 1937–41; assoc. prof., Duke U., 1941–46; research prof., U. of N.C., 1946–59; DEAN, SOCIAL SCIENCES, RESEARCH PROF., ANTHROPOLOGY, U. OF PITTSBURGH, 1959– . Carnegie fellow, 1940–41; research assoc., Carnegie Institution of Washington 1942, 1946; chmn., Committee on Latin American Culture, National Research Council, 1946–51; traveling representative in Latin America, UNESCO, 1950; National Institute of Mental Health grant (Guatemala), 1963; Selection Committee, Doherty Foundation. Membership: American Anthropological Association; American Association for the Advancement of Science; American Association of Physical Anthropologists; American Ethnological Society; American Sociological Society. Research: Peru, Ecuador, and Guatemala; modern Latin American culture. Author: Problems of Ideological Choice in Contemporary Latin America (Actas, XXXIII Congreso Internacional de Americanistas, 1958); Changing Depths in Latin America (Journal of Inter-American Studies, Oct. 1960); Possible Cultural Maladjustments in Modern Latin America (Journal of Inter-American Studies, Apr. 1963). Language: Spanish 5,5,4,3; Portuguese 4,3,1,1; French 4,3,1,1; German 3,2,1,1. Office: Dean of Social Science, U. of Pittsburgh, Pittsburgh 13, Pa.

GILLMOR, FRANCES, b. Buffalo, N.Y., May 21, 1903. ANTHROPOLOGY: FOLKLORE. B.A., U. of Ariz., 1928; M.A., 1931; Litt. D., Universidad Nacional Autónoma de México, 1957. Instr., U. of Ariz., 1931–32; instr., U. of N. Mex., 1932–34; asst. prof., U. of Ariz., 1934–44; assoc. prof., 1944–52; PROF., ENGLISH, U. OF ARIZ., 1952– . Guggenheim f e l l o w (Spain), 1959–60. Membership: American Anthropological Association; American Association of University Professors; American Folklore Society; Authors League of America; Modern Language Association; Phi Beta Kappa; Phi Kappa Phi; Sociedad Folklórica de México; Sociedad de Geografía e Historia de Honduras. Research: folklore and preconquest history of Mexico; comparison of village fiestas and folk drama in Spain, Mexico, and the Southwest. Author: Flute of the Smoking Mirror: A Biography of Nezahualcoyotl (1949); The King Danced in the Market Place: A Biography of Moteczuma I l h u i c a m i n a (1964); Spanish Texts of Three Dance Dramas from Mexican Villages (Humanities Bulletin, U. of Ariz., 1942). Language: Spanish 4,4,4,4; Portuguese 2,1,1,1; French 3,1,2,1. Home: Box 4605, University Station, Tucson, Ariz. 85717. Office: Dept. of English, U. of Ariz., Tucson, 85721.

GILMORE, N(EWTON) RAY, b. Chicago, Ill., Jan. 23, 1924. HISTORY. B.A., U. of Mich., 1948; M.A., 1948; Ph. D., U. of Calif., Berkeley, 1956. Instr., San Francisco State Coll., 1956; instr., U. of Calif., Los Angeles, 1957; instr., San Jose State Coll., 1957–58; INSTR., HISTORY, MONTEREY PENINSULA COLL., 1958– . Buenos Aires Convention exchange fellow (Mexico), 1952–53. Membership: American Association of University Professors; American Historical Association; Conference on Latin American History; Hispanic American Society; Pacific Coast Council on Latin American Studies. Research: Mexican national history. Author: Henry George Ward, British Publicist for Mexican Mines (Pacific Historical Review, Feb. 1963); The Bracero in California (Pacific Historical Review, Aug. 1963); Mexico and the Spanish American War (Hispanic American Historical Review, Nov. 1963). Language: Spanish 4,4,3,3; French 3,2,1,2. Home: 1031 North Hanna, Gilroy, Calif. Office: Dept. of History, Monterey Peninsula Coll., Monterey, Calif.

GILMORE, ROBERT LOUIS, b. Monroe, Iowa,

Sept. 8, 1913. HISTORY. B.A., Creighton U., 1935; M.A., 1939; Ph. D., U. of Calif., Berkeley, 1949. Officer, Tri-Metrogon Mapping Program, U.S. Army Air Corps (Brazil and British Guiana), 1943–44, 1945; asst. prof., Vanderbilt U., 1951–55; analyst, Office of Intelligence Research, U.S. Dept. of State, 1956–60; ASSOC. PROF., HISTORY, OHIO U., 1960– . Institute of International Education maintenance fellowship (Colombia), 1942. Membership: American Historical Association; Conference on Latin American History; Ohio Academy of History. Research: late 18th and early 19th centuries in Colombia; Mexico. Author: Caudillism and Militarism in Venezuela, 1810–1910 (1964); Nueva Granada's Socialist Mirage (Hispanic American Historical Review, May 1956); The Imperial Crisis, Rebellion, and the Viceroy: Nueva Granada in 1809 (Hispanic American Historical Review, Feb. 1960). Language: Spanish 5,4,3,3; Portuguese 4,2,2,1; French 4,1,1,1. Home: 18 Grand Park Blvd., Athens, Ohio 45701. Office: Dept. of History, Ohio U., Athens, 45701.

GJELSNESS, RUDOLPH H., b. Reynolds, N. Dak., Oct. 18, 1894. LIBRARY SCIENCE. A.B., U. of N. Dak., 1916; B.L.S., U. of Ill., 1920; Litt. D. (honorary), Luther Coll., 1953; LL.D. (honorary), U. of N. Dak., 1958. Reference librarian, A.E.F.U. (France), 1919; head, Order Dept., U. of Oreg., 1920–22; senior bibliographer, U. of Calif., Berkeley, 1922–24; asst. librarian, U. of Mich., 1925–28; chief, Preparation Div., New York Public Library, 1928–32; librarian and prof., U. of Ariz., 1932–37; PROF., CHMN., LIBRARY SCIENCE, U. OF MICH., 1937– ; American dir., Summer Library School (Bogotá, Colombia), 1942; dir., Benjamin Franklin Library (Mexico, D.F.), and vis. prof., National School of Anthropology, National U. of Mexico, 1943–44. American Scandinavian Foundation fellow (Norway), 1924–25; consultant to the president, U. of Baghdad (Iraq), 1962–63. Membership: American Library Association; Arizona Library Association; Association of American Library Schools; Bibliographical Society of America; Michigan Academy of Arts, Sciences and Letters; Michigan Library Association; Phi Beta Kappa. Research: library science education; university library administration; cataloging and classification; copyright and publishing history. Author: American Library Association Catalog Rules (1941); Catálogo colectivo de publicaciones periódicas (1949); The American Book in Mexico (1957). Language: Spanish 3,3,3,3; French 3,3,3,3; German 3,3,3,3; Norwegian 5,5,4,4. Home: 1030 Ferdon Rd., Ann Arbor, Mich. Office: Dept. of Library Science, U. of Mich., Ann Arbor.

GLADE, WILLIAM P., JR., b. Wichita Falls, Tex., July 29, 1929. ECONOMICS. B.B.A., U. of Tex., 1950; M.A., 1951; Ph. D., 1955. Instr.-asst. prof., U. of Md., 1957–60; asst. prof., U. of Wis., 1960–63; ASSOC. PROF., ECONOMICS, U. OF WIS., 1963– . Farmer scholarship, U. of Tex. (Mexico), 1953; Ford Foundation fellow, 1958–59; U. of Md. research grant, 1958; U. of Wis. research grant (Peru), 1961, (Colombia), 1963. Membership: American Economics Association; Hispanic American Society; Midwest Council of the Association for Latin American Studies. Research: economic development in underdeveloped areas and associated institutional or social changes; international marketing; community development in Colombia; labor economics; economic structure of Mexico, Guatemala, and Peru. Author: The Political Economy of Mexico (1963); Las empresas gubernamentales descentralizadas (Problemas Agrícolas e Industriales de México, 1959); Social Backwardness, Social Reform, and Productivity in Latin America (Inter-American Economic Affairs, Winter 1961). Language: Spanish 4,4,3,3; Portuguese 3,2,2,2; French 3,2,2,2. Home: 653 Pickford St., Madison, Wis. Office: Commerce Bldg., U. of Wis., Madison.

GLAUERT, EARL THEODORE, b. St. Louis, Mo., Mar. 24, 1928. HISTORY. Ph. D., U. of Pa., 1962. ASST. PROF., HISTORY, U. OF CALIF., LOS ANGELES, 1960– . American Philosophical Society fellow, 1958; Doherty fellow (Argentina), 1958; Foreign Policy Research Institute fellow, 1959; Ford Foundation fellow (Argentina), 1963–64; lectr., U.S. Peace Corps, 1963. Membership: American Historical Association; Pacific Coast Council of Latin American Studies. Research: social and intellectual history; cultural nationalism in Argentina. Author: Ricardo Rojas and the Emergence of Argentine Nationalism (Hispanic American Historical Review, Jan. 1963. Language: Spanish 5,4,3,3; German 3,2,2,2. Home: 2310 Malcolm Ave., Los Angeles, Calif. 90064. Office: Dept. of History, U. of Calif., Los Angeles, 90024.

GLICK, EDWARD B., b. Brooklyn, N.Y., Feb. 12, 1929. POLITICAL SCIENCE. B.A., Brooklyn Coll., 1950; M.A., U. of Fla., 1952; Ph. D., 1955. Instr., U. of Fla., 1955–56; dir., Commission on International Affairs, American Jewish Congress, 1956–59; lectr., City Coll. (N.Y.), 1957–58; POLITICAL SCIENTIST, SPECIAL STUDIES STAFF, SYSTEM DEVELOPMENT CORPORATION, 1959– ; lectr., Public Affairs Lecture Bureau (N.Y.), 1961– ; Hunter Coll., 1962; PROFESSORIAL LECTR., SCHOOL OF INTERNATIONAL SERVICE, AMERICAN U., 1963– . U. of Fla. graduate fellow, 1952–55; consultant, Latin American Dept., Jewish Agency for Israel, 1956; Latin American consultant, American Jewish Committee, 1960; American Jewish Committee grant (Mexico), Summer 1963. Membership: American Political Science Association; Hispanic American Society; Inter-American Council of Washngton; International Political Science Association; Phi Kappa Phi; Pi Sigma Alpha; Society for International Development. Research: Latin American-Israeli relations; Latin American disarmament; Latin American relations with the United Nations; Cuba. Author: El papel desempeñado por América Latina en la consideración del problema de Palestina por Las Naciones Unidas (1956); Latin America and the Palestine Problem (1958); Straddling the Isthmus of Tehuantepec (1959). Language: Spanish 4,3,3,2; Portuguese 2,1,1,1; French 3,3,3,3; German 3,3,3,2; Hebrew 4,4,4,4. Home: 1708 Glenbrook Rd., Fairfax, Va. 22030. Office: System Development Corporation, 5821 Columbia Pike, Falls Church, Va.

GLICK, MILTON LOUIS, b. Baltimore, Md., Sept. 2, 1926. ECONOMICS. B.A., N.Y.U., 1949; M.A., U. of Chicago, 1952; Ph. D., 1963. Industrial relations analyst, Wage Stabilization Board, 1952-53; instr., Ill. Institute of Technology, 1954-55; commodity-industry economist, Headquarters, Ordnance Weapons Command, 1955-59; instr.-ASST. PROF., ECONOMICS, WITTENBERG U., 1959- . Membership: American Economic Association. Research: effect of economic development on returns to labor in agriculture in Mexico. Language: Spanish 2,1,1,1; French 2,1,1,1. Home: 200 West Harding Rd., Springfield, Ohio 45504. Office: Dept. of Economics, Wittenberg U., Springfield, 45501.

GLICKMAN, ROBERT JAY, b. New York, N.Y., Aug. 29, 1928. SPANISH AMERICAN LITERATURE. B.A., Brooklyn Coll., 1948; M.A., Brown U., 1951; Ph. D., U. of Calif., Los Angeles, 1963. Instr., U. of Calif., Riverside, 1958-60; instr., Harvard U., 1960-63; ASST. PROF., ITALIAN AND HISPANIC STUDIES, U. OF TORONTO, 1963- . Membership: American Association of Teachers of Spanish and Portuguese; Canadian Association of Hispanists; Modern Language Association. Research: modernist poets of Latin America. Language: Spanish 5,5,5,5; Portuguese 4,4,4,4; French 4,4,4,4; Italian 4,4,4,4. Home: 276 St. Clair Ave. West, Toronto 7, Canada. Office: Dept. of Italian and Hispanic Studies, U. of Toronto, Toronto 5.

GODFREY, ERWINA EDWARDS, b. Buckeye, Ky., Aug. 3, 1916. POLITICAL SCIENCE. A.B., Transylvania Coll., 1937; M.A., U. of Ky., 1957; Ph. D., 1960. Teacher, American School (Rio de Janeiro), 1943-46; instr., U. of Ky., 1957-58; ASST. PROF., SOCIAL SCIENCE, CENTRAL MO. STATE COLL., 1960- ; dir., Latin American Institute, Central Mo. State Coll., Summer 1963. Southern Fellowships Fund fellow, 1958-60. Membership: American Political Science Association; Mid-West Latin American Society; Mid-West Political Science Association; Missouri Council of the Social Studies; Missouri Political Science Association; National Education Association. Research: international relations; Brazil. Author: Foreign Aid to Brazil from Private U.S. Sources (Journal of Inter-American Studies, Apr. 1963). Co-author: Voting Participation of 18 to 21 Year Old Students in Kentucky (1959). Language: Spanish 3,2,1,1; Portuguese 3,3,3,2; French 2,2,1,1. Home: 502 Jefferson St., Warrensburg, Mo. Office: Dept. of Social Science, Central Mo. State Coll., Warrensburg.

GODFREY, WILLIAM SIMPSON, JR., b. Philadelphia, Pa., Mar. 25, 1916. ANTHROPOLOGY. A.B., Harvard U., 1939; M.A., 1951; Ph. D., 1952. Instr., U. of Chicago, 1950-51; asst. prof.-PROF., ANTHROPOLOGY, BELOIT COLL., 1951- . Membership: American Anthropological Association; American Association of Physical Anthropologists; American Association of University Professors; Society for American Archaeology; Wisconsin Academy of Science, Arts and Letters. Research: archeology; Mexico; Guatemala. Language: Spanish 4,3,3,3; French 4,3,3,3; German 2,2,-,-. Home: 1229 Chapin St., Beloit, Wis. 53511. Office: Dept. of Anthropology, Beloit Coll., Beloit.

GOERING, THEODORE JAMES, b. Pretty Prairie, Kans., May 3, 1935. ECONOMICS. B.S., Kans. State U., 1957; M.S., Mich. State U., 1958; Ph. D., 1962. Research assoc., Mich. State U. (Cali, Colombia), 1960-62; asst. prof., U. of Calif., Berkeley, 1962-63; ADMINISTRATOR, U.S. PEACE CORPS (GUATEMALA), 1963-65. American Farm Economics Association travel grant (France), 1964. Membership: Alpha Zeta; American Farm Economics Association; Delta Phi Epsilon; Gamma Sigma Delta; Phi Kappa Phi. Research: economic development; agricultural economics; international trade; community development in Guatemala; Colombia. Author: Public Law 480 in Colombia (Journal of Farm Economics, Nov. 1962); United States Cotton Price Policy and Foreign Production (California Agriculture, Mar. 1963). Co-author: A Review of United States Agricultural Surplus Disposal in Colombia (Michigan Agricultural Experiment Station Bulletin, 1963). Language: Spanish 4,4,3,3. Home: R.F.D. 2, Box 88, Pretty Prairie, Kans. Office: U.S. Peace Corps, American Embassy, Guatemala, Guatemala.

GOGGIN, MARGARET ENID, b. Nyack, N.Y. LIBRARY SCIENCE. A.B., Maryville Coll., 1940; B.S., George Peabody Coll., 1942; M.S., U. of Ill., 1948; Ph. D., 1957. Reference asst., Joint University Library (Nashville), 1942-43; acting reference librarian, 1943-45; vis. instr., Peabody Library School, 1943-45, Summer 1948; readers' adviser, Youngstown Public Library (Ohio), 1945-46; bibliographer and reference librarian, Office of Technical Services, U.S. Dept. of Commerce, 1946-47; asst. to the dir. of libraries, asst. prof., U. of Fla., 1949-50; head, Dept. of Reference and Bibliography, assoc. prof., 1950-62; vis. lectr., Library School, U. of Okla., Summer 1959; ASST. DIR., READERS' SERVICES, LIBRARIES, ASSOC. PROF., LIBRARY SCIENCE, U. OF FLA., 1962- . Katherine L. Sharp fellow, U. of Ill., 1947-48; Southern Fellowship Fund fellow, 1956-57; Rockefeller Foundation grant (Haiti), Summer 1958; library consultant, Daytona Beach Junior Coll., Mar. 1961; Rockefeller Foundation research grant (Paris, France), Winter 1961. Membership: American Documentation Institute; American Library Association; Association of Research Libraries; Beta Sigma Phi; Florida Library Association; Southeastern Library Association. Research: bibliography; archival materials in Haiti. Author: For Every Reference Librarian—A Development Program (The Southeastern Librarian, Winter 1961); Services of Colleges and Universities of the Southeast for Business and Industry (Southeastern Libraries, Summer 1963). Editor: Sources for the Study of the Peruvian Aprista Movement (1955). Language: Spanish 2,2,1,1; French 4,3,3,3. Home: 4024 NW. 15th St., Gainesville, Fla. Office: Libraries, U. of Fla., Gainesville.

GOINS, JOHN F., b. Birmingham, Ala., Dec. 21, 1915. ANTHROPOLOGY. B.A., U. of Calif., Berkeley, 1948; Ph. D., 1953. Instr.-asst. prof., U. of Calif., Riverside, 1954-62; assoc. prof., 1962-63; ASSOC. PROF., CHMN., ANTHROPOLOGY, U. OF CALIF., RIVERSIDE, 1963- . Doherty fellow (Bolivia), 1951-52; Social Science Research Council grant (Ecuador), 1961-

62; consultant, Div. of Evaluation, U.S. Peace Corps (Ecuador), Summer 1963. Membership: American Anthropological Association; American Ethnological Society; Institute of Andean Studies; Kroeber Anthropological Society; Pacific Coast Council of Latin American Studies; Southwestern Anthropological Association. Research: Andean culture history; ethnology of South America; law, government and art of preliterate and peasant peoples, ; Bolivia; Peru; Ecuador. Author: Present Distribution of Indian Languages in Highland Bolivia (1950) ; Law as a Means to Change (Journal of Inter-American Studies, 1962). Language: Spanish 4,4,4,4; French 4,1,1,1; German 3,1,1,1. Home: 3578 Mt. Vernon Ave., Riverside, Calif. 92507. Office: Dept. of Anthropology, U. of Calif., Riverside, 92502.

GOLD, ROBERT LEONARD, b. Ossining, N.Y., Sept. 25, 1932. HISTORY. B.S., Columbia U., 1957; M.A., Bowling Green State U., 1958; Ph. D., U. of Tex., 1964. Teacher, Rockland County Board of Public Instruction (N.Y.), 1958–59; instr., State U. of Iowa, 1959–61; ASST. PROF., HISTORY, U. OF SOUTH FLA., 1963– . Membership: American Association of University Professors; American Historical Association; Florida Historical Society. Research: modern Mexico; Spanish borderlands during the colonial period. Author: The Restoration of St. Augustine (Florida Guide, Jan. 1962) ; Politics and Property during the Transfer of Florida from Spanish to English Control, 1763–65 (Florida Historical Quarterly, July 1963); The Settlement of the East Florida Spaniards in Cuba, 1763–66 (Florida Historical Quarterly, Feb. 1964). Language: Spanish 5,4,3,3; French 3,2,2,1. Home: 99 Wynona Ave., Staten Island 14, N.Y. Office: Dept. of History, U. of South Fla., Tampa 12.

GOLDE, PEGGY JEAN, b. St. Louis, Mo., Sept. 29, 1930. ANTHROPOLOGY. B.A., Antioch Coll., 1953; Ph. D., Harvard U., 1963. RESEARCH ASSOC., HARVARD SCHOOL OF PUBLIC HEALTH, 1962– ; LECTR., SOCIAL RELATIONS, HARVARD U., 1963– . Ford Foundation fellow, 1954; Thomas Dana scholar, 1955; Doherty grant, 1959–61; Social Science Research Council fellow, 1961–62. Membership: American Anthropological Association. Research: social anthropology; Indian religion and art in Latin America; public health in Peru; Indian culture in Mexico. Co-author: Some Aspects of the Folklore of Water Witching in the United States (Journal of American Folklore, Oct.–Dec. 1958) ; A Sentence Completion Procedure for Assessing Attitudes toward Old People (Journal of Gerontology, July 1959). Language: Spanish 3,4,4,2; Portuguese 1,-,-,-; French 2,-,-,-; Nahuatl -,4,3,-. Home: 1 Newport Rd., Cambridge 40, Mass. Office: Harvard School of Public Health, 692 Huntington Ave., Boston 15, Mass.

GOLDKIND, VICTOR, b. Brooklyn, N.Y., Mar. 21, 1926. ANTHROPOLOGY. B.S., George Washington U., 1949; M.A., Mich. State U., 1959; Ph. D., 1963. Instr., Mich. State U., 1960–61; ASST. PROF. ANTHROPOLOGY, SAN DIEGO STATE COLL., 1961– . Consultant on Costa Rica, U.S. Dept. of State, 1955–56; Wenner-Gren Foundation grant (Yucatan, Mexico), 1964. Membership: American Anthropological Association; Rural Sociological Society. Research: social and cultural anthropology; peasant communities in Costa Rica and Yucatan, with emphasis on economic and political factors and rural-urban relations and migration. Author: Sociocultural Contrasts in Rural and Urban Settlement Types in Costa Rica (Rural Sociology, Dec. 1961) ; Ethnic Relations in Southeastern Mexico: A Methodological Note (American Anthropologist, Apr. 1963). Language: Spanish 4,4,4,4; French 3,3,2,2; German 3,3,3,3. Home: 2851 Barnard St., San Diego, Calif. 92110. Office: Dept. of Anthropology, San Diego State Coll., San Diego, 92115.

GOLDMAN, FRANK PERRY, b. New York, N.Y., May 25, 1912. SOCIOLOGY AND EDUCATION. B.A., Tulane U., 1948; M.A., 1949; Doutor em ciências, Universidade de São Paulo, 1961. Research assoc., Escola de Sociologia e Política (São Paulo), 1950–52; teacher, São Paulo Graded School, 1952–53; chief of staff, city and state surveys (São Paulo), 1952–53, 1957–58; field researcher, Serviço de Proteção aos índios (Rio de Janeiro), 1953–56; teacher, Universidade de São Paulo, 1953–59; chair, Social Research, Pontifícia Universidade Católica (São Paulo), 1957–59; CHAIR, EDUCATIONAL SOCIOLOGY, FACULDADE DE FILOSOFIA, CIENCIAS Y LETRAS DE RIO CLARO, 1959– . field researcher, U.S. Peace Corps study in Brazil, U. of Tex., 1962–63. Institute of International Education grant, 1949; Tulane U. grant, 1950, consultant in rural industrialization, Tecelagem Parahyba (Brazil), 1952–54; College Entrance Examinations Board (São Paulo), 1956–58, (Rio Claro), 1959–64; coordinator, Escola de Educação, Faculdade de Filosofia (Rio Claro), 1960; Fundação de Amparo às Pesquisas grant (São Paulo), 1962. Membership: American Anthropological Association; American Folklore Society; American Sociological Society; Centro de Estudos Etnológicos; Centro de Pesquisas Folclóricas; International Congress of Americanists; Phi Sigma Iota; Sociedade Brasileira de Sociologia. Research: problems in education; community studies; community approach to sociology and education; Brazil. Author: Três educadores norteamericanos no Brasil (Anhembi, May 1957) ; Uma tentativa de colonização no litoral sul de São Paulo por imigrantes oriundos do sul dos Estados Unidos após a Guerra Civil (Revista de História, 1957). Co-author: Itanhaem (1958). Language: Spanish 4,4,-4,4; Portuguese 4,4,4,4; French 2,2,2,2. Home: Rua Onze, 1579, Rio Claro, São Paulo, Brazil. Office: Faculdade de Filosofia, Ciências e Letras, Rio Claro, São Paulo.

GOLDRICH, DANIEL, b. Cleveland, Ohio, Mar. 29, 1933. POLITICAL SCIENCE. B.A., Antioch Coll., 1955; M.A., U. of N.C., 1957; Ph. D., 1959. Asst. prof.-research assoc., Bureau of Social and Political Research, Mich. State U., 1959–63; ASSOC. PROF., POLITICAL SCIENCE, RESEARCH ASSOC., INSTITUTE FOR COMMMUNITY STUDIES, U. OF OREG., 1963– . Social Science Research Council fellow, 1958–59; Ford grant (Panama), Summer 1961; Carnegie grant (Costa Rica), Summer 1963. Membership: American Association of University Professors; American Political

Science Association; Hispanic American Society. Research: political behavior research: the rising elites in Latin America and their political orientations; the politics of urbanization in Latin America, particularly the extent and quality of involvement in politics of slum dwellers. Author: Radical Nationalism: Political Orientations of Panamanian Law Students (1962); The Rulers and the Ruled: Political Power and Impotence in American Communities (1964); Toward a Theory of Politicization (in Cultures and Societies of Latin America, 1965). Language: Spanish 4,4,3,2; Portuguese 1,1,1,1; French 2,2,1,1. Home: 2240 Birch Lane, Eugene, Oreg. Office: Dept. of Political Science, U. of Oreg., Eugene, 97403.

GOLDSEN, ROSE K., b. Newark, N.J., May 19, 1918. SOCIOLOGY. B.A., N.Y.U., 1943; MA., Yale U., 1944; Ph. D., 1953. Research assoc., Institute of Human Relations, Yale U., 1943-45; study dir., Bureau of Applied Social Research, Columbia U., 1946-48; SENIOR RESEARCH ASSOC.-ASSOC. PROF., SOCIOLOGY, CORNELL U., 1949– . Sterling fellow, Yale U.; Fulbright prof., U. of Bordeaux, U. of Rennes (France), 1957-58; vis. prof., U. of Buenos Aires, 1962-63; Latin American Committee, Cornell U.; consultant, American Jewish Committee. Membership: American Sociological Society: International Psychological Association. Research: methodology; problems of underdeveloped countries; Puerto Rican migrants in New York; methods of data gathering among Indian populations in Peru. Author: Values and Occupational Selection (1964). Co-author: Puerto Rican Journey (1950); What College Students Think (1960). Language: Spanish 4,4,4,4; Portuguese 3,2,2,1; French 4,4,4,4; Italian 3,2,2,1. Home: 907 Cayuga Heights Rd., Ithaca, N.Y. Office: Dept. of Sociology, Cornell U., Ithaca.

GOMEZ, MICHAEL ALBERT, b. New Orleans, La., Nov. 21, 1929. ECONOMICS. B.S., La. State U., 1952; M.A., 1955; Ph. D., Ohio State U., 1962. Instr., Okla. State U., 1955-57; researcher, Cleveland Metropolitan Services Commission, Summers 1957, 1958; instr., Ohio State U., 1957-61; vis. prof., George Peabody Coll. for Teachers, Summer 1960; asst. prof., Lafayette Coll., 1961-63; ECONOMIST, DIV. OF INTERNATIONAL FINANCE, BOARD OF GOVERNORS OF THE FEDERAL RESERVE SYSTEM, 1963– ; assoc. professorial lectr., George Washington U., 1964– . Organization of American States research fellow (Peru), 1961; consultant, International Economic Services (Brazil), Fall 1963. Membership: American Economic Association; Pi Gamma Mu. Research: Latin American economic development and finance, especially international economic policies of Brazil, Peru, Mexico, and Venezuela; economic aspects of integration of the Andean Indian. Author: Economic Growth of the South (Leadership Conference, George Peabody College, Summer 1960); Export Growth and Diversification: Peruvian Experience (Federal Reserve Board Review of Foreign Developments, Mar. 1964); The Role of International Technical Cooperation in the Interregional Development of Peru (The American Economist, Summer 1964). Language: Spanish 4,4,4,3; Portuguese 3,3,3,3; French 1,1,1,1. Home: 1069 North Manchester St., Arlington, Va. Office: Board of Governors of the Federal Reserve System, 20th St. and Constitution Ave., Washington, D.C.

GÓMEZ SICRE, JOSÉ R., b. Matanzas, Cuba, July 6, 1916. ART. Licenciado, U. of Havana, 1939; Ph. D., 1941. Ministerio de Hacienda (Cuba), 1935-45; CHIEF, DIV. OF VISUAL ARTS, PAN AMERICAN UNION, 1946– . Consultant, Cuban exhibition, Museum of Modern Art (N.Y.), 1944; permanent contributor, Américas (Washington, D.C.), 1948– . Research: Latin American art and culture. Author: Cuban Painting Today (1944); Museum Guide in Latin America (1956); Four Artists of the Americas (1956). Language: Spanish 5,5,5,5; Portuguese 5,5,2,2; French 5,3,3,3; Italian 5,5,4,3. Home: 1756 Lanier Pl., NW., Washington 9, D.C. Office: Div. of Visual Arts, Pan American Union, Washington 6, D.C.

GONZALEZ, ALFONSO, b. New York, N.Y., Mar. 21, 1927. GEOGRAPHY. A.B., Clark U., 1949; M.A., Northwestern U., 1950; Ph. D., U. of Tex., 1962. Research asst., U. of Tex. (Mexico), 1955-56; instr.-asst. prof., San Diego State Coll., 1957-60; asst. prof., Northeast La. State Coll., 1960-62; vis. prof., Kent State U., Summer 1962; asst. prof., Southern Ill. U., 1962-63; ASST. PROF., GEOGRAPHY, U. OF SOUTH FLA., 1963– . National Defense fellow in Spanish, U. of Calif., Los Angeles, Summer 1963. Membership: American Association of University Professors; American Economic Association; Association for Latin American Studies; Association of American Geographers; Hispanic American Society; National Council for Geographic Education; Population Reference Bureau; Sigma Xi. Research: population and economic development; economy, land utilization, resources, and population in Mexico. Collaborator: Coastal Study of Southwest Mexico (1957, 1958). Language: Spanish 5,5,5,5; Portuguese 2,2,2,1; French 2,2,2,2. Home: 2710 College Circle, Tampa, Fla., 33612. Office: Social Science Div., U. of South Fla., Tampa, 33620.

GONZÁLEZ, MANUEL PEDRO, b. Canary Islands, 1893. SPANISH AMERICAN LITERATURE. J.D., U. of Havana, 1920; Ph. D., 1922. Prof., U. of Calif., Los Angeles, 1924-58; PROF. EMERITUS, SPANISH AMERICAN LITERATURE, U. OF CALIF., LOS ANGELES, 1958– . First president, International Institute of Professors of Ibero-American Literature, 1938-40. Membership: Cuban Academy of Language. Research: José Martí. Author: Fuentes para el estudio de José Martí (1950); Trayectoria de la novela en México (1951); José María Heredia (1955). Language: Spanish 5,5,5,5; French 4,4,4,4. Office: Dept. of Spanish, U. of Calif., Los Angeles 24.

GONZÁLEZ, NANCIE L. SOLIEN DE, b. Chicago, Ill., Dec. 9, 1929. ANTHROPOLOGY. B.S., U. of N. Dak., 1951; M.A., U. of Mich., 1956; Ph. D. 1959. Prof., U. of San Carlos (Guatemala), Summers 1957– ; vis. lectr., U. of Calif., Berkeley, 1959-60; ANTHROPOLOGIST, INSTITUTO DE NUTRICIÓN DE CENTRO AMÉRICA

PANAMÁ, 1961- . Doherty fellow (Guatemala, British Honduras, Honduras), 1956–57. Membership: American Anthropological Association; Congress of Americanists. Research: social anthropology, especially social and community organization; health and diet; Guatemala. Author: West Indian Characteristics of the Black Carib (Southwestern Journal of Anthropology, Autumn 1959); Household and Family in the Caribbean (Social and Ecnomic Studies, Mar. 1960); Breast-feeding, Weaning, and Acculturation (Journal of Pediatrics, Apr. 1963). Language: Spanish 4,4,4,4; Portuguese 2,2,1,1; French 2,1,1,1. Home: Apartado Postal 1379, Guatemala, Guatemala.

GOODMAN, EDWARD J., b. Dubuque, Iowa, Nov. 19, 1916. HISTORY. A.B., Loras Coll., 1938; M.A., Columbia U., 1939; Ph. D., 1951. Instr., Notre Dame Coll. (N.Y.), 1940–41; instr., Seton Hall U., Spring 1946; asst. prof., U.S. Naval Academy, 1946–50; PROF. HISTORY, XAVIER U., 1950– ; DIR., HISPANIC STUDIES, 1962– . Roberts fellow, Columbia U., 1938–40. Membership: American Historical Association; American Society of International Law. Research: exploration of South America; nationalism; Spanish history. Author: Spanish Nationalism in the Struggle Against Napoleon (1958). Editor: The U.S. and Latin America Look at Each Other (1959); Colombia, Ecuador, and Venezuela: Their Peoples and Economics (1962). Language: Spanish 3,3,3,3; Portuguese 3,2,2,1; French 3,1,1,1. Home: 5601 Sunny Woods Lane, Cincinnati, Ohio 45239. Office: Dept. of History, Xavier U., Cincinnati, 45207.

GOODSELL, CHARLES TRUE, b. Kalamazoo, Mich., July 23, 1932. POLITICAL SCIENCE. A.B., Kalamazoo Coll., 1954; M.P.A., Harvard U., 1958; M.A., 1959; Ph. D., 1961. ASST. PROF., PUBLIC ADMINISTRATION, U. OF P.R., 1960– . Membership: American Political Science Association; American Society for Public Administration; Political Science Association of Puerto Rico. Research: comparative public administration in Latin America. Author: Administration of a Revolution: Development of Public Administration in Puerto Rico under Rexford Tugwell (1964). Language: Spanish 4,2,2,2; French 2,1,1,1; German 3,2,2,2. Home: Faculty Residences B–2, Río Piedras, P.R. Office: School of Public Administration, U. of P.R., Río Piedras.

GOODSELL, JAMES NELSON, b. Evanston, Ill., June 7, 1929. HISTORY AND JOURNALISM. B.A., The Principia Coll., 1951; M.A., Mexico City Coll., 1952. Instr., Mexico City Coll., 1953, 1955; asst. American news editor, The Christian Science Monitor, 1957–63; LATIN AMERICAN EDITOR, NEWS DEPT., THE CHRISTIAN SCIENCE MONITOR, 1964– . Membership: American Historical Association; Conference on Latin American History; Sigma Delta Chi. Research: United States and Latin American news; British Empire; colonial municipal formation in Cartagena, Colombia. Language: Spanish 4,4,4,3; Portuguese 3,3,3,2; French 2,2,1,1; Japanese 1,2,2,1; Korean 3,2,2,2. Home: 184 Village St., Millis, Mass. Office: The Christian Science Monitor, One Norway St., Boston 15, Mass.

GORDON, BRUCE R., b. Schenectady, N.Y., Mar. 13, 1916. SPANISH AMERICAN LITERATURE. A.B., Brown U., 1937; M.A., N.Y. State Coll. for Teachers, 1942; Ph. D., Syracuse U., 1950. Instr., Oneonta State Teachers Coll., 1941–42; instr.-asst. prof., Colgate U., 1947–50; chmn., Romance Languages, Emory U., 1950–63; PROF., FRENCH AND SPANISH, HEAD, LINGUISTICS AND FOREIGN LANGUAGES, U. OF ALASKA, 1963– . Membership: American Association of Teachers of French; American Association of Teachers of Spanish and Portuguese; American Association of University Professors; Instituto Internacional de Literatura Iberoamericana. Research: culture and civilization of France, Spain, and Latin America. Author: Integration of Laboratory and Classroom (Modern Language Journal, Feb. 1953); Early Translations of French Romantics in Mexico (Symposium, May 1953); The Validity of a Second Year Cultural Course in Foreign Languages (Kentucky Foreign Language Quarterly, 1956). Language: Spanish 4,4,4,4; French 5,5,5,5; German 3,2,2,2; Italian 3,2,2,1. Home: Box 46, College, Alaska 99735. Office: Dept. of Linguistics and Foreign Languages, U. of Alaska, College, 99735.

GORDON, BURTON LEROY, b. Asotin, Wash., Feb. 13, 1920. GEOGRAPHY. A.B., San Francisco State Coll., 1942; Ph. D., U. of Calif., Berkeley, 1953. PROF., CHMN., GEOGRAPHY, U. OF N. MEX., 1955– ; exchange lectr., U. of London, 1962–63. Office of Naval Research grant (Colombia), 1950–53; Johns Hopkins U. fellow, 1953–54; U. of Calif. and Office of Naval Research grant (Panama, Costa Rica), Summers 1954–58; consultant and researcher for Jicarilla Apache Indian Tribe. Membership: Panama Archaeological Society; Rocky Mountain Council for Latin American Studies. Research: cultural anthropology; geography and ecology in the Sinú country of Colombia; Indian tribes in Panama and Costa Rica. Author: Human Geography and Ecology in the Sinú Country (Ibero-Americana, 1957); A Domesticated Wax-producing Scale Insect Kept by the Guaymí Indians of Panama (Ethnos, no. 1–2, 1957); Shell-mounds of Bocas del Toro Province, Panama (The Panama Archaeologist, 1962). Language: Spanish 3,3,3,2; German 3,3,3,2; Italian 2,2,2,1. Home: 318 Tulane Pl., NE., Albuquerque, N. Mex. Office: Dept. of Geography, U. of N. Mex., Albuquerque.

GORDON, LINCOLN, b. New York, N.Y., Sept. 10, 1913. ECONOMICS AND POLITICAL SCIENCE. A.B., Harvard Coll., 1933; Ph. D., Oxford U., 1936. Asst. prof., Harvard U., 1936–42; program vice chmn., War Production Board, 1942–46; prof., Harvard Business School, 1946–49; dir., Program Div., Office of Special Representative in Europe, Economic Cooperation Administration, 1949–50; economic adviser to special asst. to president, The White House, 1950–52; minister for economic affairs, Embassy (London), U.S. Dept. of State, 1952–55; prof., Harvard U., 1955–61; UNITED STATES AMBASSADOR TO BRAZIL, U.S. DEPT. OF STATE, 1961– . Consultant, Alliance for Progress, U.S. Dept. of State, 1960–61; consultant, Ford Foundation (Brazil, Chile, Argentina);

Economic Advisory Board, Committee for Economic Development. Membership: American Academy of Arts and Sciences; American Association for the Advancement of Science; American Economic Association; Council on Foreign Relations; Royal Economic Society; Society for Economic Development; World Peace Foundation. Research: economic development policies; international economic relations; Latin American economic problems; role of government in Brazilian economic development. Author: United States Manufacturing Investment in Brazil (1962); A New Deal for Latin America (1963). Co-author: Government and the American Economy (1958). Language: Spanish 3,3,2,2; Portuguese 4,4,4,4; French 4,3,3,3; German 3,2,2,2. Home: 68 Snake Hill Rd., Belmont 78, Mass. Office: American Embassy, Rio de Janeiro, Brazil.

GORDON, WENDELL C., b. Birmingham, Ala., Oct. 9, 1916. ECONOMICS. B.A., Rice Institute, 1937; M.A., American U., 1938; U. of Mexico, 1939; Ph. D., N.Y.U., 1940; U. of Havana, 1946. PROF., ECONOMICS, U. OF TEX., 1940– . Membership: American Economic Association; Royal Economic Society. Research: international economics. Author: Economy of Latin America (1950); International Trade: Goods, People, and Ideas (1958); Foreign Investments (Business Review of the University of Houston, Fall 1962). Language: Spanish 5,4,4,3; Portuguese 5,–,3,3,3; French 5,4,4,3. Office: Dept. of Economics, U. of Tex., Austin, 78712.

GORENSTEIN, SHIRLEY SLOTKIN, b. New York, N.Y., Mar. 4, 1928. ANTHROPOLOGY. B.A., Queens Coll., 1949; M.A., Columbia U., 1953; Ph. D., 1963. Lectr., Queens Coll., 1961–63; ASSOC. IN ANTHROPOLOGY, COLUMBIA U., 1963– . N.Y. State Regent fellow; American Association of University Women fellow; special consultant on Latin American culture, National Education Television. Membership: American Anthropological Association; Society for American Archaeology. Research: New World archeology, especially archeology of Peru and Mexico; pre-Columbian military organization. Language: Spanish 3,2,2,3; French 3,2,2,3; German 3,3,–,3. Home: 865 West End Ave., New York, N.Y. 10025. Office: Columbia U., Morningside Heights, New York, 10027.

GORMLY, MARY B. San Francisco, Calif., Dec. 14, 1919. LIBRARY SCIENCE. B.A., U. of Wash., 1947; M.A., U. of the Americas, 1948; M.S.L.S., U. of Wash., 1959. Instr., U. of the Americas, 1948–49; instr., Coronet Hall (Mexico City), 1953–54; librarian and asst. curator, The Amerind Foundation, Inc. (Dragoon, Ariz.), 1959–61; SOCIAL SCIENCES LIBRARIAN, CALIF. STATE COLL., LOS ANGELES, 1962– . Research asst., Centro de Estudios Antropológicos del Norte de México (La Paz, Baja California), Summer 1953. Membership: American Anthropological Association; American Ethnological Society; American Indian Ethnohistorical Conference; Pacific Coast Council on Latin American Studies; Western History Association. Research: Latin American bibliography and reference materials; ethnohistory of Mesoamerica; prehispanic history of Mexico. Author: Spanish Documentary Material Pertaining to the Indians of the Northwest Coast (Davidson Journal of Anthropology, Summer 1955). Language: Spanish 4,4,3,4; Portuguese 4,3,2,3; French 3,3,2,2. Home: 714 West Washington St., Alhambra, Calif. 90801. Office: Calif. State Coll., 5151 State College Dr., Los Angeles, 90032.

GOSNELL, CHARLES FRANCIS, b. Rochester, N.Y., July 7, 1909. LIBRARY SCIENCE. A.B., U. of Rochester, 1930; B.S., Columbia U., 1932; M.S. 1937; Ph. D., N.Y.U., 1943. Reference asst, New York Public Library, 1931–45; assoc. prof. and librarian, Queens Coll., 1937–45; assoc., School of Library Service, Columbia U., 1943–47; state librarian and asst. commissioner of education, State of N.Y., 1945–62; DIR. OF LIBRARIES, PROF., LIBRARY ADMINISTRATION, N.Y.U., 1962– . Consultant in bibliography, Instituto de Estudios Históricos (Madrid), 1934; chmn., Committee on Library Cooperation with Latin America, American Library Association, 1939–41; U.S. delegate, UNESCO Conference on Public Library Service (São Paulo), 1951; surveyor, UNESCO Pilot Library (Medellín, Colombia), 1959; consultant, Ford Foundation (Brazil), 1963; chmn., Advisory Committee to U. of Brasília, American Library Association, 1963– . Membership: American Library Association; Council of National Library Association; National Association of State Librarians; Society for Colonial History. Research: library administration; book selection. Author: Spanish Personal Names (1938); Official Document Book: New York State Freedom Train (1950); Obsolete Library Books (Scientific Monthly, May 1947). Language: Spanish 3,3,3,3; Portuguese 3,3,3,3; French 2,2,2,2; Dutch 2,2,2,2; German 2,2,2,2. Home: 11 Orchard Circle, Suffern, N.Y. 10901. Office: Libraries, N.Y.U., Washington Sq., New York, 10003.

GOULD, LYMAN JAY, b. New York, N.Y., May 5, 1925. POLITICAL SCIENCE. A.B., Colby Coll., 1948; M.A., U. of Mich., 1949; Ph. D., 1958. Instr., U. of Vt., 1953–57; asst. prof., 1957–61; ASSOC. PROF., POLITICAL SCIENCE, U. OF VT., 1961– . U. of Mich. teaching fellow, 1952; U. of Vt. faculty research grant, U. of Vt., Summer 1960; Ford Foundation-U. of Vt. Program of Non-Western Studies Research travel grant (P.R.), Summer 1963; coordinator, Program of Latin American Studies, U. of Vt. Membership: American Political Science Association. Research: Latin American constitutional; American constitutional law; U.S. policy towards Puerto Rico, 1900–1917. Author: The Politics of Religion (in People, Power, and Politics, 1961). Co editor: People, Power, and Politics (1961). Language: Spanish 5,5,5,5; French 2,2,2,1. Home: 195 South Willard, Burlington, Vt. 05401. Office: Dept. of Political Science U. of Vt., Burlington, 05401.

GRABAN, MICHAEL, b. Helvetia, Pa., Nov. 7 1905. JOURNALISM. A.B., Ohio U. 1931; M.A., U. of Nev., 1950; Ph. D., Inter American U. (Mexico), 1958. Teacher High School (Yreka, Calif.), 1945–48 instr., U. of Nev., 1948–50; TEACHER MODERN LANGUAGES, PUBLICITY DIR SHASTA COLL., 1950– . Membership American Association of University Profes sors; California Teachers Association; For eign Language Association of Norther

California; Sigma Delta Chi. Research: comparison between Mexican and United States periodicals. Language: Spanish 4,4,4,4; Slovak 5,5,4,4; Russian 4,3,3,3. Home: 3330 Sunset Dr., Redding, Calif. Office: Dept. of Modern Languages, Shasta Coll., Redding.

GRADO, LOUIS M., b. El Paso, Tex., Feb. 11, 1924. EDUCATION. B.S., N. Mex. State U., 1949; M.A., Colo. State Coll., 1950; Ph. D., State U. of Iowa, 1955. ASSOC. PROF., ELEMENTARY EDUCATION, EASTERN ILL. U., 1955– ; teacher education adviser, U.S. Agency for International Development (Nicaragua), 1961–63. Membership: National Education Association; National Society for Colleges of Teacher Education; Phi Delta Kappa. Research: teacher education; elementary curriculum and supervision; educational psychology; evaluation of pre-service preparation of elementary teachers; Nicaragua. Language: Spanish 5,5,4,2. Home: 784 10th St., Charleston, Ill. Office: Eastern Ill. U., Charleston.

GRAHAM, JOHN ALLEN, b. Del Rio, Tex., July 13, 1936. ANTHROPOLOGY. A.B., U. of Tex., 1958; Ph. D., Harvard U., 1963. ASST. PROF., ANTHROPOLOGY, U. OF CALIF., BERKELEY, 1962– . Membership: American Anthropological Association; Society for American Archaeology. Research: Mesoamerican archeology, particularly Maya archeology and epigraphy; Mexico; Guatemala. Author: Sobre la escritura Maya (in El desarrollo cultural de los mayas, 1964). Language: Spanish 4,4,4,4; German 3,1,1,1. Linguistic studies: Maya; Nahuatl. Home: 925 Spruce St., Berkeley 7, Calif. Office: Dept. of Anthropology, U. of Calif., Berkeley 4.

GRAHAM, RICHARD, b. Anápolis, Brazil, Nov. 1, 1934. HISTORY. B.A., Coll. of Wooster, 1956; M.A., U. of Tex., 1957; Ph. D., 1961. Editorial asst., Hispanic American Historical Review, 1958; ASST. PROF., HISTORY, CORNELL U., 1961– . Social Science Research Council fellow (Brazil), 1959–60; American Philosophical Society grant, Summer 1962. Membership: American Historical Association; Conference on Latin American History; Hispanic American Society. Research: Brazilian nineteenth century history. Author: Mauá and Anglo-Brazilian Diplomacy, 1862–1863 (Hispanic American Historical Review, May 1962); A questão Christie, 1862–1863 (Revista de Historia, Jan. 1962). Language: Spanish 5,5,4,3; Portuguese 5,5,5,5; French 3,1,1,1; German 2,1,1,1; Italian 3,2,1,1. Home: R.F.D. 1, Dryden, N.Y. Office: Dept. of History, Cornell U., Ithaca, N.Y.

GRAY, RICHARD BUTLER, b. Fort Atkinson, Wis., May 29, 1922. POLITICAL SCIENCE. B.A., U. of Wis., 1947; M.A., Fletcher School of Law and Diplomacy, 1949; Ph. D., U. of Wis., 1957. Asst. dir., Instituto-Cultural Dominico-Americano (Ciudad Trujillo, Dominican Republic), 1949–51; instr., Villanueva U. (Havana), 1956–57; asst. prof., C. W. Post Coll., 1957–58; vis. prof., U. of Wis., Summer 1958, 1962; ASSOC. PROF., GOVERNMENT, FLA. STATE U., 1958– . Kemper Knapp fellow, U. of Wis.; Buenos Aires Convention grant (Cuba), 1955–56; consultant in Latin American Affairs, Conference on International Affairs, Auburn U., 1961; consultant, Teachers for Africa Program, Columbia U.; dir., Inter-departmental Committee on International Affairs, Fla. State U. Membership: American Academy of Political and Social Science; American Association of University Professors; American Political Science Association; Asociación de Antiguos Alumnos del Seminario Martiano; Association for Latin American Studies; Southeastern Conference on Latin American Studies; Southern Political Science Association. Research: charismatic leadership in Latin American politics; José Martí; Cuban politics; Cuban refugee problem. Author: Study Guide to the History of the Latin American Nations (1953); José Martí, Cuban Patriot (1962); José Martí and Social Revolution in Cuba (Journal of Inter-American Studies, Apr. 1963). Language: Spanish 4,4,4,3; Portuguese 3,2,1,1; French 3,2,1,1. Home: 2805 Coldstream Dr., Tallahassee, Fla. Office: Dept. of Government, Fla. State U., Tallahassee.

GRAY, WILLIAM HENRY, b. Greenville, Tex., Sept. 13, 1901. HISTORY. A.B., Trinity Coll. (Tex.), 1922; A.M., U. of Chicago, 1924; Ph. D., 1937. Dean, Instituto Politécnico (P.R.), 1922–23; teacher, Morton High School & Junior Coll. (Ill.), 1924–40; PROF., HISTORY, DIR., INTERNATIONAL STUDENT AFFAIRS, PA. STATE U., 1940– . Chmn., Pa. State Committee on International Understanding. Membership: American Academy of Political and Social Science; American Association of University Professors; American Historical Association; Conference on Latin American History. Research: diplomatic history; Latin American political and economic history. Author: Exploring American Neighbors (1942–1963); American Diplomacy in Venezuela, 1835–1865 (Hispanic American Historical Review, Nov. 1940); Bolivar's Conquest of Guayaquil (Hispanic American Historical Review, Nov. 1947). Language: Spanish 4,4,4,3; Portuguese 3,2,2,1; French 2,1,1,1; German 1,1,1,1; Italian 1,1,1,1. Home: 31 Orlando Apartments, State College, Pa., 16801. Office: 108 Sparks Bldg., University Park, Pa., 16802

GREEN, JAMES LEROY, b. Centralia, Wash., Nov. 6, 1919. ECONOMICS. B.A., Wash. State U., 1941; M.A., U. of Minn., 1948; Ph. D., 1950. Asst. prof., Southern Methodist U., 1949–51; senior assoc., Griffenhagen and Associates (Chicago), 1951–53; consultant in management (Ark., Tex., Okla.), 1953–56; economic and financial adviser to the Minister of Finance (Colombia), dir. of industrial development, 1956–57; prof., chmn., Air Force Institute of Technology, Wright-Patterson Air Force Base, 1957–60; PROF., ECONOMICS, U. OF GA., 1960– . Research seminar, Ford Foundation, U. of Va., 1962, 1964; business economics seminar, General Electric, U. of Chicago, 1963. Membership: American Economic Association; American Society for Public Administration; Beta Gamma Sigma; Phi Kappa Psi; Southern Economic Association. Research: management; business and economic development; economic growth and fluctuations; public finance; Colombia. Author: Corporación Nacional de Producción: Estatutos (1957); Understanding Problems in Latin America's

Economy (Commercial and Financial Chronicle, Oct. 1959). Language: Spanish 3,2,2,2. Home: 200 Colonial Dr., Athens, Ga. 30601. Office: Coll. of Business Administration, U. of Ga., Athens, 30601.

GREENFIELD, SIDNEY MARTIN, b. New York, N.Y., Apr. 30, 1932. ANTHROPOLOGY AND SOCIOLOGY. A.B., Brooklyn Coll., 1954; Ph. D., Columbia U., 1959. Instr., Conn. Coll., 1958–59; asst. prof., Purdue U., 1959–62; staff editor, International Encyclopedia of the Social Sciences, 1962–63; ASSOC. PROF., ANTHROPOLOGY AND SOCIOLOGY, U. OF WIS., MILWAUKEE, 1963– . Social Science Research Council fellow (Barbados, West Indies), 1956–57; Purdue Research Foundation grant (Brazil), Summer 1960; Social Science Research Council fellow, 1964. Membership: American Anthropological Association; American Ethnological Association; Society for Applied Anthropology. Research: community organization and development; land tenure and settlement patterns. Author: Industrialization and the Family in Sociological Theory (American Journal of Sociology, Nov. 1961); Social Change and Labor Commitment in Southeastern Minas Gerais (Inter-American Economic Affairs, 1963). Language: Portuguese 3,3,3,2. Home: 3016 North Prospect Ave., Milwaukee 11, Wis. Office: Dept. of Sociology, U. of Wis., 3203 North Downer Ave., Milwaukee 11.

GREENLEAF, RICHARD EDWARD, b. Hot Springs National Park, Ark., May 6, 1930. HISTORY. B.A., U. of N. Mex., 1952; M.A., 1953; Ph. D., 1956. Part-time instr., U. of N. Mex., 1954–57; ASSOC. PROF., CHMN., HISTORY AND INTERNATIONAL RELATIONS, U. OF THE AMERICAS, 1957– ; assoc. graduate dean, 1957–62; ACADEMIC VICE PRESIDENT, 1962– . Knights Templar research grant (Mexico), 1954; Rotary Foundation research fellow (Mexico), 1955–56; U. of the Americas research fellow (Spain), 1962. Membership: American Historical Association; Conference on Latin American History. Research: Mexico. Author: Victoriano Huerta: A Reappraisal (1960); Zumárraga and the Mexican Inquisition, 1536–1543 (1962); Mexican Inquisition Materials in Spanish Archives (The Americas, Winter 1964). Language: Spanish 5,4,4,4; Portuguese 4,3,3,3; French 4,3,–,3. Home: 405 Hermosa NE., Albuqureque, N. Mex. Office: Dept. of History, U. of the Americas, Km. 16, Carretera México-Toluca, México 10, D.F.

GREER, VIRGINIA LEONARD, b. Garnet, Mont., Aug. 1, 1900. HISTORY. Third Year Diploma, Teacher's Coll. (Oreg.), 1923; B.A., U. of Oreg., 1929; M.A., 1935; Ph. D., U. of N. Mex., 1954. Teacher, Oreg. Public Schools, 1920–43; instr., dean, U. of Oreg. and University High School, 1943–53; teacher, U.S. Army I. & E. Program (Japan), 1946–47; TEACHER, HISTORY, VENTURA UNION HIGH SCHOOL DISTRICT (CALIF.), 1954– . Consultant, 1948 Oregon Course of Study in the Social Sciences. Membership: California State Teachers' Association; National Education Association; Pacific Coast Council on Latin American Studies; Phi Lambda Theta. Research: Nicaragua. Author: State Department Policy in Regard to the Nicaraguan Election of 1924 (Hispanic American Historical Review, Nov. 1954). Language: Spanish 3,1,1,1; French 3,3,3,1. Home: Apt. 1, 1793 Evans, Ventura, Calif. Office: Ventura High School, 2155 East Main St., Ventura.

GREEVER, JANET GROFF, b. Philadelphia, Pa., Sept. 12, 1921. HISTORY. B.A., Bryn Mawr Coll., 1942; M.A., 1945; M.A., Radcliffe Coll., 1951; Ph. D., 1954. Instr., Bryn Mawr Coll., 1949–50; INDEPENDENT RESEARCH AND STUDY, 1954– ; asst. prof., History, Wash. State Coll., Spring 1963. History fellow, Bryn Mawr Coll., 1944–45; graduate fellow, Radcliffe Coll., 1945–47; American Association of University Women fellow, 1948–49. Membership: American Historical Association; Conference on Latin American History; Hispanic American Society. Research: Bolivia, 19th century; colonial period in Latin America. Co-author: Idaho (in World Book Encyclopedia, 1960). Language: Spanish 4,2,2,2; Portuguese 2,1,1,1; French 4,2,2,2; German 2,1,1,1; Italian 2,1,1,1. Home: 315 South Hayes St., Moscow, Idaho 83443.

GREGORY, GUSTAV ROBINSON, b. Cass City, Mich., Sept. 1, 1915. ECONOMICS. B.S., Central Mich. U., 1938; B.S.F., U. of Mich., 1940; M.F., 1940; Ph. D., U of Calif., Berkeley, 1953. Forest economist, Southern Forest Experiment Station (Tex.), U.S. Dept. of Agriculture, 1945–49; PROF., NATURAL RESOURCE ECONOMICS, U. OF MICH., 1952– ; chief, Analysis and Survey Section, Forest Economics Branch, United Nations Food and Agriculture Organization (Italy), 1961–62. Baker fellow, Bidwell fellow, and Giannini fellow, U. of Calif., Berkeley, 1949–50, 1950–51, 1951–52; consultant, U.S. Dept. of the Treasury, 1963; consultant, United Nations Food and Agriculture Organization (Mexico), 1963, 1964. Membership: American Economic Association; American Farm Economic Association; Michigan Academy of Science; Society of American Foresters. Research: natural resource economics; forest products and forest resources; Latin American timber trends. Author: An Economic Approach to Multiple Use (Forest Science, Mar. 1955); Forest Growth Goals in A Private Enterprise Economy (Journal of Forestry, Nov. 1955). Language: Spanish 3,3,3,2; French 3,2,1,1; German 2,2,1,1; Italian 2,2,2,1. Home: 2704 Brockman Blvd., Ann Arbor, Mich. Office: School of Natural Resources, U. of Mich., Ann Arbor.

GREGORY, PETER, b. New York, N.Y., Sept. 29, 1924. ECONOMICS. B.A., Ohio Wesleyan U., 1948; M.A., Harvard U., 1950; Ph. D., 1957. Asst. dir., Manpower Resources Project, Social Science Research Center, U. of P.R., 1953–57; vis. asst. prof., Yale U., 1957–58; ASST. PROF., ECONOMICS, U. OF MINN., 1958– ; vis. assoc. prof., N.Y. State School of Industrial and Labor Relations, Cornell U., 1962–64. Ford Foundation fellow, Harvard Business School, 1959–60; consultant, Dept. of Labor Relations U. of Chile, 1962–64. Membership: American Economic Association; Industrial Relations Research Association; Mid-West Economic Association. Research: labor economics; wage levels and structures in the manufacturing sector of Chile; cost incidence of social security in Chile; manpower and labor force problems of industrialization, labor mobility, and wages in

Puerto Rico. Author: The Labor Market in Puerto Rico (in Labor Commitment and Social Change in Developing Areas, 1960). Co-author: Wages, Productivity and Industrialization in Puerto Rico (1964). Language: Spanish 4,4,4,4; Portuguese 3,2,2,1; German 3,3,3,3; Greek 3,4,4,2. Home: 132 Cecil St., SE., Minneapolis, Minn., 55414. Office: Dept. of Economics, U. of Minn., Minneapolis, 55455.

GREIFER, ELISHA, b. New York, N.Y., Dec. 27, 1924. POLITICAL SCIENCE. B.S., Harvard U., 1946; M.A., 1953; Ph. D., 1958. Information specialist, U.S. High Commissioner for Germany, U.S. Depts. of Army and State (Germany), 1946–51; instr., Wheaton Coll., 1956–58; instr., Vassar Coll., 1958–59; asst. prof., 1959–61; dir., Binational Center, U.S. Information Agency (Tucumán, Argentina), 1961–63; DIR., BINATIONAL CENTER (GUAYAQUIL, ECUADOR), U.S. INFORMATION AGENCY, 1964– . Vassar Coll. research grant (Cuba), Summer 1960. Membership: American Political Science Association. Research: church and state in Cuba; culture in Argentina and Ecuador. Author: Joseph de Maistre and the Revolt against the Eighteenth Century (American Political Science Review, Sept. 1962). Editor: On God and Society, by J. de Maistre (1958). Language: Spanish 4,4,4,4; French 3,2,2,3; German 4,3,3,3. Home: 2011 Poplar St., Waukegan, Ill. Office: Binational Center, U.S. Information Service, Consulate General, Guayaquil, Ecuador.

GRIEDER, (RONALD) TERENCE, b. Cedar Rapids, Iowa, Sept. 2, 1931. ART. B.A., U. of Colo., 1953; M.S., U. of Wis., 1956; Ph. D., U. of Pa., 1962. Instr., U. of Wis.-Milwaukee, 1956–57; asst. instr., U. of Pa., 1957–59; instr., Conn. Coll., 1960–61; ASST. PROF., ART, U. OF TEX., 1961– . Smith-Mundt fellow (Guatemala), 1959–60; National Defense Education Act fellow (South America), Summer 1963. Membership: College Art Association; Society for American Archaeology. Research: 19th and 20th century art and culture in Latin America; history of pre-Columbian art, especially Maya art. Author: Manifestaciones de arte maya en la región de Petexbatun (Antropología e Historia de Guatemala, July 1960); Representation of Space and Form on Maya Pottery (American Antiquity, Apr. 1964); New Figurative Painting in Argentina (Art Journal, Sept. 1964). Language: Spanish 4,3,3,3; Portuguese 2,2,1,1; French 4,3,3,3; German 2,2,1,1. Home: 111½ West 33rd St., Austin 5, Tex. Office: Dept. of Art, U. of Tex., Austin 12.

GRIFFIN, CHARLES CARROLL, b. Tokyo, Japan, May 24, 1902. HISTORY. A.B., Harvard Coll., 1922; M.A., Columbia U., 1933; Ph. D., 1937. Clerk, Cía. Argentina de Cemento Portland, 1923–24; sales representative, Cía. Uruguaya de Cemento Portland, 1925–30; research asst., European Mission (Spain), Library of Congress, 1931–32; instr.-PROF., HISTORY, VASSAR COLL., 1934– ; asst. chief, Div. of Research and Liaison, Office of American Republics Affairs, U.S. Dept. of State, 1943–44; vis. prof., U. of Wis., 1949–50, U. of Chile, 1954, Harvard U., 1959–60. University fellow, Columbia U., 1933–34; Buenos Aires Convention exchange prof. (Venezuela), 1940–41; Advisory Committee, Handbook of Latin American Studies, 1958– ; chmn., Conference on Latin American History, 1960. Membership: Academy of American Franciscan History; Academy of History of Venezuela, Chile, and Cuba; American Geographical Society; American Historical Association; Sociedade Capistrano de Abreu (Rio de Janeiro). Research: independence period in Spanish America; archival research. Author: The United States and the Disruption of the Spanish Empire, 1810–1822 (1937); The National Period in the History of the New World (1961); Los temas sociales y económicos en la época de la independencia (1962). Language: Spanish 4,4,4,4; Portuguese 3,2,1,1; French 3,2,2,2; German 2,2,2,1; Italian 2,2,1,1. Home: 79 Raymond Ave., Poughkeepsie, N.Y. Office: Box 141, Vassar Coll., Poughkeepsie.

GRIFFIN, JAMES BENNETT, b. Atchison, Kans., Jan. 12, 1905. ANTHROPOLOGY. Ph. B., U. of Chicago, 1927; M.A., 1930; Ph. D., U. of Mich., 1936. Research assoc., U. of Mich., 1936–41; asst.-assoc. curator, Museum of Anthropology, U. of Mich., 1937–45; asst. prof., 1945–49; CURATOR OF ARCHEOLOGY, 1945– ; DIR., MUSEUM OF ANTHROPOLOGY, 1946– ; PROF., ANTHROPOLOGY, U. OF MICH., 1949– . President, Committee on Anthropology, Pan American Institute of Geography and History, 1954–59; Committee on Latin American Anthropology, National Research Council, 1956. Membership: American Anthropological Association; American Association for the Advancement of Science; International Union of Prehistoric and Protohistoric Sciences; Society for American Archaeology. Research: archeology; Mexican prehistory. Author: The Fort Ancient Aspect (1943). Co-author: Archaeological Survey of Lower Mississippi Valley (1951). Editor: Archaeology of Eastern United States (1952). Language: Spanish 3,1,1,1; French 3,1,1,1. Home: 360 Evergreen Pl., Ann Arbor, Mich., 48104. Office: Museum of Anthropology, U. of Mich., University Museums Bldg., Ann Arbor, 48104.

GRIFFIN, WILLIAM JAMES, b. College Springs, Iowa, Sept. 26, 1907. BRAZILIAN LITERATURE. B.A., Park Coll., 1929; M.A., U. of Iowa, 1930; Ph. D., 1939. Instr., Independence Jr. Coll., 1931–35; instr., St. Cloud State Coll., 1935–43; head, Language and Literature, 1939–43; U.S. Navy, 1943–46; vis. prof., U. of Brazil, 1946–48; assoc. prof., Ill. State Normal U., 1948; PROF., ENGLISH, GEORGE PEABODY COLL. FOR TEACHERS, 1948– . Smith-Mundt lectr., U. of Lisbon, 1957; Carnegie Foundation grant. Membership: American Folklore Society; American Studies Association; Association for Latin American Studies; National Council of Teachers of English; Tennessee Folklore Society; Tennessee Philological Association. Research: Brazilian poetry; English language structure and history; folklore. Author: Brazilian Literature in English Translation (Inter-American Review of Bibliography, Jan.-June 1955); Teaching Machines and Programmed Textbooks in the High School English Curriculum (High School Journal, Feb. 1962). Translator: The Anguish of Pity, by Vinicius de Morais (Texas Quarterly, Dec. 1961). Language:

Spanish 3,2,2,2; Portuguese 4,3,3,3; French 3,1,1,1; German 2,1,1,1. Home: 3601 Wilbur Foster Dr., Nashville, Tenn., 37204. Office: Dept. of English, George Peabody Coll., Nashville, 37205.

GRIFFITH, WILLIAM J., b. Kanopolis, Kans., Dec. 20, 1908. HISTORY. B.A., Southwestern Coll. (Kans.), 1930; M.A., U. of Wichita, 1937; Ph. D., U. of Calif., Berkeley, 1942. Unit head, Div. of Education, Office of Inter-American Affairs, 1942–44; special representative in Guatemala, Inter-American Educational Foundation, Office of Inter-American Affairs, 1944–47; asst. prof., Tulane U., 1947–50; assoc. prof., 1950–55; consultant in Guatemala, Foreign Operations Administration, 1954–55; PROF., HISTORY, TULANE U., 1955– ; vis. prof., U. of Colo., Summer 1961. Board of Editors, Hispanic American Historical Review, 1952–57; Social Science Research Council fellow, 1958. Membership: American Historical Association; Mississippi Valley Historical Association; Sociedad de Geografía e Historia de Guatemala; Southern Historical Association. Research: Central America since Independence; Spanish borderlands. Author: The Hasinai Indians of East Texas as seen by Europeans, 1687–1772 (1954); Santo Tomás, anhelado emporio del comercio en el Atlántico (1959); Juan Galindo, Central American Chauvinist (Hispanic American Historical Review, Feb. 1960). Language: Spanish 4,4,4,4; French 3,2,1,1. Home: 360 Audubon St., New Orleans, La., 70118. Office: Dept. of History, Tulane U., New Orleans, 70118.

GRIMES, JOSEPH EVANS, b. Elizabeth, N.J., Dec. 10, 1928. LINGUISTICS. B.A., Wheaton Coll., 1950; M.A., Cornell ,U. 1958; Ph. D., 1960. Translator, Wycliffe Bible Translators, Inc., 1950– ; LINGUIST, SUMMER INSTITUTE OF LINGUISTICS (MEXICO), 1960– . Inter-American Program in Linguistics and Language Teaching. Membership: American Anthropological Association; Association for Computing Machinery; Linguistic Society of America; Society for Applied Anthropology. Research: descriptive linguistics; computation; anthropology; Huichol of Mexico. Author: Huichol Syntax (1964); Measures of Linguistic Divergence (IX International Congress of Linguistics, 1964); Huichol Economics (América Indígena, Oct. 1961). Language: Spanish 4,4,4,4; Portuguese 2,2,1,1; French 3,1,1,1; Greek 3,1,1,1; Huichol 3,4,4,4. Linguistic studies: Huichol; Itonama; Kru; Nahuatl. Home: Héroes 53, México 3, D.F. Office: Summer Institute of Linguistics, Box 1960, Santa Ana, Calif.

GROLLIG, FRANCIS XAVIER, S. J., b. Cincinnati, Ohio, July 9, 1922. ANTHROPOLOGY. A.B., Loyola U., 1947; Ph. L., 1949; A.M., 1952; S.T.B., 1954; Ph. D., Ind. U., 1959. ASST. PROF., ANTHROPOLOGY, LOYOLA U. (ILL.), 1959– . Buenos Aires Convention grant (Guatemala), 1958; Fulbright research grant (Peru), 1961; organizer and dir., Hispanic American Academic Adventure Program, Loyola U. Membership: American Anthropological Association; Archeological Institute of America; Sigma Xi. Research: ethnology in Peru and Guatemala; Mexico. Author: An Urgent Task of Research in Guatemala (Bulletin, International Committee on Urgent Anthropological and Ethnological Research, 1960); The Vanishing Folk-Religion of the Mayan Indians (Actas, XXXIV International Congress of Americanists, 1960); Sod Houses and Floating Islands: Peruvian Primitives (in América Indígena, 1964). Language: Spanish 3,3,-3,3; French 1,1,1,1; Latin 3,3,3,3. Office: Dept. of Anthropology, Loyola U., 6525 Sheridan Rd., Chicago, Ill. 60626.

GROPP, ARTHUR ERIC, b. Kendall, Kans., Nov. 10, 1902. LIBRARY SCIENCE: BIBLIOGRAPHY. B.S., Kans. State Teachers Coll., 1927; B.A., U. of Ill., 1930; M.A., 1931. Librarian, Middle American Research Institute, Tulane U., 1931–42; librarian, Biblioteca Artigas-Washington (Montevideo, Uruguay), American Council of Learned Societies, 1942–43, American Library Association, 1944–48, U.S. Dept. of State, 1948–50; dir. of course for librarians, Asociación de Ingenieros del Uruguay, 1943–45; dir., Escuela de Biblioteca, Universidad de la República, 1946–47; LIBRARIAN, COLUMBUS MEMORIAL LIBRARY, PAN AMERICAN UNION, 1950– . Chmn., Committee on Library Cooperation with Latin America, American Library Association, 1935–42; Rockefeller Foundation grant (Central America, West Indies), 1937–38; contributing editor, Handbook of Latin American Studies, 1938–46; adviser, Survey of Agricultural Information Services in Latin America, 1951; Advisory Committee on Scientific Information Services of the Inter-American Institute of Agricultural Sciences, 1953–56; consultant to Uruguay, U.S. Dept. of State, 1963. Membership: American Library Association; Asociación de Bibliotecarios del Uruguay; District of Columbia Library Association; Inter-American Council. Research: library administration; bibliography in the Americas; agricultural libraries. Author: Guide to Libraries and Archives in Central America and West Indies (1941); Union List of Latin American Newspapers in Libraries of the United States (1953); Bibliografía sobre las bibliotecas nacionales de los países latinoamericanos y sus publicaciones (1960). Language: Spanish 5,5,5,5; Portuguese 4,3,1,1; French 2,1,1,1; German 4,3,3,3. Home: 5113 Western Ave., NW., Washington, D.C. 20016. Office: Columbus Memorial Library, Pan American Union, Washington, D.C. 20006.

GROSSMAN, WILLIAM LEONARD, b. New York, N.Y., Apr. 4, 1906. ECONOMICS AND BRAZILIAN LITERATURE. B.A., Harvard U., 1927; M.A., 1928; LL.B., 1932; J.S.D., N.Y.U. 1936. Asst. prof., N.Y.U., 1939–48; chmn., Transport Economics, Instituto Technológico da Aeronáutica (São José dos Campos, Brazil), 1948–52; assoc. prof.-PROF., CHMN., TRANSPORTATION, N.Y.U., 1952– . Consultant, Brazilian Ministry of Aeronautics, 1948–52. Membership: American Academy of Political and Social Science; American Society of Traffic and Transportation. Research: transportation; Brazilian-American economic relations; economic development of Brazil; translation of Brazilian literature; Machado de Assis. Author: Ocean Freight Rates (1956); Fundamentals of Transportation (1959). Translator: Epitaph of a Small Winner, by Machado de Assis (1952). Language: Spanish 1,1,1,1; Portuguese 4,

3,3,3; French 4,2,2,2. Home: 29 Washington Square West, New York, N.Y., 10011. Office: N.Y.U., Washington Square, New York, 10003.

GRUNWALD, JOSEPH, b. Vienna, Austria, June 25, 1920. ECONOMICS. B.S., Johns Hopkins U., 1943; Ph. D., Columbia U., 1950. Lectr., Rutgers U., 1946–47; lectr., Columbia U., 1947; asst. prof., Adelphi Coll., 1947–50; economic adviser, Government of P.R., 1950–52; acting dir., Economics Div., Puerto Rican Planning Board, 1951–52; asst. prof., City Coll. (N.Y.), 1952–54; prof., dir., Institute of Economic Research, U. of Chile, 1954–63; vis. prof., Yale U., 1961–63; DIR., ECONOMIC AND SOCIAL DEVELOPMENT STUDIES, THE BROOKINGS INSTITUTION, 1963– . Faculty research grant (Norway), 1949; co-founder, Puerto Rican Economic Association, 1950; ex-officio adviser, Government of Chile, 1955–61; consultant on Latin America, W. R. Grace and Company, Ford Motor Company, 1955–63; Rockefeller Foundation research grant, U. of Chile, 1959–61; consultant, Ford Foundation, 1960– , U.S. Dept. of State, 1962, U.S. Agency for International Development, Interamerican Bank for Reconstruction and Development, and Joint Committee on Latin American Studies, American Council of Learned Societies-Social Science Research Council, 1962– ; Advisory Committees, Institute of International Education, Brookings Institution, Twentieth Century Fund, Carnegie Endowment for International Peace, Alliance for Progress Study Group, Council on Foreign Relations. Membership: American Economic Association; Interamerican Planning Society; International Development Society; National Planning Society; Regional Science Association. Research: economic development; economic integration in Latin America; economic planning; Chilean economy. Author: Desarrollo económico de Chile, 1940–1956 (1956); Survey and Perspectives of Chile's Economic Development (1959); Resource Aspects of Latin American Economic Development (in Natural Resources and International Development, 1964). Language: Spanish 5,5,4,4; Portuguese 4,3,2,2; French 3,3,2,–; German 5,5, 5,4; Norwegian 3,3,1,1. Home: 8206 Kenfield Ct., Bethesda, Md. Office: The Brookings Institution, 1775 Massachusetts Ave. NW., Washington, D.C., 20036.

GUDSCHINSKY, SARAH CAROLINE, b. Bay City, Mich., May 8, 1919. LINGUISTICS. B.S., Central Mich. Coll. of Education, 1940; M.A., U. of Pa., 1956; Ph. D., 1958. FIELD RESEARCHER, INSTR., TECHNICAL CONSULTANT, SUMMER INSTITUTE OF LINGUISTICS (MEXICO), 1948–55, (BRAZIL), 1958– . Membership: Linguistic Circle of New York; Linguistic Circle of America; Sociedade Brasileira de Antropologia. Research: literacy; descriptive and comparative linguistics; Amerindian languages and cultures in Mexico and Brazil. Author: Proto-popotecan (1959); ABC's of Lexicostatistics, Glottochronology (Word, Aug. 1956); Mazatec Dialect History (Language, 1959). Language: Spanish 4,3,2,2; Portuguese 4, 3,3,2; German 2,2,1,1. Linguistic studies: Mazatec; Ofaie. Home: 1008 3rd St., Bay City, Mich. Office: Summer Institute of Linguistics, Box 1960, Santa Ana, Calif.

GUERNSEY, JAMES LEE, b. Henryville, Ind., June 22, 1923. GEOGRAPHY AND CITY PLANNING. B.S., Ind. State Coll., 1947; M.A., Ind. U., 1948; Ph. D, Northwestern U, 1953. Asst. prof., Ind. State Coll., 1948–53; assoc. prof., U. of Louisville, 1953–57; PROF., GEOGRAPHY, DIR., EXPERIMENT STATION, IND. STATE COLL., 1957– . Consultant, Kentucky Dept. of Conservation, 1954–57; consultant, City Planning Associates, 1959–62; consultant, Battelle Memorial Institute, 1963; National Science Foundation grant; Resources for the Future grant. Membership: Association of American Geographers; Indiana Academy of Science; National Council for Geographic Education. Research: economic geography; regional planning; physical geography. Author: El Salvador (in The American Peoples Encyclopedia, 1959); South America (in The American Peoples Encyclopedia, 1959); Reflections on the Operation of the Alliance for Progress (Proceedings of a Public Affairs Conference on Latin America, Oct. 1963). Language: Spanish 2,–,–,–; French 2,–,–,–. Home: 100 Monterey, Terre Haute, Ind. Office: Dept. of Geography, Ind. State Coll., Terre Haute.

GUERRA, EMILIO L., b. Hoboken, N.J., Aug. 27, 1909. EDUCATION AND LANGUAGE. A.B., City Coll. (N.Y.), 1931; M.S., 1933; Ph. D., N.Y.U., 1942. Teacher and supervisor, Foreign Languages, High School Div., Board of Education of the City of N.Y., 1931–57; ADJUNCT ASSOC. PROF., FOREIGN LANGUAGES, SCHOOL OF EDUCATION, N.Y.U., 1937– ; supervisor, English as a Second Language, High School Div., Board of Education of the City of N.Y., 1957–63; ACTING DIR., BUREAU OF FOREIGN LANGUAGES, BOARD OF EDUCATION OF THE CITY OF N.Y., 1963– . Smith-Mundt lectr., Universidad Central de Ecuador, 1956, Universidad de Guayaquil (Ecuador), 1957; Fulbright lectr., Universidad Nacional de Buenos Aires (Argentina), 1958; chmn., Committee on Teacher Selection for Educational Exchange with Latin America. Membership: American Association of Teachers of French; American Association of Teachers of Spanish and Portuguese; American Association of University Professors; Modern Language Association; National Education Association; Phi Delta Kappa. Research: methods and materials for secondary education; teaching foreign languages on the secondary school level; English as a foreign language. Author: Applied Linguistics and the Teacher of Spanish (High Points, Apr. 1963). Co-author: Getting to Know Spain and Latin America (1957); A First Course in Spanish (1961). Language: Spanish 5,5,5,5; French 4,4,4,4; Italian 4,4, 4,4. Linguistic studies: French; Italian; Spanish. Home: 116–40 Park Lane South, Kew Gardens, N.Y. 11418. Office: Board of Education of the City of N.Y., 110 Livingston St., Brooklyn, N.Y. 11201.

GUEST, FLORIAN FRANCIS, O.F.M., b. Alameda, Calif., Aug. 29, 1914. HISTORY. M.A., St. Louis U., 1952; M.A., Catholic U. of America, 1958; Ph. D., U. of Southern Calif., 1961. RESEARCH, HISTORY, FRANCISCAN FATHERS OF CALI-

FORNIA. Membership: Academy of American Franciscan History; California Historical Society. Research: the four presidios of Spanish California in their relationship with the California missions. Author: The Establishment of Branciforte (California Historical Quarterly, Mar. 1962). Language: Spanish 3,3,3,3. Home and office: Franciscan Fathers of Calif., Old Mission, Santa Barbara, Calif.

GUICE, C. NORMAN, b. Summit, Miss., Feb. 2, 1911. HISTORY. B.A., Hendrix Coll., 1931; M.A., Duke U., 1937; Ph. D., U. of Calif., Berkeley, 1952. Instr., Stephens Coll., 1942–43; lectr., U. of Mich., 1947; ASSOC. PROF., HISTORY, WAYNE STATE U., 1947–. Mills traveling fellow, U. of Calif. (Mexico), 1941–42; consultant, Committee on the Accreditation of Service Experiences, American Council on Education, 1954, 1956, 1958; Fulbright lectr. (Peru), 1959–60; Rockefeller grant (Peru), Summer 1960; Wayne State U. faculty research fellow (Peru and Chile), Summer 1962. Membership: American Historical Association; Conference on Latin American History; Detroit Historical Society; Michigan Historical Society. Research: Peru during the War of the Pacific. Author: Texas in 1804 (Southwestern Historical Quarterly, July 1955); Trade Goods for Texas (Southwestern Historical Quarterly, Apr. 1957); The Latin American University (Graduate Comment, Wayne State University, Dec. 1960). Language: Spanish 4,4,4,3; Portuguese 1,–,–,–; French 2,2,–,–; German 1,–, –,–. Home: 92 Mapleton Rd., Grosse Point Farms 36, Mich. Office: Dept. of History, Wayne State U., Detroit 2, Mich.

GUTHRIE, JOSEPH HUNTER, S.J., b. New York, N.Y., Jan. 8, 1901. PHILOSOPHY. S.T.D., Gregorian U. (Rome), 1932; Ph. D., Sorbonne, 1937. Prof., Woodstock Coll., 1937–40; prof., chmn., Philosophy, Fordham U., 1940–42; dean, Graduate School, Georgetown U., 1942–48; president, 1948–53; PROF., CHMN., PHILOSOPHY, ST. JOSEPH'S COLL., 1953– . Suarez Anniversary lectr. (Spain), 1949; Latin American specialist lectr., U.S. Information Agency, 1955, 1958. Research: contemporary philosophy; existentialism; Teilhard de Chardin; pre-Socratics; culture, economy and education in Haiti; communism in El Salvador, Costa Rica, Chile and Venezuela. Author: Modern Trends in American Culture (1923); Problème de l'histoire de la philosophie (1937); Symposium on American Catholic Education (1944). Language: Spanish 3,3,2,2; Portuguese 2,2,1,1; French 4,4,4,4; German 4,4,4,3; Italian 3,3,2,2. Office: Dept. of Philosophy, St. Joseph's Coll., Philadelphia, Pa. 19131.

GUZMAN, LOUIS ENRIQUE, b. Los Angeles, Calif., Oct. 29, 1920. GEOGRAPHY. B.A., U. of Calif., Los Angeles, 1949; M.A., 1951; Ph. D., U. of Chicago, 1956. Agricultural technician, Div. of Agriculture and Natural Resources, Institute of Inter-American Affairs (Panama), 1953–55; agricultural program officer, International Cooperation Administration (Panama), 1957–59; ASSOC. PROF., GEOGRAPHY, SAN FERNANDO VALLEY STATE COLL., 1959– . U.S. Office of Naval Research grant (Guatemala, British Honduras), Summer 1962; Fulbright prof. (Peru), 1963–64. Membership: American Association for the Advancement of Science; American Geographical Society; Association of American Geographers; Association of Pacific Coast Geographers. Research: agricultural resources; ancient agricultural sites of Mesoamerican Indians; agricultural resources of Panama. Author: Farming and Farmlands in Panama (1956); Las terrazas de los antiguos mayas montañeses (Revista Interamericana de Ciencias Sociales, 1962). Co-author: The Soils and Agriculture of the Llanos de Coclé, Panama (1957). Language: Spanish 5,5,5,5; Portuguese 3,3,2,1. Home: 16422 Bircher St., Granada Hills, Calif. Office: Dept. of Geography, San Fernando Valley State Coll., Northridge, Calif.

GUZMAN-RIVAS, PABLO, b. Manila, Philippines, Jan. 27, 1911. GEOGRAPHY. Ph. D., U. of Tex., 1960. ASSOC. PROF., GEOGRAPHY, U. OF COLO., 1956– . U.S. Office of Naval Research grant (Mexico), 1955–56; chmn., Committee on Latin American Studies, U. of Colo.; assoc. editor, Rocky Mountain Social Science Journal. Membership: Association of American Geographers; Rocky Mountain Social Science Association. Research: regional and historical geography; Mexico. Author: Trans-Pacific Galleon Trade (Revista Geográfica, July–Dec. 1960). Collaborator: Coastal Study of Southwest Mexico (1960–1962). Language: Spanish 5,5,5,5; Portuguese 4,4,1,1; French 4,1,1,1. Office: Dept. of Geography, U. of Colo., Boulder.

GWIN, JAMES MARTIN, b. Blair County, Pa., Oct. 2, 1906. ECONOMICS: MARKETING. B.S., U. of Conn., 1931; M.A., American U., 1941; Ph. D., Cornell U., 1949. Marketing specialist, Conn. Dept. of Agriculture, 1931–39; marketing specialist, U. of Md., 1939–50; dir., Md. Extension Service, 1950–55; general manager, Poultry and Egg National Board (Chicago, Ill.), 1955–58; manager of marketing, Ralston Purina Company (St. Louis; Mexico; Venezuela), 1958–64; VIS. PROF., ECONOMICS, SOUTHERN ILL. U., 1964– . Head, British Guiana Project, U. of Md.; assoc. editor, Poultry Science. Membership: American Association for the Advancement of Science. Research: marketing of perishable products; marketing of eggs and poultry. Author: Marketing Poultry Products (1960); Successful Broiler Growing (1961). Language: Spanish 3,3,2,2; French 3,3,2,2. Home: 72 Frederick Lane, St. Louis, Mo., 63122. Office: Dept. of Economics, Southern Ill. U., East St. Louis, Ill.

H

HAAG, HERMAN MARTIN, b. Poplar Bluff, Mo., June 19, 1903. ECONOMICS: MARKETING. B.S., U. of Mo., 1930; Ph. D., Cornell U., 1933. Information agent, Farm Credit Administration (St. Louis, Mo.), 1933; information assoc. (Washington, D.C.), 1933–36; asst.-assoc. prof., U. of Mo., 1936–45; research dir., Missouri Farmers Association, 1945–57; consultant, Ford Foundation (Rangoon, Burma), 1957–59; PROF., AGRICULTURAL INDUSTRIES, SOUTHERN ILL. U., 1959– . Grant for Mexican grain marketing study, Agricultural Development Council. Membership: American Farm Economics Association; Canadian Agricultural Economics Society; International Association of Agricultural Economics. Research: agricultural economics;

marketing of grains in Yaqui Valley, Sonora, Mexico; agricultural development in low income countries. Co-author: Operations and Practices of Illinois Egg Handlers (1962); Analysis of Weekly Unloads of Fresh Fruits and Vegetables, Chicago, May 1959–Dec. 1962 (1963). Language: Spanish 3,2,1,1; German 2,2,1,1. Home: 706 Taylor Dr., Carbonale, Ill. 62901. Office: 226 Agriculture, Southern Ill. U., Carbondale, 62903.

HAAS, LEZ LEWIS, b. Berkeley, Calif., Mar. 10, 1911. ART. A.B., U. of Calif., Berkeley, 1939; M.A., 1942; 1948–49. Instr.-prof., chmn., Art, U. of N. Mex., 1946–63; PROF., HEAD, ART, U. OF ARIZ., 1963– . Membership: American Association of University Professors; College Art Association; Society for American Archaeology. Research: painting; Amerindian art; indigenous art of Mexico. Language: Spanish 4,3,3,2; French 4,2,2,1; German 1,1,1,1. Home: 101 West Yvon Dr., Tucson, Ariz., 85704. Office: Dept. of Art, Coll. of Fine Arts, U. of Ariz., Tucson, 85721.

HAASE, YNEZ DURNFORD, b. Fillmore, Calif., Aug. 5, 1921. GEOGRAPHY. A.B., U. of Calif., Berkeley, 1949; M.A., 1952. Cartographer, U. of Calif., Berkeley, 1954–57; field geographer (Peru), U.S. Office of Naval Research, 1957–58; asst. research historian, Navajo Tribe (Ariz.), 1959–60; assoc. research geographer, Jicarilla Apache Tribe (N. Mex.), 1959–60; senior cartographer, U. of Calif., Berkeley, 1960; land use specialist, Spartan Air Services (Buenos Aires), 1961–63; instr., U.S. Peace Corps Training Center, U. of N. Mex., 1963–64; RESEARCH GEOGRAPHER, U. OF N. MEX., 1963–. Consultant, N. Mex. Mapping Board; II Congreso Nacional de la Historia del Perú. Membership: American Geographic Society; California Historical Society; Friends of the Bancroft Library; New Mexico Historical Society; Phi Alpha Theta. Research: cartography; photo interpretation; annotation of land use; native agriculture, land use and terrain of Peru and Argentina; desert cultures in Hispanic America. Author: Environment, Settlement and Land Use in Jicarilla Claim Area (1959); Geography of Northern Peru (1960); A Survey of Peruvian Fishing Communities (1962). Language: Spanish 5,5,5,4; Portuguese 1,1,1,1; French 3,1,1,1; German 3,3,3,1. Home: Box 369, Route 2, Fillmore, Calif. 93015. Office: Dept. of Geography, U. of N. Mex., Albuquerque.

HABERSTROH, CHADWICK JOHN, b. Livingston, Mont., July 19, 1927. ECONOMICS. B.A., U. of Minn., 1948; M.A., Columbia U., 1950; Ph. D., U. of Minn., 1958. Labor economist, US. Dept. of Labor, 1950–52; instr., U. of Minn., 1953–54; asst. prof., Mass. Institute of Technology, 1957–62; PROF., MANAGEMENT, U. OF DENVER, 1962– . Senior research fellow, Carnegie Institute of Technology, 1954–57; Fulbright lectr., Universidad de Cuenca (Ecuador), 1959; participant, Organization of American States-Inter-American Defense Board-Economic Commission for Latin American Conference on Tax Administration (Buenos Aires), 1961. Membership: American Association for the Advancement of Science; American Association of University Professors; American Economic Association; American Sociological Association; Institute of Management Sciences; Society for Applied Anthropology; Society for General Systems Research. Research: behavioral science; organizational behavior and theory, including control systems; commercial institutions in Ecuador; organizational problems of tax office in Argentina. Author: Some Theories of Organization (1960); Organization Structure—Social and Technical Elements (Industrial Management Review, Nov. 1961); The Legitimacy of Managerial Authority (Industrial Management Review, May 1964). Language: Spanish 4,3,4,4; Portuguese 1,1,1,1; French 1,1,1,1; German 2,2,2,2. Home: 2931 South Franklin St., Englewood, Colo., 80110. Office: Dept. of Management, U. of Denver, 1445 Cleveland Pl., Denver, Colo., 80202.

HADDICK, JACK ALLEN, b. Olden, Tex., June 12, 1920. HISTORY. B.A., Tex. Coll. of Arts & Industries, 1949; M.A., U. of Tex., 1950; Ph. D., 1954. Lectr., Mexico City Coll., 1954; ASSOC. PROF., HISTORY, U. OF HOUSTON, 1955– . E D. Farmer International Scholar (Mexico), 1954; chmn., Regional Interviewing Committee, International Education Exchange Program, U.S. Dept. of Health, Education, and Welfare, 1963. Membership: American Historical Association; Texas Gulf Coast Historical Association. Research: independence period in Mexico; Spain. Author: The Deliberative Juntas of 1808: A Crisis in Mexican Democracy (in Essays in Mexican History by C. E. Castañeda and T. Cotner, 1958). Language: Spanish 4,3,3,3. Home: 4395 Harvest Lane, Houston 4, Tex. Office: Dept. of History, U. of Houston, 3801 Cullen Blvd., Houston 4.

HADDOX, BENJAMIN EDWARD, b. Orlando, Fla., Dec. 11, 1923. SOCIOLOGY. A.B., Stetson U., 1945; B.D., Southern Baptist Theological Seminary, 1950; M.A., U. of Fla., 1960; Ph. D. 1962. Asst. prof., Miss. State U., 1962–64; ASST. PROF., ACTING CHMN., SOCIOLOGY, STETSON U., 1964– . United States Steel Foundation fellow, U. of Fla., 1960–62; Technical Committee, regional study of low-income rural families, 1962–64. Membership: American Sociological Association; National Council for Family Relations; Population Reference Bureau; Southern Sociological Society. Research: race relations; low income rural families in southeastern United States; study of the institution of religion in Colombia. Language: Spanish, 3,2,2,3; Portuguese 1,1,1,1; French 1,1,1,1. Home: 414 South Woodward, DeLand, Fla., 32720. Office: Dept. of Sociology, Stetson U., DeLand, 32720.

HADLEY, PAUL E., b. South Ovid, Mich., July 17, 1914. POLITICAL SCIENCE: INTERNATIONAL RELATIONS. A.B., Occidental Coll., 1934; A.M., U. of Southern Calif., 1946; Ph. D., 1955. Teacher, El Monte Union High School (Calif.), 1935–42; dir., Centro Cultural Paraguayo-Americano (Asunción), U.S. Dept. of State, 1942–44; head, Cultural Institutes Unit, 1945; ASSOC. PROF., INTERNATIONAL RELATIONS, U. OF SOUTHERN CALIF., 1945– . Woodrow Wilson Fellowship Selection Committee; Committee on Leaders and Specialists, American Council on Education; consultant, Modern Language Association of Southern California. Membership: Pacific Coast Council on Latin American Studies; Phi Beta Kappa; Western Political Science

Association. Research: regional and general international relations; Alliance for Progress; comparative literature. Author: Cuba and Coexistence (Institute on World Affairs, 1962); Internal Institutions and External Assistance: Some Political Implications of the Alliance for Progress (Western Political Quarterly Supplement, 1962); Tensions of Development in Latin America (Institute on World Affairs, 1963). Language: Spanish 4,4,3,3; Portuguese 2,1,1,1; French 3,3,2,2; German 3,2,2,1. Home: 127 South Adams, Glendale, Calif., 91205. Office: Dept. of International Relations, U. of Southern Calif., Los Angeles, 90007.

HAGEN, EVERETT EINAR, b. Holloway, Minn., July 5, 1906. ECONOMICS. B.A., St. Olaf Coll., 1927; M.A., U. of Wis., 1936; Ph. D., 1941. Instr., Mich. State Coll., 1937–42; economist, U.S. Government, 1942–48; prof., U. of Ill., 1948–51; economist, Robert R. Nathan Associates, Inc., 1951–53; PROF., ECONOMICS, CENTER FOR INTERNATIONAL STUDIES, MASS. INSTITUTE OF TECHNOLOGY, 1953– ; PROF., POLITICAL SCIENCE, 1964– . Consultant to: U.S. Economic Cooperation Administration, 1948; U.S. Dept. of the Treasury, 1949–51; U.S. Council, International Chamber of Commerce, 1955; President's Task Force on Foreign Economic Assistance, 1961; Ford Foundation on evaluation of university teaching of economics in Brazil, 1961; U.S. Agency for International Development (Argentina), 1962; Government of El Salvador, 1962–63. Membership: American Economic Association; Royal Economic Society. Research: economics of development; psychoanalytical theory of personality, as an instrument for understanding the process of social change involved in economic development; Colombia; Argentina. Author: Handbook for Industry Studies (1958); On the Theory of Social Change (1962). Editor: Planning Economic Development (1964). Language: Spanish 3,2,2,1; French 2,2,2,1. Home: 100 Memorial Dr., Cambridge, Mass., 02142. Office: Center for International Studies, Mass. Institute of Technology, Cambridge, 02139.

HAHN, PAUL G., b. Portales, N. Mex., Dec. 28, 1927. ANTHROPOLOGY. B.A., U. of Fla., 1952; Ph. D., Yale U., 1961. Curator, Southeast Museum of North American Indian (Marathon, Fla.), 1957–59; asst. prof., U. of Miss., 1959–62; assoc. prof., 1962–63; interim asst. prof., U. of Fla., 1963–64; NATIONAL INSTITUTE OF MENTAL HEALTH FELLOW, ANTHROPOLOGY, U. OF FLA., 1964– . Membership: American Anthropological Association; American Ethnological Society; American Ethnohistoric Conference; Current Anthropology Association; Florida Anthropological Society; Society for American Archaeology; Society for Applied Anthropology. Research: cultural anthropology; Cuban archeology. Author: College Cheating (Mississippi Magazine, Spring 1961). Language: Spanish 4,4,3,3; French 3,1,1,1. Home: 937 NW. 40th Ter., Gainesville, Fla. Office: Dept. of Anthropology, U. of Fla., Gainesville.

HAIGH, ROGER MALONE, b. Atkinson, Nebr., Feb. 6, 1937. HISTORY. B.A., Nebr. State Teachers Coll., Peru, 1957; M.A., U. of Fla., 1958; Ph. D., 1963. ASST. PROF., HISTORY, NORTH TEX. STATE U., 1963– . Graduate fellow, U. of Fla., 1961–63. Research: the relationship of informal group solidarities to the independence movement. Language: Spanish 4,2,2,1; Portuguese 2,1,1,1; Danish 3,3,3,3. Home: 1108–11 Palmwood Dr., Denton, Tex. Office: Dept. of History, North Tex. State U., Denton.

HAIGHT, CHARLES HENRY, b. Chicago, Ill., May 27, 1909. HISTORY. B.A., U. of Calif., 1946; M.A., 1947; Ph. D., Stanford U., 1956. Instr., Stanford U., 1955–56; instr., U. of Calif., 1956–58; INSTR., HISTORY, COLL. OF SAN MATEO, 1958– . Membership: American Historical Association. Research: Mexico, the colonial period and the Mexican Revolution. Language: Spanish 4,4,4,4; French 4,2,2,1. Home: 1247 Shafter St., San Mateo, Calif. Office: Dept. of History, Coll. of San Mateo.

HALE, CHARLES ADAMS, b. Minneapolis, Minn., June 5, 1930. HISTORY. B.A., Amherst Coll., 1951; M.A., U. of Minn., 1952; Diplôme, Université de Strasbourg, 1953; Ph. D., Columbia U., 1957. Instr., U. of N.C., 1956–57; asst. prof., Lehigh U., 1957–62; ASST. PROF., HISTORY, AMHERST COLL., 1963– . Fulbright scholar (France), 1952–53; Doherty fellow (Mexico), 1955–56; American Council of Learned Societies-Social Science Research Council grant (Peru), 1962–63. Membership: American Historical Association; Phi Beta Kappa. Research: Mexico. Author: The War with the United States and the Crisis in Mexican Thought (The Americas, Oct. 1957); Alamán, Antunano, y la continuidad del liberalismo (Historia Mexicana, Oct.–Dec. 1961). Language: Spanish 4,4,4,4; Portuguese 3,2,1,1; French 4,4,4,3. Home: 50 Lincoln Ave., Amherst, Mass. Office: Dept. of History, Amherst Coll., Amherst.

HALE, KENNETH LOCKE, b. Evanston, Ill., Aug. 15, 1934. ANTHROPOLOGY: LINGUISTICS. B.A., U. of Ariz., 1955; M.A., Ind. U., 1956; Ph. D., 1959. Asst. prof., U. of Ill., 1961–64; ASSOC. PROF., ANTHROPOLOGY, U. OF ARIZ., 1964– . National Science Foundation fellow (Australia), 1959-61. Membership: American Anthropological Association; Sigma Xi. Research: American Indian languages, especially Uto-Aztecan and Athabascan; Australian aboriginal languages; grammar of Papago. Author: Internal Diversity in Uto-Aztecan I, II (International Journal of American Linguistics, 1958–59); Jemez and Kiowa Correspondences in Reference to Kiowa-Tanoan (International Journal of American Linguistics, Oct. 1962). Co-author: Typological and Comparative Grammar of Uto-Aztecan (1962). Language: Spanish 4,4,4,4; Portuguese 3,3,3,3; French 3,3,3,3. Linguistic studies: Lardil; Navajo; Papago; Xhosa. Home: Route 5, Box 245, Tucson, Ariz. Office: Dept. of Anthropology, U. of Ariz., Tucson.

HALL, JEROME, b. Chicago, Ill., Feb. 4, 1901. LAW. Ph. B., U. of Chicago, 1922; J.D., 1923; S.J.D., Harvard Law School, 1935; J.S.D., Columbia U., 1935; LL.D. (honorary), U. of N. Dak., 1958. Prof., U. of N. Dak., 1929–32; prof., La. State U., 1935–36; DISTINGUISHED SERVICE PROF. OF LAW, IND. U., 1939– ; specialist, U.S. Dept. of State Educational Exchange Program (Far East and India), Summer 1954. Fulbright lectr. (United Kingdom), 1954–55, (Germany), 1961; Ford Foundation grant for South American lecture tour, 1960; honorary dir., Korean Legal Institute; dir., American Foreign Law Association; honorary president, Latin American Sociological Society. Membership: American Foreign Law Association; Latin American Sociological Society. Research: jurisprudence; criminal law; comparative law; South American legal philosophy. Author: General Principles of Criminal Law and Procedure (1947, 1960); Studies in Jurisprudence and Criminal Theory (1959); Comparative Law and Social Theory (1963). Language: French 3,–,2,3. Home: 530 South Jordan Ave., Bloomington, Ind. Office: School of Law, Ind. U., Bloomington, 47405.

HALL, JOHN OLIVER, b. Bentonville, Ark., June 4, 1914. POLITICAL SCIENCE. A.B. U. of Okla., 1936; M.P.A., U. of Pittsburgh, 1964. City manager, Nowata (Okla.), 1938–39, El Reno (Okla.), 1939–41, Muskogee (Okla.), 1946–50, Pueblo (Colo.), 1950–52; public administration adviser, Institute of Inter-American Affairs, U.S. International Cooperation Administration (Ecuador), 1952–53; (Uruguay), 1953–56; assoc. chief of party, U. of Pa.-U. of Karachi (Pakistan), 1957–59; city manager, Savannah (Ga.), 1959–62; DIR., OVERSEAS PROGRAMS, GRADUATE SCHOOL OF PUBLIC AND INTERNATIONAL AFFAIRS, U. OF PITTSBURGH, 1962– . Membership: American Academy of Political and Social Science; American Society for Public Administration; International City Managers' Association; Society for International Development. Research: national and municipal administration; international and comparative higher education; national economic and social development. Author: Public Administration in Uruguay (1954); A Study of the Secretariat of the National Council of Government (1955); A Study of the Administrative Reorganization of the Ministry of Public Health (1956). Language: Spanish 4,4,4,4; Portuguese 2,2,1,1. Home: 4210 Centre Ave., Pittsburgh, Pa., 15213. Office: Graduate School of Public and International Affairs, U. of Pittsburgh, Pittsburgh, 15213.

HALL, MARGARET ESTHER, b. Little Valley, N.Y., Mar. 19, 1905. LIBRARY SCIENCE AND LAW. B.L.S., Syracuse U., 1929; LL.B., 1935. Branch asst., Buffalo Public Library, 1927–28; law librarian, Syracuse U., 1929–32; asst. librarian, Law Library, U. of N.C., 1935–38; legal research librarian, Law Library, Columbia U., 1938–49; dir., Artigas Washington Library (Montevideo, Uruguay), U.S. Information Service, 1949–52; librarian in charge of extension services, Benjamin Franklin Library (Mexico D.F.), U.S. Information Service, 1952–55; reference librarian, U.S. Information Agency (Washington, D.C.), 1955–58; LAW LIBRARIAN, PROF. OF LAW, U. OF P.R., 1958– . Consultant, United Nations Library, First Session; International Advisory Council, Books for the People Fund, Inc.; head of secretariat, First Inter-American Congress on Peaceful Uses of Atomic Energy. Membership: American Association of Law Libraries; International Association of Law Libraries; Puerto Rican Library Association. Author: Selected Writings of Benjamin Nathan Cardozo (1947); Alexander Hamilton Reader (1957); How to Become a Citizen of the United States (1963). Language: Spanish 4,4,4,4; French 3,–,–,–. Office; Law Library, U. of P.R., Río Piedras, 00931.

HALL, ROBERT ANDERSON, JR., Raleigh, N.C., Apr. 4, 1911. LANGUAGE. B.A., Princeton U., 1931; M.A., U. of Chicago, 1935; Litt. D., U. of Rome (Italy), 1934. Asst. prof., U. of P.R., 1937–39; instr., Princeton U., 1939–40; asst. prof., Brown U., 1940–46; PROF., LINGUISTICS, CORNELL U., 1946– . Consultant, UNESCO Fundamental Education Program (Haiti), 1949; Fulbright lectr., U. of Rome, 1950–51; 1957–58. Membership: American Anthropological Association; American Association of Teachers of Italian; Linguistic Society of America; Modern Language Association. Research: Haitian Creole; pidgin and creole languages; Romance languages. Author: Haitian Creole: Grammar, Texts, Vocabulary (1953); Linguistics and Your Language (1960); Cultural Symbolism in Literature (Linguistica, 1963). Language: Spanish 4,4,4,4; Portuguese 4,3,3,3; French 5,5,5,5; German 5,5,4,4; Haitian Creole 4,3,3,3; Italian 5,5,5,5. Linguistic studies: Haitian Creole; Melanesian Pidgin English; Taki-Taki. Home: 308 Cayuga Heights Rd., Ithaca, N.Y. 14850. Office: Div. of Modern Languages, Cornell U., Ithaca, 14850.

HALLER, ARCHIBALD O., b. San Diego, Calif., Jan. 15, 1926. SOCIOLOGY. B.A., Hamline U., 1950; M.A., U. of Minn., 1951; Ph. D., U. of Wis., 1954. Project assoc., Rural Sociology, U. of Wis., 1954–56; PROF., SOCIOLOGY, MICH. STATE U., 1956– . Consultant, Instituto Interamericano de Ciencias Agrícolas, 1958, Fich. State Dept. of Mental Health, 1961–62, National Institute of Mental Health, 1962; Fulbright prof., Universidade Rural do Brasil, 1962–63; Organization of American States consultant to Government of Brazil, 1962–63; Membership: American Sociological Association; Michigan Sociological Association; Ohio Valley Sociological Society; Rural Sociological Society. Research: social structure and personality; statistical analysis; rural social structure of Brazil. Author: The Occupational Aspiration Scale: Theory, Structure and Correlates (1963); Situational and Personal Antecedents of Incipient Alienation: An Exploratory Study (1964); A Measure of Level of Occupational Aspiration (Personnel and Guidance Journal, Jan. 1964). Language: Spanish 3,3,2,1; Portuguese 4,4,3,2. Home: 1009 West Grand River, East Lansing, Mich., 48823. Office: Dept. of Sociology, Mich. State U., East Lansing, 48823.

HAMILL, HUGH MAXWELL, JR., b. Philadelphia, Pa., May 23, 1928. HISTORY. B.A., Amherst Coll., 1951; M.A., Harvard U., 1953; Ph. D., 1956. Group leader, Experiment in International Living (Mexico), Summer 1950; instr., Ohio Wesleyan U., 1957–58; asst. prof., 1958–61; asst. prof., U. of Conn., 1961–63; ASSOC. PROF., HISTORY, U. OF CONN., 1963– . Doherty fellow (Mexico), 1953–54; secretary-treasurer, Conference on Latin American History, 1960–62; dir., Latin American Area Studies, Missionary Personnel Program, National Council of Churches, June 1963. Membership: American Association of University Professors; American Historical Association; Hispanic American Society; Phi Beta Kappa. Research: New Spain in late 18th century to 1821; propaganda and psychological warfare. Author: The Hidalgo Revolt: Prelude to Mexican Independence (1964); Early Psychological Warfare in the Hidalgo Revolt (Hispanic American Historical Review, May 1961). Language: Spanish 5,4,4,4; Portuguese 3,2,2,2; French 4,2,2,2. Home: R.F.D. 1, Box 113, Mansfield Center, Conn. Office: Dept. of History, U. of Conn., Storrs.

HAMILTON, CARLOS D., b. Santiago, Chile, Oct. 20, 1908. SPANISH AMERICAN LITERATURE AND LANGUAGE. B.A., Universidad de Chile, 1923; M.A., Gregorian U. (Rome), 1929; Ph. D., 1930. Lectr., Columbia U., 1952-54; lectr., Queens Coll., 1955-56; assoc. prof., Vassar Coll., 1956-61; PROF., MODERN LANGUAGES, BROOKLYN COLL., 1961– . Fulbright lectr., Instituto Caro y Cuervo (Bogotá), 1963-64. Membership: American Association of Teachers of Spanish and Portuguese; American Association of University Professors; Instituto de Cultura Hispánica (Madrid); Instituto de Estudios Legislativos (Chile); Instituto Internacional de Literatura Iberoamericana; Modern Language Association. Research: Spanish American civilization; modernista period; socio-economic conditions in Latin America. Author: Historia de la literatura hispanoamericana (1961); Antología selecta del siglo XIX (1962); Nuevo lenguaje poético (1964). Language: Spanish 5,5,5,5; Portuguese 5,4,4,4; French 5,5,5,5; Italian 5, 5,5,5; Latin 5,5,5,5. Office: Dept. of Modern Languages, Brooklyn Coll., Brooklyn 10, N.Y.

HAMILTON, DANIEL LEE, b. Recife, Brazil, Oct. 20, 1910. BRAZILIAN LITERATURE. A.B., Baylor U., 1931; A.M., Northwestern U., 1932; Ph. D., U. of Chicago, 1941. Prof., U. of Tex., 1945-50; academic dean, Army Language School, 1950-57; assoc. dean, Foreign Service Institute, U.S. Dept. of State, 1957-62; DIR., LANGUAGE DEVELOPMENT BRANCH, U.S. OFFICE OF EDUCATION, 1962– . American Council of Learned Societies grant-in-aid; Rockefeller fellow (Brazil), 1947. Membership: Modern Language Association. Research: modern Brazilian literature. Co-author: Conversas sul-americanas (1946); Contos do Brasil (1949). Language: Spanish 4, 3,3,3; Portuguese 4,4,4,3; French 4,3,3,3. Home: 3335 North Randolph, Arlington 7, Va. Office: U.S. Office of Education, 400 Maryland Ave., SW., Washington, D.C. 20008.

HAMILTON, EARL J., b. Houlka, Miss., May 17, 1899. ECONOMICS. B.S., Miss. State U., 1920; M.A., U. of Tex., 1924; Ph. D., Harvard U., 1929; Docteur Honoris Causa, U. of Paris, 1952. Asst. prof., Duke U., 1927-29; prof., 1929-44; prof., Northwestern U., 1944-47; PROF., ECONOMICS, U. OF CHICAGO, 1947– . Frederick Sheldon traveling fellow, Harvard U. (Spain); Social Science Research Council fellow, 1929-30; Guggenheim fellow, 1937-38; Joint Committee on Latin American Studies of Social Science Research Council, National Research Council and American Council of Learned Societies. Membership: American Academy of Arts and Sciences; American Association for the Advancement of Science; American Economic Association; American Historical Association; Economic History Association; Hispanic Society of America; Royal Economic Society. Research: economic history; history of economic thought; economic background of Latin American Independence, especially in Peru, Colombia, Mexico; money and banking. Author: American Treasure and the Price Revolution in Spain, 1501-1650 (1934); War and Prices in Spain, 1651-1800 (1947); El florecimiento del capitalismo y otros ensayos de historia económica (1948). Language: Spanish 5,5,4,4; Portuguese 3,–,–,–; French 5,5,4,4; Dutch 4, 4,4,4; German 4,4,4,4; Italian 5,5,4,4. Home: 1438 Bunker Rd., Flossmoor, Ill. Office: Dept. of Economics, U. of Chicago, 1126 East 59th St., Chicago 37, Ill.

HAMMEL, EUGENE ALFRED, b. New York, N.Y., Mar. 18, 1930. ANTHROPOLOGY. A.B., U. of Calif., 1951; Ph. D., 1959. Asst. prof., U. of N. Mex, 1959-61; ASSOC. PROF., ANTHROPOLOGY, U. OF CALIF., BERKELEY, 1961– . Social Science Research Council fellow (Peru), 1957-58; consultant, U.S. Peace Corps Training Program for Peru, U. of Calif., Los Angeles, Summers 1962, 1963; assoc. editor, American Anthropologist. Membership: American Anthropological Association. Research: social anthropology, especially kinship and social organization and economic history and development; ethnography of Peru. Author: Wealth, Authority, and Prestige in the Ica Valley (1961); The Family Cycle in a Coastal Peruvian Slum and Village (American Anthropologist, Oct. 1961); Social Rank and Evolutionary Position in a Coastal Peruvian Village (Southwestern Journal of Anthropology, Autumn 1962). Language: Spanish 4,4,4,3; Serbo-Croatian 4,4,3,3. Home: 2111 Los Angeles Ave., Berkeley 7, Calif. Office: Dept. of Anthropology, U. of Calif., Berkeley, 94720.

HAMMOND, GEORGE PETER, b. Hutchinson, Minn., Sept. 19, 1896. HISTORY. A.B., U. of Calif., 1920; M.A., 1921; Ph. D., 1924; LL. D., U. of N. Mex., 1954. Instr., U. of N. Dak., 1923-24; asst. prof., U. of Ariz., 1925-27; assoc. prof., U. of Southern Calif., 1927-35; prof., dean of Graduate School, U. of N. Mex., 1935-46; PROF., HISTORY, DIR., BANCROFT LIBRARY, U. OF CALIF., BERKELEY, 1946– . Native Sons of the Golden West fellow (Spain), 1922-23; U.S. delegation, 4th Assembly of Pan American Institute of Geography and History (Caracas), 1946. Membership: American Historical Association; California Historical Society; Mississippi Valley Historical Association; New Mexico Historical Society; Western History Association. Research: early history of California and New Mexico. Author: Narratives of the Coronado Expedition (1940); The Larkin Papers (1950-64). Co-author: Oñate, Colonizer of New Mexico (1953). Language: Spanish 4,3,3,3; Portuguese 2,2,2,–; French 2,2,2,–; Danish 5,5,5,5; German 3,3,3,3. Home: 810 Contra Costa Ave., Berkeley 7, Calif. Office: Bancroft Library, U. of Calif., Berkeley 4.

HAMMOND, JOHN HAYS, b. Fort Worth, Tex., Nov. 8, 1912. SPANISH AMERICAN LITERATURE AND LANGUAGE. B.A.,

Tex. Christian U., 1933; M.A., U. of Tex., 1935; Ph. D., 1948. Instr., U. of Nebr., 1937–40; instr., Princeton U., 1941–42; instr., U.S. Naval Academy, 1942–46; instr.-asst. prof., U. of Tex., 1946–50; assoc. prof.-PROF., CHMN., FOREIGN LANGUAGES, TEX. CHRISTIAN U., 1950– . U. of Tex. research fellow (Mexico), Summers 1940, 1941; American Council of Learned Societies fellow, 1951–52; Fund for the Advancement of Education fellow (Mexico), 1953–54; consultant in Spanish, National Committee on Medical Terminology. Membership: Alpha Chi; American Association of Teachers of Spanish and Portuguese; Instituto Internacional de Literatura Iberoamericana; Modern Language Association; Phi Sigma Iota. Research: Mexican and Spanish literature. Author: Francisco Santos' Debt to Gracián (1950); José María Roa Bárcena, Champion of Catholicism (The Américas, July 1949); The Hispanism of José Vasconcelos (Phi Sigma Iota Newsletter, Apr. 1960). Language: Spanish 5,5,5,5; Portuguese 2,2,2,2; French 4,4,4,4; German 3,3,3,3; Italian 3,3,3,3. Home: 2532 Greene Ave., Fort Worth 9, Tex. Office: Dept of Foreign Languages, Tex. Christian U., Fort Worth 29.

HANCOCK, RICHARD HUMPHRIS, b. Alpine, Tex., Jan. 19, 1926. SOCIOLOGY. B.S., N. Mex. State U., 1950; M.A., 1954; Ph. D., Stanford U, 1959. Livestock inspector, Hoof and Mouth Commission (Mexico), 1950–51; executive secretary, Doña Ana County Farm Bureau, 1951–61; assoc. training dir., U.S. Peace Corps, N. Mex. State U., 1962; dir., U.S. Peace Corps (El Salvador), 1962–63; DIR. OF INTERNATIONAL PROGRAMS, CENTER FOR CONTINUING EDUCATION, U. OF OKLA., 1964– . Membership: Hispanic Society. Research: rural sociology; farm economics; human resources as a factor in economic development; community development. Author: Role of the Bracero in the Cultural and Economic Development of Mexico (1959). Language: Spanish 5,5,5,5; Portuguese 3,3,3,2. Home: 2709 Meadowbrook, Norman, Okla. Office: Oklahoma Center for Continuing Education, U. of Okla., Norman.

HANKE, LEWIS ULYSSES, b. Oregon City, Oreg., Jan. 2, 1905. HISTORY. B.S., Northwestern U., 1924; M.A., 1925; Ph. D., Harvard U., 1936. Instr., Harvard U., 1934–39; dir., Hispanic Foundation, Library of Congress, 1939–51; prof., U. of Tex., 1951–61; PROF., HISTORY, COLUMBIA U., 1961– . Archibald Cary Coolidge fellow, 1933–34; Social Science Research Council fellow (Brazil), 1937–38; Rosenwald fellow, 1950. Membership: American Historical Association. Research: the Villa Imperial de Potosí. Author: The Struggle for Justice in the Spanish Conquest of America (1949); Aristotle and the American Indians (1959). Editor: Historia de la Villa Imperial de Potosí (1964). Language: Spanish 4,4,4,4; Portuguese 4,4,4,4; French 2,2,2,2. Home: Apt. 3–D, 90 Morningside Dr., New York 27, N.Y. Office: Fayerweather Hall 603, Dept. of History, Columbia U., New York, 27.

HANNA, ALFRED JACKSON, b. Tampa, Fla., May 5, 1893. HISTORY. A.B., Rollins Coll., 1917; L.H.D. (honorary), 1945. WEDDELL PROF. OF HISTORY OF THE AMERICAS, DIR., LATIN AMERICAN STUDIES, ROLLINS COLL., 1917– . Social Science Research Council and American Philosophical Society grants (France), 1952; Cross Chevalier, Order Palmes Académiques, Republic of France. Membership: American Historical Association; Southern Historical Association. Research: period of French intervention in Mexico. Author: Diplomatic Missions of the United States to Cuba to Secure the Spanish Archives of Florida (in Hispanic American Essays in Commemoration of James Alexander Robertson, 1942). Co-author: Confederate Exiles in Venezuela (1960); The Immigration Movement of the Intervention and Empire as seen through the Mexican Press (Hispanic American Historical Review, May 1947). Home: 235 Sterling Ave., Winter Park, Fla. Office: Dept. of History, Rollins Coll., Winter Park.

HANSON, SIMON GABRIEL, b. Winooski, Vt., Dec. 5, 1908. ECONOMICS. B.S., U. of Vt., 1929; M.S., 1930; M.A., Ph. D., Harvard U, 1938. Instr., Harvard U., 1931–35; lectr., American U., 1935; instr., U. of Louisville, 1937–38; instr., Mich. State U., Summer 1938; asst. prof., Carnegie Institute of Technology, 1938–39; economist, U.S. Dept. of Treasury, 1939–40; chief economist, Coordinator of Inter-American Affairs, 1941–42; asst. chief, Div. of Studies and Statistics, U.S. Dept. of State, 1942–44; adviser on Latin American development, Foreign Economic Administration, 1944–45; EDITOR AND PUBLISHER, HANSON'S LATIN AMERICAN LETTER, 1945– ; EDITOR, INTER-AMERICAN ECONOMIC AFFAIRS, 1945– ; prof., School of Advanced International Studies, 1948–49. Research: Argentina; Brazil; Uruguay. Author: Utopia in Uruguay (1938); Argentine Meat and the British Market (1938); Economic Development in Latin America (1950). Language: Spanish 5,4,3,3; Portuguese 5,–,–,–; French 5,4,5,5. Office: P.O. Box 181, Inter-American Economic Affairs, Washington, D.C.

HARBERGER, ARNOLD C., b. Newark, N.J., July 27, 1924. ECONOMICS. A.M., U. of Chicago, 1947; Ph. D., 1950. Research asst., Cowles Commission for Research in Economics, 1949; asst. prof., Johns Hopkins U., 1949–53; economist, International Monetary Fund, 1950; assoc. prof., U. of Chicago, 1953–59; PROF., ECONOMICS, U. OF CHICAGO, 1959– ; CHMN., 1964– ; economist, Mass. Institute of Technology Center for International Studies and Indian Planning Commission (New Delhi), 1961–62. Social Science Research Council faculty research fellow, 1951–53, 1954–55; staff consultant, President's Materials Policy Commission, 1951; consultant, Committee for Economic Development, 1955; consultant, U.S. Dept. of Agriculture, 1955; consultant on Chile, U.S. Dept. of State, 1955– ; Guggenheim fellow, U. of London, U. of Cambridge, 1958; Board of Editors, American Economic Review, 1959–61; consultant on fiscal survey of Argentina, Pan American Union, 1960– ; Research Advisory Committee, Office of Scientific Personnel, National Academy of Sciences, 1961–65; planning and economic policy member, Ad Hoc Committee for Evaluation of Panama's Development Plan, Organization of American States, 1961– ; consultant, U.S. Treasury Dept., 1962– , U.S. Dept. of State, 1963– ,

International Bank for Reconstruction and Development, 1963– , U.S. Dept. of Commerce, 1965. Membership: American Economic Association; Phi Beta Kappa. Research: public finance; international trade; economic development; materials policy; econometrics. Author: The Dynamics of Inflation in Chile (in Measurement in Economics, 1963); Aspectos de una reforma tributaria en América Latina (in Economía Latinoamericana, 1963); Some Notes on Inflation (in Inflation and Growth in Latin America, 1964). Language: Spanish 5,5,4,4; German 4,4,3,3. Home: 4840 South Greenwood, Chicago, Ill. 60615. Office: Dept. of Economics, U. of Chicago, Chicago, 60637.

HARDMAN DE BAUTISTA, MARTHA JAMES, b. Oct. 8, 1935. LINGUISTICS. B.A., U. of Utah, 1955; M.A., U. of N. Mex., 1957; Ph. D., Stanford U., 1963. English teacher, Universidad de San Marcos (Peru), 1958; instr., Cornell U., 1961–63; instr., Quechua Program, U.S. Peace Corps, Cornell U., Summer 1962, U. of Calif., Los Angeles, Spring 1963; ASST. PROF., SPANISH, U. OF SANTA CLARA, 1963– . Fulbright scholar (Peru), 1958–59; National Science Foundation grant (Peru), 1960–61. Membership: American Anthropological Association; Asociación de Lingüística y Filología de América Latina; Linguistic Circle of New York; Linguistic Society of America; Modern Language Association; Society for Applied Anthropology. Research: applied linguistics; Jaqaru and Kawki languages of Peru; Aymará language of Bolivia. Author: Jaqaru: Outline of Phonological and Morphological Structure (1964); Consonantal Conditioning of the Distribution of Vowel Allophones in Jaqaru (Sphinx, 1961); Estructura fonémica del jaqaru (Revista de Filología, 1964). Language: Spanish 5,5,5,5; Portuguese 3,2,1,1; French 4,2,1,1; Italian 3,1,1,1; Latin 3,1,1,1; Rumanian 3,1,1,1. Linguistic studies: Aymará; Jaqaru; Kawki; Quechua; Shipibo. Home: Apt. 4, 1150 Pierce St., Santa Clara, Calif. Office: Dept. of Foreign Languages, U. of Santa Clara, Santa Clara.

HARNER, MICHAEL JAMES, b. Washington, D.C., Apr. 27, 1929. ANTHROPOLOGY. A.B., U. of Calif., Berkeley, 1953; Ph. D., 1963. Asst. prof., Ariz. State U., 1958–61; ASST. RESEARCH ANTHROPOLOGIST, LOWIE MUSEUM OF ANTHROPOLOGY, U. OF CALIF., BERKELEY, 1961– ; TEACHER, ANTHROPOLOGY, EXTENSION DIV., 1962– ; lectr., U. of Calif., Berkeley, Summers 1902, 1903. Doherty fellow (Ecuador), 1956–57; University fellow in Anthropology, U. of Calif., Berkeley, 1957–58; Social Science Research Council fellow, 1959; American Museum of Natural History grant (Peru), 1960–61. Membership: American Anthropological Association; American Association for the Advancement of Science; American Ethnological Society; Instituto Ecuatoriano de Antropología y Geografía; Kroeber Anthropological Society; Society for American Archaeology. Research: cultural anthropology; ethnology of Ecuador and Peru; culture change in South America. Author: Jívaro Souls (American Anthropologist, Apr. 1962); Choroti (in Encylopaedia Britannica, 1963). Co-author: Melanesian Art and Ritual (1963). Language: Spanish 4,4,4,4; Portuguese 3,2,2,1; French 2,1,1,1; Chama –,2,2,–; German 3,2,2,1; Jívaro –,2,2,–. Home: 2712 Derby St., Berkeley 5, Calif. Office: Lowie Museum of Anthropology, U. of Calif., Berkeley.

HARRELL, WILLIAM ASBURY, b. Americus, Ga., Apr. 21, 1922. HISTORY AND EDUCATION. B.A., Emory U., 1945; B.D., 1948; M.A., Scarritt Coll., 1950; Ph. D., U. of Fla., 1964. Missionary, Granbury Institute (Brazil), Board of Missions of the Methodist Church, 1949–62; SPECIALIST, COMPARATIVE EDUCATION, WESTERN HEMISPHERE, U.S. OFFICE OF EDUCATION, 1964– . National Defense Foreign Language fellow in Portuguese, 1963–64. Research: the Regency period of Brazilian history; Brazilian literature; sociology. Language: Spanish 4,3,3,3; Portuguese 5,5,5,5. Home: 6312 North 36th St., Arlington, Va. Office: Bureau of International Education, U.S. Office of Education, 400 Maryland Ave. SW., Washington, D.C., 20202.

HARRINGTON, CHARLES W., b. Miami, Fla., July 29, 1923. LIBRARY SCIENCE. B.A., U. of N.C., 1944; Harvard Business School, 1945; M.A., U. of N. Mex., 1953; M.S., La. State U., 1961. Dir. of activities, Instituto Guatemalteco-Americano (Guatemala), U.S. Dept. of State, 1947–49; administrative dir., Instituto Cultural Domínico-Americano (Ciudad Trujillo), 1949–51; librarian, Extension Services, Queens Borough Public Library (N.Y.), 1961–62; HEAD LIBRARIAN, LIBRARY, CENTENARY COLL., 1962– . Buenos Aires Convention scholar (Guatemala), 1956–57. Membership: American Library Association; Louisiana Library Association. Research: library administration; Middle American history. Language: Spanish 4,4,4,4; Portuguese 1,1,1,1; French 2,2,2,2. Home: 744½ Delaware St., Shreveport, La. Office: Centenary Coll. Library, Shreveport.

HARRINGTON, DAVID N., b. Greenville, N.C., Oct. 26, 1913. ECONOMICS. B.S., U. of Mo., 1950; M.S., 1952; Ph. D., Iowa State U., 1962. Research assoc., Iowa State U., 1952–55; PROF., AGRICULTURAL ECONOMICS, U. OF MO., 1955– . Consultant, Weitz-Hettelsater Engineers (Brazil, Venezuela), 1962–63. Research: agricultural economics; cooperative business management and marketing of agricultural products; grain storage and processing facilities in Brazil. Author: Costs of Storing Reserve Stocks of Corn (U.S. Dept. of Agriculture, 1957); A Quality-Price Study of Wheat at the Country Elevator Level (1960); Marketing Facilities for Grain and Tuberous Crops in Brazil (1963). Language: Spanish 3,2,2,3; Portuguese 2,2,2,3. Home: 309 Phyllis, Columbia, Mo. Office: Coll. of Agriculture, U. of Mo., Columbia, 65202.

HARRIS, LOUIS KENNETH, b. St. Clairsville, Ohio, Mar. 11, 1923. POLITICAL SCIENCE. A.B., Ohio State U., 1945; M.A., 1946; Ph. D., U. of Calif., Los Angeles, 1956. Instr.-PROF., POLITICAL SCIENCE, KENT STATE U., 1947– ; prof., adviser, Political Science and Public Administration, U. of Tenn. and U.S. Agency for International Development, 1962–63. Membership: American Association of University Professors; American Political Science Association. Research: Latin American politics; public administration in Panama; political consequences of urbanization in Mexico City. Language: Spanish 5,4,4,4; Portuguese 4,2,1,1. Home: 3566 Dayton Ave., Kent, Ohio. Office: Dept. of Political Science, Kent State U., Kent.

HARRIS, MARVIN, b. Brooklyn, N.Y., Aug. 18, 1927. ANTHROPOLOGY. B.A., Columbia Coll., 1948; Ph. D., Columbia U., 1953. PROF., ANTHROPOLOGY, COLUMBIA U., 1953– . Ford Foundation Foreign Area fellow; Social Science Research Council area research training fellow; executive secretary, Columbia-Cornell-Harvard-Illinois Summer Field Studies Program. Research: cultural anthropology; race relations, ethnology, community studies in Brazil and Ecuador. Author: Patterns of Race (1964); The Nature of Cultural Things (1964). Co-author: Minorities in the New World (1958). Language: Spanish 4,3,3,3; Portuguese 5,5,4,4; French 4,2,2,3. Home: 325 Highwood Ave., Leonia, N.J. Office: Dept. of Anthropology, Columbia U., New York 27, N.Y.

HARRIS, WALTER DeSALLES, b. New Haven, Conn., Jan. 4, 1924. CITY PLANNING AND ARCHITECTURE. B. Arch., Yale U., 1948; M. Arch., 1950; Ph. D. (honorary), National Engineering U. (Lima, Peru), 1960. Asst. prof., Architecture, Carnegie Institute of Technology, 1950–54; ASSOC. PROF., CITY PLANNING, DIR. OF LATIN AMERICAN PROGRAMS, YALE U., 1954– . Resident adviser, International Cooperation Administration (Guatemala), 1955–57; dir., Inter-American Housing and Planning Center (Bogotá, Colombia), 1959–60; adviser, Organization of American States. 1960–61; consultant, Inter-American Housing and Planning Center (Bogotá), 1960–61; adviser on housing, urban and regional planning, Pan American Union, 1961– . Membership: Inter-American Planning Society. Research: urban and redevelopment planning; housing. Author: Public Housing Design (in Housing Yearbook, 1962–63). Co-author: Capital Formation for Housing in Latin America (1963); Housing in Peru (1964). Language: Spanish 2,2,1,1. Home: 45 Killdeer Rd., Hamden, Conn., 06517. Office: Dept. of City Planning, School of Art and Architecture, 180 York St., New Haven, Conn. 06520.

HARRISON, JOHN PARKER, b. Sacramento, Calif., May 14, 1917. HISTORY. A.B., U. of Calif., 1938; Ph. D., 1951. Latin American specialist, Exhibits and Publications, U.S. National Archives, 1951–56; assoc. dir., Humanities, Rockefeller Foundation, 1956–62; PROF., HISTORY, DIR., INSTITUTE OF LATIN AMERICAN STUDIES, U. OF TEX., 1962– . Doherty fellow, 1949–50; U.S. Dept. of Education grant, 1949–50. Research: Latin American archives; northern South America; intellectual history of Latin America. Author: Guide to Materials on Latin America in the National Archives (1961); Role of the Intellectual in Fomenting Change: The University (1964); Confrontation with Political University (Annals of the American Academy of Political and Social Science, Mar. 1961). Language: Spanish 4,4,4,3; Portuguese 3,3,3,1; French 3,2,2,3. Home: 3505 Perry Lane, Austin, Tex. Office: Institute of Latin American Studies, P.O. Box 8058, University Station, Austin 12.

HARRISON, SANDAS LORENZO, b. Panama City, Panama, Apr. 5, 1922. HISTORY. B.A., Roosevelt U., 1954; M.A., U. of Chicago, 1955; Ph. D., Ind. U., 1963. Assoc. prof., chmn., Talladega Coll., 1957–60; prof., chmn., 1962–63; ASST. PROF., HISTORY, U. OF WIS., MILWAUKEE, 1963– . Lilly fellow, Ind. U., 1960–61; Doherty fellow and Whitney Foundation fellow (Central America), 1961–62; consultant, Phelps-Stokes Fund Project for the Improvement of Instruction in the High Schools, 1957–59. Membership: American Historical Association; Association for the Study of Negro Life and History; Conference on Latin American History; Mississippi Valley Historical Association. Research: Central American Common Market; Central American union. Language: Spanish 4,4,4,4; French 2,2,1,1. Home: 4303 North 16th St., Milwaukee, Wis., 53209. Office: Dept. of History, U. of Wis., Milwaukee, 3203 North Downer Ave., Milwaukee, 53211.

HARSTON, CLIVE RICHARDS, b. Cowley, Wyo., Oct. 9, 1918. ECONOMICS. B.S., U. of Wyo., 1946; M.S., 1947; Ph. D., Wash. State U., 1951. Asst. prof., Mont. State Coll., 1951–54; assoc. prof., 1954–59; PROF., AGRICULTURAL ECONOMICS, MONT. STATE COLL., 1959– ; marketing specialist, U.S. Agency for International Development-Tex. A. & M. U. contract (Argentina), 1964–66. Mountain States Telephone Company Business-Educator exchange fellow; consultant, U.S. Dept. Agriculture, 1960–62; agricultural credit consultant, U.S. Agency for International Development (Argentina), Summer 1962. Membership: American Farm Economics Association; Western Farm Economics Association. Research: agricultural economics; livestock marketing; grain marketing; meat packing house efficiencies; feed processing efficiences; problems of agricultural credit in Argentina. Author: Livestock Shrinkage (1960); Agricultural Credit in Argentina (1962); Economic Analysis of Meat Packing Houses in Montana (1963). Language: Spanish 4,3,3,3. Home: 1108 West Babcock, Bozeman, Mont. Office: Dept. of Agricultural Economics, Mont. State Coll., Bozeman.

HART, THOMAS ARTHUR, b. Buenos Aires, Argentina, Aug. 18, 1905. EDUCATION. B.S., Coll., of William and Mary, 1930; M.A. Emory U., 1933; M.S., 1937; Ph. D., U. of Chicago, 1941. Prof., chmn., Science, West Ga. Coll., 1933–42; Lt. Col., U.S. Army (Australia, New Guinea, Philippines, Bolivia), 1942–46; dir. of malaria control, prof., Sanitation, Institute of Inter-American Affairs, 1946; dean, School of Arts and Sciences, Roosevelt U., 1947–51; chief education adviser, U.S. Government (Bolivia), 1953–57, (Brazil), 1957–59, (Haiti), 1959–61, (Venezuela), 1961–63; PROF., EDUCATION, SCIENCE EDUCATION ADVISER, U. OF PITTSBURGH FACULTIES IN ECUADOR (QUITO), 1964– . Rosenwald Fund fellow, 1938; U.S. delegate, Ministerial Conferences in Latin America on Education and Indian Affairs; consultant, Surgeon General's Office, U.S. Dept. of the Army, Summer 1951; consultant, Ministeries of Education (Bolivia, Brazil, Haiti, Venezuela, Ecuador); recipient, National Confederation of Bolivian Farm Workers Medal. Membership: Adult Education Association; American Public Health Service; American Society of Tropical Medicine; National Education Association; Pan-American Board of Education; Sigma Xi; Sociedad Boliviana de Salud Pública. Research: parasitology; rural health problems; science education; malaria control; teacher education. Author: The Army's War Against Malaria (Scientific Monthly, May 1946); Status of Nuclear Schools—Bolivia (Summary Record of Conference Sessions of the Latin American Regional Conference on Rural Elementary Education, July 1954). Co-author: Communicable Diseases—Malaria, The Southwest Pacific Area (in Preventive Medicine in World War II, vol. VI, 1963). Language: Spanish 4,4,4,3; Portuguese 2,2,2,1; French 2,2,2,1. Home: 915 South Saint Asaph St., Alexandria, Va. 22314. Office: U. of Pittsburgh Faculties in Ecuador, U.S. Agency for International Development, American Embassy, Quito, Eduador.

HARTMAN, ROBERT S., b. Berlin, Germany, Jan. 27, 1910. PHILOSOPHY. LL.B., U. of Berlin, 1932; Ph. D., Northwestern U., 1946. Asst. prof., Coll. of Wooster, 1945-48; assoc. prof., Ohio State U., 1948-55; vis. prof., Mass. Institute of Technology, 1955-56; RESEARCH PROF., CENTRO DE ESTUDIOS FILOSÓFICOS, NATIONAL U. OF MEXICO, 1956- . Lect. (Argentina, Brazil, Mexico, Paraguay, Peru); consultant, General Electric Company and American Telephone and Telegraph Company; co-editor, Kant Studien and Journal of Humanistic Psychiatry; Fulbright fellow; adviser, National Profit Sharing Commission (Mexico). Membership: Allgemeine Gesellschaft für Philosophie in Deutschland; American Philosophical Association. Research: applied and theoretical ethics. Author: The Partnership of Capital and Labor (1958); La estructura del valor (1959); Profit Sharing in Mexico (1963). Language: Spanish 5,5,5,4; Portuguese 4,4,3,2; French 5,5,4,3; German 5,5,5,5; Norwegian-Danish 5,5,4,4; Swedish 5,5,5,4. Home: Apartado 422, Cuernavaca, Morelos, México. Office: Centro de Estudios Filosóficos, Universidad Nacional Autónoma de México, México, D.F.

HARVEY, HERBERT R., b. Cornwall, N.Y., May 25, 1931. ANTHROPOLOGY. A.B., Tusculum Coll., 1952; Ph. D., Harvard U., 1962. Research assoc., Law School, U. of Chicago, 1954-55; ASST. PROF., ANTHROPOLOGY, U. OF WIS., 1962- . Thaw fellow, Hemenway fellow, Harvard U., 1953-54; Mexican Government fellow, 1957-58; consultant, Indian Claims Section, U.S. Dept. of Justice, 1958- . Membership: American Anthropological Association; Sociedad Mexicana de Antropología; Society for American Archaeology. Research: cultural anthropology; ethnology, ethnohistory, and linguistics of Middle America; Indians of the central Mexican highlands. Author: Términos de parentesco en el grupo Otomangue (1963); Cultural Continuity in Central Mexico (Actas, XXXV International Congress of Americanists, 1964); Ethnohistory of Guerrero (in Handbook of Middle American Indians). Language: Spanish 4,4,4,4; German 2,2,2,2; Nahuatl 3,1,1,1. Home: 411 Virginia Ter., Madison 5, Wis. Office: Dept. of Anthropology, U. of Wis., Madison 6.

HARWOOD, RUTH, b. Boston, Mass. ANTHROPOLOGY. B.A., Wellesley Coll., 1940; M.A., Columbia U., 1950; Ph. D., 1963. Foreign Service clerk, U.S. Dept. of State (Panama), 1944-46; asst. in Community Development Project, American Friends Service Committee (El Salvador), 1956-58; secretary, Tax Study of Venezuela, Columbia U., 1958-62; RESEARCH ASSOC., PERU PROJECT, COLUMBIA TEACHERS COLL., 1963- . Membership: American Anthropological Association. Research: community development in El Salvador; primary education in Peru. Language: Spanish 3,3,3,3; Portuguese 1,1,1,1; French 2,2,2,2. Home: Cordaville Rd., Cordaville, Mass. 01744. Office: Columbia Teachers Coll., 525 West 120th St., New York, N.Y. 10027.

HASKINS, EDWARD C., b. Ann Arbor, Mich., Aug. 1, 1918. GEOGRAPHY. B.A., U. of Wis., 1949; M.S., 1950; Ph. D., U. of Minn., 1956. Instr., Yale U., 1954-56; asst. prof., Temple U., 1956-59; ASSOC. PROF., CHMN., GEOGRAPHY, TEMPLE U., 1959- . Social Science Research Council fellow (Brazil), 1952-54; assoc., Center for Community Studies and chmn., Executive Committee, Coll. of Latin America, Temple U.; assoc., Philadelphia Council for Community Advancement. Membership: American Association of Geographers. Research: political geography; regional and metropolitan planning; agricultural geography of Bahia, Brazil. Language: Spanish 2,2,2,2; Portuguese 3,3,2,2. Home: 10 Circle Rd., Levittown, Pa. Office: Dept. of Geography, Temple U., 1922 North Broad St., Philadelphia 22, Pa.

HATTWICK, RICHARD E., b. Chicago, Ill., Jan. 23, 1938. ECONOMICS. B.A., Ohio Wesleyan U., 1960; Ph. D., Vanderbilt U., 1965. ASST. PROF., ECONOMICS, U. OF HOUSTON, 1963- . Participant, study of graduate engineering in Latin America for Latin American Science Board, National Science Foundation. Membership: American Economic Association. Research: economic development in Brazil and Mexico; education in Latin America; Sears Roebuck do Brasil as a case study in marketing and economic growth. Language: Spanish 3,2,2,1; Portuguese 4,3,4,3; German 1,-,-,-. Home: 4709 Kingfisher, Houston 35, Tex. Office: Dept. of Economics, U. of Houston, Houston.

HAUBERG, CLIFFORD A., b. Fergus Falls, Minn., Jan. 12, 1906. HISTORY. B.S., U. of Minn., 1931; M.A., 1940; Ph. D., 1950. Teacher, principal, Minn. Public Schools, 1931-37; instr., Panama Canal Zone Schools, 1937-47; asst. prof., St. Olaf Coll., 1947-64; vis. prof., U. of Panama, Summer 1955; vis. prof., Eau Clair State Coll., 1955; PROF., HISTORY, ST. OLAF COLL., 1964- . Social Science Research Council grant (Panama), 1952-53; Associated Colleges of the Midwest faculty fellow (Central America and Mexico), Summer 1962. Membership: American Association of University Professors; American Historical Association; Mississippi Valley Historical Association. Research: Panama—economic and social history since 1849. Author: Panama: Pro Mundi Beneficio (Current History, Apr. 1957); Venezuela under Betancourt (Current History, Apr. 1961); Changing Conditions in Guatemala (Current History, Feb. 1963). Language: Spanish 3,3,3,2; French 3,1,–,–. Home: R.F.D. 2, Northfield, Minn. Office: Dept. of History, St. Olaf Coll., Northfield.

HAUCH, CHARLES CHRISTIAN, b. Chicago, Ill., Apr. 26, 1913. EDUCATION. Ph. B., U. of Chicago, 1934; M.A., 1936; Ph. D., 1942. Instr., Ind. U., 1941–43; program officer, Office of Inter-American Affairs, 1943–44; specialist, Bureau of Inter-American Affairs, U.S. Dept. of State, 1944–52; program officer, Institute of Inter-American Affairs, 1952–53; asst. chief, Legislative Reference Service, Library of Congress, 1954; editorial asst., American Peoples Encyclopedia, 1954–55, Encyclopaedia Britannica, 1955–57; specialist on comparative education in the Western Hemisphere, U.S. Office of Education, 1957–62; ACTING DIR., COMPARATIVE EDUCATION BRANCH, U.S. OFFICE OF EDUCATION, 1962– . Buenos Aires Convention fellow (Dominican Republic), 1940–41. Membership: American Historical Association; Comparative Education Society; Conference on Latin American History. Research: comparative education; Caribbean; Colombia; Haiti. Author: Foreign Attitudes towards Spanish Reoccupation of the Dominican Republic (Hispanic American Historical Review, May 1947); Educational Trends in the Caribbean: European Affiliated Areas (U.S. Office of Education, Oct. 1960); Current Situation in Latin American Education (U.S. Office of Education, Sept. 1963). Language: Spanish 3,3,3,3; Portuguese 1,1,1,–; French 3,2,2,3. Home: 5418 North 21st St., Arlington, Va., 22205. Office: Comparative Education Branch, Bureau of International Education, U.S. Office of Education, Washington, D.C. 20202.

HAURY, EMIL W., b. Newton, Kans., May 2, 1904. ANTHROPOLOGY. B.A., U. of Ariz., 1927; M.A., 1928; Ph. D., Harvard U., 1934. Instr., U. of Ariz., 1928–29; research asst., 1929–30; asst. dir., Gila Pueblo (Ariz.), 1930–37; PROF., HEAD, ANTHROPOLOGY, U. OF ARIZ., 1937– ; DIR., ARIZ. STATE MUSEUM, 1938– . Guggenheim fellow (Colombia), 1949–50; Wetherill Mesa Advisory Group, National Park Service, 1959– ; Life and Social Sciences Panel, National Science Foundation, 1962– . Membership: American Academy of Arts and Sciences; American Anthropological Association; American Association for the Advancement of Science; National Academy of Sciences; Society for American Archaeology. Research: archeology; cultural chronology in the Northern Andes; early man in western America. Author: The Excavation of Los Muertos and Neighboring Ruins in the Salt River Valley, Southern Arizona (1945); Some Thoughts on Chibcha Culture in the High Plains of Colombia (American Antiquity, July 1953). Co-author: Investigaciones arqueológicas en la sabana de Bogotá, Colombia (1953). Language: Spanish 4,3, 3,1; French 2,1,1,1; German 3,3,2,1. Home: 2749 East 4th St., Tucson, Ariz. Office: Dept. of Anthropology, U. of Ariz., Tucson.

HAVENS, A. EUGENE, b. Brooks, Iowa, Dec. 22, 1936. SOCIOLOGY. B.S., Iowa State U., 1959; M.S., Ohio State U., 1960; Ph. D., 1962. DIR., LAND TENURE CENTER RESEARCH IN COLOMBIA, U. OF WIS., 1963– . Fulbright prof. (Bogotá, Colombia), 1962–63; Planning Committee for Graduate Studies in Sociology in Colombia; Sociological Commission for Agrarian Reform in Colombia; consultant, Training for Agrarian Reform in the Andean Region (Peru). Membership: American Sociological Association; Asociación Colombiana de Sociología; Association for International Development; Rural Sociological Society. Research: research methodology; community studies; social change and diffusion of innovations; Colombia. Author: Medición en la sociología (1964); Estudio socioeconómico de un area de latifundio: Cereté Córdoba (1964); Methodological Problems of Sociological Survey Research in Colombia (América Latina. Apr.–June 1964). Language: Spanish 5,5,4,4; Portuguese 4,4,2,1; French 3,2,1,1. Home: Carrera 18 #80–75, Bogotá, Columbia. Office: Land Tenure Center, U. of Wis., Madison 6.

HAVERSTOCK, NATHAN ALFRED, b. Minneapolis, Minn., May 18, 1931. JOURNALISM. A.B., Harvard, 1953. Editor, Handbook of Latin American Studies, Hispanic Foundation, Library of Congress, 1958–61; asst. editor, Saturday Evening Post, 1961–62; staff writer, Alliance for Progress, 1963–64; EVALUATOR, LATIN AMERICA, U.S. PEACE CORPS, 1964– . Consultant, U.S. Peace Corps, National Academy of Sciences, Inter-American Development Bank. Membership: American Historical Association; Inter-American Council. Research: Latin American development; politics in Mexico, Dominican Republic; the Brazilian Northeast. Author: Brazil's Hungry Millions (Saturday Evening Post, July 28, 1962); Profile of a Peace Corpsman (Saturday Evening Post, Sept. 8, 1962). Language: Spanish 4,4,4,3; Portuguese 4,4,4,3; French 3,3,2,1. Home: 296 N St., SW., Washington, D.C.

HAVIGHURST, ROBERT J., b. DePere, Wis., June 5, 1900. EDUCATION AND PSYCHOLOGY. Ph. D., Ohio State U., 1924. PROF., EDUCATION, U. OF CHICAGO, 1941–; co-dir., Centro Brasileiro de Pesquisas Educacionais, UNESCO, 1956–62. Fulbright prof., U. of Buenos Aires, 1962. Research: social psychology and education. Author: Psicología social de la adolescensia (1961); Sociedad y educación en América Latina (1962). Co-author: Society and Education in Brazil (1964). Language: Spanish 4,4,3,2; Portuguese 5,5,4,3; French 3,3,2,2; German 5,5,4,3. Home: 5844 Stony Island Ave., Chicago 37, Ill. Office: Dept. of Education, U. of Chicago, Chicago 37.

HAWKINS, CARROLL JAMES, b. Brooklyn, N.Y., Mar. 10, 1910. POLITICAL SCIENCE. A.B., West Va. U., 1934; M.A., U. of Minn., 1937; Ph. D., 1946. Teacher, Works Progress Administration, 1938–40; instr., U. of Minn., 1940–46; asst. prof.- ASSOC. PROF., POLITICAL SCIENCE, MICH STATE U., 1946–; specialist, U.S. Dept. of State, 1948–49. Consultant, Vietnamese Itinerant Mission (Paris), 1954–55; vis. prof., U. of the Andes (Bogotá), Smith-Mundt grant, 1957–58. Membership: American Political Science Association; Association for Latin American Studies. Research: political ideologies of Colombia and Mexico; international labor. Author: Ésta es la democracia (1958); An Introduction to

Contemporary Ideologies (1963) ; Harold J. Laski: A Preliminary Analysis (Political Science Quarterly, Sept. 1950). Language: Spanish 4,–,–,–; French 2,–,–,–; German 1,–,–,–. Home: Apt. 203, 802 Cherry Lane, East Lansing, Mich. Office: Dept. of Political Science, Mich. State U., East Lansing.

HAWLEY, DOROTHEA BURTON, b. Niagara Falls, N.Y., Aug. 27, 1917. GEOGRAPHY. B.S., State U. of N.Y., Coll. at Buffalo, 1938 ; M.A., Clark U., 1947 ; Ph. D., 1949. Chief, Latin American Div., U.S. Air Force Intelligence Center, 1949–52 ; administrative asst., U.S. Naval Photo Interpretation Center, 1952–54 ; administrative asst., U.S. Marine Corps Institute, 1954–56 ; intelligence research specialist, Transportation Div., U.S. Air Force, 1956–63 ; INTELLIGENCE RESEARCH SPECIALIST, U.S. DEFENSE INTELLIGENCE AGENCY, 1963– . Clark U. fellow, 1946–47. Membership: Association of American Geographers. Research: geographic study of Panama's basic economics ; Puerto Rico. Language: Spanish 2,2, 2,3. Home: 504 Cedarwood Ct., Barcroft Woods, Falls Church, Va. Office: DIAAP-IT, Arlington Hall Station, Washington, D.C. 20025.

HAWS, GARY LEWIS, b. Vernal, Utah, Apr. 12, 1935. SPANISH AMERICAN LITERATURE. B.A., Brigham Young U., 1959 ; Ph. D., U. of N. Mex., 1964. Dir. of missionaries, Church of Jesus Christ of Latter Day Saints (Northern Mexico), 1955–58 ; area studies district leader, U.S. Peace Corps Training Center for Latin America, 1963 ; ASST. PROF., HEAD, MODERN LANGUAGES, ADAMS STATE COLL. OF COLO., 1963–64. National Defense Education Act fellow in Ibero-American Studies, 1961–62. Membership: Sigma Delta Pi. Research: educational systems of Uruguay, Argentina, and Brazil in contrast to the United States. Author: Carlos Sabat Ercasty (1965). Language: Spanish 5,5,5,5 ; Portuguese 5,4,4,4 ; French 3,2,2,2 ; Nahuatl 1,1,2,1 ; Huastec, 1,2,2,1 ; Italian 3,2,2,2. Home: R.F.D. 2, Box 180, Vernal, Utah. Office: Dept. of Modern Languages, 114 Richardson Hall, Adams State Coll. of Colo., Alamosa.

HAYDON, ROSA NAVARRO, b. Redlands, Calif., Feb. 9, 1905. EDUCATION. B.A., U. of P.R. ; M.A., Columbia U., 1930. Instr.-PROF., SCIENCE EDUCATION, U. OF P.R., 1926– ; dir., Museum of Biological Sciences, U. of P.R., 1944–45. Membership: Geology Club of Puerto Rico. Research: archeology in Yucatan and Palenque ; science teaching in primary schools. Author: Nuestro Mundo, Grades 2–6 (1953–59) ; Science Program for the Elementary Schools, Grades Kindergarten–6 (1959, 1960). Coauthor: Road Log and Guide for a Geological Trip through Central and Western Puerto Rico (1959). Language: Spanish 4,4,5,5 ; Portuguese 4,4,5,5 ; French 4,4,5,5 ; Italian 4,4,5,5. Home: Apt. 5N, 711 Union St., Miramar, P.R. Office: Coll. of Education, U. of P.R., Río Piedras, P.R.

HAYN, ROLF, b. Berlin, Germany, July 6, 1923. ECONOMICS. A.B., Ind. U., 1944 ; Ph. D., U. of Wis., 1954. Vis. lectr., U. of N. Mex., 1954–55 ; asst. prof., U. of Okla., 1955–60 ; ECONOMIC AFFAIRS OFFICER, BUREAU OF GENERAL ECONOMIC RESEARCH, UNITED NATIONS SECRETARIAT, 1961– . Consultant, Dept. of Treasury (P.R.), 1957–58 ; Fulbright lectr., U. of Córdoba (Argentina), 1958–59. Membership: American Economic Association. Research: international economics and development ; economies of Peru, Argentina, and P.R. Author: Peruvian Monetary and Foreign Exchange Policy (Inter-American Economic Affairs, Spring 1955) ; Puerto Rico's Economic Growth (Inter-American Economic Affairs, Winter 1958) ; Capital Formation and Argentina's Price Cost Structure (Review of Economics and Statistics, Aug. 1962). Language: Spanish 5,5,4,4 ; Portuguese 3,1,1,1 ; French 3,2,2,1 ; German 5,5,4,4 ; Italian 4,4,3,2. Home: 21 Primrose Ave., West, White Plains, N.Y. 10607. Office: Bureau of General Economic Research, United Nations Secretariat, New York, N.Y.

HAYNER, NORMAN SYLVESTER, b. Peking, China, May 15, 1896. SOCIOLOGY. A.B., U. of Wash., 1920 ; M.A., U. of Chicago, 1921 ; Ph. D., 1923. Prof., Rockford Coll., 1922–25 ; PROF., SOCIOLOGY, U. OF WASH., 1925– ; vis. prof., U. of Southern Calif., Summers 1931, 1948 ; vis. prof., N.Y.U., Summer 1938. Social Science Research Council grants (Mexico), 1945, 1948–49 ; chmn., Wash. State Board of Prison Terms and Paroles, 1951–56 ; American Philosophical Society grant (Mexico), 1961. Membership: American Sociological Association ; International Sociological Association ; Mexican Sociological Association ; National Council on Family Relations ; Pacific Sociological Association. Research: changing social institutions in Mexico ; criminology. Author: Hotel Life (1936) ; Mexico City: Its Growth and Configuration (American Journal of Sociology, Jan. 1945) ; Correctional Systems and National Values (British Journal of Criminology, Oct. 1962). Language: Spanish 4,4,4,3 ; French 2,2,2,1 ; German, 3,3,3,2. Home: 7566 Roosevelt Way, NE., Seattle, Wash. 98115. Office: Dept. of Sociology, U. of Wash., Seattle, 98105.

HAYTON, ROBERT DERYL, b. Clarkston, Wash., Nov. 8, 1922. POLITICAL SCIENCE: INTERNATIONAL LAW. B.A., U. of Mont., 1949 ; M.A., U. of Calif., Berkeley, 1951 ; Ph. D., 1954. Intern, U.S. Dept. of State, 1951 ; ASSOC. PROF., CHMN., INTER-AMERICAN AFFAIRS COMMITTEE, HUNTER COLL., 1954– ; lectr., U.S. Defense Intelligence School, 1958– ; lectr., Foreign Service Institute, U.S. Dept. of State, 1961–62 ; lectr., Inter-American Defense Coll. (Washington, D.C.), 1962–63 ; research assoc., International Rivers Research Project, School of Law, N.Y.C., 1963 ; vis. lectr., Wellesley Coll., 1964. Doherty fellow (Chile), 1952–53 ; Pan American World Airways fellow (Chile, Argentina), 1952–53 ; Smith-Mundt prof., U. of San Carlos (Guatemala), 1960–61 ; participant, Cornell Conference on the Western Hemisphere Defense, 1962 ; Committee on Mexican Investment and Development, American Society of International Law, 1963– ; adviser on Latin America, International Mass Education Movement. Membership: American Political Science Association ; American Society of International Law ; Antarctican Society ; International Law Association ; International Political Science Association ; Military Intelligence Reserve Society. Research: international law ; Latin American political behavior; United States foreign policy; regional organization—Central American economic union; international river basin development—La Plata River Basin and Lauca River; Antarctic. Author: National Interests in Antarctica (1960); The American Antarctic (American Journal of International Law, July 1956); The Antarctic Settlement of 1959 (American Journal of International Law, Apr. 1960). Language: Spanish 5,4,4,4; Portuguese 2,2,1,1; French 3,3,2,2; German 4,5,4,4; Italian 3,2,1,1. Home: Cat Rock Rd., Cos Cob, Conn. 06807. Office: Dept. of Political Science, Hunter Coll., 695 Park Ave., New York 21, N.Y.

HEAD, BRIAN FRANKLIN, b. Chattanooga, Tenn., Dec. 23, 1933. LINGUISTICS AND LANGUAGE. M.A., Colo. Coll., 1960; M.A., U. of Wis., 1961; Ph. D., U. of Tex., 1964. Research assoc., U. of Tex., Summer 1964; ASST. PROF., ROMANCE LANGUAGES, U. OF TEX., 1964– .; ASST. PROF., ROMANCE LANGUAGES, U. OF COIMBRA (PORTUGAL), 1965– . National Defense Education Act fellow, U. of Wis., 1960–61, U. of Tex., 1961–62, 1963–64, U. of Wash., Summer 1962; Fulbright fellow, U. of Coimbra (Portugal), 1962–63. Membership: American Association of Teachers of Spanish and Portuguese; Association for Machine Translation and Computational Linguistics; International Phonetics Association; Linguistic Circle of New York; Linguistic Society of America; Modern Language Association. Research: Portuguese linguistics and phonology; structural analysis of Brazilian Portuguese; Portuguese and Brazilian literature. Co-author: Análise de sons nasais e sons nasalizados do português (Revista do Laboratório de Fonética Experimental, 1963); An Instrumental Study of Duration in French (Revista do Laboratório de Fonética Experimental, 1963). Language: Spanish 3,3,3,3; Portuguese 5,5,4,4; French 5,5,4,4; Arabic 2,2,2,2; German 3,-,-,-; Italian 3,3,3,3. Linguistic studies: Arabic; French; Hebrew; Italian; Portuguese. Home: Apt. B, 4005 Maplewood, Austin, Tex. 78722. Office: Dept. of Romance Languages, U. of Tex., Austin, 78712.

HEAD, GERALD LOUIS, b. Artesia, Calif., Mar. 27, 1936. SPANISH AMERICAN LITERATURE. A.B., U. of Calif., Los Angeles, 1959; Ph. D., 1964. ASSOC., SPANISH, U. OF CALIF., LOS ANGELES, 1963– . National Defense fellow, U. of Calif., Los Angeles, 1960–62; U. of Calif. traveling fellow (Argentina), 1962–63. Membership: Alpha Mu Gamma; Sigma Delta Pi. Research: Hispanic languages and literature; works of Benito Lynch. Language: Spanish 5,5,5,5; Portuguese 5,4,3,4; French 5,4,3,4; Italian 3,3,3,2. Office: Spanish Dept., U. of Calif., Los Angeles 24.

HEATH, DWIGHT B., b. Hartford, Conn., Nov. 19, 1930. ANTHROPOLOGY. A.B., Harvard U., 1952; Ph. D., Yale U., 1959. Instr.–ASSOC. PROF., ANTHROPOLOGY, BROWN U., 1959– ; dir. of field research, Land Tenure Center, U. of Wis. (Bolivia), 1963. Doherty fellow and Social Science Research Council grant (Bolivia), 1956–57; Brown U. research fellow (Guatemala, Mexico), Summer 1961, (Bolivia), Summer 1962; training officer, consultant, U.S. Peace Corps., 1961– . Membership: American Anthropological Association; American association for the Advancement of Science; American Ethnological Society; American Indian Ethnohistoric Conference; Association for Latin American Studies; Sociedad Boliviana de Sociología; Society for Applied Anthropology; Society for Study of Social Problems. Research: cultural change; social structure; land tenure; alcoholism; historical and economic factors; Bolivia. Author: Successes and Shortcomings of Agrarian Reform in Bolivia (1963); Drinking Patterns of the Bolivian Camba (Quarterly Journal of Studies on Alcohol, Sept. 1959); Land Tenure and Social Organization: An Ethno-historic Study from the Bolivian Oriente (Inter-American Economic Affairs, Spring 1960). Language: Spanish 4,4,3,3; Portuguese 2,2,1,1; French 3,3,2,1. Home: 47 Barnes St., Providence 6, R.I. Office: Dept. of Sociology and Anthropology, Brown U., Providence 12.

HEGEN, EDMUND EDUARD, b. Doernsdorf, Czechoslovakia, Oct. 15, 1920. GEOGRAPHY. B.A., B.E., Post Referendum, German U. (Prague), 1944; Ph. D., U. of Fla., 1962. Guest lectr., Fla. State U., Summer 1962; instr., U. of Tampa, 1961–62; ASST. PROF., GEOGRAPHY, U. OF FLA., 1962– . U. of Fla. graduate fellow, 1960–61; post-doctoral fellow in Spanish, U. of Calif., Los Angeles, Summer 1962; National Defense Education Act research grant (Colombia), 1964. Membership: Association of American Geographers; Phi Beta Kappa. Research: history and philosophy of geography; political geography; field methods; Middle and South America; northeastern Honduras; Rio Putumayo region. Author: Highways into the Upper Amazon Basin: A Study of Transandean Roads in Southern Colombia, Ecuador, and Northern Peru (1962); The Andean Cultural Frontier (Journal of Inter-American Studies, Oct. 1963). Language: Spanish 5,5,5,4; Portuguese –,3,1,–. Home: 34 SW. 24th St., Gainesville, Fla., 32602. Office: Dept. of Geography, U. of Fla., Gainesville.

HEILIGER, EDWARD MARTIN, b. Rockford, Ill., Dec. 14, 1909. LIBRARY SCIENCE. A.B., U. of the Pacific, 1933; B.S. in L.S., U. of Denver, 1935; M.A., 1941. Dir., Biblioteca Americana de Nicaragua, 1944–46; dir. adviser, Biblioteca Central, U. of Chile, 1946–48; chief, program management, overseas libraries, U.S. Dept. of State, 1949–50; dir., Biblioteca Benjamin Franklin (Mexico), U.S. Dept. of State, 1950–53; assoc. librarian, N.Y. State Library, 1953–55; Librarian and prof., U. of Ill., 1955–63; DIR. OF LIBRARIES, PROF., HISTORY, FLA. ATLANTIC U., 1963– . Chilean National Scholarship Commission, 1946–48; Mexican-American Cultural Commission, 1952–53; Advisory Committee, Inter-American Defense Coll., 1962; U.S. delegate, UNESCO Conference on Scientific Documentation (Lima, Peru), 1962. Membership: American Documentation Institute; American Library Association; Association for Higher Education; Florida Library Association; National Education Association; Southeastern Library Association; Special Libraries Association. Research: library administration and operation; use of computers in libraries. Author: Advanced Data Processing in the University Library (1962) ; What is Happening to Our Overseas Libraries? (American Library Association Bulletin, Sept. 1960). Translator : Código para clasificadores. Language : Spanish 4,4,4,3 ; Portuguese 3,2,1,1 ; French 2,2,1,1. Home : 694 Northeast 36th St., Boca Raton, Fla. Office : Fla. Atlantic U., Boca Raton.

HEIN, JOHN, b. Freiburg, Germany, Mar. 1, 1921. ECONOMICS. B.S., Columbia U., 1949 ; M.S., 1949 ; Ph. D., 1963. Research asst., Balance of Payments Div., Federal Reserve Bank of N.Y., 1950–53 ; economist, 1953–54 ; economist, West European Unit, 1954–59 ; head, Latin American Unit, 1959–60 ; head, Western European Unit, 1960–61 ; CHIEF, FOREIGN RESEARCH DIV., FEDERAL RESERVE BANK OF N.Y., 1962– . Membership : American Economic Association ; American Finance Association. Research : international monetary and financial developments and relations ; exchange rates and controls in Latin America ; financial institutions and policies ; national banking systems and money and capital markets. Author : A Note on the Use of Index Clauses Abroad (Journal of Finance, Dec. 1960) ; The Mainsprings of German Monetary Policy (Economia Internazionale, May 1964) ; Monetary Policy and External Convertibility : The German Experience, 1959–1961 (Economia Internazionale, Aug. 1964). Language : Spanish 5,5,4,3 ; Portuguese 2,–,–,– ; French 5,5,4,4 ; German 5,5,5,5 ; Italian 5,5,4,4. Office : Federal Reserve Bank of New York, 33 Liberty St., New York, N.Y. 10045.

HELGUERA, J. LEON, b. New York, N.Y., Oct. 29, 1926. HISTORY. B.A., Mexico City College, 1948 ; M.A., U. of N.C., 1951 ; Ph. D., 1958. Assoc. prof., N.C. State U., 1957–63 ; vis. prof., Universidad de Buenos Aires, Summer 1958 ; PROF., HISTORY, VANDERBILT U., 1963– . Doherty fellow (Colombia), 1953–54 ; N.C. State U. research grant (Argentina), Summer 1958 ; Organization of American States fellow (Venezuela), Summer 1962 ; consultant, Boulton Foundation of Caracas ; U.S. consultant, Bolivarian Society of Venezuela, 1963. Membership : American Historical Association ; Centro de Historia del Cauca ; Colombian Academy of History ; Conference on Latin American History ; Southeastern Conference on Latin America ; Southern Historical Association ; Venezuelan National Academy of History. Research : northern South America in the 19th century. Author : El impacto de Bolívar en la consciencia grancolombiana, 1830–1863 (Revista de la Sociedad Bolivariana de Venezuela, Dec. 1958) ; The Changing Role of the Military in Colombia (Journal of Inter-American Studies, July 1961) ; Research Opportunities in Modern Latin America : The Bolivarian Nations (The Americas, Apr. 1962). Language : Spanish 5,5,5,5 ; Portuguese 3,4,3,3 ; French 3,3,2,1 ; German 3,3,3,2 ; Russian 2,2,–,2. Home : 2613 Barton Ave., Nashville, Tenn. 37212. Office : Box 1606, Vanderbilt U., Nashville, 37203.

HELLER, JACK I., b. Passaic, N.J., July 12, 1932. ECONOMICS AND LAW. A.B., U. of Chicago, 1951 ; LL.B., Columbia Law School, 1958. Instr., researcher, Harvard Law School, 1958–61 ; international tax consultant, Organization of American States, 1961–63 ; INTERNATIONAL TAX CONSULTANT, U.S. AGENCY FOR INTERNATIONAL DEVELOPMENT, 1963– . Research : public finance ; tax reform ; public finance aspects of the Alliance for Progress. Author : Tax Incentives for Industry in Less Developed Countries (1963). Language : Spanish 3,3,3,3. Home : 646 G St. SE., Washington, D.C. Office : Agency for International Development, U.S. Dept. of State, Room 3913 NS, Washington, D.C. 20523.

HELLYER, CLEMENT DAVID, b. Glendale, Calif., Aug. 15, 1914. JOURNALISM AND HISTORY. B.A., The Principia, 1936 ; M.S., Columbia U., 1938 ; U. of Fla., 1950–52. Asst. prof., San Diego State Coll., 1947–59 ; dir., Centro Cultural Costarricense-Norteamericano (San José), 1940–50 ; asst. dir., School of Inter-American Studies, U. of Fla., 1950–52 ; public relations asst. to div. manager, General Dynamics Corporation, 1952–53 ; Latin American news editor (Mexico), The San Diego Union (Calif.), 1953–60 ; BRAZIL REPRESENTATIVE, FODOR'S MODERN GUIDES, INC., 1962– . U.S. Dept. of State lectr. (Latin America), 1952 ; participant. The American Assembly Conference on Latin America, 1959 ; Maria Moors Cabot Award, Columbia U., 1959 ; Pan American Foundation fellow (São Paulo, Brazil), 1960–62. Membership : American Association of University Professors ; Sigma Delta Chi. Research : history of labor movement in Brazil. Author : The Story of the Border Patrol (1963). Co-author : American Air Navigator (1946) ; La cultura y el periodismo en América (1953). Language : Spanish 4,4,4,4 ; Portuguese 4,4,4,4. Home and office : P.O. Box 91, Rancho Santa Fe, Calif.

HENDERSON, DAVID ALLEN, b. Greeley, Colo., June 15, 1923. GEOGRAPHY. B.S., U. of Colo., 1946 ; M.A., 1951 ; Ph. D., U. of Calif., Los Angeles, 1964. Instr., Stanford U., 1951–52 ; instr., San Diego State Coll., 1954–56 ; lectr., San Fernando State Coll. and Los Angeles State Coll., 1958–59 ; ASSOC. PROF., GEOGRAPHY, U. OF ARIZ., 1959– . Membership : American Association of University Professors ; Association of American Geographers ; Association of Pacific Coast Geographers ; California Council of Geography Teachers. Research : economic and cultural geography ; arid lands of Mexico ; evolution of agriculture and livestock raising economy in Baja California. Author : Corn Belt Cattle Feeding in East Colorado's Irrigated Valleys (Economic Geography, Oct. 1954) ; The Sierras Juarez and San Pedro Martir, Baja California, Mexico (California Geographer 1960). Language : Spanish 4,4,4,4 ; Portuguese 3,3,2,2 ; German 4,3,2,2. Home : Box 432, Greeley, Colo. Office : Dept. of Geography, Coll. of Business and Public Administration, U. of Ariz., Tucson.

HENDERSON, DONALD C., JR., b. Williamsport, Pa., Oct. 1, 1931. HISTORY AND LANGUAGE. B.A., U. of Vt., 1955 ; M.A. Johns Hopkins U., 1957 ; Ph. D., Mich. State U., 1964. Instr., Mich. State U., 1959–62 instr., Pa. State U., 1962–64 ; ASST. PROF. SPANISH, STATE U. OF N.Y., COLL. A' ONEONTA, 1964– . U. of Vt. and John Hopkins U. tuition grants ; Middle East Institute grant ; Fulbright fellow (Chile, Argentina), 1958–59 ; National Defense Foreign Language fellow in Persian. Member ship: Modern Language Association. Research: Chile; methodology of research in social science area; economics. Language: Spanish 5,5,5,5; Portuguese 1,1,1,1; French 5,3,3,3; Persian 1,2,2,1. Office: Dept. of Spanish, State U. of N.Y., Coll. at Oneonta, Oneonta.

HENDRICKS, FRANCES KELLAM, b. Blanco, Tex., Nov. 20, 1900. HISTORY. B.A. U. of Tex., 1922; M.A., 1925; Ph. D., U. of Ill., 1931. Asst. prof., Stephen F. Austin State Coll., 1927–28; prof., U. of San Antonio, 1936–42; PROF., CHMN., HISTORY, TRINITY U., 1942– . Administrative asst. for curriculum revision, Trinity U., 1958–60. Membership: American Association of State and Local Historical Societies; American Historical Association; San Antonio Historical Association; Texas State Historical Association. Research: Chile; Mexico; Texas history. Author: The First Apostolic Mission to Chile (Hispanic American Historical Review, Nov. 1942). Co-translator: Two Novels of the Revolution, by Mariano Azuela (1963). Language: Spanish 3,2,2,2. Home: 130 Stanford Dr., San Antonio 12, Tex. Office: Dept. of History, Trinity U., San Antonio 12.

HENDRICKSON, EMBERT JULIUS, b. Minneapolis, Minn., June 22, 1928. HISTORY. B.S., St. Cloud State Coll., 1950; M.A., U. of N. Dak., 1954; Ph. D., U. of Minn., 1964. ASST. PROF., HISTORY, SAN JOSE STATE COLL., 1961– . Research: inter-American relations; relations of the United States and Venezuela, 1904–14. Language: Spanish 3,2,2,1. Home: 210½ South Kendall, Thief River Falls, Minn. 56701. Office: Dept. of History, San Jose State Coll., San Jose, Calif., 95112.

HENNING, DALE A., b. Hillsboro, N. Dak., Feb. 23, 1925. ECONOMICS. B.S., U. of Pa., 1948; M.B.A., 1949; Ph. D., U. of Ill., 1954. Labor economist, U.S. Dept. of Labor, 1949; instr., U. of Ill., 1950–54; PROF., ECONOMICS, U. OF WASH., 1955– . Consultant to state governments of Brazil; consultant, Konsulentfrind Asbjorn Habberstad (Oslo), 1954–55; research grants from Ford Foundation, Institute of Management Sciences, U.S. Government; Editorial Board, Journal of the Academy of Management. Membership: Academy of Management. Research: business policy; organization theory; human relations; personnel management. Author: Planning Theory (1961); Non-Financial Controls in Smaller Enterprises (1964). Language: Portuguese 3,3,3,3; French 2,2,2,2; German 2,2,2,2; Norwegian 3,3,3,3. Office: Dept. of Economics, U. of Wash., Seattle, 98105.

HENNING, EUGENE ALBERT, b. Paris, Mo., Sept. 4, 1904. SPANISH AMERICAN LITERATURE. B.S., U. of Mo., 1929; M.A., 1935; Ph. D., U. of N. Mex., 1950. Teacher, Public High Schools (P.R.), 1924–28; high school teacher (Orange, Tex.), 1929–33; instr., high school (Joplin, Mo.), 1933–37; instr., Joplin Junior Coll., 1937–42; dean of men, 1946–48; prof., head, Modern Languages, Whitworth Coll., 1951–60; PROF., SPANISH, HEAD, MODERN LANGUAGES, HASTINGS COLL., 1960– . Membership: American Association of Teachers of French; American Association of Teachers of Spanish and Portuguese; American Association of University Professors; Phi Sigma Iota. Language: Spanish 4,4,4,4; Portuguese 2,1,1,1; French 3,3,3,3. Linguistic studies: French; Spanish. Office: Dept. of Modern Languages, Hastings Coll., Hastings, Nebr.

HERMAN, DONALD LOUIS, b. Brooklyn, N.Y., Oct. 13, 1928. POLITICAL SCIENCE. B.A., U. of Mich., 1950; M.A. Wayne State U., 1959; Ph. D., U. of Mich., 1964. ASST. PROF., POLITICAL SCIENCE, GRAND VALLEY STATE COLL., 1964– . Membership: American Political Science Association. Research: Latin American international relations; communism in Mexico. Language: Spanish 4,4,4,4; Portuguese 2,2,2,2; French 2,2,2,2. Home: 3401 West Otter Dr., Detroit 21, Mich. Office: Dept. of Political Science, Grand Valley State Coll., Allendale, Mich., 49401.

HERMAN, J(ACK) CHALMERS, b. New Orleans, La., July 20, 1914. LANGUAGE. B.A., Tulane U., 1935; M.A., 1937; Ph. D., U. of Kans., 1950. Instr., Tulane U., 1936–38, 1945–46; postal censor, U.S. Office of Censorship (Cristobal, C.Z.), 1942–45; instr.-asst. prof., U. of Kans., 1946–52; HEAD, FOREIGN LANGUAGES, EAST CENTRAL STATE COLL. (OKLA.), 1952– ; vis. prof., U. of Ariz., Fall 1954; vis. prof. San Diego State Coll., Spring 1957. Assoc. editor, Hispania; national chapter adviser, American Association of Teachers of Spanish and Portuguese. Membership: American Association of Teachers of Spanish and Portuguese; Modern Language Association; National Education Association; Sigma Delta Pi. Author: El asesino desvelado (1952); Galdos' Expressed Appreciation of Don Quijote (Modern Language Journal, Jan. 1952); Quotations and Locutions from Don Quijote in Galdos' Novels (Hispania, May 1953). Language: Spanish 4,4,4,4; French 3,2,2,2. Home: 200 East Kings Rd., Ada, Okla. Office: Dept. of Foreign Languages, East Central State Coll., Ada.

HERMITTE, MARIA ESTHER A. DE, b. Buenos Aires, Argentina, Mar. 30, 1921. ANTHROPOLOGY. Profesor en historia, U. of Buenos Aires, 1950; M.A., U. of Chicago, 1962; Ph. D., 1964. Prof., National High School (Buenos Aires), 1950–56; research assoc., Ethnographic Museum, U. of Buenos Aires, 1955–58; principal, American Community School (Buenos Aires), 1956–58; INSTR., SOCIAL SCIENCES, U. OF CHICAGO, 1964– . Secretary, Argentine Anthropological Society, 1956–57; National Technical and Scientific Research Council of Argentina fellow, U. of Chicago, 1958–60; Organization of American States fellow, 1963–64. Membership: American Anthropological Association; Society for Applied Anthropology. Research: social anthropology; supernatural power and social control in a modern Maya community in Chiapas, Mexico; Argentina. Language: Spanish 5,5,5,5; French 3,3,3,3. Home: 5514 South Blackstone, Chicago, Ill. 60637. Office: College of Social Sciences, U. of Chicago, Chicago 37.

HERNANDEZ, DAVID, b. Chicago, Ill., Dec. 31, 1928. SPANISH AMERICAN LITERATURE. B.S., U. of Ill., 1958; M.A., Fla.,

State U., 1959; Ph. D., U. of Ill., 1965. Instr., Miss. State U., 1959–60; ASST. PROF., MODERN LANGUAGES, STEPHEN F. AUSTIN STATE COLL., 1963– . Fla. State U. fellow, 1958–59. Membership: Modern Language Association. Language: Spanish 5,5,5,5; Portuguese 5,3,1,3; French 3,2,1,2; German 3,2,2,2; Italian 3,2,1,1. Linguistic studies: Portuguese; Spanish. Home: 1600 East Main St., Nacogdoches, Tex., 75961. Office: Dept. of Modern Languages, Stephen F. Austin State Coll., Nacogdoches, 75962.

HERNÁNDEZ, MARTÍN, b. Aguada, P.R., Sept. 24, 1917. ECONOMICS. B.S.A., U. of P.R., 1938; M.S., Cornell U., 1945; Ph. D., 1947. Economist, head, Agricultural Economics and Rural Sociology, U. of P.R., 1947–49; undersecretary, P.R. Dept. of Agriculture and Commerce, 1949–55; general manager, P.R. Bank for Cooperatives, 1956–57; president, 1957–59; PROF., ECONOMIC DEVELOPMENT, U. OF P.R., 1959– ; PRESIDENT, CARIBBEAN REAL ESTATE DEVELOPMENT CORPORATION, 1960– ; executive vice president, Compañía Financiera de Inversiones, Inc. (P.R.), 1960–61. Counselor, Land Authority of P.R., 1961; financial counselor, Hotel El Portal, Inc., 1961; dir., secretary-treasurer, financial counselor, Tropic Foam, Inc., and Subsidiaries, 1961– . Membership: American Association for the Advancement of Science; American Farm Economic Association; American Society for Public Administration; American Society of Agricultural Science; Phi Kappa Phi; Puerto Rico Association of Economists; Rural Sociological Society; Society for International Development. Research: economic development; finance; housing development; marketing; foreign trade; agricultural economics; sociology. Language: Spanish 5,5,5,5; Portuguese 3,–,2,1; French 3,–,2,1. Home: Apt. A–3, 1890 Orquídea St., Río Piedras, P.R. Office: Caribbean Real Estate Development Corporation. Ponce de León Ave.-Stop 24, P.O. Box 8455, Santurce, P.R.

HERNÁNDEZ-ÁLVAREZ, JOSÉ GUILLERMO, b. Jersey City, N.J., Aug. 22, 1935. SOCIOLOGY. B.A., Fordham U., 1958; M.A., 1960. INSTR., DIR. OF RESEARCH PROJECT, CENTRO DE INVESTIGACIONES SOCIALES, U. of P.R., 1962– . Membership: American Sociological Association; International Sociological Association. Research: demography; social aspects of urban planning; sociological implications of return migration in Puerto Rico; Brazil. Language: Spanish 5,5,5,5; Portuguese 4,4,4,4; French 4,2,2,2. Home: Delbrey 161, Santurce, P.R. Office: Centro de Investigaciones Sociales, U. of P.R., Río Piedras.

HERRICK, BRUCE HALE, b. Minneapolis, Minn., May 29, 1936. ECONOMICS. A.B., Carleton Coll., 1958; Ph. D., Mass. Institute of Technology, 1964. ASST. PROF., ECONOMICS, U. OF CALIF., LOS ANGELES, 1964– . Foreign Area fellow (Chile), 1962–64; Faculty Advisory Committee for the Center for Latin American Studies, U. of Calif., Los Angeles. Membership: American Economic Association. Research: economic development in Latin America; internal migration, unemployment, and economic development in post-war Chile. Language: Spanish 4,4,4,4. Home: 11600 Rochester Ave., Los Angeles, Calif., 90025. Office: Dept. of Economics, U. of Calif., Los Angeles, 90024.

HERRICK, JANE, b. Chicago, Ill., Sept. 16, 1916. HISTORY. Ph. D., Catholic U. of America, 1955. Asst. editor, Academy of American Franciscan History, 1955–57; asst. editor, The Americas, 1956–63; PROF., HISTORY, STATE COLL. AT BRIDGEWATER, 1957– . Assoc. editor for Latin American church history, New Catholic Encyclopedia. Research: Spanish America and Brazil. Author: The Reluctant Revolutionist: Hipólito da Costa (The Americas, Oct. 1957). Language: Spanish 4,2,–,–; Portuguese 4,2,–,–; French 4,3,–,–. Home: 100 Pleasant St., Bridgewater, Mass. Office: Dept. of History, State Coll., Bridgewater.

HERRING, HUBERT C., b. Winterset, Iowa, Dec. 29, 1889. HISTORY. A.B., Oberlin Coll., 1911; A.M., Columbia U., 1912; Union Theological Seminary, 1913. Prof., Latin American History, Pomona Coll. and Claremont Graduate School, 1944–58; RETIRED, 1958– . Author: Good Neighbors (1941); History of Latin America (1955). Home: 765 Indian Hill Blvd., Claremont, Calif.

HERZOG, WILLIAM A., JR., b. Lyndonville, N.Y., Apr. 14, 1927. COMMUNICATION. B.A., Wheaton Coll., 1952; M.A., Ind. U., 1962; Mich. State U., Radio program dir., Latin America Mission, Radio Station TIFC (San José, Costa Rica), Radio Station HOXO (Panama City, Panama), 1954–61; INSTR., RESEARCH ASSOC., COMMUNICATION, MICH. STATE U., 1964– . Membership: Midwest Council of the Association for Latin American Studies. Research: cross-cultural communication; international broadcasting; diffusion of information; social change in Latin America; Colombia. Author: Adoption of New Foods and Drugs (in Five Guatemalan Villages, 1964). Language: Spanish 4,4,4,3; Portuguese 3,3,2,1. Home: 1516–H Sparton Village, East Lansing, Mich. Office: Communication Dept., Mich. State U., East Lansing.

HESS, HAROLD HARWOOD, b. Lansing Mich., May 6, 1922. LINGUISTICS. B.A. Wheaton Coll., 1947; B.D., Grand Rapids Baptist Seminary, 1950; Ph. D., U. of Mich., 1962. Language analyst and translator, Summer Institute of Linguistics (Mexico), 1951–58; teacher, Summer Institute of Linguistics (Norman, Grand Forks, Seattle), Summers 1951–61; consultant, Summer Institute of Linguistics (Mexico), 1958–63; ASSOC. DIR., SUMMER INSTITUTE OF LINGUISTICS (MEXICO) 1963–; head, Phonemics, Summer Institute of Linguistics (London), Summer 1964 Membership: Language Society of America Research: translation; syntactic structure of Mezquital Otomí. Language: Spanish 4,4,3,2; Mezquital Otomí 5,4,4,4. Linguistic studies: English; Otomí; Spanish. Home R.F.D. 1, Box 2B, Williamston, Mich. Office: Instituto Lingüístico de Verano Apartado 2975, México 1, D.F.

HEUBEL, EDWARD J., b. Flushing, N.Y May 4, 1927. POLITICAL SCIENCE B.A., Yale U., 1949; M.A., U. of Minn 1952; Ph. D., 1955; Universidad Nacional Autónoma de México, 1956. Instr., U of Minn., 1952–53; Reed Coll., 1953–56 instr.-asst. prof., Wayne State U., 1956–60 dir., Brazilian Officials Project, Wayne State U., 1958; ASSOC. PROF., CHMN., POLITICAL SCIENCE, OAKLAND U., 1961– . Fulbright lectr., U. of Buenos Aires, 1957. Membership: American Political Science Association; Midwest Council of Latin-American Studies. Research: comparative government and politics of Latin America and Britain. Author: Congressional Resistance to Reform (Midwest Journal of Political Science, Nov. 1957); Pressure Groups in the United States (Revista Argentina de Politica, Aug. 1958). Language: Spanish 4,2,3,3; French 2,1,1,2; German 2,1,2,2. Home: 133 Walnut, Rochester, Mich. Office: Dept. of Political Science, Oakland U., Rochester.

HEWES, GORDON WINANT, b. San Francisco, Calif., Oct. 29, 1917. ANTHROPOLOGY. A.B., U. of Calif., Berkeley, 1938; Ph. D., 1947. Geographer, Office of Strategic Services, 1942–45; geographer, U.S. Board on Geographical Names, 1943–44; asst. prof., U. of N. Dak., 1946–49; asst. prof., U. of Southern Calif., 1949–51; asst. prof.-PROF., ANTHROPOLOGY, U. OF COLO., 1951– . Fulbright prof., Tokyo U., 1955–56; Fulbright prof., U. de San Marcos (Peru), Fall 1960. Membership: American Anthropological Association; American Ethnological Society; American Geographical Society; Association of American Geographers; Society for American Archaeology; Sigma Xi. Research: cultural anthropology; archeology; culture-history; Mexico; Peru; archeology of Nubian area in Sudan. Author: Mexicans in Search of the Mexican (American Journal of Economics and Sociology, Jan. 1954); World Distribution of Certain Postural Habits (American Anthropologist, 1955); Food Transport and the Origins of Hominid Bipedalism (American Anthropologist, 1961). Language: Spanish 4,4,4,4; Portuguese 2,2,1,1; French 3,2,2,3; German 3,3,2,2; Italian 3,2,2,1; Japanese 2,2,2,2; Russian 3,2,2,2. Home: 335 16th St., Boulder, Colo., 80302. Office: Dept. of Anthropology, U. of Colo., Boulder, 80304.

HEWITT, CLYDE EATON, b. Hudson Falls, N.Y., June 24, 1916. HISTORY. B.A., Aurora Coll., 1937; M.A., U. of Chicago, 1939; Ph. D., 1948. PROF., HISTORY, AURORA COLL., 1939– ; REGISTRAR, 1955– . Membership: American Association of Collegiate Registrars and Admissions Officers; American Historical Association. Research: Venezuela; international investment and diplomacy; Mexico. Author: A Study in Opportunity, the Story of the First United States Industrial and Machinery Trade Mission to Mexico (Dec. 1963). Co-author: Cipriano Castro, Man Without a Country (American Historical Review, Oct. 1949). Language: Spanish 3,-,-,-. Home: 231 Calumet Ave., Aurora, Ill. Office: Dept. of History, Aurora, Coll., Aurora, 60507.

HIBBEN, FRANK CUMMINGS, b. Lakewood, Ohio, Dec. 5, 1910. ANTHROPOLOGY. A.B., Princeton U., 1933; M.S., U. of N. Mex., 1935; Ph. D., Harvard U., 1940. Naturalist, American Nature Association (Washington, D.C.), 1933–34; PROF., ANTHROPOLOGY, U. OF N. MEX., 1952– ; DIR., MUSEUM OF ANTHROPOLOGY, 1959– . Ford Foundation grant (Greece), 1956; lectr., Archaeological Institute of America, 1961– ; Rhodes scholar; National Science Foundation grants. Membership: American Anthropological Association; American Association for the Advancement of Science; American Ecological Society; American Ethnological Society; Society for American Archaeology; Texas Archaeological and Palaeological Society. Research; archeology; prehistory of Mexico and Central America. Language: Spanish 4,4,4,4; German 3,3,3,3. Office: Dept. of Anthropology, U. of N. Mex., Albuquerque.

HICKMAN, JOHN MARSHALL, b. Cedar Rapids, Iowa, Sept. 7, 1930. ANTHROPOLOGY. A.B., Cornell Coll., 1952; M.A., State U. of Iowa, 1959; Ph. D., Cornell U., 1963. Research asst., Cornell-Peru Project, Cornell U., 1960–61; DIR. OF RESEARCH, BOARD OF MISSIONS OF THE METHODIST CHURCH (LA PAZ, BOLIVIA), 1963– . Social Science Research Council fellow (Peru), 1961–63. Membership: American Anthropological Association; American Sociological Association; Society for Applied Anthropology. Research: sociology; social psychology; social and cultural change; Aymará and Quechua Indians of Peru; problems of La Iglesia Metodista in Bolivia. Author: Dimensions of a Complex Concept: A Method Exemplified (Human Organization, Fall 1962); An Approach to the Study of the Assimilation Process (1963 Proceedings, American Ethnological Society, 1964). Language: Spanish 3,4,3,3; Portuguese 1,2,1,1; French 2,2,2,2; German 2,2,2,2. Home: 2910 Indian Hill Rd., SE., Cedar Rapids, Iowa 52403. Office: Board of Missions of The Methodist Church, 475 Riverside Dr., New York, N.Y. 10027.

HILDEBRAND, JOHN RAYMOND, b. Greensburg, Kans., Apr. 21, 1924. ECONOMICS. A.B., U. of Calif., Berkeley, 1949; A.M., George Washington U., 1951; Ph. D., U. of Chicago, 1959. Asst. prof., Kans. State U., 1954–55; instr., Okla. State U., 1955–56; asst. prof., Kans. State U., 1956–60; economist, International Development Services, Inc. (Guatemala), 1960–62; economist, consultant, U.S. Agency for International Development (Argentina), Summer 1962; ASSOC. PROF., ECONOMICS, TEX. TECHNOLOGICAL COLL., 1962– . Representative, Kans. State Legislature, 1955–56. Membership: American Economic Association; American Farm Economic Association; Rocky Mountain Council on Latin American Studies; Southwestern Social Science Association. Research: Latin American economic problems. Author: Latin American Economic Development, Land Reform, and U.S. Aid with Special Reference to Guatemala (Journal of Inter-American Studies, July 1962); Farm Size and Agrarian Reform in Guatemala (Inter-American Economic Affairs, Autumn 1962); Guatemalan Rural Development Program (Inter-American Economic Affairs, Summer 1963). Language: Spanish 4,3,3,2; Portuguese 2,-,-,-; French 2,-,-,-. Home: 2806 22nd St., Lubbock, Tex. Office: Dept. of Economics, School of Business Administration, Tex. Technological Coll., Lubbock, 79409.

HILDNER, ERNEST GOTTHOLD, JR., b. Detroit, Mich., Nov. 7, 1903. HISTORY. A.B., U. of Mich., 1927; M.A., 1928; Ph. D., 1932. Asst. prof., Fisk U., Summer 1934; asst. prof., Western Ill. State Teachers Coll.,

1934–38; prof., dean, Ill. Coll., 1938–58; prof., Mich. State U., Summer 1943; PROF., HISTORY, ILL. COLL., 1958– . Economic history fellow, U. of Mich. (England, Spain), 1930–31; sabbatical, Archives of the Indies (Seville, Spain), 1961. Membership: American Historical Association. Research: the Caribbean area in the mid-18th century. Author: Ensenada and the French Alliance, 1752–56 (1933); Role of the South Sea Company in the Diplomacy Leading to the War of Jenkins' Ear (Hispanic American Historical Review, Aug. 1938). Language: Spanish 4,3,3,2; Portuguese 1,-,-,-; French 1,-,-,-. Home: 1120 West College Ave., Jacksonville, Ill. Office: Dept. of History, Ill. Coll., Jacksonville.

HILGER, MARY INEZ, O.S.B., b. Roscoe, Minn., Oct. 16, 1891. ANTHROPOLOGY. B.A., U. of Minn., 1923; M.A., Catholic U. of America, 1925; Ph. D., 1939. Instr., School of Nursing (St. Cloud, Minn.), 1939–54, 1956; lectr., vis. prof., Instituto Social León XIII, Universidad de Madrid, 1955; lectr., Coll. of St. Benedict, 1957–58; vis. prof., St. Joseph's Coll., Summer 1960; vis. lectr., American Anthropological Association, 1960, 1961–62, 1963–64; vis. prof., Tokyo U., Keio U., and Japan Women's U., 1962–63; RETIRED, 1963– . American Philosophical Society grant (Chile), 1946–47; American Philosophical Society and Wenner-Gren Foundation grant (Chile, Argentina), 1951–52; honorary research assoc., Bureau of American Ethnology, Smithsonian Institution, 1955– . Membership: American Anthropological Association; American Association for the Advancement of Science; American Benedictine Academy; American Catholic Sociological Society; Instituto Indigenista Interamericano. Research: ethnographic study of child life; Araucanian Indians of Chile and Argentina. Author: Chippewa Child Life and Its Cultural Background (1951); Arapaho Child Life and Its Cultural Background (1952); Araucanian Child Life and Its Cultural Background (1957). Language: Spanish 3,2,2,2; Portuguese 1,1,1,1; French 2,2,2,1; German 5,5,5,5; Italian 2,2,2,1. Home and office: St. Benedict's Convent, St. Joseph, Minn.

HILL, A. DAVID, b. Aurora, Minn., Jan. 22, 1933. GEOGRAPHY. B.A., U. of Colo., 1954; M.A., 1959; Ph. D., U. of Chicago, 1964. Instr., San Francisco State Coll., 1962–63; instr.-ASST. PROF., GEOGRAPHY, ANTIOCH COLL., 1963– . U.S. Office of Naval Research grant (Mexico), 1961–62. Membership: American Geographical Society; Association of American Geographers. Research: cultural geography; landscape change and ecological relationships in Mexico. Author: The Changing Landscape of a Mexican Municipio, Villa Las Rosas, Chiapas (1964). Language: Spanish 4,4,3,2. Home: 405 Phillips, Yellow Springs, Ohio. Office: Dept. of Earth Sciences, Antioch Coll., Yellow Springs.

HILL, EMMA MAY, b. Madison, Ind., Apr. 4, 1921. LANGUAGE. A.B., Hanover Coll., 1942; M.A., U. of Wis., 1946; U. of San Carlos (Guatemala), 1948; Ph. D., U. of Wis., 1957; U. of São Paulo, 1962. PROF., SPANISH, HANOVER COLL., 1946– . Lilly Endowment grant (Peru), 1961. Membership: American Association of Teachers of Spanish and Portuguese; Association for Latin American Studies; Modern Language Association. Research: Brazilian literature. Language: Spanish 4,4,4,4; Portuguese 4,3,3,3; French 3,2,2,1. Office: Dept. of Spanish. Hanover Coll., Hanover, Ind.

HILL, LAWRENCE F., b. Bivins, Tex., Nov. 19, 1890. HISTORY. B.S., West Tex. State Coll., 1915; A.B., U. of Calif., 1919; M.A., 1921; Ph. D., 1923. Asst. prof.-prof., Ohio State U., 1922–59; RETIRED, 1959– ; summer vis. prof., West Tex. State Coll., 1930, U. of Mich., 1929, 1942, U. of Nev., 1931, Duke U., 1939; vis. prof., Southern Ill. U., 1962–63, U. of Kans., 1963–64. Membership: American Historical Association; Conference on Latin American History; Mississippi Valley Historical Association; Phi Beta Kappa. Research: Brazil. Author: Diplomatic Relations Between the United States and Brazil (1947). Language: Spanish 3,-,-,-; Portuguese 3,-,-,-; French 3,-,-,-. Home: 520 Ridgewood Ave., Colorado Springs, Colo.

HILLMAN, JIMMYE STANDARD, b. McLain Miss., Mar. 1, 1923. ECONOMICS. B.S. Miss. State Coll., 1942; M.S., Tex. A. & M Coll., 1946; Ph. D., U. of Calif., Berkeley 1954. Asst. prof., Miss. State Coll., 1946–50: Asst.-ASSOC. PROF., CHMN., AGRICULTURAL ECONOMICS, U. OF ARIZ 1950– ; agricultural economist, International Cooperation Administration (Brazil), 1955–57. Rockefeller fellow, 1946–48 vis. prof. (Argentina), Fall 1956; consultant, Organization of American States (Chile), Summer 1960; consultant, Institute of International Education, 1961; consultant, U.S. Agency for International Development, 1962. Membership: American Economic Association; American Farm Economic Association; Western Farm Economic Association. Research: agricultural economics; Brazil; Mexico. Author: O desenvolvimento econômico e o nordeste brasileir (Revista do Instituto Brasil-Estados Unidos Jan.-Dec. 1957); Some Aspects of Brazilia Agricultural Policy (Inter-American Economic Affairs, Summer 1958). Language Spanish 4,4,4,3; Portuguese 5,5,5,5; Frenc 3,2,1,1. Home: 730 North Alamo, Tucson Ariz. Office: Dept. of Agricultural Eco nomics, U. of Ariz., Tucson.

HILLMON, TOMMIE J., b. Vassar, Kans Dec. 9, 1924. HISTORY AND GOVERN MENT. B.A., Washburn U., 1949; M.A Syracuse U., 1951; D.S.S., 1963. Intelligence specialist, Latin American Section U.S. Dept. of the Army, 1951–53; cartographer, U.S. Navy Hydrographic Office, 1953–56; part-time geographer, asst. enginee Geonautics, Inc., 1960–63: Hispanic reference specialist, Hispanic Foundation, Library of Congress, 1963–64; ASSOC. PROF HISTORY, CHMN., SOCIAL SCIENCE, K WESLEYAN COLL., 1964– . Membership American Association of University Professors; American Historical Association Conference on Latin American Histor Research: the role of the military in Lat America. Language: Spanish 3,2,2, Home: Lyndon, Kans. Office: Dept. of S cial Science, Ky. Wesleyan Coll., Owensbor

HILTON, RONALD, b. Torquay, England, J 31, 1911. LANGUAGE. B.A., Oxford 1933; M.A., 1936; Sorbonne, 1933–34; of Madrid, 1934–35; U. of Perugia, 193 36; Oxford U., 1936–37; U. of Calif., Berk ley, 1937–39. Dir., Comité Hispano Ingl

Library (Madrid), 1936; asst. prof., U. of British Columbia, 1939-41; assoc. prof., Stanford U., 1942-49; PROF., ROMANCE LANGUAGES, DIR., INSTITUTE OF HISPANIC AMERICAN AND LUSO-BRAZILIAN STUDIES, STANFORD U., 1949– . Commonwealth Fund fellow, U. of Calif., 1937-39; officer, Cruzeiro do Sul (Brazil). Membership: American Academy of Franciscan History; American Association of Teachers of Spanish and Portuguese; American Association of University Professors; Hispanic Society of America; Modern Language Association. Research: history of Hispanic America; Luso-Brazilian culture. Author: Handbook of Hispanic Source Materials in the United States (1942, 1956). Editor: Who's Who in Latin America (1946); The Life of Joaquim Nabuco (1950). Language: Spanish 5,5,5,5; Portuguese 5,5,5,5; French 5,5,5,5; German 1,1,1,1; Italian 1,1,1,1. Home: 766 Santa Ynez, Stanford, Calif. Office: Bolivar House, Stanford U., Stanford.

HINTON, THOMAS BENJAMIN, b. Ajo, Ariz., Sept. 5, 1924. ANTHROPOLOGY. B.A., U. of Ariz., 1955; M.A., U. of Calif., Los Angeles, 1958; Ph. D., 1961. ASST. PROF., ANTHROPOLOGY, U. OF TORONTO, 1961– . Phelps Dodge graduate scholar 1955-56; U. of Calif., Los Angeles, graduate student research grants, 1955-60; National Institute of Mental Health research fellow (Mexico), 1960-61. Membership: American Anthropological Association; Sigma Xi. Research: social and cultural anthropology; Indian and mestizo groups of Northern and Western Mexico; social structure and acculturation among the Cora Indians of Nayarit, Mexico; acculturation of Indian and other minority groups to the national cultures of Latin America. Author: Indian Assimilation in Eastern Sonora (1959); Other Sonoran Tribes (in Handbook of Middle American Indians). Co-author: The Huichol and Cora (in Handbook of Middle American Indians). Language: Spanish 4,4,4,4. Home: 710 Spadina Ave., Toronto, Canada. Office: Dept. of Anthropology, U. of Toronto, Toronto 5.

HIRSCHMAN, ALBERT O., b. Berlin, Germany, Apr. 7, 1915. ECONOMICS. Diploma, Ecole H.E.C. (Paris), 1935, Institut de Statistique, 1935; London School of Economics, 1935-36; Ph. D., U. of Trieste, 1938. Chief, West Europe Section, Federal Reserve Board, 1946-52; economic adviser, National Planning Council (Bogotá, Colombia), 1952-54; senior partner, Hirschman & Kalmanoff (Bogotá), 1954-56; research prof., Yale U., 1956-58; prof., Columbia U., 1958-64; PROF., POLITICAL ECONOMY, HARVARD U., 1964– . Rockefeller fellow, U. of Calif., Berkeley, 1941-43; consultant, Rockefeller Foundation (Colombia), 1957-58, Ford Foundation, 1958-59; Board of Editors, American Economic Review, 1962-64. Membership: American Economic Association; Royal Economic Society. Research: economic, social and political development in Latin America; international economics; investment in Central America. Author: The Strategy of Economic Development (1958); Journeys Toward Progress: Studies of Economic Policy Making in Latin America (1963). Editor, contributor: Latin American Issues—Essays and Comments (1961). Language: Spanish 5,5,4,4; Portuguese 4,3,3,2; French 5,5,4,4; German 5,5,4,4; Italian 5,5,4,4. Office: Dept. of Economics, Harvard U., Cambridge 38, Mass.

HITCHCOCK, CHARLES BAKER, b. Boston, Mass., Mar. 16, 1906. GEOGRAPHY. A.B., Harvard U., 1928; A.M., Columbia U., 1933. Field asst. and cartographer, Duida Expedition (Venezuela), American Museum of Natural History, 1929-30; research asst., Hispanic American Research, American Geographical Society, 1930-38; head, Hispanic American Research, 1938-46; asst. dir., American Geographical Society, 1943-49; executive secretary, 1950-53; DIR., AMERICAN GEOGRAPHICAL SOCIETY, 1953– . Chmn., U.S. Advisory Committee on American Cartography, Pan American Institute of Geography and History, 1945-56; Advisory Committee of Bureau of Census on Census Atlases (Central America), 1951-53; U.S. delegate, Pan American Institute of Geography and History, 1941, 1946, 1948, 1950, 1952, 1955, 1956-60. Membership: American Association for the Advancement of Science; Arctic Institute of North America; Association of American Geographers; Explorers Club; Geological Society of America; Oceanographic Society; Sociedad Geográfica de Lima; Sociedad Venezolana de Ciencias Naturales. Research: cartography; Venezuela. Editor: Map of Hispanic America (1938-46). Language: Spanish 4,3,2,2; Portuguese 3,1,1,1; French 4,2,1,1. Home: Stonehill Rd., Pound Ridge, N.Y. Office: American Geographical Society, Broadway at 156th St., New York, 10032.

HIXSON, IMOGENE, b. Paris, Ark., Oct. 15, 1914. LIBRARY SCIENCE. B.S., Okla. State U., 1936; B.S.L.S., La. State U., 1949; U. of Fla., 1948-53. Teacher, Okla. Public Schools, 1936-43, 1947-48; instr., Escola Técnica de Aviação (São Paulo, Brazil), 1946-47; cataloger of Spanish and Portuguese materials, Libraries, U. of Fla., 1949-62; HEAD, CATALOG DEPT., LIBRARIES, U. OF FLA., 1962– . Acquisitions program participant, Rockefeller Foundation grant to U. of Fla. (Guianas, Venezuela, West Indies), 1956; Creole Foundation grant to U. of Fla. (Colombia, Ecuador, Peru), 1960. Membership: American Library Association; Florida Library Association; Southeastern Library Association. Research: cataloging; acquisitions of materials. Author: Impressions of Some Caribbean Libraries (Florida Libraries, Mar. 1957). Editor: Caribbean Acquisitions (1959, 1960). Language: Spanish 2,-,-,-; Portuguese 3,-,-,-. Home: 2630 West University Ave., Gainesville, Fla. Office: Catalog Dept., Library, U. of Fla., Gainesville, 32603.

HODGMAN, SUZANNE, b. Chicago, Ill., July 16, 1925. LIBRARY SCIENCE. B.A., U. of N. Mex., 1947; M.A., Tulane U., 1950; M.L.S., U. of Tex., 1960. Reference librarian, San Antonio Public Library, 1959-60; LATIN AMERICAN SPECIALIST IN ACQUISITIONS, LIBRARIES, U. OF FLA., 1960– . Tulane U. graduate fellow; Committee on Exchange and Committee on Acquisitions, Seminars on the Acquisition of Latin American Library Materials. Membership: American Library Association; Florida Library Association; Phi Sigma

Iota; Southeastern Conference on Latin American Studies; Texas Library Association. Research: acquisitions. Author: Information Available in U.S. Bibliographic Services on Latin American Printed Materials (Papers, 6th Seminar on the Acquisition of Latin American Library Materials, 1961); Cooperative Acquisitions of Latin American Library Materials (Papers, 7th Seminar on the Acquisitions of Latin American Library Materials, 1962). Language: Spanish 4,4,4,4; Portuguese 3,2,1,1; French 3,2,2,2; Italian 2,2,1,1. Home: 327 SW. 41st St., Gainesville, Fla., 32601. Office: Libraries, U. of Fla., Gainesville, 32603.

HOECKER, RAYMOND W., b. Warrenton, Mo., Aug. 15, 1913. ECONOMICS: MARKETING. B.S., Iowa State U., 1936; M.S., Cornell U., 1939; Ph. D., 1941. Asst. prof., Kans. State U., 1941–43; asst. branch chief, U.S. Dept. of Agriculture, 1943–46; dir. of sales and research, U.S. Airlines, 1946–47; prof., head, Marketing Div., U. of Md., 1947–49; BRANCH CHIEF, U.S. DEPT. OF AGRICULTURE, 1949– . Consultant, Secretary of Agriculture of P.R., 1958; consultant, United Nations (Colombia), 1961; consultant, Marketing Institute for South America (Colombia), 1961– ; consultant on African food marketing problems, United Nations Food and Agriculture Organization, 1963. Membership: American Farm Economic Association; American Marketing Association. Research: agricultural marketing; food distribution, especially at the wholesale and retail level; agricultural marketing in Colombia and Puerto Rico. Language: Spanish 1,1,1,1; Portuguese 1,1,1,1; French 1,1,1,1. Home: 9100 Autoville Dr., College Park, Md., 20740. Office: Agricultural Research Service, Federal Center Bldg., Hyattsville, Md.

HOFFMAN, H. THEODORE, b. Dayton, Ohio, Sept. 13, 1907. ECONOMICS. B.S., U. of Dayton, 1929; M.A., American U., 1938; Ph. D., 1947. Asst. inspector, U.S. Railroad Retirement Board, 1936–41; economic and financial analyst, Embassy (Colombia), U.S. Dept. of State, 1941–45; chief, North Coast South American Section, U.S. Dept. of Commerce, 1945–50; PROF., ECONOMICS, U. OF DETROIT, 1950– . Foundation for Economic Education fellow, 1959, 1960; U. of Wis. fellow, 1963. Membership: American Economic Association; Catholic Economic Association; Beta Gamma Sigma; Delta Phi Epsilon; International Association of Catholic Economists, Agronomists and Engineers; Michigan Academy of Science, Arts and Letters. Research: international economics; railway development in Colombia. Author: Marketing Areas in Venezuela (1946); Colombia's Exchange Control (Foreign Commerce Weekly, Aug. 1945). Co-author: Business Review for Professional Secretaries (1959). Language: Spanish 5,5,4,4; German 2,2,2,2. Home: 18292 Hartwell, Detroit, Mich. 48235. Office: Dept. of Economics, U. of Detroit, Detroit, 48221.

HOFFMAN, HANS, b. Koblenz, Germany, Feb. 8, 1929. ANTHROPOLOGY. A.B., Cornell U., 1951; Ph. D., Yale U., 1957. Instr., U. of Okla., 1956–57; ethnographer, American Museum of Natural History (Peru), 1957–58; vis. asst. prof., U. of Ark., 1959–61; ASST. PROF., HARPUR COLL., STATE U. OF N.Y., 1961– . Russell Sage Foundation fellow, School of Medicine, U. of Okla., 1958–59. Membership: American Anthropological Association; Arctic Institute of North America; Society for American Archaeology; Sigma Xi. Research: cultural processes; ethnohistory of the upper Amazon; Shipibo Indians of Peru. Author: Symbolic Logic and the Analysis of Social Organization (Behavioral Science, Oct. 1959); Money, Ecology, Acculturation among the Shipibo of Peru (Murdock Festschrift, 1964). Language: Spanish 3,3,3,3. Home: 12 Lawton Ave., Binghamton, N.Y. Office: Dept. of Anthropology, Harpur Coll., State U. of N.Y., Binghamton.

HOFFMAN, FRITZ LEO, b. New Braunfels, Tex., Jan. 4, 1907. HISTORY. B.A., U. of Tex., 1928; M.A., 1930; Ph. D., 1935. Instr., U. of Tex., 1930–32, Summers 1933, 1934; chmn., Social Sciences, Corpus Christi Junior Coll., 1935–37; instr., U. of Colo., 1937–39; lectr., National U.of Buenos Aires and U. of Paraguay, 1943–44; asst. prof., U. of Colo., 1939–45; assoc. prof., 1945–52; PROF., HISTORY, U. OF COLO., 1952– ; lectr., U.S. Information Agency (Argentina, Uruguay), 1956. E. D. Farmer International Scholarship, Universidad Nacional Autónoma de México, 1932–34; Laura Spelman Rockefeller fellow, U. of Tex.; Faculty fellow, U. of Colo.; Board of Editors, Hispanic American Historical Review. Membership: American Historical Association; Conference on Latin American History; Rocky Mountain Council on Latin American Studies. Research: Rosas era; River Plate history; Mexico archival research. Author: The Diary of the Alarcón Expedition into Texas (1935); The Financing of San Martín's Expeditions (Hispanic American Historical Review, Nov. 1952); El Movimiento de Mayo en los periódicos de los Estados Unidos (Trabajos y Communicaciones, Universidad Nacional de la Plata, Nov. 9, 1960). Language: Spanish 5,5,5,5; Portuguese 3,2,1,1; French 1,1,1,1; German 5,5,4,4. Home: 1360 Bluebell, Boulder, Colo. 80302. Office: Dept. of History, U. of Colo., Boulder, 80304.

HOGE, HENRY WILLIAM, b. Island, Ky., Feb. 15, 1919. LANGUAGE AND LINGUISTICS. M.A., U. of Wis., 1942; Ph. D., 1948; Columbia U., 1952–53. Instr-asst. prof., Ind. U., 1947–58; ASSOC. PROF., CHMN., SPANISH AND PORTUGUESE, U. OF WIS., MILWAUKEE, 1959– . Ford Foundation fellow, Columbia U., 1952–53; Fulbright vis. prof., Instituto Caro y Cuervo (Bogotá), 1958–59; National Defense Education Act research projects on Brazilian Portuguese, 1963. Membership: American Association of Latin American Studies; American Association of Teachers of Spanish and Portuguese; Modern Language Association; National Federation of Modern Language Associations. Research: Spanish acoustic phonetics, dialectology, and syntax syntactical analysis of contemporary Brazilian Portuguese. Author: Lope de Vega's E. principe despeñado (1954); Oral Brazilian Portuguese (1964). Language: Spanish 5,5,4,5; Portuguese 4,4,4,4; French 4,3,3,3; German 3,3,3,3; Italian 3,3,3,3. Linguistic studies; Portuguese; Spanish. Home: 4317 North Maryland, Milwaukee 11, Wis. Office

Dept. of Spanish and Portuguese, U. of Wis., Milwaukee 11.

HOHENTHAL, WILLIAM DALTON, JR., b. Corning, Calif., Mar. 13, 1919. ANTHROPOLOGY. A.B., U. of Calif., Berkeley, 1941; Ph. D., 1951. Research assoc. U. of Calif., Berkeley, 1951–52; lectr., U. of Calif., Los Angeles, 1952–53; asst. prof.-assoc. prof., San Francisco State Coll., 1953–62; vis. prof., Fundação Escola de Sociologia e Política (São Paulo, Brazil), and U. of Calif, Berkeley, 1962–64; PROF., ANTHROPOLOGY, SAN FRANCISCO STATE COLL., 1964– . U. of Calif., Berkeley, research grants (Mexico), 1948–50; Social Science Research Council fellow (Brazil), 1951–52. Membership: American Anthropological Association; American Association for the Advancement of Science; Brazilian Anthropological Association; Kroeber Anthropological Society; Southwestern Anthropological Association. Research: cultural and physical anthropology; Brazilian ethnography, culture change, and rural problems; archeological bone pathology; domestication of plants and animals. Author: Notes on the Shucurú Indians of Serra de Ararobá, Pernambuco, Brazil (Revista do Museu Paulista, 1954); As tribos indígenas do médio e baixo Rio São Francisco (Revista do Museu Paulista, 1962). Language: Spanish 5,4,4,4; Portuguese 5,5,5,4; French 4,3,3,3. Home: 140 Scenic Ct., San Bruno, Calif. Office: Dept. of Anthropology, School of Social Science, San Francisco State Coll., San Francisco 27, Calif.

HOLBROOK, HOLLIS HOWARD, b. Natick, Mass., Feb. 7, 1909. ART. Certificate, Mass. School of Art, 1934; B.F.A., Yale U., 1936; Universidad Michoacán, 1952. PROF., ART, U. OF FLA., 1938– . Board of Directors, Southern States Art League, 1946–48; president, Florida Federation of Art, 1947; president, Florida Artists Group, 1948–51. Membership: American Association of University Professors; Florida Artists Group; Florida Education Association; Florida Federation of Art; National Society of Mural Painters; Southern States Art League. Research: painting; the arts of Guatemala, Honduras, and Costa Rica; fresco painting and lithography in Mexico. Author: The Fresco Painting Technique (Design, June 1952); A Media Laboratory (American Artist, Sept. 1960); The Development of the Plastic Arts of Central America (in The Caribbean, 1961). Language: Spanish 3,2,3,3; French 3,1,2,2. Home: 1710 Southwest 35th Pl., Gainesville, Fla. Office: Art Dept., U. of Fla., Gainesville.

HOLLAND, (GEORGE) KENNETH, b. Los Angeles, Calif., May 10, 1907. EDUCATION. A.B., Occidental Coll., 1929; M.A., Princeton U., 1931. Secretary, International Student Service, 1932–33; dir. of education, Civilian Conservation Corps Camps (New England area), 1933–35; assoc. dir., American Council on Education, 1935–41; chief, education section, Office of Inter-American Affairs, 1941–42; dir., Div. of Education, Office of Inter-American Affairs, 1942–45; president, Inter-American Education Foundation, 1945–46; asst. dir., Office of International Information and Cultural Affairs, U.S. Dept. of State, 1946–48; dir., Office of Educational Exchange, U.S. Dept. of State, 1949; PRESIDENT, INSTITUTE OF INTERNATIONAL EDUCATION (N.Y.), 1950– . Technical consultant, UNESCO Conference (London), 1945; U.S. delegations, UNESCO Conferences, 1946–50; Task Force of Pan American Union for Alliance for Progress; President Eisenhower's Advisory Committee on Latin America; secretary-general, Council on Higher Education in the American Republics. Membership: Council on Foreign Relations; Education and World Affairs; Federation of French Alliances in the United States; French Institute. Research: international affairs; educational, scientific, and cultural programs in Latin America. Author: Youth in European Labor Camps (1938); Youth in the Civilian Conservation Corps (1940); A Catalyst for Inter-American Higher Education (Teachers College Record, May 1963). Language: Spanish 4,4,3,–; French 4,4,3,–. Home: 28 Avon Rd., Bronxville, N.Y. Office: Institute of International Education, 809 United Nations Plaza, New York, N.Y. 10017.

HOLLERAN, MARY PATRICIA, b. Norfolk, Conn., May 21, 1905. HISTORY. B.A., Mt. St. Vincent-on-the-Hudson, 1928; M.A., Columbia U., 1929; Ph. D., 1948. Teacher, New Haven High School (Conn.), 1931–38; prof., Catholic U. of America, Summer 1942; chmn., History, dir. of public relations, St. Joseph Coll., 1938–52; academic dean, Hampton Institute, 1952–56; PROF., CHMN., HISTORY, STATE COLL. AT WESTFIELD, 1956–. Inter-American Advisory Committee, State of Connecticut Development Commission, 1945; U.S. delegate, Inter-American Cultural Council meeting (Peru), 1956. Membership: American Association of University Professors; American Association of University Women; Delta Kappa Gamma. Research: Guatemala. Author: Church and State in Guatemala (1949); Who Should Go to College? (Journal of Higher Education, Oct. 1947); Function of a College (Journal of Higher Education, Oct. 1956). Language: Spanish 4,–,–,–; Portuguese 2,–,–,–; French 2,–,–,–. Home: 81 Broad St., Westfield, Mass. Office: Dept. of History, State Coll., Westfield

HOLMBERG, ALLAN R., b. Renville, Minn., Oct. 15, 1909. ANTHROPOLOGY. B.A., U. of Minn., 1935; Ph. D., Yale U., 1946. Field technician, Rubber Development Corporation (Bolivia), 1942–45; cultural anthropologist, Institute of Social Anthropology, Smithsonian Institution (Peru), 1946–48; PROF., CHMN., ANTHROPOLOGY, CORNELL U., 1948– ; DIR., CORNELL-PERU PROJECT (VICOS, PERU). Sterling fellow, 1945–46; Center for Advanced Study in the Behavioral Sciences fellow, 1954–55; Latin American Science Board, National Academy of Sciences, 1963– ; Joint Committee on Latin America, Social Science Research Council, 1963–64; consultant, U.S. Agency for International Development. Membership: American Anthropological Association; American Ethnological Society; Society for Applied Anthropology. Research: social anthropology; culture change in Peru. Author: Nomads of the Long Bow (1950); The Research and Development Approach to Change (Human Organization, Spring 1958); Changing Community Attitudes and Values in Peru (in Social Change in Latin America Today, 1962). Language: Spanish 4,5,4,4; Portuguese 3,3,2,1; French 2,1,1,1; Guaraní 2,2, 2,1; Quechua 1,2,2,1. Linguistic studies: Guaraní; Quechua. Home: R.F.D. 3, West Shore Dr., Ithaca, N.Y. Office: Dept. of Anthropology, Cornell U., Ithaca, 14850.

HOLMES, JACK D. L., b. Asbury Park, N.J., July 4, 1930. HISTORY. B.A., Fla. State U., 1952; M.A., U. of Fla., 1953; Universidad Nacional Autónoma de México, 1954–55; Ph. D., U. of Tex., 1959. Editorial asst., Hispanic American Historical Review, U. of Tex., 1955–56; instr., Memphis State U., 1956–58; asst. prof., McNeese State Coll., 1959–61; researcher, San Juan National Park (P.R.), U.S. National Park Service, 1962–63; ASSOC. PROF., HISTORY, U. OF ALA., BIRMINGHAM CENTER, 1963– . Mexican Government grant, 1954–55; Charles W. Hackett fellow in Latin American Studies, U. of Tex., 1959; Fulbright grant (Spain and Portugal), 1961–62. Membership: Louisiana Historical Association; Southern Historical Association. Research: Spanish Louisiana; Spanish borderlands. Author: Documentos inéditos para la historia de Louisiana (1963); Some Economic Problems of Spanish Governors in Louisiana (Hispanic American Historical Review, Nov. 1962); The Spanish-American Rivalry over the Chickasaw Bluffs, 1780–1795 (East Tennessee Historical Society Publications, 1962). Language: Spanish 5,5,5,5; Portuguese 4,4,4,4; French 4,3,3,4; German 2,2,2, 2; Italian 3,3,2,2. Home: 505 Poinciana Dr., Birmingham 9, Ala. Office: Dept. of History, U. of Ala.-Birmingham Center, 720 South 20th St., Birmingham.

HOLMES, ROLAND CLIFFORD, b. Chicago, Ill., Jan. 8, 1929. GEOGRAPHY. A.B., U. of Fla., 1953; M.S., 1958; U. of Chicago, 1956–61. Planner, Franklin County Regional Planning Commission (Ohio), 1956–57; PROF., UNIVERSIDAD NACIONAL DE SAN AGUSTÍN (AREQUIPA, PERU), 1962– . U. of Fla. grant (Guatemala), Summer 1959; Fulbright grant (Peru), 1961–62; asesor del Segundo Congreso Nacional de Geografía (Peru), 1964. Membership: Alpha Kappa Delta; American Association of Geographers; American Geographical Society of New York; Associación Nacional de Geógrafos Peruanos; Association for Latin American Studies; Phi Kappa Delta. Research: natural resources management; use of resources in arid or semiarid regions; water resources problems; irrigation in Peru. Author; Water Resources Report of the Upper Scioto River Drainage Basin (1959); Composition and Size of Flood Losses (in Papers on Flood Problems, 1961); Tipos de estudios de campo en geografía (Humánitas, 1964). Language: Spanish 3,3,3,3; Portuguese 2,1,1,1. Home: 516 North Vermont Ave., Lakeland, Fla.

HOLZAPFEL, TAMARA OSIKOWSKA, b. Russia, Oct. 25, 1935. LANGUAGE. B.A., U. of N.C., 1957; M.A., State U. of Iowa, 1960; Ph. D., 1964. Instr., State U. of Iowa, 1963–64; ASST. PROF., MODERN AND CLASSICAL LANGUAGES, U. OF N. MEX., 1964– . Centro Colombo-Americano fellow; National Defense Education Act fellow. Membership: American Association of Teachers of Spanish and Portuguese; Modern Language Association. Research: Spanish American dialectology; Antioquian dialect of Colombia. Language: Spanish 5,5,5,5; Portuguese 2,2,2,2; French 5,5,4,3; German 5,5,5,5; Russian 5,5,5,5. Office: Dept. of Modern and Classical Languages, U. of N. Mex., Albuquerque.

HOMAN, A. GERLOF, b. Slochteren, Netherlands, Sept. 9, 1925. ECONOMICS. B.A., Bethel Coll., 1949; M.S., Kans. State U., 1952; Ph. D., U. of Oreg., 1961. Research asst., Div. of Economic Research, Stanford Research Institute, 1953–55; economist, 1955–59; research assoc., Dept. of Economics, staff member, Institute of International Studies and Overseas Administration, U. of Oreg., 1959–61; senior economist, Industrial Economics Div., Stanford Research Institute, 1961–62; CHIEF, INTERNATIONAL RESEARCH SECTION, DEPT. OF ECONOMIC RESEARCH, BANK OF AMERICA N.T. & S.A., 1962– ; TEACHER, INTRODUCTORY ECONOMICS, U. OF CALIF. EXTENSION, 1964– . Rockefeller fellow, Stanford U., 1952–53. Membership: American Economic Association; American Farm Economic Association. Research: international finance and banking; agricultural investment planning; problems of financing economic growth; balance of payments factors in Latin America; role of agriculture in Mexican economic growth; foreign investment possibilities in Peru. Author: Bank of America N.T. & S.A. and Bank of America International Exposure to Transfer Risk on Dollar Credits in Foreign Countries (1964). Co-author: World Capital Markets (1960). Contributor: Problems of Economic Development of Latin America (1959). Language: Spanish 4,4,4,2; French 4,4,3,3; Dutch 5,5, 5,5; German 4,4,4,4. Home: 120 Merritt Ct., Los Altos, Calif. 94022. Office: Room 508, 300 Montgomery St., San Francisco, Calif. 94120.

HOOGSHAGEN, SEARLE W., b. Rothiemay, Mont. LINGUISTICS. B.A., Westmont Coll., 1949. LINGUIST, SUMMER INSTITUTE OF LINGUISTICS (MEXICO), 1950– . Research: Mixe Indian culture of Mexico. Author: Three Contrastive Vowel Lengths in Mixe (Sonderabdruck, aus Zeitschrift für Phonetik, 1959); Notes on the Sacred Mushroom from Coatlán (Oklahoma Anthropological Society Bulletin, 1959) Funcionarios en Coatlán (Revista Mexicana de Estudios Antropológicos, 1960). Language: Spanish 3,3,3,2. Linguistic studies Mixe. Home: Monroe, S. Dak. Office Instituto Lingüístico de Verano, Call Hidalgo No. 166, Tlalpan, México, D.F.

HOOKER, ALEXANDER CAMPBELL, JR., b Detroit, Mich., Mar. 24, 1921. SPANISH AMERICAN LITERATURE. A.B., Dartmouth Coll., 1942; M.A., Harvard U., 1947 Mexico City Coll., 1947–48; D.M.L., Middlebury Coll., 1954. Instr., Cambridge Junior Coll., 1946–47; PROF., ROMANCE LANGUAGES, RIPON COLL., 1950– . Central American faculty fellow, Associate Colleges of the Midwest, Summer 1962 Membership: American Association of Teachers of Spanish and Portuguese; American Association of University Professors Modern Language Association. Research bibliography. Translator: La controversi en los autos de Calderón, by W. J. Entwhistle (Nueva Revista de Filología Hispánica

July–Sept. 1948) ; Sobre Pedro Mexía en Inglaterra, by Philip A. Turner (Nueva Revista de Filología Hispánica, July–Sept. 1949). Language: Spanish 4,4,4,4 ; Portuguese 2,2,1,1 ; French 3,3,3,3. Home : 727 Thorne St., R.F.D. 2, Ripon, Wis. Office : Dept. of Romance Languages, Ripon Coll., Ripon.

HOPKINS, JOHN ABEL, b. Newark, Del., Apr. 4, 1897. ECONOMICS. B.S., U. of Del., 1917 ; A.M., Harvard U., 1921 ; Ph. D., 1924. Asst. prof.-prof., Iowa State Coll., 1921–44 ; Armour Research Foundation economist (Argentina), 1942 ; agricultural adviser, Embassy (Bogotá), Foreign Service, U.S. Dept. of State, 1944–45 ; chief, Latin American Div., Office of Foreign Agricultural Relations, U.S. Dept. of Agriculture, 1945–47 ; agricultural attaché (Mexico), 1947–50, (Brazil), 1950–52, (Argentina), 1953 ; counselor for economic affairs (Buenos Aires), 1953–56 ; assoc. chief, Economic Section, Latin American Div., U.S. Dept. of State, 1956–57 ; economic counselor, International Sugar Council (London), 1958–59 ; parttime economist, International Federation of Agriculture Producers, 1961–62 ; PROJECT DIR., INTER-AMERICAN COMMITTEE FOR AGRICULTURAL DEVELOPMENT, 1962– . Membership : American Economic Association ; American Farm Economic Association. Research : agricultural economics, especially farm management. Author : Changing Technology and Employment in Agriculture (1941) ; Administración Rural (1952, 1962) ; Inventory of Information Basic to Planning of Agricultural Development in Latin America—Regional Report (1963). Language: Spanish 4,4,4,2 ; Portuguese 4,3,3,2. Home : 4000 Cathedral Ave., NW., Washington, D.C. 20016. Office : Inter-American Committee for Agricultural Development, Premier Bldg. 814, 1725 Eye St., NW., Washington, D.C.

IOPPER, REX D., b. Nashville, Ind., July 4, 1898. SOCIOLOGY. A.B., Butler U., 1922 ; A.M., 1925 ; Ph. D., U. of Tex., 1943. Teacher and treasurer, Colegio Internacional (Paraguay), 1926–31 ; tutor-asst. prof., Institute of Latin American Studies, U. of Tex., 1932–46 ; vis. prof., National U. of Mexico, Summers 1943–46 ; PROF., CHMN., SOCIOLOGY AND ANTHROPOLOGY, BROOKLYN COLL., 1947– ; vis. prof., Mexico City Coll., Summer 1950 ; senior staff scientist, Special Operations Research Office, American U., 1964–65. Smith-Mundt lectr., National U. of Asunción (Paraguay), Summer 1957 ; Fulbright lectr., National U. of Buenos Aires, Summer 1959 ; Carnegie Corporation grant, 1961. Membership : Alpha Kappa Delta ; American Association for the Advancement of Science ; American Sociological Association ; Eastern Sociological Society ; Sigma Xi ; Society for the Study of Social Problems. Research : social change and development ; sociological analysis of the Latin American struggle for independence ; contemporary Latin American revolutionary movements. Author : Cybernation, Marginality, and Revolution (in The New Sociology, 1964) ; Research on Latin America : Sociology (in Research on Latin America, 1964). Co-author : The Seizure of Power : A Century of Revolution (1958). Language: Spanish 5,4,4,4 ; Portuguese 4,3, 1,1 ; French 3,1,1,1 ; Italian 3,1,1,1. Home : 128 Washington Pl., New York 14, N.Y. Office : Dept. of Sociology and Anthropology, Brooklyn Coll., Brooklyn 10, N.Y.

HOROWITZ, MORRIS A., b. Newark, N.J., Nov. 19, 1919. ECONOMICS. B.A., N.Y.U., 1940 ; Ph. D., Harvard U., 1954. Economist, Bureau of Labor Statistics, 1941–42 ; economist, Office of Defense Transportation, 1942–44 ; dir. of wage analysis, National War Labor Board, 1944–46 ; asst. prof., U. of Ill., 1947–51 ; dir. of case analysis, Wage Stabilization Board, 1951–53 ; research assoc., Harvard U., 1953–56 ; program specialist in manpower, Ford Foundation (Argentina), 1961–62 ; PROF., CHMN., ECONOMICS, NORTHEASTERN U., 1956– . Academic consultant, American Institute for Free Labor Development ; consultant to Technical Unit, Dept. of Social Affairs, Pan American Union ; research grant, Latin American Bureau, U.S. Agency for International Development. Membership : American Economic Association ; Industrial Relations Research Association. Research : labor economics and industrial relations ; international manpower statistics ; economies of Chile and Brazil ; high-level manpower in Argentina. Author : Labor Relations in the New York Hotel Industry (1960) ; Structure and Government of the Carpenters' Union (1962) ; Los recursos humanos de nivel universitario y técnico en la República Argentina (1963). Language: Spanish 3,3,3,3. Home : 5 Riedesel Ave., Cambridge, Mass. 02138. Office : Dept. of Economics, Northeastern U., Boston, Mass. 02115.

HORST, OSCAR HEINZ, b. Newark, Ohio, Mar. 4, 1924. GEOGRAPHY. B.S., Ohio State U., 1949 ; M.A., 1951 ; Ph. D., 1956. ASSOC. PROF., GEOGRAPHY, WESTERN MICH. U., 1956– ; vis. assoc. prof., Mich. State U., Summer 1962. Buenos Aires Convention grant (Guatemala), 1955 ; Knickerbocker Foundation grant (Dominican Republic), 1960–61 ; Carnegie Foundation grant (Guatemala), 1962–63 ; National Defense Foreign Language fellow, U. of Calif., Los Angeles, Summer 1963. Membership : American Association for the Advancement of Science ; American Geographical Society ; Association of American Geographers ; Association for Latin American Studies ; Michigan Academy of Science, Arts, and Letters. Research : land tenure and economic development ; economic development in Middle America ; physical landscape and land tenure in Guatemala. Language: Spanish 3,3,3,3 ; German 3,3,3,3. Home : 833 Whites Rd., Kalamazoo, Mich. Office : Dept. of Geography and Geology, Western Mich. U., Kalamazoo.

HOSELITZ, BERT FRANK, b. Vienna, Austria, May 27, 1913. ECONOMICS. LL.D., U. of Vienna, 1937 ; M.A., U. of Chicago, 1946. Instr., U. of Chicago, 1944–45 ; asst. prof., 1945–47 ; assoc. prof., Carnegie Institute of Technology, 1947–48 ; assoc. prof., U. of Chicago, 1948–52 ; expert in El Salvador, United Nations, 1952 ; PROF., ECONOMICS AND SOCIAL SCIENCE, U. OF CHICAGO, 1952– . Membership : American Economic Association ; Economic History Association ; Royal Economic Society. Research : economics of developing countries ; social conditions of economic growth in developing countries.

Author: Patterns of Economic Growth (The Canadian Journal of Economics and Political Science, Nov. 1955) ; Economic Development in Central America (Weltwirtschaftliches Archiv, 1956) ; El desarrollo económico en América Latina (Desarrollo Económico, Oct.-Dec. 1962). Language : Spanish 3,3,3,3 ; Portuguese 1,1,1,1 ; French 4,5,4,4 ; German 5,5,4,4. Home : 6024 South Ellis Ave., Chicago, Ill. 60637. Office : Research Center in Economic Development and Cultural Change, U. of Chicago, 1126 East 59th St., Chicago, 60637.

HOSKINS, LEWIS M., b. McMinnville, Oreg., Feb. 23, 1916. HISTORY. A.B., Pacific Coll., 1938 ; M.A., Haverford Coll., 1939 ; Ph. D., U. of Mich., 1946. Prof., dean of faculty, Pacific Coll., 1943–45 ; chmn. of administration, Friends Ambulance Unit, 1945–48 ; personnel secretary, American Friends Service Committee, 1949–50 ; executive secretary, 1950–59 ; PROF. CHMN., HISTORY, EARLHAM COLL., 1959– . Part-time administrator of foreign study operations and AID contract in Kenya, 1964. Research : class structure in Mexico in 17th century. Language : Spanish 2,2,2,1 ; Chinese –,1,1,– ; German 2,2,2,1. Home : 842 National Rd. West, Richmond, Ind., 47375. Office : Dept. of History, Earlham Coll., Richmond, 47375.

HOTCHKISS, JOHN C., b. Sacramento, Calif., May 17, 1930. ANTHROPOLOGY. B.A., Reed Coll., 1956 ; M.A., U. of Chicago, 1960 ; Ph. D., 1965. Instr., Washington U., 1962–63 ; ASST. PROF., ANTHROPOLOGY, STANFORD U., 1963– . National Institute of Mental Health research fellow, 1960–61. Membership : American Anthropological Association ; American Ethnological Society ; Central States Anthropological Society. Research : social anthropology ; acculturation in a Highland Maya town in Mexico. Author : Studies of Language and culture in Highland Chiapas, Mexico (Proceedings, American Ethnological Society, Spring 1963). Language : Spanish 3,4,3,1. Home : 2297 St. Francis Dr., Palo Alto Calif. Office : Encina 401, Stanford U., Stanford, Calif.

HOUSEMAN, PHILIP JOSEPH, b. Grand Rapids, Mich., Apr. 3, 1922. HISTORY. A.B., Wayne State U., 1949 ; M.A., Stanford U., 1951 ; Ph. D., 1961. Teacher, Instituto Chileno-Norteamericano de cultura, 1954–55 ; Sacramento City Unified School District (Calif.), 1958–60 ; CHMN., HISTORY, VICTOR VALLEY COLL., 1960–. Stanford U. grant, 1954 ; Buenos Aires Convention fellow (Chile), 1954–55. Membership : American Historical Association ; Bolivarian Society ; Conference on Latin American History ; Hispanic American Historical Association ; Latin American Studies Council ; Phi Delta Kappa ; Sigma Delta Pi. Research : Chilean nationalism, 1920–52. Language : Spanish 5,5,4,4 ; Portuguese 2,2,2,1 ; French 2,1,1,1 ; Italian 2,1,1,1. Home : 16222 Tejon St., Victorville, Calif. Office : P.O. Box 725, Victor Valley Coll., Victorville.

HOUSTON, JOHN ALBERT, b. Spokane, Wash., Dec. 24, 1914. POLITICAL SCIENCE. A.B., Stanford U., 1936 ; M.A., 1947 ; Ph. D., U. of Mich., 1951. Asst.-assoc. prof., U. of Miss., 1949–54 ; PROF., CHMN., POLITICAL SCIENCE, KNOX COLL., 1954– . Social Science Research Council fellow, Summer Research Institute in International Relations, 1956 ; Social Science Foundation fellow, U. of Denver, 1957 ; book review editor, Midwest Journal of Political Science, 1962–. Membership : American Political Science Association ; Midwest Conference of Political Science ; Pi Sigma Alpha. Research : international law and organization ; the role of the Latin American states in the establishment of the United Nations. Author : Latin America in the U.N. (1956) ; The United Nations and Spain (Journal of Politics, Nov. 1952) ; Latin America in International Organizations, (in Encyclopaedia Britannica, 1962). Language : Spanish 3,3,2,2 ; French 3,1,1,1. Home : 1655 North West St., Galesburg, Ill. Office : Dept. of Political Science, Knox Coll., Galesburg.

HOWELL, HERBERT B., b. Frederick, S. Dak., Dec. 8, 1911. ECONOMICS. B.S., Iowa State U., 1934 ; M.S., 1945. District extension economist, Iowa State U., 1935–40 ; supervisor and district extension economist, 1940–45 ; prof., 1945–64 ; chief, Iowa State U. Contract Group (Lima), 1962–64 ; PROF., AGRICULTURAL ECONOMICS AGRICULTURAL EXTENSION SERVICE, IOWA STATE U., 1964– . Consultant on beef products and economic development, Government of Argentina, Fall 1959, U.S. Agency for International Development (Buenos Aires), Fall 1961, Summer 1962. Membership : American Farm Economic Association ; American Society of Farm Managers and Rural Appraisers ; Society for International Development. Research : agricultural production economics ; farm management ; credit and tenure ; agrarian reform and agricultural credit in Peru ; Argentine agricultural development. Author : Better Farm Accounting (1961) ; Economies of Scale in Livestock Production (Journal of Farm Economics, Dec. 1961). Language : Spanish 3,1,2,1. Home : 3312 Ross Rd., Ames, Iowa 50010. Office : Dept. of Agricultural Economics, Iowa State U., Ames, 50010.

HOWELL, JAMES MELTON, b. Bryan, Tex. Oct. 12, 1933. ECONOMICS. B.A., Tex A. & M. U., 1956 ; Ph. D., Tulane U., 1963 Economist, Board of Governors of the Federal Reserve System, 1962–63 ; ECONOMIST, U.S. AGENCY FOR INTERNATIONAL DEVELOPMENT (SANTIAGO CHILE), 1963– . National Defense Education Act fellow, 1959–62. Membership American Economic Association ; Souther Economic Association. Research : economi development ; developmental processes of th Chilean economy ; structural change at th community level. Language : Spanish 3,3,2 1 ; French 3,1,1,1. Home : Tarleton Sta tion, Stephenville, Tex. Office : U.S. Agenc for International Development, America Embassy, Santiago, Chile.

HOWER, ALFRED, b. New York, N.Y., Jan 1915. BRAZILIAN LITERATURE. A.E U. of Mich., 1939 ; M.A., Northwestern U 1940 ; Ph. D., Harvard U., 1954. Asst. prof Rutgers U., 1947–56 ; manager, Globe Insur ance Agency (Detroit), 1956–62 ; part-tim lectr., Wayne State U., 1901–02 ; PROF PORTUGUESE AND SPANISH, U. O FLA., 1962– . Membership : American A sociation of Teachers of Spanish and Portu guese ; American Association of Universit

Professors; Modern Language Association. Research: literature and culture of Brazil; Peruvian and Mexican literature. Author: João Bernardo da Rocha and His *O Portuguez* (Studies in Romanticism, Autumn 1961). Editor: The Romantic Movement: A Selective and Critical Bibliography (Philological Quarterly, Apr. 1955). Language: Spanish 4,4,4,4; Portuguese 4,4,4,4; French 4,2,2,2; German 2,1,1,1; Italian 3,1,1,1. Home: 406 NW. 14th St., Gainesville, Fla. Office: Dept. of Foreign Languages, U. of Fla., Gainesville.

HOY, DON ROGER, b. Lincoln, Nebr., July 18, 1931. GEOGRAPHY. B.A., U. of Okla., 1953; M.A., 1954; Ph. D., U. of Ill., 1960. Field researcher, U. of Tex. (Mexico), Summer 1957; asst. prof., Ohio State U., 1960–61; ASST. PROF., GEOGRAPHY, U. OF GA., 1961– . Recipient, National Academy of Science-National Research Council contract (Guadeloupe, French West Indies), 1959–60; National Defense Foreign Language fellow, U. of Calif., Los Angeles, Summer 1963. Membership: American Geographic Society; Association of American Geographers; National Council for Geographic Education; Sigma Xi. Research: resource use; regional planning; terrain, resources, and population in Guadeloupe and Antilles; terrain of Mexico; the Caribbean. Author: Changing Agricultural Land Use of Guadeloupe (Annals, Association of American Geographers, 1962); Power Resources of Peru (Geographical Review, Oct. 1963). Co-author: Karst Landscapes of Cuba, Puerto Rico, and Jamaica (Scientific Monthly, Oct. 1957). Language: Spanish 2,2,2,1; French 3,2,2,1. Home: 220 Hillcrest Ave., Athens, Ga. Office: Dept. of Geography, U. of Ga., Athens.

HOYT, EDWARD LYDIG, b. New York, N.Y., Feb. 17, 1936. ECONOMICS. B.S., M.S., Mass. Institute of Technology; M.A., Fletcher School of Law & Diplomacy, 1962; M.A.L.D., 1963; Ph. D., 1964. DIR., BOGOTÁ OFFICE, INTERNATIONAL DEVELOPMENT FOUNDATION, 1964– . Research: international economics; Argentine development; Colombia. Language: Spanish 4,4,4,4; Portuguese –,2,2,–; French 3,3,3,3. Home: Calle 39, No. 14–29, Apt. 201, Bogotá, Colombia. Office: Fundación para el Desarrollo Internacional, Calle 24, No. 7–14, Of. 301 C, Bogotá, Colombia.

HOYT, ELIZABETH ELLIS, b. Augusta, Maine, Jan. 27, 1893. ECONOMICS. A.B., Boston U., 1913; M.A., Radcliffe Coll., 1924; Ph. D., 1925. PROF., ECONOMICS, IOWA STATE U., 1925– . Ford Foundation grant (Caribbean), 1957–58. Membership: American Economic Association. Research: employers' policies in Guatemala; culture change. Author: Primitive Trade (1926); Guatemala: Challenge to Point Four (1948); American Income and Its Use (1954). Language: Spanish 4,2,3,2; French 4,2,3,2. Office: Dept. of Economics, Iowa State U., Ames.

HUCK, EUGENE ROGER, b. Jan. 24, 1928. HISTORY. A.B., Temple U., 1952; M.A., U. of Ala., 1954; Ph. D., 1963. Part-time instr., Jacksonville State Teacher's Coll., 1956; historian, Public Information Office, U.S. Air Force, 1954–56; instr., U. of Ala., Huntsville Center, Summer 1958; teacher, Centro Colombo-Americano (Colombia), 1959; ASSOC. PROF., HISTORY, WEST GA. COLL., 1959– . Graduate fellow, U. of Ala., 1952–53, 1956–58; Buenos Aires Convention fellow (Colombia), 1958–59; Regent's Committee on Graduate Work and Research, West Ga. Coll. Membership: American Association of University Professors; Southeastern Conference on Latin American Studies; Southern Historical Association. Research: history, sociology and economics of Latin America; international relations concerning Panama. Language: Spanish 4,3,3,3; Portuguese 1,1,1,1; French 2,2,1,2. Home: 151 Howell Rd., Carrollton, Ga. 30117. Office: Div. of Social Science, West Ga. Coll., Carrollton.

HULET, CLAUDE LYLE, b. Pontiac, Mich., Dec. 22, 1920. SPANISH AMERICAN AND BRAZILIAN LITERATURES. A.B., U. of Mich., 1942; English Language Institute, Universidad Nacional de México, 1942; M.A., U. of Mich., 1947; Ph. D., 1954. Dir., Instituto Guatemalteco Americano, U.S. Dept. of State, 1945–47; profesor de Inglés, Universidad de San Carlos Borromeo (Guatemala), 1946–47; instr., U. of Mich., 1947–51; asst. prof., Washington U., 1951–58; ASST. PROF., SPANISH AND PORTUGUESE, U. OF CALIF., LOS ANGELES, 1958– . Organization of American States fellow (Brazil), 1960; book reviewer, Los Angeles Times; Advisory Committee, Center of Latin American Studies, U. of Calif., Los Angeles. Membership: American Association of Teachers of Spanish and Portuguese; American Association of University Professors; Association for Latin American Studies; Foreign Language Association of Northern California; Instituto Internacional de Literatura Iberoamericana; Modern Language Association; Philological Association of the Pacific Coast. Research: contemporary novel, short story, and essay in Spanish American and Brazilian literatures; Argentine literature; English as a foreign language; Latin American literature in English translations. Author: Algumas reminiscências do Brasil no Romantismo argentino (Hispania, Dec. 1959); La segunda generación romántica argentina: ensayo de apreciación histórico-política (Cuadernos Americanos, Jan.–Feb. 1960). Language: Spanish 5,5,5,5; Portuguese 5,5,5,5; French 4,4,3,3; German 2,2,2,1. Linguistic studies: English; Spanish. Home: 7356 Donna Ave., Reseda, Calif. Office: Dept. of Spanish and Portuguese, U. of Calif., 405 Hilgard Ave., Los Angeles 24.

HUNDLEY, NORRIS CECIL, JR., b. Houston, Tex., Oct. 26, 1935. HISTORY. B.A., Whittier Coll., 1958; Ph. D., U. of Calif., Los Angeles, 1963. Editorial asst., Pacific Historical Review, Summer 1961; acting instr., U. of Calif., Los Angeles, 1962–63; instr., U. of Houston, 1963–64; ASST. PROF., HISTORY, U. OF CALIF., LOS ANGELES, 1964– . U. of Calif., Los Angeles, fellow, 1960–62; American Philosophical Society fellow, 1963. Membership: American Historical Association; American West Historical Association; Mississippi Valley Historical Association. Research: history of American West; U.S. diplomatic history; economic development of northern Mexico's arid border region; Mexican-American controversies over the waters of the Colorado,

Tijuana, and Rio Grande Rivers. Author: Colorado Waters Dispute (Foreign Affairs, Apr. 1964). Language: Spanish 3,2,2,3; French 3,2,2,3; German 3,1,1,3. Home: 11337 Burnham St., Los Angeles, Calif. 90049. Office: Dept. of History, U. of Calif., Los Angeles, 90024.

HUNT, SHANE JOHN, b. Lynn, Mass., Feb. 2, 1933. ECONOMICS. B.S., U. of Miami (Fla.), 1954; M.A., Yale U., 1958; Ph. D., 1963. ASST. PROF., ECONOMIC GROWTH CENTER, YALE U., 1962– . Brookings Institution fellow, 1961–62. Membership: American Economic Association. Research: economic development; economics of education; national accounting and related statistical problems; Peruvian economy. Author: Income Determinants for College Graduates and the Return to Educational Investment (Yale Economic Essays, Fall 1963). Language: Spanish 3,3,3,3; French 1,-,-,-,-. Home: Contralmirante Villar 885, Miraflores, Lima, Peru. Office: Economic Growth Center, Box 1987, Yale Station, New Haven, Conn.

HUNTER, JOHN M., b. Champaign, Ill., Dec. 1, 1921. ECONOMICS. B.S., U. of Ill., 1943; M.S., 1947; M.A., Harvard U., 1949; Ph. D., 1951. Asst. prof., Mich. State U., 1950–54; assoc. prof., 1954–58; economist, Mich. State U. Advisory Group in Viet Nam, 1955–56; acting head, Economics, Mich. State U., 1956–58; dir., Centro de Estudios sobre Desarrollo Económico, Universidad de los Andes (Colombia), 1958–60; PROF., ECONOMICS, MICH. STATE U., 1960– ; Ford Foundation program specialist, adviser, Instituto de Investigaciones Económicas, Universidad de Córdoba (Argentina), 1962–64. Consultant, Special Operations Research Office, American U., 1955– . Membership: American Economic Association; Society for International Development. Research: economic development; economic history of Cuba; economic problems of Latin America; economies of Colombia and Argentina. Author: Emerging Colombia (1962); Role of Education in Latin America (1962); Sueldos diferentes en puestos similares (Ciencias Económicas, May 1960). Language: Spanish 4,3,3,3; French 2,2,2,2. Home: 632 Baldwin Ct., East Lansing, Mich. Office: Dept. of Economics, Mich. State U., East Lansing.

HUNTINGTON, SAMUEL PHILLIPS, b. New York, N.Y., Apr. 18, 1927. POLITICAL SCIENCE. B.A., Yale U. 1946; M.A., U. of Chicago, 1948; Ph. D., Harvard U., 1950. Instr.-asst. prof., Harvard U., 1950–58; research associate, Brookings Institution, 1952–53; vis. lectr., Ohio State U., Summers 1956, 1957; assoc. prof., assoc. dir., Institute of War and Peace Studies, Columbia U., 1958–62; PROF., GOVERNMENT, HARVARD U., 1962– . Social Science Research Council fellow, 1954–57; research associate, Center for International Affairs, Harvard U., 1963– ; consultant; Office of Secretary of Defense, U.S. Air Force, Institute for Defense Analysis, U.S. Navy, Hudson Institute, Historical Evaluation and Research Organization. Membership: American Political Science Association; American Society for Public Administration. Research: role of the military in Latin American politics; comparative politics and political development. Author: The Soldier and the State: The Theory and Politics of Civil-Military Relations (1957); The Common Defense: Strategic Programs in National Politics (1961). Co-author: Political Power: USA/USSR (1964) Language: Spanish 3,2,2,1; Portuguese 1,1,1,1; French 3,2,1,1; German 2,2,2,1. Home: 52 Brimmer St., Boston, Mass. Office: Littauer Center M–25, Harvard U., Cambridge, Mass. 02138.

HURT, WESLEY ROBERT, b. Albuquerque, N. Mex., Sept. 20, 1917. ANTHROPOLOGY B.A., U. of N. Mex., 1938; M.A., 1942; Ph. D., U. of Mich., 1952. Dir., Museum prof., U. of S. Dak., 1949–63; vis. prof., U. of Calif., Berkeley, 1961; DIR., MUSEUM PROF., ANTHROPOLOGY, IND. U., 1963– Smith-Mundt prof., U. of Minas Gerais (Brazil), 1956; Fulbright prof., U. of Paraná (Brazil), 1958–59. Membership American Anthropological Association American Association of Museums; Indiana Academy of Science; Sigma Xi; Society for American Archaeology. Research: archeology in southern and central Brazil. Author: A Comparative Study of the Preceramic Occupations of North America (American Antiquity, Jan. 1953); O sambaqui do Macedo (Arqueologia No. 2, Universidade do Paraná, 1960); The Cultural Complexes from Lagoa Santa Region, Brazil (American Anthropologist, Aug. 1960) Language: Spanish 4,4,4,3; Portugues 4,4,4,3; French 3,3,2,2. Home: 120 Concord Rd., Bloomington, Ind. Office: Ind. U Museum, 150 Maxwell Hall, Bloomington

HUTCHINS, JOHN A., b. Schenectady, N.Y May 13, 1919. POLITICAL SCIENCE A.B., Allegheny Coll., 1941; M.A., Fletche School of Law & Diplomacy, 1942; Ph. D American U. 1953. Dir., American Cultura Institute (Curitiba, Brazil), U.S. Dept. c State, 1944–47; ASSOC. PROF., PORTU GUESE AND SPANISH, U.S. NAVA ACADEMY, 1948– . American Council c Learned Societies fellow, 1942; Institute c International Education fellow, Universdade de São Paulo; Organization of Amer can States grant for archival researc (Brazil, Argentina, Uruguay); Chevalie Order of the Southern Cross, Brazil, 195 Sesquicentenary Medal, Brazilian Arm Archives, 1958; Legion of Merit of Honor Paraguay, 1964. Research: Latin Amer can affairs; Luso-Brazilian interests in t Plata area. Author: Motives of the Port guese in the Banda Oriental, 1816–1824 (Terceiro Colóquio Internacional de Estud Brasileiros, 1959); A política diplomáti da Côrte do Rio de Janeiro em relação Banda Oriental do Uruguai, 1808–1812 (R vista Portuguesa de História, Tomo I 1960). Language: Spanish 5,5,4,4; Port guese 5,5,5,5; French 3,2,2,–. Home: 2 Wardour Dr., Annapolis, Md. Office: Fc eign Languages Dept., U.S. Naval Academ Annapolis.

HUTCHINSON, CECIL ALAN, b. Lowesto England, Mar. 13, 1914. HISTORY. B. Cambridge U., 1937; M.A., 1941; Ph. D., of Tex., 1948. Instr., Dartmouth Col 1938–40; editor, translator, Committee Cultural Relations with Latin America, I (Conn.), 1944–45; ASSOC. PROF., H TORY, U. OF VA., 1948– . U. of grants (Mexico), 1952–53, 1955 (Sou America), 1960. Membership: Americ Historical Association; Conference on La

American History. Research: Mexico from independence to 1860, especially social and intellectual history. Author: Mexican Federalists in New Orleans and the Texas Revolution (Louisiana Historical Review, Jan. 1956); Valentín Gómez Farías and the Secret Pact of New Orleans (Hispanic American Historical Review, Nov. 1956); Asiatic Cholera Epidemic of 1833 in Mexico (Bulletin of Historical Medicine, Jan.–Feb. 1958). Language: Spanish 4,4,4,4; Portuguese 3,3,2,2; French 4,4,3,3. Home: 216 High View Lane, R.F.D. 4, Charlottesville, Va. Office: Dept. of History, U. of Va., Charlottesville.

HUTCHINSON, HARRY WILLIAM, b. New York, N.Y., Aug. 18, 1922. ANTHROPOLOGY AND PSYCHIATRY. A.B., Columbia Coll., 1948; Ph. D., Columbia U., 1954; U. of Fla., 1960–61. Prof., U. of Bahía (Brazil), 1954–56; prof., dir. of graduate studies, Escola de Sociologia e Politica (São Paulo, Brazil), 1956–59; asst. prof., Vanderbilt U., 1959–60; ASSOC. PROF., ANTHROPOLOGY AND PSYCHIATRY, U. OF FLA., 1961– . Fulbright award; U. of Fla. fellow, 1960–61; Doherty fellow. Membership: American Anthropological Association; American Association for the Advancement of Science; Society for Applied Anthropology. Research: Brazil. Author: Village and Plantation Life in Northeast Brazil (1956); Field Guide to Brazil (1961). Language: Spanish 3,3,3,3; Portuguese 5,5,5,5. Home: R.F.D. 4, Box 165NA, Gainesville, Fla. Office: Dept. of Psychiatry and Anthropology, Coll. of Medicine, U. of Fla., Gainesville.

HYMAN, ELIZABETH HANNAN, b. Lincoln, Nebr., Oct. 8, 1912. POLITICAL SCIENCE. B.A., Bryn Mawr, 1934; M.A., Radcliffe Coll., 1935; Ph. D., 1940. Research assoc., Council on Foreign Relations, 1938–40; research analyst, Coordinator of Inter-American Affairs and Board of Economic Warfare, 1941–45; assoc. editor, Private Newsletter, 1945–46; OFFICE OF RESEARCH AND ANALYSIS FOR THE AMERICAN REPUBLICS, BUREAU OF INTELLIGENCE AND RESEARCH, U.S. DEPT. OF STATE, 1946– ; CHIEF, REGIONAL AFFAIRS DIV., 1958– . Co-author: Dollars in Latin America (1941; Spanish edition, 1944). Language: Spanish 3,2,2,1; Portuguese 2,-,-,-; French 2,-,-,-; German 2,-,-,-. Home: 216 Prince St., Alexandria, Va. Office: Bureau of Intelligence and Research, U.S. Dept. of State, Washington, D.C.

I

IDUARTE, ANDRÉS, b. Villahermosa, Mexico, May 1, 1907. SPANISH AMERICAN LITERATURE. U. of Paris, 1928–30; LL.B., U. of Madrid, 1935; Ph. D., Columbia U., 1944; LL.B., U. of Mexico, 1953. Secretary, Ateneo de Madrid, 1933–36; PROF., SPANISH, COLUMBIA U., 1939– ; prof., U. of Mexico, 1930–32, 1953; prof. Institute of Intensive Learning of Portuguese and Spanish, American Council of Learned Societies, Summers 1941, 1947; prof., U. of Havana, Summers 1946, 1955; dir. general, Instituto Nacional de Bellas Artes, U. of Mexico, 1952–54; prof., U. of Oriente (Cuba), Spring 1955. Membership: Hispanic Institute; Instituto Internacional de Literatura Iberoamericana. Research: Latin American history; Spanish and Spanish American arts and law. Author: Martí escritor (1945, 1951); Un niño en la Revolución Mexicana (1950, 1954); Pláticas hispanoamericanas (1951). Language: Spanish 5,5,5,5; Portuguese 3,3,1,1; French 4,4,4,4. Linguistic studies: French; Spanish. Home: 752 West End Ave., New York 25, N.Y. Office: 521 Philosophy Hall, Columbia U., New York 27.

IRBY, JAMES EAST, b. Bowie, Tex., May 19, 1931. SPANISH AMERICAN LITERATURE. B.A., U. of Kans., 1952; M.A., National U. of Mexico, 1957; Ph. D., U. of Mich., 1962. Instr., Princeton U., 1959–61; ASST. PROF., SPANISH, PRINCETON U., 1962– . Rackham dissertation fellow, U. of Mich., 1961–62; Rockefeller Foundation grant (Brazil), 1964–65. Research: contemporary Spanish American and Brazilian literature; contemporary Mexican literature. Author: Encuentro con Borges (1962); Sobre la estructura de Hombre de la esquina rosada de Borges (Anuario de Filología, 1962). Co-editor and translator: Labyrinths: Selected Stories and Prose Writings of Jorge Luis Borges (1962). Language: Spanish 5,5,5,5; Portuguese 4,4,4,3. Home: 20 East Stanworth Dr., Princeton, N.J. Office: Dept. of Romance Languages, Princeton U., Princeton.

IRVING, EVELYN UHRHAN, b. Buffalo, N.Y., Feb. 14, 1919. SPANISH AMERICAN LITERATURE AND LANGUAGE. A.B., Fla. State U., 1941; M.A., 1947; Ph. D., U. of Ill., 1950. Prof., head, Spanish and French, S. Dak. State Coll., 1950–61; prof., National Defense Education Act Institute, U. of S. Dak., Summer 1959; dir., Summer 1961; prof., Bradley U., Summer 1962; assoc. dir., National Defense Education Act Institute (Guatemala), Bradley U., Summer 1963; VIS. PROF., SPANISH, MACALESTER COLL., 1963– . U. of Ill. fellow, 1948–50; Delta Kappa Gamma scholar (Spain), 1956–57; Social Science Research Council grant (Central America), 1962–63. Membership: American Association of Teachers of Spanish and Portuguese; Delta Kappa Gamma; Foreign Language Teachers of Minnesota; Instituto Internacional de Literatura Iberoamericana; Modern Language Association; National Education Association; Pi Gamma Mu. Research: Rubén Darío in Guatemala; modern methods of teaching foreign languages. Author: Linguistic Analysis of Góngora's Baroque Style (1954); Rubén Darío in Guatemala (Salon 13, Sept. 1962); An NDEA Institute's Influence in Changing Foreign Language Teaching Methods (Hispania, Mar. 1963). Language: Spanish 4,4,4,4; Portuguese 3,3,3,3; French 3,3,3,3; Arabic 1,1,1,1; German 3,3,3,3. Linguistic studies: French; Spanish. Home: 621 Tenth Ave., SE., Minneapolis, Minn. Office: Spanish Dept., Macalester Coll., St. Paul 1, Minn.

IRVING, THOMAS BALLANTINE, b. Preston, Canada, July 20, 1914. LANGUAGE. B.A., U. of Toronto, 1937; M. ès Lettres, Université de Montréal, 1938; Ph. D., Princeton U., 1940. Instr., U. of Calif., Berkeley, 1940–42; founder, Spanish courses, Carleton U. (Ottawa), 1942–44; dir., Colegio Nueva Granada (Bogotá), 1944–45; catedrático, Universidad de San Carlos (Guatemala), 1946–48; PROF., ROMANCE AND ORIEN-

TAL LANGUAGES, U. OF MINN., 1948– . Fulbright research fellow (Iraq), 1956–57. Membership: American Association of Teachers of Spanish and Portuguese; American Association of University Professors; American History Association; Instituto Internacional de Literatura Iberoamericana; Medieval Academy; Middle East Institute; Modern Language Association; Sociedad de Geografía e Historia de Guatemala; Sociedad de Geografía e Historia de Honduras. Research: Hispano-Arabic culture; teaching foreign languages. Author: Aventuras en Centro América (1951), Paisajes del Sur (1952); Falcon of Spain: Abdurrahman I, 756–788 (1962). Language: Spanish 5,4,4,4; Portuguese 4,3,2,1; French 5,4,3,3; Arabic 4,3,2,2; German 3,2,1,1. Linguistic studies: Arabic; Spanish. Home: 621 Tenth Ave., SE., Minneapolis, Minn. 55414. Office: Dept. of Romance and Oriental Languages, 300 Folwell Hall, U. of Minn., Minneapolis, 55455.

IRWIN-WILLIAMS, CYNTHIA CORA, b. Denver, Colo., Apr. 14, 1936. ANTHROPOLOGY. B.A., Radcliffe Coll., 1957; M.A., 1958; Ph. D., Harvard U., 1963. Codir., Research Projects in Archeology, Peabody Museum, Harvard U., 1959– ; lectr., Hunter Coll., 1963–64; RESEARCH FELLOW, AMERICAN MUSEUM OF NATURAL HISTORY (MEXICO), 1963–64. Radcliffe Coll. fellow, 1953–57; National Science Foundation fellow, 1957–60; Peabody Museum fellow, 1960–61; Ogden Mills research fellow, 1963–64. Membership: American Anthropoligical Association; American Association for the Advancement of Science; Phi Beta Kappa; Society for American Archaeology. Research: Mexican archeology and geology; origin and early developments in indigenous New World cultures. Author: Excavations at the Lo Dais Ka Site (1959); Archaic Complexes of Central Colorado (1964); Pre-ceramic and Early Ceramic Cultures of Hidalgo and Querétaro (1964). Language: Spanish 5,5,5,4; French 4,4,3,3; German 3,2,2,2; Russian 2,2,2,2. Home: 633 Mt. Lucas Rd., Princeton, N.J. Office: American Museum of Natural History, Central Park West at 79th St., New York, N.Y.

J

JACKSON, WILLIAM VERNON, b. Chicago, Ill., May 26, 1926. LIBRARY SCIENCE. B.A., Northwestern U., 1945; A.M., Harvard U., 1948; M.S., U. of Ill., 1951; Ph. D., Harvard U., 1952. Special recruit, Library of Congress, 1951–52; asst. prof., librarian, U. of Ill., 1952–58; assoc. prof., Library Science, U. of Ill., 1958–62; vis. prof., Inter-American Library School, U. of Antioquia (Colombia), Fall 1960; ASSOC. PROF., SPANISH AND PORTUGUESE, U. OF WIS., 1963– . Fulbright research grant (France), 1956–57; consultant on libraries in Latin America, U.S. Dept. of State, 1956, 1959, 1961, 1962; Fulbright lectr., U. of Córdoba (Argentina), 1958; delegate, U.S. National Committee, UNESCO meetings, 1959, 1961; adviser, International Executive Council, Inter-American Library School, 1961–63; consultant on bibliography, Hispanic Foundation, Library of Congress, 1964–65. Membership: American Association of Teachers of Spanish and Portuguese; American Library Association; Association of American Library Schools; Association of College and Research Libraries; Beta Phi Mu; Modern Language Association; Phi Beta Kappa; Theatre Library Association. Research: library development and resources; comparative librarianship; Latin American bibliography; modern Spanish drama. Author: Aspects of Librarianship In Latin America (1962); Library Guide for Brazilian Studies (1964); Education for Librarianship—Latin America (Library Trends, Oct. 1963). Language: Spanish 5,5,5,5; Portuguese 4,4,4,3; French 4,4,4,3. Home: 196 West Kathleen Dr., Park Ridge, Ill. 60068. Office: Dept. of Spanish, U. of Wis., Madison, 53706.

JAFFE, ABRAM J., b. Chelsea, Mass., Feb. 28, 1912. SOCIOLOGY. Ph. D., U. of Chicago, 1941. Statistician, U.S. Bureau of the Census, 1945–50; DIR., MANPOWER AND POPULATION PROGRAM, BUREAU OF APPLIED SOCIAL RESEARCH, COLUMBIA U., 1950– . Consultant, Dept of Labor (P.R.), 1952–56; lectr. on census procedures, United Nations, 1958; consultant, Organization for Economic Cooperation and Development, 1962; consultant, Census Office, Government of Panama, 1962–63. Membership: American Association for the Advancement of Science; American Population Association; American Sociological Society; American Statistical Association; Industrial Relations Research Association; International Population Union. Research: demography; labor statistics and analysis. Author: People, Jobs and Economic Development (1959); Agrarian Reform and Socio-Economic Change (American Journal of Economics and Sociology, July 1960). Co-author: Manpower Resources and Utilization (1951). Language: Spanish 3,2,2,2. Home: 314 Allaire Ave., Leonia, N.J. Office: Bureau of Applied Social Research, Columbia U., 605 West 115th St., New York, N.Y. 10025.

JAMES, PRESTON E(VERETT), b. Brookline, Mass., Feb. 14, 1899. GEOGRAPHY. B.A., Harvard U., 1920; M.A., 1921; Ph. D., Clark U., 1923. Asst. prof.-prof., U. of Mich., 1923–41; chief, Latin American Div., U.S. Office of Strategic Services, 1941–45; PROF., CHMN., GEOGRAPHY, SYRACUSE U., 1945– . National Research Council fellow (Latin America), 1930; Social Science Research Council fellow, 1938; technical consultant, Conselho Nacional de Geografia (Brazil), 1949–50; Ditchley Foundation Conference, 1963; Joint Committee on Latin American Studies; Committee on Geography, Research and Development Board. Membership: American Geographical Society; American Meteorological Society; Association of American Geographers; Association for Latin American Studies; International Geographical Union; National Council for the Social Studies. Research: the interpretation of contemporary conditions in light of historical geography Brazil. Author: Latin America (1942 1950, 1959); A Geography of Man (1949 1950, 1959); One World Divided (1964) Language: Spanish 4,2,2,1; Portuguese 4,3 3,1; French 4,3,2,1; German 4,2,2,1. Home 220 Standish Dr., Syracuse, N.Y. 13224 Office: Dept. of Geography, Syracuse U Syracuse, 13210.

JAMISON, EDWARD A., b. Pontiac, Ill., July 10, 1909. HISTORY. B.S., Northwestern U., 1931; M.A., Tufts Coll., 1933; Fletcher School of Law & Diplomacy, 1933–34; Ph. D., Harvard U., 1943. Inter-American Regional Affairs, Foreign Service, U.S. Dept. of State, 1947–55; deputy chief of mission, Embassy (Costa Rica), 1956–59, (Guatemala), 1959–60; alternate representative, Organization of American States Council, 1960–63; dir., Office of Inter-American Regional Political Affairs, 1960–63; POLITICAL ADVISER TO COMMANDER IN CHIEF, ATLANTIC, 1963– . Research: inter-American organizations; Organization of American States; inter-American political-military relationships; Central American governments and economics. Author: Keeping Peace in the Caribbean (The Department of State Bulletin, July 1950). Language: Spanish 4,4,4,2; Portuguese 2,2,–,–; French 2,1,1,1. Home: 503 Battery Rd., Virginia Beach, Va. Office: SACLANT Headquarters, Box 30, Norfolk, Va. 23511.

JEFFREY, WILLIAM H., b. Burlington, Vt., Jan. 24, 1921. HISTORY. B.A., Drew U., 1942; M.A., U. of Mich., 1944; Ph. D., U. of Colo., 1950. Instr., Union Coll. (Ky.), 1945–46; PROF., HISTORY, U. OF MAINE, 1946– . American Philosophical Society grant (Argentina), 1954. Membership: American Historical Association; Conference on Latin American History; Hispanic American Society; Northeast Council on Latin American Studies; Northern New England Historians Conference. Research: 19th century Argentina; Mexico. Author: Mitre and Argentina (1952); Mitre and Urquiza (Drew University Studies, Sept. 1952). Language: Spanish 3,–,–,–; German 2,2,2,2. Home: 12 Spencer St., Orono, Maine. Office: 130 Stevens Hall, U. of Maine, Orono.

JENSEN, J. GRANVILLE, b. Portland, Oreg., Dec. 18, 1911. GEOGRAPHY. B.A., Western Wash. Coll.; M.A., Clark U., 1942; Ph. D., 1946. Asst. prof., R.I. Coll. of Education, 1941–46; vis. prof., Columbia U. Teachers Coll., Summer 1946; assoc. prof., Oreg. State U., 1946–47; PROF. CHMN., GEOGRAPHY, OREG. STATE U., 1947– . Basic Resources Committee, Pan American Institute of Geography and History. Membership: Association of American Geographers. Research: problems of the ejido in Mexico; the resource base of the Mexican economy. Author: The Ejido in Mexico: A Contrast in Land Tenure (in Case Studies in World Geography, 1961); Mexico, World Sulphur Competitor (in Case Studies in World Geography, 1961); Chuquicamata (in Case Studies in World Geography, 1961). Language: Spanish 4,4,3,3. Home: 3 Sunset Dr., Corvallis, Oreg. Office: Dept. of Geography, Oreg. State U., Corvallis.

JOHANNESSEN, CARL LEWIS, b. Santa Ana, Calif., July 28, 1924. GEOGRAPHY. B.A., U. of Calif., Berkeley, 1950; M.A., 1953; Ph. D., 1959. Instr., San Francisco State Coll., Summer 1956; acting instr., U. of Calif., Davis, 1959; ASST. PROF., GEOGRAPHY, U. OF OREG., 1959– . Carnegie grants; U. of Oreg., research grant, 1964; U.S. Office of Naval Research grant, U. of Calif., Berkeley; participant, Symposium on Savanna-Forest Boundary Problems of Venezuela, 1964. Membership: American Geographical Association; Association of American Geographers; Association of Pacific Coast Geographers; Northwest Scientific Association; Pacific Coast Council of Latin American Studies; Sigma Xi. Research: physical and cultural geography; historical plant geography and cultural change in Honduras, Dominican Republic and Haiti; agricultural and domestication of plants in Costa Rica. Author: Savannas of Interior Honduras (1963); Man's Role in the Distribution of the Corozo Palm (Yearbook, Association of Pacific Coast Geographers, 1957); Higher Phosphate Values in Soils Under Trees Than in Soils Under Grass (Ecology, Apr. 1958). Language: Spanish 3,3,3,2; French 3,–, –,–; German 3,–,–,–. Home: 1284 East 21st Ave., Eugene, Oreg. Office: Dept. of Geography, U. of Oreg., Eugene.

JOHNSON, ANNITA KER, b. Mexico, D.F., May 29, 1908. LIBRARY SCIENCE. B.A., Wellesley Coll., 1930. Purchase agent and research worker, Harvey Bassler Foundation (Mexico D.F.), 1930–31; cataloger, Library of Congress, 1931–41; teacher, Pikeville Coll., 1959–61; cataloger, Candler Memorial Library, Wesleyan Coll., 1961–62; CATALOGER, HARDIN LIBRARY, TIFT COLL., 1962– . American Library Association-Carnegie fellow (Mexico), 1936–37; technical adviser to dir. of National Library (Caracas), 1939–40. Membership: American Library Association; Inter-American Bibliographical and Library Association; Southeastern Library Association; Society of Woman Geographers. Research: cataloging; geography of Venezuela. Author: Mexican Scientific Periodicals (1931); Mexican Public Documents (1941). Co-editor: Bibliography and Library Science (in Handbook of Latin American Studies 1939–41). Languages: Spanish 5,5,4,4; Portuguese 4,2,2,2; French 3,2,2,2. Home: 3850 The Prado, Macon, Ga., 31204. Office: Hardin Library, Tift Coll., Forsyth, Ga.

JOHNSON, DONALD D., b. Hartford Conn., Jan. 10, 1917. HISTORY. A.B., U. of Calif., Los Angeles, 1938; M.A., U. of Southern Calif., 1941; Ph. D., 1946. Lectr., U. of Southern Calif., 1944–46; instr.-asst. prof., Wash. State U., 1946–49; asst. prof.-prof., U. of Hawaii, 1949–60; PROF., CHMN., HISTORY, U. OF HAWAII, 1960– ; professorial lectr., Pentagon War College programs, George Washington U., U. of Md., 1962–63. Community Foundation fellow, Honolulu, 1955; Fulbright senior lectr. (Australia), 1956. Membership: American Association of University Professors; American Historical Association; Conference on Latin American History; Hawaiian Historical Society. Research: United States diplomatic history with special reference to the Pacific basin, including the west coast of Latin America. Author: The U.S. in the Pacific: A Syllabus (1957). Language: Spanish 3,2,2,2; Portuguese 1,1,1,1; French 3,2,2,2; Italian 2,1,1,1. Home: 672 Lawelawe St., Honolulu 16, Hawaii. Office: Dept. of History, U. of Hawaii, Honolulu, 96822.

JOHNSON, ERNEST ALFRED, JR., b. Methuen, Mass., Sept. 3, 1917. SPANISH AMERICAN LITERATURE. B.A., Amherst Coll., 1939; M.A., U. of Chicago, 1940; M.A.,

Harvard U., 1941; Ph. D., 1950. PROF., ROMANCE LANGUAGES, AMHERST COLL., 1948– . Rockefeller Foundation traveling fellow (South America), 1947-48. Membership: American Association of Teachers of Spanish and Portuguese; American Association of University Professors; Modern Language Association. Research: influence of French culture on Spanish American literature; works of Ricardo Güiraldes. Author: Unos datos más sobre Juan A. Pérez Bonalde (Boletín de la Academia Venezolana, Apr.-Dec. 1956); Don Segundo Sombra: ciertos valores poéticos (Hispanófila, Sept. 1960); Miguel Delibes, El Camino—A Way of Life (Hispania, Dec. 1963). Language: Spanish 4,4,4,4; Portuguese 3,3,3,3; French 4,4,4,4. Home: 195 West St., Amherst, Mass. Office: Dept. of Romance Languages, Amherst Coll. Amherst.

JOHNSON, HARVEY LEROY, b. Cleburne, Tex., Sept. 12, 1904. SPANISH AMERICAN AND BRAZILIAN LITERATURES. B.A., Howard Payne Coll., 1925; M.A., U. of Tex., 1928; Ph. D., U. of Pa., 1940. Instr., Victoria Junior Coll., 1928–30; instr., Rice U., 1930–36; prof., Cedar Crest Coll., 1937–40; prof., Northwestern U., 1940–51; PROF. SPANISH AND PORTUGUESE, IND. U., 1951– ; chmn., 1951–63. U.S. Dept. of State vis. lectr. (Latin America), 1948; consultant, U.S. Dept. of Health, Education, and Welfare, 1961–63; consultant, Hispanic Foundation, Library of Congress; Latin American Translation Program Committee, Association of American University Presses. Membership: Alpha Chi; American Association of Teachers of Spanish and Portuguese; Asociación Internacional de Hispanistas; International Institute of Arts and Letters; Instituto Internacional de Literatura Iberoamericana; Modern Language Association; Phi Sigma Iota; Sigma Delta Pi. Research: theatre, colonial writings, and general culture of Spanish America. Author: La América Española (1949); Aprende a hablar español; diálogos y ejercicios (1963). Translator: La navidad en las montañas, by Altamirano (1961). Language: Spanish 5,5,5,5; Portuguese 5,5,5,5; French 5,4,3,3; German 5,3,3,3; Italian 5,5,4,3; Nahuatl 3,1,1,1. Linguistic studies: Spanish. Home: 923 East University, Bloomington, Ind. Office: Dept. of Spanish and Portuguese, Ind. U., Bloomington.

JOHNSON, JOHN J., b. White Swan, Wash., Mar. 26, 1912. HISTORY. B.A., Central Wash. Coll., 1939; M.A., U. of Calif., Berkeley, 1943; Ph. D., 1947. PROF., HISTORY, STANFORD U., 1946– ; acting chief, Research Div., American Republics, U.S. Dept. of State, 1952–53. Mills traveling fellow, 1943–44, (Chile), 1945–46. Membership: American Historical Association; Conference on Latin American History; Pacific Coast Council on Latin American Studies. Research: the role of the military in politics and society in Latin America. Author: Political Change in Latin America (1958); The Military and Society in Latin America (1964). Editor: The Role of the Military in Underdeveloped Countries (1962). Language: Spanish 5,4,4,3; Portuguese 5,4,3,3. Office: Dept. of History, Stanford U., Stanford, Calif.

JOHNSON, KENNETH FOX, b. Lincoln, Nebr., Oct. 14, 1933. POLITICAL SCIENCE. Ph. D., U. of Calif., Los Angeles, 1963. Instr., San Diego State Coll., 1962–63; asst. prof., U. of Wyo., 1963–64; ASST. PROF., POLITICAL SCIENCE, COLO. STATE U., 1964– . Representative, People to People Program (Colombia), Summer 1960; Ford Foundation fellow (Colombia, Mexico), 1962; research assoc., Social Science Foundation, U. of Denver, 1964– . Membership: American Political Science Association; Rocky Mountain Social Science Association; Society for International Development; Western Political Science Association. Research: urbanization and political change in Latin America; political radicalism in Colombia; political alienation in Mexico and the presidential succession; Mexico; community development. Author: Causal Factors in Latin American Political Instability (Western Political Quarterly, Sept. 1964). Co-author: Measurement of Latin American Political Change (American Political Science Review, Sept. 1961). Language: Spanish 4,3,3,4; Portuguese 3,–,–,–; French 3,–,–,–. Home: 1313 Bryan, Fort Collins, Colo. Office: Dept. of Political Science, Colo. State U., Fort Collins.

JOHNSON, RICHARD A., b. Moline, Ill., Apr. 17, 1910. HISTORY. B.A., Augustana Coll., 1932; M.A., U. of Tex., 1933; Ph. D., 1938. Commercial attaché, Embassy (Bolivia), U.S. Dept. of State, 1948–50; officer-in-charge, Consulate (Guadalajara, Mexico), 1950–52; deputy chief of mission, Embassy (Dominican Republic), 1952–54; political counselor, Embassy (Spain), 1955–57; CONSUL GENERAL, CONSULATE (MONTERREY, MEXICO), U.S. DEPT. OF STATE, 1962– . Advanced University fellow, U. of Tex., 1937–38. Membership: American Foreign Service Association; American Historical Association; Conference on Latin American History; International Good Neighbor Council. Research: inter-American diplomacy. Author: The Mexican Revolution of Ayutla (1939). Language: Spanish 5,5,4,4; Portuguese 4,2,1,1; French 3,2,2,1; German 1,1,1,1; Italian 2,2,2,1. Home: American Consulate General, AP 152, Monterrey, Nuevo León, México. Office: Foreign Service, U.S. Dept. of State, Washington 25, D.C.

JONES, OAKAH L., JR., b. Providence, R.I., June 20, 1930. HISTORY. B.S., U.S. Naval Academy, 1953; M.A., U. of Okla., 1960. Instr.-ASST. PROF., HISTORY, U.S. AIR FORCE ACADEMY, 1960– ; CHMN., LATIN AMERICAN HISTORY, 1964– . Membership: Conference on Latin American History; Historical Society of New Mexico; Western History Association. Research: colonial Latin American history; Spanish borderlands. Author: Pueblo Indian Auxiliaries in New Mexico, 1763–1821 (New Mexico Historical Review, Apr. 1962); Pueblo Indian Auxiliaries and the Reconquest of New Mexico, 1692–1704 (Journal of the West, July 1963). Language: Spanish 4,3,3,4; Portuguese 2,1,1,1; French 3,2,2,2. Home: Box 8223, Station C, Albuquerque, N. Mex. Office: Dept. of History, U.S. Air Force Academy, Colo.

JONES, ROBERT CUBA, b. Gibara, Cuba May 12, 1902. SOCIAL WELFARE. A.B. Earlham Coll., 1923; U. of Chicago. Researcher, chief, Div. of Labor and Social Affairs, Pan American Union, 1942–51;

senior officer, Technical Assistance Administration, United Nations, 1949–53; social science analyst, Presidential Commission on Migratory Labor, Executive Office of the President, 1950–51; technical consultant, Mexican Social Security Institute, 1953–54; FOUNDER AND DIR., VILLA JONES INTERNATIONAL CULTURAL CENTER, 1954– . Consultant on immigration, United Nations, 1949–50; consultant, Mexican Institute of Economic Research. Membership: American Anthropological Association; American Economic Association; American Sociological Association; Mexican Anthropological Society; Mexican Society of Geography and Statistics; Mexican Sociological Society. Research: labor: social work programs; community development. Author: Mexican War Workers in the U.S. (1942): Low Cost Housing in Latin America (1943); Immigration Possibilities in Venezuela (1950); Language: Spanish 5,5,5,4; Portuguese 3,3,–,–; French 2,2,1,1; German 2,2,1,1. Home and office: 23 Chilpancingo, México, D.F., México.

JONES, TOM BARD, b. Dunkirk, N.Y., June 21, 1909. HISTORY, A.B., U. of Mich., 1931; M.A., 1932; Ph. D., 1934. PROF. HISTORY, U. OF MICH., 1935– . Membership: American Oriental Society; Archeological Institute of America. Research: ancient history. Author: Introduction to Hispanic American History (1939; revised edition, 1950); South America Rediscovered (1949); Bibliography of South American Economic History (1955). Language: Spanish 4,3,1,1; Portuguese 4,2,1,1; French 4,4,1,1; Greek 4,2,1,1. Linguistic studies: Abbadian, Hebrew, Italian, Latin. Home: 3911 East 50th St. Minneapolis, Minn. 55417. Office: Dept. of History, U. of Minn., Minneapolis 14.

JONES, WILBUR DEVEREUX, b. Youngstown, Ohio, Sept. 28, 1916. HISTORY. A.B., Youngstown Coll., 1940; A.M., Western Reserve U., 1947; Ph. D., 1949. Instr., Western Reserve U., 1948–49; instr., U. of Ga., 1949–51; asst. prof., 1951–57; assoc. prof., 1957–62; PROF., HISTORY, U. OF GA., 1962– . Membership: Conference on British Studies. Research: Anglo-Latin American relations; Argentina and Brazil; Jamaica. Author: Lord Derby & Victorian Conservatism (1956); Lord Aberdeen and the Americas (1959); Civilization through the Centuries (1960). Language: Spanish 2,2,2,–; German 3,3,3,–. Home: 420 South Milledge Ave., Athens, Ga. Office: Dept. of History, U. of Ga., Athens.

JONES, WILLIS KNAPP, b. Beacon, N.Y., Nov. 27, 1895. SPANISH AMERICAN LITERATURE. A.B., Hamilton Coll., 1917; M.A., Pa. State U., 1922; Ph. D., U. of Chicago, 1927. Vice dir., North American Academy (Montevideo), 1919–21; instr., Pa. State U., 1921–23; instr.-prof., Spanish, Miami U., 1923–63; RETIRED, 1963– . Contributing editor, Books Abroad. Membership: American Association of Teachers of Spanish and Portuguese; Comediantes; Instituto Internacional de Literatura Iberoamericana; Modern Language Association. Research: Latin American theatre. Author: Spanish American Readings (1946); Breve historia del teatro latinoamericano (1956); Spanish American Literature in Translation, A Selection of Poetry, Fiction, and Drama since 1888 (1963). Language: Spanish 5,4,3,3; Portuguese 3,–,–,–; French 4,1,1,–. Home: 320 East Vine, Oxford, Ohio 45056.

JORDAN, DAVID CRICHTON, b. Chicago, Ill., Apr. 30, 1935. POLITICAL SCIENCE. A.B., Harvard U., 1957; LL.B., U. of Va., 1960; Ph. D., U. of Pa., 1964. ASST. PROF., POLITICAL SCIENCE, PA. STATE U., 1964– . Rockefeller Foundation and U. of Pa. grant (Argentina). Membership: American Academy of Political Science. Research: international relations and law; Latin American government and politics; United States and Latin American relations; Argentine nationalism; Peruvian political parties. Language: Spanish 5,5,4,4; Portuguese 3,2,1,1; French 3,2,1,1. Home: 660 East Prospect, State College, Pa. Office: Dept. of Political Science, Pa. State U., University Park.

JORDAN, JOHN EDWARD, b. Logan, W. Va., Mar. 9, 1922 EDUCATION AND PSYCHOLOGY. A.B., Mich. State U., 1949; Th. B., Owosso Coll., 1950; M.A., Mich. State U., 1954; Ph. D., 1956. Consultant psychologist, Mich. School for the Blind, 1954– ; psychologist, Lansing Public Schools (Mich.), 1954–57; consulting psychologist, private practice, 1954–60; ASSOC. PROF., COLL. OF EDUCATION, MICH. STATE U., 1957– . Cultural affairs consultant, U.S. Dept. of State (Guatemala); specialist grant, U.S. Dept. of State, 1962, 1963. Membership: American Personnel and Guidance Association; American Psychological Association; American Rehabilitation Association; Interamerican Society of Psychology. Research: educational-vocational guidance of handicapped people; Latin American attitudes toward education. Author: The University Looks at Rehabilitation: An International Perspective (Journal of the Michigan Medical Society, May 1962); Problems and Promises of Education in Latin America (Phi Delta Kappan, Jan. 1964); La rehabilitación y educación especial en la América Latina (Revista Mexicana de Psicología, Feb. 1964). Language: Spanish 3,3,2,1; French 3,3,1,1. Home: 732 North Park, Owosso, Mich. Office: Coll. of Education, Mich. State U., East Lansing, 48823.

JORRÍN, MIGUEL, b. Havana, Cuba, May 10, 1902. POLITICAL SCIENCE. Doctor of Public Law, U. of Havana, 1924; Doctor of Civil Law, 1925. Vis. lectr., Williams Coll., 1942–44; assoc. prof., U. of N. Mex., 1944–49; PROF., GOVERNMENT, DIR., DIV. OF FOREIGN STUDIES, U. OF N. MEX., 1949– . Consultant, Encyclopaedia Britannica (Spanish edition), 1954–58; coordinator, U.S. Peace Corps Training Center, U. of N. Mex., 1962–63. Membership: Rocky Mountain Council for Latin American Studies; Western Political Science Association. Research: Latin American political thought; Latin American politics and international relations. Author: Latin American Politics (1951); Governments of Latin America (1953); Post World War II Political Developments in Latin America (1959). Language: Spanish 5,5,5,5; Portuguese 3,3,2,1; French 3,3,2,1; Italian 3,3,2, 1. Home: 415 Girard NE., Albuquerque, N. Mex. Office: Dept. of Government, U. of N. Mex., Albuquerque, 87106.

K

KAFKA, ALEXANDRE, b. Prague, Czechoslovakia, Jan. 25, 1917. ECONOMICS. B.A., Oxford U., 1940; M.A., 1946. Prof., School of Sociology and Politics (São Paulo), 1941–49; asst. chief, Latin American Div., International Monetary Fund (Washington, D.C.), 1949–51; dir., Brazilian Institute of Economics (Rio de Janeiro), 1951–56; economist, United Nations (N.Y.), 1956–59; PROF., ECONOMICS, U. OF VA., 1959– . Economic adviser, Federation of Industries of State of São Paulo, 1944–49; adviser, Brazilian delegation, Preparatory Committee of the International Trade Organization (London), 1946; technical adviser, Brazilian delegation to the Havana Conference, 1947–48; economic and financial counselor, Superintendency of Money and Credit (Rio de Janeiro). 1951– ; special adviser, Brazilian delegation, Conference of Ministers of Finance or Economics of the American States (Petrópolis), 1954; alternate governor for Brazil, International Monetary Fund, 1954; principal adviser, Ministry of Finance, 1954–55; principal representative of Ministry of Finance on Brazilian Trade and Payments Mission to Western Europe, 1955; Brazilian technical expert, Conference on Latin American Housing Finance, Organization of American States (Los Angeles), 1962. Membership: American Economic Association; Professional Economists Organization (Brazil). Research: fiscal and monetary problems; economic development; international trade. Author: Contribuições à análise do desenvolvimento econômico (1957); Theoretical Problems of Latin American Economic Growth (Proceedings of International Economic Association, 1961); Considerations on Corporate Income Taxation in Latin America (Conference on Tax Policy, Organization of American States, 1962). Language: Spanish 5,5,4,4; Portuguese 5,5,5,5; French 5,5,4,4. Home: 1621 Meadowbrook Heights Rd., Charlottesville, Va. Office: Dept. of Economics, U. of Va., Charlottesville.

KAGAN, SIOMA, b. Riga, Russia, Oct. 29, 1907. ECONOMICS. Diplom-Ingenieur, Technische Hochschule (Berlin), 1931; M.A., American U., 1949; Ph. D., Columbia U., 1954. Economic affairs officer, United Nations (N.Y., Geneva, Shanghai), 1946–48; economic consultant, International Basic Economy Corporation, 1950–51; economic consultant, National Planning Association, 1954–55; assoc. prof., Washington U., 1956–59; staff economist, Joint Council on Economic Education, 1959–60; PROF., INTERNATIONAL BUSINESS, U. OF OREG., 1960– . Lectr., Instituto para el Desarrollo de Ejecutivos en la Argentina (Buenos Aires), 1962; co-chmn., Symposium on Management Education, XIII Congress of Comité International de L'Organisation Scientifique, 1963; lectr., Instituto de Administración Científica de las Empresas (Mexico), 1964. Research: international economic relations and business operations. Author: Expansión de la población mundial y el desarrollo económico (1963); Business Decisions in a Changing International Scene (Challenge, July 1964). Co-author: Partners in Progress (1951). Language: Spanish 3,3,3,1; French 5,5,5,5; German 5,5,4,4; Russian 5,5,4,3. Home: 1050 Ferry St., Eugene, Oreg. 97403. Office: School of Business Administration, U. of Oreg., Eugene, 97401.

KAHL, JOSEPH A., b. Chicago, Ill., July 26, 1923. SOCIOLOGY AND ANTHROPOLOGY. B.A., U. of Chicago, 1947; M.A., 1948; Ph. D., Harvard U., 1952. Instr., Harvard U., 1951–54; asst. prof., research assoc., U. of N.C., 1954–55; vis. prof., Mexico City Coll., 1955; asst. prof.-PROF., SOCIOLOGY AND ANTHROPOLOGY, WASHINGTON U., 1956– ; research sociologist, Latin American Center for Research in Social Sciences, United Nations (Brazil), 1960; vis. prof., Organization of American States Program in Applied Social Sciences (Mexico), Summers 1961, 1962. Joint Committee on Latin America, Social Science Research Council-American Council of Learned Societies, 1962–64. Membership: American Anthropological Association; American Sociological Association; Midwest Sociological Society; Society for Applied Anthropology. Research: social concomitants of industrialization in Latin America; social change in Mexico since the Revolution; occupational attitudes in Brazil; social stratification in North American society. Author: The American Class Structure (1957); Some Social Concomitants of Industrialization and Urbanization (Human Organization, Summer 1959); Urbanização e mudanças occupacionais no Brasil (América Latina, Oct.–Dec. 1962). Language: Spanish 4,4,4,4; Portuguese 4,3,2,2; French 3,2,1,1. Home: 701 South Skinker Blvd., St. Louis, Mo. 63105. Office: Dept. of Sociology and Anthropology, Washington U., St. Louis, 63130.

KAHLE, LOUIS GEORGE, b. St. Louis, Mo., Nov. 20, 1912. POLITICAL SCIENCE. B.A., U. of Tex., 1935; M.A., 1937; Ph. D., 1951. Instr., Wentworth Military Academy (Mo.), 1936–40; research analyst, U.S. Office of Strategic Services, 1942–45; instr., U. of Mo., 1946–49; asst. prof., 1950–53; assoc. prof., 1953–57; PROF., POLITICAL SCIENCE, U. OF MO., 1957– . U. of Tex. fellow, 1941–42; U. of Tex. Advanced U. fellow, 1950; U. of Mo. summer research fellow, 1952, 1954, 1959, 1961. Membership: American Political Science Association; International Political Science Association; Missouri Political Science Association; Southwest Social Science Association. Research: inter-American relations; politics and government; Latin American recognition policy of the United States. Author: The Spanish Colonial Judiciary (Southwest Social Science Quarterly, June 1951); Robert Lansing and the Recognition of Venustiano Carranza (Hispanic American Historical Review, Aug. 1958); The Common Market—And Western European Political Unification (Business and Government Review, Mar.–Apr. 1963). Language: Spanish 4,4,4,3; Portuguese 2,2,1,1; French 2,1,1,1; German 4,3,2,1. Home: 112 West Ridgeley Rd., Columbia, Mo. Office: Dept. of Political Science, U. of Mo., Columbia.

KAHLER, MARY ELLIS, b. Santiago, Chile, Aug. 2, 1919. LIBRARY SCIENCE. A.B., Swarthmore Coll., 1940; B.L.S., Drexel Institute of Technology, 1949; M.A., George Washington U., 1953. Library asst., Fort Dix Post Library, 1944–48; head, Bibliographic Unit, and bibliographer, Order Div. Library of Congress, 1949–51; classifier

Personnel Div., 1951–52; editor of publications, Union Catalog Div., 1952–53; asst. chief, Serial Record Div., 1953–57; CHIEF, SERIAL RECORD DIV., LIBRARY OF CONGRESS, 1957– . Membership: American Historical Association; American Library Association; Conference on Latin American History; Society of American Archivists; Special Libraries Association Research: Latin American history. Language: Spanish 3,3,3,–; Portuguese 5,4,4,–; French 4,4,3,4; German 2,2,2,–. Home: 712 Lakeview Dr., Falls Church, Va. 22041. Office: Serial Record Div., Library of Congress, Washington, D.C., 20540.

KAISER, CHESTER CARL, b. Garland, Kans., Sept. 16, 1908. HISTORY. B.S., Kans. State Teachers Coll., 1932; M.S., 1936; M.A., U. of Southern Calif., 1940; Ph. D., American U., 1954. Instr., secondary schools, 1936–43; asst. prof., Colo. State U., 1943–45; instr., U. of Minn., 1945–46; ASSOC. PROF., HISTORY, WILLAMETTE U., 1946–; teacher, Mexico City Coll., Summer 1956. American U. research grant, 1951–53. Membership: American Association for State and Local History; American Historical Association; Mississippi Valley Historical Association. Research: United States Mexican relations; Mexico since 1876. Author: J. W. Foster y el desarrollo económico de México (Historia Mexicana, July-Sept. 1957); México en la Primera Conferencia Panamericana (Historia Mexicana, July–Sept. 1961). Language: Spanish 3,3,3,3; French 1,1,1,1. Home: 1175 Court St. NE., Salem, Oreg. Office: Dept. of History, Willamette U., Salem.

KALB, KLAUS, b. Hopfgarten, Weimar, Germany, Oct. 29, 1936. ECONOMICS. Agricultural U. (Stuttgart-Hohenheim, Germany); M.S., Kans. State U., 1961; Ph. D., Ohio State U., 1964. CONSULTANT, AGRI RESEARCH, INC. (MANHATTAN, KANS.), 1964–. Membership: American Economic Association; American Farm Economic Association; American Marketing Association. Research: agricultural economics; marketing; rice marketing system in Peru. Language: Spanish 3,3,3,3; French 1,–,–,–; German 5,5,5,5; Russian 2,1,1,2, Home: 219 West Lane Ave., Columbus, Ohio. Office: Agri Research, Inc., Manhattan, Kans.

KALMANOFF, GEORGE, b. New York, N.Y., Sept. 17, 1917. ECONOMICS. A.B., City Coll. (N.Y.), 1936; M.S., 1938. Teacher, secondary schools of New York and Washington, D.C., Wilson Teachers' Coll., 1936–42; economist, U.S. Office of Price Administration and Foreign Economic Administration, 1942–45; chief, Mexico and Central America Section, Office of International Trade, U.S. Dept. of Commerce, 1945–50; economic affairs officer, United Nations Economic Commission for Latin America, 1950–53; economic adviser, National Planning Office, Government of Colombia, 1953–54; consultant, Cauca Valley Corporation (Colombia), International Petroleum Company (Colombia), National Development Bank of Honduras, National Planning Office of El Salvador, Guayana Corporation of Venezuela, 1954–58; ECONOMIC CONSULTANT, SCHOOL OF LAW, COLUMBIA U., 1958–. Assoc. dir., Public International Development Financing Research Project, Columbia U. Law School. Membership: American Economic Association; Phi Beta Kappa; Sigma Delta Pi; Society for International Development. Research: development economics; international finance and economic relations; Colombia. Author: Colombia (in Legal Aspects of Foreign Investment, 1959). Co-author: Investment in Central America (1956); Joint International Business Ventures (1961). Language: Spanish 5,5,5,5; Portuguese 3,2,1,1; French, 3,2,2,1. Home: 47 Fernwood Lane, Roslyn, Long Island, N.Y. Office: School of Law, Columbia U., 116th St. and Amsterdam Ave., New York, 10027.

KANEL, DON, b. Bialystok, Poland, Jan. 25, 1923. ECONOMICS. B.S., U. of Wis., 1945; M.A., 1952; Ph. D., 1954. Assoc. prof., U. of Nebr., 1954–63; vis. prof., Panjab U. (India), 1959–61; ASSOC. PROF., AGRICULTURAL ECONOMICS, LAND TENURE CENTER, U. OF WIS., 1963–. Membership: American Farm Economic Association; Canadian Agricultural Economic Society; Indian Society of Agricultural Economics. Research: agricultural economics. Author: Opportunities for Beginning Farmers: Why Are They Limited? (1960); Age Components of Decrease in Number of Farmers, 1890–1954 (Journal of Farm Economics, May 1961); Farm Adjustments by Age Groups, 1950–59 (Journal of Farm Economics, Feb. 1963). Language: Spanish 2,2,1,1; Polish 4,3,3,2. Home: 5627 Crestwood Pl., Madison, Wis. 53705. Office: Land Tenure Center, U. of Wis., Madison, 53706.

KANTOR, HARRY, b. Chicago, Ill., June 2, 1911. POLITICAL SCIENCE. B.A., U. of Ill., 1946; M.A., U. of Wis., 1947; Ph. D., U. of Calif., Los Angeles, 1952. Instr., Eastern Wash. Coll., 1950–51; PROF., POLITICAL SCIENCE, U. OF FLA., 1952– ; prof., Institute of Political Education (San José Costa Rica), 1960–61. Foundation for Economic Education fellow, 1955; U. of Fla. Graduate School research grants, 1958, 1963; consultant, Institute for the Comparative Study of Political Systems. Membership: American Association of University Professors; American Political Science Association; Phi Beta Kappa; Pi Sigma Alpha; Southeastern Conference on Latin American Studies; Southern Political Science Association. Research: factors contributing to stability and instability in Latin American governments; political systems of Venezuela, Dominican Republic, and Peru. Author: The Ideology and Program of the Peruvian Aprista Movement (1953; Spanish edition, 1964); The Costa Rican Election of 1953: A Case Study (1958). Co-author: La América Latina de hoy (1961). Language: Spanish 4,4,4,4; German 2,2,1,2. Home: 3621 NW. 7th Ave., Gainesville, Fla. Office: 201 Bldg. I, U. of Fla., Gainesville.

KANY, CHARLES EMIL, b. Dolgeville, N.Y., July 6, 1895. LANGUAGE AND LINGUISTICS. A.B., U. of Mich., 1917; M.A., Harvard U., 1918; Ph. D., 1920. Assoc., Bryn Mawr Coll., 1921–22; instr., U. of Calif., Berkeley, 1922–23; asst. prof., 1923–32; assoc. prof., 1932–43; PROF., SPANISH, U. OF CALIF., BERKELEY, 1943– . Harvard U. traveling fellow (France, Spain, Italy), 1920–21; Guggenheim fellow (Spain), 1928–29; contributing editor, Handbook of Latin American Studies, 1945–51. Membership: Hispanic Society of America. Research: American Spanish divergencies; Spanish linguistics, advanced grammar, and pronunciation. Author: American-Spanish Syntax (1945, 1951); American-Spanish Semantics (1960); American-Spanish Euphemisms (1960). Language: Spanish 5,5,5,5; Portuguese 4,4, 4,4; French 5,5,5,5; German 4,4,4,4; Greek 3,3,3,3; Russian 4,4,4,4. Linguistic studies: French; German; Italian; Russian; Spanish. Home: 2414 Telegraph Ave., Berkeley 4, Calif. Office: Dept. of Spanish and Portuguese, U. of Calif., Berkeley, 94720.

KAPLAN, BERNICE ANTOVILLE, b. New York, N.Y., Apr. 21, 1923. ANTHROPOLOGY. A.B., Hunter Coll., 1943; A.M., U. of Chicago, 1948; Ph. D., 1953. Instr., U. of Wis., 1946–47; instr., Colleges of the Seneca, 1948–49; ASST. PROF., ANTHROPOLOGY, WAYNE STATE U., 1949– (intermittently); lectr., Extension, U. of Calif., Berkeley, 1960–61; lectr., Summer School and Extension, U. of Mich., 1955– (intermittently). Wenner-Gren Foundation grant (Paracho, Michoacán, Mexico), 1948; Fulbright fellow (Peru), 1957–58. Membership: Alpha Kappa Delta; American Anthropological Association; American Association of Physical Anthropologists; Central States Anthropological Society; Sigma Xi. Research: social anthropology; community organization, culture and society in Mexico and Peru. Author: The Changing Functions of the Huanancha Dance in Paracho, Michoacán (Journal of American Folklore, Oct.–Dec. 1951); Ethnic Identification in an Indian Mestizo Community (Phylon, June 1953); Mechanization in Paracho, a Craft Community (Alpha Kappa Deltan, Winter 1960). Language: Spanish 4,3,3,3; French 3,2,2,2; Russian 2,–,–,–. Home: 31339 Pierce Rd., Birmingham, Mich. Office: Dept. of Sociology and Anthropology, Wayne State U., Detroit 2, Mich.

KAPLAN, SHELDON ZACHARY, b. Boston, Mass., Nov. 15, 1911. LAW. B.A., Yale U., 1933; B.A. in Juris, Oxford U., 1937; M.A., 1945; U. of Paris. Asst. to the legal adviser, U.S. Dept. of State, 1946–49; staff consultant, Foreign Affairs Committee, U.S. House of Representatives, 1949–57; COUNSEL, WILKINSON, CRAGUN AND BARKER, 1962– . Consultant on international economics, American Association for the United Nations; Committee on Latin American Law, American Bar Association; general counsel, Latin American Sugar Council. Membership: American Bar Association; American Society of International Law; D.C. Bar Association; Institute of World Polity; Inter-American Bar Association; Washington Foreign Law Society. Research: foreign aid; American business interests; commodities in inter-American trade; Central America. Author: The 80th Congress and the U.N. (U.S. Dept. of State Publication 3302, 1948); The Mutual Security Act and Overseas Private Investment (U.S. House of Representatives Committee on Foreign Affairs, June 1953). Co-author: Background Information on the Soviet Union (81st Congress House Report 3135, Sept. 1950). Language: Spanish 4,4,3,3; French 1,1,1,1; German 1,1,1,2. Home: 7810 Moorland Lane, Bethesda, Md. Office: Wilkinson, Cragun and Barker, 1616 H St., NW., Washington, D.C. 20006.

KARNES, THOMAS L., b. Kenosha, Wis., Aug. 21, 1914. HISTORY. A.B., Colo. U., 1940; M.A., Stanford U., 1949; Ph. D., 1953. Instr., Stanford U., 1951–54; assoc. prof., Tulane U., 1954–64; PROF., HISTORY, TULANE U., 1964– . Inter-American exchange fellow (Costa Rica), 1950–51; American Philosophical Society fellow (Guatemala), 1955; assoc., Middle American Research Institute. Membership: Conference on Latin American History; Mississippi Valley Historical Association; Phi Beta Kappa; Southwestern Social Science Association; Western History Association. Research: United States-Latin American relations; Central American history. Author: The Failure of Union: Central America, 1824–1960 (1961); The Origins of Costa Rican Federalism (The Americas, Jan. 1959); Hacia la federación centroamericana (Las Américas, May 1962). Language: Spanish 4,3,4,3; French 2,1,1,1. Home: 1301 Waltham St., Metairie, La. Office: Dept. of History, Tulane U., New Orleans, La. 70118.

KARSEN, SONJA PETRA, b. Berlin, Germany, Apr. 11, 1919. SPANISH AMERICAN LITERATURE. Bachiller, Universidad Nacional (Colombia), 1937; B.A., Carleton Coll., 1939; M.A., Bryn Mawr Coll., 1941; Ph. D., Columbia U., 1950. Instr., Lake Erie Coll., 1943–45; instr., U. of P.R., 1945–46; instr., Syracuse U., 1947–50; instr., Brooklyn Coll., 1950–51; asst. to the Deputy Director-General and program officer for Latin America, UNESCO (Paris, France), 1951–54; asst. prof., Sweet Briar Coll., 1955–57; assoc. prof., CHMN., SPANISH, SKIDMORE COLL., 1957– ; PROF., 1961– . Foreign Exchange student, 1938–39; Bryn Mawr scholar, 1939–41; U.S. Dept. of State grants-in-aid (Colombia), 1946–47; Skidmore Coll. faculty research grants (Mexico), 1959, 1961, 1963. Membership: American Association of Teachers of Spanish and Portuguese; American Association of University Professors; American Association of University Women; Instituto Internacional de Literatura Iberoamericana; Modern Language Association; National Geographic Society. Research: Mexican literature. Author: Guillermo Valencia, Colombian Poet, 1873–1943 (1951); Educational Development in Costa Rica with UNESCO's Technical Assistance, 1951–1954 (1954); Jaime Torres Bodet: A Poet in a Changing World (1963). Language: Spanish 5,5,5,5; Portuguese 3,1,1,1; French 5,5,5,5; German 5,5,5,5; Italian 3,2,2,1. Home: 160 Lincoln Ave., Saratoga Springs, N.Y. Office: Dept. of Romance Languages, Skidmore Coll., Saratoga Springs.

KARST, KENNETH LESLIE, b. Los Angeles, Calif., June 26, 1929. LAW. A.B., U. of Calif., Los Angeles, 1950; LL.B., Harvard U., 1953. Attorney, Latham & Watkins (Calif.), 1953–54, 1956–57; PROF., LAW, OHIO STATE U., 1958– . Ford Foundation fellow (Latin America), 1962–63. Membership: American Bar Association; Inter-American Bar Association; State Bar of California. Research: comparative law; intersection of law and social-economic development; land reform in Venezuela; civil and constitutional law in Argentina and Mexico. Author: Latin American Legal Institutions: Problems for Comparative Study (1964); Law and Legal Institutions (Social Science Research Council, 1964). Language: Spanish 4,4,4,4; Portuguese 3,3,2,2;

French 2,2,1,1. Home: 1820 Baldridge Rd., Columbus, Ohio 43221. Office: Coll. of Law, Ohio State U., 1659 North High St., Columbus, 43210.

KASTEN, LLOYD, A. W., b. Watertown, Wis., Apr. 14, 1905. BRAZILIAN LITERATURE. B.A., U. of Wis., 1926; M.A., 1927; Ph. D., 1931. Instr., U. of Fla., 1927–28; asst. prof.-PROF., SPANISH, U. OF WIS., 1928– . Markham traveling fellow; Guggenheim fellow. Membership: American Association of Teachers of Spanish and Portuguese; Linguistic Society of America; Medieval Academy of America; Modern Language Association; Oriental Society of America. Research: Spanish language and medieval literature; the novel in Brazil. Author: Seudo Aristóteles—Poridat de las Poridades (1957). Editor: General Estoria, Part II, by Alfonso X (1957–1961); Libro de las Cruzes, by Alfonso X (1961). Language: Spanish 5,5,4,4; Portuguese 5,4,3,3; French 5,4,3,3. Home: 3734 Ross St., Madison, Wis. 53705. Office: Dept. of Spanish and Portuguese, U. of Wis., Madison, 53705.

KATZ, SAUL MILTON, b. New York, N.Y., Apr., 7, 1915. ECONOMICS. B.S., Cornell U., 1940; M.S., 1943; M.P.A., Harvard U., 1950; A.M., 1951; Ph. D., 1953. Staff specialist, economic consultant, Production Marketing Administration, U.S. Dept. of Agriculture, 1951–53; head, Import Proposals Section, 1953–55; chief, Export Projects Branch, 1955–57; program coordinator for Latin America, 1957–59; program officer, International Cooperation Administration, U.S. Dept. of State, 1959–61; PROF., ECONOMIC AND SOCIAL DEVELOPMENT, GRADUATE SCHOOL OF PUBLIC AND INTERNATIONAL AFFAIRS, U. OF PITTSBURGH, 1961– . Consultant, Organization of American States, U.S. Agency for International Development; Committee on Comparative Administration in Latin America. Membership: American Economic Association; American Farm Economic Association; American Statistical Association; Society for International Development. Research: national development and planning; agricultural development; development administration. Author: Administración de la planificación para el desarrollo nacional (1964). Co-author: Proposed Program of Study and Research on Development Administration in Latin America: An Outline (1962); A Selected List of United States Readings on Development (1963). Language: Spanish 4,4,4,4; French 3,3,3,3; German 4,4,4,4. Home: 1240 Malvern Ave. Pittsburgh 17, Pa. Office: Graduate School of Public and International Affairs, U. of Pittsburgh, Pittsburgh, 15213.

KAVETSKY, JOSEPH, b. New York, N.Y.; Mar. 11, 1918. EDUCATION AND LANGUAGE. B.A., Brooklyn Coll., 1939; M.A., Columbia U., 1948; Ed. D., 1954. General supervisor and curriculum technician, P.R. Dept. of Education, 1948–49; lectr., Columbia U., 1952–56; PROF., EDUCATION, DIR., CURRICULUM AND TEACHING, U. OF P.R., 1962– . Consultant, Ford Foundation Puerto Rican Study in New York, 1952–56; Smith-Mundt prof., U. of Guadalajara (Mexico), 1958–59; Smith-Mundt prof., Instituto Tecnológico y de Estudios Superiores de Monterrey, 1960–61; consultant, Bi-National Center (Mexico); consultant, U.S. Peace Corps in P.R.; consultant, U.S. Armed Forces, U.S. Peace Corps, P.R. Dept. of Education; editor, Pret (P.R.). Membership: Association for Supervision and Curriculum Development; Puerto Rico English Teachers Association; Puerto Rico Teachers Association. Research: curriculum development; problems relating to foreign language learning and teaching; teaching English and Spanish as foreign languages; educational institutions of Mexico, especially universities; Puerto Rico. Author: A Manual for the Teaching of American English to Spanish-Speaking Children in Puerto Rico (1949); Teaching English to Puerto Rican Pupils, Grades 1–6 and Secondary School (1957); English as a Second Language (in Encyclopedia of Educational Research, 1960). Language: Spanish 5,5,5,5; French 3,1,1,1; German 1,4,2,1; Italian 3,3,3,1. Home: Apt. E-4, Faculty Residences, U. of P.R., Río Piedras. Office: Coll. of Education, U. of P.R., Río Piedras.

KEEN, BENJAMIN, b. Bethlehem, Pa., Apr. 25, 1913. HISTORY. A.B., Mohlenburg Coll., 1936; M.A., Lehigh U., 1939; Ph. D., Yale U., 1941. Research assoc., Strategic Index of Latin America, Yale U., 1941–43; instr., 1943–45; asst. prof., Amherst Coll., 1945–46; prof., W. Va. U., 1946–56; editor, G. and C. Merriam Co., 1956–59; PROF., HISTORY, JERSEY CITY STATE COLL., 1959– . Bulkeley fellow, Yale, 1940–41; chmn., Prize Committee, Conference on Latin American History, 1964. Membership: Conference on Latin American History. Research: Mexico; revolutionary Latin American history. Author: David C. DeForest and the Revolution of Buenos Aires (1947); Readings in Latin American Civilization (1955); The Life of the Admiral Christopher Columbus, by his Son Ferdinand (1959). Language: Spanish 4,4,4,4; French 4,3,3,3. Home: 170 Summit Ave., Upper Montclair, N.J. Office: Dept. of History, Jersey City State Coll., Kennedy Blvd., Jersey City.

KEEPPER, WENDELL EDGAR, b. Hillsboro, Ill., Sept. 7, 1910. ECONOMICS. B.S., U. of Ill., 1934; M.S.A., Cornell U., 1936; Ph. D., 1938. Prof., Pa. State Coll., 1938–50; vis. prof., Inter-American Institute of Agricultural Sciences (Costa Rica), 1948–49; DEAN, SCHOOL OF AGRICULTURE, SOUTHERN ILL. U., 1950– ; agricultural officer, United Nations Food and Agriculture Organization (Caracas), 1956; rural institutions officer, United Nations Food and Agriculture Organization (Rome), 1960–62. Consultant, United Nations Food and Agriculture Organization, (Cochabamba, Bolivia), 1964. Research: agricultural economics; farm management; agricultural education, organization, and operation. Author: Agriculture and International Trade (Pa. Agricultural Extension Service, Dec. 1943); Costs and Labor Used in Hay Harvesting by Various Methods (Pa. Agricultural Experiment Station, Sept. 1947); Place of Research for Increasing Labor Production (Inter-American Institute of Agriculture Science Information Bulletin, Aug. 1949). Language: Spanish 4,4,4,3. Home: R.F.D. 4, Kent Dr., Carbondale, Ill. Office: School of Agriculture, Southern Ill. U., Carbondale, 62903.

KELEMEN, PÁL, b. Budapest, Hungary, Apr. 24, 1894. ART. Lecture tours (Latin America), U.S. Dept. of State, 1945; vis.

prof., U. of Tex., 1953; U.S. specialist lecture tour, U.S. Dept. of State, 1956. Lectr., National Gallery of Art (Washington, D.C.), Metropolitan Museum of Art (N.Y.); chmn., Protection and Salvage of Artistic and Historic Monuments in War Areas, World War II, 1943–44; trustee, Textile Museum (Washington, D.C.); Order of Merit of Ecuador. Membership: Royal Anthropological Institute; Société des Americanistes. Research: early Christian art; art of pre-Columbian America; art of Spain and Portugal and their colonial empires. Author: Battlefield of the Gods, Essays on Mexican Art, History and Exploration (1937); Baroque and Rococo in Latin America (1951); Medieval American Art, Masterpieces of the New World before Columbus (1956). Language: Spanish 5,4,4,3; Portuguese 3,3,1,1; French 5,4,4,4; Dutch 3,2,1,1; German 5,5, 5,5; Hungarian 5,5,5,5; Italian 4,4,3,2; Latin 4,3,–,–. Home: P.O. Box 447, Norfolk, Conn., 06058.

KELLER, FRANK L., b. Highland Park, Ill., Mar. 27, 1918. ECONOMICS AND GEOGRAPHY. B.A., U. of Ill., 1940; Ph. D., U. of Md., 1949. Major and chief, Middle American Section, Intelligence (Washington, D.C.), 1941–44; Lt. Col. and asst. military attaché, Embassy (Bolivia), U.S. Dept. of State, 1944–46; asst. prof., Rutgers U., 1949–50; prof., Tulane U. Summer School (Guatemala), 1951; field dir., Economic Development Program, Institute of Inter-American Affairs (Bolivia), 1952–53; acting dir., Bureau of Economics and Business Research, Tulane U., 1953–57; prof., 1957–62; economist and prof., Latin American Institute of Economic and Social Planning, United Nations (Chile), 1962–63; PROF., ECONOMICS, TULANE U., 1962– ; vis. prof., Geography, U. of Calif., Berkeley, 1963. Laverne Noyes scholar, 1936–40; Social Science Research Council grant, 1940; Census Atlas Committee, 1950 Census of the Americas; consultant, U.S. Technical Co-operation Administration (La Paz, Bolivia), 1951. Membership: American Economic Association; Association of American Geographers; Regional Science Association; Sociedad Geográfica de La Paz, Bolivia; Southern Economic Association. Research: natural resource planning; land tenure; economic development; economics and geography of Latin America. Author: Institutional Barriers to Economic Development—Some Examples from Bolivia (Economic Geography, Oct. 1955); Guatemala—the Road Back (Latin American Report, Mar. 1956); Odeca-Common Market Experiment in an Underdeveloped Area (Journal of Latin American Studies, Apr. 1963). Language: Spanish 5,5,5,5; Portuguese 4,3,3,3; French 4,2,2,2. Home: 620 Jefferson Ave., Metairie, La. Office: Dept. of Economics, Tulane U., New Orleans, La., 70118.

KELLEY, DAVID HUMISTON, b. Albany, N.Y., Apr. 1, 1924. ANTHROPOLOGY. B.A., Harvard Coll., 1949; Ph. D., Harvard U., 1957. Asst. prof.-assoc. prof., Tex. Technological Coll., 1958–63; ASSOC. PROF., ANTHROPOLOGY, U. of NEBR., 1964– . Fulbright fellow, Universidad de San Marcos (Peru), 1957–58; Fulbright lectr., Universidad Nacional (Uruguay), 1963–64. Membership: American Anthropological Association; Institute of Andean Studies; Society for American Archaeology. Research: archeology; decipherment of Maya hieroglyphs; problems of trans-Pacific contacts; agricultural history of the New World; comparative linguistics of Uto-Aztecan and Polynesian materials. Author: Calendar Animals and Deities (Southwestern Journal of Anthropololgy, Autumn 1960); A History of the Decipherment of Maya Script (Anthropological Linguistics, Nov. 1962). Co-author: New Evidence for Pre-ceramic Maize on the Coast of Peru (Ñawpa Pacha, 1963). Language: Spanish 5,4,4,4; French 4,3,3,2; German 3,1,1,1. Home: 1816 C St., Lincoln, Nebr., 68502. Office: Dept. of Anthropology, U. of Nebr., Lincoln 8.

KELLY, WILLIAM HENDERSON, b. Bisbee, Ariz., Nov. 23, 1902. ANTHROPOLOGY. B.A., U. of Ariz., 1936; M.A., Harvard U., 1941; Ph. D., 1944. Instr., U. of Conn., 1942–43; instr., Harvard U., 1943–46; research assoc., Peabody Museum, 1946–47; assoc. prof., McGill U., 1947–48; research assoc., Peabody Museum, Harvard U., 1948–49; asst. prof., U. of Minn., 1949–52; PROF., ANTHROPOLOGY, DIR., BUREAU OF ETHNIC RESEARCH, U. OF ARIZ., 1952– . U.S. representative, Board of Governors of the Inter-American Indian Institute. Membership: American Anthropological Association; American Sociological Association; Society for Applied Anthropology. Research: Southwestern Indians; Cocopa Indians of Mexico. Author: Indians of the Southwest (1953); Papago Indians of Arizona (1963); Methods and Resources for the Construction of a Navajo Population Register (1964). Language: Spanish 3,3,2,2. Home: 5837 East Hawthorne, Tucson, Ariz. Office: Dept. of Anthropology, U. of Ariz., Tucson.

KELSO, PAUL, b. New Albany, Ind., Oct. 9, 1907. POLITICAL SCIENCE. B.A., Ball State Teachers Coll., 1933; M.A., U. of Wis., 1938; Ph. D., Ohio State U., 1944. Reporter, Muncie Star (Ind.), 1933–37; lectr., U. of Calif., Los Angeles, 1943–46; historian, Caribbean Div., U.S. Air Force, 1943–46; PROF., GOVERNMENT, U. OF ARIZ., 1946– . Membership: American Political Science Association; International City Managers' Association; Southwestern Political Science Association; Western Political Science Association. Research: public administration; Mexican government and administration. Author: Phoenix—A Decade of Council-Manager Government (1960); Budget Making in Arizona (1964); 1952 Elections in Arizona (Western Political Quarterly, Mar. 1953). Language: Spanish 4,2,2,4. Home: 2617 East Linden St., Tucson, Ariz. Office: Dept. of Government, U. of Ariz., Tucson, 85721.

KENNEDY, JOHN J(OSEPH), b. Cortland, N.Y., Sept. 13, 1914. POLITICAL SCIENCE. B.A., U. of N. Mex., 1936; A.M., Columbia U., 1938; Ph. D., 1954. Regional specialist, Office of International Information and Cultural Affairs, U.S. Dept. of State, 1946–48; vis. prof., U. of P.R., 1948–50; asst. prof., U. of Notre Dame, 1951–56; assoc. editor, Review of Politics, 1955–60; assoc. prof., U. of Notre Dame, 1956–60; assoc. prof., U. of Va., 1960–61; prof., 1961–64; DIR., PROGRAM OF LATIN AMERICAN STUDIES, CHMN., GOVERNMENT AND INTERNATIONAL STUDIES, U. OF NOTRE DAME, 1964– . Council on Foreign Relations fellow, 1958–59. Membership: American Political Science Association; Pi Sigma Alpha. Research: international relations; comparative government, ideological factors, and the political thought of Latin America; church-state relations. Author: Catholicism, Nationalism and Democracy in Argentina (1958); Accountable Government in Argentina (Foreign Affairs, Apr. 1959); Dichotomies in the Church (Annals of the American Academy of Political and Social Science, Mar. 1961). Language: Spanish 5,5,4,4; Portuguese 3,2,1,1; French 3,2,1,1. Home: 1937 Inglewood Pl., South Bend, Ind., 46616. Office: Dept. of Government and International Studies, U. of Notre Dame, Notre Dame, Ind., 46556.

KENNELLY, ROBERT ANDREW, b. Jamestown, N. Dak., Oct. 6, 1919. GEOGRAPHY. B.A., State U. of Iowa, 1948; M.A., 1950; Ph. D., 1952. Instr., State U. of Iowa, 1951–52; asst. prof., Long Beach State Coll., 1952–57; head, Social Science, 1957–58; assoc. prof., 1957–61; CHMN., SOCIAL SCIENCE, LONG BEACH STATE COLL., 1958– ; PROF., GEOGRAPHY, 1961– ; vis. prof., Central Wash. State Coll., Summers 1962, 1963. Editor, The California Geographer, 1960– . Membership: Association of American Geographers; Association of Pacific Coast Geographers; California Council of Geography Teachers; Gamma Theta Upsilon; Los Angeles Geographical Society; Pacific Coast Council of Latin American Studies. Research: economic geography; Mexico. Author: The Location of the Mexican Steel Industry (Revista Geográfica, 1955); The Cattle Feeding Industry of the Imperial Valley (Yearbook, Association of Pacific Coast Geographers, 1960). Language: Spanish 3,4,3,2; French 1,1,1,1. Home: 1451 Iroquois Ave., Long Beach, Calif., 90815. Office: Dept. of Geography, Long Beach State Coll., Long Beach, 90804.

KENNY, MICHAEL, b. London, United Kingdom, June 22, 1923. ANTHROPOLOGY. B.A., Oxford U., 1951; diploma, 1952; M.A., 1957; B.Sc., 1958. Chief of studies, Vox Language Institute (Madrid), 1952–54; lectr., British Council (Madrid), 1954–57; ASSOC. PROF., ANTHROPOLOGY, CATHOLIC U. OF AMERICA, 1959– ; dir., Latin American Institute, 1962–64. Organization of American States fellow (Cuba, Mexico), 1960–62; National Science Foundation grant (Mexico), 1961–62. Membership: American Anthropological Association; Association of Social Anthropologists; Institute of Ibero-American Studies; Inter-American Council; Sigma Xi. Research: cultural anthropology, especially rural-urban and overseas migration; Mediterranean area and Latin America. Author: A Spanish Tapestry: Town and Country in Castile (1961); 20th Century Spanish Expatriates in Cuba (Anthropological Quarterly, Apr. 1961); 20th Century Spanish Expatriates in Mexico (Anthropological Quarterly, Oct. 1962). Language: Spanish 4,4,4,4; Portuguese 2,3,–,–; French 3,3,3,2; Hindustani –,1,1,–. Home: 3621 10th St., NE., Washington, D.C. Office: Dept. of Anthropology, Catholic U. of America, Washington 17.

KENSINGER, KENNETH M., b. Altoona, Pa., June 4, 1931. ANTHROPOLOGY: LINGUISTICS. B.A., Wheaton Coll., 1953; M.A., U. of Pa., 1964. Researcher, Summer Institute of Linguistics (Peru), 1953–63; INSTR., ANTHROPOLOGY, U. OF PA., 1964– . Teaching fellow, U. of Pa., 1963–64; National Institute of Mental Health fellow, 1964– . Membership: American Anthropological Association; Philadelphia Anthropological Society. Research: cultural and social anthropology; social organization; ethnolinguistics; South American Indians; development of methods and models for the formal analysis of lexical and cultural data. Author: The Phonological Hierarchy of Cashinahua (in Studies in Peruvian Indian Languages, 1963). Language: Spanish 4,4,3,3; Portuguese 3,2,1,3; French 3,1,1,1; Cashinahua 5,5,4,4. Linguistic studies: Cashinahua. Home: 3921 Walnut St., Philadelphia, Pa. 19104. Office: Dept. of Anthropology, U. of Pa. Museum, 33rd and Spruce Sts., Philadelphia, 19104.

KENYON, ROBERT GORDON B., b. Peace Dale, R.I., Mar. 19, 1914. HISTORY, R.I.U., 1934–35; B.A., Pa. Military Coll., 1948; M.A., U. of N. Mex., 1949; Ph. D., 1952. Vis. instr., Beloit Coll., 1953; assoc prof., Nebr. State Teachers Coll., 1953–58; head, Social Science, Ark. State Coll., 1958–60; CHMN., DIV. OF HISTORY AND SOCIAL SCIENCE, SOUTHERN COLO. STATE COLL., 1960– . Membership: American Association of University Professors; American Historical Association; Conference on Latin American History. Research: Central America, Mexico, and Brazil. Author: Gabino Gainza and Central America's Independence from Spain (The Americas, Jan. 1957); The Sugar-Cane Cycle of José Lins do Rego (The Americas, Jan. 1958); Mexican Influence in Central America, 1821–1823 (Hispanic American Historical Review, May 1961). Language: Spanish 3,3,2,2; Portuguese 4,3,3,3; French 4,4,4,3. Home: 325 Henry Ave., Pueblo, Colo. Office: Div. of History and Social Science, Southern Colo. State Coll., Pueblo.

KERSON, ARNOLD LEWIS, b. New Haven, Conn., Aug. 9, 1931. SPANISH AMERICAN LITERATURE. B.A., Yale U., 1953; Ph. D., 1963. Asst. instr., Yale U., 1953–56; instr., Wesleyan U., 1956–58; instr., Yale U., 1958–60; instr., Trinity Coll., 1960–64; ASST. PROF., SPANISH, TRINITY COLL., 1964– . Membership: American Association of Teachers of Spanish and Portuguese; Modern Language Association. Research: culture and literature of the colonial period. Language: Spanish 5,5,5,5; French 4,3,3,3; German 3,2,2,2; Latin 5,–,–,4. Home: 1335 Trinity Coll., Hartford, Conn. 06106. Office: 90 Vernon St., Hartford, 06106.

KEY, HAROLD HAYDEN, b. Jacksboro, Tex., Mar. 6, 1914. ANTHROPOLOGY: LINGUISTICS. B.A., U. of Tex., 1938; M.A., 1961; Ph. D., 1963. Purchase agent, Mexico Branch, Summer Institute of Linguistics and Wycliffe Bible Translators, Inc., 1946–48; linguistic investigator, 1948–53; asst. dir., Mexico Branch, 1953–55; dir., Bolivia Branch, 1955–63; DIR., EXTENSION SERVICE, SUMMER INSTITUTE OF LINGUISTICS AND WYCLIFFE BIBLE TRANSLATORS, INC., 1963– . Research: morphology of Cayuvava; Bolivia; Mexico. Author: Phonotactics of Cayuvava (International Journal of American Linguistics, Apr. 1961). Co-author: Vocabulario Mejicano de la Sierra Zacapoaxtla, Puebla

(1953); The Phonemes of Sierra Nahuatl (International Journal of American Linguistics, Jan. 1953). Language: Spanish 3,3,3,3. Linguistic studies: Cayuvava; Sierra Nahuatl. Home and office: Summer Institute of Linguistics Box 1960, Santa Ana, Calif.

KEY, MARY RITCHIE, b. San Diego, Calif., Mar. 19, 1924. LINGUISTICS. M.A., U. of Tex., 1959; Ph. D., 1963. LINGUIST, MISSIONARY, SUMMER INSTITUTE OF LINGUISTICS, 1946– . Research: unwritten Indian languages; comparative phonology of the Tacanan languages. Co-author: Vocabulario Mejicano de la Sierra de Zacapoaxtla, Puebla (1953); The Phonemes of Sierra Nahuatl (International Journal of American Linguistics, Jan. 1953). Language: Spanish 4,4,4,4. Linguistic studies: Cavineña; Chama; Tacana. Home and office: Summer Institute of Linguistics, Box 1960, Santa Ana, Calif.

KEY, RICHARD MICHAEL, b. Poland, Sept. 4, 1922. LANGUAGE. B.A., Queen's Coll., 1945; M.A., Columbia U., 1948; Ph. D., U. of Kans., 1956. Instr., U. of Kans., 1948–53; instr., Rutgers U., 1953–55; asst. prof., Purdue U., 1955–56; binational center dir., U.S. Information Agency (Argentina), 1956–60; cultural affairs officer (Panama), 1960–63; DEPUTY CHIEF, ENGLISH TEACHING DIV., U.S. INFORMATION AGENCY, 1963– . Research: Spanish; Latin American history. Language: Spanish 5,5,5,5; Portuguese 2,2,1,1; French 3,3,3,3; German 2,2,2,2. Home: 4750 Chevy Chase Dr., Chevy Chase, Md. Office: English Teaching Div., U.S. Information Agency, Washington, D.C.

KIDDER, FREDERICK ELWYN, b. White Bear Lake, Minn., Sept. 22, 1919. LIBRARY SCIENCE. A.B., U. of Calif., Berkeley, 1940; B.L.S., 1950; M.A., 1952. Principal asst., Bancroft Library, U. of Calif., Berkeley, 1949–50; asst. librarian and lectr., Inter American U. (P.R.), 1955–56; asst. dir., School of Inter American Studies, U. of Fla., 1956–57; lectr., Inter American U., 1957–59; Latin American bibliogapher, U. of Fla., 1959–60; librarian, P.R. Nuclear Center (Mayagüez), 1961–62; LECTR. SOCIAL SCIENCES, U. OF P.R., 1962– . U. of Fla.-Rockefeller Foundation grant, 1961–62; Southern Fellowships Fund grant, 1962. Membership: American Association of Teachers of Spanish and Portuguese; American Association of University Professors; American Library Association; American Political Science Association; Conference on Latin American History; Inter-American Bibliographical and Library Association; Political Science Association of Puerto Rico; Sociedad de Bibliotecarios de Puerto Rico; Southeastern Conference on Latin American Studies. Research: political Puerto Rico; acquisition of Latin American library materials. Author: Survey of Investigations in Progress in the Field of Latin American Studies (1956); Latin America and UNESCO: The First Five Years (1960); Theses on Pan American Topics (1962). Language: Spanish 5,5,4,4; Portuguese 3,3,1,1; French 3,2,2,1; German 2,1,1,1; Russian 1,1,1,1. Home: Apartado 3294, Mayagüez, P.R. 00709. Office: Dept. of Social Sciences, U. of P.R., Mayagüez, 00709.

KIDDLE, LAWRENCE BAYARD, b. Cleveland, Ohio, Aug. 20, 1907. LANGUAGE. A. B., Oberlin Coll., 1929; A.M., U. of Wis., 1930; Ph. D., 1935. Asst. prof., Spanish, U. of N. Mex., 1935–38; instr., Princeton U., 1938–40; assoc. prof., Tulane U., 1940–43; Lt. Comdr., U.S. Naval Reserve, Jefe del Departamento, Letras e Idiomas, Escuela Naval del Perú, 1945–47; PROF., SPANISH, U. OF MICH., 1947– . Advanced Placement Program Spanish Committee, 1955–60; National Defense Education Act Fellowships Screening Committee, 1962; Fulbright prof. of linguistics, Instituto Caro y Cuervo (Bogotá), 1963–64. Membership: American Association of Teachers of Spanish and Portuguese; Linguistic Society of America; Modern Language Association. Research: Spanish dialectology. Co-editor: Antología de cuentos hispanoamericanos (1956); Antología de cuentos españoles (1960); El Libro de las cruces, by Alfonso X, (1961). Language: Spanish 5,5,5,5; Portuguese 5,3,2,2; French 5,5,4,4; German 3,1,1,1. Linguistic studies: Spanish. Home: 431 Crest Ave., Ann Arbor, Mich. Office: Dept. of Romance Languages, U. of Mich., Ann Arbor.

KIEMEN, MATHIAS CHARLES, O.F.M., b. Chippewa Falls, Wis., Jan. 10, 1917. HISTORY. B.A., Our Lady of Angels Seminary, 1940; M.A., Catholic U., 1946; Ph. D., 1954. Editor, The Americas, 1953–63; VIS. ASSOC. PROF., HISTORY, GEORGETOWN U., 1954– ; RESIDENT MEMBER, DIR., ACADEMY OF AMERICAN FRANCISCAN HISTORY, 1963– ; vis. assoc. prof., Catholic U., 1963–64. Instituto para Alta Cultura (Portugal) fellow, 1950–51; Brazilian Dept. of State fellow, 1953; U.S. specialist in Brazil, U.S. Dept. of State, 1957; Organization of American States grant (Brazil), 1963. Membership: American Historical Association; Catholic Historical Association; Centro de Estudos Históricos Ultramarinos (Lisbon); Conference on Latin American History. Research: Brazil; colonial church history; the Indian policy of Portugal in Brazil during the colonial period. Author: The Indian Policy of Portugal in the Amazon Region, 1614–1693 (1954); The Indian Policy of Portugal in Maranhão (The Americas, Oct. 1948, Apr. 1949); Status of Brazilian Indian since 1820 (The Americas, Spring 1964). Language: Spanish 4,3,3,3; Portuguese 4,4,4,3; French 3,2,1,1; German 3,3,2,1; Italian 2,2, 1,1. Home and office: Academy of American Franciscan History, Box 5966, Washington, D.C. 20014.

KIETZMAN, DALE WALTER, b. Gary, Ind., July 18, 1924. LINGUISTICS. B.A., Wheaton Coll., 1946; M.A., Northwestern U., 1952. Linguist, Summer Institute of Linguistics (Peru, Mexico), 1946–53; DIR., SUMMER INSTITUTE OF LINGUISTICS (BRAZIL), 1956– . National Defense Education Act fellow in Portuguese, Stanford U., 1961–62. Membership: Associação Brasileira de Antropologia. Research: anthropology; africanisms in Brazil. Author: Afinidades culturales de las Amahuacas del Perú (Perú Indígena, June 1952); Tendências de ordem lexical da aculturação linguística em terena (Revista de Antropologia, June 1958). Language: Spanish 4,3,3,3; Portuguese 5,4,4,4. Linguistic studies: Amahuaca. Home: Rua Livreiro Francisco

Alves, 50, Rio de Janeiro, Brazil. Office: Summer Institute of Linguistics, P.O. Box 1960, Santa Ana, Calif.

KILGORE, WILLIAM JACKSON, b. Dallas. Tex., Apr. 30, 1917. PHILOSOPHY. A.B., Baylor U., 1938; Th. M., Southern Baptist Theological Seminary, 1941; Th. D., 1943; Ph. D., U. of Tex., 1958. Prof., Buenos Aires International Seminary, 1944–49; PROF., CHMN., PHILOSOPHY, BAYLOR U., 1949– ; vis. asst. prof., U. of Tex., Summer 1958. Danforth Foundation grant, 1957–58; American Council of Learned Societies grant (Central America), 1961. Membership: American Association of Universities; American Philosophical Association; Comisión Americana al Homenaje de Alejandro Korn; Southwestern Philosophical Association. Research: history of the philosophy of ideas in Latin America. Author: Una evaluación crítica de la filosofía de Alejandro Korn (1963); La filosofía de Francisco Romero (1964); Notes on the Philosophy of Education of Andrés Bello (Journal of the History of Ideas, Oct. 1961). Language: Spanish 5,5,4,4; Portuguese 4,4,1,1; French 2,2,1,1; Italian 2,3,1,1. Home. 3409 Lyle, Waco, Tex. Office: Dept. or Philosophy, Baylor U., Waco.

KINDBERG, WILLARD ROY, b. Orange, N.J., June 1, 1928. LINGUISTICS. B.A., Wheaton Coll., 1952. LINGUISTIC INVESTIGATOR, TRANSLATION CONSULTANT, SUMMER INSTITUTE OF LINGUISTICS (PERU), 1953– . Research: Campa tribe of Peru. Author: Campa Morphology (1960); A Problem in Multiple Stresses (Word, Dec. 1956). Language: Spanish 3,3,3,3; Campa 4,4,4,4. Linguistic studies: Campa. Home: Casilla 2492, Lima, Perú. Office: Summer Institute of Linguistics, Box 1960, Santa Ana, Calif.

KING, ARDEN ROSS, b. Francis, Utah, Dec. 10, 1916. ANTHROPOLOGY. A.B., U. of Utah, 1938; Ph. D., U. of Calif., Berkeley, 1947. Instr., U. of Wash., 1944–47; instr.-PROF., ANTHROPOLOGY, TULANE U., 1947– . Wenner-Gren research fellow (Guatemala), 1952. Membership: American Anthropological Association; American Association of Physical Anthropology; American Ethnological Society; Society for American Archaeology. Research: central Andean archeology; modern cultural anthropology of Middle America, especially northern Guatemala. Language: Spanish 4,4,3,3; Portuguese 2,1,1,1; French 4,4,3,3; German 4,3,3,2. Home: 1301 Pine St., New Orleans, La. 70118. Office: Dept. of Anthropology, Tulane U., New Orleans, 70118.

KING, CHARLES LESTER, b. Gosford, Calif., Feb. 15, 1922. LANGUAGE. B.A., U. of N. Mex., 1948; M.A., U. of Southern Calif., 1950; Ph. D., 1953. Instr., La. State U., 1953–54; asst. dir.-dir., Bi-National Centers, U.S. Information Agency (Bolivia, Uruguay, Colombia, Iran), 1954–60; SPECIALIST, LANGUAGE INSTITUTE SECTION, U.S. OFFICE OF EDUCATION, 1960– . Chmn., Committee on Honor Programs and Fellowship Selection, American Association of Teachers of Spanish and Portuguese, 1961–. Membership: American Association of Teachers of Spanish and Portuguese; Modern Language Association; Phi Sigma Iota; Sigma Delta Pi. Research: Spanish: contemporary Spanish literature; English as a second language; National Defense Education Act language institutes. Author: Sender: Aragonese in New Mexico (Modern Language Journal, May 1952); Sender's Spherical Philosophy (Publications of the Modern Language Association, Dec. 1954). Language: Spanish 5,5,5,5; French 2,2,1,1; German 2,1,1,1; Latin 2,-,-,-; Persian 1,2,2,1. Home: 7003 Essex Ave., Springfield, Va. Office: Language Institute Section, Div. of College and University Assistance, U.S. Office of Education, Washington, D.C. 20202.

KING, JAMES F., b. Spokane, Wash., Feb. 16, 1913. HISTORY. B.A., U. of Minn., 1934; M.A., U. of Calif., Berkeley, 1935; Ph. D., 1939. Assoc. divisional asst., Div. of American Republics, U.S. Dept. of State, 1940–41; instr.-asst. prof., Northwestern U., 1941–44; asst. prof.-PROF., HISTORY, U. OF CALIF., BERKELEY, 1944– ; chmn., 1953–56; chmn., Center for Latin American Studies, 1956–60; assoc. dean, Graduate Div., 1960– . Rockefeller Foundation traveling fellow (Brazil, Venezuela, Colombia), 1937–38; managing editor, Hispanic American Historical Review, 1945–49; Rockefeller Foundation grant (Spain, Great Britain), 1950–51; chmn., Conference on Latin American History, 1962. Membership: American Historical Association; Pacific Coast Council of Latin American Studies; Phi Beta Kappa. Research: history of the period, 1750–1890; Spain and Spanish American independence; the Negro in Spanish America. Author: Evolution of the Free Slave Trade Principle in Spanish Colonial Administration (Hispanic American Historical Review, Feb. 1942); The Latin American Republics and the Suppression of the Slave Trade (Hispanic American Historical Review, Aug. 1944); The Colored Caste and American Representation in the Cortes of Cadiz (Hispanic American Historical Review, Feb. 1953). Language: Spanish 5,5,5,5; Portuguese 4,4,4,4; French 3,2,2,2; German 3,2,2,2; Italian 2,2,2,2. Home: 715 Santa Barbara Rd., Berkeley 7, Calif. Office: Dept. of History, U. of Calif., Berkeley 4.

KING, MARY ELIZABETH, b. Williamsport, Pa., Sept. 7, 1929. ANTHROPOLOGY. A.B., Cornell U., 1951; M.A., Columbia U., 1958; Ph. D., 1965. Asst. to state archeologist, Pa. State Museum, 1951–52; museum asst., Textile Museum, 1953–54; librarian, 1954–59; CURATOR, WESTERN HEMISPHERE TEXTILES, TEXTILE MUSEUM, 1957– ; instr., American U., Summer 1963; lectr., Howard U., 1963– . Asst. to Junius Bird, American Musuem of Natural History, June 1953; American Philosophical Society grant (Peru), 1957. Membership: American Anthropological Association; Anthropological Society of Washington; Sigma Xi; Society for American Archaeology. Research: ethnology and archeology of North and South America, especially material culture; prehistoric textiles and baskets of Peru, Mexico and the southwest United States. Author: A Preliminary Study of a Shaped Textile from Peru (1956); A New Type of Peruvian Ikat (1958); An Unusual Border Construction from Peru (Needle and Bobbin Club Bulletin, 1957). Language: Spanish 3,3,3,2; German 2,1,1,1. Home: 409 6th St. SE., Washington, D.C. 20003. Office:

Textile Museum, 2320 S St. NW., Washington, D.C. 20008.

KINGSBURY, ROBERT C., b. Lakewood, Ohio, May 3, 1924. GEOGRAPHY. A.B., U. of Miami, 1949; M.A., U. of Kans., 1951. Instr., U. of Miami, 1949–50, 1951–52; research assoc., American Geographical Society, 1954–57; ASST. PROF., GEOGRAPHY, IND. U., 1957– . U.S. Office of Naval Research grants (West Indies), 1957, 1958, 1959; cartographic editor, Weather Research Bulletin and Journal of Geography. Membership: American Congress on Surveying and Mapping; American Society of Photogrammetry; Association of American Geographers; National Council for Geographic Education. Research: cartographic design; history of maps and mapping. Author: Geography of Grenadines; Grenada; Trinidad and Tobago; British Virgin Islands (1960). Co-author: India: A Compendium (1962); An Atlas of Latin American Affairs (1965). Language: Spanish 3,1,1,2; French 2,1,1,1; Hindi 1,2,2,1. Home: 3525 Longview Ave., Bloomington, Ind. Office: Dept. of Geography, Ind. U., Bloomington.

KIRK, PAUL LIVINGSTON, b. Stockton, Calif., May 19, 1927. LINGUISTICS. B.A., Lewis and Clark Coll., 1952; M.A., U. of Wash., 1962. LINGUIST, SUMMER INSTITUTE OF LINGUISTICS (MEXICO), 1953– . National Defense fellow, U. of Wash. 1960–63. Membership: Linguistic Circle of New York; Linguistic Society of America. Research: descriptive linguistics; Mazatec Indians of Mexico. Author: Ma3na3 Xu⁴jun⁴ (1960). Co-author: Number in Kiowa: Nouns, Demonstratives and Adjectives (International Journal of American Linguistics, Jan. 1954). Language: Spanish 3,3,3,3; Mazatec 4,4,4,4. Linguistic studies: Kiowa; Mazatec. Home: c/o Summer Institute of Linguistics, Box 1960, Santa Ana, Calif. Office: Summer Institute of Linguistics, Apartado 22067, Tlalpan, México 22, D.F.

KIRSNER, ROBERT, b. Lithuania, July 9, 1921. LANGUAGE. B.A., U. of Cincinnati, 1943; M.A., 1945; M.A., Princeton U., 1947; Ph. D., 1949. Instr., Princeton U., 1945–49; PROF., ROMANCE LANGUAGES, U. OF CINCINNATI, 1949– ; prof., National Defense Education Act Institute, San Francisco State U., Summer 1959, Mich. State U., Summer 1961; resident dir., Rollins Coll. Semester Program, Universidad de los Andes (Colombia), 1964. Smith-Mundt vis. prof., National U. of Guatemala, 1951. Membership: American Association of Teachers of Spanish and Portuguese; American Association of University Professors; Instituto Internacional de Literatura Iberoamericana; Modern Language Association. Research: Spanish and Latin American Literatures, civilizations and language. Author: The Novels and Travels of Camilo José Cela (1964). Co-author: Paisajes del Sur, an Anthology of Spanish American Literature and Life (1954); ¡Repasar! A Review of Spanish Grammar (1954). Language: Spanish 5,5,5,5; Portuguese 3,4,2,2; French 3,4,3,2. Linguistic studies: French; Spanish. Home: 7020 Elbrook Ave., Cincinnati 37, Ohio. Office: Dept. of Romance Languages, U. of Cincinnati, Cincinnati 21.

KISER, J(ESSE) DORRANCE, b. Nuyaka, Okla., Feb. 7, 1922. ART. B.A.A., Auburn U., 1946; M.A.A., 1947; Teachers' Coll., Columbia U., Summers 1950–52. Instr., Auburn U., 1949–54; instr., U. of Wash., 1954–55; technical illustrator, Boeing Airplane Company, Summer 1955; ASST. PROF., ART, U. OF MINN., 1955–. U. of Minn. grant-in-aid (Mexico), 1961–62. Membership: American Association of University Professors; American Craftsmen Council; Print Council of America. Research: mural painting; pre-Columbian art and archeology; Mexican murals. Language: Spanish 3,3,3,3; French 2,2,1,1; Italian 2,2,2,1. Home: 6004 London Rd., Duluth, Minn., 55804. Office: Dept. of Art, U. of Minn., Duluth, 55812.

KITCHEN, JAMES D., b. Bayard, Iowa, Mar. 30, 1920. POLITICAL SCIENCE. B.A., U. of Calif., Los Angeles, 1947; M.A., 1949; Ph. D., 1955. Public administration analyst, U. of Calif., Los Angeles, 1948–55; asst. prof., Southern Ill. U., 1955–57; asst. prof., San Diego State Coll., 1957–62; ASSOC. PROF., POLITICAL SCIENCE, SAN DIEGO STATE COLL., 1962–. Doherty fellow (Guatemala), 1953–54; Southern Ill. U. grant (Guatemala), Summer 1956; Fulbright lectr., Central U. (Ecuador), 1960–61; Fulbright lectr. and consultant (Trinidad), 1964. Membership: American Society for Public Administration; Western Governmental Research Association; Western Political Science Association, Research: public administration; municipal government and administration in Guatemala. Author: How the Cities Grew (1952); Metropolitan Coast (1957); National Personnel Administration in Uruguay (Inter-American Economic Affairs, Summer 1950). Language: Spanish 4,4,4,4. Home: 6051 Howell Dr., La Mesa, Calif. Office: Public Administration Center, San Diego State Coll., San Diego 15.

KLEIN, HERBERT SANFORD, b. New York, N.Y., Jan. 6, 1936. HISTORY. A.B., U. of Chicago, 1957; M.A., 1959; Ph. D., 1963. Instr., U. of Chicago, 1962–63; ASST. PROF., HISTORY, U. OF CHICAGO, 1963– . Doherty fellow (Bolivia), 1960–61; Fulbright travel grant (Bolivia), Summer 1963. Membership: Conference on Latin American History. Research: Latin American colonial history; ethnohistory of the Maya; Bolivian history since 1900. Author: The War of the Castes in Chiapas, Mexico (Anthropology Tomorrow, Dec. 1960). Language: Spanish 5,4,4,3; Portuguese 3,1,1,1. Home: 5530 South Kimbark Ave., Chicago 37, Ill. Office: Dept. of History, U. of Chicago, Chicago 37.

KLEINECKE, DAVID CARMAN, b. Chicago, Ill., May 30, 1927. LINGUISTICS AND MATHEMATICS. A.B., U. of Calif., 1950; Ph. D., 1953. Instr., U. of Calif., 1953–54; member of staff, Sandia Corporation (Calif., N. Mex.), 1954–58; assoc. research engineer, U. of Calif., 1958–62; MEMBER, PROFESSIONAL STAFF, GENERAL ELECTRIC-TECHNICAL MILITARY PLANNING OPERATION, 1962– . Membership: American Association for Computing Machinery; American Geophysical Union; American Linguistic Society; American Mathematical Society; Society for Industrial and Applied Mathematics. Research: South American Indian languages; montaña history and sociology of Peru; Venezuela; physics; operations research; computers. Author: An

Etymology for Pidgin (International Journal of American Linguistics, 1960). Language: Spanish 3,2,2,2; Portuguese 2,1,1,1; French 3,1,1,1. Linguistic studies: Arawak; Chibcha; Mojo; Quechua. Home: 225 Dawlish Pl., Santa Barbara, Calif. Office: General Electric-TEMPO, 735 State St., Santa Barbara.

KNAPP, FRANK AVERILL, JR., b. Wellington, Kans., Sept. 24, 1922. HISTORY AND POLITICAL SCIENCE. B.A., U. of Okla., 1943; M.A., U. of Tex., 1949; Ph. D., 1950. Research asst., Institute of Latin American Studies, U. of Tex., 1950; prof., U. of Tex., 1950–51; staff officer, U.S. Army, 1951–52; U.S. GOVERNMENT 1952– . Research: contemporary Latin America; 19th century Mexico; economic development and economic trends in Latin America. Author: The Life of Sebastian Lerdo de Tejada (1951 [Spanish edition, 1962]); Precursors of American Investment in Mexican Railroads (Pacific Historical Review, Feb. 1952); Mexican Fear of Manifest Destiny in California (in Essays in Mexican History, 1958). Language: Spanish 4,4,4,4; Portuguese 2,–,–,–; French 3,2,2,2. Home: Apt. 515, 825 New Hampshire Ave., NW., Washington, D.C., 20037.

KNOWLTON, CLARK S., b. Salt Lake City, Utah, Dec. 31, 1919. SOCIOLOGY. B.A., Brigham Young U., 1948; M.A., 1949; Ph. D., Vanderbilt U., 1955. Instr., Ga. Southern Coll., 1952–58; instr., N. Mex. Highlands U., 1958–62; CHMN., SOCIOLOGY, TEX. WESTERN COLL., 1962– . Cordell Hull fellow (Brazil), 1950–51. Membership: American Academy of Political and Social Science; American Association for the Advancement of Science; American Sociological Society; National Council on Family Relations; Rocky Mountain Social Science Association; Rural Sociological Association; Society for Applied Anthropology; Southern Sociological Society; Southwestern Social Science Association. Research: area and regional planning; social and spatial mobility of the Syrian and Lebanese community in São Paulo, Brazil; problems of migration, acculturation, assimilation, and social disorganization among Spanish-speaking groups in the Southwest and Mexican groups in Chihuahua. Author: Sirios e Libaneses (1960); Spanish-Americans in New Mexico (Sociology and Social Research, July 1961); Patron-Peon Pattern among Spanish-Americans in New Mexico (Social Forces, Oct. 1962). Language: Spanish 5,5,4,3; Portuguese 5,5,3,2; French 3,1,1,1. Home: 5028 Jordan Lane, El Paso, Tex. 79922. Office: Box 140, Tex. Western Coll., El Paso, 79902.

KNOWLTON, ROBERT, b. Akron, Ohio, Jan. 16, 1931. HISTORY. B.A., Miami U., 1953; M.A., Western Reserve U., 1959; Ph. D., State U. of Iowa, 1963. U.S. Army (Panama), 1955–56; ASST. PROF., HISTORY, WIS. STATE COLL., 1962– . University fellow, State U. of Iowa, 1961–62. Membership: American Historical Association; Midwest Council of the Association for Latin American Studies. Research: Mexico since Independence; the Mexican Reforma. Language: Spanish 3,3,3,3; German 2,2,2,2. Home: 1217 College Ave., Stevens Point, Wis. Office: Dept. of History, Wis. State Coll., Stevens Point.

KNOX, A. J. GRAHAM, b. Thames, New Zealand, Oct. 10, 1931. HISTORY. B.A., U. of New Zealand, 1955; M.A., U. of S.C., 1957; Ph. D., U. of Fla., 1962. Catedrático auxiliar, Universidad de P.R., 1959–62; ASST. PROF., HISTORY, HOWARD U., 1962– . Membership: Institute of Race Relations (London); Inter-American Council (Washington, D.C.); Phi Beta Kappa. Research: Antillian area; race relations in Jamaica, 1838–1962; social development in Latin America. Author: Problems of Establishing a Free Society in Jamaica, 1838–1865 (Caribbean Studies, Jan. 1963). Language: Spanish 4,4,4,4; Portuguese 2,2,1,1; Hindustani 1,2,2,1. Home: Apt. 2, 2940 Southern Ave., SE., Washington 20, D.C. Office: Dept. of History, Howard U., Washington, D.C.

KNOX, JOHN BALLENGER, b. Mayesville, S.C., Sept. 16, 1909. SOCIOLOGY. B.A., Davidson Coll., 1930; M.A., U. of N.C., 1934; Ph. D., Harvard U., 1939. Instr., American U. of Beirut, 1930–32; executive secretary, Students International Union, 1937–38; personnel asst., Standard Oil Company, 1938–40; assoc. prof., Alabama Coll., 1940–41; chief of employee relations, U.S. War Production Board, 1942; dir. of civilian personnel, U.S. Navy, 1942–46; PROF., SOCIOLOGY, U. OF TENN., 1946– ; vis. prof., U. of Buenos Aires, 1957; vis. lectr., National U. of Colombia, 1959. Consultant on personnel administration, General Foods Corporation, Summer 1941; participant, 12th National Congress of Sociology (Mexico), 1961; consultant in Mexico, Hemisphere Research Corporation, 1961. Membership: American Sociological Association; Industrial Relations Research Association; International Institute of Sociology; Southern Sociological Society. Research: social psychology; industrial sociology; demography; isolation; Argentine industrial sociology. Author: The Sociology of Industrial Relations (1955); Absenteeism and Turnover in an Argentine Factory (American Sociological Review, June 1961); Las bases sociales de la industrialización (Revista Mexicana de Sociología, Sept.-Dec. 1961). Language: Spanish 4,4,4,4; French 3,3,3,3. Home: 4627 Wye Way Rd., Knoxville, Tenn. Office: Dept. of Sociology, U. of Tenn., Knoxville.

KNOX, ROBERT BAKER, b. Prineville, Oreg., Nov. 22, 1917. SPANISH AMERICAN LITERATURE. B.A., U. of Oreg., 1940; M.A., 1942; Ph. D., U. of Mich., 1952. Instr.-PROF., FOREIGN LANGUAGES, WASH. STATE U., 1949– . Membership: American Association of Teachers of Spanish and Portuguese; American Comparative Literature Association; Modern Language Association; Pacific Coast Conference on Latin American Studies; Pacific Northwest Conference on Foreign Languages; Philological Association. Research: the novel; Mexican and Andean novel. Author: La Mariposa Negra and The Raven (Symposium, Spring 1957); Notes on the Identity of Pedro Gutiérrez de Santa Clara and Some Members of his Family (Revista de Historia de América, June 1958); Some Varieties of the Spanish Novel in the Nineteen Fifties (Proceedings, Pacific Northwest Conference on Foreign Languages, 1960). Language: Spanish 5,4,4,4; Portuguese 4,2,2,3; French 5,4,4,4; German 3,–,–,–. Home: 1622 Charlotte St., Pullman, Wash. 99163. Office:

Dept. of Foreign Languages, Wash. State U., Pullman, 99163.

KOCHER, JOHN BERCHMANS, SISTER, O.P., b. Millbrook, Ill., Oct. 26, 1911. SPANISH AMERICAN AND BRAZILIAN LITERATURE. B.A., Fla. State Coll. for Women, 1932; M.A., Catholic U. of America, 1942; Ph. D., U. of Wis., 1956. Assoc. prof., Rosary Coll., 1942–48; prof., 1950–51; 1952–61; dir., Instituto Santo Domingo (Cochabamba, Bolivia), 1961–63; PROF., SPANISH AND PORTUGUESE, ROSARY COLL., 1963– . Brazilian Government fellow, 1951–52. Membership: Modern Language Association; Sigma Delta Pi. Research: Spanish American and Brazilian civilization; methodology of foreign language teaching; works of Machado de Assis; English as a foreign language. Author: Gabriela Mistral and the Franciscan Concept of Life (Renascence, Autumn 1952). Language: Spanish 5,5,5,4; Portuguese 5, 4,4,4; French 4,3,2,3; German 2,1,1,1; Latin 3,-,-,-. Home and office: Dept. of Spanish and Portuguese, Rosary Coll., River Forest, Ill., 60305.

KOLB, GLEN L., b. Omena, Mich., Apr. 11, 1914. SPANISH AMERICAN LITERATURE. B.A., U. of Mich., 1941; M.A., 1942; Ph. D., 1953. Instr., U. of Mich., 1948–49; instr., Conn. Coll., 1949–53; asst. prof., 1953–64; ASSOC. PROF., SPANISH, CONN. COLL., 1964– . Membership: American Association of Teachers of Spanish and Portuguese; Instituto Internacional de Literatura Iberoamericana; Modern Language Association. Research: Latin American history and civilization; culture of Mexico. Author: Don Juan del Valle y Caviedes; A Study of the Life, Time, and Poetry of a Spanish Colonial Satirist (1959); Aspectos estructurales de Doña Bárbara (Revista Iberoamericana, Jan.–June 1962); Simbolismo y universalidad en Ollantay (Hispania, May 1963). Language: Spanish 5,5,5,5; Portuguese 3,3,3,3; French 4,4,4,4. Home: 125 Mohegan Ave., New London, Conn. Office: Dept. of Spanish, Conn. Coll., New London.

KOLINSKI, CHARLES JAMES, b. Milwaukee, Wis., July 17, 1916. HISTORY. B.A., George Washington U., 1941; M.A., U. of Fla., 1961; Ph. D., 1963. Officer-in-charge, Consulate (Cape Verde Islands), Foreign Service, U.S. Dept. of State, 1940–43; asst. attaché, economic officer (Portugal), 1948–53, (Brazil), 1953–54; consul, economic officer (Guayaquil, Ecuador), 1957–59; second secretary, economic and political officer (Paraguay), 1959–60; asst. prof., Rollins Coll., 1963–64; ASSOC. PROF., HISTORY, FLA. ATLANTIC U., 1964– . Lake Forest Coll. scholarship, 1934–35; student asst., Hispanic American Historical Review, 1961–62; National Defense Foreign Language fellow in Spanish, U. of Fla., 1962–63. Membership: Phi Alpha Theta; Phi Kappa Phi; Pi Gamma Mu. Research: history and peoples of Brazil and the La Plata area. Author: Independence or Death: The Story of the Paraguayan War (1964); The Death of Francisco Solano (The Historian, Nov. 1963). Language: Spanish 5,5,5,5; Portuguese 5,5,5,5; French 3,3,3,2; German 2,2, 2,2; Italian 3,3,3,2. Office: Dept. of History, Fla. Atlantic U., Boca Raton.

KOLMER, LEE R., b. Waterloo, Ill., Jan. 4, 1928. ECONOMICS: MARKETING. B.S., Southern Ill. U., 1952; M.S., Iowa State U., 1952; Ph. D., 1954. Research assoc., Iowa State U., 1953–54; asst. prof., Southern Ill., U., 1954–55; PROF., ECONOMICS, IOWA STATE U., 1956– . Marketing consultant, Iowa State U., Peru Project, Summer 1963. Membership: American Farm Economic Association. Research: economics of marketing; agricultural commodity marketing; management education cooperatives. Author: Consumer Marketing Bulletin: I. Consumer Decision Making (1960); Consumer Marketing Bulletin: III. Understanding Consumers and Markets (1961); Methodology for Problem Solving with Industry Groups (Journal of Farm Economics, Dec. 1963). Language: Spanish 3,2,2,1; German 3,3,3,1. Home: 4719 Dover Dr., Ames, Iowa. Office: Dept. of Economics, Iowa State U., Ames, 50010.

KOMAREK, VIOLA WYCKOFF, b. New Shrewsbury, N.J., Aug. 13, 1908. ECONOMICS. B.S., N.Y.U., 1931; A.M., 1933; Ph. D., Columbia U., 1945. Asst. field agent, U.S. Dept. of Labor, 1934; statistician, National Industrial Recovery Act, 1934–35; asst. economic analyst, U.S. Dept. of Treasury, 1935–39; instr., Iowa State U., 1939–43; asst. prof., Vassar Coll., 1943–45; asst. prof., Wellesley Coll., 1945–47; PROF., ECONOMICS, N.Y.U., 1947– . Membership: American Economic Association; Metropolitan Economic Association of New York. Research: international economics; labor economics; consumer economics; economic development of Brazil. Author: The Public Works Wage Rate (1946); Brazilian Standards of Living (Estadística, Sept. 1962). Co-author: Economic Behavior (1939). Language: Portuguese 2,2,2,2; French 2,–, –,2. Home: 281 Van Emburgh Ave., Ridgewood, N.J. Office: Dept. of Economics, N.Y.U., Washington Square Coll., New York 3, N.Y.

KORTH, EUGENE HENRY, S.J., b. Mankato, Minn., Nov. 23, 1917. HISTORY. B.A., St. Louis U., 1941; Ph. L., 1943; M.A., 1945; S.T.L., 1950; Ph. D., U. of Tex., 1956. Instr., St. Louis U. High School, 1943–46; ASSOC. PROF., HISTORY, MARQUETTE U., 1956– ; chmn., 1958–60; DEAN, COLL. OF LIBERAL ARTS, 1960– . Doherty fellow (Chile), 1953–54. Membership: American Historical Association; Catholic Historical Association; Conference on Latin American History; Jesuit Educational Association; Jesuit Historical Association; Wisconsin State Historical Society. Research: colonial and national periods; Mexico; Chile; church-state relations; education. Author: Modern European History (1946); Pre-Registration and Registration Procedures (1961); Economic Aspects of German Intervention in the Spanish Civil War, 1936–1939 (Mid-America, July 1960). Language: Spanish 4,4, 3,2; Portuguese 2,2,1,1; French 3,2,1,1; German 3,3,2,1. Home and office: Coll. of Liberal Arts, Marquette U., 1131 West Wisconsin Ave., Milwaukee, Wis. 53233.

KOZOLCHYK, BORIS, b. Marianao, Havana, Cuba, Dec. 6, 1934. LAW. Doctorate, U. of Habana, 1956; LL.B., Faculté Internationale de Droit Comparé, 1959; LL.M., School of Law, U. of Mich., 1960. Vis. prof., School of Law, U. of Chile, Summers 1959, 1961, 1962; PROF., LAW, SOUTHERN METHODIST U., 1960– . Ford fellow, U. of Miami, 1956; Cook fellow, U. of

Mich., 1960. Membership: American Association of Law Schools; American Association of University Professors; American Foreign Law Association; Inter-American Bar Association. Research: comparative inter-American law, especially commercial law; legal systems of Chile, Mexico, and Uruguay; letters of credit in inter-American trade. Author: Comparative Law, Another Approach (Journal of Legal Education, 1961); Comparative Law and Practice Training (Foreign Exchange Bulletin, 1963–64); Reflexiones en torno a la enseñanza del derecho en el Hemisferio Occidental (Estudios Jurídicos, 1964). Language: Spanish 5,5,5,5; Portuguese 4,5,3,2; French 4,4,2,1; Italian 3,3,2,1; Yiddish 5,5,5,5. Home: 1700 Main St., Santa Monica, Calif. 90406. Office: School of Law, Southern Methodist U., Dallas 22, Tex.

KRAESSEL, ALFRED, b. Vienna, Austria, Mar. 23, 1925. ECONOMICS. B.A., Universidad de San Marcos (Peru), 1942; B.S., 1945; Ph. D., 1948. Member, Project Staff, San Marcos U., 1946–48; vis. reader, Mich. State U., 1948–49; asst. prof., U. of Bridgeport, 1949–52; asst. prof., research assoc., U. of Chicago, 1953–54; asst. prof., Rutgers U, 1954–57; asst. prof., U. of Buffalo, 1957–58; asst. prof., Ithaca Coll., 1958–59; PROF., ECONOMICS, SETON HALL U., 1959– . Ford Foundation faculty fellow, Princeton U., 1961. Membership: American Association of University Professors; American Economic Association. Research: price theory; economic development and problems of Latin America; socio-cultural aspects of developing nations; international trade. Author: Economic Development of the Huauaga Region in Peru (1954); Equilibrium of the Firm and Effect of Sales Taxes (Journal of Business, Dec. 1962). Language: Spanish 5,5,5,5; Portuguese 3,3,2,1; French 3,2,2,1; German 5,5,5,5. Home: 689 Prospect Ave., West Orange, N.J. 07052. Office: Dept. of Economics, Seton Hall U., South Orange, N.J.

KRAUSE, ANNEMARIE E., b. Herzfelde, Germany, Dec. 4, 1901. GEOGRAPHY. B.S., U. of Minn., 1928; M.S. U. of Ill., 1930; Ph. D., U. of Chicago, 1952. Asst. prof., Southern Ill. U., 1930–52; ASSOC. PROF. GEOGRAPHY, SOUTHERN ILL. U., 1952– . American Philosophical Society grant. Membership: Association of American Geographers; Illinois Geographical Society; Midwest Council of the Association for Latin American Studies; National Council for Geographic Education. Research: economic geography; colony settlements in Paraguay. Author: Mennonite Settlements in the Paraguayan Chaco (1952). Language: Spanish 3,3,3,3; German 5,5,5,5. Home: 904 Carter, Carbondale, Ill. 62901. Office: Dept. of Geography, Southern Ill. U., Carbondale, 62903.

KRAUSE, WALTER, b. Canby, Oreg., Jan. 12, 1917. ECONOMICS. B.A., U. of Oreg., 1942; M.A., 1943; A.M., Harvard U., 1944; Ph. D., 1945. Asst. prof., U. of Tex., 1945–47; asst. prof., Dartmouth Coll., 1947–50; prof., U. of Utah, 1950–54; adviser, International Cooperative Administration, U.S. Dept. of State, 1955–58; prof., State U. of Iowa, 1958–62; PROF., ECONOMICS, U. OF CALIF., RIVERSIDE, 1962– . Consultant, Pan American Union, Washington, D.C. Membership: American Economic Association. Research: economic development; international economics; Latin American economy. Author: The International Economy (1955); Economic Development: The Underdeveloped World and the American Interest (1961); Report on Latin America (1961). Office: Dept. of Economics, U. of Calif., Riverside.

KRIEGER, ALEX DONY, b. Duluth, Minn., Dec. 11, 1911. ANTHROPOLOGY. B.A., U. of Calif., Berkeley, 1936; M.A., U. of Oreg., 1939; Sc. D., Universidad Nacional de México, 1955. Project supervisor, Statewide Archeological Survey, U. of Tex., Works Progress Administration, 1939–41; archeologist, U. of Tex., 1941–47; research scientist, U. of Tex., 1947–56; museum dir., City of Riverside (Calif.), 1956–60; vis. assoc. prof., U. of Calif., Riverside, 1958–59; lectr., U. of Wash., 1960; RESEARCH PROF., ANTHROPOLOGY, U. OF WASH., 1961– . Consultant, River Basin Surveys (Texas), Smithsonian Institution, 1946–52; Viking Fund Medal and Award in Archeology, 1948; Wenner-Gren Foundation grants, 1948–50, Summers 1954, 1955; National Park Service grants (Texas, Mexico), Summers 1950–52; collaborator on field projects, National Park Service, 1952–54; collaborator, Instituto Nacional de Antropología e Historia (Mexico), 1952–55; consultant, American Philosophical Society-Universidad de Puebla (Mexico), 1960–62; National Science Foundation fellow, 1961; Pan American Union travel grant, 1962; Bollingen Foundation fellow, 1962–63; Guggenheim fellow, 1963–64. Membership: American Anthropological Association; Society for American Archaeology; Texas Archeological Society. Research: archeology and culture history of the New World; Middle American and Andean civilizations; racial origins of the American Indians; Pleistocene geology and paleontology. Author: The Travels of Alvar Nuñez Cabeza de Vaca in Texas and Mexico, 1534–1536 (in Homenaje a Pablo Martínez del Río, 1961); Early Man in the New World (in Prehistoric Man in the New World, 1964); New World Lithic Typology Project: Part II (American Antiquity, 1964). Language: Spanish 4,3,3,2; Portuguese 2,1,1,1; French 2,1,1,1; German 3,1,1,1. Home: 209 Lake Washington Blvd., Seattle, Wash. 98122. Office: Dept. of Anthropology, U. of Wash., Seattle, 98105.

KROEBER, CLIFTON BROWN, b. Berkeley, Calif., Sept. 7, 1921. HISTORY. A.B., U. of Calif., Berkeley, 1943; M.A., 1947; Ph. D., 1951. Lectr., U. of Calif. Extension Div., Berkeley, 1950–51; asst. prof., U. of Wis., 1951–55; ASSOC. PROF., HISTORY, OCCIDENTAL COLL., 1955– ; assoc. prof., Guadalajara Summer School (Mexico), Summers 1960, 1963. Heller traveling fellow (Argentina), 1949–50; Area Research fellow, Social Science Research Council, 1949–50; Haynes Foundation summer fellow, 1959. Membership: American Association of University Professors; American Historical Association; Conference on Latin American History; Pacific Coast Council on Latin American Studies; Western History Association. Research: Mexico and the Río de la Plata region. Author: The Growth of the Shipping Industry in the Río de la Plata Region, 1794–1860 (1957); The Mobilization of Philip II's Revenue in Peru, 1590–1596 (The Economic History Review, Apr. 1958); El Consulado de Buenos Aires en el proceso de la Revolución de Mayo, 1794–1810 (Trabajos y Comunicaciones, Universidad Nacional de la Plata, No. 9, 1960). Language: Spanish 4,4,4,4; French 2,2,1,1; German 2,2,1,1. Home: 1701 Linda Rosa Ave., Los Angeles, Calif. 90041. Office: Dept. of History, Occidental Coll., Los Angeles, 90041.

KRUMM, ROGER VINCENT, b. Decorah, Iowa, Feb. 1, 1919. LIBRARY SCIENCE. A.B., Luther Coll., 1940; M.A., U. of Denver, 1951. CHEMISTRY LIBRARIAN, U. OF FLA., 1951– ; Serials Dept., Centro de Documentación Científica y Técnica (México, D.F.), June 1960; Catalog Dept., Biblioteca, Universidad Autónoma de México, July 1960. Editor, Fla. Section, American Chemical Society Publication, FLACS, 1958–; translation consultant, Minute Maid Company, 1963– . Membership: American Chemical Society; Florida Library Association; Gamma Sigma Epsilon; Special Libraries Association. Research: chemical librarianship and chemical literature. Author: Journals Most Frequently Abstracted by Chemical Abstracts (in Scientific Serials, 1954). Co-author: Lista de Publicaciones en su Hemeroteca (1960). Language: Spanish 4,4,5,4; Portuguese 2,1,1,1,1; French 5,2,2,2,; German 5,2,2,2. Home: 1804 NW. 5th Ave., Gainesville, Fla. 32601. Office: U. of Fla., Gainesville, 32603.

KRUSE, CORNELIUS, b. Sappington, Mo., Apr. 21, 1893. PHILOSOPHY. B.D., Yale U., 1915; A.M., 1917; Ph. D., 1922; L.H.D. (honorary), Lawrence Coll., 1952. Instr., U. of Ill., 1920; assoc., 1921–23; assoc. prof., Wesleyan U., 1923–28; prof., 1928–61; chmn., Philosophy, 1930–61; PROF. EMERITUS, PHILOSOPHY, WESLEYAN U., 1961–; vis. prof., U. of N.C., 1962–63; vis. prof., U. of Fla., 1963–64. Cultural Mission to Latin America, Coordinator's Office for Inter-American Affairs, 1943; executive dir., American Council of Learned Societies, 1947–48; vice president, International Congress of Philosophy (São Paulo), 1954; vice president, Congress of Interamerican Society of Philosophy (Santiago), 1956; U.S. specialist, U.S. Dept. of State Mission to Latin America, Summer 1956; U.S. specialist, International Educational Exchange, Summer 1958. Membership; American Philosophical Association; Institut International de Philosophie; Interamerican Society of Philosophy. Research: Latin American philosophers and their points of view. Co-author: The Nature of Religious Experience (1937); The Nature of Man (1950); Essays in East-West Philosophy (1951). Language: Spanish 5,5,4,3; Portuguese 4,4,2,1; French 5,5,5,4; German 5,5,5,5; Italian 5,3,3,3; Russian 5,3,3,3. Home: Randolph Rd., Middletown, Conn. Office: Dept. of Philosophy, Wesleyan U., Middletown.

KUBLER, GEORGE ALEXANDER, b. Los Angeles, Calif. July 26, 1912. ART AND ARCHITECTURE. B.A., Yale U., 1934; M. A., 1936; Ph. D., 1940. PROF., HISTORY OF ART, YALE U., 1938– ; vis. prof., U. of Chicago, 1946; anthropologist, Smithsonian Institution (Peru), 1948–49; chief of mission, UNESCO Mission on Conservation and Restoration of Cuzco, Peru, 1951–56. American Council of Learned Societies fellow (Mexico). 1941; Guggenheim fellow, 1943–57; editor-in-chief, Art Bulletin, 1945–47; Smith-Mundt lectr. (Mexico), 1958; Fulbright research fellow (Spain, Portugal), 1963–64. Membership: College Art Association; Hispanic Society of America; Société des Américanistes de Paris. Research: history of primitive art; archeology. Author: Mexican Architecture of the 16th Century (1948); Art and Architecture of Spain and Portugal (1959); Art and Architecture of Ancient America (1962). Language: Spanish 4,4,4,4; Portuguese 3,3,3,3; French 4,4,4,4; German 3,3,3,3; Italian 3,3,3 3. Linguistic studies: Nahuatl; Quechua. Home: 406 Humphrey St., New Haven 11, Conn. Office: Dept. of History of Art, Yale U., New Haven 11.

KUNKEL, JOHN HOWARD, b. Berlin, Germany, Nov. 14, 1932. SOCIOLOGY. B.A., Pomona Coll., 1954; M.A., U. of Mich., 1955; Ph. D., 1960. ASST. PROF., SOCIOLOGY, ARIZ. STATE U., 1959– . Membership: American Anthropological Association; American Economic Association; American Sociological Association. Research: nation and peasant communities in Mexico; social change and economic development in Latin America, especially Mexico. Author: Economic Autonomy and Social Change in Mexican Villages (Economic Development and Cultural Change, Oct. 1961); Psychological Factors in the Analysis of Social Change (Journal of Social Issues, Jan. 1963). Language: Spanish 4,4,4,4; French 2,2,2,1; German 5,5,5,5. Home: 1715 Cutler Dr., Tempe, Ariz. Office; Dept. of Sociology. Ariz. State U., Tempe.

KURTH, WILLIAM H., b. Union Hill, N.J., July 4, 1917. LIBRARY SCIENCE. A.B., U. of Va., 1941; M.S., Catholic U. of America, 1958. Asst. chief, Order Div., Library of Congress, 1945–59; head, Circulation Dept., National Library of Medicine (Bethesda, Md.), 1959–62; Latin American bibliographer, Library, U. of Calif., Los Angeles, 1962–63; HEAD, ACQUISITIONS DEPT., LIBRARY, U. OF CALIF., LOS ANGELES, 1963– . Consultant in library services, Veterans Administration. Membership: American Library Association. Research: booktrade and libraries in South America. Author: Circulation of Books in the Americas (1960). Language: Spanish 3,3,3,–; French 2,2,2,2; German 2,2,2,2. Home: 1516 Camden Ave., Los Angeles, Calif. 90025. Office: Acquisitions Dept., Library, U. of Calif., Los Angeles, 90024.

KUTISH, FRANCIS A., b. New Hampton, Iowa, Apr. 23, 1915. ECONOMICS. B.S., Iowa State U., 1938; M.S., 1941. Instr., Iowa State U., 1941–58; asst. prof., 1958–62; PROF., AGRICULTURAL MARKETING, IOWA STATE U., 1962– ; agricultural marketing specialist, U.S. Dept. of Agriculture (El Salvador), 1963–65. Adviser, International Cooperation Administration (Santiago, Chile), 1958; adviser, U.S. Agency for International Development Bogotá, Colombia), 1962. Membership: American Farm Economic Association; International Conference of Agricultural Economists; Sigma Delta Chi. Research: agricultural economics; farm management;

marketing; foreign economic development and planning in agriculture; Central America. Language: Spanish 3,3,3,3. Home: R.F.D. 3, Ames, Iowa. Office: Dept. of Agriculture, Iowa State U., Ames.

KYLE, LEONARD R., b. Louisville, Ohio, Oct. 21, 1918. ECONOMICS. B.S., Mich. State U., 1940; M.S., Purdue U., 1948; Ph. D., 1953. Extension economist, U. of Ill., 1953–54; extension economist, Mich. State U., 1954–57; economist, Mich. State U. Colombian Project (Colombia), 1957; PROF. and EXTENSION ECONOMIST. AGRICULTURAL ECONOMICS, MICH. STATE U., 1959– . Research: agricultural economics; farm management; problems of individual agricultural producer. Author: Costo de producción de leche (1959). Language: Spanish 2.2.1,–. Home; 2340 Shawnee Trail, Okemos, Mich. Office; Dept. of Agricultural Economics, Mich. State U., East Lansing.

L

LaBARGE, RICHARD ALLEN, b. Salt Lake City, Utah, May 6, 1934. ECONOMICS. A.B., U. of Mich., 1954; M.A., Tulane U., 1955; Ph. D., Duke U., 1959. Asst. prof., Southern Methodist U., 1957–60; financial analysist, Ford Motor Company, 1960–62; SPECIAL LEGISLATIVE ANALYST, FORD MOTOR COMPANY, 1962– . Research assoc., Middle American Research Institute, Tulane U. (Guatemala), Summer 1955; Social Science Research Council fellow (Costa Rica, Honduras, Panama), 1956–57. Membership: American Economic Association; American Statistical Association; Phi Beta Kappa; Southern Economic Association; Southwestern Social Science Association. Research: political science; legislative analysis; Isthmian America. Author: Impact of the United Fruit Company on the Economic Development of Guatemala, 1946–1954 (1960); The Role of Foreign Capital in the Economic Development of Honduras, 1946 to 1956 (in Economic Development and International Trade, A Perspective, 1959); The Imputation of Values to Intra-Company Exports, The Case of Bananas (Social and Economic Studies, June 1961). Language: Spanish 4,4,4,4; Portuguese 3,1,1,1; French 4,3,3,3. Home: 2819 Trenton Dr., Trenton, Mich. 48183. Office: Ford Motor Company, 992 Central Office Bldg., Dearborn, Mich. 48121.

LA BARRE, WESTON, b. Uniontown, Pa., Dec. 13, 1911. ANTHROPOLOGY. A.B., Princeton U., 1933; Ph. D., Yale U., 1937. Instr., Rutgers U., 1938–43; asst. prof.-PROF., ANTHROPOLOGY, DUKE U., 1946– . Sterling fellow (Bolivia), 1937–38; National Science Foundation senior fellow, 1962–63; consultant in anthropology, Group for the Advancement of Psychiatry. Membership: American Anthropological Association. Research: culture and personality; ethnology; social anthropology. Author: Aymará Indians (1948); The Human Animal (1954); The Peyote Cult (1960). Language: Spanish 3,3,3,3; French 5,4,4,3; German 2,2,1,2; Italian 4,4,3,2. Linguistic studies: Aymará. Home: Mt. Sinai Rd., Durham, N.C. Office: Dept. of Sociology and Anthropology, Duke U., Durham.

LADD, JOHN, b. New York, N.Y., Mar. 3, 1923. ANTHROPOLOGY. B.A., Swarthmore Coll., 1949; M.P.A., Princeton U., 1951; Ph. D., Harvard U., 1963. Research asst., United Nations, 1950; international relations officer, British desk, U.S. Dept. of State, 1951–55; archeologist, Harvard U. (Guatemala), 1963; RESEARCH FELLOW, PEABODY MUSEUM, HARVARD U., 1964– . Consultant, Educational Services, Inc. (Cambridge, Mass.). Membership: American Anthropological Association; Society for American Archeology. Research: archeology; Mayan site of Chichén Itzá in Yucatán, México; Altar de Sacrificios, Guatemala; Panama; British Honduras. Language: Spanish 3,3,3,3; German 2,2,2,2. Home: 140 Upland Rd., Cambridge 40, Mass. Office: Peabody Museum, Harvard U., Cambridge.

LADO, ROBERT, b. Tampa, Fla., May 31, 1915. LINGUISTICS. B.A., Rollins Coll., 1939; A.M., U. of Tex., 1945; Ph. D., U. of Mich., 1950. Instr., U. of Mich., 1945–50; asst. dir., Language Institute, U. of Mich., 1946–53; assoc. dir., 1953–56; dir., 1956–60; DIR., INSTITUTE OF LANGUAGES AND LINGUISTICS, GEORGETOWN U., 1960– ; DEAN, 1961– . U.S. lecture grant (South America), 1953, (Mexico), 1955; guest lectr. (Latin America, Japan, Thailand, Great Britain); developer, Advisory Committee on the Training of Teachers (Tokyo); United States coordinator, Fulbright Program on Teaching of English in Spain. 1963; co-founder. Departmento Lorenzo Herves y Panduro de Investigaciones Lingüísticas (Madrid), 1963. Membership: Linguistic Society of America; Modern Language Association. Research: structure, sound system, lexicon, and cultural patterns of English as compared with those of other languages. Author: Linguistics Across Cultures (1957); Language Testing (1961); Language Teaching: A Scientific Approach (1964). Home: 5404 Newington Rd., Washington, D.C. Office: Institute of Languages and Linguistics, Georgetown U., Washington, D.C.

LAMB, RUTH S., b. St. Louis, Mo., Apr. 19, 1913. SPANISH AMERICAN LITERATURE. B.A., Pomona Coll., 1936; M.A., Claremont Graduate School, 1937; Ph. D., U. of Southern Calif., 1943. Instr., Northwestern U., 1942–44; PROF., SPANISH AND LATIN AMERICAN LITERATURE, SCRIPPS COLL., 1944– . Del Amo fellow (Spain), 1956; Fulbright prof., Universidade de São Paulo, 1963; chmn., Textbooks for Spanish and Portuguese Committee, Modern Language Association. Membership: American Association of Teachers of Spanish and Portuguese; Instituto Internacional de Literatura Iberoamericana; Modern Language Association; Pacific Coast Council for Latin American Studies. Research: Argentine literature; contemporary Latin American novel and poetry; modern Mexican literature and history; modern novel in Brazil. Author: History of the Mexican Theatre (1958, 1963); Cuentos Guatemaltecos (1960); Latin America: Sites and Insights (1963). Language: Spanish 5,5,5,5; Portuguese 4,4,4,4; French 4,4,4,4; German 2,2,2,2; Italian 3,3,3,2. Linguistic studies: Portuguese; Spanish.

Home: 4442 East Live Oak Dr., Claremont, Calif. Office: Dept. of Romance Languages, Scripps Coll., Claremont.

LAMB, URSULA SCHAEFER, b. Essen, Germany, Jan. 15, 1914. HISTORY. U. of Berlin (Germany), 1932–35; Smith Coll., 1935–36; M.A., U. of Calif., Berkeley, 1937; Ph. D., 1949. Lectr., Barnard Coll., 1943–49; assoc., 1949–51; tutor, Spanish, Brasenose Coll. (England), 1960; RESEARCH ASSOC., LECTR., HISTORY, YALE U., 1963– . Exchange student, Smith Coll., 1935–36; Walter Loewy scholar, U. of Calif., 1936–39; American Council of Learned Societies grant, 1943; Columbia U.-Social Science Research Council grant (Spain), 1947. Membership: American Historical Association; Conference on Latin American History; Society of the History of Discoveries. Research: Latin American colonial history; use of 16th century sources. Author: Frey Nicolás de Ovando, Gobernador de las Indias, 1501–1509 (1956); Religious Conflicts in the Conquest of Mexico (Journal of the History of Ideas, Oct. 1956). Language: Spanish 5,5,3,3; Portuguese 4,2,1,1; French 5,5,3,2; German 5,5,5,5. Home: 166 Linden St., New Haven, Conn. Office: Dept. of History, Yale U., New Haven.

LANCASTER, C. MAXWELL, b. York, Ala., 1911. SPANISH AMERICAN LITERATURE. A.M., Ind. U., 1931; Oxford U., 1931–35; Johns Hopkins U., 1935. Teacher, Ind. U., 1930–31; assoc. prof., Howard Coll., 1934–39; vis. prof., Vanderbilt U., 1939–41; asst. prof., 1942–46; assoc. prof., 1946–57; PROF., ROMANCE LANGUAGES, VANDERBILT U., 1957– . Ind. U. fellow, 1930–31; Rhodes scholar, Oxford U., 1931–35; Order of Merit, Bernardo O'Higgins (Chile), 1950. Membership: American Association of Teachers of French; Association of American Rhodes Scholars; Modern Language Association. Research: translations; Chilean and Spanish epic of the late 16th and early 17th centuries. Translator: Saints and Sinners in Old Romance; Poems of Feudal France and England (1942). Co-translator: The Araucaniad, a Version of English Poetry of Alonso de Ercilla y Zúñiga's La Araucana (1945); Arauco Tamed, by Pedro de Oña (1948). Office: Dept. of Romance Languages, Vanderbilt U., Nashville 4, Tenn.

LANCE, BETTY RITA GOMEZ, b. San José Costa Rica, Aug. 28, 1923. SPANISH AMERICAN LITERATURE. B.S., Central Mo. State Coll., 1944; M.A., U. of Mo., 1947; Ph. D., Washington U., 1959. Instr., U. of Mo., 1948–50; instr., Mathematics, N. Mex. A. and M. Coll., 1951–52; science instr., Bayless Senior High School (Mo.), 1955; asst. instr., Washington U., 1955–59; U. of Ill., 1959–61; ASST. PROF., SPANISH, KALAMAZOO COLL., 1961– ; coordinator, National Defense Education Act Spanish Language Institute, Kalamazoo Coll., Summer 1962. Membership: American Association of Teachers of Spanish and Portuguese; American Association of University Professors; Modern Language Association. Research: modern and contemporary periods. Author: Acerca de Jorge Luis Borges (La Nueva Democracia, Oct. 1958); Héctor Velarde—un estudio (La Nueva Democracia, July 1959). Language: Spanish 5,5,5,5; Portuguese: 3,3,3,3; French 3,3,3,3; German 3,1,1,1; Italian 3,3,3,3. Home: 1562 Spruce Dr., Kalamazoo, Mich. Office: Dept. of Spanish, Kalamazoo Coll., Kalamazoo.

LANDES, RUTH, b. New York, N.Y., Oct. 8, 1908. ANTHROPOLOGY. B.S., N.Y.U., 1928; M.S.W., N.Y. School of Social Work, 1929; Ph. D., Columbia U., 1935. Instr., Brooklyn Coll., 1937; instr., Fisk U., 1937–38; staff assoc., Carnegie Corporation (N.Y.), 1939; research staff, Coordinator of Inter American Affairs, 1941; representative, President's Committee on Fair Employment, 1941–45; dir., interim Fair Employment Practices Committee Program (N.Y.), 1945; researcher, Los Angeles Metropolitan Welfare Council, 1946–47; research dir., American Jewish Committee, 1948–51; lectr., New School for Social Research, 1953–55; lectr., William Alanson White Psychiatric Institute (N.Y.), 1953–54; vis. prof., U. of Southern Calif., 1957–58; dir., Geriatrics Research Program, Los Angeles City Health Dept., 1958–59; vis. prof., dir., Education and Anthropology Training Project, Claremont Graduate School and U. Center, 1959–62; prof., Columbia U., Summer 1963; vis. prof., Tulane U., Spring 1964; PROF., ANTHROPOLOGY, McMASTER U., 1965– . Social Science Research Council grants, 1932–33, 1934–35, 1935–36, (Brazil), 1938–39; Columbia U. research fellow, 1933–40; Fulbright scholar (Britain), 1951–52. Membership: American Anthropological Association. Research: social anthropology; culture in Brazil; Mexico as background for the Southwest; American ethnic groups. Author: The City of Women (1947); Negro Fetish Worship in Brazil (Journal of American Folklore, Oct.-Dec. 1940); Biracialism in American Society: A Comparative View (American Anthropologist, Dec. 1955). Language: Spanish 3,4,3,1; Portuguese 4,4,4,3; French 3,4,3,3; German 3,4,3,2. Home: 219 West 12th St., Claremont, Calif. Office: Dept. of Sociology and Anthropology, McMaster U., Hamilton, Ontario, Canada.

LANDSBERGER, HENRY A., b. Dresden, Germany, Aug. 5, 1926. SOCIOLOGY AND PSYCHOLOGY. B.S., London School of Economics and Political Science, 1948; Ph. D., Cornell U., 1954. Research assoc., Cornell U., 1954–55; asst. research officer, Institute of Statistics, U. of Oxford (England), 1955–56; asst. dir., Social Science Research Center, Cornell U., 1956–58; asst. prof., 1956–60; ASSOC. PROF., INDUSTRIAL RELATIONS, CORNELL U., 1961–; prof., Facultad de Ciencias Económicas, Cornell U.-Universidad de Chile contract (Chile), 1961–65. Social Science Research Council fellow, 1964–65; consultant, U.S. Agency for International Development Mission (Chile), 1964–65. Membership: American Psychological Association; American Sociological Association; Industrial Relations Research Association. Research: sociology of economic development and complex organization; social psychology; Latin American peasant movement; Latin American labor movements and the role of the Church in relation to the labor movement and reform. Author: The Chilean Labor Leader: A Preliminary Report on His Background and Attitudes (Industrial and

Labor Relations Review, Apr. 1964); El administrador de personal chileno: informe preliminar (Instituto de Organización y Administración, Universidad de Chile, July 1964). Language: Spanish 4,4,4,4; Portuguese 1,1,1,1; French 2,1,1,1; German 5,5, 4,4. Office: N.Y. State School of Industrial and Labor Relations, Cornell U., Ithaca, N.Y. 14850.

LANDY, DAVID, b. Savannah, Ga., June 4, 1917. ANTHROPOLOGY. B.A., U. of N.C., 1949; M.A., 1950; Ph. D., Harvard U., 1956. Field dir., Family Life Project, U. of P.R., 1951–53; research assoc., Harvard Medical School, 1956–60; asst. prof., Boston U. School of Social Work, 1956–60; research assoc., co-principal investigator, Mass. Mental Health Center, 1956–60; assoc. prof., Graduate School of Public Health, U. of Pittsburgh, 1960–63; PROF., CHMN., ANTHROPOLOGY, U. OF PITTSBURGH, 1963–. Executive Committee, American Indian Ethnohistoric Conference; assoc. editor, Ethnology; dir., Field Training Project under National Science Foundation grant, U. of Pittsburgh—Stanford U.— U. of Nev. (Mexico; Nev.). Membership: American Anthropological Association; American Association for the Advancement of Science; American Sociological Association; Society for Applied Anthropology. Research: cultural anthropology; comparative medical systems; primitive and folk medicine; cultures of the Caribbean and Mesoamerica; family organization and socialization in rural Puerto Rico. Author: Tropical Childhood: Cultural Learning and Transmission in a Rural Puerto Rican Village (1959); Tuscarora Tribalism and National Identity (Ethnohistory, Summer 1958); Problems of the Person Seeking Help in Our Culture (Social Welfare Forum, 1960). Language: Spanish 4,4,4,4; French 2,1,1,1. Home: 6636 Dalzell Pl., Pittsburgh, Pa. 15217. Office: Dept. of Anthropology, U. of Pittsburgh, Pittsburgh, 15213.

LANE, GEORGE B., JR., b. San Antonio, Tex., Nov. 18, 1930. POLITICAL SCIENCE. B.A., Trinity U., 1951; Ph. D., American U., 1962. Intelligence officer, U.S. Air Force, 1953–58; research asst., Special Operations Research Office, American U., Summer 1959; Latin American affairs analyst, U.S. Dept. of Health, Education, and Welfare, 1962–64; EDUCATION RESEARCH AND PROGRAM SPECIALIST, LANGUAGE AND AREA CENTERS SECTION, U.S. OFFICE OF EDUCATION, 1964–. Massey Foundation fellow, American U., 1959–60; National Defense Foreign Language fellow in Portuguese, U. of Tex., Summer 1963. Membership: American Academy of Political and Social Science; American Political Science Association; Pi Gamma Mu; Pi Sigma Alpha. Research: Latin American foreign affairs; socio-political development; Brazilian social change; Peruvian education. Language: Spanish 3,3,3,3; Portuguese 3,3,2,2; French 1,–,–,–; Mandarin Chinese 1,2,2,1. Home: 9624 Brunett Ave., Silver Spring, Md. Office: U.S. Office of Education, Dept. of Health, Education, and Welfare, Washington, D.C.

LANGMAN, IDA KAPLAN, b. Borzna, Russia, Feb. 7, 1904. LIBRARY SCIENCE: BIBLIOGRAPHY AND BOTANY. B.S., U. of Pa., 1930; M.S., 1947. Teacher, Philadelphia School Board, 1922–50; museum teacher, 1950–56; research fellow, U. of Pa., 1956–65; translator and abstractor, Biological Abstracts, 1961–65; FREE LANCE TRANSLATOR AND ABSTRACTOR, 1965– . U.S. Office of Education travel and maintenance grant (Mexico), 1948–49; National Science Foundation grant, U. of Pa., 1956–60 (Mexico), 1956–57, 1962–63; American Philosophical Society, 1961–62. Membership: Academia Nacional de Ciencias de México; American Association for the Advancement of Science; American Institute of Biological Sciences; American Society of Plant Taxonomists; American Translators Association; International Association of Plant Taxonomists; Sociedad Botánica de México. Research: taxonomy; plant geography; translating and abstracting biological literature; botanical bibliography with emphasis on Mexico; museum education. Author: A Selected Guide to the Literature on the Flowering Plants of Mexico (1965); Mexican Libraries Move Ahead (International Institute of Education News Bulletin, Mar. 1960); Travel and Descriptive Works Prior to 1800 Useful for Studies in Mexican Botany (Revista Interamericana de Bibliografía, July–Sept. 1960). Language: Spanish 5,5,4,4; Portuguese 4,3,3,2; French 3,3,3,2; Italian 2,–,–,–. Home: 248 Harvey St., Philadelphia, Pa. 19144. Office: Div. of Biology, U. of Pa., Philadelphia, 19104.

LANNING, EDWARD PUTNAM, b. Northville, Mich., Sept. 21, 1930. ANTHROPOLOGY. B.A., U. of Calif., 1953; Ph. D., 1960. Archeological field asst. (Peru), 1956–57; catedrático, Universidad Nacional Mayor de San Marcos (Peru), 1958; instr., Sacramento State Coll., 1959–60; senior museum anthropologist, R. H. Lowie Museum, U. of Calif., Berkeley, 1960–61; ASST. PROF., ANTHROPOLOGY, COLUMBIA U., 1963– . Fulbright teaching grant, Universidad Nacional Mayor de San Marcos (Peru), 1961–63. Membership: Institute of Andean Studies; Society for American Archaeology. Research: archeology; South American culture history; early man in South America; origins and development of agriculture; origins of Andean ancient civilizations; Peru. Author: A Ceramic Sequence for the Piura and Chira Coast, Northern Peru (1963); Early Lithic Industries of Western South America (American Antiquity, Oct. 1961); A Pre-agricultural Occupation on the Central Corst of Peru (American Antiquity, 1963). Language: Spanish 5,5,5,5; Portuguese 3,1,1,1; French 3,2,2,2; German 3,1,1,1. Home: Apt. 3-R, 142 Montague St., Brooklyn 1, N.Y. Office: Dept. of Anthropology, Columbia U., New York 27, N.Y.

LANNING, JOHN TATE, b. Linwood, N.C., Sept. 13, 1902. HISTORY. A.B., Trinity Coll., 1924; A.M., U. of Calif., Berkeley, 1925; Ph. D., 1928. Instr.-prof., Duke U., 1927–61; JAMES B. DUKE PROF. OF HISTORY, DUKE U., 1961– ; lectr., U. of Chile and U. of Córdoba, 1931; lectr., George Washington U., 1935; Trumbull lectr., Yale U., 1943. Guggenheim Latin American exchange fellow, 1930–31; American Council of Learned Societies grant, 1932; assoc. managing editor, Hispanic American Historical Review, 1935–39; managing editor, 1939–45; Duke U. research grants (Mexico), 1936, 1942, (Guatemala), 1938, (Spain), 1949; Social Science Research Council grant, 1941; Committee on Inter-American Cultural and Artistic Relations, 1942; Carnegie Revolving Fund Prize, 1955; Bolton Prize, 1956; Serra Award, Academy of American Franciscan History, 1958; Medal of Merit, U. of Ariz., 1960; Board of Advisory Editors, Hispanic American Historical Review, The Americas, and Latin American Review; chmn., Council on Research, Duke U. Membership: American Historical Association; Conference on Latin American History; Phi Beta Kappa; Sociedad Cubana de Estudios Históricos e Internacionales; Sociedad de Geografía e Historia de Guatemala. Research: academic, intellectual, and cultural history of the Spanish Empire. Author: Academic Culture in the Spanish Colonies (1940); The University in the Kingdom of Guatemala (1955); The Eighteenth Century Enlightenment in the University of San Carlos de Guatemala (1956). Language: Spanish 5,5,4,4; Portuguese 4,4,4,4; French 4,4,4,4; German 4,4,4,4; Greek 4,4,4,4; Latin 4,4,4,4. Home: 3007 Surrey Rd., Hope Valley, Durham, N.C. Office: 120 Allen Bldg., Duke U., Durham.

LAREW, LEONOR A., b. New York, N.Y., May 29, 1925. LANGUAGE. B.S., N.Y.U., 1946; National U. of Mexico, 1947–49; M.A., N.Y.U., 1950; Ph. D., U. of Mo., 1960. Reporter, El Universal (México, D.F.), 1946–48; secretary to the editor, El Diario de Nueva York, 1949–51; instr., U. of Tenn., 1950–51; teacher, Spring Glen School (Conn.), 1954–55; teacher, Hamden High School (Conn.), 1955–56; instr., U. of Mo., 1956–60; ASSOC. PROF., FOREIGN LANGUAGES, STATE U. OF N.Y. COLL. AT GENESEO, 1960– ; master demonstration teacher, Secondary School Level, National Defense Education Act Summer Institute, Rosary Coll., Summer 1961; master demonstration teacher, Foreign Languages in Elementary Schools, National Defense Education Act Summer Institute, Washington U., Summer 1963. Fels Foundation graduate fellow, U. of Mo. Membership: American Association of Teachers of Spanish and Portuguese; American Association of University Professors; Modern Language Association. Research: Spanish; methods of teaching a foreign language in elementary schools. Author: The Optimum Age for Initiation of a Foreign Language (The Modern Language Journal, May 1961); Tape Recorder versus the Teacher in Spanish Classes (The Elementary School Journal, Jan. 1962); Teach Poetry to Your High School Students (Hispania, Dec. 1962). Language: Spanish 5,5,5,5; Portuguese 2,1,1,1; French 3,1,1,1. Home: 58 Lima Rd., Geneseo, N.Y. Office: Dept. of Foreign Languages, State U. of N.Y., Coll. at Geneseo, Geneseo, 14454.

LARSON, DAVID LLOYD, b. New York, N.Y., Feb. 22, 1930. POLITICAL SCIENCE. A.B., Dartmouth Coll., 1952; A.M., Fletcher School of Law and Diplomacy, 1957; M.A.L.D., 1958; Ph. D., 1963. ASST. PROF,. GOVERNMENT, TUFTS U., 1958– ; lectr., consultant, Naval War Coll., 1964–65. Fletcher fellow; Clayton fellow; consultant, Systems Analysis Research Corporation. Membership: American Academy of Political and Social Science; American Economic Association; American Political Science Association; American Society of International Law. Research: international relations; international law and organization; United States foreign policy towards Yugoslavia, 1941–63; Caribbean area and Central America. Author: The Cuban Crisis of 1962: Selected Documents and Chronology (1963). Language: Spanish 3,1,1,1; Portuguese 3,1,1,1; French 3,1,1,1; German 3,3,2,2. Home: 28 Thornberry Rd., Winchester, Mass. 01890. Office: Dept. of Government, Tufts U., Medford, Mass. 02155.

LARSON, MILDRED LUCILLE, b. St. Lawrence, S. Dak., Mar. 29, 1925. LINGUISTICS. A.B., Wheaton Coll., 1947; M.A., U. of Mich., 1958. Literary worker, Summer Institute of Linguistics (Mexico), 1950–52; summer school staff, U. of Okla., Summers 1951, 1952, 1957, 1958, 1962, 1964; LINGUIST, SUMMER INSTITUTE OF LINGUISTICS (PERU), 1952– . Research: Aguaruna tribe of Peru. Author: Gramática aguaruna castellana (1963); Comparación de los vocabularios aguaruna y huambisa (Tradición, 1957); Emic Classes Which Manifest the Obligatory Tagmemes in Major Independent Clause Types of Aguaruna (in Peruvian Indian Languages, 1963). Language: Spanish 3,3,3,2. French 3,-,-,-. Linguistic studies: Aguaruna. Home: Solway, Minn. Office: Summer Institute of Linguistics, Box 1960, Santa Ana, Calif.

LASKER, GABRIEL WARD, b. Huntington, Yorkshire, England, April 29, 1912. ANTHROPOLOGY AND ANATOMY. Ph. D., Harvard U., 1945. ASSOC. PROF., ANATOMY, SCHOOL OF MEDICINE, WAYNE STATE U., 1946– . Fulbright research fellow (Peru), 1957–58; Fulbright lectr. (Chile), 1958; chmn., Conference of Biological Editors. Membership: American Anthropological Association; American Association for the Advancement of Science; American Association of Physical Anthropologists. Research: physical anthropology of living peoples. Author: Human Evolution (1963); The Teaching of Anthropology (1963); Physical Anthropology, 1953–1961 (1964). Language: Spanish 5,4,4,4. Office: Dept. of Anatomy, School of Medicine, Wayne State U., Detroit 7, Mich.

LASSEY, WILLIAM RAYMOND, b. Cartwright, N. Dak., Sept. 27, 1934. COMMUNICATION AND ECONOMICS. Ph. B., Mont. State Coll., 1956; M.S., 1961; Ph. D., Mich. State U., 1964. Asst. dir., Research Project on Communication, American International Association (San José, Costa Rica), 1962–64; ASST. INSTR., COMMUNICATION, DATA ANALYSIS CONSULTANT, MICH. STATE U., 1964– . Membership: American Economic Association; Interamerican Society of Psychology. Research: cross-cultural social and communication research; economic and social change; human resource development; computer data processing and analysis; Middle America. Author: Employment Opportunities in International Technical Cooperation (1961). Language: Spanish 4,4,4,3; Portuguese 4,3,3,2. Home: 1537 J Spartan Village, East Lansing, Mich. 48823. Office: Dept. of Communication, Mich. State U., East Lansing, 48823.

LASTRA, YOLANDA, b. Mexico, D.F., Sept. 13, 1932. LINGUISTICS. B.A., Smith Coll., 1954; M.A., Georgetown U., 1957; Ph. D., Cornell U., 1963. Linguist, Foreign Service Institute, 1957; teacher, Binational Center (Mexico, D.F.), 1957–59; asst. coordinator, Interamerican Program in Linguistics and Language Teaching (Ithaca, N.Y.), 1962–63; ASST. PROF., INSTITUTE OF LANGUAGES AND LINGUISTICS, GEORGETOWN U., 1963– . Consultant, Institute of Cultural Relations (Anápolis, Brazil). Membership: Asociación de Lingüística y Filología de América Latina; Linguistic Society of America; Modern Language Association. Research: Spanish linguistics; Chichimeco Jonaz of Mexico; Cochabamba Quechua syntax; Peru. Language: Spanish 5,5,5,5; Portuguese 4,3,1,1; French 4,4,4,3; Italian 4,4,3,2. Linguistic studies: Quechua. Home: 1851 Columbia Rd., NW., Washington, D.C. Office: Institute of Languages and Linguistics, Georgetown U., Washington, D.C.

LAUGHLIN, ROBERT MOODY, b. Princeton, N.J., May 29, 1934. ANTHROPOLOGY. B.A., Princeton U., 1956; M.A., Harvard U., 1959; Ph. D., 1963. MIDDLE AMERICAN ETHNOLOGIST, SMITHSONIAN INSTITUTION, 1962– . Membership: American Anthropological Association. Research: ethnography; folklore; myths and dreams of Tzotzil Indians of Chiapas, Mexico; lowland Mazatec Indians of Oaxaca, Mexico; compilation of Tzotzil dictionary. Author: El símbolo de la flor en la religión de Zinacantán (Estudios de Cultura Maya, 1962). Language: Spanish 4,4,4,3; French 4,3,3,3; German 3,2,2,2; Tzotzil 4,4,4,4. Office: Bureau of American Ethnology, Smithsonian Institution, Washington 25, D.C.

LAUTERBACH, ALBERT, b. Austria, July 24, 1904. ECONOMICS. Dr. Rer. Pol., U. of Vienna (Austria), 1925, Lectr., Extension Coll. in Vienna, 1927–38; Central European correspondent, The Financial News (London), 1927–38; research member, Institute for Advanced Study, Princeton U., 1940–41; asst. prof., U. of Denver, 1941–42; member, Economics Dept., Brooklyn Coll., 1940, 1943, 1946; researcher in international economics, Carnegie Endowment for International Peace, 1943–45; PROF. ECONOMICS, SARAH LAWRENCE COLL., 1963– ; chmn., Social Science faculty, 1946–48, 1956–57, 1960–61; vis. assoc. prof., N.Y.U., 1947; lectr., International Summer Seminar (Alpbach, Austria), and Summer School of European Studies (Zurich), 1950, 1954; research assoc., Brookings Institution, 1955, 1962. Consultant, Committee for Economic Development, 1943–44; research fellow, consultant, Survey Research Center, U. of Mich., 1951–52, 1956; Smith-Mundt lectr., U. of Chile, 1956; public member, New York State Minimum-Wage Board, 1956–57; Fulbright prof., Catholic U. of Chile, 1959–60; senior development economist, United Nations Technical Assistance Mission to Western Samoa, 1962; Brookings research prof. (Brazil, Mexico, Peru, Venezuela), 1962–63; Carnegie Corporation research grant; Social Science Research Council grant. Membership: American Association of University Professors; American Economic Association; Metropolitan Economic Association of New York; Society for International Development. Research: political economy; social and psychological aspects of economic development; management attitudes towards economic development in Latin America. Author: Economic Security and Individual Freedom (1948); Man, Motives, and Money: Psychological Frontiers of Economics (1959); Managerial Attitudes in Chile (1961). Language: Spanish 4,4,4,3; Portuguese 3,3,2,1; French 4,4,4,3; German 5,5,5,5. Home: 545 West 236th St., Bronx 63, N.Y. Office: Dept. of Social Science, Sarah Lawrence Coll., Bronxville 8, N.Y.

LAYTON, ROBERT L., b. Salt Lake City, Utah, May 31, 1925. GEOGRAPHY. B.S., U. of Utah, 1951; M.S., 1952; Ph. D., Syracuse U., 1962. Missionary, Church of the Latter Day Saints (Argentina), 1947–49; ASSOC. PROF., CHMN., GEOGRAPHY, BRIGHAM YOUNG U., 1954– . Participant, National Science Foundation Summer Institute in Cartography, U. of Wash., 1963. Membership: Association of American Geographers; Association of Pacific Coast Geographers; Phi Beta Kappa. Research: economic and urban geography; cartography. Language: Spanish 4,4,3,3; Portuguese 3,3,2,1; French 2,1,1,1. Home: 490 East 1980 North, Provo, Utah. Office: Dept. of Geography, 167HGB, Brigham Young U., Provo.

LEACOCK, SETH, b. Angleton, Tex., Aug. 10, 1924. ANTHROPOLOGY. Ph. D., U. of Calif., Berkeley, 1958. ASST. PROF., ANTHROPOLOGY, U. OF CHICAGO, 1959– . Social Science Research Council fellow (Brazil), 1956–57; National Science Foundation fellow (Brazil), 1962–63. Membership: American Anthropological Association; American Ethnological Society. Research: acculturation of the Mavé Indians of Brazil; lower class religious cult in Belém, Brazil. Author: Ceremonial Drinking in an Afro-Brazilian Cult (American Anthropologist, Apr. 1964). Language: Spanish 2,1,1,1; Portuguese 4,4,3,3; French 4,2,2,2; German 2,1,1,1. Home: 1300 East 56th St., Chicago 37, Ill. Office: Dept. of Anthropology, U. of Chicago, Chicago 37.

LEAL, LUIS, b. Linares, Mexico, Sept. 17, 1907. SPANISH AMERICAN LITERATURE. B.S., Northwestern U., 1940; M.A., U. of Chicago, 1941; Ph. D., 1950. Instr., U. of Chicago, 1942–43, 1946–48; asst. prof., 1948–52; assoc. prof., U. of Miss., 1952–56; vis. prof., U. of Ariz., 1955–56; assoc. prof., Emory U., 1956–59; assoc. prof., U. of Ill., 1959–62; PROF., SPANISH, U. OF ILL., 1962– ; vis. prof., U. of Wis., Summer 1960; prof., U. of Ariz. National Defense Education Act Summer Institute (Guadalajara, Mexico), Summers 1962, 1963. Editor literario, Revista Iberoamericana; Latin America Studies Committee, U. of Ill. Membership: American Association of Teachers of Spanish and Portuguese; Association of Latin American Studies; Instituto Internacional de Literatura Iberoamericana; Modern Language Association. Research: Spanish American novel and short story; Mexican literature, especially short story; works of Mariano Azuela. Author: México, civilizaciones y culturas (1955); Breve historia del cuento mexicano (1956); Mariano Azuela, vida y obra (1961). Language: Spanish 5,5,5,5; Portuguese 2,2,2,2; French 2,2,2,2; Italian 3,3,3,3. Home: 207 West Iowa, Urbana, Ill.

61801. Office: Dept. of Spanish, U. of Ill., Urbana.

LEAVITT, STURGIS ELLENO, b. Windham, Maine, Jan. 24, 1888. SPANISH AMERICAN LITERATURE. A.B., Bowdoin Coll., 1908; M.A., Harvard, 1913; Ph. D., 1917. Instr., Northwestern U., 1913-14; instr., Harvard U., 1915-17; asst. prof., U. of N.C., 1917-18; assoc. prof., 1918-21; prof., 1921-45; Kenan prof. of Spanish, 1945-60; KENAN PROF. EMERITUS, SPANISH, U. OF N.C., 1960- . Editor, Humanities in the South, 1935-45; editor, South Atlantic Bulletin, 1935-59; dir., Inter-American Institute, U. of N.C., 1945-59. Membership: American Association of Teachers of Spanish and Portuguese; Instituto Internacional de Literatura Iberoamericana; Modern Language Association; Southern Humanities Conference. Research: Spanish 17th century literature; Spanish American bibliography. Author; Chilean Literature, a Bibliography of Literary Criticism, Biography, and Literary Controversy (1923); The Estrella de Sevilla and Claramonte (1931); Revistas hispanoamericanas: Indice bibliográfico (1960), Language: Spanish 5,5,4,4; Portuguese 2,2,1,1; French 3,-,3,3. Home: P.O. Box 1169, Chapel Hill, N.C. Office: Dept. of Romance Languages, U. of N.C., Chapel Hill.

LeDOUX, MARJORIE ELIZABETH, b. Breaux Bridge, La., Apr. 21, 1920. LIBRARY SCIENCE. B.A., Southwestern La. Institute, 1941; M.A., Tulane U., 1951; M.S., La. State U., 1952. Reference librarian, Library, Loyola U., 1952-54; reference librarian, Howard-Tilton Library, Tulane U., 1954-56; librarian, Library, School of Medicine, La. State U., 1956-62; LIBRARIAN, LATIN AMERICAN LIBRARY, TULANE U., 1962- . Middle American Research Institute graduate asst. fellow. Membership: American Library Association; Louisiana Library Association; New Orleans Library Club; Seminar on the Acquisition of Latin American Library Materials; Southeastern Conference of Latin American Studies. Research: Latin American literature. Language: Spanish 5,5,5,4; Portuguese 2,3,2,1; French 5,5,5,4. Home: 7230 Plum St., New Orleans, La. 70118. Office: Latin American Library, Tulane U., New Orleans.

LEEDS, ANTHONY, b. New York, N.Y., Jan. 26, 1925. ANTHROPOLOGY. B.A., Columbia Coll., 1949; Ph. D., Columbia U., 1957. Part-time lectr., Columbia U., 1953-54, 1959-60; instr., Hofstra Coll., 1956-59; asst. prof., City Coll. (N.Y.), 1959-61; part-time lectr., Catholic U. of America, 1961-62; chief, Urban Development Program, Organization of American States, 1961-63; part-time professorial lectr., American U., 1962-63; ASSOC. PROF., ANTHROPOLOGY, RESEARCH ASSOC., INSTITUTE OF LATIN AMERICAN STUDIES, U. OF TEX., 1963-. Social Science Research Council grant (Venezuela), 1958; American Philosophical Society grant, 1960-. Membership: American Anthropological Association; American Association for the Advancement of Science; American Ethnological Society; Society for the Scientific Study of Religion. Research: cultural anthropology; acculturation of Llanos Indians of Venezuela; socio-political organization of Brazil. Author: The Port-of-Trade in Pre-European India as an Ecological and Evolutionary Type (Proceedings, American Ethnological Society, 1961); Ecological Determinants of Chieftanship among the Yaruro Indians of Venezuela (Akten, 34 Internationalen Amerikanisten Kongress, 1962); Fatôres culturais em educação: Brasil, Índia, Estados Unidos, União Soviética (Educacão e Ciências Sociais, 1962). Language: Spanish 4,4,4,3; Portuguese 4,4,4,4; French 3,3,2,3; Dutch 2,1,1,1; German 3,4,4,3; Russian 1,1,1,1. Home: 903 West 31st St., Austin, Tex. Office: Dept. of Anthropology, U. of Tex., Austin 12.

LEEDS, WILLARD LODOWICK, b. Glendale, Calif., Jan. 15, 1915. EDUCATION. A.B., San Jose State Coll., 1941; M.S., Calif. Institute of Technology, 1943; Ph. D., U. of Ill., 1952. Weather officer, U.S. Navy (P.R., Panama, Trinidad, British and Dutch Guiana), 1943-44; meteorologist, Pan American-Grace Airways (Peru, Bolivia, Ecuador, Colombia), 1945-47; vis. expert in education, Kyushu U. (Japan), U.S. Dept. of Army, 1949-50; asst. prof., U. of Nebr., 1950-52; assoc. prof., dir. of instruction, Fla. State U., 1952-53; prof., coordinator of evening and summer programs, San Francisco State Coll., 1953-63; senior adviser, U. of Chicago Pakistan Education Project (Lahore), 1959-61; DIR., INTERNATIONAL EDUCATION AND GRADUATE STUDIES IN EDUCATION, U. OF WIS., MILWAUKEE, 1963-. Dir., comprehensive high school projects for Venezuela and Dominican Republic, U. of Wis.; consultant, College of Education, U. of P.R. Membership: American Association of Colleges for Teacher Education; Midwest Council of the Association for Latin American Studies; National Education Association; National Science Teachers Association; National Society for Study of Education. Research: science education; secondary education; analysis of teaching in three unified classes in a junior high school; meteorology; earth science curriculum planning. Author: Weather and You (1956, 1964). Language: Spanish 3,3,3,3; Portuguese 2,2,1,1; French 1,1,1,1. Home: 4620 North Woodburn St., Milwaukee, Wis. 53211. Office: School of Education, U. of Wis.-Milwaukee, 3203 North Downer Ave., Milwaukee, 53211.

LEHMANN, SHIRLEY JEANNE, b. Syracuse, N.Y., Oct. 12, 1930. POLITICAL SCIENCE. B.A., Oberlin Coll., 1952; M.A., Radcliffe Coll., 1955; Ph. D., 1961. Instr., Vassar Coll., 1958-61; ASST. PROF. IN RESEARCH, FOREIGN AREA STUDIES DIV., AMERICAN U., 1962-. Fulbright fellow (France), 1953-54; American Association of University Women and Fulbright travel grants, 1961; guest scholar, Mass. Institute of Technology Center for International Studies and Brookings Institution, 1962; National Defense Education Act fellow in Portuguese, U. of Tex., Summer 1963. Membership: Phi Beta Kappa. Research: comparative government; international relations; political system and social dynamics of Brazil; political system of Peru; French Socialist Party, 1905-1914. Language: Spanish 3,2,1,1; Portuguese 3, 2,2,1; French 5,4,4,4; German 3,2,2,2. Home: 2105 N St. NW., Washington, D.C. Office: Foreign Area Studies Div., American U., 5010 Wisconsin Ave. NW., Washington, D.C.

LEMAIRE, MINNIE ETHEL, b. Taunton, Mass., July 15, 1908. GEOGRAPHY. B.A., Wheaton Coll., 1930; M.A., Clark U., 1932; Ph. D., 1935. Instr., State Teachers Coll. (La Crosse, Wis.), 1935–43; chmn., Geography, State Teachers Coll (East Stroudsburg, Pa.), 1943–47; PROF., GEOGRAPHY, MT. HOLYOKE COLL., 1947– . Membership: American Association of University Professors; American Association of University Women; American Geographical Society; Association of American Geographers; International Federation of University Women; National Council for Geographic Education; Society of Woman Geographers. Research: land use in the tropics. Author: Iguazu Falls, South America (School Science and Mathematics, Oct. 1942); El Salvador (Economic Geography, July 1946); Manioc (Journal of Geography, Dec. 1950). Language: Spanish 3,3,3,2; French 4,3,2,2. Home: 190 Brattle St., Holden, Mass. Office: Dept. of Geology and Geography, Mt. Holyoke, Coll., South Hadley, Mass.

LEMUS, GEORGE, b. Del Rio, Tex., Apr. 14, 1928. SPANISH AMERICAN LITERATURE AND POLITICAL SCIENCE. Universidad Nacional Autónoma de México, 1946–48; B.A., U. of Tex., 1952; M.A., 1956; Ph. D., 1963. Language training instr., U.S. Air Force Language School, Lackland Air Force Base (Tex.), 1957–58; instr., Loyola U. of Los Angeles, 1958–60; part-time instr., Santa Monica City Coll., 1959–60; asst. prof., San Diego State Coll., 1960–65; part-time instr., Grossmont Coll., 1963– ; ASSOC. PROF., SPANISH, SAN DIEGO STATE COLL., 1965– . Spanish Government scholar, Dirección General de Relaciones Culturales (Madrid), Summer 1957; chmn., Latin American Studies Committee, San Diego State Coll., 1963– ; dir., San Diego State Mexico City Summer Program, Universidad Iberoamericana, 1964–65. Membership: American Association of Professors of Spanish and Portuguese; Association for Latin American Studies; Pacific Coast Council on Latin American Studies. Research: literature and historical literature of Mexico; Latin American political literature and government. Author: Francisco Bulnes: Su vida y sus obras (1964); Pedagogía mexicana y norteamericana, comparada (Hispania, Sept. 1962). Language: Spanish 5,5,5,5; Portuguese 5,4,–,–; French 5,4,4,3. Home: 8405 Lake Baca Dr., San Diego, Calif. 92119. Office: Dept. of Spanish, San Diego State Coll., 5402 College Ave., San Diego, 92115.

LEONARD, IRVING ALBERT, b. New Haven, Conn., Dec. 1, 1896. HISTORY AND SPANISH AMERICAN LITERATURE. Ph.B., Yale U., 1918; M.A., U. of Calif., Berkeley, 1925; Ph. D., 1928. Prof., U. of the Philippines, 1921–22; teacher, Petaluma High School (Calif.), 1922–23; asst. dir., Humanities, Rockefeller Foundation, 1937–40; prof., Brown U., 1940–42; PROF., ROMANCE LANGUAGES AND HISTORY, U. OF MICH., 1942– . American Council of Learned Societies fellow (Spain), 1930–31, (Mexico), 1932; Guggenheim fellow, 1935; Fulbright prof., Oxford U., 1952. Membership: American Association of Teachers of Spanish and Portuguese; Hispanic Society of America. Research: cultural history of Spain and Spanish America. Author: Don Carlos de Sigüenza, Mexican Savant (1929); Books of the Brave (1949); Baroque Times in Old Mexico (1959). Language: Spanish 5,5,4,4; Portuguese 4,3,1,1; French 3,2,1,1. Home: 1328 Forest Ct., Ann Arbor, Mich. Office: Dept. of History, U. of Mich., Ann Arbor.

LEONARD, OLEN E., b. Poolville, Tex., Jan. 31, 1909. SOCIOLOGY AND ANTHROPOLOGY. B.S., Fredericksburg Teachers Coll., 1931; Ph. D., La State U., 1944. Rural sociologist, U.S. Dept. of Agriculture, 1936–46; dir., Cooperative Agricultural Experiment Stations (Bolivia), 1946–48; assoc. prof., U of Tex., 1948–49; prof., Mich. State U., 1949–52; sociologist, project dir., Interamerican Institute of Agricultural Sciences, Organization of American States (Cuba), 1952–62; prof., Bureau of Ethnic Research, U. of Ariz., 1962–63; rural sociologist, United Nations, 1963–64; ASST. TO CHIEF, FOREIGN POPULATION BRANCH, ECONOMIC AND STATISTICAL ANALYSIS DIV., U.S. DEPT. OF AGRICULTURE, 1964– . Consultant on Latin America, Office of Foreign Agricultural Relations, U.S. Dept. of Agriculture, 1948–49. Membership: American Anthropological Association; American Sociological Association; American Statistical Association; Rural Sociological Society. Research: Latin American social organization and institutions; social factors and economic development in Latin America; demography; Bolivia. Author: The Role of the Spanish Land Grant in the Social Organization of a Spanish Village (1949); Santa Cruz, Bolivia: Study of an Area (1950); Bolivia: Land and People (1954). Language: Spanish 5,5,5,4; Portuguese 4,4,3,2; French 4,2,2,1. Office: Foreign Population Branch, Economic and Statistical Analysis Div., U.S. Dept. of Agriculture, Washington, D.C.

LESLIE, CHARLES M., b. Lake Village, Ark., Nov. 8, 1923. ANTHROPOLOGY AND SOCIOLOGY. Ph. B., U. of Chicago, 1949; M.A., 1950; Ph. D., 1959. Instr., Southern Methodist U., 1950–51; instr., U. of Minn., 1954–56; ASSOC. PROF., ANTHROPOLOGY, POMONA COLL., 1956– . Ford Foundation research grant (Mexico), 1953–54; Social Science Research Council grant (Mexico), Summer 1960; Fulbright travel grant (India), 1961; International Center for Medical Research and Training, Johns Hopkins U. fellow, 1962; National Science Foundation fellow, 1962; National Institute of Mental Health grant, 1963. Membership: American Anthropological Association; American Ethnological Society; American Folklore Society; Royal Anthropological Institute; Society for Applied Anthropology; Southwestern Anthropological Association. Research: cultural anthropology; medical sociology; Mexico. Author: Now We Are Civilized (1960); Anthropology of Folk Religion (1960); The Rhetoric of the Ayurvedic Revival (Man, May 1963). Language: Spanish 4,4,3,2; French 3,1,1,1. Home: 122 East 7th St., Claremont, Calif. Office: Dept. of Sociology and Anthropology, Pomona Coll., Claremont.

LEVETT, ELLA PETTIT, b. Elizabeth, N.J., Sept. 19, 1905. HISTORY. M.A., U. of S.C., 1934; Ph. D., U. of Chicago, 1941; M.A., Middlebury Coll., 1950; Ph. D., U. of Salamanca (Spain), 1961. Teacher, North

Charleston High School (S.C.), 1928–37; asst. in Latin American History, U. of Chicago, 1941–42; prof., Hunter Coll., 1944–45; PROF., LATIN AMERICAN HISTORY, SPANISH, CHMN., FOREIGN LANGUAGES, HARDIN-SIMMONS U., 1945– . University fellow, U. of Chicago; Buenos Aires Convention fellow (Colombia); Spanish Government grant. Membership: American Historical Association; American Association of University Women; Modern Language Association; Pi Gamma Mu; Sigma Delta Pi; South Central Modern Language Association; West Texas Historical Association. Research: United States-Latin American relations; Spanish philology; John Steinbeck and the Hispanic World. Author: Loyalism in the American Colonies (Proceedings, South Carolina Historical Association, 1936); Negotiations for Release from the Inter-oceanic Obligations of the Clayton-Bulwer Treaty (1945). Language: Spanish 4,4,4,4; Portuguese 2,2,1,1; French 2,2,1,1; German 3,2,1,1. Home: 1801 University, Abilene, Tex. Office: Dept. of Spanish, Hardin-Simmons U., Abilene.

LEVIN, NORMAN BALFOUR, b. New York, N.Y., Jan. 14, 1922. LINGUISTICS. B.S., U. of Tex., 1949; M.A., 1954; Ph. D., U. of Pa., 1961. Chmn., Spanish High School Program, Board of Education (Brentwood, N.Y.), 1954–57; vis. instr., U. of Pa., 1957–58; asst. prof., U. of N. Dak., 1958–61; American specialist, Office of Communications, Engineering and Technical Services Div., U.S. Dept. of State, 1961–62; assoc. dir., National Defense Education Act Summer Institute, Howard U., Summers 1962, 1963; ASST. PROF., ROMANCE LANGUAGES, HOWARD U., 1962– ; instr., American U., 1963. West German Government grant, 1962. Membership: American Association of University Professors; Linguistic Association of Great Britain; Linguistic Society of America; Modern Language Association; National Education Association; Washington Linguistics Club. Research: American Indian linguistics; applied Spanish linguistics. Author: The Assiniboine Language (1964); The Origin and Development of Urdu (Proceedings, Linguistic Circle of Manitoba and North Dakota, May 1959); A Study of Contrasts in Modern Foreign Language Problems (The North Dakota Teacher, Apr. 1960). Language: Spanish 5,5,5,5; Portuguese 2,2,2,2; French 5,5,5,5; Italian 2,2,2,2; Russian 3,3,3,3. Linguistic studies: Assiniboine; Bamilike; Bubi. Home: 7405 Alaska Ave., NW., Washington, D.C., 20012. Office: Dept. of Romance Languages, Howard U., Washington, 20001.

LEVY, JAMES ROBERT, b. Newark, N.J., Sept. 3, 1937. HISTORY. B.A., Columbia Coll., 1959; M.A., Columbia U., 1961; Ph. D., U. of Pa., 1964. Instr., U. of Pa., 1962–63; INSTR., HISTORY, POMONA COLL., 1963– . U. of Pa. and Rockefeller Foundation fellow (Argentina), 1962. Membership: American Historical Association; Conference on Latin American History. Research: social and intellectual developments in Latin American history; 19th century nationalism and liberalism in Argentina. Language: Spanish 4,3,3,2; Portuguese 2,2,1,1; French 2,1,1,1. Home: Norton Hall, Pomona Coll., Claremont, Calif. Office: Pearsons 109, Pomona Coll., Claremont.

LEWALD, HERALD ERNEST, b. Königsberg, Germany, Oct. 31, 1922. SPANISH AMERICAN LITERATURE. B.A., U. of Minn., 1951; M.A., 1955; Ph. D., 1960. Asst. to manager, Argentinisches Tageblatt (Buenos Aires), 1946–47; legal adviser, Maryland Casualty Company (Minneapolis), 1952–53; instr., Ga. Institute of Technology, 1954–57; instr., U. of Minn., 1957–58; ASST. PROF., SPANISH, CARLETON COLL., 1958– ; vis. prof., Calif. State Coll., Fullerton, 1962–63. Membership: American Association of Teachers of Spanish and Portuguese; American Association of University Professors; Modern Language Association; Phi Beta Kappa. Research: sociological aspects of Spanish American literature; cultural analysis of the big-city society of Buenos Aires. Author: El costumbrismo porteño como intérprete sociológico (Cultura, Fall 1963); Aim and Function of Costumbrismo Porteño (Hispania, Sept. 1963); Problems in Culture Teaching (Modern Language Journal, Oct. 1963). Language: Spanish 5,5,5,5; Portuguese 2,2,2,1; French 4,4,4,3. Home: 208 College, Northfield, Minn. Office: Dept. of Spanish, Carleton Coll., Northfield.

LEWIS, DARRELL RICHARD, b. St. Paul, Minn., July 31, 1936. ECONOMICS. B.A., Luther Coll., 1960; Ph. D., La. State U., 1963. ASST. PROF., ECONOMICS, DIR., LATIN AMERICAN STUDIES PROGRAM, LUTHER COLL., 1963– ; vis. prof., U. of Wyo., Summer 1964. Woodrow Wilson fellow; National Defense doctoral fellow; Foundation for Economic Education fellow; vis. consultant on Project Social Studies, U. of Minn., Summer 1964. Membership: American Association of University Professors; American Economic Association; Midwest Economic Association. Research: Latin American economic development, capital utilization, and fiscal reform; economic structures, fiscal policies, post-war development policies, and balance of payments of Brazil and Mexico; economic education in secondary and higher education. Language: Spanish 3,2,2,2; German 3,3,3,3. Home: 302 View St., Decorah, Iowa. Office: Dept. of Economics, Luther Coll., Decorah.

LEWIS, FRANK MARSHALL, b. Indianapolis, Ind., Nov. 18, 1921. POLITICAL SCIENCE. A.B., Ind. U. 1943; M.A., Northwestern U., 1949; Ph. D., U. of Tex., 1955. Instr., U. of Tex., 1955–56; asst. prof., U. of S. Dak., 1956–59; assoc. prof., 1960–63; vis. assoc. prof., U. of Colo., Fall 1963; ASSOC. PROF., GOVERNMENT, U. OF S. DAK., 1964– . Buenos Aires Convention scholar and Doherty fellow (Chile), 1954–55; Foreign Policy Research Institute fellow, U. of Pa., 1959–60. Membership: American Academy of Political and Social Science; American Political Science Association; Midwest Conference of Political Scientists; Midwest Council of the Association for Latin American Studies. Research: political parties of Latin America; Chilean politics. Language: Spanish 4,3,3,3; Portuguese 2,2,2,2. Home: 323 Elm St., Vermillion, S. Dak. Office: Dept. of Government, U. of S. Dak., Vermillion.

LEWIS, OSCAR, b. New York, N.Y., Dec. 25, 1914. ANTHROPOLOGY. B.S.S., City Coll. (N.Y.), 1936; Ph. D., Columbia U., 1940. PROF., ANTHROPOLOGY, U. OF ILL., 1948– . American Council of Learned Societies grant, 1942; field dir., Inter-American Indian Institute, 1943–44; consultant, Ford Foundation, 1952–54; Guggenheim fellow (Mexico), 1955, 1963; Wenner-Gren Foundation grant; research in P.R., Social Security Administration, 1963. Membership: American Anthropological Association; American Ethnological Society. Research: social and applied anthropology: Mexico, El Salvador, Puerto Rico, and Cuba. Author: Life in a Mexico Village: Tepoztlan Restudied (1951); Five Families (1959); The Children of Sánchez (1961). Language: Spanish 4,4,4,4; French 2,2,1,1. Home: 605 South Busey, Urbana, Ill. Office: Dept. of Anthropology, U. of Ill., Urbana.

LEYBURN, JAMES GRAHAM, b. Hedgesville, W. Va., Jan. 17, 1902. SOCIOLOGY AND ANTHROPOLOGY. B.A., Duke U., 1920; M.A., 1921; M.A., Princeton U., 1922; Ph. D., Yale U., 1927. Prof., Hollins Coll., 1922–24; asst., Princeton U., 1924–25; prof., Yale U., 1927–47; PROF., SOCIOLOGY, WASHINGTON AND LEE U., 1947– . Membership: American Anthropological Association; American Sociological Association; Southern Sociological Society; Virginia Social Science Association. Research: race and ethnic relations; Haiti. Author: Frontier Folkways (1935); The Haitian People (1941); The Scotch-Irish: A Social History (1962). Language: Spanish 2,1,1,1; Portuguese 1,1,1,1; French 4,3,3,3; Dutch 1,1,1,1; German 1,1,1,1. Home: 30 University Pl., Lexington, Va. Office: Dept. of Sociology, Washington and Lee U., Lexington.

LICHTBLAU, MYRON I., b. New York, N.Y., Oct. 10, 1925. SPANISH AMERICAN LITERATURE. B.A., City Coll. (N.Y.), 1947; M.A., Universidad Nacional Autónoma de México, 1948; Ph. D., Columbia U., 1957. Instr., Ind. U., 1957–59; ASSOC. PROF., ROMANCE LANGUAGES, SYRACUSE U., 1959– . Committee on Latin American Area Studies. Membership: American Association of Teachers of Spanish and Portuguese; Instituto Internacional de Literatura Iberoamericana; Modern Language Association. Research: Argentine and Mexican literature; Spanish American novel. Author: The Argentine Novel in the 19th Century (1959); Manuel Gálvez; Las dos vidas del pobre Napoleón (1963); Los cuentos de Eduardo Mallea (Humánitas, Jan. 1961). Language: Spanish 5,5,5,5; Portuguese 3,2,–,–; French 4,3,3,3. Home: 251 Mountainview Ave., Syracuse, N.Y. Office: Dept. of Romance Languages, Syracuse U., Syracuse 10.

LIDA, RAIMUNDO, b. Lemberg, Austria, Nov. 15, 1908. SPANISH AMERICAN LITERATURE. M.A., Universidad de Buenos Aires, 1931; Ph. D., 1943. Investigator, Instituto de Filología, Universidad de Buenos Aires, 1931–38; assistant prof., Universidad Nacional de La Plata (Argentina), 1936–47; secretary, Instituto de Filología, Universidad de Buenos Aires, 1938–47; dir., Centro de Estudios Literarios, El Colegio de México, 1947–52; vis. prof., Ohio State U., Summer 1951, Spring 1952; PROF., ROMANCE LANGUAGES AND LITERATURES, HARVARD U., 1953– . Guggenheim fellow, 1939–40, 1959–60; Editorial Committee, Nueva Revista de Filología Hispánica (Mexico); Editorial Committee, Sur (Buenos Aires). Membership: Asociación Internacional de Hispanistas; Medieval Academy of America; Modern Language Association. Research: 17th century literature; Spanish and Spanish American 20th century poetry; 19th and 20th century prose; cultural life in Argentina and Mexico. Author: Belleza, arte y poesía en la estética de Santayana (1943); Los cuentos de Rubén Darío (1950); Letras Hispánicas (1958). Language: Spanish 5,5,5,5; Portuguese 2,2,2,1; French 3,3,3,2; German 2,2,1,1. Office: Dept. of Romance Languages and Literatures, 218 Boylston Hall, Harvard U., Cambridge, Mass. 02138.

LIETZ, PAUL STANTON, b. Mexico, D.F., May 3, 1906. HISTORY. A.B., Loyola U. (Ill.), 1929; A.M., 1935; Ph. D., 1940. Teacher, Loyola Academy (Chicago), 1931–40; PROF., HISTORY, LOYOLA U. (ILL.). 1940– ; summer vis. prof., U. of Havana, 1947, U. of San Marcos and Catholic U. (Peru), 1950. U.S. Dept. of State grants (Cuba, Peru), Summers 1947, 1950; Newberry Library fellow in Philippine Studies, 1953–55; Editorial Staff, Mid-America; Bolton Prize Committee, 1964. Membership: American Catholic Historical Association; American Historical Association; Conference on Latin American History. Research: Spanish colonial history; history of the Philippines; Mexico. Author: Calendar of Philippine Documents in the Ayer Collection of the Newberry Library (1956); Alzina's Historia de Viscayas (Bibliographical Society of the Philippines, Occasional Papers, 1962). Language: Spanish 5,4,3,3; Portuguese 3,3,2,1; French 4,3,2,1; Latin 3,–,–,–. Home: 1233 Arthur Ave., Chicago 26, Ill. Office: Dept. of History, Loyola U., Chicago 26.

LIEUWEN, EDWIN, b. Harrison, S. Dak., Feb. 8, 1923. HISTORY. A.B., U. of Calif., Berkeley, 1947; M.A., 1948; Ph. D., 1951. Vis. instr., U. of Calif., Los Angeles, 1951–52; chief, Latin American Branch, Intelligence, U.S. Government, 1952–53; vis. asst. prof., U. of Calif., Berkeley, 1954–55; chief, Latin American Section, Intelligence, U.S. Government, 1955–57; PROF., CHMN., HISTORY, U. OF N. MEX., 1957– . Doherty fellow (Venezuela), 1950–51; Fulbright lectr., U. of Utrecht (Netherlands), 1953–54; Carnegie fellow, Council on Foreign Relations, 1957–58; Rockefeller research fellow (Mexico), 1963–64. Membership: American Historical Association; Conference on Latin American History; Council on Foreign Relations. Research: Mexico; petroleum industry in Venezuela; Latin American politics. Author: Petroleum in Venezuela: A History (1954, 1955); Arms and Politics in Latin America (1959, 1961); Venezuela (1961, 1964). Language: Spanish 5,4,3,3; Portuguese 3,2,1,1; French 3,2,1,1. Home: 309 Dartmouth NE., Albuquerque, N. Mex. Office: Dept. of History, U. of N. Mex., Albuquerque.

LIGHTMAN, JACOB BEN, b. Boston, Mass., Apr. 9, 1904. SOCIAL WELFARE. A.B. George Washington U., 1928; LL.B., 1928; M.S.S., State U. of N.Y., 1933. Lawyer (Washington, D.C.), 1928–29; asst. to dir.,

American Joint Distribution Committee, 1933–37; executive dir., Jewish Community Council of Houston (Tex.), 1937–43; dir. for Latin America, American Joint Distribution Committee (Buenos Aires), 1943–50; dir. of community relations, American Jewish Committee (Paris), 1950–51; dir., National Conference for Israel and Jewish Rehabilitation (Montreal), 1952–55; ASSOC. PROF., SCHOOL OF SOCIAL WORK, McGILL U., 1955– . Welfare consultant, U.S. International Cooperation Administration (Costa Rica), Summer 1959; consultant, U.S. International Cooperation Administration-Council on Social Work Education (Madras, India), 1960–61. Membership: Canadian Association of Social Workers; Canadian Conference of Social Work; International Conference of Social Work; Pan American Conference of Social Work. Research: international welfare; refugee aid; social work education. Author: Challenge and Opportunity in Welfare Programmes for the Undeveloped and Developing Areas (The Social Worker, June–July 1962); The Community Organization Approach in Training for International Social Work (Social Work Review, July 1963). Language: Spanish 5,5,4,4; Portuguese 3,2,2,1; French 4,4,3,2; German, 4,4, 4,3. Home: 531 Grosvenor Ave., Montreal 6, Quebec, Canada. Office: School of Social Work, McGill U., 3506 University St., Montreal 2.

LINARES DE SAPIR, OLGA, b. David, Panama, Nov. 10, 1936. ANTHROPOLOGY. B.A., Vassar Coll., 1958; M.A., Radcliffe Coll., 1961; Ph. D., Harvard U., 1964. INSTR., ANTHROPOLOGY, HARVARD U., 1964– . Ogden fellow, 1963–64. Membership: American Anthropological Association. Research: South American archeology and ethnology; archeological investigations in the Chiriqui Gulf Region of Panama. Language: Spanish 5,5,5,5; Portugese 3,3,1,1; French 4,4,5,3. Home: Apartado 76, David, Panama. Office: Peabody Museum, Harvard U., Cambridge, Mass.

LIPP, SOLOMON, b. New York, N.Y., Oct. 15, 1913. SPANISH AMERICAN LITERATURE AND EDUCATION. B.S., City Coll. (N.Y.), 1934; M.S., 1935; Ph. D., Harvard U., 1949. Teacher, Works Progress Administration (N.Y.), 1936–41; educational consultant, Federal Works Agency (Washington, D.C.), 1941–42; PROF., MODERN LANGUAGES, BOSTON U., 1947– ; vis. prof., Northeastern U., Emerson Coll., Brandeis U., 1949–55. Smith-Mundt grant, U. of San Carlos (Guatemala), 1956, U. of Costa Rica, 1958; Fulbright scholar, National U. of Córdoba (Argentina), 1963. Membership: American Association of Teachers of Spanish and Portuguese; Association for Latin American Studies; Modern Language Association; New England Federation of Modern Language Teachers; New England Pan American Society; Phi Delta Kappa; Phi Sigma Iota. Research: history of educational philosophy in Hispanic America; Spanish and Spanish American philosophy; foreign language teaching methodology. Author: Francisco Giner de los Ríos Modern Educator of Spain (History of Education Quarterly, Sept. 1952) Mario Monteforte Toledo, Contemporary Guatemalan Novelist (Hispania, Sept. 1961); Latin American Perspective: Threat or Promise (Graduate Journal, 1962–1963). Language: Spanish 5,5,5,5; Portuguese 4,2,2,2; French 3,2,2,2; German 3,3,-3,3; Italian 3,3,3,2; Yiddish 5,5,5,5. Home: 58 Myrtle St., West Newton 65, Mass. Office: Dept. of Modern Languages, Boston U., 236 Bay State Rd., Boston, Mass.

LISS, SHELDON B., b. Nov. 3, 1936. HISTORY. B.A., American U., 1958; M.A., Duquesne U., 1962; Ph. D., American U., 1964. Executive-administrator, Public Relations, private corporation in Mexico and U.S., 1958–62; ASST. PROF., LATIN AMERICAN STUDIES, IND. STATE COLL., 1964– . Membership: American Historical Association; American Political Science Association; Hispanic American Society; Phi Alpha Theta. Research: the Chamizal conflict between Mexico and the United States; Cuba. Language: Spanish 5,4,4,4; Portuguese 3,2,1,1; French 3,2,2,3; German 1,3,1,1; Rumanian 3,3,1,1. Home: 1817 North Quinn St., Apt. 306, Arlington, Va. 22209. Office: Dept. of Latin American Studies, Ind. State Coll., Terre Haute.

LIST, GEORGE HAROLD, b. Tucson, Ariz., Feb. 9, 1911. MUSIC. B.S., Columbia U., 1951; M.A., 1945; Ph. D., Ind. U., 1954. Supervisor of instrumental music, Elmont Public Schools (N.Y.), 1941–43; head, Music Dept., High School (Floral Park, N.Y.), 1943–44; instr., Colo. Coll., 1945–46; asst. prof., Miami U., 1946–48; assoc. prof., 1948–53; DIR. ARCHIVES OF FOLK AND PRIMITIVE MUSIC, IND. U., 1954– ; lectr., Anthropology, 1954–55; LECTR., MUSIC, 1958– ; prof., Ethnomusicology and Folklore Research, Universidad Nacional (Bogotá), 1964–65. Fund for the Advancement of Education fellow, 1952; councilor, Society for Ethnomusicology, 1960– ; Fulbright research award, 1964–65; host and co-organizer, Second Inter-American Conference in Ethnomusicology, Ind. U., Apr. 1965. Membership: American Anthropological Association; American Folklore Society; American Musicological Society; International Folk Music Council (London); Junta Nacional de Folclor (Bogotá); Society for African Music (Union of South Africa). Research: ethnomusicology; folklore; folk music of the coastal regions of Colombia; music of the Jívaro Indians of Ecuador and Peru. Author: Music in the Culture of the Jívaro Indians of the Ecuadorian Montaña (Inter-American Music Bulletin, Mar.-May 1964); Impresiones de etnomusicología y folklore en América Latina (Revista Musical Chilena, June-Sept. 1964); Etnomusicología en educación alta (Revista Musical Chilena, Sept.-Dec. 1964.) Language: Spanish 3,3,2,3; French 3,2,1,1; German 2,2,2,1. Home: 2512 East 7th St., Bloomington, Ind. 47405. Office: Archives of Folk and Primitive Music, Maxwell Hall 013, Ind. U., Bloomington, 47405.

LITTON, GASTON, b. Granite, Okla., Oct. 16, 1913. LIBRARY SCIENCE. A.B., U. of Okla., 1934; M.A., 1940; Ph. D., Georgetown U., 1942. Asst., National Archives, 1937–45; dir.-librarian, American Library (Managua, Nicaragua), 1946–48; archivist and prof., U. of Okla., 1948–56; dir., Inter-American Library School (Medellín, Colombia), 1956–58; CHIEF, INTER-AMERICAN LIBRARY SCHOOL, 1959– . Adviser, National Library (Brazil), 1945; U.S. Dept.

of State specialist, Universidade do Paraná (Brazil), 1953; consultant, U. of Panama, 1956; U.S. Dept. of State specialist, vis. prof., U. of Panama, 1959; consultant, Canal Zone libraries, 1960. Membership: Oklahoma Library Association; Society of American Archivists. Research: organization of library programs; development of teaching materials and library school curriculum; archival science; bibliography of Colombia. Author: History of Oklahoma (1957). Co-author: Cherokee Cavaliers (1939). Language: Spanish 5,5,5,5; Portuguese 4,4,3,2; French 2,3,1,1. Home: Apartado aéreo 5023, Medellín, Colombia. Office: Inter-American Library School, Universidad de Antioquia, Medellín, Colombia.

LLOYD-JONES, DONALD J., b. New York, N.Y., May 25, 1931. ECONOMICS AND GEOGRAPHY. B.A., Swarthmore Coll., 1952; M.B.A., Columbia U., 1954; Ph. D., 1960. Instr., Columbia U., 1952–62; research asst., National Academy of Science, 1956–57; DIR., AMERICAN AIRLINES, INC. (NEW YORK), 1957– . Membership; American Economic Association; American Geographical Society; American Statistical Association. Research: economic development geography; economic development in Colombia and Brazil. Language: Spanish 4,4,4,3; Portuguese 3,3,3,2: French 2,2,2,3; German 2,2,2,1. Home: 8 Branford Rd., Hastings-on-Hudson, N.Y. Office: American Airlines, 633 Third Ave., New York, N.Y. 10017.

LOCKLEY, LAWRENCE CAMPBELL, b. Salem, Oreg., Nov. 21, 1899. ECONOMICS. B.A., U. of Calif., 1920; M.A., 1921; M.A., Harvard U., 1928; Ph. D., 1931. Prof., chmn., Marketing, Temple U., 1930–35; chief, Census Service, U.S. Bureau of the Census, 1935; market analyst, Curtis Publishing Company, 1935–42; div. manager, Center for Market Research, E. I. duPont de Nemours & Company, 1942–45; prof., N.Y.U., 1946–51; dean, School of Commerce, U. of Southern Calif., 1951–59; vis. prof., Columbia U., 1959–60; PROF., CHMN., MARKETING, U. OF SANTA CLARA, 1960– . Chief of party, International Cooperation Administration Seminars in Mexico, 1956; adviser, International Cooperation Administration (Costa Rica), 1958; lectr., International Cooperation Administration (Nicaragua), 1961; editor, Journal of Retailing; head, Market Guide Projects, U.S. Agency for International Development, 1963, 1964. Membership: American Economic Association; American Marketing Association; American Statistical Association; Beta Gamma Sigma. Research: marketing; business organization; census problems and government statistics. Author: Use of Motivation Research in Marketing (1960); A Guide to Market Data in Central America (1964); A Market Guide to Peru (1964). Language: Spanish 3,3,3,3. Home: 616 Morse St., San Jose, Calif. 95126. Office: Dept. of Marketing, U. of Santa Clara, Santa Clara, Calif. 95050.

LOCKLIN, (DAVID) PHILIP, b. Richford, Vt., Mar. 1, 1897. ECONOMICS. A.B., Middlebury Coll., 1920; A.M., Harvard U., 1922; Ph. D., U. of Ill., 1926. Asst. prof.-assoc. prof., U. of Ill., 1927–41; principal transport economist, Interstate Commerce Commission, 1935; PROF., ECONOMICS, U. OF ILL., 1941– ; dir., Inter-territorial Freight Rate Studies, U.S. Board of Investigation and Research 1942–43 ; vis. prof., U. of Calif., Berkeley, 1952–53 ; Transport Planning Group, World Bank and Government of Argentina, 1960–61. Membership: American Economic Association; American Finance Association; American Political Science Association ; American Society of Traffic and Transportation. Research : transport economics; transportation planning in Argentina. Author: Railroad Regulation Since 1920 (1928) ; Economics of Transportation (1960) ; The Literature on Railway Rate Theory (Quarterly Journal of Economics, Feb. 1933). Language: Spanish 3,1,1,1; Portuguese 1,1,1,1; French 3,1,1,1; German 3,1,1,1. Home: 1106 South Garfield St., Urbana, Ill., 61801. Office: Dept. of Economics, 226 David Kinley Hall, U. of Ill., Urbana.

LOFTIN, MARION T., b. Coushatta, La., Sept. 10, 1915. SOCIOLOGY. B.A., Northwestern La. State Coll., 1936 ; M.A., La. State U., 1941 ; Ph. D., Vanderbilt U., 1952. Teacher, La. Public Schools, 1935–40 ; assoc. prof., Southeastern La. Coll., 1946–47 ; PROF., HEAD, SOCIOLOGY AND RURAL LIFE, MISS. STATE U., 1949– . Simón Bolívar fellow (Brazil), Vanderbilt U., 1948–49 ; Technical Committee to Honduras, Organization of American States, 1960–61. Membership : American Sociological Association ; Rural Sociological Society ; Southern Sociological Society. Research : rural sociology ; the Japanese in Brazil ; rural organization in Brazil and Honduras. Author: Problems in Health and Medical Services (1955) ; Social Factors Related to the Health of Older People (1959) ; A Research Note on Data Collection (Rural Sociology, Sept. 1961). Language: Spanish 4,3,3,2 ; Portuguese 4,3,3,2 ; French 3,2,2,2. Home: P.O. Box 156, State College, Miss. Office: Dept. of Sociology and Rural Life, Miss. State U., State College.

LOGAN, RAYFORD W., b. Washington, D.C., Jan. 7, 1897. HISTORY. A.B., Williams Coll., 1917 ; A.M., Harvard U., 1932 ; Ph. D., 1936. Prof., chmn., Va. Union U., 1925–30 ; prof., chmn., Atlanta U., 1933–38 ; PROF., HISTORY, HOWARD U., 1938– ; CHMN., 1942– . Advisory Committee, Coordinator of Inter-American Affairs, 1941–42 ; Fulbright fellow (France), 1951–52 ; Advisory Committee on Latin America, Institute of International Education, 1962– . Membership : American Historical Association ; Conference on Latin American History ; Inter-American Council (Washington, D.C.) ; International Institute of Arts and Letters ; Phi Beta Kappa. Research : colonial administration ; race relations in the Caribbean ; diplomatic history of Haiti. Author: Diplomatic Relations of the United States with Haiti, 1776–1891 (1941). Language: Spanish 1,2,2,2 ; Portuguese 3,–,–,– ; French 1,1,1,1. Home: 1519 Jackson St. NE., Washington, D.C. Office: Dept. of History, Howard U., Washington.

LONG, ROBERT GRANT, b. Crystal Falls, Mich., Dec. 19, 1918. GEOGRAPHY. B.A., U. of Mich., 1941 ; A.M., Syracuse U., 1943 ; Ph. D., Northwestern U., 1949. Case geographer, U.S. Dept. of the Interior, 1943–44 ; cartographic officer, U.S. Navy, 1944–46 ; ASSOC. PROF., GEOGRAPHY, U. OF TENN., 1949– . Social Science Research Council fellow (Brazil), 1948. Membership: Association of American Geographers; National Council for Geographic Education. Research: economic geography; land use. Author: Volta Redonda: Symbol of Maturity in the Industrial Progress of Brazil (Economic Geography, Apr. 1948); O vale do médio Paraiba (Revista Brasileira de Geografia, July–Sept. 1953); Latin America (in Compton's Encyclopedia, 1963). Language: Spanish 2,2,2,1; Portuguese 3,2,2,1; French 3,1,1,1; German 1,1,1,1. Home: 138 Sunrise Dr., Knoxville, Tenn., 37919. Office: Dept of Geology and Geography, U. of Tenn., Knoxville, 37916.

LONGLAND, JEAN ROGERS, b. Boston, Mass., Jan 11, 1913. LIBRARY SCIENCE. A.B., Wheaton Coll., 1935; S.B., Simmons Coll., 1936. First cataloger, The Hispanic Society of America, 1936–46; asst. curator for Portuguese books, 1946–53; CURATOR OF THE LIBRARY, THE HISPANIC SOCIETY OF AMERICA, 1953– . Membership: American Translators Association; Brazilian Cultural Society; New York Technical Services Librarians; Special Libraries Association. Research: Luso-Brazilian materials; Portuguese and Brazilian literature. Language: Spanish 4,4,3,4; Portuguese 4,4,4,4; French 4,4,4,4. Home: 2201 Amsterdam Ave., New York, N.Y. 10032. Office: The Hispanic Society of America, Broadway at 155th St., New York, 10032.

LONGYEAR, JOHN MUNRO, III, b, Houghton, Mich., July 30, 1914. ANTHROPOLOGY. A.B., Cornell U., 1936; Ph. D., Harvard U., 1940. Research assoc., Div. of Historical Research, Carnegie Institute of Washington, 1938–42; PROF., ANTHROPOLOGY, COLGATE U., 1948– . Research fellow, Andean Institute, 1941–42; research fellow, Peabody Museum, Harvard U., 1946–48. Membership: American Anthropological Association; American Association for the Advancement of Science; Sociedad Mexicana de Antropología; Society for American Archaeology. Research: archeology of the southern Maya area and Central America. Author: Archaeological Investigations in El Salvador (1944); Copan Ceramics: A Study of Southeastern Maya Pottery (1952); An Archaeological Survey of El Salvador (in Handbook of Middle American Indians). Language: Spanish 3,3,3,3; Portuguese 1,1,1,1; French 3,1,1,1. Home: Preston Hill Rd., Hamilton, N.Y. Office: Dept. of Anthropology, Colgate U., Hamilton.

LOOMIS, CHARLES P., b. Broomfield, Colo., Oct. 26, 1905. SOCIOLOGY. B.S., N. Mex. State Coll., 1928; M.S., N.C. State Coll., 1929; Ph. D., Harvard U., 1932. Asst. prof., N.C. State Coll., 1929–32; senior agricultural economist, Bureau of Agricultural Economics, U.S. Dept. of Agriculture, 1936–42; chief, div. of extension and training, Office of Foreign Agricultural Relations, 1940–44; vis. lectr., Harvard U., 1942–44; RESEARCH PROF., HEAD, SOCIOLOGY AND ANTHROPOLOGY, MICH. STATE U., 1944– . Chief, Refugee Organization of United Nations for the Indian countries. Membership: American Anthropological Association; American Sociological Association; National Planning Association; Rural Sociological Society; Society for Applied Anthropology. Research: rural sociology; United States-Mexican border relations; resettlement potential and agricultural development in Peru and Bolivia; technological assistance in Costa Rica. Author: Turrialba—Social Systems and Change (1957); Social Systems (1960); Modern Social Theories (1961). Language: Spanish 5,4,4,3; French 4,–,–,–; German 5,4,4,3. Office: Dept. of Sociology and Anthropology, Mich. State U., East Lansing.

LOOS, EUGENE EMIL, b. Menomonic, Wis., Nov. 17, 1927. LINGUISTICS. B.A., San Diego State Coll., 1949; B.D., Fuller Theological Seminary, 1952; M.A., U. of Mich., 1960. LINGUIST, SUMMER INSTITUTE OF LINGUISTICS, 1952– . Research: anthropology and literacy in native languages of the jungles of eastern Peru. Author: Quirica I, II, III, IV (Capanahua Primers) (1961); Capanahua Narration Structure (1963). Language: Spanish 4,4,4,4; Capanahua 4,4,4,4. Linguistic studies; Capanahua; Huitoto. Home: 5341 Rex Ave., San Diego, Calif. Office: Instituto Lingüístico de Verano, Casilla 2492, Lima, Perú.

LOPES, ALBERT R., b. Oceano, Calif., May 10, 1911. SPANISH AMERICAN AND BRAZILIAN LITERATURES AND LANGUAGE. B.A., U. of Calif., 1931; M.A., 1931; Ph. D., U. of Calif., Berkeley, 1935. Instr., U. of Calif., 1935–36; prof., head, Modern Languages, Loyola U. (La.), 1936–39; asst. prof., U. of N. Mex., 1939–43; instr., U.S. Naval Academy, 1943–46; assoc. prof., U. of N. Mex., 1946–47; PROF., MODERN LANGUAGES, U. of N. MEX., 1947– . Membership: American Association of Teachers of Spanish and Portuguese; Instituto Internacional de Literatura Iberoamericana; Modern Language Association. Research: Brazilian writers. Author: Conversas sul-americanas (1946); Functional Spanish (1956). Language: Spanish 5,5,5,5; Portuguese 5,5,5,5; French 4,4,3,3; Italian 4,5,4,3. Home: 205 Sycamore, N.E., Albuquerque, N. Mex. Office: Dept. of Modern and Classical Languages, U. of N. Mex., Albuquerque.

LOTHROP, SAMUEL KIRKLAND, b. Milton, Mass., July 6, 1892. ANTHROPOLOGY. A.B., Harvard U., 1915; Ph. D., 1921. Archeologist, Harvard U. (P.R., Guatemala, Honduras), 1915–17, (Panama), 1933, 1940, 1951, (Costa Rica), 1948–49; archeologist, Carnegie Institution of Washington (Guatemala, Yucatan), 1923, (Guatemala), 1932–33; archeologist, Museum of American Indian, Heye Foundation (New Mexico, Central America), 1924, (Chile, Paraguay, Argentina, Peru), 1924–25, (Central America), 1926, (Guatemala), 1928, (Chile), 1929; asst. curator, Peabody Museum, Harvard U., 1935–42; archeologist, Institute of Andean Research (Peru), 1941–42; curator, Andean Archeology, Robert S. Peabody Museum, Harvard U., 1943–62; RETIRED, 1963– . Loubat Prize, Columbia U.; U. of Pa. Museum fellow; Kidder Medal for American Archeology, 1957; Huxley Memorial Medal, 1960; Wenner-Gren Foundation Medal in Archeology, 1961. Membership: American Anthropological Association; American Association for the Advancement of Science; National Academy of Science; Royal Anthropological Institute; Société des Américanistes; Society for American Archaeology. Research: Latin American archeology and ethnology. Author: Tulum, an Archaeological Study of Eastern Yucatan

(1923); Indians of Tierra del Fuego (1928); Coclé, an Archaeological Study of Central Panama (Part I, 1937; Part II, 1941). Language: Spanish 4,4,4,4; Portuguese 2,2, 1,–; French 3,3,2,–. Linguistic studies: Cacaopera; Ona; Yahgan. Home: 65 Partridge Lane, Belmont, Mass. Office: Peabody Museum, Harvard U., Cambridge, Mass.

LOTT, LEO B., b. Lehi, Utah, Mar. 5, 1919. POLITICAL SCIENCE. B. Ph., Gonzaga U., 1942; M.A., U. of Wis., 1951; Ph. D., 1954. ASST. PROF., POLITICAL SCIENCE, OHIO STATE U., 1954– ; vis. lectr., U. of Wis., Summer 1956. Doherty fellow (Venezuela), 1952–53. Membership: American Association for the United Nations; American Political Science Association. Research: political systems of Latin America; Venezuela; Paraguay. Author: Executive Power in Venezuela (American Political Science Review, June 1956); The 1952 Venezuelan Election: The Lesson for 1957 (Western Political Quarterly, Sept. 1957); The Nationalization of Justice in Venezuela (Inter-American Economic Affairs, Summer 1959). Language: Spanish 4,2,2,3; Portuguese 1,1,1,1; French 2,1,1,1. Dept. of Political Science, Ohio State U., 216 North Oval Dr., Columbus, Ohio 43210.

LOU, DENNIS WINGSOU, b. Canton, China, Oct. 6, 1924. HISTORY. B.A., Phillips U., 1953; M.A., Tex. Christian U., 1956; Ph. D., Ind. U., 1963. Chmn., Talladega Coll., 1961–62; ASSOC. PROF., SOCIAL SCIENCE, STATE U. OF N.Y., COLL. AT ONEONTA, 1963– . Tex. Christian U. fellow, 1954–56; Asian History and Latin American History fellow, Ind. U., 1959–61; senior faculty fellow, University Committee of Oriental Studies, Columbia U., 1962–63. Membership: American Academy of Social and Political Sciences; American Historical Association; Asian Studies Association; Pacific Institute, Far East Prehistory Association; Pan American Union Latin American Conference. Research: China's cultural relations with Latin America; the possible early relationship between the Chinese civilization and the high culture of America. Author: Folklore of Si-chow (Chi Heng School Journal, Hong Kong, 1941); Rain Worship Among the Ancient Chinese and the Nahua-Maya Indians: A Comparative Study of Cultural Similarities (Academia Sinica, 1957). Language: Spanish 4,3,2,2; Portuguese 1,–,–,–; French 3,3,2,2; Chinese 5,5,5,5; Japanese 3,3,3,2. Home: 107 Spruce St., Oneonta, N.Y. Office: Dept. of History, State U. of N.Y., Coll. at Oneonta, Oneonta.

LOUNSBURG, FLOYD GLENN, b. Stevens Point, Wis., Apr. 25, 1914. ANTHROPOLOGY: LINGUISTICS. B.A., U. of Wis., 1941; M.A., 1946; Ph. D., Yale U., 1949. Asst. prof., Yale U., 1949–55; assoc. prof., 1955–61; PROF., ANTHROPOLOGY, YALE U., 1961– . Center for Advanced Study in the Behavioral Sciences fellow, 1963–64. Membership: American Anthropological Association; American Ethnological Society; Linguistic Society of America. Research: Brazilian ethnology; aboriginal tribes in Mato Grosso, Brazil; 16th century Yucatec kinship terminology; Inca kinship system. Author: Field Methods and Techniques in Linguistics (in Anthropology Today, 1953); Linguistics and Psychology (in Psychology, A Study of a Science, 1963); The Structural Analysis of Kinship Semantics (Proceedings, Ninth International Congress of Linguists, 1964). Language: Spanish 4,3,3,3; Portuguese 4,4,4,4; French 4,2,2,2; German 4,4,4,4. Linguistic studies: Iroquoian languages; Quechua. Home: 52 Hellstrom Rd., East Haven, Conn. Office: Dept. of Anthropology, Yale U., New Haven, Conn. 06520.

LOUNSBURY, JOHN FREDERICK, b. Perham, Minn., Oct. 26, 1918. GEOGRAPHY. B.S., U. of Ill., 1942; M.S., 1946; Ph. D., Northwestern U., 1951. Assoc. dir., Rural Land Classification Program, Dept. of Agriculture and Commerce (P.R.), 1949–51; asst. prof.-prof., chmn., Earth Sciences, Antioch Coll., 1951–61; vis. prof., Northwestern U., Summer 1951; Ind. U. Conservation Workshop, Summers 1955–57; Wesleyan U., Summer 1957; U. of Ga., Fall 1959; Mich. State U., Summers 1960, 1963; HEAD, GEOGRAPHY, COORDINATOR OF SPECIAL INSTRUCTIONAL PROGRAMS, EASTERN MICH. U., 1961– . Representative in Bolivia, Technical Cooperation Administration, U.S. Dept. of State, 1951; consultant, research analyst, Dayton Metropolitan Community Studies, Inc.-Ford Foundation, 1957–59, and Industrial Development Corporation (Mich.), 1961–63; Advisory Committee on Geography to U.S. Dept. of State, Pan American Institute of Geography and History, 1962– ; dir., Geography in Liberal Education Project, Association of American Geographers-National Science Foundation, 1963– . Membership: American Association for the Advancement of Science; American Geographical Society; Association of American Geographers; Association of Latin American Studies; Gamma Theta Upsilon; Michigan Academy of Science, Arts and Letters; National Council for Geographic Education; National Planning Association; Regional Science Association; Sigma Xi. Research: economic geography; land use; industrial and economic area development. Author: Rural Settlement Types and Patterns of Puerto Rico (1952); Farmsteads in Puerto Rico and Their Interpretive Value (Geographical Review, July 1955); Economic Development in Latin America: Puerto Rico as a Case Study (Papers, Michigan Academy of Science, Arts and Letters, 1964). Language: Spanish 2,2,2,2; French 3,3,2,2. Home: 737 Mansfield, Ypsilanti, Mich. Office: Dept. of Geography, Eastern Mich. U., Ypsilanti.

LOWENTHAL, DAVID, b. New York, N.Y., Apr. 26, 1923. GEOGRAPHY AND HISTORY. B.S., Harvard Coll., 1943; M.A., U. of Calif., Berkeley, 1950; Ph. D., U. of Wis., 1953. Asst. prof., chmn., Geography, Vassar Coll., 1952–56; RESEARCH ASSOC., AMERICAN GEOGRAPHICAL SOCIETY, 1957– . Fulbright research fellow, U. of the West Indies (Jamaica), 1956–57; consultant, U. Coll. of the West Indies, 1959– ; Institute of Race Relations Commission (London), 1961–65; Humid Tropics Commission, International Geographical Union. Membership: American Anthropological Association; American Historical Association; Association of American Geographers; Society for the History of Discoveries. Research: historical geography of the Guianas; the Caribbean; population; race relations in the Caribbean. Author: The West Indies Federation (1961); Physical Resources of the British Caribbean (in The Economy of the West Indies, 1960); Levels of West Indian Government (Social and Economic Studies, 1962). Language: Spanish 2,1,1,1; French 4,4,4,4; Dutch 2,2, 1,1; German 3,3,3,3. Home: 75 Riverside Dr., New York 24, N.Y. Office: American Geographical Society, Broadway at 156th St., New York 32.

LOWY, SARA JAROSLAVSKY, b. Paraná, Argentina, June 25, 1916. SPANISH AMERICAN LITERATURE. Profesora, Instituto Nacional del Profesorado Secundario (Buenos Aires), 1939; M.A., State U. of Iowa, 1950. Instr., State U. of Iowa, 1948–50; lectr., Columbia U., 1950–51; instr., La. State U., 1954–55; 1959–60; vis. prof., Universidad Nacional Autónoma de México, Summer 1963. Research: 19th century Argentine literary criticism; the United States as seen by Latin American writers. Author: Alberto Gerchunoff: vida y obra (1957); La literatura en los periódicos argentinos (Revista de la Universidad de Buenos Aires, 1946). Co-author: La cultura argentina en el decenio 1852–1862 (1947). Language: Spanish 5,5,5,5; Portuguese 3,4, –,–; French 5,5,3,3. Home: 534 Highland Park Dr., Baton Rouge, La. 70808.

LOZANO, ANTHONY GIRARD, b. San Antonio, Tex., Jan. 30, 1938. LINGUISTICS AND LANGUAGE. B.A., U. of Tex., 1960; Ph. D., 1964. Asst. dir., Languages, Universidad del Valle (Cali, Colombia), 1962–63; 1ST LIEUTENANT, U.S. ARMY, 1964–66. Rockefeller grant (Colombia); National Defense Education Act fellow in Spanish; Ford Foundation fellow. Membership: Linguistic Society of America. Research: applied and descriptive linguistics; English as a second language; spoken styles in Colombian Spanish; transformational grammar. Author: Intercambio de español e inglés en San Antonio, Texas (Archivum, 1962); English (Journal of the Asociación Colombiana de Profesores de Inglés, 1963); Basic English Sentences (Language Learning, 1964). Language: Spanish 5,5,5,5; Portuguese 5,3,1,1; French 5,3,3,3. Home: 1514 Lawndale, San Antonio, Tex. 78209.

LOZANO, CARLOS, b. Zamora, Mexico, Jan. 12, 1913. SPANISH AMERICAN LITERATURE. B.A., U. of Calif., Berkeley, 1941; Ph. D., 1962. Asst. prof., George Washington U., 1959–63; assoc. prof., St. Louis U., 1963–64; ASSOC. PROF., HISPANIC AMERICAN AND SPANISH PENINSULAR LITERATURES, U. OF OREG. 1964– . Therese F. Collin traveling fellow, U. of Calif., Berkeley; contributing editor, Handbook of Latin American Studies. Membership: American Association of Teachers of Spanish and Portuguese; Comediantes; Modern Language Association. Research: Spanish American colonial and contemporary literature; modernism; the novel; contemporary poetry; influence of Rubén Darío in Spain; Spanish mystic and Golden Age literature. Author: The Elemental Odes of Pablo Neruda (1961). Co-author: Novelistas hispanoamericanos contemporáneos (1964). Translator: My Horse González, by Fernando Alegría (1964). Language: Spanish 5,5,5,5; Portuguese 5,4,4,3; French 5,5,4,4; Italian 5,5,4,4. Office: Dept. of Modern Languages, U. of Oreg., Eugene.

LUDWIG, ARMIN KONRAD, b. Toledo, Ohio, Dec. 30, 1930. GEOGRAPHY. B.S., Ball State Teachers Coll., 1952; M.A., Mich. State U., 1955; Ph. D., U. of Ill., 1962. ASST. PROF., GEOGRAPHY, COLGATE U., 1958– . National Defense fellow in Portuguese, U. of Tex., Summer 1962; Social Science Research Council grant (Brazil), 1963–64. Membership: Association of American Geographers. Research: urban geography; the motivations for and patterns of migrations of people and movement of goods; the role of government planning in the movement of people and goods into and from the new Distrito Federal, Brazil and the functional structure of Brasilia and the Distrito Federal. Author: The Transportation Structure of the Lower Wabash Valley (1962). Language: Spanish 2,2,2,1; Portuguese 4,3,3,3. Home and office: Dept. of Geography, Colgate U., Hamilton, N.Y.

LUEBKE, BENJAMIN H., b. Toutle, Wash., Apr. 26, 1901. SOCIOLOGY. B.S., Oreg. State Coll., 1925; M.S., Kans. State Agricultural Coll., 1926; Ph. D., U. of Fla., 1959. Agricultural missionary, Methodist Church (Chile), 1920–31; assoc. agricultural economist, U. of Tenn., 1935–57; asst. prof., Berea Coll., 1957–58; ASSOC. PROF., SOCIOLOGY, TENN. POLYTECHNIC INSTITUTE, 1959– . Membership: Alpha Kappa Delta; American Sociological Society; Association of American University Professors; Rural Sociological Society; Southern Sociological Society. Research: rural sociology; delineation of rural communities in the state of Oaxaca, Mexico; international border contacts in Juárez, Mexico. Author: Migration from a Southern Appalachian Community (Land Economics, Feb. 1958). Co-author: Types of Farming in Tennessee (1960). Language: Spanish 5,3,3,4. Home: 1721 Lake Ave., Knoxville, Tenn. Office: Dept. of Sociology, Tenn. Polytechnic Institute, Box 131 A, Cookeville, Tenn.

LUND, HARRY, b. North Mankato, Minn., July 29, 1911. LANGUAGE. A.B., U. of Minn., 1942; U. of P.R., 1947–50; Ph. D., U. of Madrid, 1953. Asst., Veterans Administration (P.R.), 1946–47; English teacher, Ramírez Business Coll. (P.R.), 1946–49; interpreter, Mayo Clinic, Summer 1954; English teacher, Public High School (Minn.), 1954; ASSOC. PROF., SPANISH, PAN AMERICAN COLL., 1954– . Membership: American Association of Teachers of Spanish and Portuguese. Research: Spanish. Author: Escribiendo Español (1959); Ejercicios de acento y de la ortografía (1961); Calderón de la Barca (1963). Language: Spanish 5,5,5,3; French 3,1,1,1; Danish 2,3,3,1; German –,2,2,–. Linguistic studies: Spanish. Home: 1001 West Mahl, Edinburg, Tex. Office: Dept. of Spanish, Pan American Coll., Edinburg.

LUPER, ALBERT T(HOMAS), b. Jacksonville, Tex., Jan. 10, 1914. MUSIC. Certificate, Lisbon Conservatory, 1931; B. Mus., Tex. Christian U., 1934; M. Mus., U. of Rochester, 1938; Eastman School of Music, U. of Rochester, 1948–51. Prof., John Tarleton Coll., 1935–38; instr.-asst. prof., U. of Tex., 1938–48; asst. prof., U. of Iowa, 1948–59; PROF., MUSIC, U. OF IOWA, 1959– . U. of Tex. fellow (Mexico), 1941; participant, International Conference on

Brazil, 1958; 7th U.S. Conference on UNESCO, 1959; Advisory Board, Inter-American Institute for Musical Research, Tulane U. Membership: American Association of University Professors; American Choral Foundation; American Musicological Society; Association for Latin American Studies; College Music Association; International Association of Music Libraries; International Musicological Society; Music Library Association; Society for Ethnomusicology. Research: musicology; Renaissance music; 20th century music; colonial church music in Mexico; Portuguese music. Author: Music of Argentina (1941); Portuguese Polyphony in the 16th and Early 17th Centuries (Journal of the American Musical Society, Summer 1950). Co-author: Music of Latin America (1942). Language: Spanish 4,4,4,4; Portuguese 5,5,5,4; French 4,3,3,3; German 3,2,2,1; Italian 3,2,2,1. Home: 213 McLean St., Iowa City, Iowa 52241. Office: Dept. of Music, U. of Iowa, Iowa City, 52240.

LUTZ, E. RUSSELL. b. Lancaster, Pa., June 1, 1902. LAW. A.B., George Washington U., 1922; LL. B., Yale U., 1926; Law School, George Washington U., 1926–28. Asst. solicitor and asst. legal adviser, U.S. Dept. of State, 1926–37; attorney, asst. general counsel, U.S. Maritime Commission, 1937–41; dir., vice president, American President Lines, 1942; executive vice president, 1943–49; manager, Washington office, W. R. Grace & Company, 1949–50; vice president, Grace Line, Inc., 1950–54; VICE PRESIDENT, OFFICER IN CHARGE OF WASHINGTON AREA, W. R. GRACE & COMPANY, 1954– . Industry representative, Fourth Meeting of Consultation of Ministers of Foreign Affairs, Organization of American States, 1951; Committee on Shipping Conferences and Freight Rates, Inter-American Economic and Social Council, 1952–57; industry observer, Third Extraordinary Meeting of the Inter-American Economic and Social Council of the Organization of American States, 1953, Tenth Inter-American Conference, 1954, Economic Conference of the Organization of American States, 1957. Membership: American Society of International Law; American Bar Association; Federal Bar Association; Inter-American Bar Association; Maritime Law Association of the United States; Maritime Administrative Bar Association. Research: international law; maritime law. Author: Treatment of Private Property of Aliens on Land in Time of War (American Society of International Law Proceedings, Apr. 1933); Recent Arbitration Between the United States and Panama (Federal Bar Association Journal, Apr. 1934). Collaborator: Convicting the Innocent (1932). Language: Spanish 1,1,1,1; French 1,1,1,1. Home: 1427 34th St. NW., Washington, D.C., 20007. Office: 1511 K St. NW., Washington, 20005.

LYNCH, JAMES B. Jr., b. Miona, Va., Sept. 23, 1919. ART. A.B., Harvard U., 1941; A.M., 1947; Ph. D., 1960. Instr., Pine Manor Junior Coll., 1951–55; ASSOC. PROF., FINE ARTS, BOSTON U., 1955– . Bacon traveling fellow, Harvard U. (Mexico), 1949. Membership: College Art Association. Research: Italian Renaissance; pre-Columbian art; contemporary art in Mexico. Author: Orozco's House of Tears (Journal of Inter-American Studies, July 1961); Raphael's Small St. George in the Louvre (Gazette des Beaux-Arts, Apr. 1962). Language: Spanish 3,-,-,-; Portuguese 1, -,-,-; French 3,-,-,-. Home: 5 Squirrel Rd., Wellesley Hills, Mass. Office: Dept. of Fine Arts, Boston U., 725 Commonwealth Ave., Boston, Mass.

LYONS, MARION, S.C.H., b. Brockton, Mass., Apr. 30, 1913. GEOGRAPHY. B.A., Mt. St. Vincent Coll., 1931; M. Ed., Boston Coll., 1938; Ph. D., Clark U., 1963. Teacher, Sisters of Charity (Roxbury, Mass.), 1936–55; AUTHOR AND LECTR., SISTERS OF CHARITY (WELLESLEY, MASS.), 1955– . National Council for Geographic Education fellow. Membership: Gamma Theta Upsilon; National Council of Geographic Education; New England Association of History Teachers; New England-Saint Lawrence Geography Society. Research: present and potential industrial growth of Cali, Colombia. Author: Neighbors Across the World (1959); Southern Neighbors (1960); My World of Neighbors (1961). Language: Spanish 3,3,3,3; Portuguese 1,1,1,1; French 3,3,3,3; German 3,3,3,3; Latin 3,1,1,3. Home and office: Academy of the Assumption, Wellesley Hills, Mass., 02181.

M

McADAMS, JOHN, b. Vega Baja, P.R., July 15, 1916. POLITICAL SCIENCE. A.B., U. of P.R., 1937; A.M., Fordham U., 1938; Ph. D., 1952. Instr., U. of P.R., 1939–40; U.S. Army (P.R., Panama, Colombia, Brazil, Paraguay), 1940–45; instr., editor, Latin American Section, Command and General Staff School, U.S. Army, 1945–47; DIR. OF PUBLICATIONS, PAN AMERICAN UNION, 1949– . Contributor, Encyclopaedia Britannica Yearbook, 1950–54, and National Catholic Education Yearbook, 1962; book reviewer, Review of Inter-American Bibliography, The Americas. Membership: American Political Science Association; Public Personnel Association; Society for Personnel Administration. Research: educational institutions in Latin America; economic and social organization in Latin America. Language: Spanish 5,5,-5,5; Portuguese 4,4,3,1; French 4,3,3,2. Home: 5606 Forest Pl., Bethesda, Md. 20014. Office: Dept. of Publications, Pan American Union, Washington, D.C., 20006.

McALEES, DANIEL CLARK, b. Reading, Pa., Feb. 6, 1937. EDUCATION. A.B., Albright Coll., 1958; M.A., Mich. State U., 1959; Ph. D. 1963. COORDINATOR, REHABILITATION COUNSELOR TRAINING, COLO. STATE COLL., 1963– . Overseas Study grant (Guatemala), U.S. Dept. of State; research asst. (Guatemala), Mich. State U., 1961–62; consultant on rehabilitation and special education, Instituto de Investigaciones y Mejoramiento Educativo (Guatemala). Membership: American Personnel and Guidance Association; American Psychological Association; American Rehabilitation Counseling Association; Colorado Rehabilitation Association; International Society for Rehabilitation of the Disabled; National Rehabilitation Association; National Society for Crippled Children and Adults. Research: rehabilitation; special education; psychology; analysis of special education in Guatemala. Author: Manual explicativo sobre el significado del cociente intelectual (1962); Un análisis de la construcción y aplicación de los items de un test sociométrico (1963); Special Education in Guatemala (Mich. State U. World Horizons in Special Education Lecture Series, July 1963). Language: Spanish 3,3,3,2. Home: 2907 11th Street Rd., Greeley, Colo. Office: Colo. State Coll., Greeley.

McALISTER, LYLE NELSON, b. Twisp, Wash., Feb. 14, 1916. HISTORY. B.S., State Coll. of Wash., 1938; M.A., U. of Calif., Berkeley, 1947; Ph. D., 1950. Instr.,-assoc. prof., U. of Fla., 1950–59; prof., chmn., 1959–63; PROF., HISTORY, DIR., CENTER FOR LATIN AMERICAN STUDIES, U. OF FLA., 1963– . Doherty fellow (Mexico), 1949–50; American Philosophic Society grant, 1953, 1955; chmn., Robertson Prize Committee, Conference on Latin American History, 1957; Rockefeller Foundation grant, 1962. Membership: American Association of University Professors; American Historical Association; Association for Latin American Studies. Research: New Spain; civil-military relations in Latin America; social organization in colonial Latin Amerca. Author: The Fuero Militar in New Spain (1957); The Reorganization of the Army of New Spain, 1763–1767 (Hispanic American Historical Review, Feb. 1953); Social Structure and Social Change in New Spain (Hispanic American Historical Review, Aug. 1963). Language: Spanish 5,4,4,4; Portuguese 3,3,3,2; French 3,1,1,1. Home: 2712 SW. 5th Pl., Gainesville, Fla. Office: Center for Latin American Studies, Library 450, U. of Fla., Gainesville.

McANDREW, JOHN, b. New York, N.Y., May 4, 1904. ARCHITECTURE AND ART. S.B., Harvard Coll., 1924; M. Arch., Harvard Graduate School of Architecture, 1940. Instr., Art, Vassar Coll., 1932–36; curator of architecture, Museum of Modern Art (N.Y.), 1936–40; prof., Instituto Nacional de Antropología (Mexico), 1943; PROF., ART, WELLESLEY COLL., 1944– ; vis. prof. of architecture, Mass. Institute of Technology, 1948–52. Editorial Board, Art in America; Inter-American Committee on Artistic Relations grant (Mexico), 1939. Membership: College Art Association; Italia Nostra; Sociedad de Arquitectos Colombianos; Sociedad de Arquitectos Mexicanos; Society of Architectural Historians. Research: Mexican architecture. Author: Open-Air Churches of 16th Century Mexico (1965). Co-author: Catalogue of Painting and Sculpture at Wellesley (1959). Editor: Guide to Modern Architecture, Northeast States (1940). Language: Spanish 4,4,4,3; Portuguese 1,1,1,1; French 4,4,4,3; German 3,3,3,2; Italian 3,2,2,2. Home: 107 Dover Rd., Wellesley 81, Mass. Office: Dept. of Art, Wellesley Coll., Wellesley 81.

McBRIDE, GEORGE McCUTCHEN, b. Benton, Kans., Oct. 11, 1876. GEOGRAPHY. B.A., Park Coll., 1898; Ph. D., Yale U., 1921; LL.D., U. of Calif., 1961. Prof., Instituto Inglés (Santiago, Chile), 1901–07; dir., Instituto Americano (La Paz, Bolivia), 1907–15; asst., Wesleyan U., 1915–17; asst., Yale U., 1916–17; librarian and asst. editor, American Geographical Society, 1917–22; prof., U. of Calif., Los Angeles, 1922–47; technical adviser, Ecuador-Peru Boundary Commission (Lima, Peru; Quito, Ecuador) U.S. Dept. of State, 1942–49; PROF. EMERITUS, GEOGRAPHY, U. OF CALIF., LOS ANGELES 1947– . American Geograpical Society honorary fellow, 1922; Carnegie Endowment for International Peace lectr. to South America, 1930, and Central America, 1938; American Geographical Society Livingstone Medal, 1956. Membership: American Geographical Society; Association of American Geographers; Association of Pacific Coast Geographers; Los Angeles Geographical Society; Pacific Geographical Society; Pi Gamma Mu; Sociedad Geográfica de Lima. Research; land tenure systems in Latin America; tropical highlands of America; political geography. Author: Agrarian Indian Communities of Highland Bolivia (1921); Land Systems of Mexico (1923); Chile: Land and Society (1931). Language: Spanish 5,5,5,5; Portuguese 4,4,–,– ; French 2,2,–,– ; Italian 3,–,–,–. Home: 921 West Bonita, Claremont, Calif.

McBRYDE, FELIX WEBSTER, b. Lynchburg, Va., Apr. 23, 1908. GEOGRAPHY. B.A., Tulane U., 1930; Ph. D., U. of Calif., Berkeley, 1940. Instr., Ohio State U., 1937–42; geographer, U.S. War Dept., 1942–45; cultural geographer, Institute of Social Anthropology (Peru), Smithsonian Institution, 1945–47; representative, Institute of Andean Research (Peru), 1947–48; geographer, U.S. Bureau of Census, 1948–56; lectr., U. of Md., 1951–63; dir. of surveys and regional planning, Gordon A. Friesen Associates, Inc. (Washington, D.C.), 1956–58; president, F. W. McBryde Associates, Inc. (Washington, D.C.), 1958– ; PHYSICAL GEOGRAPHER, U.S. ARMY CORPS OF ENGINEERS, INTER-AMERICAN GEODETIC SURVEY (C.Z.), 1964– . U. fellow, U. of Colo., 1930–31; research fellow, Clark U., 1931–32; field research fellow (Guatemala), Clark U. and Carnegie Institution of Washington, 1932; Social Science Research Council fellow (Guatemala, El Salvador), 1935–36; National Research Council fellow (Mexico, Guatemala), 1940–41; technical adviser and chief of mission for First Census of Ecuador, 1949–51; orientation lectr., Foreign Service Institute, U.S. Dept. of State, 1953–57; representative of President Miguel Ydígoras Fuentes (Guatemala), 1957–63; Latin American representative, Institute of Modern Languages Inc., 1963– ; president and organizer, Inter-American Institute of Modern Languages and Inter-American Linguistic Research Institute (Guatemala), 1963– ; consultant, Inter-American Statistical Institute, Pan American Institute of Geography and History, and Inter-American Geodetic Survey. Membership: American Anthropological Association; American Association for the Advancement of Science; American Congress on Surveying and Mapping; American Geographical Society; American Geophysical Union; American Meteorological Society; Association of American Geographers; Ecuadorian Institute of Anthropology and Geography; Ecuadorian Institute of Natural Sciences; Inter-American Council; Lima Geographical Society; Mexican Society of Geographers and Statisticians. Research: ethnogeography; geo-demography; cartog raphy; regional and cultural geography of Latin America; natural resources of Latin America. Author: Sololá: A Guatemalan Town and Cakchiquel Market Center (1933); Cultural and Historical Geography of Southwest Guatemala (1947); Plan de coordinación hospitalaria en Costa Rica (1959). Language: Spanish 5,5,5,5; Portuguese 3,3,2,2; French 3,2,1,3; German 2,1,1,2; Italian 3,3,1,2. Home: 10100 Falls Rd., Rockville, Md., 20854. Office: Natural Resources Div., Inter-American Geodetic Survey, U.S. Army, Fort Clayton, C.Z.

McCARRAN, MARGARET-PATRICIA, S.N.-J.M., b. Reno, Nev., July 22, 1904. HISTORY. Mus. B., Mt. St. Mary's Coll. (Calif.), 1931; M.A., Catholic U. of America, 1946; Ph. D., 1952. ASSOC. PROF., SOCIAL SCIENCES, COLL. OF THE HOLY NAMES, 1952– . Membership: Academy of Political Science; Pi Gamma Mu. Language: Spanish 3,-,-,2; French -,2,-,2; Latin -,3,-,2. Home and office: Coll. of the Holy Names, 3500 Mountain Blvd., Oakland 19, Calif.

McCARTY, KIERAN, O.F.M., b. Tama, Iowa, June 19, 1925. HISTORY. B.A., San Luis Rey Coll., 1946; M.A., Catholic U. of America, 1960. RESIDENT MEMBER, ACADEMY OF AMERICAN FRANCISCAN HISTORY, 1958– ; technical consultant, Instituto Nacional de Antropología e Historia, 1960–61; EDITOR, THE AMERICAS, 1963– ; INSTR., HISTORY, CATHOLIC U. OF AMERICA, 1964– . Organization of American States fellow (Mexico), 1961. Research: archival studies in Mexico; colonial church history. Author: Los Franciscanos en la Frontera Chichimeca (1962); Apostolic Colleges of the Propagation of the Faith: Old and New World Background (The Americas, July 1962). Language: Spanish 4,4,4,4; Portuguese 3,3,3,3; French 2,2,2,2; German 2,2,2,2; Italian 2,2,2,2,. Home and office: Academy of American Franciscan History, 9800 Kentsdale Dr., Box 5966, Washington, D.C. 20014.

McCONNELL, THOMAS RAYMOND, b. Mediapolis, Iowa, May 25, 1901. EDUCATION. A.B., Cornell Coll., 1924; A.M., U. of Iowa, 1928; Ph. D., 1933. Faculty, Cornell Coll., 1925–36; assoc. prof.-prof., U. of Minn., 1936–50; assoc. dean-dean, Coll. of Science, Literature, and the Arts, 1940–50; chancellor, U. of Buffalo, 1950–54; PROF., EDUCATION, U. OF CALIF., BERKELEY, 1954– ; CHMN., CENTER FOR THE STUDY OF HIGHER EDUCATION, 1956– . Fellow, Center for Advanced Study in the Behavioral Sciences, 1959–60; chmn., Ford Foundation group to recommend grant programs to Chilean universities, 1962; consultant, U. of Chile, 1962; Presidents Kennedy and Johnson's Committee, on Higher Education in the District of Columbia; Research Committee, Educational Testing Service; Committee on Appraisal and Development, Junior College Student Personnel Services; Advisory Council, Cooperation Research Branch, Office of Education, U.S. Dept. of Health, Education, and Welfare. Membership: American Council of Education; American Educational Research Association; American Psychological Association; Institute for College and University Administrators; National Education Association; National Society for Study of Education. Research: student characteristics and development; organization, administration and coordination of higher education. Author: Liberal Education and the University (1954); A General Pattern for American Public Higher Education (1962). Co-author: The Diverse College Student Population (in The American College, 1962). Language: Spanish 2,2,1,2; French 2,2,1,1. Office: Center for the Study of Higher Education, 4606 Tolman Hall, U. of Calif., Berkeley, 94720.

McCORKLE, (HOMER) THOMAS, JR., b. Comfort, Tex., July 30, 1914. ANTHROPOLOGY. A.B., U. of Calif., Berkeley, 1938; Ph. D., 1954. Instr., U. of Calif., Santa Barbara, 1954–55; field dir., Committee for Cultural Study of Mexican Americans, 1955; research anthropologist, Coll. of Medicine, U. of Iowa, 1956–60; research anthropologist, Pa. State Health Dept., 1960–63; SUPERVISING SOCIAL SCIENTIST, DIV. OF DENTAL PUBLIC HEALTH, U.S. DEPT. OF HEALTH, EDUCATION, AND WELFARE, 1963– . Doherty fellow (Venezuela), 1952–53. Membership: American Anthropological Association; American Association for the Advancement of Science; Sigma Xi; Society for Applied Anthropology. Research: cultural anthropology; community development and health services; health and medical behavior of special groups; group beliefs and practices related to teeth, mouth, and dental health; social behavior and value systems of elite groups; culture of poverty. Author: Chiropractic: A Deviant Theory of Disease . . . (Human Organization, Spring 1961); Three Medical Systems: China, West, Middle East (Journal of the National Medical Association, Mar. 1963); Developing a Behavioral Science Service (Public Health Reports, May 1963). Language: Spanish 5,4,4,4; Portuguese 3,2,2,2; French 3,2,2,2. Home: 2645 Shasta Rd., Berkeley 8, Calif. Office: Dental Health Center, 14th Av. and Lake St., San Francisco 18, Calif.

McCRARY, J. SMITH, b. San Antonio, Tex., Jan. 8, 1926. SOCIOLOGY. B.A., Southern Methodist U., 1948; M.A., 1949; Ph. D., Washington U., 1956. Instr. and lectr., Southern Ill. U., 1949–56; asst. prof., U. of Chattanooga, 1956–58; assoc. prof., U. of Omaha, 1958–60; PROF., CHMN., SOCIOLOGY, HANOVER COLL., 1960– . Lilly Foundation grant, 1961, (Mexico), 1962; American Association for Middle Eastern Studies grant, U. of Utah, 1963. Membership: American Sociological Association; Indiana Academy of Social Science; Mid-West Sociological Society; National Council on Family Relations; Pan American Union Gerontological Society. Research: social anthropology; sociological theory in Mexico for the teaching of sociology and current sociological research; Anthropological studies of rural Mexico. Author: Role, Status, and Participation of the Aged in a Small Community (1956); Modern Theories of Public Assistance (Public Aid in Illinois, Feb. 1957). Co-author: People of Coaltown (1958). Language: Spanish 4,4,4,3; Portuguese 1,1,1,1; French 3,3,3,3; Arabic 3,3,3,3; Greek 2,2,2,2. Home: 225 Crestwood Dr., Madison, Ind. Office: Dept. of Sociology, Hanover Coll., Hanover, Ind., 47243.

McCROCKLIN, JAMES H., b. Boerne, Tex., May 3, 1923. POLITICAL SCIENCE. B.A., U. of Tex., 1943; M.A., 1947; Ph. D., 1954. Instr.-PROF., CHMN., GOVERNMENT, TEX. COLL. OF ARTS & INDUSTRIES, 1947– . Mayor, Kingsville, Tex., 1958– ; seminar moderator, National War Coll. 1962. Membership: American Association of University Professors; American Political Science Association; Pi Sigma Alpha; Southern Political Science Association; Southwestern Political Science Association; Southwestern Social Science Association. Research: government; Garde d'Haiti; Mexico; municipal administration. Author: Garde d'Haiti, 1915–1934 (1956). Co-author: Our National Constitution (1955); Political Parties and Their Determinants (1959). Language: Spanish 2,2,2,2. Home: 1201 West Lee, Kingsville, Tex. Office: Dept. of Government, Tex. Coll. of Arts & Industries, Kingsville.

McDONALD, RONALD H., b. Orange, Calif., May 19, 1935. POLITICAL SCIENCE. B.A., Pomona Coll., 1957; M.A., U. of Calif., Los Angeles, 1958; Ph. D., 1963. Instr., U. of Calif., Los Angeles, 1962–63; ASST. PROF., POLITICAL SCIENCE, SYRACUSE U., 1963– . Congressional fellow, American Political Science Association, 1960–61; Social Science Research Council fellow (Mexico), 1961–62; Latin American Program Committee, Syracuse U. Membership: American Political Science Association; Pi Gamma Mu; Western Political Science Association. Research: political beliefs and ideologies; Mexico; theory of communications. Author: Ideology and Political Appeals: A Theory for Analysis of Contemporary Belief Systems (1963). Language: Spanish 4,4,3,3, ; Portuguese 2,1,1,1 ; French 3,1,1,1. Home: 1216 Westcott, Syracuse 10, N.Y. Office: Dept. of Political Science, Maxwell Graduate School, Syracuse U., Syracuse 10.

MACDONALD, WILLIAM DICKSON, b. Halifax, Canada, July 5, 1913. LAW. B.A., U. of Toronto, 1936; LL.B., 1939; Barrister-at-law, Osgoode Hall Law School (Toronto), 1939; LL.M., U. of Mich., 1947; S.J.D., 1956. Prices officer, Canadian Wartime Prices and Trade Board, 1942–44; asst. enforcement counsel, 1945–46; asst. prof., Wayne U., 1946–48; PROF., LAW, COLL. OF LAW, U. OF FLA., 1948– ; U.S. specialist, L'Ecole Royale D'Administration and Faculté de Droit (Cambodia), Spring 1959; vis. prof., Faculté Internationale de Droit Comparé (Luxembourg), 1960. Committee on Associate Membership for Canadian and Latin American Law Schools, Association of American Law Schools, 1951– ; Ford Foundation law faculty fellow (Europe and Brazil), 1961–62; National Defense Education Act travel grant (Brazil), 1963; Committee on Exchange of Foreign Professors, Association of American Law Schools, 1964– . Membership: American Society of International Law; Inter-American Bar Association. Research: international law; comparative law: comparative family property law; law school in Brazil. Author: Fraud on the Widow's Share (1960). Language: Spanish 4,4,4,4; Portuguese 4,4,4,4; French 4,4,4,4: Cambodian 1,2,2,1; Dutch 2,2,2,2; German 3,3,3,3. Home: 2244 NW. Fourth Pl., Gainesville, Fla. Office: Coll. of Law, U. of Fla., Gainesville.

McGANN, THOMAS FRANCIS, b. Cambridge, Mass., Mar. 25, 1920. HISTORY. B.A., Harvard U., 1941; M.A., 1949; Ph. D., 1952. U.S. naval attaché in Latin America, 1942–46; teaching fellow, instr., asst. prof., Harvard U., 1950–58; assoc. prof.-PROF., LATIN AMERICAN HISTORY, U. OF TEX., 1958– ; vis. prof., Stanford U., 1962–63. Lowery fellow, Milton fellow, Harvard U.; U. of Texas research fellow. Membership: American Historical Association; Conference on Latin American History. Research: Argentina; colonial Peru; inter-American relations; Spain. Author: Argentina, the United States, and the Inter-American System, 1880–1914 (1957). Editor: Portrait of Spain (1963). Translator: A History of Argentine Political Thought, by José Luis Romero (1963). Language: Spanish 5,5,-4,3; Portuguese 3,2,1,1; French 3,2,2,1. Home: 4615 Crestway Dr., Austin, Tex. Office: Dept. of History, U. of Tex., Austin 12.

McGARRY, DANIEL D., b. Los Angeles, Calif., Oct. 10, 1907. HISTORY. M.A., U. of Calif., Los Angeles, 1938; Ph. D., 1940. Instr., Mt. St. Joseph's Coll., 1940–43; asst. prof., Ind. U., 1946–50; PROF., MEDIEVAL HISTORY, SAINT LOUIS U., 1950– . U of Calif., Los Angeles, and American Philosophical Society fellowships. Membership: American Historical Association; Catholic Historical Association; Conference on Latin American History; Medieval Academy. Research: medieval history; history of education; medieval Europe. Author: Metalogicon of John of Salisbury (1955); Sources of Western Civilization (1962); Educational Methods of the Franciscans in Spanish California (The Americas, Jan. 1950). Language: Spanish 4,4,3,2; French 3,3,3,2. Home: 20 Parkland, Glendale 22, Mo. Office: Dept. of History, Saint Louis U., St. Louis 3, Mo.

McGIMSEY, CHARLES ROBERT, III, b. Dallas, Tex., June 18, 1925. ANTHROPOLOGY. B.A. of N. Mex., 1949; M.A., Harvard U., 1954; Ph. D., 1958. Towing locomotive operator, Panama Canal Company, 1955–57; instr., asst. curator, U. of Ark., 1957–58; asst. prof., 1958–62; DIR., MUSEUM, U. OF ARK., 1959– ; ASSOC. PROF., ANTHROPOLOGY, 1962– . Thaw fellow, Harvard U., 1960; Winthrop fellow, Harvard U., 1950–52; editor, Arkansas Archeologist, 1959– ; co-editor, Quarterly Notes, Southeast Museums Conference, 1963– . Membership: American Anthropological Association; Society for American Archeology. Research: archeology of Panama. Author: Monagrillo Culture of Panama (1954). Language: Spanish 3,3,3,2. Home: 435 Hawthorne, Fayetteville, Ark. 72701. Office: Dir., U. of Ark. Museum, Fayetteville, 72703.

McGRADY, DONALD LEE, b. Greenhurst, Md., Jan. 17, 1935. SPANISH AMERICAN LITERATURE. A.B., Swarthmore Coll., 1957; M.A., Harvard U., 1958; Ph. D., Ind. U., 1961. Instr.-asst. prof., U. of Tex., 1961–64; ASST. PROF., SPANISH, U. OF CALIF., SANTA BARBARA, 1964– . Peaslee Scholar, Universidad de los Andes, 1955; Organization of American States grant, 1960–61; Social Science Research Council grant. Membership: American Association of Teachers of Spanish and Portuguese; Modern Language Association.

Research: poetry of Jorge Isaacs; the novel and poetry of Colombia. Author: La novela histórica en Colombia, 1844–1959 (1962); Sobre una alusión literaria en la novela Pax (Revista Iberoamericana, Jan.-June 1962); Was Mateo Alemán in Italy? (Hispanic Review, Apr. 1963). Language: Spanish 5,5,5,5; Portuguese 3,3,3,3; French 2,2,2,2; Italian 2,2,2,2. Home: 165 Carlo Dr., Goleta, Calif. Office: Dept. of Spanish and Portugese, U. of Calif., Santa Barbara, 93018.

McGREEVE, WILLIAM PAUL, b. Greenville, Ohio, Apr. 14, 1938. ECONOMICS. A.B., Ohio State U., 1960; Ph. D., Mass. Institute of Technology, 1965. Research assoc., Committee of Nine, Alliance for Progress, 1962; ASST. PROF., ECONOMICS, U. OF OREG., 1964– . Woodrow Wilson fellow, 1960–61; Foreign Area Fellowship Program fellow (Colombia), 1963–64. Research: economic development, especially of Colombia; rural-urban migration in Latin America; government-foreign minerals company relations in Latin America. Author: Problem of Underemployment in Latin America (Activist, May 1965). Language: Spanish 4,4,4,3; French 3,1,1,1. Home: 1957 Potter St., Eugene, Oreg. 97403. Office: Dept. of Economics, U. of Oreg., Eugene, 97403.

MACHADO, MANUEL ANTHONY, JR., b. Nogales, Ariz., June 4, 1939. HISTORY. B.A., U. of Calif., Santa Barbara, 1961; M.A., 1962; Ph. D., 1964. ASST. PROF., SOCIAL SCIENCES, STATE U. OF N.Y., COLL. AT PLATTSBURGH, 1964– . John Hay Whitney Foundation opportunity fellow, 1962–63; Organization of American States summer research fellow (Mexico), Summer 1963. Membership: Pacific Coast Council of Latin American Studies. Research: modern Latin American history; Mexican-United States cooperation in control of foot and mouth disease. Language: Spanish 5,5,5,5; Portuguese 4,2,1,1; French 2,1,1,1. Office: Div. of Social Sciences, State U. of N.Y., Coll. at Plattsburgh, Plattsburgh, N.Y.

McKERN, THOMAS WILTON, b. Nukualofa, Tongan Islands, Dec. 27, 1920. ANTHROPOLOGY. B.A., U. of Wis., 1942; M.A., 1948; Ph. D., U. of Calif., 1955. Anthropologist, American Graves Registration Service, U.S. Dept. of the Army (Saipan), 1948; instr., San Francisco State Coll., 1954–55; physical anthropologist, Quartermaster Research and Development Center (Natick, Mass.), 1956–58; ASSOC. PROF., ANTHROPOLOGY, U. OF TEX., 1959– . Consultant, Centro de Investigaciones Sociales, A.C. (Monterrey, Mexico). Membership: American Anthropological Association; American Association of Physical Anthropology. Research: physical anthropology; paleoanthropology; primatology; biological nature of prehistoric populations in Mexico; Old and New World prehistory; population genetics; osteological identification. Author: Skeletal Age Changes in Young American Males (1957); Origins of Man—A Notebook for Students of Physical Anthropology (1963); Paleolithic Man from the Crimea (American Journal of Physical Anthropology, Sept. 1962). Language: Spanish 2,2,1,1; French 2,2,1,1. Home: 2904 Enfield Rd., Austin, Tex. Office: Dept. of Anthropology, U. of Tex., Austin 12.

McLEAN, MALCOLM DALLAS, b. Rogers, Tex., Mar. 10, 1913. SPANISH AMERICAN LITERATURE. B.A., U. of Tex., 1936; M.A., Universidad Nacional Autónoma de México, 1938; Ph. D., U. of Tex., 1951. Field editor in charge of Spanish translators, Texas Historical Records Survey, 1938–39; asst. dir., archivist, San Jacinto Museum of History (Houston), 1939–41; research analyst, Mexico and Central America Desk, U.S. War Dept., 1941–46; Spanish translator, Library, U. of Tex., 1946–47; instr. U. of Tex., 1947–51; asst. prof.-assoc. prof., U. of Ark., 1951–56; dir., U.S. Information Agency, Binational Center (Tegucigalpa, Honduras), 1956–59 (Guayaquil, Ecuador), 1959–61; ASSOC. PROF., SPANISH, TEX. CHRISTIAN U., 1961– . E. D. Farmer International fellow, Universidad Nacional Autónoma de México, 1937–38. Membership: American Association of Teachers of Spanish and Portuguese; Instituto Internacional de Literatura Iberoamericana; Modern Language Association; Phi Beta Kappa; Phi Sigma Iota; Texas Foreign Language Association; Texas State Historical Association; Texas State Teachers Association. Research: 19th century Mexican literature; cultural heritage of the Mexican-United States borderlands; research methods; bibliography. Author: El contenido literario de El Siglo Diez y Nueve (1940); Vida y obra de Guillermo Prieto (1960). Co-author: Handbook for Translators of Spanish Historical Documents (1941). Language: Spanish 5,5,5,5; Portuguese 3,3,1,1; French 4,3,1,1. Home: 2555 Cockrell, Fort Worth, Tex. 76109. Office: Dept. of Spanish, Tex. Christian U., Fort Worth, 76129.

MacLEISH, WILLIAM HITCHCOCK, b. Boston, Mass., Aug. 7, 1928. JOURNALISM. B.A., Yale U., 1950. Special Projects editor, Visión, Inc., 1958–64; DIR., LATIN AMERICAN YEAR, CORNELL U., 1964– . Institute of Current World Affairs fellow (Peru), 1954–56; consultant, U.S. Dept. of State. Research: coverage of economic and social development. Author: Land and Liberty (Visión, Dec. 1962); Latin America: A Positive View (Visión, May 1963); Economic Integration in Latin American (Visión, Dec. 1963). Language: Spanish 4,4,4,2; Portuguese 3,2,1,1. Home: 627 Highland Rd., Ithaca, N.Y. Office: Cornell U., Ithaca, 14850.

MACLEOD, MURDO JOHN, b. Imtarfa, Malta, Apr. 22, 1935. HISTORY. M.A., U. of Glasgow (Scotland), 1959; U. of Guatemala, Summer 1959; M.A., U. of Fla., 1961; Ph. D., 1962. Asst. dir., Inter-American Studies, U. of Fla., 1961–62; ASST. PROF., LATIN AMERICAN HISTORY, U. OF PITTSBURGH, 1962– . Xiralt travel fellow, U. of Glasgow, 1957; assistant de langue anglaise, French Government, 1957–58; U. of Fla. fellow, 1959–63; Pan American Foundation travel grant (Guatemala), 1959; U.S. Agency for International Development—U. of Pittsburgh Program (Ecuador), 1963–65. Membership: American Academy of Social and Political Sciences; American Historical Association; Conference on Latin American History; Phi Alpha Theta; Phi Beta Kappa. Research: history and analysis of social protest with emphasis on the Indo-Andean Republics; political novelists in Latin

American politics in 19th and 20th centuries. Author: Colonial Central America (in The Caribbean: The Central American Area, edited by A. Curtis Wilgus, 1961); The Haitian Novel of Social Protest (Journal of Inter-American Studies, Apr. 1962). Language: Spanish 4,5,4,4; Portuguese 2,2,2,1; French 4,5,4,4; Gaelic 3,5, 5,1; German 2,2,1,1. Office: Dept. of History U. of Pittsburgh, Pittsburgh 13, Pa.

McMAHON, DOROTHY ELIZABETH, b. Troy, N.Y., Dec. 2, 1912. SPANISH AMERICAN LITERATURE. A.B., U. of Ariz., 1935; A.M., 1938; Ph. D., U. of Southern Calif., 1947. PROF., HEAD, SPANISH, U. OF SOUTHERN CALIF., 1944– . Del Amo fellow (Spain), 1948–49. Membership: American Association of Teachers of Spanish and Portuguese; American Association of University Professors; Conference on Latin American History; Modern Language Association; Pacific Coast Council for Latin American Studies; Phi Beta Kappa; Philological Association of the Pacific Coast. Research: contemporary Hispanic literature; Spanish American colonial history. Author: Variations in the Text of Zaraté's Historia del descubrimiento y conquista del Perú (Hispanic American Historical Review, Nov. 1953); Zaraté's Historia del descubrimiento y conquista del Perú (Papers of the Bibliographic Society of America, Apr. 1955); Indian in Romantic Literature of the Argentine (Modern Philology, Aug. 1958). Language: Spanish 5,5,4,4; Portuguese 3,2,–,1; French 4,3,3,3; German 1,3,1,1. Home: 6577 4th Ave., Los Angeles 43, Calif. Office: Dept. of Spanish, U. of Southern Calif., Los Angeles 7.

MacMICHAEL, DAVID CHARLES, b. Albany, N.Y., June 5, 1928. HISTORY. B.A., Hampden-Sydney Coll., 1952; M.A., U. of Oreg., 1961; Ph. D., 1964. INSTR., HISTORY, DOMINICAN COLL. OF SAN RAFAEL, 1962– . National Defense fellow, U. of Oreg., 1959–62. Research: American relations with the Dominican Republic, 1871–1940. Language: Spanish 2,–,–,–. Home: 645 Cedarberry Lane, San Rafael, Calif. 94903. Office: Dominican Coll. of San Rafael, San Rafael, 94905.

McMURRY, JOHN H., b. Ann Arbor, Mich., Feb. 22, 1921. GEOGRAPHY. B.A., U. of Mich., 1942; M.P.A., 1947; Ph. D., 1950. Instr., Mich. State U., 1947–48; asst. prof., assoc. prof., Fla. State U., 1950–62; PROF., CHMN., GEOGRAPHY, WATERLOO LUTHERAN U. (ONTARIO, CANADA), 1962– . U.S. Office of Naval Research grant; consultant, Mich. Dept. of Conservation, Florida Forest Service, and Florida Land Use and Control Commission. Membership: Association of American Geographers; Community Planning Association of Canada; Florida Academy of Science; Michigan Academy of Science. Research: resources management; public land policies; oceanography; terrain analysis. Author: Land Policy and Program in Michigan (1951); Organization of Florida Resource Agencies (1956); Classification of Florida's Gulf Coast (Annals, Association of American Geographers, 1960). Language: Spanish 3,3,3,3; French 3,3,3,3; German 3,3,3,3. Home: R.F.D. 1, Waterloo, Ontario, Canada. Office: Dept. of Geography and Geology, Waterloo Lutheran U., Waterloo.

McNEELY, JOHN GORDON, b. Avon, S. Dak., Nov. 24, 1912. ECONOMICS. B.S., S. Dak. State Coll., 1933; M.S., 1934; Ph. D., U. of Wis., 1941. Agricultural economist, U.S. Dept. of Agriculture (Ark., Miss., Nebr.), 1939–47; prof., Tex. A. & M. U., 1947–58; LEADER OF RESEARCH, DEPT. OF AGRICULTURAL ECONOMICS AND SOCIOLOGY, TEX. A. & M. U., 1960– . Ford Foundation vis. prof., U. of Poona (India), 1958–59; consultant, Operation Beef (Argentina), 1960–62; consultant to Syria, Ford Foundation, 1962–64; dir., Tex. A. & M. U.-U.S. Agency for International Development agricultural project in Argentina. Membership: American Farm Economic Association; International Association of Agricultural Economists; Western Farm Economic Association. Research; agricultural economics; marketing and land tenure; agricultural economic programs for Argentina. Author: Texas Farm Commodity Prices, 1947–1952 (1953); Some Problems of Price Analysis for Rice (1959); Wool Marketing Problems in Texas (1961). Language: Spanish 1,1,1,1; Portuguese 1,1,1,1; French 2,1,1,1. Home: 317 Brookside, Bryan, Tex. 77803. Office: Dept. of Agricultural Economics and Sociology, Tex. A. & M. U., College Station, 77843.

McNEELY, JOHN HAMILTON, b. Evansville, Ind., Mar. 2, 1917. HISTORY. B.A., American U., 1938; M.A., George Washington U., 1939; Ph. D., U. of Tex., 1958. ASSOC. PROF., HISTORY, TEX. WESTERN COLL., 1946– . Membership: Texas State Historical Association. Research: Central America; land reform in Mexico. Language: Spanish 3,3,3,–. Home: 1828 Cliff Dr., El Paso, Tex. Office: Dept. of History, Tex. Western Coll., El Paso.

McNEELY, SAMUEL SIDNEY, JR., b. New Orleans, La., May 24, 1915. EDUCATION AND LANGUAGE. Dott. in Lett., U. of Rome, 1939; Ph. D., La. State U., 1940. Instr., La. State U., 1946–47; civil education officer, Supreme Commander for Allied Powers (Japan), 1947–52; administrator, assoc. prof., La. State U. Caribbean Area Program (P.R.), 1952–53; assoc. prof., La. State U. Caribbean Area Program (C.Z.), 1953–55; foreign student adviser, assoc. prof., U. of Houston, 1955–58; DIR., INTERNATIONAL OFFICE, ASSOC. PROF., ENGLISH, TULANE U., 1958– . Creole Foundation travel grant (Caribbean), 1958; Board of Directors, National Association for Foreign Student Affairs. Membership: American Association of University Professors; National Association for Foreign Student Affairs. Research: English as a foreign language; education in the Caribbean. Author: Education in the Caribbean Countries (1958). Language: Spanish 4,4,4,4; Portuguese 3,2,2,2; French 3,2,2,2; Italian 4,4,3,4; Japanese 1,3,3,1. Linguistic studies: English. Office: International Office, Tulane U., New Orleans, La. 70118.

MACNEISH, RICHARD STOCKTON, b. New York, N.Y., Apr. 29, 1918. ANTHROPOLOGY. B.A., U. of Chicago, 1940; M.A., 1944; Ph. D., 1948. Dir., Summer Field School, U. of Ky., 1948; senior archeologist, National Museum of Canada (Ottawa), 1949–63; DIR., PROYECTO ARQUEOLÓGICO-BOTÁNICO TEHUACÁN (PUEBLA, MEXICO), R. S. PEABODY FOUNDATION FOR ARCHAEOLOGY, 1963– . U. of Chicago grant (Mexico), 1945-46; Lilly Research Fund grant, 1947; Viking Fund grants (Mexico), 1948, 1949; Harvard U. grants (Mexico), 1953, 1954; American Philosophical Society grants (Mexico), 1953, 1954, 1955, (Honduras, Guatemala), 1958; American Academy of Arts and Sciences grants (Mexico), 1954, 1955; De Kalb Seed Company grant (Mexico), 1954; Guggenheim fellow (Mexico), 1955; Canada Council grant, 1958; New World Archaeological Foundation grant (Mexico), 1959; Rockefeller Foundation grant, 1961; National Science Foundation grants (Mexico), 1961, 1962, 1963, 1964; Permanent Council, Union Internationale des Sciences Préhistoriques et Protohistoriques. Membership: American Anthropological Association; American Association for the Advancement of Science; Arctic Institute for North America; Society for American Archaeology. Research: archeology; origin of agriculture and civilization in Tehuacán, Puebla, Mexico; archeology of northeastern Mexico; United States and Canadian archeology. Author: An Early Archaeological Site Near Pánuco, Vera Cruz (1954); Preliminary Archaeological Investigations in the Sierra de Tamaulipas, Mexico (1958). Co-author: The Santa Marta Rock Shelter, Ocozocoautla, Chiapas, Mexico (1962). Language: Spanish 4,4,3,2. Office: R. S. Peabody Foundation for Archaeology, Phillips Academy, Andover, Mass.

McNELLY, JOHN TAYLOR, b. Lancaster, Wis., Oct. 2, 1923. COMMUNICATION AND JOURNALISM. B.A., U. of Wis., 1946; M.A., 1957; Ph. D., Mich. State U., 1961. Newsman, Reuters (London), 1952-53; newspaper editor (Calif. and Idaho), 1953-56; news editor, U. of Wis. News Service, 1956-57; instr., Mich. State U., 1957-61; asst. dir. of research, Programa Interamericano de Información Popular (San José, Costa Rica), 1961-62; ASST. PROF., COLL. OF COMMUNICATION ARTS, SCHOOL OF JOURNALISM, MICH. STATE U., 1962- ; vis. lectr., Berlin Institute for Communication in Developing Countries, 1965. Coordinator, Mich. State U. seminars on communication for foreign professionals and technicians, 1959-60; lectr., Centro Internacional de Estudios Superiores en el Periodismo para América Latina (Quito), 1963. Membership: American Association for Public Opinion Research; Association for Education in Journalism; Phi Kappa Phi; Sigma Delta Chi. Research: the role of mass communication in international development; international flow of news; use of survey research in investigating problems of mass communication; mass communication in Latin America. Author: Meaning Intensity and Interest in Foreign News Topics (Journalism Quarterly, Spring 1962); Media Use and Socioeconomic Status in a Latin American Capital (Gazette, 1963). Co-author: Media Use and Political Interest at the University of Costa Rica (Journalism Quarterly, Spring 1964). Language: Spanish 4,4,4,4; Portuguese 3,2,1,1; French 2,1,1,1. Home: 842 Huntington Rd., East Lansing, Mich. Office: Coll. of Communication Arts, School of Journalism, Mich. State U., East Lansing.

McNICOLL, ROBERT EDWARDS, b. St. Louis, Mo., Feb. 4, 1907. HISTORY. A.B., U. of Miami, 1931; M.A., Duke U., 1936; Ph. D., 1938. Prof., co-dir., Hispanic American Institute, U. of Miami, 1933-55; vis. prof., U. of Havana, 1940-41, Summers 1940-55; divisional asst., Cultural Relations, U.S. Dept. of State, 1943-45; prof., Southern Ill. U., 1945-46; divisional asst., Intelligence Resources, U.S. Dept. of State, 1946-47; editor, Journal of Inter-American Studies, Pan American Foundation, 1952-64; DIR., BI-NATIONAL CULTURAL CENTER (CUZCO, PERU), U.S. INFORMATION AGENCY, 1964- . Pan American Foundation grant (Chile), 1956-58; consultant, Duke U. Hispanic Program, Ford Foundation. Membership: Asociación de Artistas y Escritores Americanos (Cuba); Conference on Latin American History; El Ateneo (El Salvador). Research: contemporary relations in Latin America; intellectual history. Author: Educación Interamericana (1942); Intellectual Origins of Aprismo (Hispanic American Historical Review, Aug. 1943). Translator: Bolívar and the Political Thought of the Spanish-American Revolutions, by V. A. Belaúnde (1938). Language: Spanish 5,5,4,4; Portuguese 3,3,2,3; French 3,2,2,2. Office: Journal of Inter-American Studies, Box 13625, Gainesville, Fla.

MacPHAIL, DONALD DUGALD, b. Dayton, Ohio, Mar. 13, 1922. GEOGRAPHY. B.S., Mich. State U., 1947; M.A, U. of Mich., 1949; Ph. D., 1953. District mapping chief, Rural Land Classification Program, Dept. of Agriculture and Commerce (P.R.), 1950-51; asst. prof., Western Wash. State Coll., 1952-56; vis. lectr., Mich. State U., Summer 1956; asst. prof., U. of Colo., 1956-60; ASSOC. PROF., GEOGRAPHY, U. OF COLO., 1961- ; chmn., 1961-63. Teaching fellow, U. of Mich., 1949-52; Fulbright prof. and head, Sección de Geografía Regional y Planificación, Instituto de Geografía, U. of Chile, 1959; U. of Colo. faculty research fellow (Chile), 1960; consultant, Organization of American States and Utah State U. on Land and Water Resources Center (Venezuela); vice-chmn., Population Committee, Commission on Geography, Pan American Institute of Geography and History; Committee on Desert and Arid Zones Research, American Association for the Advancement of Science; consultant, U.S. Agency for International Development (Guatemala), 1962; National Defense fellow in Spanish, U. of Calif., Los Angeles, Summer 1963. Membership: American Association for the Advancement of Science; American Association of University Professors; American Geographical Society; Association of American Geographers; Colorado Education Association. Research: regional development; land-use inventory; geomorphology; airphoto interpretation; regional geography of Mexico; Chile. Author: The Cattle Farms of Southern Puerto Rico (in Symposium on the Geography of Puerto Rico, 1955); Puerto Rican Dairying: A Revolution in Tropical Agriculture (Geographical Review, Apr. 1963); Estructuras Regionales (in El hombre en las tierras áridas de los Estados Unidos, 1963). Language: Spanish 4,4,4,4; Portuguese 1,1,1,1; French 3,3,3,2. Home: 10 South 32nd St., Boulder, Colo. 80302. Office: Dept. of Geography, U. of Colo., Boulder, 80304.

McPHEETERS, DEAN WILLIAM, b. Milton,

Iowa, Jan. 6, 1917. LANGUAGE. B.S., U. of Ill., 1940; M.A., U. of Fla., 1941; Ph. D., Columbia U., 1952. Instr., La. State U., 1947–49; PROF., SPANISH AND PORTUGUESE, SYRACUSE U., 1951– ; chmn., Undergraduate Program of Latin American Studies, Syracuse U., 1952–61. American Council of Learned Societies grant (Brazil), Summer 1941; consultant, H. P. Krause (N.Y.), 1950– ; consultant, Dept. of Education, State of New York, Spring 1961. Membership: American Association of Teachers of Spanish and Portuguese; Modern Language Association; New York Linguistic Society; New York State Federation of Language Teachers. Author: An Unknown Early Seventeenth-Century Codex of the Crónica Mexicana of H. Alvarado Tezozómoc (Hispanic American Historical Review, Nov. 1954); The Distinguished Peruvian Scholar, Cosme Bueno, 1711–1789 (Hispanic American Historical Review, Nov. 1955); Xicotencatl, símbolo republicano y romántico (Nueva Revista de Filología Hispánica, July–Dec. 1956). Language: Spanish 5,5,5,5; Portuguese 4,4,4,4; French 4,4,4,4; German 3,3,3,3; Italian 3,3,3,3. Linguistic studies: Portuguese; Spanish. Home: 126 Westminster Ave., Syracuse, N.Y. 13210. Office: Dept. of Romance Languages, Syracuse U., Syracuse, 13210.

McPHERSON, WOODROW WILSON, b. Haw River, N.C., Apr. 11, 1917. ECONOMICS. B.S., N.C. State, 1938; M.S., La. State U., 1940; Ph.D., Harvard U., 1950. Economist, Bureau of Agricultural Economics, U.S. Dept. of Agriculture, 1940–48; prof., N.C. State Coll., 1949–59; adviser, Planning Board, Government of Pakistan, 1955–57; head, Economics and Statistical Research, Div. of Tropical Research, United Fruit Company (Honduras), 1959–62; GRADUATE RESEARCH PROF., ECONOMICS, U. OF FLA., 1962– . Consultant on Trinidad, U.S. Agency for International Development, 1963; consultant on economics of tropical operations, United Fruit Company. Membership: American Economic Association; American Farm Economic Association; American Statistical Association; International Association of Agricultural Economists. Research: economic and agricultural development; political systems. Author: Credit for Economic Development in Agricultural Production (Pakistan Economic Journal, 1956). Co-author: Application of Linear Programming in an Analysis of Economic Changes in Farming (Review of Economics and Statistics, Nov. 1957). Language: Spanish 2,2,2,2; Portuguese 1,1,1,1; French 2,1,1,1. Home: 3942 SW. 6th Pl., Gainesville, Fla. Office: Dept. of Economics, U. of Fla., Gainesville, 32603.

McQUOWN, NORMAN ANTHONY, b. Peoria, Ill., Jan. 30, 1914. ANTHROPOLOGY: LINGUISTICS. A.B., U. of Ill., 1935; M.A., 1936; Ph. D., Yale U., 1940. Instr., National School of Anthropology (Mexico), 1939–42; language technician, Service Forces, U.S. Army, 1943–45; lectr., Hunter Coll., 1945–46; asst. prof., U. of Chicago, 1946–51; assoc. prof., 1951–58: PROF., ANTHROPOLOGY, U. OF CHICAGO, 1959– . Rockefeller Foundation fellow (Mexico), 1938–39, 1949; research fellow, Dept. of Indian Affairs, Republic of Mexico, 1940–41; American Council of Learned Societies research fellow, 1941–43; Carnegie Institution fellow (Mexico), 1946–47, (Guatemala), 1948; representative of Linguistic Society of America in El Consejo de Lenguas Indígenas (Mexico). Membership: American Anthropological Association; Association for the Advancement of Science; Linguistic Society of America. Research: language in culture; Indian languages of Mexico (Chiapanec, Cuitlatec, Huastec, Nahuatl, Tarascan, Totonac, Tzeltal, Tzotzil, Yucatec), and Guatemala (Aguacatec, Cakchiquel, Chuh, Jacaltec, Kekchi, Mam, Pokomam, Pokonchi, Quiché, Xinca). Author: El tzeltal hablado (1957–58); The Indigenous Languages of Latin America (American Anthropologist, 1955); Los orígenes y la diferenciación de los mayas según se infiere del estudio comparativo de las lenguas mayanas (in Desarrollo cultural de los mayas, 1964). Language: Spanish 4,4,4,4; Portuguese 3,3,1,1; French 4,4,2,2; Esperanto 5,5,3,4; German 4,4,3,3; Italian 4,3,1,1; Russian 3,3,2,1. Linguistic studies: Huastec; Mam; Totonac; Turkish. Home: Apt. 3, 5708 South Drexel Ave., Chicago, Ill. 60637. Office: Dept. of Anthropology, U. of Chicago, 1126 East 59th St., Chicago, 60637.

MADAY, BELA CHARLES, b. Prague, Czechoslovakia, Nov. 3, 1912. SOCIOLOGY AND ANTHROPOLOGY. Ph. D., Pazmany U. (Hungary), 1937. Professorial lectr., Technical U. (Hungary), 1942–44; prof., Defense Language Institute, 1948–57; lectr., Monterey Peninsula Coll., 1956–57; PROF. IN RESEARCH, AMERICAN U., 1958– . Coordinator, Bolivian Area Studies, Peace Corps Training Program, Brandeis U., 1964. Membership: American Anthropological Association; Anthropological Society of Washington: Sociological Society of Washington. Research: sociology and cultural change in Panama, Colombia, Brazil and Bolivia. Co-author: U.S. Army Area Handbook for Colombia (1961); U.S. Army Area Handbook for Panama (1962); U.S. Army Area Handbook for Brazil (1964). Language: Spanish 3,3,2,2; Portuguese 2,2,1,1; French 2,2,1,1; German 4,4,4,4; Hungarian 5,5,5,5; Italian 3,3,2,2. Home: 4528 49th St., NW., Washington, D.C. 20016. Office: American U., 5010 Wisconsin Ave., NW., Washington, D.C. 20016.

MADDOX, JAMES GRAY, b. Rison, Ark., Feb. 4, 1907. ECONOMICS. B.S.A., U. of Ark., 1927; M.S., U. of Wis., 1930; M.P.A., Harvard U., 1948; Ph. D., 1950. Economist, U.S. Dept. of Agriculture, 1935–39; div. dir., Farm Security Administration, 1939–53; asst. to chief, Bureau of Agricultural Economics, 1943–47; asst. dir., American International Association, 1949–52; vice president, International Development Services, 1953; staff member, American Universities Field Staff, 1953–58, (Mexico), 1955–57; PROF., AGRICULTURAL ECONOMICS, N.C. STATE COLL., 1958– . Membership: American Economic Association; American Farm Economic Association. Research: economic development; land economics; international economics. Author: Technical Assistance by Religious Agencies in Latin America (1956); Field Letters and Reports on Mexico (American Universities Field Staff, 1956–57). Language: Spanish 2,2,3,1. Home: Route 6, Box 266, Raleigh, N.C. Office: Dept. of Agricultural Economics, N.C. State Coll., Raleigh.

MADDOX, JAMES ROBERT, b. Flat Rock, Ill., Aug. 13, 1910. ECONOMICS. B.S., U. of Ill., 1942; M.A., 1943; Ph. D., 1951. PROF., ECONOMICS, U. of DENVER, 1946– . Research: international economics; Mexico; Latin American economics; money and banking; economic development. Membership: American Economic Association; Pi Gamma Mu; Rocky Mountain Council on Latin American Studies. Spanish 3,–,–,–,–. Home; 6463 South Ulster, Englewood, Colo. Office: Dept. of Economics, U. of Denver, Denver 10, Colo.

MADSDEN, WILLIAM, b. Shanghai, China, Dec. 26, 1920. ANTHROPOLOGY. B.A., Stanford U., 1946; Ph. D., U. of Calif., Berkeley, 1955. Asst. prof., U. of Tex., 1955–61; asst. prof., U. of Calif., Berkeley, Summer 1956; vis. prof., U. of Calif., Santa Barbara, Summer 1957; assoc. prof., U. of Tex., 1961–63; vis. prof., U. of Calif., Berkeley, Summer 1963; vis. prof., U. of P.R., Summer 1964; PROF., ANTHROPOLOGY, PURDUE U., 1964– . Center for Advanced Studies in the Behavioral Sciences fellow, 1963–64; Wenner-Gren Foundation fellow (Mexico). Membership: American Anthropological Association; American Association for the Advancement of Science; Centro de Investigaciones Sociales, A.C. (Monterrey, Mexico). Research: Mexican-American acculturation in South Texas; Nahuatl acculturation in the Valley of Mexico; socio-cultural aspects of addiction in California. Author: Christo-Paganism: A Study of Mexican Religious Syncretism (1957); The Virgin's Children: Life in an Aztec Village Today (1960); Mexican-Americans of South Texas (1964). Language: Spanish 3,3,3,3; Portuguese 2,1,1,1; French 3,2,2,2; German 2,1,1,2. Home: 168 Creighton Rd., West Lafayette, Ind. Office: Dept. of Anthropology, Purdue U., West Lafayette.

MAGNER, JAMES A., RT. REV., b. Wilmington, Ill., Oct. 23, 1901. HISTORY AND PHILOSOPHY. B.A., St. Mary of the Lake Seminary, 1923; M.A., 1924; S.T.D., Urban U. (Rome), 1928; Ph. D., Academy of St. Thomas (Rome), 1929. Instr., Quigley Preparatory Seminary, 1929–40; PROCURATOR AND ASST. TREASURER, BUSINESS AND FISCAL OFFICE, CATHOLIC U. OF AMERICA, 1940– ; DIR., CATHOLIC U. PRESS, 1941– . Membership: American Catholic Historical Association; Catholic Association for International Peace; Institute of Ibero-American Studies, Catholic U. of America. Research: Mexican history; social ethics. Author: Men of Mexico (1942); The Latin American Pattern (1943); Mental Health in a Mad World (1953). Language: Spanish 3,4,3,3; Portuguese 2,2,1,1; French 3,3,2,2; German 2,2,2,1; Greek 1,1,1,1; Latin 3,3,2,2. Home and office: The Catholic U. of America, 620 Michigan Ave., NE., Washington, D.C. 20017.

MAGURN, JOSEPH JOHN, b. Somerville, Mass., Oct. 30, 1916. ECONOMICS. A.B., Harvard Coll., 1938; LL.B. George Washington U. School of Law, 1949. Vice consul, Consulate (Paramaribo, Surinam), U.S. Dept. of State, 1943–44; economist, U.S. Dept. of Commerce, 1944–58; ECONOMIST, CHECCHI AND COMPANY, 1958– . Research: finance law; private investment in Venezuela and Colombia; industrial possibilities of Costa Rica and Nicaragua; economic development in Argentina and Honduras. Author: Investment in Venezuela (1953); Investment in Mexico (1956); Investment in Central America (1957). Language: Spanish 4,4,4,4; Portuguese 3,3,3,3; French 3,3,3,3; Dutch 3,3,3,3. Home: 3912 Blackthorn St., Chevy Chase, Md. Office: Checchi and Company, 1612 K St., NW., Washington, D.C. 20006.

MAK, CORNELIA, b. Paterson, N.J. LINGUISTICS. MISSIONARY, LINGUIST, SUMMER INSTITUTE OF LINGUISTICS (MEXICO), 1947– . Research: descriptive linguistics; highland Mixtecos of Mexico. Author: A Comparison of Two Mixtec Tonemic Systems (International Journal of American Linguistics, Apr. 1953); The Tonal System of a Third Mixteco Dialect (International Journal of American Linguistics, Jan. 1958). Co-author: Proto-Mixtec Phonology (International Journal of American Linguistics, Jan. 1960). Language: Spanish 4,4,4,–; French 1,–,–,–; Dutch 2,4,2,–. Linguistic studies: Mixtec. Home: 104 Ruth Ave., Hawthorne, N.J. 07506. Office: Summer Institute of Linguistics, Box 1960, Santa Ana, Calif.

MALAGÓN BARCELÓ, JAVIER, b. Toledo, Spain, May 24, 1911. HISTORY AND LAW. Bachiller, Instituto de San Isidro, 1927; Maestro de Primera Enseñanza, Escuela Normal de Maestros, 1929; LL.D., Universidad de Madrid, 1934. Asst., Universidad de Madrid, 1932–34, 1935–36; librarian, Sala de Lectura Francisco Giner, 1931–35; librarian, Museo Laboratorio Jurídico Ureña, 1935–39; asst. prof., 1936–39; catedrático, Universidad de Santo Domingo, 1940–46; member, Centro de Estudios Históricos, El Colegio de México, 1946; vis. prof., Universidad de P.R., Summers 1947, 1949; prof., El Colegio de México, 1947; catedrático, Universidad Nacional Autónoma de México, 1948–49; vis. prof., American U., Summer 1956, 1960–61, 1963–64; TECHNICAL SECRETARY, FELLOWSHIP AND PROFESSORSHIP PROGRAM, ORGANIZATION OF AMERICAN STATES, 1958– ; lectr., Catholic U. of America, 1964. Ministerio de Educación (Spain) scholarship, 1932; Universidad de Madrid grants (Germany), 1934, 1935–36; Universidad de Santo Domingo research grant to Archivo Nacional de Cuba, 1941; secretary, Revista de Historia de América and Boletín Bibliográfico de Antropología Americana (Mexico), 1947–55; Rockefeller Foundation grant, 1950, 1952–53; dir., Inter-American Review of Bibliography, Pan American Union, 1955–61; Advisory Board, Handbook of Latin American Studies, 1955–63; consultant, Comisión de Historia de México, 1955, U.S. Dept. of Justice, 1955–56; Biblioteca Nacional de México, 1957, Committee on International Exchange of Persons, 1958; advisory editor, The Americas, 1955; assoc. editor, Hispanic American Historical Review, 1956–60; Serra Award of the Americas, 1962. Membership: Academia Nacional de Historia y Geografía (Mexico); American Historical Association; Conference on Latin American History; Instituto de Estudios Afroamericanos (Mexico); Pan American Institute of Geography and History; Sociedad Mexicana de Historia. Research: history of Spanish law, metropolitan and colonial. Author: Programa de historia del derecho español en Indias (1941); La literatura jurídica española del Siglo de Oro en la Nueva España (1959); Toledo and the New World in the XVI Century (1963). Language: Spanish 5,5,5,5; Portuguese 4,4,1,1; French 4,4,3,2; German 3,3,3,1; Latin 3,-,-,1. Home: 4840 43rd Pl., NW., Washington, D.C. Office: Organization of American States, 1725 I St., NW., Washington 6.

MALKIEL, YAKOV, b. Kiev, Russia, July 22, 1914. LANGUAGE AND LINGUISTICS. Ph. D., U. of Berlin, 1938. Supply instr., U. of Wyo., 1942; lectr., U. of Calif., Berkeley, 1942–45; instr., 1945–46; asst. prof., 1946–48; assoc. prof., 1948–52; PROF., SPANISH AND PORTUGUESE, ASSOC. GRADUATE DEAN, U. OF CALIF., BERKELEY, 1952– . Research fellow (Argentina), 1948; Guggenheim fellow, 1948–49, 1959. Membership: Linguistic Society of America; Modern Language Association; Société de Lingüistique Romane. Research: Romance philology; theory of literary and historical research. Author: Reconstruction of Hispano-Latin Word Families (1954); Typology of Historical Grammars (Lingua, Dec. 1961). Language: Spanish 5,5,4,4; Portuguese 4,3,3,3; French 5,5,4,4; German 5,5,4,4; Russian 5,5,4,4. Home: 1 Arlington Lane, Berkeley 7, Calif. Office: 4333 Dwinelle Hall, U. of Calif., Berkeley 4.

MANCHESTER, ALAN K., b. Camden, N.J., July 2, 1897. HISTORY. A.B. Vanderbilt U., 1920; M.A., Columbia U., 1922; Ph. D., Duke U., 1930. School administrator, Methodist Church (Brazil), 1922–27; Instr.-PROF., HISTORY, DUKE U., 1929– ; asst. dean-DEAN, 1934– ; cultural attaché, Embassy (Brazil), U.S. Dept. of State, 1951–52. Assoc. managing editor, Hispanic American Historical Review, 1939–44; specialist, International Educational Exchange Program, U.S. Dept. of State, 1954, 1955; consultant, U.S. Dept. of State, 1956, 1958; member-at-large, U.S. National Commission for UNESCO, 1958–62; consultant, Brazilian Institute, N.Y.U., 1958; U.S. representative, Inter-American Cultural Council, Organization of American States, 1959– . Research: Brazilian history, particularly the 19th century; the Portuguese Empire. Author: British Preeminence in Brazil (1933); Constitutional Dictatorship in Brazil (in Studies in Hispanic America Affairs: South American Dictators During the First Century of Independence, 1937); Dom Pedro Segundo, the Democratic Emperor (in Brazil, 1947). Language: Spanish 3,3,2,1; Portuguese 4,4,4,2. Home: 406 Swift Ave., Durham, N.C. 27705. Office: Dept. of History, Duke U., Durham.

MANCHESTER, PAUL THOMAS, b. Barkeyville, Pa., Sept. 27, 1893. SPANISH AMERICAN LITERATURE. B.A., Park Coll., 1914; M.A., Vanderbilt U. 1921; Ph. D., Peabody, Coll., 1927. Teacher, Instituto Inglés (Santiago, Chile), 1914–17; prof., Ogden Coll., 1918–19; asst. prof., Vanderbilt U., 1919–27; prof., chmn., Foreign Languages, Colo. State Coll., 1927–28; prof., chmn., Romance Languages, Vanderbilt U., 1928–63; PROF. EMERITUS, ROMANCE LANGUAGES, VANDERBILT U., 1963– ; VIS. PROF., ROMANCE LANGUAGES, JACKSONVILLE U., 1963– . Orden al Mérito Bernardo O'Higgins, Government of Chile, 1952. Membership: American Association of Teachers of French; American Association of Teachers of Spanish and Portuguese; Kappa Delta Pi; Modern Language Association; Phi Beta Kappa; Phi Sigma Iota; Sigma Delta Pi. Research: nineteenth century Spanish literature; poetry; literary criticism; translations. Author: Joyas Poéticas (1950); Translator: The Araucaniad (1945); Arauco Tamed (1948). Language: Spanish 5,4,4,4; French 5,4,4,4. Linguistic studies: French; Spanish. Home: Timber Lane, Nashville 12, Tenn. Office: Dept. of Romance Languages, Jacksonville U., Jacksonville, Fla.

MANDELL, STUART LESTER, b. New York, N.Y., Jan. 16, 1924. ECONOMICS: MARKETING. A.B., Brooklyn Coll., 1946; M.B.A., Syracuse U., 1948. PROF., HEAD, ECONOMICS AND MANAGEMENT, LOWELL TECHNOLOGICAL INSTITUTE, 1948– ; instr., U. of Mich., 1955–56; ASSOC. DIR., INTERNATIONAL MARKETING INSTITUTE, 1960–. Consultant on marketing in Latin America, U.S. Agency for International Development; dir., Summer Program in Marketing Management, Harvard Business School. Membership: American Academy of Advertising; American Economic Association; American Marketing Association; Association for Education in International Business. Research: international trade. Author: Foreign Competition in American Industrial Markets (1958); Boston Conference on Distribution (1961, 1962, 1963); Wool Grease, The Economics of Recovery and Utilization (June 1955). Language: Spanish 3,3,2,2; Portuguese 2,2,1,1; French 1,1,1,1. Home: 52 Columbus Ave., Haverhill, Mass. 01830. Office: Lowell Technological Institute, Lowell, Mass. 01854.

MANDELSTAMM, ALLAN BERYLE, b. Saginaw, Mich., Oct. 18, 1928. ECONOMICS. A.B., U. of Mich., 1950; M.A., 1951; Ph. D., 1962. Instr., U. of Mich., 1954–56; instr., Northwestern U., 1957–59; asst. prof., Vanderbilt U., 1959–63; ASSOC. PROF., ECONOMICS, MICH STATE U., 1963– . Consultant on manpower problems in South America, U.S. Agency for International Development; Rockefeller Foundation fellow, 1959, 1960, 1961, 1962; Ford Foundation Seminar fellow, 1962. Membership: American Association of University Professors; American Economic Association; Industrial Relations Research Association; Midwest Economic Association; Southern Economic Association. Research: labor and manpower; money and banking; history of economic thought. Language: Spanish 4,4,4,4; French 3,3,2,3; German 3,2,2,3; Italian 3,3,3,3; Russian 2,1,1,1. Home: 2738 Woodruff Ave., Lansing, Mich. 48912. Office: Dept. of Economics, Mich. State U., East Lansing.

MANGER, WILLIAM, b. Richmond, Va., Sept. 22, 1899. POLITICAL SCIENCE. LL.B., Georgetown U., 1921; M.S., 1924; Ph. D., 1926. Clerk-div. chief and counselor, Pan American Union, 1915–46; asst. secretary general, Organization of American States, 1946–58; DIR., LATIN AMERICAN STUDIES PROGRAM, GEORGETOWN U., 1959–. Research: international relations; inter-American regional system. Author: Pan America in Crisis (1961). Editor: The Alliance for Progress: A Critical Appraisal

(1963). Language: Spanish 4,4,4,4. Home: 3001 Birch St., NW., Washington, D.C. 20015. Office: Latin American Studies Program, Georgetown U., Washington, D.C.

MANGIN, WILLIAM, b. Syracuse, N.Y., June 2, 1924. ANTHROPOLOGY. B.A., Syracuse U., 1948; Ph. D., Yale U., 1954. Field dir., Cornell U. (Vicos, Peru), 1951–53; ASSOC. PROF., ANTHROPOLOGY, SYRACUSE U., 1954–; vis. prof., Universidad de San Marcos (Lima), 1957–59; deputy dir., U.S. Peace Corps (Peru), 1962–64. National Institute of Mental Health grant (Lima), 1957–59; Harry Stack Sullivan Institute of Psychoanalysis grant (Peru), 1960; Social Science Research Council grant. Membership: American Anthropological Association; Sigma Xi. Research: cultural anthropology; Indian community development in Peru; migration to urban areas in Peru. Author: Drinking Among Andean Indians (Quarterly Journal of Alcoholic Studies, Mar. 1957); Organización social en Vicos (Etnología y Arqueología, May 1960); Mental Health and Migration to Cities (New York Academy of Science, 1960). Language: Spanish 4,5,4,3; Portuguese 3,3,2,1; French 2,2,1,1; Quechua –,2,–,–. Home: 712 Ackerman Ave., Syracuse, N.Y. Office: Dept. of Anthropology, Syracuse U., Syracuse.

MANLEY, VAUGHN PORTER, b. Sioux City, Iowa, Aug. 24, 1930. GEOGRAPHY. A.B., Stanford U., 1952; M.A., San Diego State Coll., 1954; D.S.S., Syracuse U., 1958. Asst. prof., Wis. State Coll., 1958–59; asst. prof., Drake U., 1959–62; ASST. PROF., ECONOMICS, IOWA STATE U., 1962– . National Science Foundation grants, Summers 1961, 1962, 1963. Membership: Association of American Geographers; Farm Economic Association; Phi Alpha Theta. Research: regional economic patterns of farming; Chilean resources. Language: Spanish 4,4,4,4. Home: 6429 University Ave., Des Moines, Iowa 50311. Office: Dept. of Economics, Iowa State U., Ames.

MANN, LAWRENCE DALE, b. Chico, Calif., Nov. 13, 1931. CITY AND REGIONAL PLANNING. A.B., Harvard U., 1954; M.C.P., 1959; Ph. D., 1960. Instr., Harvard U., 1960–61; asst. prof., U. of N.C., 1961–64; PROGRAM SPECIALIST, FORD FOUNDATION, MINISTRY OF PUBLIC WORKS, COMMUNITY FACILITIES PROGRAM (SANTIAGO, CHILE), 1964– . Frank Knox fellow: Ford Foundation vis. prof., U. of Litoral (Rosario, Argentina), Summer 1963. Membership: American Institute of Planners: International Federation of Housing and Planning; Regional Science Association. Research: sociological and economic aspects of planning; regional development and urbanization policy as related to national economic development. Author: Community Decision Making Studies (Journal of American Institute of Planners, Feb. 1964); French Regional Planning (Journal of American Institute of Planners, May 1964). Language: Spanish 4,3,3,2; Portuguese 2,1,1,1; French 4,4,4,2. Home: Box 469, Chapel Hill, N.C. Office: Ford Foundation, Ismael Valdes Vergara 340, Dto. 11, Santiago, Chile.

MANNERS, ROBERT ALAN, b. New York, N.Y., Aug. 21, 1913. ANTHROPOLOGY. B.A., Columbia U., 1935; M.A., 1939; Ph. D., 1950. Instr., U. of Rochester, 1950–52; asst. prof., Brandeis U., 1952–56; assoc. prof., 1956–61; PROF., ANTHROPOLOGY, BRANDEIS U., 1961– ; CHMN., 1962– . U. of P.R. and Rockefeller Foundation grants (P.R.), 1948–49. Membership: African Studies Association; American Anthropological Association; American Association of University Professors; American Ethnological Society. Research: culture change; Caribbean history and ethnology. Co-author: People of Puerto Rico (1956). Editor: Africa Speaks (1960); Process and Pattern in Culture (1964). Language: Spanish 4,3,3,3; French 4,3,2,2. Home: 134 Sumner St., Newton Center, Mass. Office: Dept. of Anthropology, Brandeis U., Waltham 54, Mass.

MANNO, FRANCIS J., b. Clermont, Pa., Dec. 24, 1914. HISTORY. B.A., B.S., Georgetown U., 1941; Ph. D., 1954. Prof., St. Mary's Coll. (Kans.), 1955–57; prof., Villanova U., 1957–63; PROF., HISTORY, STATE OF N.Y., COLL. AT BROCKPORT, 1963– . Vis. fellow, Ohio State U., Summer 1957. Membership: American Academy of Social and Political Science; American Association of University Professors; American Historical Association; Conference on Latin American History; Phi Alpha Theta. Research: diplomatic history of the United States and Mexico. Author: Yucatán en la guerra entre México y los Estados Unidos (Revista de la Universidad de Yucatán, July–Aug. 1963). Language: Spanish 3,3,3,3; French 3,3,3,3; Italian 5,5,5,5. Home and office: Dept. of History, State U. of N.Y., Coll. at Brockport.

MANSFIELD, CHARLES YARROW, b. New Haven, Conn., Feb. 8, 1934. ECONOMICS. A.B., Oberlin Coll., 1955; M.P.A., Princeton U., 1958; Ph. D., 1963. Research assoc., Patent, Trademark, and Copyright Research Institute, George Washington U., 1962–63; ECONOMIST, INTERNATIONAL MONETARY FUND, 1963– . George Washington U. Committee on National Wealth. Research: financial and economic analysis; economic structure of Mexico; International Monetary Fund missions in Chile and Peru. Author: The Riskiness of Research and Development Performed by Large Firms (Patent, Trademark, and Copyright Journal, Winter 1963). Language: Spanish 4,4,4,3; Portuguese 1,1,1,1; French 3,3,3,3. Home: 4926 Eskridge Ter., Washington, D.C. 20016. Office: International Monetary Fund, 19th and H Sts., NW., Washington, D.C.

MARBUT, FREDERICK BROWNING, b. Columbia, Mo., Aug. 8, 1905. JOURNALISM. A.B., George Washington U., 1938; M.A., Harvard U., 1939; Ph. D., 1950. Sports editor, The Panama American (Panama), 1929–30; copy-reader, The Washington Evening Star (D.C.), 1930; wire editor, Associated Press (Conn.), 1930–33; reporter, Associated Press (Washington, D.C.), 1933–38; instr.-assoc. prof., Kent State U., 1941–44; PROF., JOURNALISM, PA. STATE U., 1944– . Smith-Mundt lectr. (Bolivia), 1957; U.S. Dept. of State lectr. (Ecuador, Venezuela, Argentina, Chile, Uruguay), 1959; Smith-Mundt lectr. (Jamaica), 1960; Smith-Mundt prof., The National U. of Nicaragua, 1962–63; lectr., Centro International de Estudios Superiores en el Periodismo para América Latina (Quito), 1963. Membership: American Association of Teachers of Journalism; American Association of University Professors; Association for Education in Journalism; International Press Institute; Sigma Delta Chi. Research: press and governmental relationships; freedom of the press; world history of the press; U.S. history. Author: Chile Has Law to Enforce Ethics (The Quill, Apr. 1961); Latin American Journalism (The Penn State Journalist, May 1963); The Press of Latin America (The Penn State Journalist, Sept. 1963). Language: Spanish 5,4,4,3; French 4,3,2,1; German 2,2,2,1. Home: Pennsylvania Furnace, Pa. Office: 215 Carnegie Bldg., Pa. State U., University Park.

MARCHANT, ANYDA, b. Rio de Janeiro, Brazil, Jan. 27, 1911. LAW. A.B., National U. (George Washington U.), 1931; M.A., 1933; LL.B., 1936. Law clerk, Schuster and Feuille (N.Y.), 1936–39; handbook asst., Hispanic Foundation, Library of Congress, 1940; research librarian, chief of Anglo-American section, asst., Latin American section, Law Library, Library of Congress, 1940–45; legal asst., Brazilian Traction Company (Rio de Janeiro), 1947–48; assoc., Covington & Burling, 1948–50; Latin American analyst, Bureau of Foreign and Domestic Commerce, U.S. Dept. of Commerce, 1951–53; ATTORNEY, INTERNATIONAL BANK FOR RECONSTRUCTION AND DEVELOPMENT, 1954– . Research: comparative law; Latin American history and culture. Author: Dom João's Botanical Garden (Hispanic American Historical Review, May 1961); The Captain's Widow (The Americas, Summer 1963); Matthew F. Maury's New Virginia (The Southwest Review, Summer 1963). Language: Spanish 3,3,3,3; Portuguese 5,5,4,4; French 4,3,3,4; Italian 2,2,2,2. Home: 2011 Hanover St., Silver Spring, Md. 20190. Office: International Bank for Reconstruction and Development, 1818 H St., NW., Washington, D.C.

MARICHAL, JUAN, b. Tenerife, Canary Islands, Feb. 2, 1922. SPANISH AMERICAN LITERATURE. Bachelier-ès-lettres, U. of Algiers, 1941; A.M., Princeton U., 1948; Ph. D., 1949; A.M. (honorary), Harvard U., 1958. Instr., Instituto Luis Vives (Mexico, D.F.), 1944–45; instr., Princeton U., 1946–48; instr., Middlebury Coll. Summer School, 1946–48; instr., Johns Hopkins U., 1948–49; asst. prof., Harvard U., 1949–53; assoc. prof., Bryn Mawr Coll., 1953–58; assoc. prof., Harvard U., 1958–61; PROF., ROMANCE LANGUAGES AND LITERATURES, HARVARD U., 1961– . Guggenheim fellow (Spain), 1959; Organization of American States fellow (Mexico), Summer 1960. Membership: American Association of Teachers of Spanish and Portuguese; Hispanic Society of America; Modern Language Association. Research: Spanish and Latin American intellectual history; intellectual history of Latin America since 1810. Author: La voluntad de estilo (1957); Montaigne in Spain (Nueva Revista de Filología Hispánica, Jan.–June (1953). Editor: Ensayos de literatura hispánica (1958). Language: Spanish 5,5, 5,5; French 5,5,5,5. Home: 29 Lancaster St., Cambridge, Mass. 02140. Office: Widener Library 708, Harvard U., Cambridge, 02138.

MARITANO, NINO, b. Turin, Italy, 1919. ECONOMICS. B.A., Turin U., 1941; M.A., Louvain U., 1951; Ph. D., Georgetown U., 1958. Asst. prof., State U. of Genoa (Italy), 1957–58; ASST. PROF., ECONOMICS, ST. THOMAS COLL., 1959– . Hill Family Foundation grant (Central America), 1961, (South America), 1962; Rockefeller Foundation grant, 1963. Membership: American Economic Association; Catholic Economic Association; Econometric Association; Midwest Economic Association; Minnesota Economic Association. Research: Central American Common Market; Latin American Free Trade Association; labor economics; agricultural economics; Latin American economic development problems. Author: An Alliance for Progress, the Challenge and the Problem (1963); A Theory of Static Equilibrium (Econométrica, June 1958); Economic Development and Growth: Challenge of the 60's (Review of Social Economy, Spring 1962). Language: Spanish 5,5,5,4; Portuguese 4,5,4,4; French 5,5,5,4; Italian 5,5,5,4; German 4,4,4,3. Office: St. Thomas Coll., 2115 Summit Ave., St. Paul, Minn.

MARKMAN, SIDNEY DAVID, b. Brooklyn, N.Y., Oct. 10, 1911. ART AND ARCHITECTURE. A.B., Union Coll., 1934; M.A., Columbia U., 1936; Ph. D., 1943. Prof., Universidad Nacional de Panamá, 1941–45; PROF., ART, DUKE U., 1947– . Chmn., Junta de Conservación y Restauración de Monumentos Históricos de Panamá, 1942–45; Duke U. Research Council grants (Central America), 1949–62; Philosophical Society grant (Spain), 1959; Fulbright research scholar (Spain), 1961–62. Membership: Archaeological Institute of America; Society of Architectural Historians. Research: architecture of colonial Central America, especially Guatemala. Author: San Cristobal de las Casas y su arquitectura (1963); Colonial Architecture of Antigua, Guatemala (1965); Santa Cruz, Antigua, and the Spanish Colonial Architecture of Central America (Journal, Society of Architectural Historians, Mar. 1956). Language: Spanish 5,5,5,4; Portuguese 2,1, 1,1; French 5,2,2,1; German 4,4,2,1. Home: 919 Urban Ave., Durham, N.C. Office: Dept of Art, Duke U., Durham.

MARTIN, GENE ELLIS, b. Omaha, Nebr., Apr. 4, 1926. GEOGRAPHY. B.A., U. of Wash., 1949; M.A., 1952; Ph. D., Syracuse U., 1955. Vis. prof., U. of Chile, 1953; asst. prof., U. of Ga., 1955–56; vis. asst. prof., Syracuse U., Summer 1956; asst. prof.-ASSOC. PROF., GEOGRAPHY, U. OF OREG., 1956– ; vis. prof., Universidad Nacional de Buenos Aires, Summer 1959; vis. assoc. prof., U. of Minn., Summer 1961, U. of Wash., Summer 1964. Doherty fellow (Chile), 1953–54; Rockefeller grant (Argentina), 1962–63; U. of Oreg. research grants (Colombia), 1962, 1963. Membership: Association of American Geographers. Research: rural settlement and land tenure of Hispanic South America; land division in central Chile; land tenure in Argentina and Colombia. Author: La división de la tierra en Chile central (1960). Language: Spanish 4,4,4,3; Portuguese 2,2,2,1; French 3,2,2,1; German 2,2,2,1. Home: 3185 University St., Eugene, Oreg. Office: Dept. of Geography, U. of Oreg., Eugene.

MARTIN, JOHN LEWIS, b. Huntington, W. Va., Jan. 6, 1911. SPANISH AMERICAN LITERATURE. A.B., Marshall U., 1933;

M.A., U. of Ky., 1934; Ph. D., U. of Pittsburgh, 1940. PROF., SPANISH, MARSHALL U., 1935–. Membership: National Education Association; West Virginia Education Association. Research: literature of Colombia. Author: El Alférez Real (1940); Las obras literarias de José Milla (1947); What the Elementary Instructor Needs to Know in Teaching Foreign Languages (West Virginia Scholastic Journal, Mar. 1963). Language: Spanish 5,5,4,5; French 4,4,3,4; Italian 3,3,–,3. Home: 21 Tynes Lane, Huntington, W. Va. Office: Dept. of Spanish, Marshall U., Huntington.

MARTIN, JOHN W., b. Winnipeg, Canada, June 20, 1922. LINGUISTICS AND LANGUAGE. B.A., U. of Wash., 1949; M.A., 1956; Ph. D., 1956. Instr., head, English, Universidad Autónoma de Guadalajara (Mexico), 1946–47; instr., U. of Wash., 1953–56; asst. prof., Wash. State U., 1956–57; asst. prof., Fresno State Coll., 1957–60; vis. assoc. prof., National Defense Education Act Institute, N.Y.U., Summer 1961; assoc., Center for Applied Linguistics (Washington, D.C.), 1961; VIS. ASSOC. PROF., DIR., INSTITUTO LINGUÍSTICO COLOMBO-AMERICANO (U. OF CALIF., LOS ANGELES), 1961–. Organizer, Center for Applied Linguistics Conference (P.R.), Fall 1961; Fulbright lectr. (Ecuador), 1960–61; consultant, Minister of Education (Colombia), 1961. Membership: Inter-American Program in Linguistics and Language Teaching; Linguistic Circle of New York. Research: Romance linguistics; language teaching; English as a foreign language; planning of teacher development programs in Latin America; a contrastive analysis of Spanish and English. Author: Some Uses of the Old Spanish Past Subjunctives (Romance Philology, Aug. 1958); Remarks on the Origin of the Portuguese Inflected Infinitive (Word, 1960). Language: Spanish 5,5,5,5; Portuguese 4,4,2,3; French 4,3,2,3. Linguistic studies: English; Spanish. Office: Instituto Lingüístico Colombo-Americano, Apartado Aéreo 13407, Bogotá, Colombia.

MARTIN, NORMAN FRANCIS, S.J., b. Half Moon Bay, Calif., July 8, 1914. HISTORY. U. of Santa Clara, 1933–35; A.B., Gonzaga U. (Wash.), 1941; M.A., 1942; S.T.L., Colegio Máximo San Miguel (Argentina), 1948; M.A., Mexico City Coll., 1950; Ph. D., Universidad Nacional Autónoma de México, 1957. Instr., U. of Santa Clara, 1942–43; Colegio Centro América (Nicaragua), 1943–45; Colegio de San Bartolomé (Colombia), 1944–45; prof., U. of Santa Clara, 1958–62; WRITER, JESUIT INSTITUTE OF HISTORY (ROME), 1963– . Guggenheim fellow (Europe), 1962–63. Membership: American Catholic Historical Association; American Historical Association; Conference on Latin American History; Pacific Coast Council on Latin American Studies. Research: social and economic aspects of Mexican colonial history; Jesuit achievements in Baja California in the 17th and 18th centuries. Author: Los Vagabundos de la Nueva España, Siglo XVI (1957); Instrucción del Virrey Marqués de Croix que deja a su sucesor Antonio María Bucareli (1960). Language: Spanish 5,5,5,5; Portuguese 4,4,3,3; French 4,3,3,3; Italian 4,3,3,3. Linguistic studies: Greek, Hebrew, Italian, Latin. Home: Faculty Residence, U. of Santa Clara, Santa Clara, Calif. Office: Jesuit Institute of History, Via dei Penitenzieri 20, Rome 6, Italy.

MARTINEZ, ANGELINA, b. Ponce, P.R., Aug. 27, 1920. LIBRARY SCIENCE; BIBLIOGRAPHY. B.A., Inter American U. (P.R.), 1943; B.S.L.S., La. State U., 1945; M.S., U. of Ill., 1957. Asst. librarian, Inter American U., 1943–44, 1945–46; junior cataloger, Organization of American States, Spring 1946; head librarian, Inter American Institute of Agricultural Sciences (Costa Rica), 1946–59; documents librarian and subject specialist in the biological sciences, U. of Calif., Davis, 1959–62; HEAD, REFERENCE DEPT., SUBJECT SPECIALIST IN THE BIOLOGICAL SCIENCES AND AGRICULTURE, U. OF CALIF., DAVIS, 1962– . Rockefeller fellow, 1944–45, 1956–57; Executive Committee, Inter American Institute of Agricultural Sciences, 1946–59; Organizing Committee of First Technical Meeting of Latin American Agricultural Librarians, 1953; Committee to Study Organization and Arrangement of the Bibliography of Agriculture, 1962. Membership: American Library Association; Beta Phi Mu; California Library Association. Research: reference work and bibliography in the biological sciences and agriculture. Author: Problems of Latin American Agricultural Libraries and Proposed Program of Activities of the Inter-American Association of Agricultural Librarians (International Association of Agricultural Librarians and Document Quarterly Bulletin, 1957). Co-author: Cacao Bibliography (1954); Corn Bibliography (1960). Language: Spanish 5,5,5,5; Portuguese 3,–,–,–; French 3,–,–,–; Italian 3,–,–,–. Home: 903 Craig Pl., Davis, Calif. 95616. Office: University Library, U. of Calif., Davis, 95616.

MARTINEZ, JOHN R., b. Midvale, Utah, Jan. 31, 1927. HISTORY. B.A., Brigham Young U., 1950; M.A., U. of Calif., Berkeley, 1953; Ph. D., 1957. Asst. prof., Brigham Young U., 1956–57; ASSOC. PROF., HISTORY, ARIZ. STATE U., 1957– . John Hay Whitney fellow (Mexico). Membership: Pacific Coast Council for Latin American Studies; Rocky Mountain Council on Latin America. Research: intellectual and cultural history; current political and diplomatic problems; Mexican emigration to the United States, 1848–1930. Author: Sarmiento and Rodó on Democracy (1960); The Changing Role of the Military (Bureau of Government Research, Ariz. State U., 1962); Three Cases of Communism: Cuba, Brazil, and Mexico (1964). Language: Spanish 5,5,5,5; Portuguese 3,3,3,3; French 3,3,3,3; German 2,2,2,2. Home: 607 West 19th St., Tempe, Ariz. Office: Dept. of History, Ariz. State U., Tempe.

MARTÍNEZ, MANUEL GUILLERMO, b. Mexico, D.F., July 13, 1897. HISTORY AND SPANISH AMERICAN LITERATURE. B.S., Georgetown U., 1928; Ph. D., Georgetown U., 1932; M.A., Catholic U. of America, 1936; Ph. D., 1947. Research asst., Inter-American High Commission, 1919–25; clerk, Chancery, Embassy of Mexico (Washington, D.C.), 1925–30; PROF., SPANISH AND HISPANIC AMERICAN CIVILIZATION, INSTITUTE OF LANGUAGES AND LINGUISTICS, GEORGETOWN U., 1930– . Staff mem-

ber, U.S. Secretary of State Colby's delegation to South America, 1920; Pan American Highway Commission, 1923; Georgetown U. representative, Fourth Pan American Commercial Congress, 1932. Membership: American Association of Teachers of Spanish and Portuguese; American Association of University Professors; Hispanic American Academy of Arts and Sciences; Instituto de las Españas; Pi Gamma Mu. Research: Mexican historiography. Author: Don Joaquín García Icazbalceta—His Place in Mexican Historiography (1947; Spanish edition, 1950); Don Joaquín García Icazbalceta (Review of Inter-American Bibliography, Apr.–June 1951). Language: Spanish 5,5,5,5; Portuguese 3,3,2,2; French 3,3,2,2. Home: 7111 Beechwood Dr., Chevy Chase, Md. 20015. Office: Institute of Languages and Linguistics, Georgetown U., Washington, D.C. 20007.

MARTINS, HEITOR MIRANDA, b. Belo Horizonte, Brazil, July 22, 1933. BRAZILIAN LITERATURE AND LANGUAGE. B.A., Universidade de Minas Gerais, 1959; Ph. D., 1962. Instr., U. of N. Mex., 1960–62; ASST. PROF., PORTUGUESE, TULANE U., 1962– ; vis. asst. prof., U. of Tex., 1963. Membership: American Association of Teachers of Spanish and Portuguese; Associação Mineira de Escritôres; Linguistic Society of America; Modern Language Association. Research: paleography; structure of the novel; colonial and romantic periods in Portuguese literature. Author: Sirgo nos cabelos (1961); Manuel de Galhegos: Monarquia dual e restauração (1964); Notas para uma metodologia da língua portuguêsa no exterior (Revista do Livro, 1961). Language: Spanish 4,4,4,4; Portugese 5,5,5,5; French 4,4,3,3; Italian 4,3,3,3; Latin 3,-,-,-. Home: Apt. 521, 6440 South Claiborne, New Orleans, La. 70125. Office: Dept. of Spanish and Portuguese, Tulane U., New Orleans, 70118.

MARTORELL, IRMA B., b. San Juan, P.R., Aug. 20, 1923. SOCIAL WELFARE. B.A., U. of P.R., 1945; M.S., Simmons Coll., 1952. Public welfare worker, Dept. of Public Welfare (P.R.), 1945–46; caseworker, Travelers Aid Society (Miami, Fla.), 1947–49; medical social worker, Dept. of Health (P.R.), 1949–51; casework supervisor, State Insurance Fund (P.R.), 1952–53; medical social worker, Veterans Administration Hospital (Calif.), 1953–56; clinical social worker, National Institute of Health (Md.), 1957–61; FAMILY SERVICES TECHNICIAN, BUREAU OF FAMILY SERVICES, U.S. DEPT. OF HEALTH, EDUCATION, AND WELFARE, 1961– . Medical social work consultant, Ministry of Public Health and Social Assistance (Guatemala), 1957; consultant, International Service, U.S. Dept. of Health, Education, and Welfare. Membership: Colegio de Trabajadores Sociales de Puerto Rico; National Association of Social Workers. Research: medical and psychiatric social work. Author: Employment Problems Encountered by Epileptic Patients (Social Service Review of Puerto Rico, 1953); Social Service in the State Insurance Fund (Órgano Fondo Seguro del Estado, 1953). Language: Spanish 5,5,5,5; Portuguese 3,3,3,3; French 3,3,3,3; Italian 3,3,3,3. Office: Repatriation Unit, Bureau of Family Services, U.S. Dept. of Health, Education, and Welfare, Washington, D.C. 20006.

MARTZ, JOHN D., b. Latrobe, Pa., July 8, 1934. POLITICAL SCIENCE. A.B., Harvard U., 1955; A.M., George Washington U., 1960; Ph. D., U. of N.C., 1963. ASST. PROF., POLITICAL SCIENCE, U. OF N.C., 1963– ; U.S. EDITORIAL DIR., U. OF N.C. AND FACULTAD LATINOAMERICANA DE CIENCIAS SOCIALES. Buenos Aires Convention grant (Colombia), 1956–57; National Defense Education Act fellow, 1960–62; Ford Foundation foreign area fellow (Colombia, Venezuela), 1962–63. Membership: American Political Science Association; Hispanic American Society; Pi Gamma Mu; Southeastern Conference on Latin American Studies; Southern Political Science Association. Research: Acción Democrática; political thought of Latin America. Author: Central America: Crisis and Challenge (1959); Colombia: A Contemporary Political Study (1962); Dynamics of Change in Latin American Politics (1964). Language: Spanish 4,4,4,4; Portuguese 3,3,2,2; French 3,3,2,2. Home: 218 Ransom St., Chapel Hill, N.C. Office: Institute of Latin American Studies, U. of N.C., Chapel Hill.

MARY TERESE AVILA, SISTER, B.V.M., b. Quincy, Mass., Aug. 17, 1917. BRAZILIAN LITERATURE.B.A., Mills Coll., 1939; M.A., U. of Ariz., 1944; Ph. D., U. of Wis., 1965. Instr., Lawrence Coll., 1944–49; teacher, Xavier High School (Phoenix, Ariz.), 1951–55, Salpointe High School (Tucson, Ariz.), 1955–57; instr., Mundelein Coll., 1957–59; ASST. PROF., SPANISH AND PORTUGUESE, MUNDELEIN COLL., 1963– . National Defense Education Act fellow, U. of Wis. Membership: American Association of Teachers of Spanish and Portuguese; Phi Kappa Phi; Sigma Delta Pi. Research: contemporary Brazilian novel; Machado de Assis; effect of the Cuban revolution on religious organizations; contemporary literature of Spain. Author: The Biblical Significance of the Symbolism in Esaú e Jacó (Revista das Letras, Winter 1964). Language: Spanish 5,5,5,5; Portuguese 5,4,4,4; French 4,3,3,3. Home: Mount Carmel, Dubuque, Iowa. Office: Dept. of Spanish and Portuguese, Mundelein Coll., 6363 Sheridan Rd., Chicago, Ill. 60626.

MASON, J(OHN) ALDEN, b. Philadelphia, Pa., Jan. 14, 1885. ANTHROPOLOGY. A.B., U. of Pa., 1907; Ph. D., U. of Calif., 1911; Litt. D., Franklin & Marshall Coll., 1958. Student delegate, International School of Mexican Archeology and Ethnology, 1911–13; field investigator, Puerto Rican Insular Survey, 1914–15; asst. curator, Field Museum of Natural History, 1917–23; asst. curator, American Museum of Natural History, 1924–25; curator emeritus, Museum, U. of Pa., 1926–55; EDITOR, NEW WORLD ARCHAEOLOGICAL FOUNDATION, BRIGHAM YOUNG U., 1958– . Membership: American Anthropological Association; American Association for the Advancement of Science; Eastern States Archaeological Federation; Society for American Archaeology; Society for Pennsylvania Archaeology. Research: archeology; ethnology; Indian languages; folklore; Mexico; Caribbean region; Peru. Author: Archaeology of Santa Marta, Colombia (1931, 1936, 1940); The Languages of

South American Indians (1950); The Ancient Civilizations of Peru (1957). Language: Spanish 4,4,4,3; Portuguese 2,1,1,1; French 2,1,1,1. Linguistic studies: Papago; Tepecano; Tepehuan. Home: 725 Conestoga Rd., Berwyn, Pa. Office: University Museum, 33rd and Spruce Sts., Philadelphia 4, Pa.

MASSEY, WILLIAM CLIFFORD, b. San Mateo, Calif., June 17, 1917. ANTHROPOLOGY A.B., U. of Calif., Berkeley, 1940; Ph. D., 1947. Asst. prof., U. of Wash., 1950–56; lectr., Instituto Nacional de Antropología e Historia (Mexico), Fall 1954; technical writer, Boeing Airplane Company (Seattle), 1956–57; assoc. prof., U. of Fla., 1958–61; assoc. prof., La. State U., 1962; assoc. prof., U. of Fla., 1962–63; RESEARCH DIR., MUSEO DEL SUR (LA PAZ, MEXICO), 1964– . American Philosophical Society grant (Mexico), 1954; U. of Wash. Graduate School grant (Baja California), 1952–53; National Science Foundation grant (Baja California), 1963–64. Research: Mexican archeology, community studies, and demography especially of Baja California; Latin American physical and cultural geography, and history. Author: Tribes and Languages of Baja California (Southwestern Journal of Anthropology, Winter 1947); Cultural Distinction of Aboriginal Baja California (in Homenaje a Pablo Martínez del Río, 1961). Co-author: Comparative Studies of North American Indians (American Philosophical Society, July 1957). Language: Spanish 5,4,4,4; Portuguese 4,1,1,1; French 5,3,2,1; German 3,2,1,1. Home: Calle Álvaro Obregón 1065, La Paz, Baja California Sur, México. Office: Dept. of Anthropology, U. of Fla., Gainesville, 32603.

MASSON, FRANCIS GEORGE, b. Pilares de Nacozari, Sonora, Mexico, Mar. 11, 1929. ECONOMICS. B.A., Wash. State U., 1950; M.A., Ohio State U., 1951; Ph. D., 1954. Research analyst, Ohio Legislative Service Commission, 1955–56; economic affairs officer, United Nations Economic Commission for Latin America, 1956–57; member, Klein and Saks Economic and Financial Mission to Chile, 1957–58; assoc. dir. of research, National Planning Association, 1958–61; international economist, U.S. Tariff Commission, 1961–62; senior specialist in trade and finance, Balance of Payments Div., U.S. Dept. of Commerce, 1962–64; DEPUTY COORDINATOR FOR LATIN AMERICA, U.S. AGENCY FOR INTERNATIONAL DEVELOPMENT, 1964– . Consultant, Merck, Inc., Clevite Corp., National Planning Association; District of Columbia Public Finance Advisory Board. Membership: American Economic Association; District of Columbia Political Science Association; Phi Beta Kappa; Phi Kappa Phi; Pi Sigma Alpha. Research: economic programming and planning; econometrics; balance of payments; aid requirements of Latin American countries; public administration. Author: El sistema de previsión chileno (1958); Invisible Trade Barriers between Canada and the United States (1963); El servicio nacional de salud, informe de la misión Klein and Saks (Boletín, Servicio Nacional de Salud, Santiago, Feb. 1958). Language: Spanish 5,5,5,5; Portuguese 4,3,2,1; French 4,4,4,4; Russian 3,2,1,1. Home: 5527 Nevada Ave. NW., Washington, D.C. 20015. Office: Office of Program Coordination, U.S. Agency for International Development, Washington 25, D.C.

MASUR GERHARD S., b. Berlin, Germany, Sept. 17, 1901. HISTORY. U. of Marburg (Germany), 1921; Ph. D., U. of Berlin, 1925. Privatdozent, U. of Berlin, 1930–35; prof., Escuela Normal Superior (Colombia), 1936–45; PROF., HISTORY, SWEET BRIAR COLL., 1947– ; vis. prof., U. of Va., 1949–51, U. of N. Mex., 1953, Free U. of Berlin, 1960, U. of Calif., Berkeley, 1963–64. Rockefeller grant, 1945–47, 1954–55; Guggenheim fellow, 1955; Fulbright lectr., 1960. Membership: American Historical Association; Conference of Latin American History; Conference on Central European History. Research: Latin American independence period; history of ideas. Author: Simon Bolivar (1948). Language: Spanish 5,5,4,4; Portuguese 3,2,–,–; French 5,4,3,2; German 5,5,5,5. Office: Dept. of History, Sweet Briar Coll., Sweet Briar, Va.

MATE, HUBERT EMERY, b. Lima, N.Y., Sept. 2, 1917. SPANISH AMERICAN AND BRAZILIAN LITERATURES. A.B., Howard Coll., 1937; M.A., U. of Ala., 1938; Ph. D., Northwestern U., 1949. Instr., U. of Ala., 1938–39; instr., Ind. U., 1946–49; asst. prof., U. of Ala., 1949–53; assoc. prof., 1953–58; asst. dean, 1955–59; PROF., ROMANCE LANGUAGES, U. OF ALA., 1958– ; acting dean, 1959–61; DEAN, ACADEMIC LIAISON OFFICER, 1961– . Rockefeller Foundation research assoc. (Brazil), 1941–42; American Council of Learned Societies lectr., U. of São Paulo, 1941–42; cavaleiro, Cruzeiro do Sul (Brazil). Membership: American Association of Teachers of Spanish and Portuguese; American Association of University Professors; Association of Latin American Studies; Modern Language Association; Southeastern Society of Latin American Studies; Southern Humanities Conference. Research: modernista movement; the contemporary novel in Spanish America and Brazil. Author: Um exame crítico dos contos de Taunay (Revista Iberoamericana, July 1950); Social Aspects of Novels of López y Fuentes and Alegría (Hispania, Sept. 1956); Spanish on Television at the University of Alabama (Hispania, Sept. 1958.) Language: Spanish 5,5,5,5; Portuguese 5,5,5,5; French 5,4,4,4. Linguistic studies: French; Portuguese; Spanish. Home: 2713 Claymont Cir., Tuscaloosa, Ala. Office: Dept. of Romance Languages, Box N, U. of Ala., University.

MATHER, EUGENE (COTTON), b. West Branch, Iowa, Jan. 3, 1918. GEOGRAPHY. A.B., U. of Ill., 1940; M.S., 1941; Ph. D., U. of Wis., 1951. Research analyst, U.S. Office of Strategic Services, 1942–45; asst.-assoc. prof., U. of Ga., 1947–56; lectr., U. of British Columbia, 1956–57; PROF., GEOGRAPHY, U. OF MINN., 1957– ; CHMN., 1961– . Member of Board, Nederlandse Vereniging voor Economische en Sociale Geografie. Membership: Association of American Geographers; Canadian Association of Geographers. Research: geography of South America. Author: Southeastern Excursion Guidebook (1952); A Linear-Distance Map of Farm Population in the United States (Annals of Association of American Geographers, Sept. 1944); The

Production and Marketing of Wyoming Beef Cattle (Economic Geography, Apr. 1950). Language: Spanish 1,1,1,1,; French 3,-,-,-. Home: Route 3, River Falls, Wis. Office: Dept. of Geography, U. of Minn., Minneapolis 14.

MATHEWS, THOMAS GEORGE, b. Bloomington, Ind., Oct. 31, 1925. HISTORY. B.A., Oberlin Coll., 1949; M.A., Columbia U., 1953; Ph. D., 1957. Vis. lectr., U. of P.R., Mayagüez, 1950-53; asst. prof., 1953-57; vis. lectr., Mexico City Coll., 1954; consultant, Hispanic Foundation, Library of Congress, 1956; assoc. prof., chmn., U. of P.R., Mayagüez, 1957-61; Latin American specialist, Embassy (Cuba), U.S. Dept. of State, 1960; DIR., INSTITUTE OF CARIBBEAN STUDIES, U. OF P.R., 1961- . Membership: American Historical Association; Conference on Latin American History. Research: politics in Puerto Rico; confederation in the Caribbean. Author: Puerto Rican Politics and the New Deal (1960); Rafael Altamira: An Appreciation (Hispanic American Historical Review, Aug. 1952); Plans for a Confederation of the Greater Antilles (Caribbean Historical Review, Dec. 1954). Language: Spanish 4,4,4,4; Portuguese 2,3,2,-; French 2,2,1,-. Home: Ruta Rural 2, Buzón 39, Beverly Hills, P.R. Office: Institute of Caribbean Studies, U. of P.R., Río Piedras.

MATILLA, ALFREDO, b. Madrid, Spain, May 22, 1910. POLITICAL SCIENCE AND MUSIC. Lic., U. of Madrid, 1930; Dr., 1936. Prof., dir., Diplomatic School (Dominican Republic), 1940-45; prof., Conservatory of Music (Dominican Republic), 1942-45; PROF., SOCIAL SCIENCE, U. OF P.R., 1946- ; DIR. OF CULTURAL ACTIVITIES, 1947- ; PROF., HISTORY OF MUSIC, CONSERVATORY OF MUSIC OF P.R., 1960- . Consultant, Festival Casals, Inc., 1956-64. Membership: American Society of International Law. Author: Los grandes procesos del mundo (1931); La conciencia de la paz (1946). Language: Spanish 5,5,5,5; Portuguese 3,2,1,1; French 4,5,4,4; Italian 4,4,3,3. Home: Reparto Santa Ana, Calle Temple E-17, Río Piedras, P.R. Office: Dept. of Social Science, U. of P.R., Río Piedras.

MATLUCK, JOSEPH H., b. Brooklyn, N.Y., Nov. 25, 1917. LANGUAGE AND LINGUISTICS. B.A., Brooklyn Coll., 1940; M.A., Mexico City Coll., 1949; Ph. D., National U. of Mexico, 1951. Instr., Northwestern U., 1951-55; ASSOC. PROF., SPANISH AND ROMANCE LINGUISTICS, U. OF TEX., 1955- ; vis. prof., audio-visual consultant, U. of P.R., 1958-59; vis. prof., U. of N. Mex., 1960-61, Summer 1961, N.Y.U., Summer 1962, Mexico City Coll., Spring 1963, El Colegio de México, Spring 1963. National Testing Committee, American Association of Teachers of Spanish and Portuguese; Farmer fellow (Mexico), 1957, 1960; U. of Tex. research scholar (Mexico), 1960, Fall 1963, (Italy), 1963-64; Baird scholar (Mexico), 1963; Fulbright research scholar in Romance linguistics (Rome), 1963-64. Membership: American Association of Teachers of Spanish and Portuguese; American Association of University Professors; American Library of Recorded Dialect Studies; Linguistic Society of America; Modern Language Association. Research: Romance linguistics; Latin American dialectology; educational television and radio; English as a foreign language. Author: La pronunciación en el español del Valle de México (1951); The Comic Strip: A Source of Anglicisms in Mexican Spanish (Hispania, May 1960); Fonemas finales en el consonantismo puertorriqueño (Nueva Revista de Filología Hispánica, July-Dec. 1961). Language: Spanish 5,5,5,5; Portuguese 4,4,2,2; French 3,2,2,3; German 2,2,2,2; Italian 5,4,4,4; Yiddish 5,5,5,5. Linguistic studies: Italian; Spanish. Home: 3903 Bailey Lane, Austin, Tex. Office: Dept. of Romance Languages, U. of Tex., Austin 12.

MATSON, DANIEL SHAW, b. Mediapolis, Iowa, May 17, 1908. LINGUISTICS. A.B., U. of Ariz., 1930; M.A., San Luis Rey Coll., 1944; National U. of Mexico, 1951. Missionary, Papago Indian Agency, 1940-50; instr., U. of Ariz., 1950-54; management analyst, U.S. Army Ordnance Depot, 1956-60; SCIENTIFIC LINGUIST, OPERATIONAL RESEARCH SPECIALIST, U.S. ARMY ELECTRONIC PROVING GROUNDS, COMMUNICATIONS ELECTRONICS AGENCY (FORT HUACHUCA, ARIZ.), 1960- . Membership: Arizona Education Association; Sigma Delta Pi. Research: American and Mexican Indian Languages. Author: Southwestern Chronicle, Papago Recordings (Arizona Quarterly, Spring 1953). Co-editor: Cordero's Description of the Apache (New Mexico Historical Review, Oct. 1957). Language: Spanish 5,5,5,4,4; Portuguese 2,2,1,1; German 5,3,3,3; Latin 4,4,3,3; Papago -,4,4,-. Linguistic studies: Papago; Pima. Home: P.O. Box 1336 Sierra Vista, Ariz. 85635. Office: U.S. Army Combat Developments Command, Communications Electronics Agency, Fort Huachuca, Ariz.

MATTESON, ESTHER L. M., b. Nov. 8, 1912. LINGUISTICS. B.A., Seattle Pacific Coll., 1958; Ph. D., U. of Calif., Berkeley, 1963. LINGUISTIC ADVISER, SUMMER INSTITUTE OF LINGUISTICS (BOLIVIA), 1944- . Research: mountain areas of indigenous languages in Peru; Piro tribe of Peru; Tzeltal of Mexico; Bolivia. Author: The Piro of the Urubamba (Kroeber Anthropological Society Papers, Spring 1954); Piro Phonemics and Morphology (Kroeber Anthropological Society Papers, Fall 1954); Analyzed Piro Text: A Boy and a Jaguar (Kroeber Anthropological Society Papers, Spring 1955). Language: Spanish 4,4,4,4; Piro 4,4,4,4. Linguistic studies: Piro (Arawakan). Home: 8133 Winthrope St., Oakland 5, Calif. Office: Instituto Lingüístico de Verano, Casilla 64, Riberalta, Beni, Bolivia.

MATTHEWS, HERBERT LIONEL, b. New York, N.Y., Jan. 10, 1900. JOURNALISM. A.B., Columbia Coll., 1922. Reporter, war correspondent, foreign correspondent, The New York Times, 1922-48; EDITORIAL WRITER, THE NEW YORK TIMES, 1948- . Research: Latin America; Western Europe; Cuba. Author: The Fruits of Fascism (1943); The Cuban Story (1961); Cuba (1964). Language: Spanish 4,-,-,-; Portuguese 2,-,-,-; French 4,-,-,-; Italian 4,-,-,-. Home: 174 East 74th St., New York 21, N.Y. Office: The New York Times, New York 36.

MAUCK, ELWYN ARTHUR, b. Toledo, Iowa, May 5, 1910. POLITICAL SCIENCE. A.B., Cornell Coll., 1932; A.M., Columbia U., 1933; Ph. D., 1937. Asst. prof., U. of N.C., 1937–42; chief, reports and awards office, Office of Civilian Defense, 1942–45; vis. prof., U. of P.R., 1945–46; chief, O & M Div., War Assets Administration Regional Office (Nashville, Tenn.), 1946–47; prof., U. of Md., 1947–49; chief, Fiscal Research Bureau, State of Md., 1948–53; div. chief, Public and Business Administration, International Cooperation Administration (Rio de Janeiro, Brazil), 1953–57; prof. and principal public administration adviser, N.Y.U. (Ankara, Turkey), 1958–59, U. of Minn. (Seoul, Korea), 1959–62; PROF., PUBLIC AND INTERNATIONAL AFFAIRS, U. OF PITTSBURGH, 1962– ; prof. and chief of party, U. of Mich. (Taipei, Taiwan), 1963–64. Roberts fellow, Columbia U.; public administration adviser, U. of Minas Gerais (Belo Horizonte, Brazil); consultant, State of Md. Membership: American Political Science Association; American Society for Public Administration; Pi Sigma Alpha; Southern Political Science Association. Research: public administration. Language: Spanish 1,1,1,–; Portuguese 2,2,2,–; French 2,1,–,–; German 2,2,2,–. Home: 1767 Beechwood Blvd., Pittsburgh, Pa. 15217. Office: Graduate School of Public and International Affairs, U. of Pittsburgh, Pittsburgh, 15213.

MAXWELL, HENRY JAMES, b. Glenwood, Iowa, Feb. 1, 1919. BRAZILIAN LITERATURE. B.A., U. of Nebr., 1940; M.A., U. of Wis., 1941; Ph. D., 1955. Instr., Ind. U., 1950–52; asst. prof.-assoc. prof., Wabash Coll., 1952–63; ASSOC. PROF., SPANISH AND PORTUGUESE, TEX. TECHNOLOGICAL COLL., 1963– . Membership: American Association of Teachers of Spanish and Portuguese; Modern Language Association. Research: modern Brazilian novel. Author: Bilac, Olavo Braz Martins dos Guimarães (in Encyclopedia Americana, 1964). Language: Spanish 5,5,4,4; Portuguese 5,4,3,3. Home: 2603 21st St., Lubbock, Tex. 79410. Office: Dept. of Spanish and Portuguese, Tex. Technological Coll., Lubbock, 79409.

MAXWELL, THOMAS JAMES, b. Bryantville, Mass., June 22, 1924. ANTHROPOLOGY. B.A., Coll. of Wooster, 1947; M.A., U. of Mo., 1953; Ph. D., Ind. U., 1962. Research asst., Indian Land Claims, Ind. U., 1954–56; PROF., CHMN., SOCIOLOGY AND ANTHROPOLOGY, INTER AMERICAN U., 1956– ; ACADEMIC DIR., 1963– ; vis. prof., Institute of Cooperatives, U. of P.R., 1963. Dir., Institute in Anthropology for High School Students, National Science Foundation (P.R.), Summer 1963; Fulbright grant, Summer Institute in Indian Civilization (Mysore, India), 1964. Membership: American Anthropological Association; American Ethnological Association; Institute of Caribbean Culture; Instituto Indigenista Interamericano; Sigma Xi. Research: community studies; culture and social problems of Puerto Rico; social structure of a Puerto Rican housing project; Mexico. Author: Ottawa and Chippewa Occupany of Royce Area 205 (1956); Agricultural Ceremonies of the Central Andes During Four Hundred Years of Spanish Contact (Ethnohistory; Winter 1956). Language: Spanish 4,4,4,4; Portuguese 2,–,–,–; French 1,–,–,–: Biblical Greek 1,–,–,–; German 2,2,2,2; Hindi 1,–,1,–. Home and office: Inter American U., San Germán, P.R. 00753.

MAY, PHILLIP ALLAN, b. Providence, R.I., June 6, 1929. ECONOMICS. A.B., U. of Calif., Los Angeles, 1957; M.A., 1959; Ph. D., 1965. Research economist, Rand Corporation (Santa Monica, Calif.), 1960–61; lectr., U. of Calif., Riverside, 1961–62; assoc., U. of Calif., Los Angeles, 1962–64; PROF., ECONOMICS, NORTHERN MICH. U., 1964– . Research: Panama and the Central American customs union; effects of the customs union on value of Central American output. Language: Spanish 3,2,2,3. Home: 509 Lakewood Lane, Marquette, Mich. Office: Dept. of Economics, Northern Mich. U., Marquette.

MAYBURY-LEWIS, DAVID H. P., b. Hyderabad, Pakistan, May 5, 1929. ANTHROPOLOGY. B.A., Cambridge U., 1952; M.A., 1956; M. Sc., U. of São Paulo, 1956; M.A., Oxford U., 1956; Ph. D., 1960. Research asst., Oxford U., 1959–60; ASST. PROF., SOCIAL ANTHROPOLOGY, HARVARD U., 1960– . Fellow in anthropology, U. of São Paulo, 1955–56; Center for Advanced Study in the Behavioral Sciences fellow, 1964–65. Membership: American Anthropological Association; Association of Social Anthropologists; Royal Anthropological Institute of Great Britain. Research: social anthropology; Indians of Central Brazil; sociology of upland Brazil; comparative social structure; sociology of development in Brazil. Author: Akwě-Shavante Society (1964); On the Analysis of Dual Organizations (Bijdragen Tot de Taal-Land-en Volkenkunde, 1960); Parallel Descent and the Apinayé Anomaly (Southwestern Journal of Anthropology, Summer 1960). Language: Spanish 5,5,4,5; Portugese 5,5,5,5; French 5,5,5,5; Danish 5,5,5,5; German 5,5,4,4; Italian 3,3,3,2; Russian 3,3,3,3. Home: A-13 Adams House, Harvard U., Bow St., Cambridge 38, Mass. Office: Dept. of Social Relations, Harvard U., 9 Bow St., Cambridge 38.

MAYERS, MARVIN KEENE, b. Canton, Ohio, Oct. 25, 1927. ANTHROPOLOGY: LINGUISTICS. B.A., Wheaton Coll., 1949; B.D., Fuller Theological Seminary, 1952; M.A., U. of Chicago, 1958; Ph. D., 1960. FIELD RESEARCHER, ADMINISTRATIVE DIR., TECHNICAL STUDIES DIR., SUMMER INSTITUTE OF LINGUISTICS (CENTRAL AMERICA), 1953– . National Science Foundation grant, 1954: Organization of American States grant (Guatemala), 1959. Research: phonemics; dialect survey; Guatemala. Author: Pocomchi Texts (1958); The Pocomchi, A Sociolinguistic Study (1961); Pocomchi Verb Structure (International Journal of American Linguistics, July 1957). Language: Spanish 4,4,3,3. Linguistic studies: Pocoman (Mayan); Pocomchi (Mayan). Home: 1525 Dale Dr., Silver Spring, Md. Office: Summer Institute of Linguistics, Apartado 74, Guatemala, Guatemala.

MAYNARD, EILEEN A., b. Clifton Springs, N.Y., Nov. 12, 1922. ANTHROPOLOGY. B.S., Geneseo State Teachers Coll., 1944; M.A., Syracuse U., 1957; Ph. D., Cornell U., 1963. Anthropologist, U.S. Peace Corps (Peru), 1962; ANTHROPOLOGIST, COR-

NELL U.-PERU PROJECT (Lima), 1963– . Smith-Mundt grant. Research: cultural anthropology; village ethnography of Palín, Guatemala; community development in Peru. Author: The Peace Corps in Peru: The First Months (1963); Patterns of Community Service Development in Selected Communities of the Mantaro Valley, Peru (1964). Language: Spanish 4,3,3,3. Home: Calle General Orbegoso 174 (Breña), Lima, Peru. Office: Cornell-Peru Project, Dept. of Anthropology, Cornell U., Ithaca, N.Y.

MAYNE, ALVIN, b. Chicago, Ill., May 14, 1914. ECONOMICS AND STATISTICS. B.A., U. of Chicago, 1935; M.B.A., 1937. Economist, Moody's Investor's Service, 1945–48; lectr., Wharton School, U. of Pa., 1948–51; consultant, Office of the President, 1951–54; ECONOMIC ADVISER, GOVERNOR OF PUERTO RICO, 1954– ; PLANNING ADVISER, U.S. COORDINATOR, ALLIANCE FOR PROGRESS, U.S. AGENCY FOR INTERNATIONAL DEVELOPMENT, 1962– . Editor, Journal of Economics and Statistics in Puerto Rico. Membership: American Economic Association; American Statistical Association; Puerto Rico Economic and Statistics Society; Sigma Xi. Research: economic development plans for Central America and Caribbean. Author: Planning Economic and Social Programs in Puerto Rico (1960); Designing and Administering Regional Economic Plan (1960). Language: Spanish 4,3,3,2. Office: Office of the Governor, Commonwealth of Puerto Rico, San Juan.

MAYOL, JOSEFINA M., b. Havana, Cuba, Jan. 28, 1918. LIBRARY SCIENCE. A.B., U. of Tampa, 1940; B.S., George Peabody Coll., 1941. Head librarian, Estación Experimental Agronómica de Santiago de las Vegas (Havana), 1941–45; head, Technical Services, Biblioteca Pública, Sociedad Económica Amigos del País (Havana), 1948–53; prof., Escuela Cubana de Bibliotecarios, 1950–53; cataloger, Miami Public Library, 1953–55; head librarian, prof., Centro Regional de Educación Fundamental para América Latina (Patzcuaro, México), 1955–61; prof., Escuela Interamericana de Bibliotecología, Universidad de Antioquia (Medellín, Colombia). 1961–62; cataloger and prof., U. of P.R., 1963; REFERENCE LIBRARIAN, MIAMI PUBLIC LIBRARY, 1963– . American Library Association Special Committee on Cooperation with Latin American Catalogers and Classifiers. Membership: American Library Association; Asociación Cubana de Bibliotecarios; Asociación Interamericana de Bibliotecarios Agrícolas; Florida Library Association. Research: cataloging; library science education; library programs in community education and fundamental education projects. Author: Ex-libris cubanos (1951); La biblioteca en la escuela (1960). Co-author: Cuban Libraries (Library Quarterly, Apr. 1952). Language: Spanish 5,5,5,5; Portuguese 2,1,1,1; French 3,2,1,1. Home: 3024 SW. 26th St., Miami, Fla. 33133. Office: Miami Public Library, 1 Biscayne Blvd., Miami.

MAZZARA, RICHARD A., b. New York, N.Y., June 29, 1926. BRAZILIAN AND SPANISH AMERICAN LITERATURES. B.A., Queens Coll., 1948; M.A., Johns Hopkins U., 1949; Ph. D., U. of Kans., 1959. Instr., French, U. of Kans., 1950–55; instr., Spanish, Amherst Coll., 1955–57; instr., Colby Coll., Summer 1957; ASSOC. PROF., ROMANCE LANGUAGES, FRANKLIN AND MARSHALL COLL., 1957– . Fulbright fellow (Paris). 1953–54: National Defense Education Act fellow, U. of Tex., Summer 1962, U. of Wis., Summer, Fall 1963; Organization of American States fellow (Brazil), Summer 1964. Membership: American Association of Teachers of French; American Association of Teachers of Spanish and Portuguese; American Association of University Professors; Modern Language Association. Research: modern Brazilian drama; 17th century French literature. Author: Some Picaresque Elements in Concolorcorvo's Lazarillo de ciegos caminantes (Hispania, May 1963); Poetry and Progress in Jorge Amado's Gabriela, cravo e canela (Hispania, Sept. 1963); Gilberto Freyre and José Honório Rodrigues: Old and New Horizons for Brazil (Hispania, May 1964). Language: Spanish 5,5,4,4; Portuguese 4,5,3,3; French 5,5,4,4; German 2,2,1,1; Italian 4,4,2,2. Home: 924 First St., Lancaster, Pa. Office: Dept. of Romance Languages, Franklin and Marshall Coll., Lancaster.

MEAD, ROBERT G., JR., b. Cleveland, Ohio, Dec. 30, 1913. SPANISH AMERICAN LITERATURE. A.B., U. of Calif., Los Angeles, 1941; M.A., 1942; Ph. D., U. of Mich., 1949. Research analyst, Latin America, Office of Strategic Services, 1942–45; research analyst, Latin America, U.S. Dept. of State, 1945–47; PROF., FOREIGN LANGUAGES, U. OF CONN., 1949– . Editor, Hispania, 1957–62; editorial committee, Hispanic American Report; Spanish consultant, Harcourt, Brace, and World, Inc.; foreign language consultant, U.S. Office of Education; Executive Council, American Association of Teachers of Spanish and Portuguese. Membership: American Association of University Professors; Instituto Internacional de Literatura Iberoamericana; Modern Language Association. Research: the essay and the history of ideas in Spanish America; Mexican literature. Author: Breve historia del ensayo hispanoamericano (1956); Temas Hispanoamericanos (1959). Editor: Iberoamérica (1962). Language: Spanish 5,5,5,5; Portuguese 4,3,–,–; French 4,4,4,4; Italian 2,2,–,–. Home: 4 Westwood Rd., Storrs, Conn. Office: Dept. of Foreign Languages, U. of Conn., Storrs.

MEADER, ROBERT ELI, b. Rochester, N.H., Oct. 8, 1912. LINGUISTICS. Missionary, South American Indian Mission (Brazil), 1936–56; LINGUISTIC CONSULTANT, SUMMER INSTITUTE OF LINGUISTICS (BRAZIL), 1958– . Membership: Associação Brasileira da Antropologia. Research: Brazil. Language: Spanish 3,2,2,1; Portuguese 5,5,4,4; French 3,1,1,1; Guaraní 3, 1,1,2. Linguistic studies: Guaraní; Iranxe; Nambiguarian; Tupí. Home: 13 Lawton St., Rome, Ga. Office: Summer Institute of Linguistics, Box 1960, Santa Ana, Calif.

MECHAM, J(OHN) LLOYD, b. San Bernardino, Calif., July 16, 1893. POLITICAL SCIENCE. A.B., U. of Calif., Berkeley, 1916; M.A., 1917; Ph. D., 1923. Instr., Columbia U., 1922–24; asst. prof., Washington U., 1924–25; prof., U. of Tex., 1925–63; PROF. EMERITUS, GOVERNMENT, U.

of TEX., 1963– . Native Sons of the Golden West traveling fellow, U. of Calif., 1920–21. Membership: American Political Science Association. Research: Latin American governments and relations. Author: Francisco de Ibarra y Nueva Vizcaya (1927); Church and State in Latin America (1934); The United States and Inter-American Security Cooperation (1962). Language: Spanish 4,3,3,3. Home: 2809 West Fresco Dr., Austin, Tex. Office: Dept. of Government, U. of Tex., Austin.

MEEK, GEORGE D., b. Beloit, Wis., July 26, 1936. JOURNALISM. B.A., Syracuse U., 1957. Assoc. editor, Register Magazine (Washington, D.C.), 1959–60; MANAGING EDITOR, AMERICAS MAGAZINE, PAN AMERICAN UNION, 1960– . Inter American Press Association fellow, U. of Chile, 1958–59. Membership: Phi Beta Kappa; Sigma Delta Chi. Research: Latin American affairs; Chile. Language: Spanish 4, 4,4,3; Portuguese 4,4,4,2. Home: 210 North Columbus St., Arlington 3, Va. Office: Pan American Union, Washington, D.C. 20006.

MEEK, HOWARD BAGNALL, b. Chelsea, Mass., Oct. 30, 1893. ECONOMICS AND BUSINESS. S.B., Boston U., 1917; M.A., U. of Maine, 1920; Ph. D., Yale U., 1933; Sc. D. in Ed. (honorary), Boston U., 1949. Instr., U. of Maine, 1918–20; instr., Yale U., 1920–22; prof., dean, School of Hotel Administration, Cornell U., 1922–61; EXECUTIVE DIR., COUNCIL ON HOTEL, RESTAURANT, AND INSTITUTIONAL EDUCATION 1961– . Consultant on hotel rationing, U.S. Office of Price Administration (Washington, D.C.), 1943–44; consultant on hotel standards, Economic Development Administration (P.R.), 1952–53; consultant on hotels, International Cooperation Administration, U.S. Operations Mission to Costa Rica, 1962; consultant on education for restaurant industry, National Restaurant Association, 1962–64; consultant on education for tourism, Coll. of the Virgin Islands. Membership: American Association of University Professors; American Economic Association; American Hotel Association; American Statistical Association; Cornell Society of Hotelmen; National Restaurant Association; New York State Hotel and Motel Association. Research: hotel and restaurant administration; education for the mass housing and feeding industries, public hospitality, and tourism. Author: A Code of Minimum Standards for the Tax Exempt Hotels of Puerto Rico (1953); The Tourism of Costa Rica (1962): A Classification System for the Hotels of Costa Rica (1962). Language: Spanish 4,3,3,2; French 4,–,–,–. Home: 422 Highland Rd., Ithaca, N.Y., 14850. Office: Council on Hotel, Restaurant, and Institutional Education, Statler Hall, Ithaca, 14850.

MEGGERS, BETTY J., b. Washington, D.C., Dec. 5, 1921. ANTHROPOLOGY. B.A., U. of Pa., 1943; M.A., U. of Mich., 1944; Ph. D., Columbia U., 1952. RESEARCH ASSOC., DIV. OF ARCHAEOLOGY, SMITHSONIAN INSTITUTION 1954– . Membership: American Anthropological Association; American Ethnological Society; American Geographical Society; Anthropological Society of Washington; Society for American Archaeology. Research: archeology: Brazil; Ecuador; Venezuela; British Guiana. Co-author: Archeological Investigations at the Mouth of the Amazon (1957); Archeological Investigations in British Guiana (1960). Co-editor: Aboriginal Cultural Development in Latin America (1963). Language: Spanish 4,3,3,2; Portuguese 4,3,2,2; French 4,2,1,1. Home: 1227 30th St. NW., Washington 7, D.C. Office: Div. of Archeology, Smithsonian Institution, Washington 25.

MEIER, MATT S., b. Covington, Ky., June 4, 1917. HISTORY. B.A., U. of Miami, 1948; M.A., Mexico City Coll., 1949; Ph. D., U. of Calif., Berkeley, 1954. Research asst., Documents Div., Bancroft Library, lectr., Extension Div., U. of Calif., Berkeley, 1953–54; vis. lectr., San Francisco State Coll., Summers 1953, 1954, 1955; asst. prof., Bakersfield Coll., 1955–63; asst. prof., Fresno State Coll., Spring 1963; assoc. prof., Long Beach State Coll., Summer 1963; ASST. PROF., HISTORY, U. OF SANTA CLARA. 1963– . Fulbright lectr. (Argentina), 1958–59. Membership: American Association of University Professors; American Historical Association. Research: the Díaz period in Mexico, especially the economic aspect. Editor: Folsom Letter (Sacramento County Historical Society Golden Notes, Apr.–May 1955). Language: Spanish 5,4,4,4; Portuguese 3,3,2,1; French 3,2,2,1; German 3,3,2,2; Italian 3,2,2,1. Home: 591 Remington Ave. Sunnyvale, Calif. Office: Dept. of History, U. of Santa Clara, Santa Clara, Calif.

MEIGHAN, CLEMENT WOODWARD, b. San Francisco, Calif., Jan. 21, 1925. ANTHROPOLOGY. B.A., U. of Calif., Berkeley, 1949; Ph. D., 1953. Archeologist, lectr., U. of Calif., Berkeley, 1950–52; instr.-PROF., ANTHROPOLOGY, U. OF CALIF., LOS ANGELES 1952– ; CHMN., 1961– . Membership: American Anthropological Association; Society for American Archaeology. Research: archeology; Mexico. Language: Spanish 4,3,3,3; French 4,2,2,2. Home: 2727 Marquette Dr., Topanga, Calif. Office: Dept. of Anthropology, U. of Calif., Los Angeles 24.

MEIGS, PEVERIL, b. New York, N.Y., May 5, 1903. GEOGRAPHY. A.B., U. of Calif., Berkeley, 1925; Ph. D., 1932. Prof., Calif. State Coll., 1929–42; exchange prof., La. State U., 1938–39; geographer, U.S. Office of Strategic Services, 1942–47; analyst, Bibliography Project, Arctic Institute of North America—Library of Congress, 1947–49; geographer-CHIEF, EARTH SCIENCES DIV., U.S. ARMY NATICK LABORATORIES, 1949– . U. of Calif., grant (Mexico), 1930–31; Social Science Research Council grant, 1939; president, Arid Zone Commission, International Geographical Union, 1950–64. Membership: American Association for the Advancement of Science; American Geographical Society; American Meteorological Society; Association of American Geographers; Association of Pacific Coast Geographers; Phi Beta Kappa; Royal Geographical Society. Research: physical geography; climatology; environmental research. Author: The Dominican Mission Frontier of Lower California (1935); The Kiliwa Indians of Lower California (1939); World Distribution of Arid and Semiarid Homoclimates (in Arid Zone Hydrology, 1953). Language: Spanish 4,4,4,4; French 3,2,2,2; German 3,2,2,2. Home: 147 Pelham Island Rd., Wayland, Mass. 01778. Office: U.S. Army Natick Laboratories, Kansas St., Natick, Mass. 01762.

MENDELOWITZ, DANIEL M., b. Linton, N. Dak., Jan. 28, 1905. ART. B.A., Stanford U., 1926; M.A., 1927. Asst. prof., San Jose State Coll., 1927–34; PROF., ART AND EDUCATION, STANFORD U., 1934– . Membership: National Art Education Association; Pacific Arts Association. Research: art education; pre-Columbian cultures of Ecuador, Guatemala, Mexico, and Peru; Latin American colonial arts. Author: Children Are Artists (1953, 1963); A History of American Art (1960). Language: French 3,3,3,2; Italian 3,2,3,2. Home: 800 Lathrop Dr., Stanford, Calif. Office: Dept. of Art, Stanford U., Stanford.

MENDEZ, MARGARITA CASTRO, b. San José, Costa Rica, Oct. 19, 1912. SPANISH AMERICAN LITERATURE. B.S., U. of Minn. 1942; M.A., 1946; Ph. D., Columbia U., 1964. Instr., U. of Minn., 1944–46; instr., Syracuse U., 1946–47; instr., Russell Sage Coll., 1947–50; ASSOC. PROF., SPANISH, MARYMOUNT COLL., 1950– ; instr., Western Reserve U., Summers 1950–52, 1960–61. U. of Minn. fellow. Membership: American Association of University Professors; Hispanic Institute in the United States; Modern Language Association. Research: costumbrista literature in Costa Rica. Language: Spanish 5,5,5,5; Portuguese 4,4,2,1; French 4,3,2,1; Italian 4,-,-,-. Linguistic studies: Portuguese; Spanish, Home: 25 Central Park West, New York 23, N.Y. Office: Dept. of Spanish, Marymount Coll., Tarrytown, N.Y.

MENEZ, JOSEPH F., b. Attleboro, Mass., Nov. 6, 1917. POLITICAL SCIENCE. A.B., U. of Notre Dame, 1945; M.A., 1946; Ph. D. 1953. Instr., U. of Detroit, 1946–47; instr., Loyola U. (Ill.), 1947–53; asst. prof., 1953–58; assoc. prof., chmn., Political Science, 1958–63; PROF., POLITICAL SCIENCE, LOYOLA U., 1963– . John F. O'Hara fellow, U. of Notre Dame, 1950; Fulbright lectr. (Peru), 1960–61. Membership: American Academy of Political and Social Science; American Political Science Association; Mid-West Political Science Association. Research: constitutional and political comparison of the executive office in Latin America and the United States; Latin American political theory; Latin American government and politics; Peru. Author: Presidents and Constitutions in the Americas (Mid-America, Jan., Apr. 1954); A Brief in Support of the Supreme Court (Northwestern U., Law Review, Mar.–Apr. 1959); The Vice Presidency of the United States (Queen's Quarterly, Spring 1958). Language: Spanish 4,5,5,4; Portuguese 4,5,4,3; French 3,1,1,1. Home: 7305 South Paxton Ave., Chicago 49, Ill. Office: Dept. of Political Science, Loyola U., 820 North Michigan Ave., Chicago, 11.

MENTON, SEYMOUR, b. New York, N.Y., Mar. 6, 1927. SPANISH AMERICAN AND BRAZILIAN LITERATURES. B.A., City Coll. (N.Y.) 1948; M.A., Universidad Nacional de México, 1949; Ph. D., N.Y.U. 1952. Teacher, New York City Board of Education, 1949–52; instr., Dartmouth Coll., 1952–54; teacher, N.Y.U., Summers 1953, 1957; asst. prof.-PROF., SPANISH AMERICAN LITERATURE, U. OF KANS., 1954– ; prof., Universidad de San Carlos (Guatemala), Summers 1955, 1956, 1958; prof., Universidad de Costa Rica, 1960; prof., National Defense Education Act Summer Institute, U. of Ariz. (Guadalajara, Mexico), 1963. Smith-Mundt grant (Brazil) 1961; contributing editor, Handbook of Latin American Studies, 1962– ; editor, Hispania, 1963– . Membership: American Association of Teachers of Spanish and Portuguese; American Association of University Professors; Instituto Internacional de Literatura Iberoamericano; Modern Language Association. Research: prose fiction in Central America and Mexico; contemporary Spanish American and Brazilian novel; naturalism. Author: Saga de México (1955); Historia de la novela guatemalteca (1960); Antología histórico-crítica del cuento hispanoamericano (1964). Language: Spanish 5,5,5,5; Portuguese 4,4,4,4; French 4,4,3,3. Home: 709 Lawrence Ave., Lawrence, Kans. Office: Dept. of Romance Languages, U. of Kans., Lawrence.

MENZEL, DOROTHY, b. Prague, Czechoslovakia, Nov. 3, 1924. ANTHROPOLOGY. B.A., Swarthmore Coll., 1946; Ph. D., U. of Calif., Berkeley, 1954. Research assoc., U. of Calif., Berkeley, 1954–59; asst. research anthropologist, U. of Calif., Berkeley, 1960–63; LECTR., ANTHROPOLOGY, U. OF CALIF., BERKELEY, 1963– . National Science Foundation fellow, 1955–57, 1958; Fulbright fellow (Peru), 1959–60; Ogden Mills fellow, American Museum of Natural History, 1962–63. Membership: American Anthropological Association; Institute of Andean Studies; Kroeber Anthropological Society; Society for American Archaeology. Research: Peruvian archeology. Author: Problemas en el estudio del Horizonte Medio en la arqueología peruana (Revista del Museo Regional de Ica, June 1958); The Inca Occupation of the South Coast of Peru (Southwestern Journal of Anthropology, Summer 1959); Archaism and Revival on the South Coast of Peru (Selected Papers, 5th International Congress of Anthropological and Ethnological Sciences, Sept. 1960). Language: Spanish 4,4,4,4; Portuguese 1,1,1,1; French 2,2,1,1; Czech 2,3,2,1; German 4,4,3,3. Home: 2206–A McKinley Ave., Berkeley 3, Calif. Office: Dept. of Anthropology, U. of Calif., Berkeley 4.

MERCER, LUCILLE E., b. McConnelsville, Ohio, June 27, 1901. LANGUAGE. B.S., Ohio State U., 1923; diploma, U. of Madrid, 1925; M.A., 1928; Ph. D., 1940. Instr. Ohio State U., 1926–27; PROF. CHMN., SPANISH, BALDWIN-WALLACE COLL., 1927– ; instr., Fla. State U., Summer 1928. Carnegie Foundation fellow (Chile, 1938–39. Membership: American Association of Teachers of Spanish and Portuguese; Delta Kappa Gamma; Modern Language Association: Sigma Delta Pi. Author: First Inter-American Congress of Women (Delta Kappa Gamma Journal, Winter 1947): Women in Latin America (Delta Kappa Gamma Bulletin, Winter 1947); Modern Languages for Today (Journal of Education, 1950). Language: Spanish 5,4,4,4; Portuguese 4,-,-,-; French 5,4,4,4. Home: 155 Westbridge Dr., Berea, Ohio. Office: Dept. of Spanish, Baldwin-Wallace Coll., Berea.

MERRIFIELD, WILLIAM RICHARD, b. Chicago, Ill., Sept. 28, 1932. LINGUISTICS. B.A., Wheaton Coll., 1954; M.A., Cornell U., 1963. LINGUIST, BIBLE TRANSLATOR, SUMMER INSTITUTE OF LINGUIS-

TICS AND WYCLIFFE BIBLE TRANSLATORS, INC., 1955– . Linguistic consultant, Gamio Center (Mexico); National Defense Education Act fellow, Cornell U., 1962–64. Membership: American Anthropological Association; Linguistic Society of America; Sociedad Mexicana de Antropología. Research: culture change and applied anthropology; Mexico; literacy; lexicography. Author: A Laboratory Manual for Morphology-Syntax (1962): Chinantec Kinship in Palantla, Oaxaca, Mexico (American Anthropologist, 1959): Palantla Chinantec Syllable Types (Anthropological Linguistics, 1963). Language: Spanish 3,3,3,3; French 3,–,–,–; Chinantec 3,3,3,3; German 3,–,–,–; Linguistic studies: Chinantec; Kiowa. Home: 820 Saverien Dr., Sacramento 25, Calif. Office: Instituto Lingüistico de Verano, Apartado Postal 2975, México 1, D.F.

MESA, ROSA QUINTERO, b. Havana, Cuba, Oct. 14, 1923. LIBRARY SCIENCE. Degree in Pharmacy, Universidad de la Habana, 1945; degree in library science, 1959. Asst. librarian, Biblioteca Nacional (Havana), 1959–60; librarian, Ruston Academy (Havana), 1960–61; ASST., DOCUMENTS DEPT., LIBRARIES, U. OF FLA., 1961– . Research: Latin American government publications. Language: Spanish 5,5,5,5; Portuguese 2,2,2,2; French 1,1,1,1; Italian 2,2,2,2. Home: 1812 NW. 2nd Ave., Gainesville, Fla. 32601. Office: Documents Dept., Libraries, U. of Fla., Gainesville, 32603.

MESTRE, JOSE A., b. Havana, Cuba, May 2, 1923. ECONOMICS AND LAW. Dr. en leyes, Havana U., 1944. Partner, Bufete-Mestre (Havana), 1944–60; secretary, Legal Dept., Vanidades Continental (N.Y.), 1960-63; secretary, Legal Dept., Bohemia Libre (N.Y.), 1960–62; LATIN AMERICAN EDITOR, BUSINESS INTERNATIONAL (N.Y.) 1961— . Research: economic research in Mexico, Brazil, Colombia, Peru, Ecuador, Uruguay. Author: Mexico: Business Problems and Opportunities (1962); Economic Integration in Latin America (Business International, Jan. 1963). Language: Spanish 5,5,5,5; Portuguese 4,3,2,2; French 3,3,3,2; German 3,3,3,3; Latin 3,2,2,3. Home: 3555 Oxford Ave., New York 63, N.Y. Office: 757 Third Ave., New York 17.

METRAUX, RHODA, b. Brooklyn, N.Y., Oct. 18, 1914. ANTHROPOLOGY. B.A., Vassar Coll., 1934; Ph. D., Columbia U., 1951. ASSOC. DIR., STUDIES IN ALLOPSYCHIC ORIENTATION, AMERICAN MUSEUM OF NATURAL HISTORY, 1961– . Anthropologist, UNESCO Pilot Project in Fundamental Education (Marbial Valley, Haiti), 1948–49; Social Science Research Council grant (Montserrat, British West Indies), 1953–54. Membership: American Anthropological Association; American Association for the Advancement of Science; American Ethnological Association; New York Academy of Sciences; Society for Applied Anthropology. Research: cultural anthropology; culture change in contemporary societies; Haiti. Co-author: The Study of Culture at a Distance (1953); Themes in French Culture (1954). Language: Spanish 2,2,2,1; Portuguese 1,1,1,1; French 3,3,2,1; German 4,4,3,2. Home: 193 Waverly Pl., New York, N.Y. 10014. Office: Studies in Allopsychic Orientation, American Museum of Natural History, 79th St. and Central Park West, New York, 10024.

METZGER, DUANE GERALD, b. Grand Rapids, Mich., Feb. 13, 1930. ANTHROPOLOGY. M.A., U. of Chicago, 1957; Ph. D., 1964. Asst. prof., Stanford U., 1960–63; ASST. PROF., ANTHROPOLOGY, INSTITUTE OF COMMUNICATIONS RESEARCH, U. OF ILL., 1963– . Membership: American Anthropological Association. Research: language and culture; cognition; cultures of Middle America; culture of Chiapas, Mexico. Author: A Formal Ethnographic Analysis of Tenejapa Ladino Weddings (American Anthropologist, Dec. 1963); Tenejapa Medicine: The Cures (Southwestern Journal of Anthropology, Summer 1963). Language: Spanish 3,3,3, 2; Tzeltal 3,2,2,1. Home: 7 Florida Dr., Urbana, Ill. Office: 137 Davenport Hall, U. of Ill., Urbana.

MEYER, BENJAMIN FRANKLIN, b. San Antonio, Tex., Aug. 18, 1903. JOURNALISM. Baylor U. Staff correspondent, San Antonio Express, 1919–21; managing editor, Daily Record (Cuero, Tex.), 1921–23; news editor, News Tribune (Waco), 1923–25; telegraph editor, Record News (Wichita Falls, Tex), 1925–26; general manager, Electra News (Electra, Tex.), 1926–27; correspondent and asst. chief, Associated Press (Atlanta), 1927–38; chief of Bureau (Mexico, D.F.), 1938–41; executive representative for Caribbean (Havana), 1941–43; chief of bureau and special correspondent (Santiago, Chile), 1943–45; sales representative (Charlotte, N.C.), 1945–46; manager, Sales, Midwest Div. (Chicago), 1946–48; Caribbean chief (Havana), 1948–54; CORRESPONDENT-EDITOR, LATIN AMERICAN AFFAIRS, ASSOCIATED PRESS (WASHINGTON, D.C.), 1954– . Research: Latin American news and public affairs. Language: Spanish 5,5,5,4. Home: 2632 South Grant St., Arlington, Va. 22202. Office: The Associated Press, 1300 Connecticut Ave., NW., Washington, D.C. 20036.

MEYER, MARY EDGAR, SISTER, O.S.F., b. Concord Hill, Mo., Apr. 10, 1900. LANGUAGE. B.A., Ind. U., 1929; M.A., St. Louis U., 1933; Ph. D., U. of Mich., 1948. PROF., CHMN., ROMANCE LANGUAGES, MARIAN COLL., 1943– . Lilly Endowment grant, Purdue U., Summer 1959; Ind. U. fellow, Russian Workshop, Summer 1960. Membership: American Association of Teachers of Spanish and Portuguese; International Mark Twain Society; Midwest Council of the Association of Latin American Studies; Modern Language Association. Research: contemporary Latin American literature; English as a foreign language. Author: The Sources of Hojeda's La Cristiada (1953); Walt Whitman's Influence on Latin American Poets (The Americas, July 1952). Translator: Quelques Vertus Rares, by Raoul Plus (1950). Language: Spanish 5,5,5,5; Portuguese 3,3,3,3; French 4, 4,4,4; German 5,5,5,5; Italian 3,3,3,3; Russian 2,2,2,2. Home and office: Dept. of Romance Languages, Marian Coll., Indianapolis, Ind. 46222.

MEYER, MICHAEL CARL, b. Albuquerque, N. Mex., Sept. 6, 1935. HISTORY. B.A., U. of N. Mex., 1957; U. of Wis., 1957–58; Mexico City Coll., 1958–59; M.A., U. of N. Mex., 1961; Ph. D., 1963. Vis. asst. prof., U. of

N. Mex., Summer, 1963; ASST. PROF., HISTORY, U. OF NEBR., 1963– . National Defense Education Act fellow, 1962–63; U. of Nebr. faculty research grant, 1964; consultant, U.S. Peace Corps Training Programs, U. of N. Mex., U. of Nebr. and Los Angeles City Coll.; Latin American Studies Committee, U. of Nebr. Membership: American Historical Association; Mississippi Valley Historical Association. Research: modern Mexico; General Pascual Orozco, Jr., in the Mexican Revolution. Author: Albert Bacon Fall's Mexican Papers (New Mexico Historical Review, Jan. 1965). Language: Spanish 5,5,4,4; Portuguese 4,4,3,2; French 3,2,1,1. Home: 643 Eastridge Dr., Lincoln, Nebr. Office: Dept. of History, U. of Nebr., Lincoln.

MEYER, MORTON ALLAN, b. Brooklyn, N.Y., Dec. 18, 1917. STATISTICS. Statistics and census adviser to Uruguay, International Cooperation Administration, 1955–58; chief, Computer Programming Branch, U.S. Bureau of the Census (Washington, D.C.), 1958–60; asst. to chief, Demographic Operations Div., 1960; asst. chief, 1961; CHIEF, DEMOGRAPHIC OPERATIONS DIV., U.S. BUREAU OF THE CENSUS, 1961– . Statistical adviser to Argentina, Organization of American States, Nov. 1962; statistical adviser to Peru, U.S. Agency for International Development, Nov. 1964. Membership: Academy of Political Science; American Association for the Advancement of Science; American Statistical Association; Foreign Service Association; Society for International Development. Research: collection and processing of statistical data from censuses and sample surveys; development of technical specifications and systems analysis. Language: Spanish 4,4,4,3; French 1,2,1,1. Home: 2303 Fairlawn St., SE, Washington, D.C. 20031. Office: Demographic Operations Div., Bureau of the Census, Washington, D.C. 20233.

MICHEL, JOSEPH, b. Autlan, Mexico, Mar. 19, 1922. LANGUAGE. B.A., De La Salle U., 1944; M.A., Universidad Nacional de México, 1952; Ph. D., U. of N. Mex., 1961. Chmn., Foreign Language, St. Michael's Coll., 1952–59; dir., Foreign Language Teaching, N. Mex. State Dept. of Education, 1959–61; INSTR., ROMANCE LANGUAGES, DIR., LANGUAGE RESEARCH AND DEVELOPMENT CENTER, U. OF TEX., 1961– . Consultant, Modern Language Association; consultant, Education Association; editor, News Bulletin, State Dept. of Education (N. Mex.), 1959–61. Membership: American Association of Teachers of Spanish and Portuguese; American Association of University Professors; Modern Language Association. Research: foreign language teaching; linguistics; Mexican literature; English as a foreign language. Author: Un siglo de cuento corto en la literatura mexicana (1952); Yuxtaposición de La Gloria de don Ramiro y Tirano Banderas (1961). Language: Spanish 5,5,5,5; Portuguese 3,3,–,–; French 4,4,4,3; German 1, –,–,–. Linguistic studies: English; Spanish. Home: 5404 Ridge Oak, Austin, Tex., 78731. Office: Sutton Hall 408, U. of Tex., Austin, 78712.

MILCZEWSKI, MARION ANTHONY, b. Saginaw, Mich., Feb. 12, 1912. LIBRARY SCIENCE. A.B., U. of Mich., 1936; B.S.L.S., U. of Ill., 1938; M.S., 1940, Asst. to executive secretary, American Library Association (Chicago), 1940–42; asst. dir.-dir., International Relations Office, American Library Association (Washington, D.C.), 1942–47; survey dir., Tennessee Valley Library Council, 1947–49; asst. librarian, U. of Calif., Berkeley, 1949–60, DIR., LIBRARIES, U. OF WASH., 1960– . Katherine Sharpe fellow, U. of Ill., 1939; adviser in establishment of Biblioteca Benjamin Franklin (Mexico), 1941; Fulbright research grant (England), 1954–55; Rockefeller Foundation consultant, Universidad del Valle (Colombia), 1962; Ford Foundation consultant, Universidad de Oriente (Venezuela), 1963; International Relations Committee, American Library Association. Membership: American Association of University Professors; American Library Association; Pacific Northwest Library Association. Research: university libraries. Author: Libraries of the Southeast (1949); A Report of a Survey of the Libraries of the Universidad del Valle (1962); A Survey of the Libraries of the Universidad de Oriente (1963). Language: Spanish 4,4,4,3; Portuguese 2,2,1,1; French 3,2,1,1. Home: 3621 NE. 100, Seattle 55, Wash. Office: Library, U. of Wash., Seattle 98105.

MILES, JAMES FRANKLIN, b. Richland County, S.C., June 10, 1913. ECONOMICS. A.B., U. of S.C., 1938; M.A., 1939; Ph. D., Cornell U., 1951. Head, Reports and Accounts, State Dept. of Education (Columbia, S.C.), 1941–42; head, Reports Section, U.S. Dept. of Agriculture (Atlanta, Ga.), 1942–44; assoc. extension economist, U.S. Dept. of Agriculture, 1944–47; ASSOC. PROF., ECONOMICS, CLEMSON U., 1947– . Consultant, Point Four Program (El Salvador), 1961; researcher, U.S. Dept. of Agriculture (Costa Rica, 1963; Panama, 1963). Membership: American Farm Economics Association; Southern Agricultural Workers Association; Southern Economic Association. Research: agricultural economics; dairy and poultry marketing research; economic development; foreign trade; Central America. Author: El Salvador, Cotton Newcomer Competes for Markets (1961); Marketing Bananas, Tomatoes and Eggs in San Salvador (1961); Food Balance and Prospects for Agricultural Trade in Panama and Costa Rica (1963). Language: Spanish 2,2,2,2; French 2,2,2,2. Home: P.O. Box 1041, Clemson, S.C. 29631. Office: Dept. of Agricultural Economics and Rural Sociology, Clemson U., Clemson.

MILES, PAUL M., b. Denver, Colo., Mar. 14, 1917. LIBRARY SCIENCE. B.A., U. of Denver, 1940; M.A., U. of Calif., Berkeley, 1947; Mexico City Coll., 1948–49; B.S., 1950. Reference librarian, Library, U. of Calif., Los Angeles, 1950–51; geology librarian, 1951–52; international documents librarian, 1952–54; industrial relations librarian, 1951–59; ASST. UNIVERSITY LIBRARIAN, LIBRARY, U. OF CALIF., LOS ANGELES, 1959– . Library planning consultant, National U. of Colombia, 1962; library building consultant, Ariz. State U., 1962, U. of Calif., Davis, 1963, U. of Calif., Irving, 1963. Membership: American Library Association; California Library Association. Research: Hispanic American history and economics; university library administration, organization, and buildings in Latin America. Author: Los problemas actuales de las bibliotecas de la Universidad Nacional de Colombia (1962); Survey and Report on the Matthews Library, Arizona State University (1962). Editor: Industrial Relations Thesis and Dissertations (1955–58). Language: Spanish 5,5,5,5; Portuguese 3,3,2,2; French 4,2,1,2; German 3,2,1,–. Office: Asst. University Librarian, Library, U. of Calif., Los Angeles 24.

MILES, SUZANNE WHITELAW, b. Mt. Carroll, Ill., June 7, 1922. ANTHROPOLOGY. A.M., U. of Chicago, 1948; Ph. D., Harvard U., 1954. Curator, Wis. Museum of History, 1945–47; instr., U. of Wis., 1947–50; asst. prof., Brandeis U., 1958–61; RESEARCH FELLOW, BOLLINGEN FOUNDATION (GUATEMALA), 1961– ; catedrática, Universidad de San Carlos, 1963. Doherty fellow, 1954–55; Bollingen Foundation fellow, 1956–58. Membership: American Anthropological Association; Royal Anthropological Society of Great Britain; Society for American Archaeology. Research: archeology, ethnography, ethnology, and history of Middle America. Author: The 16th Century Pokom-Maya (Transactions, American Philosophical Society, Nov. 1957); Sculpture of Guatemala—Chiapas (in Handbook of Middle American Indians); 16th Century Ethnography of Guatemala (in Handbook of Middle American Indians). Language: Spanish 5,5,4,4; Portuguese 4,4,3,3; French 4,4,2,3; German 4,4,2,1; Maya 4,4,3,3. Home: 3a Avenida 14–64, Zona 1, Guatemala, Guatemala. Office: Bollingen Foundation, 140 East 62nd St., New York 21, N.Y.

MILLER, DAVID LYNN, b. Royal Oak, Mich., Nov. 1, 1922. HISTORY AND EDUCATION. B.A., Wesleyan U., 1947; M.A., Mexico City Coll., 1948; Ph. D., U. of Mich., 1960. Vis. prof., Mexico City Coll., Summer 1951; asst. manager, Migration Center (Mexico), Farm Placement Service, U.S. Dept. of Labor, 1951–53; instr., Mexico City Coll., 1952; supervisor of employee communication, Chrysler Corporation, 1953–57; COORDINATOR OF EXTENSION, EDUCATIONAL SERVICE, LOS ANGELES STATE COLL., 1958– . Boston Globe Memorial fellow (Mexico), 1947–48; Orla B. Taylor fellow, U. of Mich., 1949–50; teaching fellow, U. of Mich., 1951. Membership: American Association of University Professors; American Society of Training Directors; Personnel Managers Committee, Los Angeles Chamber of Commerce. Research: Mexico; administration of educational programs. Language: S p a n i s h 4,3,3,3; French 2,2,2,2. Home: 2504 Baltusrol Dr., Alhambra, Calif. 91803. Office: Los Angeles State Coll., 5151 College Dr., Los Angeles, Calif. 90032.

MILLER, E. WILLARD, b. Turkey City, Pa., May 17, 1915. GEOGRAPHY. B.S., Clarion State Coll., 1937; M.S., U. of Nebr., 1939; Ph. D., Ohio State U., 1942. Instr., Ohio State U., 1941–42; asst. prof., Western Reserve U., 1943–44; geographer, U.S. Office of Strategic Services, 1944–45; assoc. prof., Pa. State U., 1945–49; head, Geography, 1945–63; PROF. GEOGRAPHY, PA. STATE U., 1949– ; ASST. DEAN OF RESIDENT INSTRUCTION, COLL. OF MINERAL INDUSTRIES, 1964– . U.S. representative, Committee on Basic Natural Resources, Pan American Institute of Geography and History; book review editor Producers Monthly Magazine, 1947– ; geographic editor, Thomas Y. Crowell Company; adviser, Unicorn Press, Funk and Wagnalls. Membership: American Association for the Advancement of Science; American Geographical Society; American Geophysical Union; Association of American Geographers; International Institute of Arts and Letters; National Council for Geographic Education; Pi Gamma Mu; Sigma Xi. Research: mineral geography; resource development in Mexico, Central America, and Venezuela. Author: Exploring Earth Environments: A World Geography (1964); Petroleum in the Economy of Venezuela (Economic Geography, Apr. 1940). Maps: Geography of Latin America, by Fred Carlson (1943). Language: Spanish 2,–,–,–; French 4,3,3,3. Home: 200 East Irwin Ave., State College, Pa. Office: Dept. of Geography, Pa. State U., University Park, Pa.

MILLER, FRANK C., b. Quincy, Ill., Feb. 11, 1932. ANTHROPOLOGY. B.A., Carleton Coll., 1954; Ph. D., Harvard U., 1960. Instr.-asst. prof., Carleton Coll., 1958–63; ASSOC. PROF., ANTHROPOLOGY, U. OF MINN., 1964– . Ford Foundation fellow and Woodrow Wilson fellow, 1954–55; National Science Foundation fellow, 1956–57, Cambridge U., 1963–64; Doherty fellow (Mexico), 1957–58; consultant in anthropology, Mental Health Project for Indian Boarding Schools (Flandreau, S. Dak.), 1963–65. Membership: American Anthropological Association; American Association of University Professors; Central States Anthropological Society; Seminario de Estudios Mayas (Mexico). Research: culture change; inter-cultural health programs: Indian and mestizo cultures and land reform in Mexico. Author: The Influence of Decision-making on the Process of Change: The Case of Yalcuc (Alpha Kappa Deltan, Winter 1960). Language: Spanish 3,3,3,2; Portuguese 1,1,1,1; French 1,1,1,1. Home: 1710 Logan Ave., South, Minneapolis, Minn. Office: Dept. of Anthropology, U. of Minn., Minneapolis, 55455.

MILLER, GUSTAVUS HINDMAN, b. Chattanooga, Tenn., Nov. 3, 1917. BRAZILIAN LITERATURE AND LANGUAGE. A.B., U. of Mich., 1940; M.A., 1948; Ph. D., 1956. Chmn., Dept. of Air Force Administration, Escola Técnica de Aviação (São Paulo, Brazil), 1946–48; instr., U. of Tex., 1948–49; instr., U. of Mich., 1953–55; ASST. PROF., SPANISH AND PORTUGUESE, DUKE U., 1955– . Membership: American Association of Teachers of Spanish and Portuguese; Modern Language Association. Research: Spanish and Portuguese language teaching programs. Language: Spanish 4,4,4,4; Portuguese 4,4,4,4; French 3,2,2,2. Linguistic studies: Portuguese; Spanish. Home: Bartram Dr., Chapel Hill, N.C. Office: Dept. of Romance Languages, Duke U., Durham, N.C.

MILLER, HUBERT JOHN, b. Hays, Kans., Dec. 9, 1927. HISTORY. B.A., U. of Dayton, 1951; M.A., St. Louis U., 1954; Ph. D., Loyola U. (Ill.), 1964. Teacher, Academy of the Sacred Heart (Mo.), 1951–53; St. John's High School (St. Louis, Mo.), 1953–54; Escuela Americana (El Salvador), 1955–56; dir., Instituto de Inglés (El Salvador), 1956; ASST. PROF., HISTORY, ST.

MARY'S U. OF TEX., 1960– . Fellowship lectr., Loyola U. (Ill.), 1956–59; Smith-Mundt grant (Guatemala), 1959–60. Membership: American Historical Association; Hispanic American Historical Association; Pi Gamma Mu. Research: church and state question in Guatemala during the national period. Language: Spanish 5,3,3,3; German 3,4,4,3. Home: 5803 Angie Pl., San Antonio, Tex., 78240. Office: Dept. of History, St. Mary's U., San Antonio, 78228.

MILLER, PATRICK HENRY, b. Vicksburg, Miss., Feb. 16, 1929. LAW. B.B.A., U. of Miami, 1953; LL. B., 1954; Universidad Javeriana (Bogotá, Colombia), 1959. Special agent, Federal Bureau of Investigation, 1954–58; attorney, International Petroleum Company, 1958–63, (Bogotá), 1959–60; CORPORATE SECRETARY, ATTORNEY, INTERNATIONAL PETROLEUM COMPANY, 1963– . Membership: Florida Bar Association. Research: Latin American legal, economic, and political problems. Language: Spanish 4,4,4,4. Home: 5340 SW. 59th Ave., Miami, Fla. Office: International Petroleum Company, Ltd., 396 Alhambra Circle, Coral Gables, Fla.

MILLER, ROBERT RYAL, b. Lake Andes, S. Dak., Oct. 3, 1923. HISTORY. B.A., U. of Calif., Berkeley, 1948; M.A., 1951; Ph. D., 1960. Asst. prof., U. of Southwestern La., 1959–60; ASST. PROF., HISTORY, N. MEX. STATE U., 1960– . Coordinator, U.S. Peace Corps Training Program, 1962– . Membership: American Historical Association; Conference on Latin American History; Mississippi Valley Historical Association; Sigma Xi; Western History Conference. Research: Mexico and Spain, especially the 19th century. Author: The American Legion of Honor in Mexico (Pacific Historical Review, Aug. 1961); Plácido Vega: A Mexican Secret Agent in the United States (The Americas, Oct. 1962); Lew Wallace and the French Intervention in Mexico (Indiana Magazine of History, Mar. 1963). Language: Spanish 4,4,4,4; Portuguese 2,2,1,1; French 2,1,1,1. Home: Box 945, University Park, N. Mex. Office: Dept. of History, N. Mex. State U., University Park, 88070.

MILLER, WALTER SCOTT, b. Altoona, Pa., Oct. 29, 1910. LINGUISTICS. FIELD INVESTIGATOR, CHARTER MEMBER, SUMMER INSTITUTE OF LINGUISTICS, 1936– ; BIBLE TRANSLATOR, CHARTER MEMBER, WYCLIFFE BIBLE TRANSLATORS, INC., 1942– . Research: Mixe region of Oaxaca, Mexico; Bible translation; folklore. Author: Cuentos mixes (1956). Language: Spanish 4,5,4,5. Linguistic studies: Mixe. Home: Hidalgo 8, Mitla, Oaxaca, México. Office: Instituto Lingüístico de Verano, A.C., Héroes 53, México 3, D.F.

MILLS, DOROTHY HURST, b. Huntington Beach, Calif., Jan. 8, 1928. LANGUAGE. B.A., U. of Southern Calif., 1949; M.A., 1950; Ph. D., 1955. Teacher, Torrance High School (Calif.), 1953–54; teacher, Paramount High School (Calif.), 1955; teacher, Lynwood High School (Calif.), 1955–56; asst. prof., Long Beach State Coll., 1956–61. Del Amo Foundation scholar, U. of Madrid, 1950; Smith-Mundt grant, Universidad Veracruzana (Mexico), 1961–62. Membership: Phi Beta Kappa; Phi Kappa Phi; Pi Lambda Theta; Sigma Delta Pi. Research: teacher training programs for English and Spanish; analysis of the morphology of the diminutives ito, illo, ico, uelo and of their increments as used in Spanish America. Author: Spanish Case (Hispania, Feb. 1951). Lanuage: Spanish 5,5,4,4,; French 2,1,1,1. Linguistic studies: English, Spanish. Home: 610 Park Lane, Santa Ana, Calif.

MINER, WILLIAM D., b. Table Grove, Ill., June 26, 1914. HISTORY. A.B., Knox Coll., 1936; M.A., Ind. U., 1948; Ph. D., 1950. Lectr., Southern Ill. U. High School, 1950; PROF., HISTORY, ASST. DEAN OF STUDENTS, EASTERN ILL. U., 1950– . Membership: Conference on Latin American History; Mississippi Valley Historical Association; National Education Association. Research: Spanish borderlands; American West. Language: Spanish 2,-,-,-. Home: Lincoln Highway Rd., Charleston, Ill. 61920. Office: Dept. of History, Eastern Ill. U., Charleston.

MINGER, RALPH ELDIN, b. Gregory, S. Dak., Oct. 19, 1925. HISTORY. B.A., U. of Southern Calif., 1949; Ph. D., 1958. Instr., Immaculate Heart Coll., 1957–59; lectr.-ASSOC. PROF., U.S. DIPLOMATIC HISTORY, SAN FERNANDO VALLEY STATE COLL., 1958– ; lectr., U. of Md., Summers 1962–63; vis. asst. prof., 1962–63. Editorial Board, Southern California Quarterly. Membership: American Association of University Professors; American Historical Association; American Studies Association; Mississippi Valley Historical Association; Phi Alpha Theta; Pi Sigma Alpha; Los Angeles World Affairs Council. Research: United States diplomatic relations in the Caribbean, Central America and Mexico. Author: William H. Taft and the United States Intervention in Cuba in 1906 (Hispanic American Historical Review, Feb. 1961); Panama, the Canal Zone, and Titular Sovereignty (Western Political Quarterly, June 1961). Language: Spanish 3,3,3,3; Portuguese 1,1,1,1; French 1,1,1,1. Home: 1328 Highland Ave., Glendale 2, Calif. Office: Dept. of History, San Fernando Valley State Coll., 18111 Nordhoff St., Northridge, Calif.

MINKEL, CLARENCE W., b. Austin, Minn., Feb. 9, 1928. GEOGRAPHY. B.A., Colo. State Coll., 1953; M.A., 1955; Ph. D., Syracuse U., 1960. Instr., Colo. State Coll., Summer 1955; asst. prof., N.Y.U., Summer 1960; ASST. PROF., GEOGRAPHY, COLO. STATE COLL, 1960– ; national and regional planning adviser, U.S. Agency for International Development (Guatemala), 1963–65. Watson fellow, 1956–60; U.S. Steel fellow, 1958–60. Membership: American Name Society; Association of American Geographers; Colorado Council for the Social Studies; Colorado Education Association; Rocky Mountain Council on Latin America; Rocky Mountain Social Science Association. Research: physical resources planning in Guatemala; industrial development in Venezuela. Language: Spanish 3,3,3,3; Portuguese 2,1,1,1; French 2,1,1,1. Office: Dept. of Geography, Colo. State Coll., Greeley.

MINNICH, R. HERBERT, JR., b. Lititz, Pa., July 1, 1931. SOCIOLOGY. M.S., Cornell U., 1956; U. of Fla. High school teacher, Eastern Mennonite Coll., 1953–56; foreign missionary, Mennonite Board of Missions and Charities (Brazil), 1958–62; ASST. DIR., LATIN AMERICAN LANGUAGE AND AREA PROGRAM, U. OF FLA., 1963– . Henry Strong Dennison fellow, Cornell U.; U. of Fla. fellow; Foreign Area Fellowship Program grant (Brazil), 1965. Membership: Alpha Kappa Delta; American Sociological Association; Rural Sociological Society. Research: rural sociology; social change; Brazil. Author: A Manual of Social Science Material for Missionaries (1958). Co-author: Latin-American Content Courses at Selected American Universities (1964). Language: Spanish 4,3,3,3; Portuguese 5,5,5,4; German 3,2,2,2. Home: 157 Hess Blvd., Lancaster, Pa. Office: Latin American Language and Area Program, U. of Fla., Gainesville, 32603.

MINOR, DOROTHY ANNA HENDRICH, b. Dorrance, Kans., July 4, 1925. LINGUISTICS. A.B., Wheaton Coll., 1949. LINGUIST, SUMMER INSTITUTE OF LINGUISTICS (PUCALLPA, PERU). 1951– . Research: culture and customs of Witoto people of Peru; compilation of primers in Witoto language. Author: Huitoto Rabenico Books 1–6 (1958, 1961, 1964); Huitoto Cuellena Books 1–3 (1959, 1960). Language: Spanish 2,2,2,2; Witoto 3,3,3,2. Linguistic studies: Witoto. Home: c/o Leo J. Hendrich, 928 St. James Pl., Wichita, Kans., 67206. Office: Instituto Lingüístico de Verano, Casilla 2492 Lima, Perú.

MINOR, EUGENE EDWARD, b. Tempe, Ariz., Jan. 23, 1922. LINGUISTICS. B.A., Wheaton Coll., 1949. LINGUIST, TRANSLATOR, SUMMER INSTITUTE OF LINGUISTICS (PERU), 1951– . Research: descriptive linguistics in aboriginal languages; culture, customs and folkways of Witotos in Peru. Author: Jesucristo Neupued—Marco Cuegapue, The Gospel According to St. Mark (1961); Witoto Vowel Clusters (International Journal of American Linguistics, 1956); The Structure and Contexts of Witoto Predicates in Narrative Speech (in Studies in Peruvian Indian Languages, 1963). Language: Spanish 3,3,3,2; Muináni Witoto 3,4,4,3. Linguistic studies: Muináni Witoto. Home: c/o Leo J. Hendrich, 928 St. James Pl., Wichita, Kans., 67206. Office: Instituto Lingüístico de Verano, Casilla 2492, Lima, Perú.

MINTZ, SIDNEY WILFRED, b. Dover, N.J., Nov. 16, 1922. ANTHROPOLOGY. B.A., Brooklyn Coll., 1943; Ph. D., Columbia U., 1951. PROF., ANTHROPOLOGY, YALE U., 1951– . Guggenheim fellow, 1957; consultant, Overseas Development, Ford Foundation, 1957–63; Social Science Research Council faculty research fellow (Haiti), 1958–59; consultant, Cultural Affairs, Pan American Union, 1958–63; consultant, Institute of Caribbean Affairs, U. of P.R., 1960–63; lectr., Foreign Service Institute, U.S. Dept. of State, 1961–63; consultant, Latin American Section, Foreign Area Fellowship Program, 1961–63. Membership: American Anthropological Association; American Ethnological Society; Royal Anthropological Institute of Great Britain and Ireland. Research: organization of departments of anthropolgy at foreign universities; Latin American peasantries; Caribbean area; educational institutions in Mexico; Puerto Rico; Haiti; Jamaica. Author: Worker in the Cane (1960); Cañamelar; The Contemporary Culture of a Rural Puerto Rican Proletariat (in The People of Puerto Rico, 1956). Language: Spanish 4,4,4,3; Portuguese 2,3,1,1; French 3,3,2,2; Dutch 2,1,1,1; German 3,3,2,2; Haitian Creole 4,4,4,3. Home: 104 York Sq., New Haven, Conn. Office: Dept. of Anthropology, Yale U., 51 Hillhouse Ave., New Haven.

MITCHELL, C. CLYDE, JR., b. Nashville, Tenn., Nov. 12, 1915. ECONOMICS. B.A., U. of Tex., 1937; M.A., 1940; M.P.A., Harvard U., 1942; Ph. D., 1949. Prof., chmn., Agricultural Economics, U. of Nebr., 1949–56; adviser, United Nations Food and Agriculture Organization and Ministry of Economy (Mexico), 1956–57; member, Harvard U.-Pakistan Planning Team, 1957–59; chief, United Nations Food and Agriculture Organization Mission in Colombia, 1959–63; CHIEF, COMITÉ INTERAMERICANO DE DESARROLLO AGRÍCOLA PLANNING MISSION (BRAZIL), 1963– . U. of Tex. graduate fellow, 1937–38; Littauer fellow, Harvard U., 1941–42, 1948–49; Fulbright prof., U. of Rome (Italy), 1956; vis. prof., Universidad del Valle (Colombia), 1961. Membership: American Economic Association; American Farm Economic Association. Research: economic development; food and agricultural development of Mexico, Colombia, Brazil. Author: Land Reform in Asia—a Case Study (1952). Language: Spanish 4,4,4,3 Portuguese 3,3, 3,3; French 3,2,2,2; German 2,2,2,2; Italian 2,2,2,2. Home and office: Food and Agriculture Organization of the United Nations, Rua Jardim Botánico 1008, Rio de Janeiro, Brazil.

MITCHELL, ELEANOR, b. Orange, N.J., Apr. 4, 1907. LIBRARY SCIENCE. B.A., Douglass Coll., 1928; B.S., Columbia U., 1929; M.A., Smith Coll., 1936. Asst. curator of books and photographs, Art Dept., Smith Coll., 1929–36; asst. to dir., The Graduate House in Florence (Italy), 1936–37; librarian, Fine Arts Dept., U. of Pittsburgh, 1937–42; asst. to dir., Biblioteca Pública del Estado de Jalisco (Mexico), 1942–43; chief, Art Div., New York Public Library, 1943–51; art and museum specialist, UNESCO (Paris), 1948–49; dir. of library service, U.S. Information Agency (Rome), 1951–54; librarian specialist, Biblioteca Pública Departamental (Cali, Colombia) and Escuela Interamericana de Bibliotecología (Medellín), U.S. Dept. of State, 1955–57; executive dir., Fine Arts Committee, People-to-People Program, 1957–61; secretary pro tem, Books for the People Fund, Pan American Union, 1961–62; bibliographic asst., Margaret S. Bryant-Rockefeller Foundation Bibliography Project; International Rice Research Institute, 1962–63; LIBRARY CONSULTANT, UNIVERSIDAD CATOLICA, SAINT LOUIS U.-U.S. AGENCY FOR INTERNATIONAL DEVELOPMENT CONTRACT (ECUADOR), 1963– . Carnegie scholar, U. of Paris, Summer 1932; American Council of Learned Societies grant, U. of Wyo., Summer 1941; consultant, Library of Congress, 1954–55; International Executive Council, Escuela Interamericana de Bibliotecología, 1956– : Board of Directors, Books for the People Fund, Inc., 1961– ; consultant, Hispanic Foundation, Library of Congress, 1963. Membership: American Association of Museums; American Federation of Arts;

American Library Association; Asociación Ecuatoriana de Bibliotecarios; Association of College and Reference Libraries; College Art Association; Society of Woman Geographers; Special Libraries Association. Research: library administration, organization and education; fine arts and book programs; international cultural relations. Author: La fille de Jephté par Degas: genèse et evolution (Gazette des Beaux-Arts, Oct. 1937); Books for the People Fund (D.C. Libraries, Apr. 1962); Contemporary Colombia: Its Bibliographic Present and Future (12th Annual Conference on the Caribbean, 1962). Language: Spanish 4,4,4,4; Portuguese 3,3,–,–; French 4,4,4,3; German 3,2,2,2; Italian 4,4,4,3; Russian 3,2,2,2. Home: William H. Mitchell, Box 68 B, R.F.D. 6, Alexandria, Va. Office: U.S. Agency for International Development, American Embassy, Quito, Ecuador.

MOLONEY, RAYMOND L., b. San Luis, Colo., July 13, 1920. LANGUAGE. B.A., U. of Colo., 1948; M.A., 1949; Ph. D., 1954. Instr., U. of Colo., 1948–54; instr., Miami U., 1954–55; asst. prof., U. of Wis., 1955–59; assoc. prof., Portland State Coll., 1959–60; PROF., CHMN., SPANISH AND PORTUGUESE, MIAMI U., 1960– . Chmn., Guidelines Committee, Dept. of Education, State of Ohio. Membership: American Association of Teachers of Spanish and Portuguese; Colorado Congress of Foreign Language Teachers; Modern Language Association. Research: Portuguese African literature. Language: Spanish 5,5,5,5; Portuguese 5,5,5,4; French 4,4,3,3. Home: 407 Sandra Dr., Oxford, Ohio, 45056. Office: Dept. of Spanish and Portuguese, Miami U., Oxford, 45056.

MOMSEN, RICHARD P., JR., b. New York, N.Y., June 14, 1923. GEOGRAPHY. A.B., Dartmouth Coll., 1950; M.A., U. of Minn., 1952; Ph. D., 1960. Asst. to president, Ted Coleman Do Brasil (São Paulo), 1945–46; Brazilian representative and mining company manager, Lindsay Light and Chemical Company (Rio Vitória, Brazil), 1948–49; field manager, D. J. Belcher and Associates (Anápolis, Brazil), 1954–55; translator, International Geographical Congress (Rio de Janeiro), 1955–56; asst. prof., Rollins Coll., 1960–63; ASSOC. PROF. GEOGRAPHY, COORDINATOR OF INTERNATIONAL STUDIES PROGRAM, BALL STATE TEACHERS COLL., 1963– ; field manager, Organization of American States (Ecuador), Summer 1963. Leader, Experiment in International Living (Brazil), 1951; geographer, Whiton Peruvian Expedition, 1961; Fulbright lectr., Coimbra U. (Portugal), 1962. Membership: American Geographical Society; Associação dos Geógrafos Brasileiros; Association of American Geographers. Research: physical geography; use of natural resources; Amazon River region of Peru; Guayas Basin, Ecuador; Brazil. Author: Argentina (1960); Routes over the Serra Do Mar (1964). Language: Spanish 4,4,4,2; Portuguese 5,5,5,3; French 4,4,3,2; German 3,3,3,2; Norwegian 3,2,2,1; Russian 1,2,2,1. Home: 318 Shellbark Rd., Muncie, Ind. Office: Dept. of Science, Ball State Teachers Coll., Muncie.

MONGUIÓ, LUIS, b. Tarragona, Spain, June 25, 1908. SPANISH AMERICAN LITERATURE. Licenciado en Derecho, U. of Madrid, 1928. Vice consul, Ministerio de Estado de España (Valparaíso, Chile), 1931–33; instr.-prof., Mills Coll., 1942–57; PROF., SPANISH, U. OF CALIF., BERKELEY, 1957– . Guggenheim fellow (Peru), 1951; American Council of Learned Societies-Social Science Research Council grant (Peru), 1960. Membership: American Association of Teachers of Spanish and Portuguese; American Association of University Professors; American Society for Aesthetics; Foreign Language Association of Northern California; International Association of Hispanists; Instituto Internacional de Literatura Iberoamericana; Modern Humanities Research Association; Modern Language Association; Philological Association of the Pacific Coast. Research: Peruvian literature. Author: César Vallejo, vida y obra (1952); La poesía postmodernista peruana (1954); Sobre un escritor elogiado por Cervantes (1960). Language: Spanish 5,5,5,5; Portuguese 3,3,3,3; French 4,4,4,4; Italian 4,4,4,4. Linguistic studies: French; Italian; Spanish. Home: 1180 Keeler Ave., Berkeley 8, Calif. Office: Dept. of Spanish and Portuguese, U. of Calif., Berkeley, 94720.

MONSEN, RAYMOND JOSEPH, JR., b. Payson, Utah, Mar. 13, 1931. ECONOMICS. B.S., U. of Utah, 1953; M.A., Stanford U., 1954; Ph. D., U. of Calif., Berkeley, 1960. Asst. prof., Brigham Young U., 1960–63; ASSOC. PROF., ECONOMICS, U. OF WASH., 1963– . Consultant, U.S. Government and U.S. Navy. Membership: American Economic Association; Association for Comparative Economics; Western Economic Association. Research: business administration; Latin American economic conditions; ideologies of modern American capitalism. Author: Modern American Capitalism (1963); Business Prospects for Venezuela (Business Horizon, Winter 1963–64). Language: Spanish 2,–,–,–; Portuguese 3,–,–,–. Home: 2000 East Galer St., Seattle, Wash. Office: Coll. of Business Administration, U. of Wash., Seattle.

MONTAVON, PAUL A., b. Lima, Peru, July 22, 1920. ECONOMICS. M.A., Catholic U., 1947; Ph. D., 1949. Asst. prof., Quincy Coll. (Ill.), 1949–52; ASST. PROF., ECONOMICS, U. OF NOTRE DAME, 1952– . Smith-Mundt fellow (Venezuela), 1960–61; dir., U.S. Peace Corps Training Program, Summer 1963. Membership: American Association of University Professors; American Economic Association; Midwest Economic Association. Research: price theory; public finance; statistical methods; Venezuela. Author: Consumer Debt and Inflation (Review of Social Economy, Mar. 1957); Inflation Control and Political Considerations (Review of Politics, Jan. 1959). Co-author: Economic Aspects of Social Life (1955). Language: Spanish 5,4,4,3; Portuguese 2,2,1,1; French 4,2,2,2. Home: 1795 Ponader Dr., South Bend 15, Ind. Office Dept. of Economics, U. of Notre Dame Notre Dame, Ind.

MONTGOMERY, JAMES HOUSTON, b. Greensboro, N.C., Oct. 22, 1930. LIBRARY SCIENCE. B.A., Guilford Coll., 1953; M.A. U. of N.C., 1957; U. of Calif., Los Angeles 1957–59; M.A.L.S., George Peabody Coll. 1963. Teacher, Boydton High School (Va.) 1953–54; teacher, Escuela Eugenio María de Hostos (Mayagüez, P.R.), 1954–55; asst. prof., Carson-Newman Coll., 1959–60; asst. prof., Bloomsburg State Coll., 1960–61; BIBLIOGRAPHER AND CATALOG LIBRARIAN, JOINT UNIVERSITY LIBRARIES (NASHVILLE, TENN.), 1963– . Participant, 8th and 9th Seminars on the Acquisition of Latin American Library Materials. Membership: American Library Association. Research: acquisitions and cataloging; Spanish and Spanish-American literature. Author: Latin Americana in the Joint University Libraries (Tennessee Librarian, Summer 1964). Language: Spanish 4,4,4,4; Portuguese 3,3,3,3; French 3,3,3,3. Home: 2005 Blakemore Ave., Nashville, Tenn., 37203. Office: Joint University Libraries, 419 21st Ave. South, Nashville, 37203.

MOORE, BRUCE R., b. Council Bluffs, Iowa, Mar. 19, 1929. LINGUISTICS. M.A., Ind. U., 1961. LINGUIST, TRANSLATOR, SUMMER INSTITUTE OF LINGUISTICS, 1953– . Research: Indian languages of Ecuador. Author: A Statistical Morphosyntactic Typology Study of Colorado (International Journal of American Linguistics, Oct. 1961); Second Thoughts on Measuring Naturalness (The Bible Translator, Apr. 1964). Language: Spanish: 4,4,4,3; Colorado 3,3,3,3. Linguistic studies: Colorado. Home: Casilla 1007, Quito, Ecuador. Office: Summer Institute of Linguistics, Box 1960, Santa Ana, Calif.

MOORE, FREDERICK T., b. Chicago, Ill., May 10, 1920. ECONOMICS. M.A., U. of Wis., 1941; Kent Coll. of Law; Ph. D., U. of Calif., 1951. Chief asst. in statistics, U. of Calif., Berkeley, 1946–48; lectr., 1948–50; asst. prof., U. of Ill., 1950–51; chief, Interindustry Analysis, U.S. Dept. of the Interior, 1951–53; CHIEF, ECONOMICS GROUP, RAND CORPORATION, 1953– . Consultant, Center for Development Studies (Venezuela), and National Economic Development Bank of Brazil; lectr., Institute of Social Studies (The Hague). Membership: American Economic Association. Research: statistics, development strategies and policies; economic development of Brazil, Chile, and Venezuela. Author: Studies in Economic Planning (1961); Models for Economic Development (1963); The World Bank and Its Economic Missions (Review of Economics and Statistics, Feb. 1960). Language: Spanish 3,3,2,2; Portuguese 3,3,2,2. Home: 8 Hesketh St., Chevy Chase, Md. Office: Rand Corp., 1000 Connecticut Ave., Washington, D.C.

MOORE, JAMES MAXWELL, b. Bogota, N.J., Oct. 21, 1914. HISTORY. A.B., U. of Calif., Berkeley, 1936; M.A., 1938; Ph. D., 1943. Asst. prof., Xavier U. (Cincinnati), 1947–49; prof., Rocky Mountain Coll., 1949–50; prof., chmn., Social Science, Boise District Coll., 1950–57; prof., Lake Erie Coll., 1957–60; PROF., HISTORY, NORWICH U., 1960– . Membership: American Association of University Professors; American Committee for Irish Studies; American Historical Association. Research: Latin American population growth; modern European history. Author: The Roots of French Republicanism (1962); Population Increase and Economic Potential in Latin America (1963). Language: Spanish 5,3,3,3; French 5,3,3,3; Gaelic 5,3,3,3; German 5,3,3,3; Russian 3,3,3,3. Home: 57 Central St., Northfield, Vt. Office: Dept. of Social Science, Norwich U., Northfield.

MOORE, JOHN PRESTON, b. Lexington, Va., Nov. 1, 1906. HISTORY. B.A., Washington & Lee U., 1927; M.A., Harvard U., 1930; Ph. D., Northwestern U., 1942. Instr., U. of Ark., 1934–36; asst. prof., The Citadel, 1938–42; PROF., HISTORY, LA. STATE U., 1946– . Howard Houston fellow, Washington & Lee U., Rumford scholarship, Harvard U.; Guggenheim fellow (Spain), 1960–61. Membership: Phi Beta Kappa. Research: Spanish colonial history; Peru and Ecuador in the 18th century. Author: The Cabildo in Peru Under the Hapsburgs (1954). Language: Spanish 5,4,4,3; Portuguese 2,1,1,1; French 5,4,3,3. Home: 4888 Sweetbriar Pl., Baton Rouge, La. Office: Dept. of History, La. State U., Baton Rouge.

MOORE, O. ERNEST, b. Fort Worth, Tex., Oct. 5, 1896. ECONOMICS. M.S.S., New School for Social Research, 1946. Economist, Federal Reserve Bank of N.Y., 1935–39; chief of Foreign Research Div., 1939–46; manager, Research Dept., 1946–53; financial and economic adviser, United Nations (Haiti), 1951–52, 1953, 1956; financial adviser, U.S. Fiscal Mission (La Paz, Bolivia), and acting executive dir. of National Monetary Stabilization Commission, 1956–57; economist, Klein and Saks Mission (Santiago, Chile), 1957–58, (Port-au-Prince, Haiti), 1958–59; adviser, Government of Venezuela, 1959; finance officer, Brown Engineers (N.Y.), 1959–60; economist, Klein and Saks Mission to Ecuador, 1960–61; economist, Centro de Estudios Monetarios Latinoamericanos (Mexico, D.F.), 1961–62; GENERAL PARTNER, INTERNATIONAL ECONOMIC SERVICES, 1962– . Membership: Academy of Political Science; American Economic Association; American Finance Association; Foreign Policy Association; National Planning Association; Society for International Development. Research: finance; economic development; economic structure and relationships of Bolivia, Brazil, Chile, Ecuador, Haiti, Mexico, Venezuela. Author: Stabilization of the Bolivian Peso (1958); El departamento de investigaciones económicas de un banco central (1962–63); Evolución de las instituciones financieras en México (1963). Language: Spanish 5,4,4,4; Portuguese 4,3,3,3; French 5,5,5,5; German 4,4,3,3; Italian 3,2,1,1. Office: International Economic Services, 60 East 42nd St., New York, N.Y. 10017.

MOORE, SALLY FALK, b. New York, N.Y., Jan. 18, 1924. ANTHROPOLOGY AND LAW. B.A., Columbia U., 1943; LL.B., 1945; Ph. D., 1957. Assoc. attorney, Spence, Hotchkiss, Parker and Duryea (N.Y.), 1945; attorney, U.S. War Dept. (Nuremberg), 1946; asst., Dept. of Anthropology, Columbia U., 1950–52; ASST. PROF., ANTHROPOLOGY, U. OF SOUTHERN CALIF., 1963– . Ansley Prize, Columbia U., 1957. Membership: American Anthropological Association; Royal Anthropological Institute of Great Britain. Research: comparative law and politics; kinship and social structure; law and government of Inca and Aztec civilizations. Author: Power and Property in Inca Peru (1958); Asymmetrical Cross-cousin Marriage (American Anthropologist,

1963); Descent and Symbolic Filiation (American Anthropologist, 1964). Language: Spanish 4,2,2,1; Portuguese 2,1,1,1; French 5,5,4,4; German 2,2,–,1. Home: 12438 Rochdale Lane, Los Angeles 49, Calif. Office: Dept. of Anthropology, U. of Southern Calif., Los Angeles.

MOORHEAD, MAX LEON, b. Grand Junction, Colo., Dec. 28, 1914. HISTORY. B.A., U. of Okla., 1937; M.A., 1938; Ph. D., U. of Calif., Berkeley, 1942. Asst. prof., U. of Okla., 1945–51; assoc. prof., 1951–56; PROF., HISTORY, U. OF OKLA., 1956– ; vis. prof., U. of Tex., 1962–63. American Philosophical Society research grant (Mexico), 1950; contributor, Encyclopaedia Britannica and Britannica Book of the Year, 1938–42, 1945–50, 1962. Membership: Conference on Latin American History; Mississippi Valley Historical Association; Phi Alpha Theta; Phi Beta Kappa; Western History Association. Research: 18th century Mexico; archival research; history of trade and transportation in Mexico. Author: New Mexico's Royal Road: Trade and Travel on the Chihuahua Trail (1958); The Private Contract System of Presidio Supply in Northern New Spain (Hispanic American Historical Review, Feb. 1961). Editor: Commerce of the Prairies, by Josiah Gregg (1953). Language: Spanish 4,3,3,3; Portuguese 2,1,1,1; French 2,1,1,1; German 2,1,1,1. Home: 1228 Caddell, Norman, Okla. Office: Dept. of History, U. of Okla., Norman.

MORALES-CARRIÓN, ARTURO, b. Havana, Cuba, Nov. 16, 1913. HISTORY AND INTERNATIONAL RELATIONS. B.A., U. of P.R., 1935; M.A., U. of Tex., 1936; Ph. D., Columbia U., 1950. Prof., U. of Miami, 1939–40; div. asst., U.S. Dept. of State, 1940–43; chmn., U. of P.R., 1945, 1951–52; consultant, Hispanic Foundation, Library of Congress, 1946–47; vis. lectr., Columbia U., 1947–49; vice president, Committee on Teaching World History, United Nations Educational, Scientific, and Cultural Organization, 1950–51; under-secretary, Dept. of State, Commonwealth of P.R., 1953–61; deputy asst. secretary, Inter-American Affairs, U.S. Dept. of State, 1961–64; SPECIAL ADVISER TO SECRETARY GENERAL, ORGANIZATION OF AMERICAN STATES, 1964– . Membership: Academia Colombiana de la Historia; Institute of Puerto Rican Culture; Inter-American Academy; Pan American Institute of Geography and History; Sociedad Peruana de Historia. Research: Latin America and international organizations of the regional system. Author: Puerto Rico and the Non-Hispanic Caribbean: A Study in the Decline of Spanish Exclusivism (1952). Co-author: Introducción a la historia de Europa en el siglo XIX (1940); La enseñanza de la historia en Puerto Rico (1953). Language: Spanish 5,5,5,5; Portuguese 3,–,4,–; French 3,3,3,–; German 1,1,1,–; Italian 2,2,1,–; Home: 5520 Westbard Ave., Westwood, Bethesda, Md. Office: Organization of American States, Pan American Union, 17th and Constitution Ave., NW., Washington, D.C.

MORELLO-FROSCH, MARTHA EUGENIA, b. Argentina, Sept. 13, 1928. SPANISH AMERICAN LITERATURE. M.A., Ohio State U., 1954; M.A., 1956; Ph. D., 1958. Cultural executive secretary, American Information Center (Rosario, Argentina), 1950–52; instr., Ohio State U., 1958–61; asst. prof., 1961–64; prof., National Defense Education Act Institute, Ohio State U., Summer 1963; ASSOC. PROF., ROMANCE LANGUAGES, OHIO STATE U., 1964– . Panamerican scholar, Ohio State U., 1952–54; American Philosophical Society fellow, 1962. Membership: American Association of Teachers of Spanish and Portuguese; American Association of University Women; Hispanófila Society; Instituto Internacional de Literatura Iberoamericana; Modern Language Association. Research: 20th century Spanish and Spanish American literature, especially poetry. Author: Metáfora cósmica y ciudadana en Leopoldo Lugones (Revista Iberoamericana de Literatura, Nov. 1957); Salinas y Guillén: dos formas de esencialidad (Revista Hispánica Moderna, Jan. 1961); Elementos populares en la poesía de Jorge Luis Borges (Asomante, July 1962). Language: Spanish 5,5,5,5; Portuguese 3,4,3,2; French 5,4,3,4; German 2,3,2,2; Italian 5,5,5,5. Linguistic studies: French; Italian; Spanish. Home: 2899 Neil Ave., Columbus 2, Ohio. Office: Romance Language Dept., Ohio State U., Columbus 10.

MORENO, LAUDELINO, b. Burgos, Spain, Nov. 19, 1901. HISTORY, GEOGRAPHY, LITERATURE, AND INTERNATIONAL LAW. Ph. D. (history), U. of Madrid, 1923; LL.D., 1925; Ph. D. (natural science), 1926; Ph. D. (economics), 1928. Prof., Universidad Central (Spain), 1922–39; vis. prof., Universidad Central (Ecuador), 1929, Universidad Nacional Autónoma de México, 1932; prof., Universidad de Santo Domingo (Dominican Republic), 1939–41; prof., Universidad de Guatemala, 1941–47; prof., Universidad Central de Venezuela, 1947–50; ASSOC. PROF., SPANISH, U. OF SOUTHERN CALIF., 1950– ; vis. prof., U. of Colo., 1963. Delegate, League of Nations; attaché, Spanish Embassy (Mexico), 1932–33. Membership: American Association of University Professors; International Association for Instruction of History; Pan American Institute of Geography and History; Sociedad de Geografía e Historia de Guatemala; Sociedad de Geografía e Historia de Honduras. Author: Historia de las relaciones interestatuales de Centroamérica (1928); Filosofía del Derecho (1944); Derecho consular guatemalteco (1946). Language: Spanish 5,5,5,5; Portuguese 5,4,4,4; French 5,5,4,4; Italian 4,4,4,3; Tagalog 4,4,4,3. Home: 735 West 47th St., Los Angeles, Calif., 90037. Office: Dept. of Spanish, U. of Southern Calif., Los Angeles 7.

MORGNER, AURELIUS, b. New York, N.Y., May 23, 1917. ECONOMICS. B.S., U. of Mo., 1938; M.A., 1940; Ph. D., U. of Minn., 1955. Instr., U. of Minn., 1942–46; lectr., Northwestern U., 1946–47; assoc. prof., Tex. A. & M. U., 1947–56; prof., 1956–58; acting dir. of graduate studies, Escola de Sociologia, Universidade de São Paulo (Brazil), 1958–60; PROF., CHMN., ECONOMICS, U. OF SOUTHERN CALIF., 1962– . Assoc. editor, Sociologia, 1958– ; Smith-Mundt vis. prof. (Brazil), 1958–60; assoc. editor, Latin American Handbook, 1960– ; Ford Foundation fellow, Columbia U. Membership: American Economic Association; American Finance Association; Pacific Coast Council of Latin Americanists; Royal Economic Society; Western Economic Association. Research: economic development; Brazil. Author: Implicações sociológicas e econômicas do atual inflação no Brasil (Sociologia, May 1959). Co-author: Problems in the Theory of Price (1954). Contributor: Resistências à mudança (1960). Language: Spanish 3,–,–,–; Portuguese 4,4,4,3; French 4,3,3,3. Home: 3768 South Flower St., Los Angeles 7, Calif. Office: Dept. of Economics, U. of Southern Calif., Los Angeles 7.

MORÍNIGO, MARCOS A., b. Asunción, Paraguay, Oct. 7, 1904. LANGUAGE, U. of Buenos Aires, 1932; U. of Paris, 1936–38; Ph. D., U. of Buenos Aires, 1945. Prof., U. of Tucumán, 1938–46; prof., U. of Southern Calif., 1947–50; prof., U. of Caracas, 1950–51; prof., U. of Fla., 1951–53; prof., U. of Southern Calif., 1953–57; prof., U. of Buenos Aires, 1957–62; PROF., SPANISH, U. OF ILL., 1962– . Membership: American Association of Teachers of Spanish and Portuguese; American Association of University Professors; Asociación Interuniversitaria Argentina de Filología; Asociación Internacional de Hispanistas; Modern Language Association. Research: Spanish philology; relationship between Spanish and American Indian languages; history of Spanish in America; American lexicography. Author: Hispanismos en el Guaraní (1931); América en el teatro de Lope de Vega (1946); Programa de filología hispánica (1959). Language: Spanish 5,5,5,5; Portuguese 4,3,3,3; French 4,4,4,4; German 3,2,2,1; Guaraní 5,5,5,5; Italian 4,4,3,3. Linguistic studies: Guaraní. Home: 705 West Ohio, Urbana, Ill. Office: Dept. of Spanish, Italian, and Portuguese, U. of Ill., Urbana.

MORRIS, JAMES OLIVER, b. Akron, Ohio, Feb. 8, 1923. HISTORY AND LABOR RELATIONS. A.B., Hiram Coll., 1948; M.S., U. of Mich., 1951; Ph. D., 1954. PROF., N.Y. STATE SCHOOL OF INDUSTRIAL AND LABOR RELATIONS, CORNELL U., 1955– ; chief of party, U.S. Agency for International Development-Cornell U. contract (Chile), 1959–62. Fulbright research grant (Chile), 1958–59. Research: labor relations in the Western Hemisphere; labor relations system in Chile; labor unions in the United States. Author: Conflict within the American Federation of Labor (1958). Co-author: Afiliación y finanzas sindicales en Chile, 1932–1959 (1962). Language: Spanish 4,4,4,4. Home: 7 Winthrop Pl., Ithaca, N.Y. Office: N.Y. State School of Industrial and Labor Relations, Cornell U., Ithaca, 14850.

MORRISON, PAUL CROSS, b. Racine, Ohio, Aug. 26, 1906. GEOGRAPHY. B.S., Ohio State U., 1928; M.A., 1933; Ph. D., Clark U., 1941. Instr., Ohio State U., 1930–31; instr.-PROF., GEOGRAPHY, MICH. STATE U., 1931– . Consultant, Inter-American Institute of Agricultural Sciences (Turrialba, Costa Rica), 1948, 1949, 1951; Fulbright lectr., Ochanomizu U. and Tokyo Education U. (Tokyo, Japan), 1955–56; National Defense Foreign Language fellow, U. of Calif., Los Angeles, Summer 1962; vis. prof. and consultant, U. of P.R., Summer 1962. Membership: American Geographical Society; Association of American Geographers; Michigan Academy of Science, Arts and Letters; National Council of Geographic Education; Phi Kappa Phi; Sigma Xi. Research: economic geography; population and settlement; Middle America. Author: Aspects of the Urban Geography of Turrialba, Costa Rica (Ochanomizu University Studies in Art and Culture, Jan. 1957); Caribbean America (in World Geography, 1958): Middle America, Land of Too Many and Too Little (Journal of Geography, Mar. 1961). Language: Spanish 3,2,2,2; Portuguese 2,1,1,1; French 2,1,1,1. Home: 520 Sycamore Lane, East Lansing, Mich., 48823. Office: Dept. of Geography, Mich. State U., East Lansing.

MORSE, RICHARD McGEE, b. Summit, N.J., June 26, 1922. HISTORY. B.A., Princeton U., 1943; M.A., Columbia U., 1947; Ph. D., 1952. Lectr.-asst. prof., Columbia U., 1949–58; dir., Institute of Caribbean Studies, U. of P.R., 1958–61; vis. lectr., Harvard U., 1960; prof., chmn., State U. of N.Y., Coll. at Long Island, 1961–62; vis. lectr., Brooklyn Coll., 1962; assoc. prof., Yale U., 1962–63; PROF., HISTORY, YALE U., 1963– . Woodrow Wilson fellow, 1946–47; U.S. Dept. of State grant (Brazil), 1947–48; consultant, Economics Faculty, U. of Nuevo León, 1958–60; consultant, Ford Foundation, 1958– ; Albert J. Beveridge Award Committee, 1963– . Membership: Conference on Latin American History; Phi Beta Kappa. Research: Brazilian history; comparative history of the Americas. Author: From Community to Metropolis: A Biography of São Paulo, Brazil (1958); Toward a Theory of Spanish American Government (Journal of the History of Ideas, Jan. 1954); Some Characteristics of Latin American Urban History (American Historical Review, Jan. 1962). Language: Spanish 4,4,4,4; Portuguese 4,4,4,4; French 4,4,4,4. Home: Sunbrook Rd., Woodbridge, Conn. Office: Dept. of History, Yale U., New Haven, Conn.

MORTON, LUIS M., JR., b. Laredo, Tex., Nov. 29, 1925. HISTORY AND EDUCATION. B.S., U. of Houston, 1948; LL.B., St. Mary's U., 1951; M.L., U. of Houston, 1953; Ph. D., U. of Tex., 1956. Instr., Odessa Coll., 1956–60; dean of admissions, 1960–61; DEAN OF DAY COLL., ODESSA COLL., 1961– . Membership: Phi Alpha Theta; Phi Delta Kappa; Pi Sigma Alpha Research: the Mexican Revolution; junior college education. Author: The Profs Go Back to School (Texas Outlook, Nov. 1960); The Faculty Incentive Plan at Odessa College (Junior College Journal, Dec. 1960); The Faculty Incentive Plan at Odessa College (The Bulletin, National Association of Secondary School Principals, Oct. 1961). Language: Spanish 5,5,5,5; Portuguese 3,3,3,3; French 2,2,2,2. Home: 1440 Englewood Lane, Odessa, Tex. Office: P.O. Box 3752, Odessa Coll., Odessa.

MORTON, WARD McKINNON, b. Fredericksberg, Tex., Mar. 29, 1907. POLITICAL SCIENCE. A.B., South Tex. State Coll., 1929; M.A., U. of Tex., 1935; Ph. D., 1940. Instr.-asst. prof., U. of Ark., 1938–49; asst. prof., Wayne State U., 1948; assoc. prof.-PROF., GOVERNMENT, SOUTHERN ILL. U., 1949– . Institute of Latin American Studies fellow (Mexico), U. of Tex.,

1940–41; Smith-Mundt vis. prof., Universidad Autónoma de Nicaragua, 1960. Membership: American Association of University Professors; American Political Science Association; Midwest Political Science Conference. Research: political theory; Latin American comparative government; Mexico. Author: Woman Suffrage in Mexico (1963); The Mexican Constitutional Congress of 1916–17 (Southwestern Social Science Quarterly, June 1952); The Mexican Establishment in Operation (Proceedings, Fourteenth Caribbean Conference, 1964). Language: Spanish 4,4,4,4; Portuguese 2,2,–,–; French 2,2,–,–; German 2,2,–,–; Italian 2,2,–,–. Home: 809 West Mill, Carbondale, Ill. Office: Dept. of Government, Southern Ill. U., Carbondale.

MOSELEY, EDWARD HOLT, b. Selma, Ala., July 13, 1931. HISTORY. B.S., U. of Ala., 1953; M.A., 1957; U. of Nuevo León (Mexico), 1959–60; Ph. D., U. of Ala., 1963. ASST. PROF., HISTORY, LA. POLYTECHNIC INSTITUTE, 1960– . U.S. Dept. of State grant (Mexico), 1959–60. Membership: Louisiana Historical Association; Southern Historical Association; Southwestern Social Sciences Association. Research: 19th century Mexico; the Mexican Revolution; Mexican novel of the Revolution. Language: Spanish 4,3,3,3; German 2,2,2,2. Home: Glenwood Dr., Ruston, La. Office: Dept. of History, La. Polytechnic Institute, Ruston.

MOSER, GERALD MAX, b. Leipzig, Germany, Jan. 3, 1915. BRAZILIAN LITERATURE. Licencié es lettres, U. of Paris, 1935; diploma 1937; docteur de l'Université, 1939. Instr., Bridgewater Coll., 1939–41; instr., Cornell U., 1943–44; instr., U. of Wis., 1944–45; asst. prof., U. of Ill., 1945–49; ASSOC. PROF., SPANISH AND PORTUGUESE, PA. STATE U., 1949– . American Council of Learned Societies scholar, U. of Chicago, 1941, U. of Wis., 1945; Fulbright research fellow, U. of Lisbon, 1962–63. Membership: American Association of Teachers of Spanish and Portuguese; Modern Language Association. Research: literary history of Brazil. Author: Les Romantiques Portugais et l'Allemagne (1939); A sensibilidade brasileira de Manuel Bandeira (Revista Iberoamericana, Sept. 1955); O Brasil do poeta Manuel Bandeira (in La cultura y la literatura iberoamericana, 1957). Language: Spanish 4,4,4,4; Portuguese 4,4,4,4; French 4,4,4,4. Linguistic studies: Portuguese. Home: 295 South Osman St., State College, Pa. Office: 214 Sparks Bldg., University Park, Pa.

MOSES, CARL C(ALVIN), b. Princeton, W. Va., Apr. 14, 1921. POLITICAL SCIENCE. A.B., Coll. of William and Mary, 1947; M.A., U. of N.C., 1955; Ph. D., 1958. Instr., U. of N.C., 1954–56; asst. prof., Va. Polytechnic Institute, 1957–60; vis. asst. prof., U. of Fla., 1960–61; assoc. prof., Va. Polytechnic Institute, 1961–64; ASSOC. PROF., POLITICAL SCIENCE, WAKE FOREST COLL., 1964– . National Defense Foreign Language fellow, 1963. Membership: Southeastern Conference on Latin American Studies. Research: comparative government; Latin American government and politics. Language: Spanish 4,3,3,3. Office: Dept. of Political Science, Wake Forest Coll., Winston-Salem., N.C., 24060.

MOTTEN, CLEMENT GILE, b. Colorado Springs, Colo., Feb. 16, 1917. HISTORY. B.S., Trinity Coll. (Conn.), 1938; Universidad Nacional de México, 1941; Ph. D., U. of Pa., 1947. PROF., HISTORY, DIR. OF INTERNATIONAL CULTURAL ACTIVITIES, TEMPLE U., 1946– ; vis. prof., U. of Pa., 1962–63. Social Science Research Council fellow (Mexico), 1945–46; Beveridge Award, American Historical Association, 1948; Doherty fellow (Chile), 1950; Smith-Mundt lectr., U. of Havana (Cuba), 1959–60; Organization of American States research fellow (South America), 1960; Latin American Adviser, American Friends Service Committee; Board of Directors, International Institute of Philadelphia. Membership: American Historical Association; Conference on Latin American History. Research: university education and political organization in Latin America. Author: Mexican Silver and the Enlightenment (1950). Editor: Latin American Development Programming and United States Investments (1956). Language: Spanish 4,4,4,4; Portuguese 3,2,1,1; French 4,3,3,2; German 2,3,2,1; Italian 2,2,1,1. Home: 22 Pennock Ter., Lansdowne, Pa. Office: Dept. of History, Temple U., Philadelphia 22, Pa.

MOUSHEY, EUGENE WILSON, b. Fort Wayne, Ind., Dec. 28, 1922. LIBRARY SCIENCE. B.A., U. of Mich., 1948; M.A., 1949; B.S., 1950; A.M.L.S., 1951. Librarian and teacher, Wis. State Coll., 1951–62; teacher, Universidad Nacional de El Salvador, 1957–58; teacher, Escuela Interamericana de Bibliotecología (Medellín, Colombia), 1963–64; ASST. LIBRARIAN, DOCUMENTS AND REFERENCE, LIBRARY, WIS. STATE COLL., 1964– . Membership: American Library Association; Association of Wisconsin State College Faculties; Wisconsin Library Association. Research: cataloging and classification; reference; library science education. Language: Spanish 5,5,5,5; Portuguese 2,1,1,1; French 3,2,2,2. Home: 751 Jackson St., Oshkosh, Wis. Office: Library, Wis. State Coll., Oshkosh.

MOWLL, JACK USHER, b. Cleveland, Ohio, Oct. 16, 1915. GEOGRAPHY. B.A., Johns Hopkins U., 1948; Ph. D., 1956. Dir., economic research, Martin-Marietta Corporation (Baltimore), 1954–59; dir., regional planning, Penn-Jersey Transportation Study (Philadelphia), 1959–61; CONSULTANT, 1961– . Membership: American Economic Association; American Geographical Society; Association of American Geographers; Regional Science Association; Society for International Development. Research: economic geography; regional development planning; transportation economics and planning; feasibility of industrial development; Panama. Language: Spanish 3,3,3,2. Home: 632 Overhill Rd., Ardmore, Pa.

MOZLEY, LOREN N., b. Brookport, Ill., Oct. 2 1905. ART. U. of N. Mex., 1923–26; independent study, France, Italy, 1929–31 Instr., dir. of field school, U. of N. Mex. 1936–38; PROF., ART, U. OF TEX. 1938– ; prof. extraordinario, National U of Mexico, Summers 1942–45; vis. prof. U. of Southern Calif. Research: painting; Latin American colonial art. Author: A Note on José Guadalupe Posada (1946) Yankee Artist (Bulletin, Museum of Moderr Art, Oct. 1936); The Colonial Churche

(Liturgical Arts, May 1955). Language: Spanish 4,4,4,3; Portuguese 2,1,2,–; French 4,4,3,3. Home: 311 Buckeye Trail, Austin, Tex. Office: Dept. of Art, U. of Tex., Austin.

MUDIE, JOHN HOWARD, b. Hackensack, N.J., July 13, 1927. ECONOMICS. A.B., Dartmouth Coll., 1949; M.B.A., U. of Pa., 1951; Ph. D., U. of Tex., 1960. Asst. prof., Tex. A. & M. Coll., 1955-56; ASST. VICE PRESIDENT, GOVERNMENT DEVELOPMENT BANK FOR P.R., 1956– . Teaching fellow, U. of Tex., 1954-55. Membership: American Economic Association; Economic and Statistical Association of Puerto Rico; Society for International Development. Research: public relations; role of the government development bank in Puerto Rico's economic program; Caribbean area. Language: Spanish 4,4,4,4; French 3,2,2,2; German 2,3,2,1. Home: 601 Darlington Apts., Santurce, P.R. Office: Government Development Bank for P.R., P.O. Box 4591, San Juan, P.R.

MULLER, HERMAN JOSEPH, S.J., b. Cleveland, Ohio, Apr. 9, 1909. HISTORY. M.A., Loyola U. (Ill.), 1936; S.T.L., St. Louis U., 1943; Ph. D., Loyola U. (Ill.), 1950. Instr., Xavier U., 1943-47; instr., Loyola U. (Ill.), 1950-52; asst. prof., John Carroll U., 1952-56; assoc. prof., U. of Detroit, 1956-64; CHMN., 1959– ; PROF., HISTORY, U. OF DETROIT, 1964– . Membership: American Catholic Historical Association; American Historical Association; Michigan Academy of Arts and Sciences; Phi Alpha Theta. Research: Anglo-Hispanic American trade relations in the 17th and 18th centuries; the Renaissance and the Reformation; Europe, 1914-1939. Author: Trade Interests of XVIII Century British Travel (Mid-America, July 1951); British Travel Writers and the Jesuits (Mid-America, Jan. 1953); British Business and Spanish America, 1700-1800 (Mid-America, Jan. 1957). Language: Spanish 2,1,1,1; Portuguese 1,1,1,1; French 3,2,2,1; German 2,3,3,1; Latin 3,3,3,3. Home and office: Dept. of History, U. of Detroit, 4001 West McNichols, Detroit 21, Mich.

MUNN, HENRY LUSK, b. Chicago, Ill., Jan. 11, 1924. ECONOMICS: MARKETING. B.S., De Paul U., 1948; M.B.A., U. of Chicago, 1949; Ph. D., 1957. Instr., De Paul U., 1949-52; administrative asst. to dean, Wright Jr. Coll., 1952-57; assoc. prof., Ariz. State U., 1957-59; PROF., MARKETING, SAN FERNANDO VALLEY STATE COLL., 1959– ; vis. prof., U. of Calif., Los Angeles, 1963-64; SENIOR MARKETING CONSULTANT, WESTERN MANAGEMENT CONSULTANTS (PHOENIX), 1964– . Ford Foundation marketing fellow, U. of Calif., 1958; National Defense Foreign Language fellow, U. of Calif., 1963; consultant, Color Research Institute, Marplan; Educational Advisory Committee, Consumers Union of the United States. Membership: Academy of Management; American Marketing Association. Research: marketing and consumer research; consumer behavior in the marketplace in Mexico. Author: Brand Perception as Related to Age, Income and Education (Journal of Marketing, Jan. 1960); Group Interviews Reveal Consumer Buying Behavior (Journal of Retailing, Fall 1961); The Significance of the Retirement Market (Journal of Retailing, Summer 1964). Language: Spanish 2,2,2,2. Home: 8553 Chimineas Ave., Northridge, Calif., 91324. Office: School of Business Administration, San Fernando Valley State Coll., Northridge.

MUNRO, DANA G., b. Providence, R.I., July 18, 1892. HISTORY. A.B., Brown U., 1912; A.B., U. of Wis., 1912; U. of Munich, 1912-13; Ph. D., U. of Pa., 1917; LL.D., Brown U., 1940. Economist, U.S. Dept. of State, 1919-20; economist, Consulate (Valparaiso, Chile), Foreign Service, 1920-21; staff, Div. of Latin American Affairs, 1921-25, first secretary, Legation (Panama), 1925-27 (Nicaragua), 1927-29; chief Div. of Latin American Affairs, 1929-30; minister to Haiti, 1930-32; prof., Princeton U., 1932-61; dir., Woodrow Wilson School of Public and International Affairs, 1939-58; RETIRED, 1958– . Carnegie Peace Endowment grant (Central America), 1914-16; Carnegie vis. prof. (South America), 1935; president, Foreign Bondholders Protective Council, 1938– ; National Advisory Committee on Inter-American Affairs, 1959-61. Membership: American Historical Association; Council for Latin American Affairs; Inter-American Academy. Research: United States diplomatic history; history of intervention policy in the Caribbean. Author: The Five Republics of Central America (1918); The Latin American Republics, a History (1942); Intervention and Dollar Diplomacy in the Caribbean (1964). Language: Spanish 4,3,3,3; Portuguese 3.2,1,1; French 4,3,2,1; German 2,2,2,1. Home: 345 Harrison St., Princeton, N.J.

MUNRO, EDWIN CLAIR, b. Hotchkiss, Colo., Mar. 11, 1909. BRAZILIAN LITERATURE AND LANGUAGE. B.A., U. of Denver, 1939; M.A., U. of N. Mex., 1940; Ph. D., U. of Wis., 1949. Instr., Spanish, Newcomb Coll., Tulane U., 1946-47; PROF., SPANISH AND PORTUGUESE, STATE U. OF N.Y., ALBANY, 1948– . U. of Tex. Center for Latin American Area Studies fellow, Summer 1963. Membership: American Association of Teachers of Spanish and Portuguese; American Association of University Professors; Modern Language Association. Research: medieval Spanish; modern Brazilian novel. Author: Foreign Languages in Elementary Schools, A Bridge to Cultural Understanding (New York State Education Journal, May 1954). Language: Spanish 5,5,4,5; Portuguese 4,4,4,3; French 4,4,3,3; German 2,1,1,1; Italian 3,2,2,2. Linguistic studies: Spanish. Home: Star Rt., Altamont, N.Y. Office: Dept. of Romance Languages, State U. of N.Y., 135 Western Ave., Albany.

MUNROE, ROBERT L., b. Baltimore, Md., July 1, 1932. ANTHROPOLOGY. A.B., U. of Calif., Berkeley, 1958; Ph. D., Harvard U., 1964. Research fellow, Laboratory of Human Development, Harvard U., 1964; ASST. PROF., ANTHROPOLOGY, PITZER COLL., 1964– . National Institutes of Health fellow, Harvard U., 1962-63. Research: cultural practices and personality study of the Black Carib, British Honduras. Language: Spanish 2,1,1,1; Portuguese 1,1,1,1; French 2,1,1,1; Russian 2,2,2,2. Home: 825 Maryhurst Dr., Claremont, Calif. Office: Dept. of Anthropology, Pitzer Coll., Claremont.

MUNSTER, JOE HENRY, JR., b. Austin, Tex., July 28, 1912. LAW. B.A., U. of Tex., 1933; M.A., 1933; LL.B., 1936; S.J.D., Northwestern U., 1952. Naval officer, U.S. Navy, 1941-61; PROF., LAW, SCHOOL OF LAW, WESTERN RESERVE U., 1961– . Membership: American Association of Law Schools; American Association of University Professors; American Bar Association; American Economic Association; Federal Bar Association. Research: legal-economic problems; government control of business; Central America. Author: Savants, Sandwiches and Spacesuits (Science, Sept. 1964). Co-author: Military Evidence (1959, 1962, 1964). Language: Spanish 3,3,3,3; Portuguese 2,2,2,2; French 2,2,2,2; German 3,3,3,3. Home: 2300 Overlook Rd., Cleveland Heights, Ohio 44106. Office: School of Law, Western Reserve U., Cleveland, 44106.

MURDOCH, RICHARD KENNETH, b. Ancón, C.Z., May 8, 1913. HISTORY. A.B., Harvard Coll., 1936; M.A., U. of Calif., Los Angeles, 1940; Ph. D., 1947. Asst. prof., Carnegie Institute of Technology, 1947-56; vis. instr., U. of N.C., 1950-51, 1955-56; ASSOC. PROF., HISTORY, U. OF GA., 1956– ; DIR., UNIVERSITY CENTER, 1959– . National Defense Foreign Language post-doctoral fellow in Spanish, U. of Calif., Los Angeles, Summer 1963. Membership: American Association of University Professors: American Historical Association; Bolivarian Society; Hispanic American Historical Association; Mississippi Valley Historical Association; Southeastern Conference on Latin American Studies. Research: Argentina; Brazil; Chile; borderlands. Author: The Georgia-Florida Frontier, 1793–1796 (1951); Citizen Mangourit and the Projected Attack on East Florida in 1794 (Journal of Southern History, Nov. 1948); The Battle of Orleans, Mass., 1814, and Associated Events (American Neptune, Winter 1963–64). Language: Spanish 4,3,3,3; Portuguese 2,-,-,-; French 4,3,3,3; German 3,3,3,3; Russian 1,-,-,-. Home: Box 1292, Athens, Ga. Office: Dept. of History, U. of Ga., Athens.

MURGUÍA, THEODORE INFANTE, b. San Bernardino, Calif.. Jan. 25, 1925. SPANISH AMERICAN LITERATURE AND LINGUISTICS. A.B., Park Coll., 1951; M.S., Kans. State U., 1952; M.A., U. of Wash., 1958; Ph. D., 1961. Asst. prof., U. of Calif., Santa Barbara, 1958-62; ASST. PROF., FOREIGN LANGUAGES, SAN FRANCISCO STATE COLL., 1962– . Membership: American Association of Teachers of Spanish and Portuguese: Foreign Language Association of Northern California; Linguistic Circle of New York. Research: Spanish linguistics; the gaucho in literature. Author: The Timeless Aspect of Don Segundo Sombra (Hispania, Mar. 1963); The Application of Linguistics to the Classroom Situation (Hispania, May 1963). Language: Spanish 5,5,5,5; French 3,3,3,3; Italian 3,3,3,3. Linguistic studies: English; French; Italian; Latin; Spanish. Home: 50 Duval Dr., South San Francisco, Calif. Office: Dept. of Foreign Languages, San Francisco State Coll., 1600 Holloway, San Francisco 27, Calif.

MURRA, JOHN VICTOR, b. Odessa, Russia, Aug. 24, 1916. ANTHROPOLOGY. B.A., U. of Chicago, 1936; M.A., 1942; Ph. D., 1956. Instr., U. of Chicago, 1943–47; asst. prof.-assoc. prof., U. of P.R., 1947–49; lectr., Vassar Coll., 1949–51; prof., 1954–61; vis. prof., Universidad de San Marcos (Peru), 1958–59; vis. prof., Proyecto 104, Asuntos Sociales, Organization of American States (Mexico), Summer 1961; vis. prof., Yale U., 1961–63; PRINCIPAL INVESTIGATOR, INSTITUTE OF ANDEAN RESEARCH (PERU), 1963– . Social Science Research Council fellow (Ecuador), 1941–42 (Peru), 1946–47; Vassar Faculty fellow (Peru), 1958–59; Editorial Board, Revista del Museo Nacional (Peru). Membership: American Anthropologcal Association; American Ethnological Society; Instituto de Estudios Peruanos; International African Institute; Society for African Studies; Society for American Archaeology. Research: cultural anthropology; provincial life in Inca times; Andean and African ethnology. Author: On Inca Political Structure (1958); Rite and Crop in the Inca State (in Culture in History, 1960). Language: Spanish 4,5,4,3; French 5,5,4,3; Quechua 3,3,3,2; Rumanian 5,5,4,4; Russian 4,5,4,3. Home: 1100 Dámaso Beraún, Huánuco, Perú. Office: Casilla 61, Huánuco, Perú.

MURRAY, PAUL VINCENT, b. Chicago, Ill., July 15, 1908. HISTORY. B.A., St. Ambrose Coll., 1933; M.A., Catholic U. of America, 1934. Instr., Universidad Nacional de México, Summers 1935, 1943, 1944; teacher, American High School (Mexico, D. F.), 1936–39; principal, 1939–46; co-founder, dean, vice-president, president, Mexico City Coll., 1940–61; ADMINISTRADOR GENERAL, MEXICO CITY CENTER OF BILINGUAL STUDIES, 1961– . Knights of Columbus fellow, Catholic U. of America, 1933–36; founding member: Mexican American Institute of Cultural Relations, 1942, Colegio Tepeyac, 1944, Colegio Junípero Serra, 1956, Lomas High School, 1961, Mexico City Center, 1951. Membership: American Catholic Historical Association; Sociedad Mexicana de Geografía y Estadística. Research: church-state relations in Mexico. Author: The Church and the First Mexican Republic, 1820–1830 (American Catholic Historical Society, Mar. 1937); Tres norteamericanos y su participación en el desarrollo del Tratado McLane-Ocampo, 1856–1860 (Revista Estudios Históricos, Cuaderno No. 3, 1946). Co-author: Inglés elemental (1937–). Language Spanish 5,5,5,3; Portuguese 3,2,-,-; French 3,-,-,-; Italian 5,-,-,-. Home: Corregidores 1516, México 10, D.F. Office: San Luis Potosí 154, México 7.

MYREN, DELBERT THEODORE, b. Eleva Wis., Nov. 13, 1925. COMMUNICATION B.S., U. of Wis., 1951; U. of Bonn (Germany), 1951–52; M.S., U. of Wis., 1953 Ph. D., 1955. Instr., U. of Wis., 1954–55 AGRICULTURAL INFORMATION SPECIALIST, ROCKEFELLER FOUNDATION (MEXICO), 1955– ; vis. prof., U. of Wis. 1963. Membership: Asociación Latinoamericana de Fitotecnistas; Rural Sociological Society; World Conference of Agricultural Economists. Research communication of information; factors limiting the diffusion of knowledge and adoption of improved practices among different farm sectors Author: Training for Extension Work in Latin America (América Latina, Apr.–Jun 1964). Co-author: Resultados de un est dio sobre la lectoría de Agricultura Técnica en México (Agricultura Técnica en México, Winter 1962) ; La difusión y adopción del maíz híbrido en cuatro municipos del Estado de Guanajuato (Agricultura Técnica en México, Summer 1963). Language: Spanish 4,4,4,3 ; Portuguese 2,2,1,1 ; French 1,-,-,- ; German 3,3,3,3. Home: Loma Bonita 20, Lomas Altas, Mexico 10, D.F. Office: Rockefeller Foundation, Londres 40, Mexico 6.

MYREN, RICHARD ALBERT, b. Madison, Wis., Aug. 9, 1924. LAW. B.S., U. of Wis., 1948 ; LL.B., Harvard Law School, 1952. Research chemist, U.S. Dept. of Agriculture, 1948–49 ; asst. prof.-assoc. prof., U. of N.C., 1952–56 ; asst. prof.-ASSOC. PROF., POLICE ADMINISTRATION, IND. U., 1956– . Consultant, Children's Bureau, U.S. Dept. of Health, Education, and Welfare, 1960–62 ; special adviser, President's Committee on Juvenile Delinquency and Youth Crime ; special adviser to International Association of Chiefs of Police Delinquency Project. Membership : Society for International Development. Research : international comparative law ; comparative study of the administration of the criminal law ; Argentina. Author: Indiana Conservation Officers' Manual of Law and Practice (1961) ; Legal Foundations of the Indianapolis Police Department (1963). Co-author: Police Work with Children (1962). Language: Spanish 2,2,2,2 ; German 2,2,2,2. Home: 2403 Browncliff Lane, Bloomington, Ind. Office: Dept. of Police Administration, Ind. U., Bloomington.

N

NADER, LAURA, b. Winsted, Conn., Sept. 30, 1930. ANTHROPOLOGY. B.A., Wells Coll., 1952 ; Ph. D., Harvard U., 1961. ASST. PROF., ANTHROPOLOGY, U. OF CALIF., BERKELEY, 1960– . Mexican Government fellow, 1957–58 ; consultant, Arthur D. Little, Inc., 1958–60 ; Institute for International Studies (Berkeley, Calif.) grant ; fellow, Center for Advanced Studies in the Behavioral Sciences (Stanford, Calif.), 1963–64. Membership : American Anthropological Association. Research : social anthropology ; social organization, particularly village law systems of Mexican Zapotec and Trique Indian groups. Author: Talea and Juquila: A Comparison of Zapotec Social Organization (1964) ; Conflict Resolution in Two Mexican Communities (American Anthropologist, 1963) ; An Analysis of Zapotec Law Cases (Ethnology, 1964). Language: Spanish 4,4,4,4 ; Arabic –,5,4,–. Home: 2694 Hilgard, Berkeley 9, Calif. Office: Dept. of Anthropology, U. of Calif., Berkeley 4.

NARVAEZ, RICARDO AUGUSTO, b. Jayuya, P.R., Dec. 24, 1921. LANGUAGE AND LINGUISTICS. B.S., Concordia Coll., 1943 ; M.A., U. of Minn., 1948 ; Ph. D., 1959. ASST. PROF., SPANISH AND LINGUISTICS, U. OF MINN., 1946–51, 1957– ; asst. prof., English, U. of P.R., 1952–57. Smith-Mundt prof. of English, Universidad de Guadalajara (Mexico), 1959–60 ; consultant on Spanish texts for EMC Corporation (St. Paul), 1959– ; Fulbright prof., Linguistics, Instituto Caro y Cuervo (Bogotá, Colombia), 1962–63. Membership: American Association of Teachers of Spanish and Portuguese ; American Association of University Professors ; Linguistic Circle of New York ; Linguistic Society of America. Research : Spanish linguistics ; English as a foreign language. Author: Acronyms in Spanish (Language Learning, 1962) ; Algunos comentarios sobre la pronunciación del castellano en Puerto Rico (Cultura, Sept. 1963) ; From San Juan to Guadalajara (Hispania, Dec. 1963). Language: Spanish 5,5,5,5 ; Portuguese 3,3,3,2 ; French 2,2,2,1. Home: 2200 Hendon Ave., St. Paul, Minn. 55108. Office: 200 Folwell Hall, U. of Minn., Minneapolis, 55455.

NASATIR, ABRAHAM P., b. Santa Ana, Calif., Nov. 24, 1904. HISTORY. A.B., U. of Calif., 1921 ; M.A., 1922 ; Ph. D., 1926. Instr., U. of Iowa, 1926–27 ; asst. prof.-PROF., HISTORY, SAN DIEGO STATE COLL., 1928– . Native Sons of the Golden West traveling fellow (Spain), 1923–24 ; Social Science Research Council fellow (Spain and France), 1930–31 ; Fulbright fellow (France), 1950–51 ; fellow, Huntington Library, Summer 1952 ; Fulbright lecturer, U. of Chile, 1959–60 ; vice consul (Paraguay). Membership: American Historical Association ; Mississippi Valley Historical Association ; Pacific Coast Council on Latin American Studies. Research : Spain in the Mississippi Valley in the 18th century ; the French in California. Author: French Activities in California : An Archival Calendar Guide (1945) ; Before Lewis and Clark (1952) ; Latin America : Development of its Civilization (1960). Language: Spanish 4,3,4,3 ; French 4,3,3,2 ; German 2,-,-,-. Home: 3340 North Mountain View Dr., San Diego 16, Calif. Office: Dept. of History, San Diego State Coll., San Diego 15.

NASH, JUNE C., b. Salem, Mass., May 30, 1927. ANTHROPOLOGY. B.A., Barnard Coll., 1948 ; M.A., U. of Chicago, 1953 ; Ph. D., 1960. Teacher, Chicago Teachers Coll., 1963–64 ; ASST. PROF., ANTHROPOLOGY, YALE U., 1964– . National Institute of Mental Health research grants (Guatemala), 1953–54, (Mexico), 1957 ; National Institutes of Health fellow (Burma), 1960–61 ; U.S. Peace Corps lectr. Membership : American Anthropological Association ; Central States Anthropological Association. Research : Social relations in Amatenango del Valle, Guatemala ; Mexico. Author: Protestantism in a Guatemalan Indian Village (1960) ; Marriage, Fertility and Population Growth in Burma (Southwestern Journal of Anthropology, Fall 1963). Language: Spanish 4,-,-,- ; Burmese 2,-,-,-. Home : 264 Fountain St., New Haven, Conn. Office : Dept. of Anthropology, Yale U., New Haven.

NASH, MANNING, b. Philadelphia, Pa., May 4, 1924. ANTHROPOLOGY. B.S., Temple U., 1949 ; A.M., U. of Chicago, 1952 ; Ph. D., 1955. Instr., U. of Calif., Los Angeles, 1955–56 ; prof., San Carlos U. (Guatemala), 1956 ; asst. prof., U. of Wash., 1956–57 ; ASSOC. PROF., ANTHROPOLOGY, U. OF CHICAGO, 1957– . Social Science Research Council fellow (Guatemala), 1953–54 ; National Institute of Mental Health research grants (Mexico), 1957, 1959 ; National Science Foundation fellow, 1960–61. Membership : American Anthropological Association ; Royal Anthropological Institute of Great Britain and Ireland ; Sigma Xi.

Research: social and cultural change; economic development; Mesoamerican ethnology. Author: Machine Age Maya (1958); Multiple Society in Economic Development (American Anthropologist, Oct. 1957); Social Context of Economic Choice in a Small Society (Man, Nov. 1961). Language: Spanish 4,4,4,2; French 3,3,2,1; Burmese 1,2,2,1. Linguistic studies: Burmese; Tzeltal. Home: 5507 South Kenwood, Chicago 37, Ill. Office: Dept. of Anthropology, U. of Chicago, Chicago 37.

NASON, MARSHALL RUTHERFORD, b. Deloraine, Canada, Sept. 23, 1917. SPANISH AMERICAN LITERATURE AND LANGUAGE. B.A., La. State U., 1939; M.., 1947; Ph. D., U. of Chicago, 1958. Executive secretary, Div. of Latin American Relations, La. State U., 1940–47; instr.-assoc. prof., U. of N. Mex., 1947–60; vis. prof., U. of Calif., Berkeley, 1954, Summer 1955; consultant, Latin American Programs and dir. in Chile, U.S. Peace Corps, 1961–62; dir., Div. of Foreign Studies, U. of N. Mex., 1962–63; DIR., PEACE CORPS TRAINING CENTER FOR LATIN AMERICA, U. of N. MEX., 1963– . U. of Chicago fellow, 1954; Organization of American States fellow (Argentina), 1960; National Defense Education Act consultant, 1962, 1963. Membership: American Association of Teachers of Spanish and Portuguese; American Association of University Professors; Association for Latin American Studies; Instituto Internacional de Literatura Iberoamericana; Phi Sigma Iota; Rocky Mountain Council for Latin American Studies. Research: Argentine literature; community development in Latin America. Author: Seudónimo de un escritor consagrado (Revista de la Universidad, Jan.–Apr. 1962). Co-author: Charlar repasando (1951); Bibliografía de Benito Lynch (1961). Language: Spanish 5,5,4,4; Portuguese 3,3,2,2; French 2,2,1,2. Linguistic studies: American Spanish; Spanish. Home: 829 Adams St., NE., Albuquerque, N. Mex. Office: Peace Corps Training Center, U. of N. Mex., Albuquerque.

NATTIER, FRANK E., b. St. Joseph, Mo., Sept. 2, 1915. LAW. B.S.F.S., Georgetown U., 1937; LL.B., 1940; LL.M., N.Y.U., 1953. Asst. to dean, School of Foreign Service, Georgetown U., 1937–38; economics writer, Pan American Union, 1938–40; asst. and acting special representative, U.S. Office of Interamerican Affairs, Embassy (Rio de Janeiro), 1941–45; attorney, Breed, Abbott & Morgan (N.Y.), 1946–55; ATTORNEY, LAW OFFICES OF FRANK E. NATTIER, 1955– . President, American Brazilian Association, 1962–64; chmn., Committee on Latin America, National Foreign Trade Council, 1963– ; chmn., Subcommittee on Latin America, Association of the Bar of the City of New York; dir., American Foreign Law Association; Latin American Committee, American Bar Association; consultant on Bolivian investment law, U.S. Agency for International Development Mission (Bolivia). Membership: American Bar Association; American Brazilian Association; American Foreign Law Association; Association of the Bar of the City of New York. Research: legal aspects of business relationships between United States and Latin American countries, especially Brazil. Author: Some Forms of Corporate Financing in Brazil (American Journal of Comparative Law, 1955); Central American Program of Economic Integration (in A Lawyer's Guide to International Business Transactions, 1963). Contributor: Doing Business Abroad (1962). Language: Spanish 4,4,4,4; Portuguese 4,4,4,4; French 3,2,2,2. Home: 48 Spencer Ct., Hartsdale, N.Y. Office: Law Offices of Frank E. Nattier, 300 Madison Ave., New York, N.Y. 10017.

NAVA, JULIAN, b. Los Angeles, Calif., June 19, 1927. HISTORY. A.B., Pomona Coll., 1951; A.M., Harvard U., 1952; Ph. D., 1955. Teacher, Centro Venezolano-Americano (Caracas), U.S. Information Agency, 1953–54; lectr., U. of P.R., 1955–57; ASSOC. PROF., HISTORY, SAN FERNANDO VALLEY STATE COLL., 1957– . John Hay Whitney Foundation fellow, 1951 (Venezuela), 1953; Bravo Fund fellow, 1952, 1954; Fulbright exchange prof. (Spain), 1962–63; chmn., Committee to Preserve the History of Los Angeles, Mayor's Office, 1961– . Membership: American Historical Association; Conference on Latin American History; Pacific Coast Council on Latin American Studies. Research: social and cultural history of Latin America. Author: Antonio Guzmán Blanco y el progreso de Venezuela (Umbral, Mar. 1954); Orígenes del teatro criollo en Venezuela (Umbral, June 1954); La imigración a Venezuela desde el fin de la Guerra Federal al Siglo XX (Revista Shell, 1957). Language: Spanish 5,5,5,4; Portuguese 4,3,2,1; French 3,3,3,1. Home: 18240 Rayen St., Northridge, Calif. Office: Dept. of History, San Fernando Valley State Coll., Northridge.

NAVARRO, JOAQUINA, b. Madrid, Spain Sept. 1, 1916. SPANISH AMERICAN LITERATURE. B.A., Instituto Escuela (Madrid), 1934; M.A., Columbia U., 1942 Ph. D., 1954. Instr., Middlebury Summer School, 1943–54; ASSOC. PROF., CHMN. SPANISH AND PORTUGUESE, SMITH COLL., 1943– . Dir., Smith Coll. Junior Year in Mexico, 1947, 1949–50; Social Science Research Council grant, 1960–61 Membership: American Association of Teachers of Spanish and Portuguese; Modern Language Association. Research: history of Spanish; Spanish phonetics Author: La novela realista mexicana (1955). Language: Spanish 5,5,5,5; Portuguese 3,3,3,3; French 4,4,4,4; Italian 2,2,2. Linguistic studies: English; French Spanish. Home: 24 Hastings Height Northampton, Mass. Office: Dept. of Spanish and Portuguese, Smith Coll., Northampton.

NAYLOR, ROBERT ARTHUR, b. Wellwyn Garden City, England, Dec. 19, 1925. HISTORY. B.A., U. of Western Ontario, 1951 M.A., 1952; Ph. D., Tulane U., 1955 Instr., Tulane U., 1955–56; ASSOC. PROF. HISTORY, AUBURN U., 1956– ; vis. prof. U. of Pittsburgh, 1963–64; vis. assoc. prof. George Washington U., 1964– . International exchange student, Oberlin Coll., 1949–50; Governor General's Gold Medal, U. of Western Ontario, 1951; graduate fellow, Tulane U., 1953; research grant and Latin American Studies scholarship, 1954; fellow Institute of Historical Research, U. of London, 1954–55; Latin American Studies grant, Tulane U., 1955–56. Membership Southeastern Conference on Latin America

Studies; Southern Historical Association. Research: 19th century British economic penetration of Latin America. Author: British Role in Central America Prior to the Clayton-Bulwer Treaty of 1850 (Hispanic American Historical Review, Aug. 1960); A Mexican Monarchist Views the American Civil War in November, 1861 (Iowa Civil War Journal, Mar. 1962); Research Opportunities in Modern Latin America: Central America and Mexico (The Americas, Apr. 1962). Language: Spanish 4,3,3,3. Home: 739 McKinley Ave., Auburn, Ala. Office: Dept. of History, Auburn U., Auburn.

NEAL, JOE WEST, b. Watertown, Tenn., Oct. 25, 1916. POLITICAL SCIENCE. Ph. D., U. of Tex., 1957; DIR., INTERNATIONAL OFFICE, U. OF TEX., 1941– ; LECTR., GOVERNMENT, 1946– . Braniff International Airways grant (Cuba, Panama), 1949; Creole Foundation fellow (Venezuela), 1955: U.S. Office of Education fellow (Mexico), 1950–57; consultant, U.S. Dept. of State and Institute of International Education. Membership: American Political Science Association; National Association of Foreign Student Advisors; Southwestern Political Science Association. Research: state and local government in northeastern Mexico; U.S.-Latin American relations; educational exchange. Language: Spanish 4,4,4,3; Portuguese 3,2,1,1. Home: 2309 Shoal Creek Blvd., Austin, Tex. Office: International Office, U. of Tex., Austin, 78712.

NEALE-SILVA, EDUARDO, b. Talca, Chile, Dec. 10, 1905. SPANISH AMERICAN LITERATURE. M.A., U. of Wis., 1928; Ph. D., 1935. Instr., U. of Wis., 1928–36; asst. prof., 1936–41; assoc. prof., 1942–47; PROF., SPANISH, U. OF WIS., 1948– . Guggenheim fellow, 1940–41. Membership: American Association of Teachers of Spanish and Portuguese; Instituto Internacional de Literatura Iberoamericana; Modern Language Association. Research: Argentina; literature in Brazil, Chile, Colombia, Ecuador, Peru, and Uruguay. Author: El arte poético de José Eustasio Rivera (1959); Horizonte humano: vida de José Eustasio Rivera (1960); José Eustasio Rivera, polemista (Revista Iberoamericana, 1948). Language: Spanish 5,5,5,5; Portuguese 4,4,3,1; French 4,3,3,1. Home: 911 University Bay Dr., Madison 5, Wis. Office: Dept. of Spanish, Box 464, Bascom Hall, U. of Wis., Madison 6.

NEEDLER, MARTIN CYRIL, b. Manchester, England, Mar. 23, 1933. POLITICAL SCIENCE. A.B., Harvard U., 1954; Ph. D., 1960. Instr., Dartmouth Coll., 1959–60; instr., U. of Mich., 1960–63; ASST. PROF., POLITICAL SCIENCE, U. OF MICH., 1963– . Lectr., Venezuelan Student Leader Exchange Program, 1961, 1962; Rackham Graduate School research grant (Peru), 1962; National Defense Foreign Language fellow, U. of Calif., Los Angeles, Summer 1962; Institute for the Comparative Study of Political Systems research grant (Ecuador), 1963–64. Membership: American Political Science Association; Association for Latin American Studies; Hispanic American Society; International Political Science Association. Research: theoretical problems in comparative politics; current problems of U.S. foreign policy; Mexico; Peru;
Ecuador. Author: Latin American Politics in Perspective (1963); The Political Development of Mexico (American Political Science Review, June 1961); United States Recognition Policy and the Peruvian Case (Inter-American Economic Affairs, Spring 1963). Language: Spanish 4,4,4,4; Portuguese 1,1,1,1; French 4,3,4,4; German 4,4,4,4. Home: 1308 Granger Ave., Ann Arbor, Mich. Office: Dept. of Political Science, U. of Mich., Ann Arbor.

NEHNEVAJSA, JIRI, b. Dyjakovice, Czechoslovakia, Aug. 9, 1925. SOCIOLOGY. Ph. D., U. of Zurich, 1953. Editor, Svobodne Noviny (Brno, Czechoslovakia), 1945–48; research staff, Conservation of Human Resources Project, Columbia U., 1951; instr., U. of Colo., 1951–52; asst. prof., U. of Colo., 1952–56; asst. prof., Columbia U., 1956–61; PROF., SOCIOLOGY, U. OF PITTSBURGH, 1961– ; CHMN., 1962– . Consultant, Pan American Union, 1961–63; consultant, Institute for Defense Analysis, 1964– . Membership: Air Force Association; American Institute of Aeronautics and Astronautics; American Public Opinion Research; American Sociological Association. Research: political systems; public opinion analysis; peace and war sociology; perception of cold war issues. Contributor: Automation and Society (1959); Handbuch der empirische Sozialforschung (1963). Co-editor and contributor: Reader in Sociometry (1960). Language: Spanish 3,2,2,1, Portuguese 2,1,1,1; French 4,3,3,3; Czech 5,5,5,5; German 5,5,4,4; Russian 3,2,2,1. Home: 1520 West Ingomar Rd., Pittsburgh 37, Pa. Office: Dept. of Sociology, U. of Pittsburgh, Pittsburgh 13.

NEKVASIL, EDWARD M., b. Prague, Czechoslovakia, Apr. 30, 1923. ECONOMICS. Diploma, Prague School of Economics, 1948; M.A., U. of Chicago, 1956; Ph. D., U. of Brussels, 1960. NUMISMATISCHES INSTITUT WIEN (AUSTRIA), 1958– . Membership: American Numismatic Association. Research: Latin American finance; numismatics; relations between Latin America and Slavic countries; financial and monetary history and financial documentation in Argentina and Mexico. Language: Spanish 4,3,3,3; Portuguese 3,2,2,2; French 4,4,4,4; Czech 5,5,5,5; German 4,4,4,4; Russian 3,3,2,2; Serbo-croatian 5,5,5,5. Home: 307 3rd St. SE., Washington, D.C.

NELSON, EASTIN, b. Aspermont, Tex., Sept. 20, 1902. ECONOMICS. M.A., U. of Tex., 1929; Ph. D., 1945. Prof., U. of Panama, 1940–43; asst. prof., U. of Tex., 1943–46; vis. prof., U. of Santo Domingo (Dominican Republic), 1946; asst. prof., Wayne State U., 1946–47; PROF., ECONOMICS, U. OF TEX., 1947– ; economic analyst, Klein and Saks, Consultants (Lima, Peru), 1951; vis. prof., U. of San Carlos (Guatemala), 1954; vis. prof., U. of Guayaquil (Ecuador), Summer 1963. Membership: Southern Ecomic Association; Southwestern Social Science Association. Research: historical change measured quantitatively. Author: A Revolution in Economic Policy: An Hypothesis of Social Dynamics in Latin America (Southwestern Social Science, Dec. 1953); Product Profiles and National Income: A Method of Studying Economic Change (Inter-American Economic Affairs Quarterly, Spring 1954). Language: Spanish 5,4,4,4; Portuguese 2,–,3,1; French 3,1,2,1. Home: 609 East 45th St., Austin, Tex.

NELSON, LOWRY, b. Ferron, Utah, Apr. 16, 1893. SOCIOLOGY. B.S., Utah State U., 1916; M.S., U. of Wis., 1924; Ph. D., 1929. Editor, Utah Farmer, 1920–22; dir., Extension Div., Brigham Young U., 1922–28; dean, Coll. of Applied Science, Brigham Young U., 1929–34; asst. dir., Rural Rehabilitation Div., Resettlement Administration, 1935–36; dir., Agricultural Experiment Station, Utah State U., 1936–37; prof., U. of Minn., 1937–58; PROF. EMERITUS, SOCIOLOGY, U. OF MINN., 1958– . Agriculture Committee, International Labor Organization, 1937–52; Fulbright fellow (Italy), 1954–55; consultant, U.S. Agency for International Development (Brazil), 1957, 1958, 1960, (Chile), 1960. Membership: American Association for the Advancement of Science; American Sociological Association; Midwest Sociological Society; National Planning Association; Rural Sociological Society. Research: social aspects of agrarian reform in Mexico, Bolivia and Venezuela; frontier settlement in the Paraná; Chilean rural education. Author: Rural Sociology (1948); Rural Cuba (1950); The Mormon Village: A Pattern and Technique of Land Settlement (1952). Language: Spanish 4,1,1,2; Portuguese 3, 1,1,2; French 4,1,1,1; Italian 3,–,–,–. Home: Apt. 705, 2401 H St., NW., Washington, D.C. 20007. Office: Dept. of Sociology, U. of Minn., Minneapolis 14.

NELSON, MICHAEL, b. Wellington, New Zealand, Oct. 14, 1928. ECONOMICS. B.S., U. of New Zealand, 1950; M.A., 1952; Ph. D., Oreg. State Coll., 1956. Research economist, U. of New Zealand, 1952–54; research asst., Oreg. State Coll., 1954–56; economist, Stanford Research Institute, 1956–59; economist, Government of Chile and International Agricultural Services contract, 1959; economist, International Agricultural Services, Inc., 1959–60; ECONOMIST, STANFORD RESEARCH INSTITUTE, 1960– ; economist, International Bank for Reconstruction and Development and Government of Honduras, Stanford Research Institute contract, 1962; economic adviser, Consejo Nacional de Desarrollo (Argentina), Stanford Research Institute contract, 1962– . Fulbright scholar. Membership: American Farm Economic Association; New Zealand Association for the Advancement of Science; Sigma Xi. Research: agricultural economics; regional development and transportation; farm management in Chile; national transportation priorities of Honduras; Argentina. Author: Economic Survey of Waipukurau County (1952); Economic Development and Transport Investment Planning: A Case Study in Honduras (1963). Co-author: Use of Linear Programming in the Valuation of Intermediate Products (Journal of Land Economics, Aug. 1957). Language: Spanish 4,4,4,4. Home: Andrade 470, Acassuso, Provincia de Buenos Aires, Argentina. Office: Stanford Research Institute, Ravenswood Ave., Menlo Park, Calif.

NELSON, PAUL, b. Brooklyn, N.Y., July 29, 1929. ECONOMICS. Ph. D., U. of Okla., 1956. Staff economist, National Rural Electric Cooperative Association (Washington, D.C.), 1956–60; ECONOMIST, NATIONWIDE INSURANCE COMPANY, 1960– . Consultant, U.S. Agency for International Development; consultant, American Institute for Free Labor Development. Membership: American Economic Association; American Farm Economic Association; Society for International Development. Research: income analysis; economic conditions and financial institutions in Colombia and Peru. Language: Spanish 3, 3,3,3. Home: 3012 Sudbury Rd., Columbus 21, Ohio. Office: Nationwide Insurance Company, 246 North High St., Columbus 16.

NEMES, GRACIELA P., b. Camagüey, Cuba, Mar. 24, 1919. SPANISH AMERICAN LITERATURE. B.A., Trinity Coll. (Vt.), 1942; M.A., U. of Md., 1949; Ph. D., 1952. Instr., U. of Md., 1946–57; asst. prof., 1957–62; lectr., Catholic U. of America, Summers 1957– ; ASSOC. PROF., FOREIGN LANGUAGES AND LITERATURES, U. OF MD., 1962– . American Philosophical Society of Philadelphia grants (P.R.), Summer 1956 (Spain), Summer 1960. Membership: American Association of Teachers of Spanish and Portuguese; American Association of University Professors; Asociación Internacional de Hispanistas; Ateneo Americano de Washington; Hispanic Society of America; Modern Language Association; Phi Kappa Phi; Sigma Delta Pi. Research: Spanish American civilization; Juan Ramón Jiménez; Zenobia Camprubí de Jiménez; contemporary Hispanic literature. Author: Vida y obra de Juan Ramón Jiménez (1957); Tagore and Jiménez: Poetic Coincidences (in Tagore Centenary Volume, 1961); La importancia de Maeterlinck en un momento crítico de las letras hispanas (Revue Belge de Philologie et d'Histoire, 1962). Language: Spanish 5,5, 5,5; Portuguese 3,2,1,1; French 3,2,2,1. Linguistic studies: Spanish. Home: 6926 Pineway, University Park, Hyattsville, Md. Office: Dept. of Foreign Languages and Literatures, U. of Md., College Park.

NESBITT, PAUL H., b. Savanna, Ill., Aug. 15, 1904. ANTHROPOLOGY. B.A., Beloit Coll., 1926; M.A., U. of Chicago, 1930; Ph. D., 1938. Prof., Beloit Coll., 1930–45; technical dir., Museo Nacional de Guatemala, 1946–48; CHIEF, ARCTIC-DESERT-TROPIC INFORMATION CENTER, AIR U., 1948– . U. of Chicago fellow; U.S. Dept of Defense Research and Development Board; Air Force member, U.S. Dept. of Defense Coordinating Group for Geography. Membership: Alabama Academy of Science; American Anthropological Association; American Association for the Advancement of Science; Society for American Archaeology. Research: non-temperate areas: ecology, social sciences, earth science; New World archeology; Panama; Guatemala; Venezuela; Mexico. Author: Ethnic Studies on U.S.S.R., Middle East, South America (1955–63); The Survival Book (1960); The Lost World (1963). Language: Spanish 3, 3,3,3; French 2,2,2,2. Home: 3123 Wilmington Rd., Montgomery 5, Ala. Office: Aerospace Studies Institute, Air U. Maxwell Air Force Base, Ala.

NETT, ROGER W., b. Idaho, Mar. 18, 1921 SOCIOLOGY. B.A., Eastern Wash. Coll. 1941; Ph. D., Wash. State U., 1949. Sociologist, State of Wash., 1947–48; prof. Okla. State U., 1949–54; training officer, Air Materiel Command, U.S. Government, 1954

57; PROF., SOCIOLOGY, U. OF PITTSBURGH, 1957- ; prof., Central U. of Ecuador, U.S. Agency for International Development-U. of Pittsburgh contract, 1963-65. Membership: American Sociological Association. Research: general methodology of social science; demography of Ecuador. Author: Thorntree Meadows (1957, 1960); Introduction to Electronic Data Processing (1959); Introducción al estudio de la sistematización electrónica de datos (1961). Language: Spanish 4,4,4,4. Office: Dept. of Sociology, U. of Pittsburgh, Pittsburgh 13, Pa.

NEUENSWANDER, HELEN LUCILLE, b. Willis, Kans., Nov. 30, 1926. LINGUISTICS. R.N., Bethany Hospital School of Nursing, 1948; B.A., John Brown U., 1952. ANALYTICAL LINGUIST, MISSIONARY, NURSE, SUMMER INSTITUTE OF LINGUISTICS (GUATEMALA), 1953- . Research: unwritten Indian languages; ethnography and Achí Indian language of Guatemala. Language: Spanish 3,4,4,4; French 1,1,1,1. Linguistic studies: Achí. Home: Colony, Kans. 66015. Office: Summer Institute of Linguistics/Wycliffe Bible Translators, Box 1960, Santa Ana, Calif. 92702.

NEUMEYER, ALFRED, b. Munich, Germany, July 1, 1901. ART. Ph. D., U. of Berlin, 1925. Dir., Press Office, Staatliche Museen (Berlin), 1930-33; privatdozent, U. of Berlin, 1931-35; PROF., ART HISTORY, MILLS COLL., 1935- . Morrison grant (Mexico, Guatemala, Ecuador, Peru), 1947; Guggenheim fellow, 1958; prof. honoris causa, Free U. of Berlin, 1961; Fulbright fellow, 1962-63. Membership: College Art Association; Pacific Coast Council for Latin American Studies; International P.E.N. Club; Society of Aesthetics. Research: museum administration. Author: Cézanne Drawings (1958); Die Kunst in Unserer Zeit (1961); The Indian Contribution to Latin American Art (Art Bulletin, 1948). Language: Spanish 2,2,2,1; French 3,3,3,3; German 5,5,5,5. Home: 5575 Fernhoff Rd., Oakland 19, Calif. Office: Dept. of Art, Mills Coll., Oakland 13.

NEVINS, ALBERT J., M.M., b. Yonkers, N.Y., Sept. 11, 1915. COMMUNICATION AND JOURNALISM. Maryknoll Seminary, 1942; Litt. D. (honorary), St. Benedict Coll., 1962. Editor, Chinese-American Bulletin, 1942-45; assoc. editor, Maryknoll Magazine, 1945-52; DIR., MASS COMMUNICATIONS, MARYKNOLL FATHERS, 1945- ; dir., World Horizon Films, 1947- ; business manager, Maryknoll Magazine, 1950- ; children's editor, Our Sunday Visitor, 1952- ; editor, Maryknoll Magazine, 1952- ; editor, World Campus, 1958- ; dir., Cultivation Dept., Maryknoll Fathers, 1960- . Premier Prix, International Film Festival (Lille, France), 1957, 1961; Catholic Press Association Award, 1961; Maria Moors Cabot Prize, Columbia U., 1961; Freedom of the Press Committee, Inter-American Press Association; chmn., Latin America Committee, Catholic Press Association; consultant, Catholic Committee on Inter-American Student Problems; consultant, International Visitors' Office, National Catholic Welfare Council; cofounder, Catholic Institute of the Press. Membership: Africa Studies Association; Catholic Association for International Peace; Inter-American Press Association; Overseas Press Club. Research: mass communications in Latin America; preparation of documentary films. Author: The Making of a Priest (1957); The Maryknoll Book of People (1959); Away to the Lands of the Andes (1962). Language: Spanish 4,3,3,2; Portuguese 2,2,1,1; French 3,2,2,2. Home and office: Maryknoll Fathers, Maryknoll, N.Y. 10545.

NEWCOMER, HALE ALDEN, b. Champaign, Ill., Mar. 20, 1929. ECONOMICS: MARKETING. B.S., U. of Ill., 1951; M.B.A., U. of Tex., 1953; Ph. D., U. of Ill., 1957. Asst. prof., U. of Wash., 1956-58; asst. prof., U. of Mo., 1958-62; ASSOC. PROF., MARKETING, KENT STATE U., 1962- Consultant to Bendix Corporation, Projection on Business and Economic Development of Latin America, Fall 1964. Membership: American Marketing Association; Midwest Economic Association. Research: international marketing and international political economy; industrial development of Mexico. Author: International Aids to Overseas Investments and Trade (1964); Barter in Mexican Cotton—A New Concept in International Trade? (Journal of Marketing, Oct. 1958); Marketing's Response to the New Trade Policy (Winter Conference Proceedings, American Marketing Association, Winter 1963). Language: Spanish 4,3,3,3; Portuguese 3,2,1,1; French 2,1,1,1; Italian 2,2,1,1. Home: 1331 South Lincoln, Kent, Ohio. Office: Dept. of Marketing, Kent State U., Kent.

NEWMAN, MARSHALL THORNTON, b. New Bedford, Mass., July 15, 1911. ANTHROPOLOGY. Ph. B., U. of Chicago, 1933; M.A., 1935; Ph. D., Harvard U., 1941. Project coordinator, Institute of Andean Research (Peru), 1941-42; assoc. curator of physical anthropology, Smithsonian Institution, 1942-62; PROF., ANTHROPOLOGY, PORTLAND STATE COLL., 1962- . Board member, Div. of Anthropology and Psychology, National Research Council, 1955-57; Post-doctoral Fellowship Panel, National Research Council, 1956-59; consultant, Inter-American Studies on Atherosclerosis, Dept. of Pathology, La. State U., 1960- . Membership: American Anthropological Association; American Association of Physical Anthropologists; Anthropological Society of Washington. Research: physical anthropology; relationship of biological man to his total environment, particularly the dietary and disease aspects; biology and nutrition of the Vicos Indians of Peru. Author: Adaptation in the Physique of American Aborigines to Nutritional Factors (Human Biology, Sept. 1960); The Biological Adaptation of Man to His Environment: Heat, Cold, Altitude, and Nutrition (Proceedings, New York Academy of Science, June 1961); Ecology and Nutritional Stress in Man (American Anthropologist, Feb. 1962). Language: Spanish 3,4,3,2; French 3,3,2,2. Home: 14370 SW. Uplands Dr., Lake Oswego, Oreg. Office: Dept. of Anthropology, Portland State Coll., Portland 1, Oreg.

NEWTON, RONALD CHARLES, b. Newark, N.J., Feb. 8, 1933. HISTORY. B.A., Rutgers U., 1955; M.A., U. of Fla., 1960; Ph. D., 1963. Admin. asst., Summer School, Universidad de San Carlos (Guatemala), 1960; teacher, Bi-National Center (Buenos

Aires), Summer 1961; ASST. PROF., HISTORY, PURDUE U., 1963– . Henry Rutgers fellow, 1955; Graduate School fellow, U. of Fla., 1959–61; National Defense Foreign Language fellow, 1962–63. Membership: American Historical Association; Conference on Latin American History; Congreso Internacional de Americanistas; Southern Historical Association. Research: modern Spanish American corporate interest groups and the political process; colonial guilds and corporations; Argentine frontier in the 18th and 19th centuries. Language: Spanish 5,4,4,4; Portuguese 4,3,3,2; French 4,3,3,3; German 5,5,5,4; Italian 4,3,3,3. Home: 1034 Happy Hollow Rd., West Lafayette, Ind. Office: Dept. of History, Purdue U., West Lafayette.

NEWTON, WESLEY PHILLIPS, JR., b. Montgomery, Ala., Apr. 2, 1925. HISTORY. A.B., U. of Mo., 1949; M.A., U. of Ala., 1953; Ph. D., 1964. Expert consultant, Historical Div., Maxwell Air Force Base, U.S. Air Force, 1957–61; ASST. PROF., HISTORY, AUBURN U., 1964– . Graduate fellow, U. of Ala., 1954–57. Membership: Phi Alpha Theta. Research: aviation in Latin American-United States relations; development of aviation in Latin America. Author: What is the Alliance for Progress? (Comment, University of Alabama Quarterly, 1963). Collaborator: Air Force Combat Units of World War II (1961). Language: Spanish 3,2,2,2; Portuguese 3,1,1,1. Home: Rt. 1, Box 2–F, Montevallo, Ala. Office: Dept. of History, Auburn U., Auburn, Ala.

NICHOLLS, WILLIAM HORD, b. Lexington, Ky., July 19, 1914. ECONOMICS. A.B., U. of Ky., 1934; M.A., Harvard U., 1938; Ph. D., 1941. Instr.-assoc. prof., Iowa State Coll., 1938–44; asst. prof., U. of Chicago, 1945–48; PROF., ECONOMICS, VANDERBILT U., 1948– ; member, Turkish Mission, International Bank for Reconstruction and Development, 1950; senior staff economist, Council of Economic Advisers, 1953–54; vis. prof., Harvard U., 1961–62; economist, Fundação Getulio Vargas (Rio de Janeiro, Brazil), 1963–64. Agriculture Committee, National Planning Association, 1954– ; Board of Directors, Social Science Research Council, 1956–61; consultant on Brazil, Ford Foundation, 1960– . Membership: American Economic Association; American Farm Economic Association; International Association of Agricultural Economics; International Economic Association; Southern Economic Association. Research: agricultural economics; agriculture and economic development; economics of Brazilian agriculture. Author: Southern Tradition and Regional Progress (1960); The Importance of an Agricultural Surplus in Underdeveloped Countries (1962); Uma apreciação sôbre a economia rural no Brasil (Agricultura em São Paulo, May 1961). Language: Spanish 2,2,2,1; Portuguese 4,4,3,3; French 3,1,1,1; German 3,2,2,2. Home: 2900 Westmoreland Dr., Nashville 12, Tenn. Office: P.O. Box 1819, Vanderbilt U., Nashville 5.

NICHOLS, GRACE LAURA, b. Detroit, Mich., Mar. 11, 1901. SPANISH AMERICAN LITERATURE. B.A., U. of Wis., 1926; M.A., U. of Colo., 1929; Ph. D., U. of N. Mex., 1951. Instr., Phoenix Coll., 1947–48; manuscript editor, American Dental Association; prof., Alma Coll., 1954–61; PROF., SPANISH, CHMN., MODERN LANGUAGES, HILLSDALE COLL., 1961– . Membership: American Association of Teachers of Spanish and Portuguese; Modern Language Association. Research: Guatemalan poetry. Author: Teachers' Unions in the First Year of Occupation in Japan (Delta Kappa Gamma Bulletin, Winter 1948). Language: Spanish 5,4,4,4; Portuguese 3,2,2,2; French 4,2,2,2; German 2,–,–,–. Home: 2546 Pine St., Boulder, Colo. Office: Dept. of Modern Languages, Hillsdale Coll., Hillsdale, Mich. 49242.

NICHOLS, LAWRENCE RICHARD, b. Winston-Salem, N.C., Jan. 7, 1924. HISTORY. B.A., Wake Forest Coll., 1948; Ph. D., Duke U., 1954. Asst. prof., Queens Coll. (N.C.), 1953–56; Coll, of Charleston, 1956–62; ASST. PROF., HISTORY, EASTERN ILL. U., 1962– . Padre Varela fellow (Cuba), 1951–52; Hispanic fellow, Duke U. (Spain), 1963. Membership: American Association of University Professors; American Historical Association; Southern Historical Association. Research: Antonio Maceo, hero of Cuban independence movement. Language: Spanish 4,4,4,4; Portuguese 2,2,2,2; German 2,2,2,–. Home: R.F.D. 4, Ashby Dr., Charleston, Ill. Office: Dept. of History, Eastern Ill. U., Charleston.

NICHOLS, MADALINE WALLIS, b. Ipswich, Mass., Jan. 21, 1898. HISTORY AND SPANISH AMERICAN LITERATURE. B.A., Mt. Holyoke Coll., 1918; M.A., Cornell U., 1922; Ph. D., U. of Calif., Berkeley, 1937. Reference asst., Hispanic Foundation, Library of Congress and research asst., Committee on Latin American Studies, American Council of Learned Societies, 1939–42; editor, Agriculture in the Americas, U.S. Dept. of Agriculture, 1942–43; assoc. prof., Goucher Coll., 1943–45; asst prof., Duke U., 1945–46; lectr. in Latin American History, U. of Calif., Los Angeles, 1946–47; assoc. prof., Fla. State U., 1948–50; RETIRED, 1950– ; vis. prof., U. of N. Mex., 1950–51; honors prof. in Latin American Studies, State U. of N.Y., Coll. at Geneseo, 1963–64. Carnegie travel grant (Chile), 1937; National Committee on International Relations, American Association of University Women, 1945–46; chmn., Conference on Latin American History, 1949–50; chmn., Robertson Award Committee, 1960. Membership: Hispanic Society of America; Sociedad de Geografía e Historia de Guatemala; Unión Cultural Argentina. Research: inter-American relations. Author: Bibliographic Guide to Materials on American Spanish (1941); The Gaucho (1942; Portuguese edition, 1946; Spanish edition, 1953); A Colombian Pattern for Peace, 1819–1830 (in The Caribbean: Contemporary Colombia, 1962). Language: Spanish 5,3,3,3; Portuguese 2,2,1,1; French 3, 3,2,2; German 2,1,1,–; Italian 2,1,1,–. Home: 19 Oak St., Geneseo, N.Y. 14454. Office: Dept. of Social Studies, State U. of N.Y., Coll. at Geneseo, Geneseo.

NICHOLS, THEODORE EDWARD, b. Oakland, Calif., July 24, 1921. HISTORY. A.B., U. of Calif., Berkeley, 1944; M.A., 1946; Ph. D., 1951. Instr., U. of Ariz., Fall 1949; instr., San Francisco State Coll., Spring 1950; asst. prof., U. of Ga., 1951–56; vis. asst. prof., Yale U., 1953–54; 1956–64; PROF., HISTORY, LONG BEACH

STATE COLL., 1964- . Mills traveling fellow (Columbia), 1948-49; Carnegie Intern in General Education, Yale U., 1953-54; Del Amo Foundation fellow (Sevilla, Spain), Spring 1963. Research: Colombian and Chilean history. Author: The Establishment of Political Relations between Chile and Great Britain (Hispanic American Historical Review, Feb. 1948) ; The Rise of Barranquilla (Hispanic American Historical Review, May 1954) ; Colombia : the History of the Colonial Period (in The Caribbean : Contemporary Colombia, 1962). Language : Spanish 3,3,3,3 ; Portuguese 2,-,-,- ; French 3,2,2,1. Home: 3261 Oak Knoll Dr., Los Alamitos, Calif. Office: Dept. of History, Long Beach State Coll., Long Beach 4, Calif.

NICHOLSON, HENRY B., b. La Jolla, Calif., Sept. 5, 1925. ANTHROPOLOGY. A.B., U. of Calif., Berkeley, 1949; LL.B., 1952; M.A., Harvard U., 1955; Ph. D., 1958. PROF., ANTHROPOLOGY, U. OF CALIF., LOS ANGELES, 1956- . Doherty fellow (Mexico), 1955-56 ; National Science Foundation and U. of Calif. grants (Mexico) ; co-editor, Ethnohistory volumes, Handbook of Middle American Indians. Membership : American Anthropological Association ; Archaeological Institute of America ; Sociedad Mexicana de Antropología ; Society for American Archaeology. Research : ethnohistory and archeology of Meso-America ; pre-Hispanic and early colonial periods in central-southern Mexico. Language : Spanish 4,3,3,3 ; Portuguese 3,2,1,1 ; French 3,1,1,1 ; German 2,1,1,1 ; Nahuatl (classical) 2,,-,-,-. Home: 8353 Georgetown Ave., Los Angeles 45, Calif. Office: Dept. of Anthropology, U. of Calif., Los Angeles.

NIDA, EUGENE ALBERT, b. Oklahoma City, Okla., Nov. 11, 1914. ANTHROPOLOGY LINGUISTICS. A.B., U. of Calif., Los Angeles, 1936 ; M.A., U. of Southern Calif., 1939 ; Ph. D., U. of Mich., 1943. SECRETARY FOR TRANSLATIONS, AMERICAN BIBLE SOCIETY, 1943- . Membership : American Anthropological Association ; Linguistic Society of America ; Linguistic Society of New York. Research : Latin American language and culture. Author : God's Word in Man's Language (1952) ; Customs and Cultures (1954) ; Message and Mission (1960). Language : Spanish 4,4,4,3 ; Portuguese 3,2,3,1 ; French 4,4,4,3. Linguistic studies : Nahuatl ; Guaraní ; Haitian Creole ; Maya ; Quechua ; Spanish ; Tarahumara. Home: 33 Husted Lane, Greenwich, Conn. Office: American Bible Society, 450 Park Ave., New York 22, N.Y.

NIEMEYER, EBERHARDT VICTOR, JR., b. Houston, Tex., Sept. 28, 1919. HISTORY. Ph. D., U. of Tex., 1958. Dir., Instituto Hondureño de Cultura Interamericana (Tegucigalpa), U.S. Information Agency, 1953-55 ; dir., Instituto de Cultura Peruano Americano (Lima), 1955-56 ; asst. editor, Hispanic American Historical Review, U. of Tex., 1956-57 ; asst. prof., Tex. Coll. of Arts & Industries, 1957-58 ; vis. prof., U. of P.R., Summer 1958 ; dir., Instituto Guatemalteco Americano, U.S. Information Agency, 1958-60 ; dir., Philippine American Cultural Center (Manila), 1961-63 ; ASST. CULTURAL AFFAIRS OFFICER (MEXICO), U.S. INFORMATION AGENCY, 1963- . Carnegie Foundation grant, U. of N.C., Summer 1950. Membership: Sociedad de Geografía e Historia de Guatemala ; Sociedad Nuevoleonesa de Geografía, Historia, y Estadística ; Texas State Historical Association. Research : Mexican Constitutional Convention of 1916-17. Author : Anticlericalism in the Mexican Consitutional Convention of 1916-17 (The Americas, July 1954) ; Bernardo Reyes, fundador del moderno Nuevo León (Anales de la Sociedad de Geografía e Historia de Guatemala, 1959). Co-editor: Guide to the Hispanic American Historical Review, 1946-1955 (1958). Language : Spanish 4,4,4,4. Home: 2508 Indian Trail, Austin, Tex. 78703. Office: U.S. Information Agency, Washington, D.C. 20521.

NIGRO, FELIX ANTHONY, b. Brooklyn, N.Y., Aug. 8, 1914. POLITICAL SCIENCE. B.A., U. of Wis., 1935 ; M.A., 1936 ; Ph. D., 1948. Staff member, Griffenhagen & Associates (Venezuela), 1946-47 ; asst. prof., U. of Tex., 1948-49 ; vis. prof., U. of P.R., 1949-51 ; assoc. prof., Fla. State U., 1951-52 ; public administration consultant, Institute of Inter-American Affairs (Uruguay, Chile, El Salvador), 1952-54 ; senior assoc., J. L. Jacobs and Company, Management Consultants (Chicago), 1954 ; assoc. prof., U. of P.R., 1954-56 ; prof., Advanced School of Public Administration (Costa Rica), 1956-57 ; prof., Southern Ill. U., 1957-61 ; vis. prof., U. of Southern Calif., Spring 1960 ; PROF., POLITICAL SCIENCE, SAN DIEGO STATE COLL., 1961- . U. of Wis. fellow, 1947-48 ; consultant, International Cooperation Association (Venezuela, Chile), 1952, 1953 ; lectr., Conference of Pan American Sanitary Bureau on Water Finance and Administration (Mexico), Nov. 1960 ; lectr.-consultant, Public Administration Center (Guatemala), 1961. Research : public administration ; personnel administration ; government personnel in Latin America. Author : Administración de Personal (1956) ; Public Personnel administration (1959) ; Personnel Administration in Latin America (Personnel Administration, Nov.-Dec. 1957). Language : Spanish 5,5,5,5. Home: 6683 Hillgrove Dr., San Diego 20, Calif. Office: Dept. of Political Science, U. of Del., Newark.

NIST, JOHN ALBERT, b. Chicago, Ill., Nov. 27, 1925. BRAZILIAN LITERATURE. A.B., DePauw U., 1949 ; M.A., Ind. U., 1950 ; Ph. D., 1952. Asst. prof., Eastern Mich. U., 1952-55 ; assoc. prof., 1955-58, 1959 ; vis. prof., U. of Ariz., 1962-63 ; PROF., CHMN., ENGLISH, AUSTIN COLL., 1963- . Fulbright lectr., Universidade de São Paulo (Brazil), 1958-59 ; Social Science Research Council Latin America grant, Universidade do Brazil (Rio de Janeiro), 1961-62 ; Machado de Assis Medal, Brazilian Academy of Letters, 1964. Membership : American Association of Teachers of Spanish and Portuguese ; American Overseas Educators Organization ; Conference on College Composition and Communication ; Modern Language Association ; National Council of the Teachers of English ; National Geographic Society. Research : Modernist movement in Brazil ; modern Brazilian poetry ; English language and literature. Author : Modern Brazilian Poetry (1962) ; Contemporary Brazilian Poetry (Books Abroad, 1963). Language : Spanish 2,2,2,2 ; Portuguese 3, 3,3,3 ; French 2,2,2,2 ; German 2,2,2,2. Linguistic studies : English. Home: 2329 North Lockhart, Sherman, Tex. 75090. Office: Dept. of English, Box 621, Austin Coll., Sherman, 75091.

NORDELL, NORMAN WAYNE, b. San Diego, Calif., July 13, 1931. LINGUISTICS. B.A., Azusa Coll., 1954; San Diego State Coll. LINGUIST, SUMMER INSTITUTE OF LINGUISTICS (MEXICO), 1954– . Research: reconstruction and Bible translation. Author: On the Status of Popoluca in Zoque-Mixe (International Journal of American Linguistics, Apr. 1962). Language: Spanish 4,3,3,3; French 2,1,1,1; Mixe 3,3,3,3. Linguistic studies: Mixe. Home: 212 East 4th St., National City, Calif. Office: Instituto Lingüístico de Verano, Apartado 2975, México 1, D.F.

NORRIS, RENFRO COLE, b. Burnet, Tex., Mar. 13, 1921. EDUCATION. B.A., U. of Tex., 1948; M.A., 1951; Ph. D., U. of Mich., 1961. Television production, State Coll. of Wash., 1952–57; asst. dir., radio and television, U. of Tex., 1957–64; HEAD, BROADCASTING DIV., TEX. CHRISTIAN U., 1964– . Chmn., Conference on Mexican Broadcasting, U. of Tex., 1961; dir., Monterrey Educational Television Project, Instituto Tecnológico de Monterrey, 1963–64; UNESCO expert, Seminar on Educational Television (México, D.F.), Summer 1964. Membership: Alpha Epsilon Rho. Research: educational television; Latin American broadcasting. Author: Audience Oriented Television for Education (The Speech Teacher, Apr. 1953); TEMP–ITV in Texas (National Association of Educational Broadcasters Journal, May 1960); The Monterrey Educational Television Project (National Association of Educational Broadcasters Journal, July 1964). Language: Spanish 3,4,4,3; French 2,2,2,2. Office: Broadcast Div., Tex. Christian U., Fort Worth, Tex.

NOWOTNY, FRANZ A., b. Austria, June 6, 1934. ECONOMICS AND GEOGRAPHY. M.S., U. of Vienna (Austria), 1958; Ph. D., U. of Fla., 1960. Asst. prof., St. Francis Coll., 1961–63; assoc. prof., East Carolina Coll., 1963–64; ASSOC. PROF., ECONOMICS, ST. FRANCIS COLL., 1964– . U. of Fla. research grant. Membership: American Economic Association; Association of American Geographers. Research: recent economic development in Guatemala; Central America; La Plata republics. Language: Spanish 5,5,4,4; French 4,3,2,3; German 5,5,5,5; Italian 4,3,2,3. Home and office: Dept. of Economics, St. Francis Coll., Biddeford, Maine.

NÚÑEZ, BENJAMIN, b. Salta, Argentina, July 13, 1912. ANTHROPOLOGY: LINGUISTICS. Licenciado, Universidad de Buenos Aires, 1945; M.A., Colombia U., 1952; Ph. D., 1957. Prof., National Coll. (Salta, Argentina), 1947–51; PROF., INSTITUTE OF LANGUAGES AND LINGUISTICS, GEORGETOWN U., 1957– ; prof., Catholic U. (Ponce, P.R.), Summer 1963. Organization of American States summer grant (Argentina), 1959; Georgetown U. grant (Argentina), Summer 1962; consultant, Center for Intercultural Communication (Ponce, P.R.); Fulbright lectr., Catholic U. of Buenos Aires, 1964–65. Membership: American Anthropological Association; Anthropological Society of Washington, D.C.; Linguistic Circle of New York; Linguistic Society of America; Name Society; Society of Americanists. Research: cultural anthropology; lexicography of Argentine Spanish. Author: Fundamental Education: The Peruvian Case (1959). Language: Spanish 5,5,5,5; Portuguese 3,3,4,–; French 3,3,4,3. Linguistic studies: Argentine Spanish. Office: Institute of Languages and Linguistics, Georgetown U., Washington, D.C. 20007.

NUNEZ, THERON ALDINE, JR., b. Pittsburgh, Pa., Mar. 16, 1930. ANTHROPOLOGY. A.B., Fla. State U., 1955; M.A., 1956; Ph. D., U. of Calif., Berkeley, 1963. Instr., Fla. State U., 1957–58; ASST. PROF., ANTHROPOLOGY, U. OF FLA., 1963– . National Science Foundation grant. Membership: American Anthropological Association. Research: Spanish American culture; social structure and culture change; peasant society in Mexico. Author: The Creek War and Creek Nativism, 1813–1814 (Ethnohistory, 1958); Tourism, Tradition, and Acculturation: Weekendismo in a Mexican Village (Ethnology, July 1963). Language: Spanish 4,4, 3,3; German 2,2,2,1. Home: 4111 Northwest 11th St., Gainesville, Fla. Office: Dept. of Anthropology, U. of Fla., Gainesville.

NUNLEY, ROBERT E., b. Red Jacket, W. Va., Mar. 10, 1931. GEOGRAPHY. B.S., Marshall Coll., 1952; M.A., 1953; Ph. D., U. of Mich., 1958. Instr., Marshall Coll., 1952–53; strategic intelligence analyst, Latin American Section, Office of the Asst. Chief of Staff, 1953–55; instr.-asst. prof., Wayne State U., 1957–62; ASSOC. PROF., GEOGRAPHY, ASSOC. DIR., LATIN AMERICAN STUDIES, U. OF KANS., 1962– . Buenos Aires Convention fellow, 1953; National Academy of Sciences-National Research Council fellow (Costa Rica), 1956–57; National Science Foundation fellow, Northwestern U., Summer 1961; Status and Trends in Geography Committee, 1962– . Membership: American Association of University Professors; American Geographic Society; Association of American Geographers; Midwest Council for Latin American Studies; Phi Beta Kappa; Population Association of America; Regional Science Association. Research: manpower; distribution of population; Central America. Author: The Distribution of Population in Costa Rica (1960); Kansas University Faculty Interest in Latin America (1963). Language: Spanish 5,4,4,4; Portuguese 3,2, 1,1; German 3,2,1,1. Home: 1101 Ohio, Lawrence, Kans. Office: Dept. of Geography and Meteorology, U. of Kans., Lawrence, 66045.

NUNN, FREDERICK McKINLEY, b. Portland, Oreg., Oct. 29, 1937. HISTORY. B.A., U. of Oreg., 1959; U. of Calif., Berkeley, 1960; M.A., U. of N. Mex., 1963; Ph. D., 1963. Coordinator, El Salvador-Costa Rica U.S. Peace Corps Projects, U. of Okla., Summer 1963; ASST. PROF., HISTORY, ELBERT COVELL COLL., U. OF THE PACIFIC, 1963– . National Defense Education Act graduate fellow in Ibero-American Studies, U. of N. Mex., 1959–63; Doherty fellow (Chile and Peru), 1962. Membership: American Association of University Professors; American Historical Association. Research: Brazilian history and literature; the armed forces and political change in Latin America; Chilean history and politics. Language: Spanish 5,5, 5,5; Portuguese 5,5,5,4; French 4,3,3,2; German 2,2,1,1; Italian 4,3,1,1. Home: 814 North Tuxedo, Stockton, Calif. 95204. Office: Dept. of History, Elbert Covell Coll., U. of the Pacific, Stockton.

NUTINI, HUGO G., b. Peumo, Chile, June 26, 1928. ANTHROPOLOGY. B.S., Chilean Naval Academy, 1947; M.A., U. of Calif., Los Angeles, 1958; Ph. D., U. of Calif., Los Angeles, 1962. Asst. prof., Los Angeles State Coll., 1962–63; anthropologist, Pan American Union, 1962–63; ASST. PROF., ANTHROPOLOGY, U. OF PITTSBURGH, 1963– . Chilean Foreign Ministry fellow, 1950; Baker grant, U. of Calif., Los Angeles (Chile), Summer 1958; Social Science Research Council fellow (Mexico), Summer 1959, 1960–62; Pan American Union fellow, 1959–61. Membership: American Anthropological Association; American Association of Applied Anthropology; Institute of the Royal Anthropological Association. Research: social anthropology; social structure in Mexico; Mesoamerican and South American ethnology. Author: Roman Social Organization (Commentary, Apr. 1959); Polygyny and Clan Organization in a Nahuatl-Speaking Village (American Anthropologist, Feb. 1961); Polygyny and Family Structure (Ethnology, June 1963). Language: Spanish 5,5,5,5; Portuguese 4,3,3,3; French 4,4,4,3; Italian 5,5,5,5; Nahuatl –,3,3,–. Home: 3720 Parkview Ave., Pittsburgh 13, Pa. Office: Dept. of Anthropology, U. of Pittsburgh, Pittsburgh 13.

NUTTALL, DONALD ANDREW, b. San Diego, Calif., Mar. 14, 1926. HISTORY. A.B., San Diego State Coll., 1951; M.A., 1959; Ph. D., U. of Southern Calif., 1964. Instr.-ASST. PROF., HISTORY, WHITTIER COLL., 1961– . Membership: American Historical Association; California Historical Society. Research: Pedro Fages and the advance of the northern frontier of New Spain, 1767–1782. Language: Spanish 3,2,2,2. Home: 11045 Trudie St., Whittier, Calif. Office: Dept. of History, Whittier Coll., Whittier.

O

OBAID, ANTONIO H., b. Rancagua, Chile, May 22, 1917. LANGUAGE. B.A., Carleton Coll., 1941; M.A., U. of Nebr., 1942; Ph. D., U. of Minn., 1953. Instr., Carleton Coll., 1942–44; PROF., SPANISH, CARLETON COLL., 1946– ; vis. prof., U. of N. Mex., Summer 1963. Ford Foundation fellow (Spain), 1953–54; Hill Family Foundation study travel grant (Latin America), 1958. Membership: American Association of Teachers of Spanish and Portuguese; Modern Language Association; Phi Beta Kappa. Research: Chilean literature and language. Author: An Alliance for Progress: The Challenge and the Problem (1963). Language: Spanish 5,5,5,5; Portuguese 3,3,1,1; French 4,4,3,3; Arabic 1,3,2,1; Russian 3,3,3,3. Home: 305 Maple St., Northfield, Minn. 55057. Office: Dept. of Spanish, Carleton Coll., Northfield, 55057.

OBERG, KALERVO, b. Nanaimo, British Columbia, Canada, Jan. 15, 1901. ANTHROPOLOGY. B.A., U. of British Columbia, 1928; M.A., U. of Pittsburgh, 1930; Ph. D., U. of Chicago, 1933. Economic analyst, U.S. Dept. of Agriculture (N. Mex.), 1939–42; anthropologist, Office of the Coordinator of Inter-American Affairs (Ecuador, Peru), 1942–43; economic analyst, Food Div., Foreign Economic Administration (Washington, D.C.), 1944–45; anthropologist, Institute of Social Anthropology, Smithsonian Institution, (Escola de Sociologia e Política, U. of São Paulo), 1946–53; anthropological research consultant, U.S. Agency for International Development (Rio de Janeiro), 1953–59; community development adviser (Paramaribo, Surinam), 1959–63; PROF., ANTHROPOLOGY, CORNELL U., 1963– . Social Science Research Council fellow (Uganda), 1934–36; International African Institute grant, London School of Economics, 1937. Membership: American Anthropological Association; Royal Anthropological Society of Great Britain; International African Institute. Research: peasant communities of Surinam and Brazil; primitive Indian tribes of Brazil; community development in Brazil. Author: The Indians of the Northern Mato Grosso (1949); Types of Social Structures Among the Lowland Tribes of South and Central America (American Anthropologist, June 1955); The Marginal Peasant in Rural Brazil (1959). Language: Spanish 4,3,2,3; Portuguese 5,4,4,3; French 3,2,1,1; German 3,1,1,1. Home: Lansing Apts. G2–5, Ithaca, N.Y. 14850. Office: Dept. of Anthropology, Cornell U., Ithaca, 14850.

OBERHELMAN, HARLEY DEAN, b. Clay Center, Kans., June 30, 1928. SPANISH AMERICAN LITERATURE AND LANGUAGE. B.S., U. of Kans., 1950; M.A., 1952; Ph. D., 1958. Instr., U. of Kans., 1955–56; HEAD, FOREIGN LANGUAGES, TEX. TECHNOLOGICAL COLL., 1958– . Fulbright lectr., National U. of Tucumán (Argentina), 1961–62; State of Texas research grant (Uruguay), 1962; assoc. editor, Hispania, 1962– . Membership: American Association of Teachers of Spanish and Portuguese; American Overseas Educators Organization; Modern Language Association; Rocky Mountain Conference of Latin American Studies. Research: modern and contemporary literature of Spanish America; literature of the River Plate; linguistics and methodology of teaching Spanish and English as a foreign language; language laboratory operations. Author: Español Moderno, Book I (1964); La Revista Azul y el modernismo mexicano (Journal of Inter-American Studies, July 1959); Contemporary Uruguay as Seen in Amorim's First Cycle (Hispania, May 1963); Language: Spanish 4,4,4,4; Portuguese 3,3,2,1; French 4,3,2,2. Linguistic studies: English; Spanish. Home: 3005 54th St., Lubbock, Tex., 79413. Office: Dept. of Foreign Languages, Tex. Technological Coll., Lubbock, 79409.

OBERLITNER, THOMAS BILLING, b. Gettysburg, Ohio, Feb. 8, 1914. POLITICAL SCIENCE. A.B., U. of Southern Calif., 1946; A.M., U. of Calif., Berkeley, 1947; Ph. D., Stanford U., 1950. Latin American area specialist, U.S. Dept. of Defense, 1953–56; deputy chief, Latin American branch, Office of Research, U.S. Information Agency, 1956–60; part-time instr., American U., 1959–60; RESEARCH OFFICER, U.S. ARMY COMBAT DEVELOPMENTS COMMAND COMMUNICATIONS-ELECTRONICS AGENCY, 1960– ; part-time vis. lectr., U. of Ariz., 1961–62. Membership:

Pi Sigma Alpha. Research: United States and Mexico, 1921–32; Chile, Ecuador, and Bolivia. Language: Spanish 4,3,3,3; Portuguese 2,–,–,–; French 2,–,–,–. Home: 7229 Flamenco Dr., Tucson, Ariz. 85710. Office: U.S. Army Combat Developments Command Communications-Electronics Agency, Fort Huachuca, Ariz. 85613.

O'CONNOR, JAMES R., b. Newton, Mass., Apr. 20, 1930. ECONOMICS. B.S., Columbia U., 1955; Ph. D., 1964. Instr., Barnard Coll., 1958–64; ASST. PROF., ECONOMICS, WASH. U., 1964– . Contributor, Bibliography of Latin American Agrarian Reform, Inter-American Development Bank. Membership: American Economic Association. Research: political economy; Cuba. Author: On Cuban Political Economy (Political Science Quarterly, June 1964); Stalemate in Latin America (Studies on the Left, Fall 1964); The Foundations of Cuban Socialism (Studies on the Left, Fall 1964). Language: Spanish 4,4,3,3; Portuguese 1,1,1,1; French 2,2,2,1. Home: 6908 Millbrook Blvd., University City, Mo. Office: Dept. of Economics, Wash. U., St. Louis, Mo.

OFFICER, JAMES E., b. Boulder, Colo., July 28, 1924. ANTHROPOLOGY. A.B., U. of Ariz., 1950; Ph. D., 1964. Asst. information officer, American Embassy (Santiago, Chile), 1951–53; radio-television announcer (Tucson), 1954–60; instr., U. of Ariz., 1955–60; ASSOC. COMMISSIONER, BUREAU OF INDIAN AFFAIRS, U.S. DEPT. OF THE INTERIOR, 1961– . Member, Secretary Udall's Task Force on Indian Affairs, 1961; vis. prof., Training Centers for Indian Community Development (Mexico, Bolivia), 1964; consultant to U.S. Dept. of State on Inter-American Indian Institute. Membership: American Anthropological Association; Society for American Archaeology; Society for Applied Anthropology. Research: Indian community development; American Indians; Spanish-speaking minority of the Southwest; Mexican folkways; Chile. Author: Indians in School (1956); A Note on the Elias Family of Tucson (Arizona and the West, Winter 1959). Language: Spanish 4,4,4,4; Portuguese 2,1,1,1; French 2,1,1,1; German 2,1,1,1. Home: 320 N St., SW., Washington, D.C. 20024. Office: Bureau of Indian Affairs, U.S. Dept. of the Interior, Washington, D.C.

OGELSBY, JOHN C. M., b. Philadelphia, Pa., (Sept. 22, 1931. HISTORY. A.B., Stanford U., 1953; U. of London, 1955–56; M.A., U. of Wash., 1960; Ph. D., 1963. ASST. PROF., HISTORY, U. OF VICTORIA (CANADA), 1961– . Teaching fellow, U. of Wash., 1958–60; University grant, 1964. Membership: Canadian Historical Association; Conference on Latin American History; Hispanic American Society; Navy Records Society. Research: 18th century Caribbean history; colonial period in history of New World; logwood trade in the Caribbean. Author: Graduate Research in Europe (The Historian, May 1963); British and Panama, 1742 (Caribbean Studies, July 1963); Argentina: No Habrá Progreso (Canadian Forum, Nov. 1963). Language: Spanish 3,3,3,2; French 3,3,3,1. Home: 2671 Margate, Victoria, British Columbia, Canada. Office: Dept. of History, U. of Victoria, Victoria.

OLDMAN, OLIVER, b. New York, N.Y., July 19, 1920. LAW AND ECONOMICS. S.B., Harvard Coll., 1942; LL. B., Harvard Law School, 1953. PROF., LAW, DIR. OF TRAINING, INTERNATIONAL PROGRAM IN TAXATION, HARVARD LAW SCHOOL, 1955– . Committee on Latin American Affairs, Harvard U.; consultant on fiscal reform in Costa Rica, United Nations. Membership: American Bar Association; International Association of Assessing Officers; National Tax Association. Research: tax law and public finance; taxation in Argentina, El Salvador, Mexico, and Venezuela. Author: Tax System of Argentina: A Survey of Issues (Public Finance, 1961); Controlling Income Tax Evasion (Organization of American States, 1963). Co-author: Fiscal System of Venezuela (1959). Language: Spanish 2,2,2,2; French 2,2,2,2. Home: 15 Buckingham St., Cambridge, Mass. 02138. Office: Harvard Law School, Langdell Hall, Cambridge, 02138.

OLIVER, COVEY (THOMAS), b. Laredo, Tex., Apr. 21, 1913. LAW AND EDUCATION. (B.A., U. of Tex., 1933; LL. B., 1936; LL.M., Columbia U., 1953; J.S.D., 1954. Assoc. prof., U. of Tex., 1936–41; senior attorney, Board of Economic Warfare, 1942; Foreign Service auxiliary, U.S. Dept. of State, 1942–45; div. chief, U.S. Dept. of State, 1945–49; Walter Perry Johnson Prof., School of Law, U. of Calif., Berkeley, 1949–56; PROF., LAW, SCHOOL OF LAW, U. OF PA., 1956– . Carnegie Endowment lectr., Hague Academy of International Law, 1955; Fulbright fellow and lectr. (São Paulo), 1962; U.S. member, Inter-American Juridical Committee, Organization of American States; Board of Editors, American Journal of International Law. Membership: American Bar Association; American Society of International Law; International Law Association; Phi Beta Kappa; Philadelphia Bar Association; Texas Bar Association. Research: international transactions law; international public law; maritime law; international organizations law and policy; Latin American university organization and administration. Author: Restatement of the Foreign Relations Law of the United States (1962); The Interamerican Security System and the Cuban Crisis (1962). Contributor: Law and Politics in the World Community (1953). Language; Spanish 5,5,4,4; Portuguese 5,5,3,3; French 4,4,2,2. Home: 35 Violet Lane, Lansdowne, Pa., Office: School of Law, U. of Pa., Philadelphia 4.

OLIVERA, GUIDO FRANCISCO, b. Colón, Cuba, Sept. 15, 1914. LIBRARY SCIENCE: BIBLIOGRAPHY. A.B., B.S., Havana Institute, 1937; Doctor in Law, Havana U., 1941; M.S.L.S., Syracuse U., 1965. Counselor at law (Havana, Cuba), 1941–45; counselor at law, asst. head, Tax Dept., Morán, Valdés, Rodríguez and Forcade (Havana, Cuba), 1945–50, head, tax dept., 1950–60; counselor at law, Chamber of Commerce of the Republic of Cuba, 1950–60; LATIN AMERICAN BIBLIOGRAPHER, ORDER DEPT., MAIN LIBRARY, SYRACUSE U., 1962– . Membership: Asociación Cubana de Especialistas en Asuntos Económicos y Fiscales; Cuban Bar Association. Research: tax law; bibliography of Argentina, Paraguay and Uruguay. Language: Spanish 5,5,5,5; Portuguese 3,3,1,1; Italian 2,2,–,1. Home: 249

West Borden Ave., Syracuse, N.Y. 13205. Office: Order Dept., Main Library, Syracuse U., Syracuse, 13210.

OLIVERA, OTTO HUGO, b. Pedro Betancourt, Cuba, Apr. 20, 1919. SPANISH AMERICAN LITERATURE. Doctorate, Universidad de la Habana, 1945; M.A., La. State U., 1947; Ph. D., Tulane U., 1953. Instr., Tulane U., 1950–54; ASSOC. PROF., ROMANCE LANGUAGES, CHMN., LATIN AMERICAN CONCENTRATION, SYRACUSE U., 1954– . Dir., Syracuse Semester in Guatemala, 1961, 1963; consultant, Experiment in International Living, 1963. Membership: American Association of Teachers of Spanish and Portuguese; American Association of University Professors; Instituto Internacional de Literatura Iberoamericana; Modern Language Association; New York Federation of Language Teachers. Research: literature of Spanish Antilles, Spanish Caribbean, and Central America; poetry of Cuba. Author: Breve historia de la literatura antillana (1957); El romanticismo de José Eustasio Rivera (Revista Iberoamericana, Feb. 1952); María, tema predilecto de Isaacs (Symposium, 1960). Language: Spanish 5,5,5,5; Portuguese 3,4,2,2; French 2,-,-,-; Italian 2,3,1,1. Linguistic studies: English; Portuguese; Spanish. Home: 114 Conan St., Syracuse 7, N.Y. Office: Dept. of Romance Languages, Syracuse U., Syracuse 10.

OLMSTED, DAVID L., b. Jamestown, N.Y., Mar. 11, 1926. ANTHROPOLOGY: LINGUISTICS. A.B., Cornell U., 1947; M.A., 1948; Ph. D., 1950. Instr., Northwestern U., 1950–51; asst. prof., Yale U., 1951–54; asst. prof.-PROF., ANTHROPOLOGY, U. OF CALIF., DAVIS, 1954– . Social Science Research Council faculty research fellow, 1957–58; Guggenheim fellow, 1961. Membership: American Anthropological Association; Linguistic Society of America. Research: dialectology of New World Spannish and Portuguese; comparative linguistics of African languages spoken in New World; Hokan ethnology. Author: A History of Palaihnihan Phonology (1964); Palaihnihan and Shasta I: Labial Stops (Language, Jan.–Mar. 1956); Palaihnihan and Shasta II: Apical Stops (Language, Apr.–June 1957). Language: Spanish 3,3,3,3; Portuguese 3,2,2,2; French 3,2,2,2; Russian 4,4,4,3. Linguistic studies: Achumawi; Atsugewi; Basque; Bricamu; Lucumi; Shasta; Tequistlatecan; Tlapanecan; Yoruba. Home: 717 Miller Dr., Davis, Calif. Office: Dept. of Anthropology, U. of Calif., Davis.

OLSON, DONALD W., b. Sandstone, Minn., Mar. 6, 1922. LINGUISTICS. B.A., Wheaton Coll., 1948; M.A., Ind. U., 1957. LINGUISTIC INVESTIGATOR, SUMMER INSTITUTE OF LINGUISTICS, 1950– ; teacher, English, Ind. U., 1957; teacher, English, Hartford Seminary Foundation, 1963–64. Membership: Linguistic Society of America. Research: Pame and Zapotec Indians of Mexico; divisive and nondivisive affixes in Pame. Author: Spanish Loan Words in Pame (International Journal of American Linguistics, Oct. 1963); Pame Texts (Tlalocán, 1963). Co-author: Classification of Consonant Clusters (Language, 1958). Language: Spanish 4,4,4,3; Pame 2,2,2,2; Cheyenne 1,1,1,1; Zapotec 2,2,2,2. Linguistic studies: Cheyenne, Pame, Zapotec. Home: Box 483, Sandstone, Minn. 55072. Office: Summer Institute of Linguistics, Box 1960, Santa Ana, Calif.

OLSON, ERNEST CHARLES, b. Chicago, Ill., Aug. 6, 1911. ECONOMICS. B.A., U. of Chicago. Economist, War Production Board, 1942–44; economist, U.S. Dept. of State, 1944–47; economist, Latin American Section, Div. of International Finance, Federal Reserve Board, 1947–55; head, Latin American Section, 1952–55; CONSULTING ECONOMIST, BANK OF AMERICA (SAN FRANCISCO), 1956– . Adviser, Government of Guatemala, 1949; member, Federal Reserve Missions to Paraguay, 1951; adviser, Central Bank of Ecuador, 1957; adviser, Central Reserve Bank of El Salvador, 1961, 1964; adviser, Government of Nicaragua, 1962. Membership: American Economic Association; American Finance Association; American Statistical Association; Western Economic Association. Research: international trade and finance; monetary and fiscal policy; banking legislation with special emphasis on developing countries. Author: Factors Affecting International Differences in Production (Papers and Proceedings, American Economic Association, May 1948). Co-author: Public Finance and Economic Development in Guatemala (1952). Language: Spanish 3,3,2,2. Home: 322 Highland Ave., San Rafael, Calif. Office: Bank of America, N.T. & S.A., 300 Montgomery St., San Francisco, Calif.

OLTROGGE, DAVID FREDERICK, b. Waverly, Iowa, June 28, 1936. LINGUISTICS. LINGUIST, SUMMER INSTITUTE OF LINGUISTICS, 1960– . Research: descriptive linguistics; Jicaque language of Central Honduras. Language: Spanish 3,3,3,3. Linguistic studies: Jicaque. Home: 3325 West Lynwood, Phoenix, Ariz. 85018. Office: Summer Institute of Linguistics, P.O. Box 1960, Santa Ana, Calif. 92702.

O'NEILL, GEORGE CARACENA, b. New York, N.Y., Mar. 22, 1921. ANTHROPOLOGY AND ENGINEERING. B.A., Columbia Coll., 1944; Ph. D., Columbia U., 1962. Field archeologist, River Basin Surveys, Smithsonian Institution (S. Dak.), 1951–52; instr., Hunter Coll., 1954–55; architectural engineer and space designer, Rodger's Associates (N.Y.), 1955–57; project coordinator, Hilton Hotels International (N.Y., Canada, Cuba, Trinidad), 1957–60; account executive, Lippincott & Margulies (N.Y.), 1960–61; ASST. PROF., ANTHROPOLOGY, CITY COLL. (N.Y.), 1961– . Doherty fellow (Mexico), 1952–53; Voss Fund award, American Museum of Natural History (Mexico), 1953; Tishman scholar award, Columbia U., 1954; consultant and research dir., Puerto Rican Social Services, Inc. (N.Y.), 1964; Institute for Community Research and Development, City Coll.; research dir., Center for Latin American Studies, City Coll. Membership: American Anthropological Association; Centro de Investigaciones Antropológicas de México; Interamerican Society of Psychology; Sociedad Mexicana de Antropología; Society for American Archaeology; Society for International Development. Research: archeology; fossil man in Middle America; civil and architectural engineering; Mexico. Author: Report of Discovery of Fossil Man and Lithic Industry at Aztahuacan, Mexico (American

Antiquity, 1954) ; Una contribución geológica- arqueológica al problema de niveles de lagos de la cuenca de México (Revista Mexicana de Estudios Antropológicos, 1954–55) ; Vocational Rehabilitation Needs of Disabled Puerto Ricans in New York City (Puerto Rican Social Services, Apr. 1964). Language: Spanish 5,5,5,4 ; Portuguese 1,1,1,1 ; French 3,3,3,3. Home : 2 Ellwood St., New York, N.Y. 10040. Office: Center for Latin American Studies, City Coll. (N.Y.), Convent Ave. at 138th St., New York, 10031.

OPPERMAN, HENRY JAMES, b. Long Beach, Calif., Mar. 15, 1925. EDUCATION. B.A., U. of Calif., Santa Barbara, 1948 ; M.A., Stanford U., 1965. Instr., Santa Maria Union High School and Junior Coll. (Calif.), 1948–51 ; instr., Hartnell A. & M. Coll. 1951–54 ; trade and industrial education adviser, Foreign Operations Administration, U.S. Dept. of State (Managua, Nicaragua), 1954–59 ; adviser, International Cooperation Administration, U.S. Dept. of State (Cali, Colombia), 1959–61 ; vocational education adviser, U.S. Agency for International Development, U.S. Dept. of State (Tehran, Iran), 1962–64 ; RESEARCH ASST., SCHOOL OF EDUCATION, STANFORD U., 1964– . Membership : American Vocational Association ; Epsilon Pi Tau ; Kappa Delta Pi ; National Planning Association. Research : training programs for vocational-industrial teachers ; shop organization and management ; curriculum development. Author : Technical Vocabulary, Spanish English-Mechanical (1958). Language : Spanish 4,4,4,4 ; Portuguese 3,3,2,– ; Farsi –,2,2,–. Home : 153 Pier St., Shell Beach, Calif. Office : School of Education, Stanford U., Stanford, Calif.

ORJUELA, HÉCTOR HUGO, b. Bogotá, Colombia, July 29, 1930. SPANISH AMERICAN LITERATURE AND LANGUAGE. B.A., M.A., North Tex. State U., 1952 ; Ph. D., U. of Kans., 1960. Instr., Va. Military Institute, 1956–58 ; asst. prof., 1958–60 ; ASST. PROF., LATIN AMERICAN LITERATURE, U. OF SOUTHERN CALIF., 1960– . Good-Neighbor scholar, North Tex. State U., 1951 ; vis. prof., National Defense Education Act Institute, Tex. Technical Coll., Summer 1961 ; asst. prof., National Defense Education Act Institute, U. of Southern Calif., Summers 1962–64. Membership : American Association of Teachers of Spanish and Portuguese ; Instituto Caro y Cuervo ; Instituto de Literatura Iberoamericana ; Modern Language Association. Research : Latin American poetry ; Colombian bibliography. Author : Biografía y bibliografía de Rafael Pombo (1964) ; Revaloración de una vieja polémica literaria (1964). Co-author : Spanish Conversational Review Grammar (1964). Language : Spanish 5,5,5,5 ; Portuguese 4,4,3,3 ; French 4,4,3,3. Home : 10261½ West 35th St., Los Angeles 7, Calif. Office : Dept. of Spanish, U. of Southern Calif., Los Angeles 7.

ORNE, JERROLD, b. St. Paul, Minn., Mar. 25, 1911. LIBRARY SCIENCE. M.A., U. of Minn., 1933 ; Ph. D., U. of Chicago, 1939 ; B.S., U. of Minn., 1940. Librarian and prof,. Knox Coll., 1941–43 ; librarian, Washington U., 1946–51 ; librarian, Air U., Maxwell Air Force Base, 1951–57 ; LIBRARIAN, U. OF N.C., 1957– . Library of Congress fellow, 1940–41 ; consultant in library education (Cuba), Library of Congress-U.S. Dept. of State, Summers 1950, 1951 ; assoc. editor, American Documentation, 1953–57 ; consultant, Library of Congress, National Aeronautics and Space Administration, and U.S. Dept. of Commerce ; editorial consultant, Library Journal, 1962–64. Membership : American Association of University Professors ; American Library Association ; Associated Research Libraries ; Association of Southeastern Research Libraries ; North Carolina Library Association. Research : documentation. Author : Language of the Foreign Book Trade (1949, 1962) ; The Future of Libraries in Cuba (Missouri Library Association Quarterly, Sept. 1950) ; Planning a New Library School in Cuba (Library of Congress Information Bulletin, Sept. 1950). Language : Spanish 4,4,4,4 ; Portuguese 3,2,1,1 ; French 5,5,5,5 ; German 3,3,1,1 ; Italian 5,5,3,3. Home : 529 Dogwood Dr., Chapel Hill, N.C. Office : Library, U. of N.C., Chapel Hill.

ORR, CAROLYN, b. Brownsville, Tex., Sept. 20, 1925. LINGUISTICS. B.A., Columbia Bible Coll., 1947 ; M.A., Ind. U., 1958 ; U. of Tex. Teacher (Chadbourn, N.C.), 1948–50 ; LINGUIST, SUMMER INSTITUTE OF LINGUISTICS (ECUADOR), 1950– . Research : language learning ; translation ; Quichua reading materials ; Ecuador ; Peru. Author : Ecuador Quichua Phonology (1962) ; Ecuador Quichua Clause Structure (1962). Language : Spanish 3,3,3,3 ; Quichua 4,4,4,4. Linguistic studies : Quichua. Home : 2324 Cravens Rd., Fort Worth, Tex. Office : Instituto Lingüístico de Verano, Casilla 1007, Quito, Ecuador.

ORREGO-SALAS, JUAN ANTONIO, b. Santiago, Chile, Jan. 18, 1919. MUSIC. Diploma, Catholic U. of Chile, 1943 ; M.A., U. of Chile, 1944 ; Ph. D., 1952. Prof., National Conservatory, U. of Chile, 1943–61 ; lectr., Catholic U. of Santiago, 1946–48 ; music critic, El Mercurio (Santiago), 1949–61 ; dir., Instituto de Extensión Musical, U. of Chile, 1956–59 ; chmn., Music, Catholic U. of Chile, 1958–61 ; PROF., MUSIC, DIR., LATIN AMERICAN MUSIC CENTER, IND. U., 1961– . Rockefeller Foundation scholar, 1944–55 ; Guggenheim fellow, 1945–46, 1954–55 ; editor, Revista Musical Chilena, 1949–56 ; Rockefeller Foundation grant, 1961–62. Membership : American Musicological Society ; Asociación de Educación Musical (Chile) ; Asociación Nacional de Compositores (Chile) ; Music Teachers National Association : Instituto de Investigaciones Musicales (Chile) ; International Society for Contemporary Music. Research : composition ; art, folk, and primitive music ; folkmusic and literature of contemporary music with emphasis on the trends of nationalistic developments in Chile. Author : A Journey through Latin American Music (1963) ; The Young Generation of Latin American Composers (1963) ; Chilean Contemporary Music (1963). Language : Spanish 5,5,5,5 ; Portuguese 3,4,2,2 ; French 4,4,4,4 ; German 3,2,2,2. Home : R.F.D. 2, Box 234X, Bloomington, Ind. Office : Latin American Music Center, School of Music MA-318, Ind. U., Bloomington.

OSBORN, HENRY A., JR., b. Birmingham, Ala., June 4, 1924. LINGUISTICS. A.B., Ind. U., 1948 ; M.A., 1957 ; Ph. D., 1962. Missionary-linguist, Wycliffe Bible Translators, 1945–47 ; MISSIONARY, LINGUIST, BAPTIST MID-MISSIONS, 1952– . Research : translation of Biblical materials in Spanish and American Indian languages ; Mexico ; Peru ; Venezuela. Author : Textos folklóricos en Guarao (Boletín Indigenista Venezolano, Mar. 1958). Language : Spanish 5,5,4,4 ; Portuguese 4,4,3,1 ; French 2,1,1,1 ; German 3,1,1,1 ; Warao 5,4,4,4. Linguistic studies : Amahuaca ; Warao. Home : 1463 Ryar Rd., Jacksonville, Fla. 32216. Office : Baptist Mid-Missions, 1740 East 12th St., Cleveland 14, Ohio.

OSBORNE, CAROLYN M., b. Teh Chow, China, Jan. 25, 1919. ANTHROPOLOGY. B.A., U. of N. Mex., 1938 ; M.A., 1941. Curator of Anthropology, Washington State Museum, U. of Wash., 1951–52 ; ANTHROPOLOGY AID, WETHERILL MESA PROJECT, MESA VERDE NATIONAL PARK, 1960– . Research : archeology ; material culture ; primitive textiles. Author : Shaped Breechcloths from Peru (1950). Co-author : A Burial Cave in Baja California (1961). Co-editor : Textiles of Ancient Peru (1962). Language : Spanish 4,3,2,2 ; French 4,1,1,–. Home and office : Mesa Verde National Park, Colo. 81330.

OSWALD, J. GREGORY, b. Chicago, Ill., Mar. 18, 1922. HISTORY. B.A., U. of Calif., Berkeley, 1948 ; M.A., Loyola U. (Ill.), 1950 ; Ph. D., Stanford U., 1958. Instr., Stanford U., 1955–58 ; ASSOC. PROF., HISTORY, U. OF ARIZ., 1958– . Mershon post-doctoral fellow, Ohio State U., 1962–63 ; consultant and project director, Hispanic Foundation, Library of Congress, 1963– . Contributing editor, Handbook of Latin American Studies. Membership : American Association for the Advancement of Slavic Studies ; Far West Slavic Conference. Research : Soviet history ; Soviet historical writing on Latin America ; an analysis of Soviet interpretations of Latin American history, particularly their emphasis on problems of Mexican history. Author : A Soviet Criticism of the Hispanic American Historical Review (Hispanic American Historical Review, Aug. 1960) ; Soviet News and Notes (Hispanic American Historical Review, Feb. 1961) ; La Revolución Mexicana en la Historiografía Soviética (Historia Mexicana, Jan. 1963). Language : Spanish 3,3,3,3 ; French 3,2,3,2 ; Czech 5,5, 5,5 ; German 4,4,4,4 ; Russian 5,5,5,5 ; Slovak 5,5,5,5. Home : 2708 East Glenn St., Tucson, Ariz. Office : Dept. of History, U. of Ariz., Tucson.

OTTE, ROBERT CHARLES, b. Douglas County, Nebr., Aug. 17, 1922. ECONOMICS. B.S., U. of Nebr., 1947 ; M.A., 1954 ; Ph. D., U. of Wis., 1956. Vocational agriculture instr., Elliott Consolidated Schools (Iowa), 1948–51 ; research asst., U. of Nebr., 1952–54 ; research asst., U. of Wis., 1954–55 ; instr., U. of Wis., 1955–56 ; agricultural economist, Economic Research Service, U.S. Dept. of Agriculture (Washington, D.C.), 1956–64 ; AGRICULTURAL ECONOMIST, ECONOMIC RESEARCH SERVICE, U.S. DEPT. OF AGRICULTURE (QUITO, ECUADOR), 1964– . Regional Research Committee of the Great Plains Council ; North Central Land Economics Committee ; Southeast Land Tenure Research Committee. Membership : American Farm Economic Association ; Soil Conservation Society of America. Research : economics of land and water use ; technical assistance in agrarian reform and colonization. Author : Local Resource Protection and Development Districts (1957) ; Present State District Laws as They Affect Watershed Programs (in Economics of Watershed Planning, 1961) ; Districts that Manage Resources (in A Place to Live, 1963). Language : Spanish 3,3,3,3. Home : Luis Cordero 942, Quito, Ecuador. Office : U.S. Dept. of Agriculture Team, U.S. AID Mission, c/o American Embassy, Quito.

OWEN, GEORGE HODGES, b. Berlin, Germany, Sept. 16, 1912. LAW. Bacc., U. of Paris, 1932 ; Diploma, Ecole des Sciences Politiques, 1935 ; LL.B., Law School, Fordham U., 1942. Lectr., Fordham U., 1939–42 ; legal asst. to U.S. member, Inter-American Committee for Political Defense (Montevideo, Uruguay), 1946–47 ; desk officer for Ecuador, Peru, Chile, Bureau of Inter-American Affairs, U.S. Dept. of State, 1947–51 ; U.S. member, Inter-American Juridical Committee (Rio de Janeiro), 1951–57 ; counselor for political affairs, Embassy (Brazil), U.S. Dept. of State, 1953–56 ; consul general (Guayaquil, Ecuador), 1956–58 ; special asst. for Antarctica, U.S. Dept. of State, 1958–62 ; CHIEF, ADVISORY OPINIONS DIV., VISA OFFICE, U.S. DEPT. OF STATE, 1962– . Alternate U.S. representative, Inter-American Council of Jurists (Buenos Aires), 1953, (Mexico), 1956. Membership : American Bar Association ; New York State Bar Association. Research : comparative private law ; civil and procedural law ; internatioanl law. Language : Spanish 5,4,4,4 ; Portuguese 4,4,3,3 ; French 5,5,4,5 ; German 3,4,4,3 ; Italian 4,3,2,1 ; Latin 3,–,–,2. Home : 3018 P St., NW., Washington, D.C. 20007. Office : U.S. Dept. of State, Washington, D.C. 20520.

OWEN, ROGER CORY, b. Port Arthur, Tex., Sept. 14, 1928. ANTHROPOLOGY. B.A., Mich. State U., 1953 ; M.A., U. of Ariz., 1957 ; Ph. D., U. of Calif., Los Angeles, 1962. ASST. PROF., ANTHROPOLOGY, U. OF CALIF., SANTA BARBARA, 1959– . Social Science Research Council fellow (Baja California, Mexico), 1958–59 ; consultant, General Motors Defense Systems Division, 1961 ; U. of Calif. faculty summer fellow, 1963. Membership : American Anthropological Association ; Arizona Archaeological and Historical Society ; Sigma Xi ; Southwestern Anthropological Association. Research : ethnography of northern Baja California ; Indians of Santa Catarina, Baja California ; peasant life in Northwest Mexico. Author : Marobavi : A Study of an Assimilated Group in Northern Sonora (Anthropological Papers, U. of Ariz., 1959). Language : Spanish 3,3,3,2. Linguistic studies : Paipai. Home : 541 Dalton Way, Goleta, Calif. Office : Dept. of Sociology and Anthropology, U. of Calif., Santa Barbara.

P

PACHECO, ARMANDO CORREIA, b. Curitiba, Paraná, Brazil, Nov. 19, 1915. PHILOSOPHY AND BRAZILIAN LITERATURE. Ph. B., Catholic U. of São Paulo, 1939 ; Ph. D., Notre Dame U., 1946. Chief, Section of Letters, Pan American Union, 1951–58 ; CHIEF, DIV. OF PHILOSOPHY AND LETTERS, PAN AMERICAN UNION, 1958– . Inter-American Committee, Organization of American States ; editor, Inter-American Review of Bibliography, Membership: Brazilian American Institute; Modern Language Association; Sociedad Iberoamericana de Filosofía. Research: Latin American philosophy and literature, particularly Brazilian philosophy and literature. Author: Machado de Assis, Romancista (1949, 1954); Joaquím Nabuco; acción y pensamiento (1950); Graça Aranha: la obra y el hombre (1951); Ensayistas del Brasil: Escuela de Recife (1952). Language: Spanish 5,5,5,5; Portuguese 5,5,5,5; French 5,5,5,5. Home: 400 Valley Lane, Falls Church, Va. Office: Div. of Philosophy and Letters, Pan American Union, Washington, D.C. 20006.

PACKENHAM, ROBERT ALLEN, b. Watertown, S. Dak., Oct. 5, 1937. POLITICAL SCIENCE. B.A., Augustana Coll., 1958; M.A., U. of Ill., 1959; Ph. D., Yale U., 1964. Intern, International Cooperation Administration, Summer 1961; FOREIGN AREA FELLOWSHIP PROGRAM FELLOW (BRAZIL), 1963-65; Yale U. fellow, 1959-62; research fellow, Brookings Institution, 1962-63. Membership: American Political Science Association. Research: foreign aid and political development; political system of Brazil. Author: Approaches to the Study of Political Development (World Politics, Oct. 1964). Language: Spanish 2,2,1,1; Portuguese 3,3,3,3; French 2,1,1,2; German 2,2,2,2. Home: 4118 Sheridan Rd., Zion, Ill. Office: c/o Dept. of Political Science, Yale U., New Haven, Conn.

PADDEN, ROBERT CHARLES, b. St. Paul, Minn., Sept. 14, 1922. HISTORY. B.A., U. of Calif., Santa Barbara, 1952; M.A., U. of Calif., Berkeley, 1954; Ph. D., 1959. Lectr., U. of Calif., Berkeley, 1957-58; asst. prof., 1958-64; ASSOC. PROF., HISTORY, ST. NORBERT COLL., 1964- . Membership: American Historical Association; Conference on Latin American History. Research: ethnohistory; the ethnohistory of nationalism; cultural history of mestizaje in Mexico; colonial Church in New Spain; Araucanian C h i l e . Language: Spanish 4,4,4,4; Portuguese 4,4,3,3; French 3,3,2,3; German 3,3,2,3; Italian 3,3,2,3. Home: R.F.D. 2, West De Pere, Wis. Office: Dept. of History, St. Norbert Coll., West De Pere.

PADGETT, L. VINCENT, b. Salina, Kans., Jan. 6, 1924. POLITICAL SCIENCE. B.S.S., Northwestern U., 1950; Ph. D., 1955. Asst. prof., Tex. Technological Coll., 1954-55; ASSOC. PROF., POLITICAL SCIENCE, SAN DIEGO STATE COLL., 1956- . Doherty fellow (Mexico), 1952-53; dir., Second Inter-American Seminar, Eighth Inter-American Municipal Congress, 1960; Social Science Research Council fellow (Mexico), Summer 1963. Membership: American Political Science Association; Pacific Coast Council of Latin American Studies. Research: Latin American comparative government; Mexico. Author: Mexico's One-Party System: A Reevaluation (American Political Science Review, Dec. 1957); Power Structure and Decision-making in a Mexican Border City (American Journal of Sociology, Jan. 1960); Community Development in the Western Hemisphere (San Diego State Coll. Public Affairs Research Institute, Aug. 1961). Language: Spanish 5,5,4,3. Home: 5845 Yorkshire Ave., La Mesa, Calif. Office: Dept. of Political Science, San Diego State Coll., San Diego, Calif., 92115.

PADILLA, ELENA, b. San Juan, P.R., Apr. 9, 1923. ANTHROPOLOGY. B.A., U. of P.R., 1943; M.A., U. of Chicago, 1947; Ph. D., Columbia U., 1951. Research assoc., U. of Ill., 1952-53; instr., Cornell Medical Coll., 1953-54; research assoc., Columbia U., 1954-57; senior consultant, New York City Community Mental Health Board, 1959-61; dir. of research, 1961-63; CHIEF RESEARCH SCIENTIST, NEW YORK CITY COMMUNITY MENTAL HEALTH BOARD, 1963- ; ASSOC. PROF., GOVERNMENT, N.Y.U., 1963- . U. of P.R. fellow, U. of Chicago and Columbia U.; Research Review Subcommittee, Interdepartmental Health Council (N.Y.); consultant, Postgraduate Center for Psychotherapy, Inc. Membership: American Anthropological Association; American Public Health Association; New York City Public Health Association; Society for Applied Anthropology. Research: public health; mental health; social science applications to planning; social change; Puerto Rico. Author: Up from Puerto Rico (1958); Social Rural Types in the Caribbean Region (1958). Co-author: People of Puerto Rico (1956). Language: Spanish 5,5,5,5; Portuguese 3,3,3,3; French 4,4,4,5. Home: 372 Central Park West, New York, N.Y. Office: New York City Community Mental Health Board, 93 Worth St., New York.

PAGE, A. NAYLAND, b. Luling, Tex., July 30, 1931. HISTORY. B.A., Tex. Coll. of Arts & Industries, 1952; M.A., 1953; Ph. D., U. of Okla., 1958. ASSOC. PROF., HISTORY, TEX. COLL. OF ARTS & INDUSTRIES, 1959- . Fulbright fellow (Chile), 1958-59. Membership: American Association of University Professors; Hispanic American Historical Association; Southwestern Social Science Association. Research: current political parties and attitude in South America; Chile. Language: Spanish 4,4,4,3. Office: Dept. of History, Tex. Coll. of Arts & Industries, Kingsville, Tex.

PAINTER, NORMAN WELLINGTON, b. Osage, Tex., Feb. 23, 1918. SOCIOLOGY. B.A., Baylor U., 1947; M.A., Tulane U., 1949; Ph. D., Mich. State U., 1956. Prof., Central U. of Venezuela, 1952-59; lectr., U. of Ill., 1959-61; DEPUTY CHIEF, RESEARCH, U.S. INFORMATION AGENCY, 1961- . Consultant, Creole Petroleum Corporation (Venezuela); Mich. State U. grant (Costa Rica), 1950-51. Membership: American Sociological Association; Inter-American Council (Washington, D.C.). Research: social and cultural change in Latin America; Venezuela; demographic and social organization in Costa Rica. Author: Aplicación de métodos de delineación ecológica en Latinoamérica (Acta Científica Venezolana, Mar.-Apr. 1953). Co-author: Rural Population Stability, Central District of Turrialba Canton, Costa Rica (Rural Sociology, Dec. 1952); Demographic Characteristics of the Population (in Turrialba: Social Systems and the Introduction of Change, 1953). Language: Spanish 5,5,5,5; Portuguese 2,3,2,1; French 2,1,1,1. Home: 1730 Wilmart St., Rockville, Md. Office: U.S. Information Agency, Washington, D.C., 20025.

PALMER, THOMAS WAVERLY, b. Tuscaloosa, Ala., Feb. 25, 1891. LAW. A.B., U. of Ala., 1910; LL.B., Harvard U., 1913; LL.D. (honorary), U. of Ala., 1954. Attorney for Chile Exploration Company, and U.S. consular agent (Chuquicamata, Chile), 1919–22; counsel, representative abroad, official, Standard Oil Company (N.J.), 1922–48; president, dir., Ancon Insurance Company and Balboa Insurance Company (Havana), 1949–56; PRIVATE CONSULTANT, 1956– . Sheldon traveling fellow (Spain), 1913–14; counsel, Petroleum Supply Committee for Latin America, Petroleum Administration for World War II; president, Panamerican Society of the United States, Inc., 1946–49, and honorary life president, 1949– ; dir., American Geographical Society of New York, 1946– ; dir., The Americas Foundation, 1961– ; officer, National Order of the Southern Cross (Brazil); commander, Order of the Liberator (Venezuela); officer, National Order of Carlos Manuel de Céspedes (Cuba). Membership: American Bar Association; Bar Association of the City of New York; Instituto da Ordem dos Advogados Brasileiros (Rio de Janeiro). Research: comparative law; private international law; negotiations, representation, and public relations in business abroad; investments in petroleum rights. Author: Digest of the Laws and Regulations of Argentina Applicable to Petroleum (1922); Gringo Lawyer (1956). Co-author: The Law and Legal Literature of Curaçao (1934). Language: Spanish 5,4,4,2; Portuguese 1,1,1,1. Home: 187 Garth Rd., Scarsdale, New York, N.Y. 10583.

PANE, REMIGIO U., b. Italy, Feb. 5, 1912. SPANISH AMERICAN LITERATURE AND BIBLIOGRAPHY. B.A., Rutgers U., 1938; M.A., 1939; Columbia U., 1939–41. PROF., CHMN., ROMANCE LANGUAGES, RUTGERS U., 1939– . Chmn., Northeast Conference on the Teaching of Foreign Languages, 1960; dir., National Defense Education Act Foreign Language Institute for secondary school teachers of Spanish and French, Rutgers U., Summers 1963, 1964. Membership: American Association of Teachers of Italian; American Association of Spanish and Portuguese; Modern Language Association; New Jersey Foreign Language Teachers Association. Research: bibliography of Latin American literature and history in translation; foreign language teaching methodology. Author: English Translations from the Spanish: 1484–1943 (1944). Language: Spanish 5,5,5,5; Portuguese 2,2,1,1; French 5,5,4,4; Italian 5,5,5,5. Office: Dept. of Romance Languages, Rutgers U., New Brunswick, N.J.

PARATORE, ANGELA, b. Madison, Wis., Jan. 6, 1912. LANGUAGE AND LINGUISTICS. B.A., U. of Wis., 1934; M.A., 1936; Ph. D., Cornell U., 1950. Asst. prof., Spanish, American Institute for Foreign Trade, 1951–52; ASSOC. PROF., LINGUISTICS, IND. U., 1952– ; prof., National Defense Education Act Language Institute, Notre Dame U., Summers 1961, 1962, Sonoma State Coll., Summer 1963. Roosevelt fellow (Mexico), 1942–43; Fulbright fellow (Italy), 1950–51; research consultant, U.S. Dept. of Health, Education, and Welfare, 1961–62. Membership: Linguistic Society of America; Modern Language Association; National Association of Foreign Student Advisers. Research: applied linguistics; teacher training in language teaching methods; English as a foreign language. Author: English Dialogues for Foreign Students (1956); English Exercises for Foreign Students (1958). Co-author: Speaking and Writing Spanish (1951). Language: Spanish 5,5,5,5; French 4,4,3,3; Albanian-,-,5,-. Linguistic studies: English; French; Spanish. Home: 818 Regent St., Madison, Wis. Office: Dept. of Linguistics, Ind. U., Bloomington.

PAREJA DIEZCANSECO, ALFREDO, b. Guayaquil, Ecuador, Oct. 12, 1908. POLITICAL SCIENCE, HISTORY, AND SPANISH AMERICAN LITERATURE. Licenciado, Universidad de Guayaquil, 1931; special doctorate, Universidad Central (Ecuador), 1960. Prof., Colegio Nacional Vicente Rocafuerte (Guayaquil, Ecuador), 1931–33; inspector general, secondary education, Ministry of Education, Government of Ecuador, 1934–36; prof., Universidad Central (Ecuador), 1950–61; prof., deputy dir., Inter-American Institute of Political Education (Costa Rica), 1961–62; assoc. prof., U. of Fla., 1962; PROF., POLITICAL SCIENCE, U. OF FLA., 1964– . Guggenheim fellow, 1963–64. Research: Ecuador; political thought in Gran Colombia. Author: Vida y leyenda de Miguel de Santiago (1952); Historia del Ecuador (1955); La lucha por democracia en el Ecuador (1956). Language: Spanish 5,5,5,5; Portuguese 3, 3,3,2; French 4,4,3,2. Home: 508 Northwest 34th Ter., Gainesville, Fla. Office: Dept. of Political Science, U. of Fla., Gainesville.

PARISEAU, EARL JOSEPH, b. Methuen, Mass., Aug. 14, 1928. BIBLIOGRAPHY. B.A., U. of Fla., 1957; M.A., American U., 1959. Asst. to editor, Handbook of Latin American Studies, Hispanic Foundation, Library of Congress, 1961; EDITOR, HANDBOOK OF LATIN AMERICAN STUDIES, 1961– ; ASST. DIR., HISPANIC FOUNDATION, LIBRARY OF CONGRESS, 1964– . Committee on Bibliography, Seminars on the Acquisition of Latin American Library Materials. Membership: American Historical Association; Conference on Latin American History; Delta Sigma Pi; Inter-American Council; Phi Alpha Theta. Research: Latin American bibliography; development of national acquisition plan for Latin America; Latin American history and economics. Editor: Handbook of Latin American Studies, No. 23–27 (1961–65). Language: Spanish 3,3,3,3; Portuguese 3,3,2,2. Home: 5515 Margate St., Springfield, Va. Office: Hispanic Foundation, Library of Congress, Washington, D.C., 20540.

PARKER, FRANKLIN DALLAS, b. Baltimore, Md., Jan. 7, 1898. HISTORY. B.A., Greenville Coll., 1939; M.A., U. of Ill., 1949; Ph. D., 1951. Asst. prof., Woman's Coll., U. of N.C., 1951–60; assoc. prof., 1960–63; ASSOC. PROF., HISTORY, U. OF N.C., 1963– . Southern Fellowships Fund grant, Summer 1955; Doherty fellow (Central America), 1955–56; Southern Fellowships Fund and Woman's College Research Council grants (Central America), 1960. Membership: Conference on Latin American History; Sociedad de Geografía e Historia de Guatemala; Southeastern Conference of Latin American Studies. Research: archival research in Central America. Author: José Cecilio del Valle and the Establishment of the Central American Confederation (1954); The Central American Republics (1964). Language: Spanish 4,4,4,4; French 4,2,2,1; German 2,1,1,1. Home: 2009 Wright Ave., Greensboro, N.C. 27403. Office: Dept. of History, U. of N.C., Greensboro, 27412.

PARKER, JOHN ALBERT. b. Kentville, Nova Scotia, Canada, Mar. 27, 1909. CITY AND REGIONAL PLANNING. B.S., Mass. Institute of Technology, 1931; M. Arch., 1933; M.C.P., 1946. Dir., Lowthorpe School of Landscape Architecture (Groton, Mass.), 1934–45; chmn., Div. of Planning, Rhode Island School of Design, 1945–46; RESEARCH PROF., INSTITUTE FOR RESEARCH IN SOCIAL SCIENCE, CHMN., CITY AND REGIONAL PLANNING, U. OF N.C., 1946– . Consultant on planning education, U.S. Agency for International Development (Santiago, Chile), Summer 1962 (Central America), Summer 1963; consultant, National Capitol Planning Commission, 1963– . Membership: American Institute of Planners; American Society of Planning Officials. Research: organization for planning; education in city and regional planning. Author: Post-Graduate Planning Education in Chile (1962); Planning Education in Central America (1963); Roles of the Planner in Urban Development (in Urban Growth Dynamics, 1962). Language: Spanish 1,1,1,1; French 1,1,1,1. Office: Dept of City and Regional Planning, U. of N.C., Chapel Hill.

PARKES, HENRY B., b. Sheffield, United Kingdom, Nov. 13, 1904. HISTORY. B.A., Oxford U., 1927; Ph. D., U. of Mich., 1929. Instr.-PROF., HISTORY, N.Y.U., 1930– . Research: American history; Western culture. Author: A History of Mexico (1938, 1949, 1960). Language: Spanish 3,1,1,1; French 3,1,1,1. Home: 210 East 15th St., New York 3, N.Y. Office: Dept. of History, N.Y.U., Washington Square East, New York 3.

PARKS, E. TAYLOR, b. Mulberry, Tenn., Aug. 14, 1898. HISTORY AND INTERNATIONAL RELATIONS. B.A., Carson-Newman Coll., 1927; M.A., U. of Tenn., 1938; Ph. D., Duke U., 1931. Instr., Duke U., 1930–32; chmn., Berea Coll., 1932–45; CHIEF, RESEARCH GUIDANCE AND REVIEW DIV., HISTORICAL OFFICE, U.S. DEPT. OF STATE, 1945– . Staff member, Joint United States-Brazil Technical Commission, 1948–49; delegate, Pan American Institute of Geography and History, 1961. Membership: American Historical Association; Conference on Latin American History; Mississippi Valley Historical Association; Southern Historical Association. Research: diplomatic history of United States and Latin America. Author: Colombia and the United States 1765–1934 (1935). Editor: American Foreign Policy: Basic Documents (1950–63); The Diary and Journal of Richard Clough Anderson, Jr., 1814–1826 (1964). Language: Spanish 3,–,–,–. Home: 3221 South 12th St., Arlington 4, Va. Office: Historical Office, U.S. Dept. of State, Washington, D.C., 20520.

PARSONS, JAMES JEROME, b. Cortland, N.Y., Nov. 15, 1915. GEOGRAPHY. A.B., U. of Calif., Berkeley, 1937; M.A., 1939; Ph. D., 1948. Instr.-PROF., GEOGRAPHY, U. OF CALIF., BERKELEY, 1947– . Guggenheim fellow (Spain), 1959–60. Membership: Academia Colombiana de Historia; Association of American Geographers. Research: economic geography. Author: Antioqueño Colonization in Western Colombia (1949); San Andres and Providencia (1956); The Green Turtle and Man (1962). Language: Spanish 4,3,3,3; Portuguese 3,3,2,2; French 3,1,1,1. Home: 670 Woodmont, Berkeley 8, Calif. Office: Dept. of Geography, U. of Calif., Berkeley 4.

PARSONS, LEE ALLEN, b. Wausau, Wis., June 15, 1932. ANTHROPOLOGY. B.A., Beloit Coll., 1954; A.M., Harvard U., 1958; Ph. D., 1964. ASSOC. CURATOR OF ANTHROPOLOGY, MILWAUKEE PUBLIC MUSEUM, 1959– . Collaborator, Seminario de Cultura Maya. Membership: American Association of Museums; Society for American Archaeology; Wisconsin Archaeological Society. Research: Middle American archeology; museology; Pacific coast of Guatemala. Author: The Nature of Horizon Markers in Middle American Archaeology (Anthropology Tomorrow, 1957); Peruvian Mortuary Art (Archaeology, Autumn 1962); Excavations at Bilbao, Sta. Lucia Cotz., Guatemala (Antropología e Historia de Guatemala, Jan. 1963). Language: Spanish 4,3,3,3; French 2,–,–,–; German 2,–,–,–. Home: 2942 North Hackett Ave., Milwaukee 11, Wis. Office: Milwaukee Public Museum, 800 West Wisconsin Ave., Milwaukee 3.

PARSONS, MARY DUDLEY, b. Hammonton, Calif., Mar. 21, 1915. LIBRARY SCIENCE. B.A., U. of Calif., 1936; Certificate in Librarianship, 1937. Asst., Library, U. of Calif., Berkeley, 1937–42; asst. in circulation and cataloging, San Antonio Public Library (Tex.), 1944–45; head, Education Library, Bindery Dept., asst. head, Serials Dept., U. of Calif., Berkeley, 1946–51; teacher and librarian, Monte Vista School (Vacaville, Calif.), 1952–55; head librarian, U. of the Americas, 1955–62; PRIVATE TUTOR, ENGLISH (DOMINICAN REPUBLIC), 1963– . Chmn., Ad Hoc Committee on Internal Reorganization of Mexico City Coll., 1961; adviser on reorganization of Escuela Nacional de Bibliotecarios y Archivistas (Mexico), Organization of American States Technical Assistance Mission, 1963. Membership: American Library Association; Asociación Mexicana de Bibliotecarios. Research: organization and administration of libraries; college libraries; acquisition of books and materials; education for librarians. Author: The College Library: Laboratory or Storehouse? (in Antología, Mexico City College, 1956); Mexico's National Book-Freedom Fair (Library Journal, June 1957). Co-author: Directory of Mexico City Libraries (1958). Language: Spanish 4,4,4,4; Portuguese 1,1,1,1; French 2,1,1,1. Home: c/o Mrs. William Boles, 42 Rodell Pl., Arcadia, Calif., 91006.

PATCH, RICHARD W., b. Lansing, Mich., Apr. 12, 1929. ANTHROPOLOGY. B.A., Cornell U., 1951; Ph. D., 1956. Vis. asst. prof., Tulane U., 1956–57; STAFF MEMBER, AMERICAN UNIVERSITIES FIELD

STAFF, INC., 1957– ; VIS. PROF., ANTHROPOLOGY, U. OF WIS., 1962– ; staff member, Land Tenure Center, 1962. Doherty fellow; Institute of Current World Affairs fellow, 1954–57; Inter-American Development Bank Mission for Rural Development of Bolivia, 1962; dir., Colonization Study for Bolivian Government and U.S. Agency for International Development, 1962. Membership: American Anthropological Association; American Ethnological Society; Midwest Council of the Association for Latin American Studies; Society for Applied Anthropology. Research: cultural anthropology; social and economic development in the Andes; land tenure and social change in Peru and Bolivia. Author: Emergent Peoples (in Expectant Peoples, 1963). Co-author: Social Change in Latin America Today (1960). Language: Spanish 5,5,5,4; Portuguese 3,3,2,1; French 4,3,3,2. Office: American Universities Field Staff, Inc., 366 Madison Ave., New York 17, N.Y.; or Dept. of Anthropology, U. of Wis., Madison 6, Wis.

PATTEN, GEORGE PHILLIP, b. Farmersburg, Ind., June 29, 1924. GEOGRAPHY. B.S., Ind. State Coll., 1948; M.A., Ohio State U., 1949; Ph. D., Northwestern U., 1955. Instr., U. of Ark., 1950–51; instr., Hunter Coll., 1954–55; asst. prof., State Coll. of Iowa, 1955–57; ASSOC. PROF., GEOGRAPHY, OHIO STATE U., 1957– . National Defense Education Act fellow, U. of Calif., Los Angeles, Summer 1963. Membership: African Studies Association; American Geographical Society; Association of American Geographers; Gamma Theta Upsilon; International Geographical Union; National Council for Geographic Education; Ohio Academy of Science; Pi Gamma Mu; Sigma Xi. Research: tropical agriculture; agricultural land use in Middle America. Author: Gabon (Focus, Oct. 1961); Republic of the Congo (Focus, Oct. 1962). Language: Spanish 3,3,3,2; French 2,1,1,1; Swahili 2,2,2,3. Home: 864 Afton Rd., Columbus, Ohio 43221. Office: Dept. of Geography, Ohio State U., 1775 South College Rd., Columbus, Ohio 43210.

PATTERSON, JERRY EUGENE, b. Fort Worth, Tex., May 2, 1931. BIBLIOGRAPHY AND HISTORY. B.A., U. of Tex., 1952; M.A., 1955; Yale U., 1955–57; Columbia U., 1958–60. ASST. EDITOR, LATIN AMERICA: A GUIDE TO THE HISTORICAL LITERATURE, LIBRARY OF CONGRESS, 1964– . Asst., Hispanic American Historical Review, 1954; asst., Historical Manuscripts Div., Yale U. Library. Membership: Conference on Latin American History. Research: rare books; the literary criticism of Pedro Henríquez Ureña; history of mining in Latin America. Author: Prescott Manuscripts (Hispanic American Historical Review, Feb. 1959); Manuscritos Mexicanos (Historia Mexicana, Jan. 1960); The Mexican War, 1846–1848 (Yale U. Library Gazette, Jan. 1960). Language: Spanish 3,3,3,1. Home: 420 East 80th, New York 21, N.Y.

PATTERSON, THOMAS CARL, b. Rutland, Vt., Nov. 5, 1937. ANTHROPOLOGY. A.B., U. of Calif., Berkeley, 1960; Ph. D., 1964. ACTING INSTR., ANTHROPOLOGY, U. OF CALIF., BERKELEY, 1963– . Fulbright fellow (Peru), 1962–63. Membership: American Anthropological Association; American Ethnological Society; Far-Eastern Prehistory Association; Institute of Andean Studies; Kroeber Anthropological Society; Prehistoric Society, Inc.; Society for American Archaeology. Research: South American archeology and ethnology; Peruvian archeology; ethnohistory of the Andean area; South American technology. Author: Contemporaneity and Cross-Dating in Archaeological Interpretation (American Antiquity, Jan. 1963). Co-author: Changing Settlement Patterns on the Central Peruvian Coast (Ñawpa Pacha, 1964). Language: Spanish 3,3,3,3; Portuguese 2,1,1,1; French 4,2,2,3; German 2,1,1,3. Home: Apt. 1, 1260 Hopkins St., Berkeley, Calif. 94720. Office: Dept. of Anthropology, U. of Calif., Berkeley, 94720.

PAUL, BENJAMIN D., b. New York, N.Y., Jan. 25, 1911. ANTHROPOLOGY. A.B., U. of Chicago, 1938; Ph. D., 1942. Community organization expert, Rural Teacher Training Program (Guatemala), Inter-American Educational Foundation, 1946; lectr.-assoc. prof., Dept. of Social Relations, Harvard U., 1946–63; lectr.-assoc. prof., School of Public Health, Harvard U., 1951–63; research assoc., Dept. of Psychiatry, Children's Medical Center (Boston), 1958–62; PROF., ANTHROPOLOGY, STANFORD U., 1963– . Research fellow, Peabody Museum, Harvard U., 1946–63; Committee on Preventive Medicine and Social Research, Social Science Research Council, 1953–59; Committee on Behavioral Science and Public Health, American Public Health Association, 1954–60; consultant, Ford Foundation, UNESCO, State Health Depts. of Calif., Mass., N. Mex., and N.Y.; Center for Advanced Study in the Behavioral Sciences fellow, 1962–63. Membership: American Anthropological Association; Society for Applied Anthropology. Research: training of medical anthropologists; processes of culture change at the community level. Author: Life in a Guatemalan Indian Village (in Cultural Patterns, 1950); Changing Marriage Patterns in a Highland Guatemalan Community (Southwestern Journal of Anthropology, Summer 1963). Editor: Health, Culture and Community (1955). Language: Spanish 3,3,3,3; French 3,2,2,2; German 2,2,1,1. Home: 622 Salvatierra St., Stanford, Calif. 94305. Office: Program in Medicine and the Behavioral Sciences, Stanford U., Stanford, 94305.

PAULING, NORMAN GEORGE, b. San Antonio, Tex., May 13, 1923. ECONOMICS. B.A., U. of Tex., 1944; M.A., 1947; Ph. D., 1952. Instr., U. of Tex., 1946–47; instr., Vanderbilt U., 1947–48; asst. district economist, Office of Price Stabilization (Shreveport, La.), 1951–52; dir., Research and Planning, Arabian American Oil Company, 1952–61; chief, Automation Impact Studies Div., U.S. Dept. of Labor, 1952–64; MANPOWER PLANNING CONSULTANT, U.S. AGENCY FOR INTERNATIONAL DEVELOPMENT (GUATEMALA), 1964– . U. of Tex. graduate fellow, 1949–50; Fulbright research fellow (New Zealand), 1950–51. Membership: A m e r i c a n Economic Association; Industrial Relations Research Association; National Planning Association; Southern Economic Association. Research: labor economics; economic development; occupational sociology; industrial relations. A u t h o r : Experience with an Industrial Research Program in the Social Sciences (University of Chicago Journal of Business, Apr. 1961); Some Neglected Areas of Research on the Effects of Technological Change on Workers (University of Chicago Journal of Business, July 1964); Labor Separations in an Underdeveloped Area: A Case Study of Worker Adjustment to Change (American Journal of Economics and Sociology, Oct. 1964). Language: Spanish 4,4,4,4; French 2,1,1,1; German 3,3,3,3. Home: 16 Calle, 14–39, zona 10, Guatemala, Guatemala. Office: U.S. Agency for International Development, Regional Office, Central America and Panama, c/o American Embassy, Guatemala.

PAULSON, BELDEN HENRY, b. Oak Park, Ill., June 29, 1927. POLITICAL SCIENCE. B.A., Oberlin Coll., 1950; M.A., U. of Chicago, 1955; Ph. D., 1962. Co-dir., Italian Service Mission (Naples), 1950–53; dir., Homeless European Land Program (Sardinia, Italy), 1957–59; consultant, United Nations High Commissioner for Refugees (Rome), 1959–61; ASST. PROF., POLITICAL SCIENCE, U. OF WIS., 1962– . Land Tenure Center-U.S. Agency for International Development research grant (Brazil), Summer 1963; U. of Wis. research grant (Italy), Summer 1964. Membership: Adult Education Association of the United States of America; American Political Science Association; Midwest Conference of Political Scientists; Midwest Council of the Association for Latin American Studies; Society for Applied Anthropology. Research: international relations; local and regional political patterns in northeast Brazil; community development; Italian communism. Author: Difficulties and Prospects for Community Development in Northeast Brazil (Inter-American Economic Affairs, Spring 1964); Local Political Patterns in Northeast Brazil: A Community Case Study (Land Tenure Center, Summer 1964). Co-author: The Community in Revolutionary Latin America (U. of Kans. Occasional Publications, no. 3, Spring 1964). Language: Spanish 2,2,2,2; Portuguese 2,2,2,2; Italian 4,4,4,4. Home: 2602 East Newberry Blvd., Milwaukee, Wis. Office: Dept. of Political Science, U. of Wis., Milwaukee, 53211.

PAYNE, WALTER ARVILLE, b. Lodi, Calif., Jan. 30, 1924. HISTORY. B.A., U. of Calif., Berkeley, 1945; M.A., Universidad de San Carlos de Guatemala, 1951; Ph. D., U. of Fla., 1955. Instr., Grant Union High School (Calif.), 1946–47; registrar, catedrático, Escuela de Verano, Universidad de San Carlos de Guatemala, 1948–51; instr., American School of Guatemala, 1950, 1958; asst. prof., asst. dir., School of Inter-American Studies, U. of Fla., 1952–58; lectr., U. of Glasgow (Scotland), 1956–57; asst. prof., U. of Fla., 1958–61; catedrático, Escuela de Verano, Universidad de San Carlos de Guatemala, 1958, 1959, 1960; ASSOC. PROF., HISTORY, U. OF THE PACIFIC, 1961– . Latin American Studies fellow, Tulane U., 1951; Homenaje de Mérito, Facultad de Humanidades, Universidad de San Carlos, 1951; asst. managing editor, Hispanic American Historical Review, 1960– . Membership: American Historical Association; Conference on Latin American History; Pacific Coast Council on Latin American Studies. Research: republican period in Central America. Author: A Central American Historian—José Milla y Vidaurre, 1822–1882 (1957); Aportes principales de la historia norteamericana (in Notes and Lectures for the Second Bolivian Economic Seminar Project, 1960); Recent Central American Relations with Non-Hemisphere States (in The Caribbean: The Central American Area, 1961). Language: Spanish 4,4,4,4; Portuguese 3,3, 3,3; French 2,2,2,2. Home: 1514 Calhoun Way, Stockton 7, Calif. Office:Dept. of History, U. of the Pacific, Stockton 4.

PAZOS, FELIPE, b. Havana, Cuba, Sept. 27, 1912. ECONOMICS. Doctor, U. of Havana, 1937; LL.D., 1938. Economist, Treasury Dept. of Cuba, 1941–42; commercial attaché, Cuban Embassy (Washington, D.C.), 1942–46; chief, Latin American Div., International Monetary Fund, 1946–49; president, Banco Nacional de Cuba, 1949–60; economic consultant, 1952–58; adviser, Government Development Bank of P.R., 1960–61; member, Committee of Nine, Organization of American States, 1962–64; ADVISER, COMMITTEE OF NINE, ORGANIZATION OF AMERICAN STATES, 1965– . Adviser, Government of El Salvador, 1961; president, Group of Experts on Planning for Economic and Social Development in Latin America, Pan American Union (Washington, D.C.), 1961; adviser, Secretariat of the Extraordinary Meeting of the Interamerican Economic and Social Council (Uruguay), 1961; Board of Editors, El Trimestre Económico. Membership: American Economic Association. Research: development plans of Chile and Honduras. Author: Inflation and Exchange Instability in Latin America (American Economic Review, May 1949); Economic Development and Financial Stability (Staff Papers, International Monetary Fund, Oct. 1953); Private Versus Public Foreign Investment (in Economic Development for Latin America, 1961). Language: Spanish 5,5,5,5; Portuguese 3,2,1,1; French 2,1,1,1. Home: 6916 Bradley Blvd., Bradley Hills, Bethesda, Md. Office: Committee of Nine, Organization of American States, Washington, D.C. 20006.

PEARSON, ROSS NORTON, b. Nebo, Ill., June 19, 1917. GEOGRAPHY. B. Ed., Ill. State Normal U., 1939; M.S., U. of Wis., 1947; Ph. D., U. of Mich., 1954. Asst. prof., Mich. State Normal Coll., 1947–51; asst. prof.-ASSOC. PROF., GEOGRAPHY, U. OF MICH., 1951– . Consultant, Agricultural Colonization Program in Guatemala, International Development Service-International Cooperation Administration, 1960; chmn., Committee on Population Studies, Pan American Institute of Geography and History; Committee on Geography for the Peace Corps, National Council for Geographic Education; National Academy of Science-National Research Council Advisory Committee on Geography to U.S. Dept. of State, Pan American Institute of Geography and History. Membership: American Geographical Society; Association of American Geographers; Michigan Academy of Science; Midwest Council of the Association of Latin American Studies; National Council for Geographic Education.

Research: population distribution; land use; land reform; settlement; geography of recreational regions. Author: Zones of Agricultural Development in Guatemala (Journal of Geography, Jan. 1963); Land Reform Guatemalan Style (American Journal of Economics and Sociology, Apr. 1963); Changes in the Distribution of Population in Argentina (Revista Geográfica, 1963). Language: Spanish 3,2,2,1. Home: 1007 Lincoln Ave., Ann Arbor, Mich. Office: Dept. of Geography, U. of Mich., Ann Arbor.

PECK, F. TAYLOR, b. Mobile, Ala., Apr. 24, 1920. EDUCATION. B.S., Spring Hill Coll.; M.A., Georgetown U., 1948; Ph. D., 1950. Research analyst, Georgetown U., 1948–49; historian, U.S. Navy, 1949; dir., Instituto Cultural Peruano Americano (Lima), 1950–54; dir., Centro Colombo-Americano (Bogotá), 1954–55; vis. prof., U. of the Andes (Bogotá), 1954–55; cultural attaché, Embassy (Bogotá), U.S. Information Service, 1955–57, (Guatemala), 1957–62; REGIONAL AFFAIRS OFFICER, U.S. INFORMATION AGENCY, 1962– . Georgetown U. fellow, 1947–48; chmn., Executive Committee, Latin American Institute. Membership: Guatemala Society of Geography and History; Latin American Council; Inter-American Institute. Research: organization, function, and operation of the Latin American university; the political and social role of the university student and student organizations in Latin America. Author: Round Shot to Rockets (1949). Language: Spanish 5,4,4,3; Portuguese 2,2,1,1; French 2,2,1,1. Home: 4561 Cathedral Ave., NW., Washington, D.C. 20016. Office: Room 1128, U.S. Information Agency-IAL, 1776 Pennsylvania Ave., NW., Washington, D.C.

PECK, ROBERT F., b. Buffalo, N.Y., Sept. 22, 1919. PSYCHOLOGY AND EDUCATION. B. Sc., State U. of N.Y., Buffalo, 1941; M. Sc., State U. of N.Y., Albany, 1942; Ph. D., U. of Chicago, 1951. Instr.-research assoc., Committee on Human Development, U. of Chicago, 1947–50; vice president, research dir., Worthington Associates (Chicago), 1950–59; assoc. prof., U. of Tex., 1954–59; PROF., EDUCATIONAL PSYCHOLOGY, U. OF TEX., 1959– ; DIR., PERSONALITY RESEARCH CENTER, U. OF TEX., 1962– . Consultant, Social Research, Inc., (Chicago), 1947–50; Interamerican Research Planning Conference, 1956; Conference on Cross-Cultural Research (Mexico City), 1957, (Monterrey, Mexico), 1959; Conference on Social and Economic Change in Contemporary Mexico (Monterrey), 1961; Planning Committee, Round Table on Culture Shock and Social Change, VII Interamerican Congress of Psychology (Mexico), 1961; U.S. delegate, symposium chmn., VIII Interamerican Congress of Psychology (Argentina), 1963; Cross-National Conference on Childhood and Adolescence (Chicago), 1964. Membership: American Psychological Association; Gerontology Association; Interamerican Society of Psychology; Sigma Xi; Society for Research in Child Development; Southwestern Psychological Association; Texas Psychological Association. Research: educational psychology; personality and culture; mental health; the psychology of moral character; cross-cultural study of conceptions of love and respect relationships in Brazil, Chile, Venezuela, Mexico, and Panama. Author: Respecto y posición social en dos culturas (Proceedings of VII Interamerican Congress of Psychology, 1963); Two Core-Culture Patterns and the Diffusion of Values Across Their Border (Proceedings of the VII Interamerican Congress of Psychology, 1963). Co-author: The Meaning of Love in Mexico and the United States (American Psychologist, 1962). Language: Spanish 4,3,2,1. Home: 3304 Glen Rose, Austin, Tex. 78731. Office: Personality Research Center, U. of Tex., Austin, 78712.

PECKHAM, EDMUND T., b. Worcester, Mass., Feb. 9, 1924. HISTORY AND POLITICAL SCIENCE. A.B., Brown U., 1948; M.A., Harvard U., 1949; Ph. D., 1954. Asst. prof., Rice U., 1952–58; assoc. prof., U. of the Pacific, 1958–62; PROF., SOCIAL SCIENCE, DEAN OF STUDENT LIFE, RAYMOND COLL., U. OF THE PACIFIC, 1962– . Business research fellow, Lever Brothers. Membership: Conference on Latin American History; Hispanic American Historical Association; Phi Beta Kappa; Phi Eta Sigma; Phi Kappa Phi. Research: United States foreign relations; inter-American diplomacy. Language: Spanish 3,3,3,3; Portuguese 2,1,1,1; French 3,2,2,3. Home: 1924 Meadow, Stockton, Calif. Office: Dept. of Social Science, Raymond Coll., U. of the Pacific, Stockton.

PEEKE, M. CATHERINE, b. Weaverville, N.C., Apr. 1, 1924. LINGUISTICS. B.A., Columbia Bible Coll., 1946; A.B., King Coll., 1947; M.A., Ind. U., 1962. LINGUIST, SUMMER INSTITUTE OF LINGUISTICS (ECUADOR), 1949– . Membership: Linguistic Society of America. Research: language analysis in Peru and Ecuador. Author: Pronombres personales en Shimigae (1959); Structural Summary of Záparo (in Ecuadorian Indian Languages: I, 1962). Co-author: Phonetic Units in the Secoya Word (in Ecuadorian Indian Languages: I, 1962). Language: Spanish 4,4,3,3. Linguistics: Andoa Shimigae); Auca; Secoya; Záparo. Home: R.F.D. 3, Box 266, Weaverville, N.C. 28787. Office: Instituto Lingüístico de Verano, Casilla 1007, Quito, Ecuador.

PEFFER, E. LOUISE, b. Natrona, Pa., Nov. 15, 1898. HISTORY. B.S., Purdue U., 1937; M.A., U. of Calif., 1939; Ph. D., 1942. Research assoc., assoc. prof.-PROF., FOOD RESEARCH INSTITUTE, STANFORD U., 1946– . Fulbright fellow (Argentina), 1958. Membership: Agricultural History Society; American Historical Association; Conference on Latin American History; Mississippi Valley Historical Association; Pacific Coast Conference on Latin American Studies. Research: agricultural history; history of Argentine cattle and beef industry. Author: The Argentine Cattle Industry Under Perón (Food Research Institute Studies, May 1960); State Intervention in the Argentine Meat Packing Industry, 1946–58 (Food Research Institute Studies, Feb. 1961); Foot-and-Mouth Disease in United States Policy (Food Research Institute Studies, May 1962). Language: Spanish 3,2,2,1; French 3,2,2,1. Home: 1314 College Ave., Palo Alto, Calif., 94306. Office: Food Research Institute, Stanford U., Stanford, Calif., 94305.

PELISSIER, RAYMOND FRANCIS, b. Hatfield, Mass., May 16, 1912. ECONOMICS. B.S., U. of Mass., 1933; M.S., 1938; Ph. D., American U., 1958. International economist, U.S. Dept. of State, 1952-53; prof., Georgetown U., 1953-60; dir., School of Business Administration, Georgetown U., 1960-64; MANAGEMENT CONSULTANT, 1964– . Research: development of management executives in Latin America. Author: American Business Managers and Technicians in Mexican Business (Inter-American Economic Affairs, Winter 1952); Intensification of Competition in Mexico Through the Entry of American Private Enterprise (Inter-American Economic Affairs, Autumn 1953); Case Method Gaining Wider Use in Training Venezuelan Businessmen (Export-Trade, Dec. 1959). Language: Spanish 5,4,3,2; Portuguese 3,-,-,-; German 1,-,-,-. Home: 5150 North Third St., Arlington, Va.

PEÑALOSA, FERNANDO, b. Berkeley, Calif., July 28, 1925. SOCIOLOGY, ANTHROPOLOGY AND LIBRARY SCIENCE. A.B., U. of Denver, 1949; A.M., 1950; Ph. D., U. of Chicago, 1956; A.M., U. of Southern Calif., 1959; Ph. D., 1963. Cataloger and head of technical services, Library, Fresno State Coll., 1952-54; instr.-asst. prof., U. of Southern Calif., 1954-59; asst. prof., Calif. State Polytechnic Coll., 1959-62; ASSOC. PROF., SOCIOLOGY AND ANTHROPOLOGY, HEAD, SOCIAL SCIENCE, CALIF. STATE POLYTECHNIC COLL., 1962– . Social Science Research Council grant-in-aid (Mexico), 1964. Membership: American Anthropological Association; American Ethnological Society; American Sociological Association; Pacific Council on Latin American Studies; Pacific Sociological Society; Sigma Xi; Southwestern Anthropological Association. Research: bibliography and social change in Mexico; urbanization in the state of Guanajuato, Mexico. Author: Mexican Book Industry (1957); Selección y adquisición de libros (1961). Language: Spanish 5,5,4,4; Portuguese 3,2,2,3; French 3,2,2,3. Home: 497 Sycamore, Claremont, Calif. Office: Dept. of Social Science, Calif. State Polytechnic Coll., Pomona.

PENDERGAST, DAVID MICHAEL, b. Oakland, Calif., May 29, 1934. ANTHROPOLOGY. B.A., U. of Calif., Berkeley, 1955; Ph. D., U. of Calif., Los Angeles, 1961. ASST. PROF., ANTHROPOLOGY, U. OF UTAH, 1960– ; FIELD DIR., BRITISH HONDURAS EXPEDITION, ROYAL ONTARIO MUSEUM (CANADA), 1964– . Membership: American Anthropological Association; American Association for the Advancement of Science; Sigma Xi; Sociedad Mexicana de Antropología; Society for American Archaeology. Research: archeology; prehistory of the Maya; Middle America. Author: Metal Artifacts in Prehispanic Mesoamerica (American Antiquity, 1962); Excavaciones en la Cueva E. Quiroz, Distrito Cayo, Honduras Británica (Estudios Mayas, 1964). Co-author: Oral Tradition as History: A Paiute Example (Journal of American Folklore, 1958). Language: Spanish 5,5,4,4; Portuguese 3,4,4,1,1; French 3,3,3,3; Dutch 3,1,1,1; German 3,3,3,4; Italian 3,1,1,1. Home: 3310 Oakwood St., Salt Lake City, Utah 84109. Office: Dept. of Anthropology, U. of Utah, Salt Lake City 12.

PENN, RAYMOND L., b. Morris, Minn., May 25, 1911. ECONOMICS. B. Ed., Wis. State Teachers Coll., 1932; Ph. D., U. of Wis., 1941. Prof., S. Dak. State Coll., 1935-40; regional research supervisor, Div. of Land Economics, U.S. Dept. of Agriculture, 1940-46; chmn., Agriculture Economics, U. of Wis., 1948-55; PROF., AGRICULTURAL ECONOMICS, U. OF WIS., 1946– ; CAMPUS COORDINATOR, LAND TENURE CENTER, 1962– . Land Tenure Center Faculty Advisory Committee, U. of Wis. Membership: American Association of University Professors; American Farm Economics Association; Canadian Farm Economics Association; Western Farm Economics Association; Wisconsin Historical Society. Research: agricultural economics; agricultural education; agricultural policy; land tenure in Latin America; land economics. Author: Public Interest in Private Property (Land) (Land Economics, May 1961); Education and Technical Assistance for Rural Development (Journal of Farm Economics, Dec. 1963). Co-author: La reforma agraria de Venezuela (Revista inter-americana de ciencias sociales, 1963). Language: Spanish 1,1,1,1. Home: 114 Vaughn Ct., Madison, Wis. Office: Land Tenure Center, U. of Wis., Madison, 53706.

PENNINGTON, CAMPBELL WHITE, b. Campbell's Station, Tenn., Feb. 2, 1918. GEOGRAPHY. B.A., U. of Tex., 1947; M.A., 1949; Ph. D., U. of Calif., Berkeley, 1959. Asst. prof., Ga. State Coll., 1956-57; ASSOC. PROF., U. OF UTAH, 1957– . American Philosophical Society grant (Mexico), 1960. Membership: Association of American Geographers. Research: cultural geography; northwestern Mexico. Author: The Tarahumar of Mexico, Their Environment and Material Culture (1963). Language: Spanish 4,4,4,4. Linguistic studies: Tarahumar; Tepehuán. Home: 480 Douglas, Salt Lake City, Utah. Office: Dept. of Geography, U. of Utah, Salt Lake City.

PEPLOW, MARIJANE EASTMAN, b. Philadelphia, Pa., Sept. 16, 1930. POLITICAL SCIENCE. A.B., Upsala Coll., 1950; M.A., School of Advanced International Studies, Johns Hopkins U., 1951; Doctorado, Universidad Católica (Quito, Ecuador), 1952. Program specialist, Pan American Union, 1959; prof., Arlington County School Board (Va.), 1960-61; PROGRAM SPECIALIST, PAN AMERICAN UNION, 1962– . Institute of International Education fellow (Ecuador); Upsala fellow; Georgetown U. fellow; School of Advanced International Studies, Johns Hopkins U. fellow. Membership: American Political Science Association; Delta Kappa Gamma; International Political Science Association. Research: international law; international relations; problems of developing areas. Language: Spanish 5,5,5,5; Portuguese 5,5,4,4; French 5,5,5,5; German 3,2,2,1; Italian 5,4,3,2; Russian 3,2,2,1. Home: 807 South Oak St., Arlington, Va. 22204. Office: Pan American Union, Washington, D.C. 20006.

PERAZA, ELENA VÉREZ, b. Havana, Cuba, July 22, 1919. LIBRARY SCIENCE: BIBLIOGRAPHY. Librarian, Universidad de la Habana, 1948: Ph. D., 1956. Librarian, Biblioteca Pública Panamericana de la Sociedad Colombista Panamericana, Habana, 1943-59; prof., Universidad de Panamá, 1949-50; librarian, Consejo Nacional de Economía (Havana), 1950-58; librarian, Archivo Nacional (Havana), 1959-60; prof., Escuela Interamericana de Bibliotecología (Medellín, Colombia), 1961; ASST. LIBRARIAN, MAIN LIBRARY, U. OF FLA., 1962- . Membership: American Library Association. Research: Cuban bibliography. Author: Publicaciones de las instituciones culturales cubanas (1949, 1954); Bibliografía bibliotecológica cubana, 1948-1955 (1949-56); El griego en Cuba (Journal of Inter-American Studies, Jan. 1959). Language: Spanish 5,5,5,5; Portuguese 4,4,3,3; French 3,-,2,1. Home: 3762 SW. 3rd Pl., Gainesville, Fla. 32603. Office: Main Library, U. of Fla., Gainesville.

PERAZA SARAUSA, FERMÍN, b. Guara, Cuba, July 7, 1907. LIBRARY SCIENCE: BIBLIOGRAPHY. Doctor en Derecho Civil, Universidad de la Habana, 1930; Doctor en Ciencias Políticas, Sociales y Económicas, 1937; librarian degree, 1950. Dir., Biblioteca Municipal de la Habana, 1933-60; prof., Escuela de Bibliotecarios, Universidad de la Habana, 1946-60; prof., Escuela Nacional de Archiveros (Havana), 1960; prof., Escuela Interamericana de Bibliotecología (Medellín, Colombia), 1961- 62;BIBLIOGRAPHER, LIBRARY, U. OF FLA., 1962- . International Consultative Committee of Bibliography, Documentation and Terminology of UNESCO, 1961; delegate, Conference on the Caribbean, U. of Fla., 1962. Membership: Academy of American Franciscan History; Institución Hispanocubana de Cultura; Instituto de Cultura Americana; Library Association (London); Sociedad Colombista Panamericana; Sociedad de Geografía y Estadística; Society of American Archivists. Research: Cuban bibliography. Author: Bibliografía cubana, 1937-1962 (26 vols., 1938-62); Biblioteca del bibliotecario (68 vols., 1942-64); Diccionario biográfico cubano (11 vols., 1951-60). Language: Spanish 5,5,5,5; Portuguese 3,-,-,-; Italian 3,-,-,-. Home: 3762 SW. 3rd Pl., Gainesville, Fla. Office: Library, U. of Fla., Gainesville.

PERKINS, DEXTER, b. Boston, Mass., June 20, 1889. HISTORY. A.B., Harvard U., 1909; Ph. D., 1914; LL.D. (honorary), U. of Rochester, 1955. Prof., U. of Rochester, 1915-53; PROF. EMERITUS, ROCHESTER U., 1954- ; John L. Senior prof., Cornell U., 1953-59; PROF. EMERITUS, CORNELL U., 1959- ; Robert Campbell prof., Wells Coll., 1963-64. Commonwealth lectr., U. Coll. (London), 1937; Pitt prof., Cambridge U., 1945-46; president, Salzburg Seminar on American Studies, 1950-62. Membership: American Association of University Professors; American Historical Association; Phi Beta Kappa. Research: American foreign policy. Author: Hands Off: A History of the Monroe Doctrine (1941; revised edition, 1963); The United States and Latin America (1961); American Quest for Peace (1962). Language: Spanish 1,-,-,-; Portuguese 1,-,-,-; French 1,-,-,-. Home: 316 Oxford St., Rochester 7, N.Y.

PERRIGO, LYNN IRWIN, b. Delphi, Ind., Feb. 21, 1904. HISTORY, B.A., Ball State Teachers Coll., 1933; M.A., U. of Colo., 1934; Ph. D., 1936. Social Studies teacher, Muncie City Schools, 1922-27; Scout executive, Muncie Council, Boy Scouts of America, 1927-33; instr.-assoc. prof., U. of Kansas City, 1936-45; dir., Midwest Inter-American Center, 1943-44; asst. dir., extension div., U. of Colo., 1946-47; PROF., CHMN., HISTORY AND SOCIAL SCIENCE, N. MEX. HIGHLANDS U., 1947- ; dir., Inter-American Workshops, U. of Kansas City, Summers 1942, 1943; Latin American specialist, Teachers' Workshop, Graduate School of Education, Harvard U., Summer 1944. Membership: American Historical Association; Mississippi Valley Historical Association; New Mexico Historical Society; Rocky Mountain Conference on Latin American Studies; Rocky Mountain Social Science Association. Research: inter-American programs. Author: Latin America, Its History and Culture (1944); Our Spanish Southwest (1960); The Rio Grande Adventure: A History of New Mexico (1964). Language: Spanish 3,2,2,3; French 2,1,1,2. Home: 1038 Fifth, Las Vegas, N. Mex. Office: Dept. of History, N. Mex. Highlands U., Las Vegas.

PETERS, THELMA PETERSON, b. Independence, Mo., Apr. 22, 1905. HISTORY. A.B., Brenau Coll., 1926; M.A., Duke U., 1938; Ph. D., U. of Fla., 1960. Teacher, Miami Edison Senior High School, 1930-57; instr., U. of Miami, 1960-61; DIR., DIV. OF SOCIAL SCIENCE, MIAMI-DADE JUNIOR COLL., 1961- . Membership: Florida Historical Association; Historical Association of Southern Florida; Southern Historical Association. Research: Bahama Islands; American history. Author: Blockade-Running During the American Civil War (Tequesta, 1945); The American Loyalists in the Bahama Islands (Florida Historical Quarterly, Jan. 1962). Language: Spanish 3,2,2,2. Home: 11377 NE. West Biscayne Canal Rd., Miami, Fla. Office: Div. of Social Science, Miami-Dade Junior Coll., 11380 NW. 27th Ave., Miami.

PETERSON, FREDRICK ALVIN, b. Sheboygan, Wis., June 23, 1920. ANTHROPOLOGY. B.A., Mexico City Coll., 1948; M.A., 1949. Field asst., Lacandon Jungle Expedition, 1950-51; field asst., Milwaukee Public Museum research project (Mexico), 1954; co-dir., Lacandon Jungle Expedition, Centro de Estudios Antropológicos de México, 1955; writer (Mexico), 1956; photographic and production editor, Mexico This Month Magazine (Mexico), 1957; archeologist, New World Archaeological Foundation (Mexico), 1958-59; field dir., 1960-61; asst. dir., Proyecto Arqueológico-Botánico Tehuacán (Mexico), 1961-63; research scientist assoc., U. of Tex., 1964; ASST. PROF., ANTHROPOLOGY, COORDINATOR OF LATIN AMERICAN STUDIES, WEST VA. WESLEYAN COLL., 1964- . Wenner-Gren Foundation grant (Mexico), 1951-52. Membership: Centro de Estudios Antropológicos de México; Instituto Interamericano; Sociedad Mexicana de Antropología y Historia. Research: Mesoamerican social anthropology and archeology; ethnography of Indian tribes; mestizo culture; community organization; urban development; Mexico; Guatemala. Author: Ancient Mexico (1959, 1961). Co-author: The Mexican Kickapoo Indians

(1956); The Santa Marta Rock Shelter (1962). Language: Spanish 5,4,4,4; German 2,2,1,1. Office: Dept. of Anthropology, W. Va. Wesleyan Coll., Buckhannon.

PETERSON, HAROLD F(ERDINAND), b. Galesburg, Ill., Oct. 1, 1900. HISTORY. A.B., Knox Coll., 1922; M.A., U. of Minn., 1925; Ph. D., Duke U., 1933. Asst. prof., State U. of N.Y., Coll. at Buffalo, 1933–42; lectr., Committee on Cultural Relations with Latin America, 1940; captain, Joint Intelligence Committee, U.S. Joint Chiefs of Staff, 1942–43; captain-lieutenant colonel, Military Intelligence Div., War Dept., 1943–46; PROF. OF LATIN AMERICAN HISTORY, STATE U. OF N.Y., COLL. AT BUFFALO, 1945– . Two research fellowships, Research Foundation, State U. of N.Y, 1960. Membership: American Historical Association; Conference on Latin American History; National Council for Social Studies. Research: United States-Argentine diplomatic relations; inter-American relations. Author: Argentina and the United States, 1810–1960 (1964). Co-author: Builders of Latin America (1942). Language: Spanish 3,3,3,2. Home: 230 Knowlton Ave., Kenmore, N.Y. 14217. Office: Dept. of History, State U. of N.Y., Coll. at Buffalo, 1300 Elmwood Ave., Buffalo, 14222.

PETERSON, PHYLLIS JANE, b. Detroit, Mich., Oct. 2, 1932. POLITICAL SCIENCE. A.B., U. of Mich., 1954; M.A., U. of Calif., Berkeley, 1957; Ph. D., U. of Mich., 1962. Resident lectr., Ind. U. (Jeffersonville), 1959–62; instr., 1962–64; instr., Ind. U., 1964; ASST. PROF., GOVERNMENT, IND. U., 1964– . Doherty fellow (Brazil), 1958–59; Social Science Research Council and Ind. U. Faculty research grants (Brazil), Summer 1963. Membership: American Political Science Association; Midwest Conference of Political Scientists. Research: Latin American government and political party systems; Brazilian political parties. Language: Spanish 5,4,4,3; Portuguese 5,4,4,3; French 4,2,1,1. Home: 18830 Saratoga, Lathrup Village, Mich. Office: Dept. of Government, Ind. U., Bloomington.

PETTIT, JOHN ALBERT, b. Elkhart, Ind., Aug. 26, 1908. LANGUAGE. A.B., Wittenberg Coll., 1929; B.D., Chicago Lutheran Seminary, 1932; M.A., U. of Chicago, 1944; Ph. D., U. of Ill., 1955. Pastor, United Lutheran Church in America (Puerto Rico), 1938–42; instr., U. of Chicago, 1944–49; asst. prof., Ill. Wesleyan U., 1949–50; HEAD, MODERN LANGUAGES, MARIETTA COLL., 1953– . U. of Chicago fellow, 1942–43; consultant, U.S. Armed Forces Institute, U. of Chicago, 1943–45; Membership: American Association of Teachers of Spanish and Portuguese; Modern Language Association; Sigma Delta Pi. Research: Indian novel in Mexico, Ecuador, and Peru; language laboratory methodology. Language: Spanish 5,5,5,5; Portuguese 4,3,3,3; French 4,4,4,4; German 3,3,3,3; Russian 2,2,2,2. Home: 513½ Wooster St., Marietta, Ohio. Office: Dept. of Modern Languages. Marietta Coll., Marietta.

PFLAUM, IRVING PETER, b. Chicago, Ill., Apr. 9, 1906. HISTORY AND JOURNALISM. Ph. B., U. of Chicago, 1928; J.D., 1930; J.D., DePaul U., 1931. Reporter, Chicago Evening Post, 1930–33; staff correspondent and bureau chief, United Press Associations of America (Spain), 1933–39; foreign news editor, The Chicago Sun-Times, 1939–61; prof., professorial lectr. Law, Journalism, Northwestern U., 1940–59; assoc., Cuba and the Caribbean, American Universities Field Staff, 1959–61; PROF., SOCIAL STUDIES, DIR., LATIN AMERICAN CENTER, INTER AMERICAN U. (P.R.), 1961– . Marshall Field Fellowship Award, 1958; consultant, Seminars, Foreign Relations Club of U.S.A.; consultant, U. of Fla. and Inter American U. Summer Seminars; Ford Foundation fellow (Cuba), 1960–61. Membership: Association of American University Professors; Political Science Association; Sigma Delta Chi. Research: Cuban revolution; the Caribbean. Author: American Universities Field Staff Reports on Cuba, 1960–1961 (1960–61); Tragic Island: How Communism Came to Cuba (1961); Arena of Decision: Latin America in Crisis (1964). Language: Spanish 4,4,4,4; Portuguese 1,1,1,1; French 2,2,1,2. Home: Box 152, Inter American U., San German, P.R. Office: Latin American Center, Inter American U., San German.

PHELAN, JOHN LEDDY, b. Fall River, Mass., July 19, 1924. HISTORY. A.B., Harvard U., 1946; M.A., U. of Calif., Berkeley, 1947; Ph. D., 1951. Asst. prof., U. of Wis., Milwaukee, 1956–58; assoc. prof., 1958–60; ASSOC. PROF., HISTORY, U. OF WIS., MADISON, 1960– . Fulbright fellow (France), 1951–52; fellow in Philippine Studies, Newberry Library, 1953–55; Guggenheim award (Archivo General de Indias, Spain), 1960–61. Membership: American Academy of Franciscan History; American Historical Association; Conference on Latin American History. Research: colonial period in Latin America with emphasis on institutional, cultural, and intellectual history. Author: The Millennial Kingdom of the Franciscans in the New World: A Study of the Writings of Gerónimo de Mendieta, 1524–1604 (1956); The Hispanization of the Philippines: Spanish Aims and Filipino Responses, 1525–1700 (1959). Language: Spanish 4,4,4,3; Portuguese 3,3,2,1; French 4,3,3,1. Home: 346 East Lakeside, Madison, Wis. Office: Dept. of History, U. of Wis., Madison.

PHILLIPS, ALLEN W., b. Providence, R.I., June 17, 1922. SPANISH AMERICAN LITERATURE. B.A., Dartmouth Coll., 1942; M.A., Universidad Nacional de México, 1948; Ph. D., U. of Mich., 1953. Instr., Hamilton Coll., 1948–49; instr., U. of Mich., 1949–55; asst. prof.-ASSOC. PROF., SPANISH, U. OF CHICAGO, 1955– ; vis. prof., U. of Calif., Berkeley, Summer 1960. Guggenheim fellow, 1960–61; American Council of Learned Societies grant, 1961; literary dir., Revista Iberoamericana, 1961–63; American Philosophical Society grant, 1963. Membership: Instituto Internacional de Literatura Iberoamericana. Research: contemporary literature in Spain and Latin America. Author: Ramón López Velarde, el poeta y el prosista (1962); Francisco González León, Poeta de Lagos (1964); Estudios y notas sobre literatura hispanoamericana (1965). Language: Spanish 5,5,5,5; French 3,3,3,3. Home: 340 Winnebago,

Park Forest, Ill. Office: Dept. of Spanish, U. of Chicago, 1050 East 59th St., Chicago 37, Ill.

PHILLIPS, JOSEPH D., b. Buena Park, Calif., Dec. 5, 1914. ECONOMICS. A.B., U. of Calif., 1937; Ph. D., Columbia U., 1951. Asst. prof., Wesleyan U. (Conn.), 1946–49; lectr., Santa Barbara Coll., 1949–51; assoc. prof., Champlain Coll., 1951–53; prof., dept. head, Idaho State Coll., 1953–56; RESEARCH PROF., ECONOMICS, U. OF ILL., 1956– ; economist, Joint Center for Urban Studies (Venezuela), 1962–63. Columbia U. fellow, 1941–42; Social Science Research Council field fellow, 1942; Social Science Research Council Demobilization Award, 1946; editor, Illinois Business Review. Membership: American Economic Association; American Statistical Association; Economic History Association. Research: economic development; the Guayana region of Venezuela. Author: Trade and Trade Control in the Pacific Area (1942); Little Business in the American Economy (1958); The Self-Employed in the United States (1962). Language: Spanish 3,3,3,3. Home: 108 West Florida Ave., Urbana, Ill. Office: Bureau of Economic and Business Research, 428 David Kinley Hall, U. of Ill., Urbana, 61803.

PICKERING, WILBUR NORMAN, b. São Paulo, Brazil, Apr. 25, 1934. LINGUISTICS. B.A., William Jennings Bryan Coll., 1956; Dallas Theological Seminary, 1956–59. LINGUIST, SUMMER INSTITUTE OF LINGUISTICS (BRAZIL), 1961– . Research: rural Brazilian life and culture, especially of the Apurinã tribe; analysis of the Apurinã language. Language: Spanish 3,3,3,3; Portuguese 4,4,4,4; Apurinã –,3,-3,–. Linguistic studies: Apurinã. Home: Caixa Postal 431, Manaus, Amazonas, Brasil, Office: Summer Institute of Linguistics, P.O. Box 1960, Santa Ana, Calif.

PICKETT, VELMA BERNICE, b. Dunning, Nebr., Aug. 14, 1912. LINGUISTICS. A.B., U. of Calif., Los Angeles, 1935; M.A., Cornell U., 1951; Ph. D., U. of Mich., 1959. INSTR.-FIELD WORKER AND TRANSLATOR, SUMMER INSTITUTE OF LINGUISTICS (MEXICO), 1943– . Membership: Linguistic Society of America. Research: analysis of unwritten languages; Isthmus Zapotec. Author: The Grammatical Hierarchy of Isthmus Zapotec (1960). Co-author: An Introduction to Morphology and Syntax (1962). Language: Spanish 4,4,4,3; French 3,1,1,1; Isthmus Zapotec 5,4,5,5. Linguistic studies: Isthmus Zapotec. Home: 1068 Devonshire Dr., Encinitas, Calif. Office: Summer Institute of Linguistics, Box 1960, Santa Ana, Calif.

PICÓ, RAFAEL, b. Coamo, P.R., Dec. 29, 1912. GEOGRAPHY, ECONOMICS, AND POLITICAL SCIENCE. B.A., U. of P.R., 1932; B.A., Clark U., 1934; Ph. D., 1938. Chmn., P.R. Planning Board (Santurce, P.R.), 1942–45; secretary, Dept. of the Treasury (San Juan, P.R.), 1955–57; PRESIDENT, GOVERNMENT DEVELOPMENT BANK FOR P.R. (SANTURCE, P.R.), 1958– . United Nations planning expert to El Salvador, 1949, Peru, 1952, Bolivia, Ecuador, and Peru, 1955; Public Administration consultant (Honduras), 1957; Ad Hoc Committee, Honduras National Plan, 1962. Membership: American Geographical Society; American Institute of Planners; American Society of Planning Officials; American Society for Public Administration; Association of American Geographers; Inter-American Planning Society; Municipal Finance Officers Association; National Housing Conference; Pan American Foundation; Society for International Development. Research: economic geography; development programs; banking; public administration; application of planning to development of government operations; Puerto Rico. Author: The Geographic Regions of Puerto Rico (1950); Geografía de Puerto Rico, Parte I: Geografía Física de Puerto Rico (1954); Puerto Rico: Planificación y Acción (1962). Language: Spanish 5,5,5,5; French 3,3,3,1. Home: 564 Independencia St., Reparto Baldrich, Hato Rey, P.R. Office: Government Development Bank for Puerto Rico, 1311 Ponce de León Ave., Santurce, P.R. 00908.

PIKAZA, OTTO, b. Sestao, Vizcaya, Spain, Sept. 1, 1928. HISTORY. Ph. D., Universidad de Sevilla (Spain), 1961. Instr., Ind. U., 1961–64; ASST. PROF., HISTORY, IND. U., 1964– . Latin American Studies Committee, Ind. U. Research: beginnings of diplomatic relations between the United States and Spain, 1776–1785; research in Archivo General de Indias; 17th century Bolivia. Author: Don Gabriel José de Zuloaga, Gobernador de Venezuela, 1737–1747 (Escuela de Estudios Hispanoamericanos, 1963). Language: Spanish 5,5,5,5; Portuguese 4,4,1,1; French 4,4,2,4; Italian 4,4,2,1. Home: West University Apts. 13, Bloomington, Ind. Office: Dept. of History, Ind. U., Bloomington.

PIKE, EUNICE VICTORIA, b. Woodstock, Conn., Nov. 6, 1913. LINGUISTICS. MISSIONARY, LINGUIST, SUMMER INSTITUTE OF LINGUISTICS (MEXICO), 1936– . Membership: Linguistic Circle of New York; Linguistic Society of America. Research: descriptive linguistics; phonology; Mazatec Indians of Oaxaca, Mexico. Author: Problems in Zapotec Tone Analysis (International Journal of American Linguistics, July 1948); Tonemic-intonemic Correlation in Mazahua (International Journal of American Linguistics, Jan. 1951). Co-author: Huasteco Intonation and Phonemes (Language, July–Sept. 1949). Language: Spanish 3,3,3,2; Mazatec 3,4,4, 3. Linguistic studies: Arabela; Chatino; Huastec; Marinahua; Mazahua; Mazatec; Mixtec; Zapotec. Home: Héroes 53, México 3, D.F. Office: Summer Institute of Linguistics, Box 1960, Santa Ana, Calif. 92702.

PIKE, FREDERICK BRAUN, b. Los Angeles, Calif., Dec. 23, 1926. HISTORY. B.A., Loyola U. (Calif.), 1949; M.A., U. of Tex., 1950; Ph. D., 1956. ASSOC. PROF., HISTORY, U. OF NOTRE DAME, 1952– ; vis. asst. prof., Rutgers U., Summer 1961; vis. prof., U. of Pa., 1964–65. Doherty Foundation grant (Chile), 1959–60; Social Science Research Council grant (Peru), 1963–64. Membership: American Historical Association; Conference on Latin American History. Research: republican history of Chile and Peru. Author: Chile and the United States, 1880–1962 (1963). Editor: Freedom and Reform in Latin America (1959); Conflict Between Church and State in Latin America (1963). Language: Spanish 4,4,3,2. Home: 307 East Pokagon St., South Bend, Ind. Office: Dept. of History, U. of Notre Dame, Notre Dame, Ind.

PIKE, KENNETH LEE, b. Woodstock, Conn., June 9, 1912. LINGUISTICS. Th. B., Gordon Coll., 1933; Ph. D., U. of Mich., 1942. PRESIDENT, SUMMER INSTITUTE OF LINGUISTICS (CALIF.), 1935– ; PROF., LINGUISTICS, U. OF MICH., 1948– . Board member, Wycliffe Bible Translators, 1935– ; Rockefeller Foundation grant. Membership: American Anthropological Association; International Phonetic Association; Linguistic Society of America. Research: descriptive linguistics; analysis, phonetics, grammar structure and theory of language; relation of language to culture; semantic structure; Indian languages in Ecuador, Bolivia, and Peru. Author: Phonetics, a Technique for the Description of Sounds (1943); Intonation of American English (1945); Phonemics (1947); Language in Relation to a Unified Theory of the Structure of Human Behavior (1954, 1955, 1960). Language: Spanish 4,4,4,1; French 3,1,1,1; Mixtec 4,4,3,2. Linguistic studies: Bilaan; Fore; Maya; Mazatec; Mixtec. Home: 1914 Wayne St., Ann Arbor, Mich. 48104. Office: Dept. of Linguistics, U. of Mich., Ann Arbor, 48104.

PINCUS, JOSEPH, b. New York, N.Y., Apr. 17, 1919. ECONOMICS. B.S.S., City Coll. (N.Y.), 1941; M.A., American U., 1947; Ph. D., 1953. Foreign affairs analyst, Div. of Research for American Republics, U.S. Dept. of State, 1949–58; tariff adviser, U.S. Overseas Mission (Honduras), 1958–61; international economist, U.S. Tariff Commission, 1961–62; program officer, U.S. Agency for International Development (Costa Rica), 1962–64; ECONOMIC ADVISER, U.S. AGENCY FOR INTERNATIONAL DEVELOPMENT MISSION (PARAGUAY), 1964– . Member, Continental-Allied team to survey Honduran industry, 1959; consultant on Central American Common Market, Wolf Engineering Company, 1961. Membership: Society for International Development. Research: international economics; Central American Common Market; Latin American Free Trade Association. Author: Breve historia del arancel de aduanas en Honduras (1959); The Industrial Development Laws of Central America (1961); The Central American Common Market (1962). Language: Spanish 4,4,4,2; Portuguese 3,2,1,1; French 3,3,2,2. Home: 161–04 Jewel Ave., Flushing 65, N.Y. Office: U.S. Agency for International Development, American Embassy, Asunción, Paraguay.

PINE, JOHN CRANE, b. East Aurora, N.Y., Oct. 25, 1921. HISTORY. B.A., Dartmouth Coll., 1945; M.A., U. of Chicago, 1948; Ph. D., U. of Colo., 1955. Instr., Hastings Coll., 1947–50; Joplin Junior Coll., 1955–56; ASSOC. PROF., HISTORY, U. OF ARK., 1956– . Membership: American Historical Association; Mississippi Valley Historical Association. Research: Latin American-United States relations. Language: Spanish 2,3,2,2; French 1,1,1,1. Home: 1228 West Cleveland, Fayetteville, Ark. Office: Dept. of History, U. of Ark., Fayetteville, 72701.

PI-SUNYER, ORIOL, b. Barcelona, Spain, Jan. 16, 1930. ANTHROPOLOGY. B.A., Mexico City Coll., 1954; A.M., Harvard U., 1957; Ph. D., 1962. Instr.-asst. prof., U. of New Brunswick, 1959–61; ASST. PROF., ANTHROPOLOGY, CASE INSTITUTE OF TECHNOLOGY, 1961– . Teaching fellow, Harvard U., 1956–59; research assoc., Center for International Studies, Mass. Institute of Technology (Mexico), 1957–58; consultant on Mexico, Ford Foundation, 1964– . Membership: American Anthropological Association. Research: social and cultural anthropology; culture history; economic development; Mexican economic development and problems of technical education. Author: Historical Background to the Negro in Mexico (Journal of Negro History, Oct. 1957); Religion and Witchcraft: Spanish Attitudes and Pueblo Reactions (Antropologica, 1960); Perspectives in Frontier Culture: New Spain and Homeric Greece (Antropologica, 1964); Culture Resistance to Technological Change (Technology and Culture, 1964). Language: Spanish 5,5,5,4; Portuguese 3,2,1,1; French 3,3,3,3; Catalán 5,5,5,3. Home: 2009 Marlindale Rd., Cleveland Heights 18, Ohio. Office: Dept. of Humanities and Social Studies, Case Institute of Technology, Cleveland 6.

PLANK, JOHN NATHAN, b. Dayton, Ohio, July 22, 1923. POLITICAL SCIENCE. A.B., Harvard Coll., 1949; M.A., Haverford Coll., 1953; Ph. D., Harvard U., 1959. Dir., American Friends Service Committee Project in Community Development (El Salvador), 1953–54; instr., Harvard U., 1959–61; asst. prof., 1961–62; prof., Fletcher School of Law & Diplomacy, 1962–63; vis. prof., Harvard U., 1962–63; dir., Office of Research and Analysis for American Republics, U.S. Dept. of State, 1963–64; DIR., POLITICAL DEVELOPMENT STUDIES, BROOKINGS INSTITUTION, 1964– . Doherty fellow (Argentina), 1957–58; consultant, Ford Foundation, 1960–61; Bliss fellow, 1961–62. Membership: American Political Science Association; Inter-American Association for Democracy and Freedom. Research: international affairs; nationalism in developing nations; political development; Peru. Author: The Alliance for Progress: Problems and Prospects (1962); What Policy for Latin America? (New York Times Magazine, June 1961); The Monroe Doctrine (New York Times Magazine, Oct. 1962). Language: Spanish, 4,4,4,3; Portuguese 3,2,1,1; French 3,2,1,1. Home: 3429 34th Pl., NW., Washington, D.C. 20016. Office: Brookings Institution, 1775 Massachusetts Ave., Washington, D.C.

PLETCHER, DAVID MITCHELL, b. Faribault, Minn., June 14, 1920. HISTORY. B.A., U. of Chicago, 1941; M.A., 1941; Ph. D., 1946. Instr., U. of Iowa, 1944–46; assoc. prof., Knox Coll., 1946–56; assoc. prof.-PROF., HISTORY, HAMLINE U., 1956– ; assoc. prof., U. of Mo., Summers 1955–59. Fulbright grant, U. of London, 1953–54; Beveridge Memorial Award, 1957; McKnight Foundation Award, 1961; Social Science Research Council grant (Mexico), 1962–63. Membership: American Historical Association; Upper Midwest Historical Association. Research: history of United States foreign relations; United States-Mexican relations. Author: Rails, Mines, and Progress: Seven American Promoters in Mexico, 1867–1911 (1958); The

Awkward Years: American Foreign Relations under Garfield and Arthur (1962). Language: Spanish 4,3,3,4; French 4,3,3,4. Home: 2130 Como Ave., St. Paul 8, Minn. Office: Dept. of History, Hamline U., St. Paul 1.

POLEMAN, THOMAS T., b. St. Louis, Mo., Nov. 28, 1928. ECONOMICS. M.A., U. of Mo., 1951; M.S., 1952; M.A., Stanford U., 1957; Ph. D., 1960. Research assoc., Food Research Institute, Stanford U., 1959-61; professorial assoc., National Academy of Science-National Research Council, 1960-61; senior economic analyst, U.S. Government, 1961-63; PROF., AGRICULTURAL ECONOMICS, CORNELL U., 1963- . Membership: American Economic Association; American Farm Economic Association; African Studies Association; Asian Studies Association. Research: economics of food and agriculture in tropical countries; agriculture and agricultural development in the Mexican tropics. Author: The Papaloapan Project: Agricultural Development in the Mexican Tropics (1964); The Food Economics of Urban Tropical Africa (Food Research Institute Studies, May 1961). Language: Spanish 4,2,2,1. Home: 155 North Sunset Dr., Ithaca, N.Y. Office: Dept. of Economics, Cornell U., Ithaca.

POLLOCK, DAVID HAROLD, b. Prince Albert, Canada, June 14, 1922. ECONOMICS. B.S., U. of Saskatchewan, 1946; M.A., U. of Chicago, 1948. Research asst., World Bank, 1949-50; economist, Economic Commission for Latin America, United Nations (Washington, D.C.), 1951-53; Economic Development Div. (Santiago), 1953-55; asst. chief, Economic Commission for Latin America (Washington, D.C.), 1955-58; deputy to the chief, Economic Development Section (Mexico), 1958-59; chief, Economic Commission for Latin America (Washington), 1959-63; special asst. to the Secretary General, United Nations (New York), 1963-64; CHIEF, ECONOMIC COMMISSION FOR LATIN AMERICA, UNITED NATIONS (WASHINGTON, D.C.), 1964- . Research fellow, U. of Chicago. Membership: American Economic Association; Society for International Development. Research: analyses and projections in the field of economic development; balance of payments analyses; commodity and tourism studies; investment analyses and projections. Author: Trends in Commodity Trade Between the United States and Latin America (Economic Commission for Latin America: Economic Bulletin for Latin America, 1961). Co-author: Economic Development of El Salvador (1959). Contributor: Economic Development of Colombia (1954). Language: Spanish 4,3,3,2; French 3,2,2,1. Home: 1118 Cresthaven Dr., Silver Spring, Md. Office: Economic Commission for Latin America, United Nations, 1725 I St., NW., Washington, D.C. 20006.

POLLOCK, HARRY E. D., b. Salt Lake City, Utah, June 24, 1900. ANTHROPOLOGY. A.B., Harvard U., 1923; M.A., 1930; Ph. D., 1936. Archeologist, Case Institution of Washington, 1928-50; dir., Dept. of Archaeology, Carnegie Institution of Washington, 1950-58; research fellow, Peabody Museum, Harvard U., 1953-63; research assoc., Carnegie Institution of Washington, 1958; CURATOR, PEABODY MUSEUM, HARVARD U., 1963- . Membership: American Anthropological Association; American Association for the Advancement of Science; Society for American Archaeology. Research: Middle American archeology; Mayan archeology. Author: Round Structures of Aboriginal Middle America (1936); Sources and Methods in Study of Maya Architecture (in Maya and Their Neighbors, 1940). Co-author: Preliminary Study of Ruins of Coba (1932). Language: Spanish 3,2,2,3. Home: 11 Berkeley Pl., Cambridge, Mass., 02138. Office: Peabody Museum, Harvard U., Cambridge, 02138.

PONSETI, HELENA PERCAS, b. Valencia, Spain, Jan. 17, 1921. SPANISH AMERICAN LITERATURE. Baccalauréat, Institut Maintenon, 1939; B.A., Barnard Coll., 1942; M.A., Columbia U., 1943; Ph. D., 1951. Instr., Russell Sage Coll., 1942-45; instr., Queens Coll., 1945-48; asst. prof., Grinnell Coll., 1948-54; assoc. prof., 1954-56; PROF., SPANISH, GRINNELL COLL., 1956- . Danforth grant (Mexico), Summer 1959; Editorial Staff, Revista Iberoamericana, 1959-61. Membership: American Association of Teachers of Spanish and Portuguese; Hispanic Institute of Columbia University; Modern Language Association. Research: poetry in Argentina; Latin American literature, analysis and criticism; Hispanic culture. Author: Women Poets of Argentina, 1810-1950 (1958); Algunas observaciones sobre la lengua de Borges (Revista Iberoamericana, June 1958); Sobre la Avellaneda y su novela Sab (Revista Iberoamericana, July-Dec. 1962). Language: Spanish 5,5,5,5; Portuguese 3,-,-,-; French 5,5,5,5; Italian 3,-,-,-. Home: 315 Ellis Ave., Iowa City, Iowa, 52241. Office: Dept. of Modern Foreign Languages, Grinnell Coll., Grinnell, Iowa.

POOLE, RICHARD STAFFORD, C. M., b. Oxnard, Calif., Mar. 6, 1930. HISTORY. A.B., St. Mary's Seminary, 1952; M.A., St. Louis U., 1958; Ph. D., 1961. Instr., Cardinal Glennon Coll., 1958-59; dean of men, 1959-63; vice president, 1963-64; PROF., HISTORY, ST. MARY'S SEMINARY, 1964- . Cardinal Glennon Coll. summer research grants (Mexico), 1960, 1962. Membership: American Catholic Historical Association; American Historical Association; Hispanic American Historical Association; Judeo-Christian Studies Institute; Mississippi Valley Historical Association. Research: church history in colonial Mexico. Author: Research Possibilities of the Third Council (Manuscripta, 1961); The Church and the Repartimientos in the Light of the Third Mexican Council, 1585 (The Americas, July 1963). Language: Spanish 4,3,3,3; Portuguese 2,1,1,1; French 2,1,1,1; Italian 2,2,1,1. Home and office: St. Mary's Seminary, Perryville, Mo.

POPPINO, ROLLIE EDWARD, b. Milwaukie, Oreg., Oct. 4, 1922. H I S T O R Y. B.A., Stanford U., 1948; M.A., 1949; Ph. D., 1953. Instr., Stanford U., 1953-54; intelligence research specialist, U.S. Dept. of State, 1954-61; lectr., American U., 1959-61; asst. prof., U. of Calif., Davis, 1961-64; ASSOC. PROF. HISTORY, U. OF CALIF., DAVIS, 1964- . Doherty fellow (Brazil), 1950-51; consultant, U.S. Dept. of State, 1962- ; Social Science Research Council fellow (B r a z i l), 1963. Membership: American Historical Association; Conference on Latin American History; Pacific Coast Council on Latin American Studies. Research: history of Brazil; communism in Latin America; Latin American international relations; socio-political change since 1900 in Latin America. Author: Cattle Industry in Colonial Brazil (Mid-America, Oct. 1949); A Century of the Revista do Instituto Histórico e Geográfico Brasileiro (Hispanic American Historical Review, May 1953); Imbalance in Brazil (Current History, Feb. 1963). Language: Spanish 4,4,3,3; Portuguese 4,5,4,3; French 3,2,1,1. Home: 1221 Eureka Ave., Davis, Calif. Office: Dept. of History, U. of Calif., Davis, 95616.

PORTELL-VILÁ HERMINIO, b. Cárdenas, Cuba, June 18, 1901. HISTORY. LL.D., Universidad de la Habana, 1927; Ph. D., 1934. Instr., Black Mountain Coll., 1935–39; prof., U. of Havana, 1939–60; vis. prof., U. of Calif., Los Angeles, 1940, U. of Fla., 1960–61; commentator, Latin American Div., Voice of America, U.S. Information Agency, 1961–63. Guggenheim fellow, 1931–33, 1935; Chubb fellow, Yale U., 1957; Rockefeller grant, 1960. Research: Cuban-United States relations. Author: Narciso López y su época (1930–58); Céspedes, el Padre de la Patria Cubana (1931); Historia de Cuba en sus relaciones con los Estados Unidos y España (1938–1941). Language: Spanish 5,5,5,5; Portuguese 4,4,4,3; French 3,3,3,3. Home: 4740 Connecticut Ave., NW., Washington, D.C.

POST, ALBERT, b. Brooklyn, N.Y., Apr. 18, 1915. ECONOMICS. A.B., U. of Ark., 1936; A.M., Columbia U., 1937; Ph. D., 1942. Attaché, Embassy (Madrid), U.S. Dept of State, 1946–49; economist, Economic Development Div., 1949–50; economist, U.S. delegations to North Atlantic Treaty Organization and Organization for European Economic Cooperation, 1950–53; economist, Commercial Policy Div., U.S. Dept. of State, 1954–55; financial attaché, Embassy (Brazil), 1955–57; financial adviser, Latin America affairs, 1957–60; economic counselor, Embassy (Guatemala), 1961–63; ADVISER, U.S. DEPT. OF TREASURY, 1963– . Council on Foreign Relations Study Group, 1960–61. Membership: American Economic Association. Research: Latin American economic integration. Language: Spanish 4,4,4,4; Portuguese 3,3,3,–; French 3,3,3,–; German 2,2,2,–. Home: 6322 32nd St., NW., Washington, D.C., 20015. Office: U.S. Dept. of State, Washington, D.C.

POTASH, ROBERT A., b. Boston, Mass., Jan. 2, 1921. HISTORY. A.B., Harvard U., 1942; A.M., 1947; Ph. D., 1953. Instr., U. of Mass., 1950–55; political analyst, U.S. Dept. of State, 1955–57; PROF., HISTORY, U. OF MASS., 1957– . Organization of American States fellow (Argentina), 1961–62; consultant, U.S. Dept. of State; Board of Editors, Hispanic American Historical Review. Membership: American Historical Association; Conference on Latin American History. Research: contemporary Argentina; 19th century Mexico. Author: El Banco de Avío de México (1959); The Historiography of Mexico Since 1821 (Hispanic American Historical Review, Aug. 1960); The Changing Role of the Military in Argentina (Journal of Inter-American Studies, Oct. 1961). Language: Spanish 4,4,4,4; Portuguese 3,3,3,2; French 3,2,2,2; German 2,2,2,2. Home: 130 Red Gate Lane, Amherst, Mass. Office: Dept. of History, U. of Mass., Amherst.

POWELL, PHILIP WAYNE, b. Chino, Calif., Oct. 30, 1913. HISTORY. B.A., U. of Calif., Berkeley, 1936; Ph. D., 1941. Divisional asst., U.S. Dept. of State, 1941–43; vis. prof., U. of Pa., 1943–44; asst. prof., Northwestern U., 1944–48; vis. prof. in Ecuador, U.S. Dept. of State, 1947; special adviser to secretariat, 9th International Conference of American States (Bogotá, Colombia), 1948; PROF., HISTORY, U. OF CALIF., SANTA BARBARA, 1948– . Rockefeller Foundation fellow (Latin America), 1938–39; American Philosophical Society grant-in-aid (Mexico), 1945; chmn., Latin American Conference of the American Historical Association, 1948; Del Amo Foundation traveling fellow, 1950, 1954–55. Membership: American Historical Association. Research: inter-American relations; Spanish-United States relations; Spanish history; Mexican colonial history. Author: Soldiers, Indians and Silver: The Northward Advance of New Spain, 1550–1600 (1952). Language: Spanish 5,5,5,4; Portuguese 4,3,3,3; French 3,3,2,1; Dutch 2,2, 1,1; German 2,2,1,1. Home: 1216 Shoreline Dr., Santa Barbara, Calif. Office: Dept. of History, U. of Calif., Santa Barbara.

POWELSON, JOHN PALEN, b. New York, N.Y., Sept. 3, 1920. ECONOMICS. Ph. D., Harvard U., 1950 Research economist, asst. chief of training, International Monetary Fund, 1950–58; prof., School of Advanced International Studies, Johns Hopkins U., 1958–64; vis. prof., U. of San Andrés (La Paz, Bolivia), 1960; dir., Program on National Accounts, Latin American Monetary Studies Center (Mexico), 1963–64; PROF., ECONOMIC DEVELOPMENT, U. OF PITTSBURGH, 1964– . Economic adviser, Government of Bolivia, 1959–60. Membership: American Economic Association; Society for International Development. Research: national income accounting; Bolivia; Mexico. Author: Economic Accounting (1955); National Income (1960); Latin America: Today's Economic and Social Revolution (1964). Language: Spanish 4,4,4,3; French 3,3,3,3. Home: 5620 Marlboro Rd., Pittsburgh, Pa. 15217. Office: Graduate School of Public and International Affairs, U. of Pittsburgh, Pittsburgh 13.

POWLISON, PAUL STEWART, b. Toracari, Bolivia, Dec. 27, 1923. LINGUISTICS. B.A., U. of Mich., 1947; M.A., 1958. LINGUIST, MISSIONARY, SUMMER INSTITUTE OF LINGUISTICS (PERU), 1950– . Ford folklore fellow, Ind. U., 1963–64. Research: folklore; Iquitos area of Peru. Author: The Yagua Kinship System (1959); La cultura Yagua reflejada en sus cuentos folklóricos (Folklore Americano, 1959); Palatalization Portmanteaus in Yagua (Word, Dec. 1962). Language: Spanish 4,4,4,3; Portuguese 2,2,1,1; French 3,1,1,1; Japanese 1,1,1,1; Quechua 1,2,1,1 Yagua 3,3,4,3. Linguistic studies: Yagua Home: 1203 South Henderson, Bloomington, Ind. 47403. Office: Instituto Lingüístico de Verano, Casilla 2492, Lima, Perú.

PREECE, MARGOT, b. Detroit, Mich., Apr. 7, 1931. JOURNALISM. B.A., U. of Fla., 1952; M.A., 1954; Radcliffe Coll., 1954-56. Instr., foreign student adviser, Fla. Southern Coll., 1952-53; asst. instr., U. of Fla., 1953-54; instr., Social Science Research Center editor, U. of P.R., 1956-61; REPORTER, THE SAN JUAN STAR (P.R.), 1962- ; CORRESPONDENT, NORTH AMERICAN NEWSPAPER A L L I A N C E (N.Y.), 1964- . Doherty fellow, Radcliffe Coll., 1954-56; consultant, P.R. Dept. of Commerce; editor, Economic Pulse of Puerto Rico, 1959-61. Membership: Puerto Rico Newspaper Guild. Research: Puerto Rico and the Caribbean. Author: Venezuela (in Encyclopedia Americana, 1954-62); Cuba (in Encyclopedia Americana, 1954-62). Language: Spanish 5,5,5,5; Portuguese 4,2,1,1; French 5,3,2,2; German 2,2,1,1; Greek 3,1,1,1; Italian 3,2,1,1; Latin 3,1,1,1; Russian 2,2,1,1. Home: Box 765, Hato Rey, P.R. Office: The San Juan Star, San Juan, P.R.

PRESCOTT, JAMES RUSSELL, b. Lincoln, Nebr., Feb. 9, 1935. ECONOMICS AND STATISTICS. B.A., U. of Calif., Berkeley, 1957; M.A., Harvard U., 1961; Ph. D., 1964. ASST. PROF. ECONOMICS AND STATISTICS, IOWA STATE U., 1963- . Woodrow Wilson, Earhart Foundation, and I.B.M. fellow; teaching fellow, Harvard U., 1961-63; U.S. Agency for International Development consultant, Institute of National Planning, Government of Peru (Lima), Summer 1964. Membership: American Economic Association. Research: Public finance; computer applications of investment project inventories in Peru. Language: Spanish 3,3,2,2; French 4,4,3,2; German 2,2,2,2. Home: 821 Hodge St., Ames, Iowa 50010. Office: Dept. of Economics, Iowa State U., Ames, 50010.

PREVITALI, GIOVANNI, b. New York, N.Y., Jan. 19, 1911. SPANISH AMERICAN LITERATURE AND LANGUAGE. B.A., Oxford U., 1934; LL.B., U. of Va., 1950; M.A., Oxford U., 1950; Ph. D., Yale U., 1959. Instr., Spanish and Italian, U. of Va., 1949-52; asst. prof., U. of Tex., 1957-59; chmn., Foreign Languages, San Francisco State Coll., 1959-60; prof., U. of P.R., 1960-61; prof., Fla. Presbyterian Coll., 1961-63; PROF., ROMANCE LANGUAGES AND LITERATURE, U. OF P.R., MAYAGÜEZ, 1964- . Ford Faculty fellow, 1952; dir. of Spanish, Summer Language Institute at Yale U., 1954-57; dean, Language Abroad Institute (Ohio). Membership: American Association of Teachers of Italian; American Association of Teachers of Spanish and Portuguese; American Association of University Professors; Dante Society of America; Institute of World Affairs; Instituto International de Literatura Iberoamericana; Modern Language Association. Research: Argentine and Brazilian literature; teaching methods for modern foreign languages. Author: Ricardo Güiraldes and Don Segundo Sombra (1963); Lo inefable en la poesía de Juan Ramón Jiménez (Atenea, 1961); El Verdadero Don Segundo Sombra (Revista Iberoamericana, 1963). Language: Spanish 5,5,5,5; Portuguese 4,4,4,4; French 4,4,4,4; German 2,2,-2,1; Italian 5,5,5,5. Linguistic studies: French; Latin; Spanish. Office: Dept. of Humanities, U. of P.R., Mayagüez, P.R.

PRICE, HARTLEY D'OYLEY, b. Brisbane, Australia. EDUCATION. B.S., Springfield Coll., 1927; B.P.E., 1928; B.S., U. of Ill., 1928; M.A., 1931; Ph. D., N.Y.U., 1946. Assoc. prof., gymnastic coach, dir. of intramural sports, U. of Ill., 1927-48; PROF., PHYSICAL EDUCATION, VARSITY GYMNASTIC COACH, DIR. OF GYMKANA, FLA. STATE U., 1948- . Fulbright prof. (India), 1958-59, (Colombia), 1961; National Defense Education Act fellow in Spanish, U. of Calif., Los Angeles, 1962. Membership: Amateur Athletic Union of the United States; American Association for Health, Physical Education and Recreation; National Collegiate Athletic Association. Research: physical education. Author: Gymnastics and Tumbling (1949. 1959); Educación física, el desarrollo de cuerpo y mente (1961). Co-author: Intramural and Recreational Sports for Men and Women (1949). Language: Spanish 3,2,2,3; Portuguese 1,1,1,-; French 2,1,1,-. Home: 1561 Yancey St., Tallahassee, Fla. Office: Dept. of Physical Education, Fla. State U., Tallahassee.

PROSKOURIAKOFF, TATIANA, b. Tomsk, Russia, Jan. 23, 1909. ANTHROPOLOGY AND PRE-COLUMBIAN ART. B.S., Pa. State Coll., 1930. ARCHEOLOGIST, CARNEGIE INSTITUTION OF WASHINGTON, 1944- . U. of Pa. Museum archeological expedition to Middle America. 1936; research assoc. in Maya art, Peabody Museum, Harvard U. Membership: American Anthropological Association; American Association for the Advancement of Science; Society for American Archaeology. Research: Middle American archeology; pre-Columbian art of Middle America; Maya hieroglyphic writing. Author: An Album of Maya Architecture (1946); A Study of Classic Maya Sculpture (1950); Historical Implications of a Pattern of Dates at Piedras Negras, Guatemala (American Antiquity, Apr. 1960). Language: Spanish 3,3,2,2; French 3,1,2,2; German 2,1,1,1; Russian 4,5,3,2. Home: 28 Healey St., Cambridge, Mass. 02138. Office: Peabody Museum, Harvard U., Cambridge, Mass. 02138.

PSUTY, NORBERT PHILLIP, b. Hamtramck, Mich., June 13, 1937. GEOGRAPHY. B.A., Wayne State U., 1959; M.A., Miami U., 1960; Ph. D., La. State U., 1965. Instr., La. State U., 1961-62; researcher, U.S. Office of Naval Research contract, Coastal Studies Institute, La. State U., 1962-64; INSTR., GEOGRAPHY, U. OF MIAMI, 1964- . Membership: American Geographical Society; Association of American Geographers. Research: physical geography, especially geomorphology and climatology; coastal morphology and regional climatology of Tabasco, Mexico. Language: Spanish 3,3,3,2; French 2,1,1,1; German 3,2,2,2. Home: 5730 NW. 3rd St., Miami, Fla. Office: Dept. of Geography, U. of Miami, Coral Gables, Fla.

PULSIFER, JOSEPHINE STURDIVANT, b. Cumberland, Maine, Sept. 27, 1915. LIBRARY SCIENCE. B.A., Barnard Coll., 1936; B.S. in L.S., Drexel Institute of Technology, 1942. Periodicals librarian, reference asst., Library, U. of Maine, 1949-52; serials cataloger, asst. head, Catalog Dept., Library, Iowa State U., 1953-55; head, Catalog Dept., Library, S. Dak. State

Coll., 1956–61; librarian, Pan American Agricultural School (Tegucigalpa, Honduras), 1961–63; CATALOGER, DESCRIPTIVE CATALOGING DIV., LIBRARY OF CONGRESS, 1963– . Membership: American Library Association; International Association of Agricultural Librarians and Documentalists; Special Libraries Association. Research: cataloging, administration, and serials, especially in agricultural and biological sciences; serials in Spanish and Portuguese Language; Spanish 3,3,3,3. Portuguese 2,1,1,1, ; French 3,3,2,2. Home: 2424 Pennsylvania Ave. NW., Washington, D.C., 20037. Office: Descriptive Cataloging Div., Library of Congress, Washington, D.C., 20540.

PULVER, GLEN CURTIS, b. Wyocena, Wis., Oct. 31, 1929. ECONOMICS. B.S., U. of Wis., 1951; M.S., 1955; Ph. D., 1956. Instr.-assoc. prof., U. of Wis., 1955–61; assoc. prof., Universidade do Rio Grande do Sul (Brazil), 1961–63; ASSOC. PROF., AGRICULTURAL ECONOMICS, U. OF WIS., 1963– . Membership: International Agricultural Economics Association. Research: agricultural economics; farm management; development opportunities for small farms in Southern Brazil. Author: An Emperical Measure of Decision Making (Research Bulletin 238, U. of Wis., June 1962); Large Milking Operations in Wisconsin (Research Bulletin 556, U. of Wis., June 1962); Vegetable Enterprise Selection in Central Wisconsin (Research Bulletin 247, U. of Wis., Jan. 1964). Language: Spanish 3,2,2,2; Portuguese 4,4,4,4; French 1,1,1,1. Home: 3 Walworth Ct., Madison, Wis. Office: Dept. of Agricultural Economics, U. of Wis., Madison.

PURKS, JAMES HARRIS, III, b. Atlanta, Ga., Aug. 21, 1936. JOURNALISM. B.A., U. of N.C., 1959; M.A., Stanford U., 1963. Reporter, The News and Observer (Raleigh, N.C.), 1957–59; reporter, The Tampa Tribune (Fla.), 1961–62; NEWSMAN, ASSOCIATED PRESS (BIRMINGHAM, ALA.), 1962– . Inter-American Press Association scholar (Chile), 1960–61; National Defense Foreign Language fellow in Spanish, Stanford U., 1962–63. Research: political science; freedom of the press in Latin America; political parties of Chile. Language: Spanish 4,4,4,4; Portuguese 2,2,2,2. Home: Apt. 412, 2909 Highland Ave., Birmingham 5, Ala. Office: The Associated Press, Birmingham.

PUTNAM, EMILIE BACA, b. Las Vegas, N. Mex., Mar. 10, 1904. SOCIAL WELFARE. A.B., U. of Mo., 1925; Smith Coll., 1937. Social worker, N. Mex. State Public Welfare Dept., 1932–34; psychiatric social worker, Brooklyn Bureau of Charities, 1936–38; supervisor of clubs and recreation, American Red Cross (New Guinea, Australia, New Caledonia, Philippines, Korea, Japan), 1943–47; social work adviser, Supreme Commander for the Allied Powers (Japan), 1947–51; community development and social work adviser, International Cooperation Administration (Peru), 1952–58; instr. in community development, International Cooperation Administration (Chile), 1958–59; (Guatemala), 1960–62; COMMUNITY DEVELOPMENT ADVISER, REGIONAL OFFICE, U.S. AGENCY FOR INTERNATIONAL DEVELOPMENT (CENTRAL AMERICA), 1962– . Membership: National Association of Social Workers. Research: community development in Central America; child welfare; psychiatric social work. Author: Japan's Children (Survey Graphic, 1951); Algunos aspectos de organización de la comunidad (1954) Community Development (National Association of Social Workers Journal, 1956. Language: Spanish 4,4,4,4; Portuguese 3,3,2,–; French 3,3,3,2. Home: 1468 Canyon Rd., Santa Fe, N. Mex. Office: Agency for International Development, U.S. Embassy, San José, Costa Rica.

Q

QUINN, ROBERT MacLEAN, b. Chicago, Ill., Oct. 28, 1920. ART. B.A., U. of Ariz., 1945; Ph. D., Johns Hopkins U., 1957. Instr.-PROF., ART, U. OF ARIZ., 1945– ; prof., Guadalajara Summer School, 1960–64. Samuel H. Kress Foundation travel grant (Spain), Summer 1959, 1962–63; regional correspondent, American Council of Learned Societies. Research: Hispano-Flemish painting; Mexican colonial art and architecture. Author: Fernando Gallego and the Retablo of Ciudad Rodrigo (1961). Language: Spanish 4,4,4,3; Portuguese 2,1,1,1; French 3,1,1,1; Dutch 3,1,1,1; German 4,4,4,3; Italian 3,1,1,1. Home: 4431 Cooper Circle, Tucson, Ariz. Office: Dept. of Art, U. of Ariz., Tucson.

QUINTERO-RAMOS, ÁNGEL MANUEL, b. Manatí, P.R., Dec. 9, 1915. ECONOMICS. B.B.A., U. of P.R., 1937; M.B.A., N.Y.U., 1939; Ph. D., 1950. Economist, P.R. Dept. of Agriculture, 1940; instr., Coll. of Business, U. of P.R., 1940–43; instr., Coll. of Social Science, 1943–44, asst. prof., 1944–50; asst. prof., Coll. of Business, 1950–51; assoc. prof., 1951–54; part-time prof., P.R. Junior Coll., 1952–54; part-time prof., Coll. of the Sacred Heart, 1953–58; prof., 1954–57; PROF., CHMN., FINANCE, U. OF P.R., 1957– . Chmn., Convention Committee, Annual Meeting of the National Committee for the Development of Small Business Management, 1958. Membership: American Economic Association; American Finance Association; Asociación Puertorriqueña de Analistas Financieros; Asociación Puertorriqueña de Economía; Catholic Business Education Association. Research: finance; money and banking; Argentina. Author: El Mercado de Valores (1962); Moneda y Banca (vol. I, 1963; vol. II, 1964); A History of Money and Banking in Argentina (1964). Language: Spanish 5,5,5,5; Portuguese 2,2,1,1; French 2,1,1,1; Italian 2,2,1,1. Home: Paseo del Parque HA-4, Garden Hills, Bayamón, P.R. Office: Dept. of Finance, U. of P.R., Río Piedras.

QUIRK, ROBERT E., b. Akron Ohio, Sept. 22, 1918. HISTORY. A.B., Wayne State U., 1946; M.A., Harvard U., 1948; Ph. D., 1951. Instr., Wayne State U., 1946–47; instr., Mexico City College, 1950; instr.-PROF., HISTORY, INDIANA U., 1950– ; vis. assoc. prof., U. of Tex., 1960. Woodbury Lowery traveling fellow (Mexico), 1949–50; Social Science Research Council fellow, 1961–62. Membership: American Historical Association; Association of Latin American Studies; Conference on Latin American History. Research: United States-Latin American relations; Mexican Revolution of 1910; church and state in

Mexico. Author: The Mexican Revolution, 1914–1915 (1960); An Affair of Honor: Woodrow Wilson and the Occupation of Veracruz (1962); The Mexican Revolution and the Catholic Church (1964). Language: Spanish 4,4,4,4; Portuguese 2,2,2,2; French 2,2,2,2; German 4,4,4,4. Office: Dept. of History, Ind. U., Bloomington.

R

RAAB, MARY RICARDA, O.S.F., b. Chicago, Ill., Apr. 9, 1926. SPANISH AMERICAN LITERATURE. B.A., Coll. of St. Teresa, 1959; Ph. D., St. Louis U., 1965. Instr., St. Louis U., 1960–62; English instr., Javeriana U. (Bogotá), 1962; English instr., Colegio de Nuestra Señora de la Paz (Bogotá), 1963; INSTR., SPANISH, COLL. OF ST. TERESA, 1964– . National Defense Education Act fellow, St. Louis U., 1959–62. Membership: Sigma Delta Pi. Research: works of José Manuel Marroquín of Colombia. Language: Spanish 4,4,4,3; Portuguese 4,3,3,3; French 3,3,3,3. Office: Dept. of Spanish, Coll. of St. Teresa, Winona, Minn. 55987.

RABASSA, GREGORY LUIS, b. Yonkers, N.Y., Mar. 9, 1922. BRAZILIAN AND SPANISH AMERICAN LITERATURES. A.B., Dartmouth Coll., 1945; M.A., Columbia U., 1947; Ph. D., 1954. Lectr., Columbia U., 1946–48; instr., 1948–54; assoc., 1954–58; asst. prof., 1958–63; ASSOC. PROF., SPANISH AND PORTUGUESE, COLUMBIA U., 1963– . Institute of Latin American Studies grant (Brazil), Summer 1962; International Bibliography Committee, Modern Language Association; assoc. editor, Odyssey Review. Membership: American Association of Teachers of Spanish and Portuguese; American Association of University Professors; Instituto Internacional de Literatura Iberoamericana; Modern Language Association; Phi Beta Kappa; Renaissance Society of America. Research: contemporary Brazilian literature; translations from Portuguese and Spanish; life and works of Padre Antônio Vieira. Author: O negro na ficção brasileira: 1888–1950 (1965); América, Europa y España: Apuntes de El Espectador (Revista Hispánica Moderna, Jan.–Apr. 1948); The Five Faces of Love in Jorge Amado's Bahian Novels (Revista de Letras, 1963). Language: Spanish 5,5,5,5; Portuguese 5, 5,4,4; French 5,3,3,3; German 2,2,2,2; Italian 5,4,3,3; Russian 2,1,1,1. Home: 90 Morningside Dr., New York, N.Y. 10027. Office: Dept. of Foreign Languages, Columbia U., New York, 10027.

RAEL, JUAN B., b. Arroyo Hondo, N. Mex., Aug. 14, 1900. SPANISH AMERICAN LITERATURE. A.B., St. Mary's Coll. (Calif.), 1923; M.A., U. of Calif., Berkeley, 1927; Ph. D., Stanford U., 1937. Instr., U. of Oreg., 1927–34; PROF., SPANISH, STANFORD U., 1934– ; CO-DIR., GUADALAJARA SUMMER SCHOOL, U. OF ARIZ., 1953– . American Philosophical Society grant; Stanford U. grant; U. of Oreg. grant. Membership: American Association of Teachers of Spanish; American Folklore Society; Modern Language Association. Research: folklore of the American Spanish Southwest and Mexico; Spanish of New Mexico; nativity folk drama. Author: An Annotated Bibliography of New Mexican Spanish Folklore (1950); The New Mexican Alabado (1951); Cuentos de Colorado y de Nuevo Méjico (1957). Language: Spanish 5,5,5,5; Portuguese 3,3,1,1. Linguistic studies: Spanish. Home: P.O. Box 7227, 574 Lasuen, Stanford, Calif. Office: Modern European Languages, Stanford U., Stanford.

RAINE, PHILIP, b. Baltimore, Md., July 24, 1908. POLITICAL SCIENCE. Certificate, U. of Madrid, 1930; B.S., Georgetown U. Foreign Service School, 1930; M.A., American U., 1956. Area chief, Foreign Service, U.S. Dept. of State, 1942–43; asst. dir. of regional div., Office of Inter-American Affairs, 1943–44; liaison officer, U.S. Dept. of State, 1945; regional specialist, 1946; asst. chief, Area Div. IV, 1947; cultural attaché (México, D.F.), 1948–52; public affairs adviser, 1952–55; political officer (São Paulo), 1955–62; DEPUTY CHIEF OF MISSION, CONSUL GENERAL, EMBASSY (SAN JOSÉ, COSTA RICA), FOREIGN SERVICE, U.S. DEPT. OF STATE, 1962– . Membership: American Political Science Association; Mexican Institute of Geography and History. Research: economic integration efforts of Central American countries and Alliance for Progress; the Brazilian military. Author: Paraguay (1956); Report on Brazil (Atlantic Monthly, 1960). Language Spanish 4,4,4,3; Portuguese 4,4,4,3; French 3,3,3,3; German 2,3,2,1. Office: American Embassy, San José, Costa Rica.

RAMEY, MARILYN LORRAINE, b. Los Angeles, Calif., Sept. 9, 1937. LIBRARY SCIENCE. A.B., Occidental Coll., 1959; M.L.S., U. of Calif., Los Angeles, 1961; M.A., Middlebury Coll., 1964. Teacher, Instituto Guatemalteco-Americano, U.S. Information Agency, 1960; librarian, Brooklyn Public Library, 1961–63. Smith-Mundt grant, U. of San Carlos (Guatemala), 1959–60. Membership: American Library Association. Language: Spanish 4,5,4,4; French 2,2,2,2. Home: 10625 Esther Ave., Los Angeles 64, Calif.

RAMIREZ, EZEKIEL S., b. Ray, Ariz., Oct. 11, 1917. POLITICAL SCIENCE. Ph. D., Stanford U., 1951. Research analyst, U.S. Dept. of Army (Austria), 1949–55; research analyst, U.S. Dept. of Defense, 1955–58; liaison attaché, Embassy (Madrid), U.S. Dept. of State, 1958–62; FOREIGN LIAISON OFFICER, U.S. DEPT. OF DEFENSE, 1962– . Research: international relations; diplomatic relations between Austria and Brazil, 1815–1889. Language: Spanish 5,5,5,5; Portuguese 5,4,3,2; French 5,3,1,1; German 5,5,3,2. Home: 524 North Livingston St., Arlington 3, Va.

RAMÍREZ, MANUEL D., b. Tampa, Fla., Dec. 30, 1914. SPANISH AMERICAN AND BRAZILIAN LITERATURES. B.A., U. of Fla., 1937; M.A., 1939; Ph. D., U. of N.C., 1959. Instr., executive secretary, Institute of Inter-American Affairs, U. of Fla., 1939–42; asst. prof., Kans. State U., 1946–60; assoc. prof., National Defense Education Act Language Institute, U. of Ala., Summers 1960, 1961, Appalachian State Teachers Coll., Summers 1962, (prof.) 1963; prof., U. of Ala., 1960–64; PROF., SPANISH, U. OF GA., 1964– . Chmn., Latin American Studies Program Committee, U. of Ala., 1962–64. Membership: American

Association of Teachers of Spanish and Portuguese; Modern Language Association; Southeastern Conference on Latin American Studies. Research: contemporary Brazilian, Colombian, Chilean, and Mexican theatre; Brazilian folklore. Author: Italian Folklore From Tampa, Florida: Proverbs (Southern Folklore Quarterly, June 1948); Color in the Prose Fiction of Valle-Inclán (Romance Notes, Nov. 1959); La luz y la oscuridad en la prosa de Valle-Inclán (Duquesne Hispanic Review, Dec. 1962). Language: Spanish 5,5,5,5; Portuguese 5,5,5,5; French 4,3,3,3; Italian 4,3,3,3. Linguistic studies: French; Italian; Portuguese; Spanish. Office: Dept. of Spanish, U. of Ga., Athens.

RANDALL, HAROLD M., b. Jefferson County, Iowa, Jan. 5, 1900. ECONOMICS AND POLITICAL SCIENCE. A.B., Parsons Coll., 1924; M.A., Georgetown U., 1927; Ph. D., 1929. Instr., Georgetown U., 1927–29; asst. commercial attaché-ambassador, U.S. Dept. of State (Chile, Argentina, Paraguay, Mexico, Cuba), 1930–59; DIR., TRAINING PROGRAM FOR INTERNATIONAL BUSINESS EXECUTIVES, BUSINESS COUNCIL FOR INTERNATIONAL UNDERSTANDING, PROF., LATIN AMERICAN STUDIES, AMERICAN U., 1959– . U.S. representative, Inter American Economic and Social Council, 1955–59; chmn., 1957–58. Membership: Inter-American Council. Research: economic and commercial investigation and analysis; international relations. Language: Spanish 5,4,4,4; Portuguese 2,1,1,1; French 2,1,2,1. Home: 3900 Watson Pl., NW., Washington 16, D.C. Office: Box 369, American U., Washington 16.

RANDALL, LAURA R., b. New York, N.Y., Nov. 18, 1935. ECONOMICS. B.A., Barnard Coll., 1957; M.A., U. of Mass., 1959; Ph. D., Columbia U., 1962. Economist, Federal Reserve Bank of New York, 1961–63; INSTR., ECONOMICS, QUEENS COLL., 1963– ; INSTR., ECONOMICS, COLUMBIA U., 1964– . N.Y. State scholar, 1955–57; Dibblie scholar, Columbia U., 1959–60; Columbia U. workshop grant, Ford Foundation (Latin America), 1960–61. Membership: American Economic Association. Research: economic development; economic history of Latin America; Mexico. Author: Economic Development, Evolution or Revolution (1964); Labour Migration and Mexican Economic Development, 1940–1950 (Social and Economic Studies, Mar. 1962); Craftsmanship (Columbia University Forum, Spring 1964). Language: Spanish 4,4,4,3; Portuguese 3,3,3,3; French 3,3,3,3; German 2,2,2,2. Home: 425 Riverside Dr., New York, N.Y. 10025. Office: Dept. of Economics, Queens Coll., Flushing 67, N.Y.

RANDALL, ROBERT WILLIAM, b. Twin Falls, Idaho, Sept. 28, 1925. HISTORY. B.A., Brown U., 1951; Ph. D., Harvard U., 1965. Trainee and program specialist, Pan American Union, 1958–59; acting chief, Social Science Section, 1959–61; coordinator of training programs in Social Affairs, 1961; lectr., U. of the Americas, 1962; asst. prof., 1963–64; ASST. PROF., HISTORY, WESTERN RESERVE U., 1964– . Membership: American Association of University Professors; American Historical Association; Delta Sigma Rho; Phi Beta Kappa. Research: economic history of Mexico; the British Real del Monte Mining Company in Mexico. Language: Spanish 3,3,3,2; Portuguese 2,1,1,1; French 2,1,1,1. Home: 2523 North Moreland Blvd., Cleveland, Ohio 44120. Office: Dept. of History, Western Reserve U., Cleveland, 44106.

RANDS, ROBERT LAWRENCE, b. Washington, D.C., May 13, 1922. ANTHROPOLOGY. B.A., U. of N. Mex., 1949; M.A., U. of Calif., Los Angeles, 1949; Ph. D., Columbia U., 1952. Asst. prof., U. of Miss., 1952–56; researcher, Bureau of American Ethnology, Smithsonian Institution (Panama), 1952; assoc. prof., U. of Miss., 1956–60; research assoc., U. Museum, U. of Pa. (Guatemala), 1960– ; prof., U. of Miss., 1960–63; vis. prof., U. of N.C., 1963; ASSOC. PROF., ASST DIR., RESEARCH LABORATORIES OF ANTHROPOLOGY, U. OF N.C., 1963– . Guggenheim fellow (Mexico), 1956–57. Membership: American Anthropological Association; American Association for the Advancement of Science; American Indian Ethnohistoric Conference; Archaeological Institute of America; Archaeological Society of North Carolina; Seminario de Cultura Maya; Sociedad Mexicana de Antropología; Society for American Archaeology; Southeastern Archaeological Conference; Southeastern Conference on Latin American Studies. Research: archeology and ethnohistory; cultural ecology; archeology in Mexico, Panama, and Guatemala; Maya art. Author: The Water Lily in Maya Art: A Complex of Alleged Asiatic Origin (Bulletin, Bureau of American Ethnology, 1953); The Ceramic Position of Palenque, Chiapas (American Antiquity, Jan. 1957); Diffusion and Discontinuous Distribution (American Anthropologist, Apr. 1958). Language: Spanish 4,4,4,3; Portuguese 1,1,1,1; French 1,1,1,1. Office: Person Hall, U. of N.C., Chapel Hill.

RAPP, MARIE A., b. Grand Rapids, Mich., Oct. 16, 1905. LIBRARY SCIENCE. A.B., Western Mich. U., 1927; A.B. in L.S., U. of Mich., 1937. Teacher, Mich. Public Schools, 1927–29; librarian, Battle Creek Public School Library, 1929–31, 1933–36; head of reference, Library, Battle Creek Coll., 1931–33; senior reference asst., Detroit Public Library, 1937–46; head, Reference Dept., Biblioteca Benjamin Franklin (México, D.F.), 1946–48; assoc. dir., 1948–51; dir., Library, Centro Regional de Educación Fundamental para América Latina (Pátzcuaro, Mexico), UNESCO, 1951–57; head, Reference Dept., Library, U. of Ill., 1957–59; head, Acquisitions Dept., Columbus Memorial Library, Pan American Union, 1959–60; HEAD, CIRCULATION DEPT., LIBRARY, U. OF ILL., 1960– . Consultant on acquisitions (Mexico, Argentina, and Brazil), Library, Inter-American Defense Coll. (Washington, D.C.), 1963. Membership: American Association of University Professors; American Library Association; Illinois Library Association. Research: acquisition of Latin American materials. Language: Spanish 5,5,5,4; Portuguese 2,2,1,1; French 5,2,1,1. Home: 401 Fullerton Pkwy., Chicago, Ill. 60614. Office: Library, U. of Ill., Navy Pier, Chicago, 60611.

RAU, HERBERT LAWRENCE, JR., b. Chicago, Ill., June 29, 1929. GEOGRAPHY. B.S., Northwestern U., 1951; M.A., 1955; Ph. D., 1958. Lectr., Northwestern U., 1954–56; asst. prof., Ball State U., 1956–58; assoc. prof., Kans. State U., 1958–64; vis. prof., George Peabody Coll. for Teachers, Summers 1962, 1964; ASSOC. PROF., GEOGRAPHY, STATE U. OF N.Y., COLL. AT BUFFALO, 1964– . Fulbright lectr., Universidade do Brasil (Rio de Janeiro), 1959–60. Membership: American Association for the Advancement of Science; Association of American Geographers; National Council for Geographic Education. Research: economic and commercial geography of Latin America, with special interest in land utilization analysis, resource development, and underdevelopment; Colombia. Author: The Electric Power Industry of East-Central Brazil (Annals, Association of American Geographers, 1960); Argentina's Changing Industrial Resource Base (Annals, Association of American Geographers, 1962); South America (in World Geography, 1964). Language: Spanish 3,2,2,2; Portuguese 2,2,2,2; French 2,1,1,1. Home: Apt. A4, 3296 Main St., Buffalo, N.Y. 14214. Office: Dept. of Geography, State U. of N.Y., Buffalo, 14214.

RAUP, PHILLIP M., b. Timken, Kans., Jan. 4, 1914. ECONOMICS. A.B., U. of Kans., 1939; M.S., U. of Wis., 1942; Ph. D., 1949. Military government officer, Office of U.S. Military Government (Berlin), 1945–49; asst. prof., U. of Wis., 1949–53; PROF., AGRICULTURAL ECONOMICS, U. OF MINN., 1953– . Brookings Institution fellow, 1941–42; consultant, Economic Development Institute, International Bank for Reconstruction and Development, 1959– ; consultant, United Nations Food and Agriculture Organization (Rome), 1960–61. Membership: American Economic Association; American Farm Economic Association; Agricultural History Society; Association for Latin American Studies; Royal Economic Society. Research: agricultural economics; land economics; world agricultural development; land reform; land and water use studies. Author: The Contribution of Land Reforms to Agricultural Development (Economic Development and Cultural Change, Oct. 1963); Rural Resource Development in an Urban Society (Journal of Farm Economics, Dec. 1963); Some Recent Developments in European Land Policy (in Land Use Policy and Problems in the United States, 1963). Language: Spanish 2,2,1,1; Portuguese 1,1,1,1; French 2,2,2,1; German 4,4,4,4; Russian 2,2,2,1. Home: 1572 Fulham St., St. Paul, Minn. 55108. Office: Dept. of Agricultural Economics, U. of Minn., St. Paul, 55101.

RAVICZ, ROBERT S., b. Minneapolis, Minn., Feb. 16, 1921. ANTHROPOLOGY. A.B., Tex. U., 1942; A.M., Harvard U., 1953; Ph. D., 1959. Advertising and sales, H. Steele y Cia. (México, D.C.), 1947–49; instr., U. of Wis., 1958–60; asst. prof., U. of Tex., 1960–61; assoc. prof., Ill. State U., 1961–63; assoc. prof., Boston U., 1963–64; PROF., ANTHROPOLOGY, SAN FERNANDO VALLEY STATE COLL., 1964– . Buenos Aires Convention grant (Mexico), 1955–56; Rockefeller Foundation grant, 1959–60; Wis. Alumni research fellow (Mexico), 1959; National Science Foundation grant (Mexico), 1963; consultant, Educational Service, Inc. (Cambridge, Mass.), 1963. Membership: American Anthropological Association. Research: social anthropology; indigenous and mestizo peoples; culture change; developments toward urbanism; native use of plant medicines; ritual kinship; Mexico. Author: La Mixteca en el estudio comparativo del hongo alucinante (1961); Compadrinazgo (in Handbook of Middle American Indians); Mixtec (in Handbook of Middle American Indians). Language: Spanish 4,4,4,4; French 3,3,3,2. Home: 23340 Hatteras St., Woodland Hills, Calif. 91364. Office: Dept. of Anthropology, San Fernando Valley State Coll., 18111 Nordhoff St., Northridge, Calif.

RAY, PHILIP ALEXANDER, b. Salt Lake City, Utah, May 27, 1911. LAW. B.A., Stanford U., 1932; LL.B., 1935. Assoc., McCutchen, Olney, Mannon & Greene, 1935–42; partner, 1946–54, 1957; general counsel, U.S. Dept. of Commerce, 1954–56; vice president, dir., J. H. Pomeroy & Company, Inc., 1958–59; Under Secretary, U.S. Dept. of Commerce, 1959–61. ATTORNEY, PRIVATE PRACTICE (SAN FRANCISCO), 1961– ; SENIOR RESEARCH ASSOC., LATIN AMERICAN AFFAIRS, HOOVER INSTITUTION ON WAR, REVOLUTION AND PEACE, STANFORD U., 1963– . Consultant, Stanford Research Institute, 1961; trustee, American Enterprise Institue for Public Policy Research (Washington, D.C.). Membership: American Arbitration Association; American Bar Association; American Law Institute; American Society of International Law; Bar Association of San Francisco; Inter-American Bar Association. Research: international investment and trade; Latin American affairs; Cold War problems; Mexico. Author: South Wind Red (1962). Language: Spanish 4,4,3,3; French 2,2,2,2. Home: 520 Roehampton Rd., Hillsborough, Calif. Office: 601 California St., Suite 1600, San Francisco 8, Calif.

RAYBURN, JOHN C., b. Bellbuckle, Tenn., Oct. 6, 1912. HISTORY. M.A., U. of Chicago, 1949; Ph. D., 1952. DIR., GRADUATE DIV., TEX. COLL. OF ARTS & INDUSTRIES, 1952– . Membership: Southwestern Social Science Association; Texas State Historical Association. Research: Venezuela and Mexico; Mexican history along the Rio Grande. Author: U.S. Investments in Venezuelan Asphalt (Inter-American Economic Affairs, Summer 1953); Investments in Venezuelan Telephones (Inter-American Economic Affairs, Autumn 1955); Rail Transportation in Venezuela (Inter-American Economic Affairs, Spring 1957). Language: Spanish 2,2,2,1. Home: 1222 West Lee, Kingsville, Tex. Office: Graduate Div., Tex. Coll. of Arts & Industries, Kingsville.

RAYMOND, JOSEPH B., b. Portales, N. Mex., Sept. 18, 1917. LANGUAGE. A.B., U. of Mo., 1940; M.A., Columbia U., 1946; Ph. D., 1951. Assoc. editor, Mexican Life Magazine, 1944–45; instr., Stephens Coll., 1946–47; instr., Washington U., 1947–49; instr., Teachers Coll., Columbia U., 1949–52; asst. prof., Pa. State U., 1952–57; asst. prof., San Jose State Coll., 1957–59; HEAD, MODERN LANGUAGES, CABRILLO COLL., 1959– . President's scholar, Teachers Coll., Columbia U., 1949–50; consultant, National Defense Education Act

Administration (Calif.), 1959–62; educational television consultant, KQED television station (San Francisco). Membership: American Association of Teachers of Spanish and Portuguese; California Teachers Association; Foreign Languages Association of California; Modern Language Association. Research: audio-visual materials; foreign languages in elementary schools; Spanish folkloric materials: English as a second language. Author: Mexican Proverbs (Western Folklore, Oct. 1953); Tensions in Proverbs: More Light on International Understanding (Western Folklore, July 1956). Co-author: Rodeo Gramatical (1951). Language: Spanish 5,5,5,5; French 4,4,4,4; German 3,3,3,2. Home: 811 Vista del Mar, Aptos, Calif. Office: Dept. of Modern Languages, Cabrillo Coll., Aptos.

REED, ERIK KELLERMAN, b. Quincy, Mass., Aug. 16, 1914. ANTHROPOLOGY. A.B., George Washington U., 1932; A.M., Harvard U., 1933; Ph. D., 1944. REGIONAL ARCHEOLOGIST, NATIONAL PARK SERVICE, U.S. DEPT. OF INTERIOR (SANTA FE, N. MEX.), 1937– . UNESCO missions (Peru), 1958, 1960. Membership: Society for American Archaeology; Spanish Colonial Arts Society. Research: physical anthropology; archeology; ruins preservation in Peru; Galapagos Islands. Author: History and Archeology of Guam (1952). Language: Spanish 4,3,3,2; Portuguese 2,1,1,1; French 4,3,3,2; German 3,2,2,1; Russian 2,–,–,–. Home: 238 Griffin St., Santa Fe, N. Mex. Office: Southwest Regional Office, National Park Service, P.O. Box 728, Santa Fe.

REEDY, DANIEL ROSS, b. Marshall, Ill., May 21, 1935. SPANISH AMERICAN LITERATURE. B.S., Eastern Ill. U., 1957; M.A., U. of Ill., 1959; Ph. D., 1962. ASST. PROF., SPANISH, U. OF N.C., 1962– . Rotary International fellow, Universidad Nacional de San Marcos (Peru), 1958–59; delegate, Allerton House Conference on Latin America, Spring 1960; U. of Ill. fellow, 1960, 1961–62. Membership: American Association of Teachers of Spanish and Portuguese; Instituto Internacional de Literatura Iberoamericana; Modern Language Association. Research: Spanish American poetry of the Colonial Period; Peruvian literature. Author: The Poetic Art of Juan del Valle Caviedes (1964); Poesías inéditas de Juan del Valle Caviedes (Revista Iberoamericana, Jan.–June 1963); A New Manuscript of the Works of Juan del Valle Caviedes (Romance Notes, Fall 1963). Language: Spanish 5,5,5,4; Portuguese 4,3,2,2; French 2,2,1,1; German 2,1,1,1; Italian 2,1,1,1; Quechua 2,1,1,1. Home: 108 Taylor St., North Forest Hills, Chapel Hill, N.C. Office: Dept. of Romance Languages, U. of N.C., Chapel Hill.

REICH, LARRY, b. New York, N.Y., Jan. 19, 1919. CITY AND REGIONAL PLANNING. B.C.P., Harvard U., 1947; M.C.P., 1948. Planner, Milwaukee County Regional Planning Dept., 1948–49; planner, Tennessee Valley Authority, 1949–51; planner, Tippets, Abbetts, McCarthy, Stratton Engineering Company (N.Y.), 1951–52; International Basic Economy Corporation Housing Corporation, 1952–53; chief, Comprehensive Plan Div., City of Philadelphia, 1953–60; ASST. COMMISSIONER, CITY PLANNING, CITY OF CHICAGO, 1960– . Consultant, Governments of El Salvador and Honduras. Membership: American Institute of Planners; American Society of Planning Officials; International Federation of Town Planning. Research: housing and building construction; capital programming; industrial development. Author: A Comprehensive Plan for San Miguel (1952); A Comprehensive Plan for Philadelphia (1960). Language: Spanish 4,4,4,3; French 4,2,3,3. Home: 1325 East 50th St., Chicago 15, Ill. Office: Rm. 800, 211 West Wacker Dr., Chicago, 60606.

REID, J. RICHARD, b. Parsons, Kans., May 1, 1914. LANGUAGE. A.B., Swarthmore Coll., 1935; Ph. D., Harvard U., 1943. Instr., Harvard U., 1939–44; PROF., CHMN., ROMANCE LANGUAGES, CLARK U., 1944– . Dir., community development projects, Friends Service Committee (Mexico), Summers 1952, 1954, 1957. Membership: American Association of Teachers of French; American Association of Teachers of Spanish and Portuguese; Linguistic Circle of New York; Linguistic Society of America; Modern Language Association. Research: contemporary Mexican literature and culture; general and descriptive linguistics; language teaching. Author: An Exploratory Survey of Foreign Language Teaching by Television in the United States (1961). Language: Spanish 4,4,4,4; Portuguese 2,2,2,1; French 4,4,4,4; Italian 3,2,2,1. Linguistic studies: French; Italian; Portuguese; Rumanian; Spanish. Home: Stafford St., Rochdale, Mass. Office: Dept. of Romance Languages, Clark U., Worcester, Mass. 01610.

REID, JOHN T., b. Vallejo, Calif., Apr. 21, 1908. SPANISH AMERICAN LITERATURE. B.A., Stanford U., 1930; M.A., 1931; Ph. D., 1936. Instr., Rice Institute, 1931–32; instr., Stanford U., 1933–38; asst. prof., Duke U., 1938–42; special assistant to Ambassador, Foreign Service (Ecuador, Cuba), U.S. Dept. of State, 1942–46; asst. prof., U. of Calif., Los Angeles, 1946–49; public affairs officer, Embassy (Venezuela), U.S. Dept. of State, 1949–53; CULTURAL OFFICER, U.S. INFORMATION AGENCY, 1953– . Federal Executive fellow, Brookings Institution, 1963–64. Research: Spanish American attitudes toward the U.S.; cultural and symbolic nationalisms in Spanish America. Author: Notes and Meditations on Contemporary Venezuelan Literature (Hispania, Aug. 1951); Symbolic Nationalism in Spanish America (Hispania, Mar. 1957). Co-author: An Outline History of Spanish American Literature (1942; 1964). Language: Spanish 5,5,5,5; Portuguese 3,3,2,2; French 4,4,3,3; German 2,2,1,1. Linguistic studies: Spanish. Home: 3325 Quebec Pl., NW., Washington 8, D.C. Office: U.S. Information Agency, Washington 25.

REIFF, DONALD G., b. Chicago, Ill., Oct. 20, 1934. LINGUISTICS. B.A., DePauw U., 1956; M.A., U. of Wis., 1958; M.A., U. of Mich., 1961; Ph. D., 1962. Instr., U. of Wash., 1962–63; ASST. PROF., LINGUISTICS, U. OF ROCHESTER, 1963– . American Council of Learned Societies grant, 1959; consultant on Spanish course, Midwest Program, Airborne Television Instruction, 1962. Membership: Linguistic

Circle of New York; Linguistic Society of America; Modern Language Association. Research: psycholinguistics; language structures; crosslingual reading skills. Language: Spanish 4,5,5,4; Portuguese 3,-2,1,1; French 4,4,4,4. Linguistic studies: English; French; Spanish. Home: 207 University Park, Rochester, N.Y. 14620. Office: Dept. of Languages and Linguistics, U. of Rochester, Rochester, 14627.

REINA, RUBEN E., b. Córdoba, Argentina, Dec. 5, 1924. ANTHROPOLOGY. B.A., U. of Mich., 1949; M.A., Mich. State U., 1951; Ph. D., U. of N.C., 1957. Instr., Women's Coll., U. of N.C., 1954–55; asst. prof., U. of P.R., 1956–57; ASSOC. PROF., ANTHROPOLOGY, ASSOC. CURATOR, U. MUSEUM, U. OF PA., 1957– . National Science Foundation fellow; Southern Fellowship Fund grant; Ford Foundation grant. Membership: American Anthropological Association; American Ethnological Society; Philadelphia Anthropological Society; Society for Applied Anthropology. Research: cultural anthropology; Guatemalan community culture; Argentine city culture. Author: Chinautla, A Guatemalan Indian Community: A Study in the Relationship of Community Culture and National Change (1960); The Potter and the Farmer: The Fate of Two Innovators in a Mayan Village (Expedition, Summer 1963). Co-author: Entrepreneurship in Argentine Culture (1962). Language: Spanish 5,5,5,5; Portuguese 3,3,3,3; French 3,3,3,3; Italian 3,3,3,3. Home: 36 Green Valley Rd., Wallingford, Pa. Office: Dept. of Anthropology, U. of Pa., Philadelphia 4.

REINHART, HELEN KATHERINE, b. Quincy, Ill., Feb. 28, 1929. HISTORY. B.A., Quincy Coll., 1950; M.A., U. of Ill., 1956; Ph. D., 1960. Instr., Superior State Coll., 1959; INSTR., SOCIAL SCIENCE, ODESSA COLL., 1960– . Fellowship, U. of Ill. Membership: American Academy of Political and Social Sciences; American Association of University Professors; American Historical Association; Conference on Latin American History; Permian Basin Historical Society. Research: political history of the Brazilian regency, 1831–1840. Language: Spanish 4,2,2,3; Portuguese 4,1,1,2; French 4,1,1,2; German 3,1,1,1. Home: 1007 West 19th St., Odessa, Tex. Office: Dept. of Social Science, Odessa Coll., Odessa.

REISCHER, OTTO RICHARD, b. Vienna, Austria, July 9, 1917. ECONOMICS. B.A., U. of Mich., 1946; M.A., Columbia U., 1948; Ph. D., 1959. Lectr., Rutgers U., 1948–50; economist, Div. of Foreign Labor Conditions, U.S. Dept. of Labor, 1950–51; asst. to economic adviser, European Program Div., Economic Cooperation Administration, 1951–52; chief, Evaluation Staff, Div. of Foreign Reporting, U.S. Dept. of State, 1952–53; assoc., Checchi and Company, 1954; vis. special lectr., U. of British Columbia, 1954–55; instr., Mich. State U., 1955–56; senior research assoc., Foreign Area Studies Div., Special Operations Research Office, American U., 1956–58; freelance economic consultant, 1958–60; assoc., EMB, Ltd., 1960–61; market consultant, Tippetts-Abbott-McCarthy-Stratton, Consulting Engineers (N.Y.), 1962; vice president, Continental-Allied Company, Inc., 1962–63: ECONOMIC ADVISER, PAKISTAN INVESTMENT ADVISORY CENTRE (KARACHI), U.S. AGENCY FOR INTERNATIONAL DEVELOPMENT-C. W. ROBINSON & COMPANY, INC., MANAGEMENT CONSULTANTS, 1963– . Staff member, Public Advisory Board for Mutual Security, 1953; consultant, National Industrial Conference Board, 1953; consultant, Economic Affairs, Pan American Union, 1959–60, 1961–63; Fulbright prof., Universidad de los Andes (Venezuela), Spring 1963. Membership: American Arbitration Association; American Economic Association; Royal Economic Society; Society for International Development. Research: economic development; economic systems; commercial policy; trade; international finance. Author: Trade Adjustment in Theory and Practice (1961); Desarrollo industrial a mediano plazo en regiones sub-desarrolladas (1963); Toward a Unification of Ethics, Law and the Social Sciences (University of Detroit Law Journal, Apr. 1963). Language: Spanish 5,4,4,3; Portuguese 3,2,1,1; French 5,5,5,4; German 5,5,5,5; Italian 5,5,4,4; Russian 3,2,2,2; Urdu 2,2,2,1. Home: 1300 North Barton St., Arlington, Va. Office: c/o AID Mission, Karachi, APO 271, New York, N.Y.

REISKY DE DUBNIC, VLADIMIR, b. Klaster, Czechoslovakia, Dec. 31, 1923. POLITICAL SCIENCE: INTERNATIONAL RELATIONS. B.A., Caslav Coll., 1943; M.A., U. of Chicago, 1951; Ph. D. 1959. Research asst., Center for the Study of American Foreign Policy, U. of Chicago, 1949–53; writer, Business International (Brazil), 1955; asst. prof., Washington Coll., 1956–60; vis. prof., dir., Center for Social Studies, Pontifical Catholic U. (Rio de Janeiro), 1962–64; research consultant, Washington Center of Foreign Policy Research, School of Advanced International Studies, 1964; PROF., FOREIGN AFFAIRS, U. OF VA., 1964– . Social Science Research Council fellow (Brazil), 1960–61; Organization of American States fellow (Brazil), 1960–62. Membership: American Political Science Association; Getúlio Vargas Foundation (Brazil); International Political Science Association; Institute of Public Law and Political Science; Masaryk Club, U. of Chicago. Research: Brazilian federal congress, federal administration and political parties; the Soviet orbit. Author: Communist Propaganda Methods: A Case Study on Czechoslovakia (1960); A política externa do Brasil no govêrno de Jânio Quadros (Síntese Política Econômica Social, Jan.-Mar. 1961). Language: Spanish 2,3,2,1; Portuguese 5,5,5,4; French 2,2,2,1; Czech 5,5,5,5; German 5,5,5,5; Polish 3,3,2,1; Russian 2,3,1,1. Home: 5 Whitfield Rd., Baltimore 10, Md. Office: Dept. of Political Science, U. of Va., Charlottesville.

RENNE, ROLAND ROGER, b. Greenwich, N.J., Dec. 12, 1905. ECONOMICS. B.S., Rutgers U., 1927; M.S., U. of Wis., 1928; Ph. D., 1930. Asst. prof., Mont. State Coll., 1930–35; assoc. prof., 1936; prof., 1936–39; head, 1939–43; PRESIDENT, MONT. STATE COLL., 1943– ; country dir., U.S. Economic and Technical Mission (Philippines), 1951–53; chief, World Bank-Food and Agriculture Organization Mission

(Peru), 1958–59. Consultant, U.S. Overseas Mission (Ethiopia), 1960; consultant, U. of Asunción (Paraguay), 1962; asst. secretary of agriculture for international affairs, U.S. Dept. of Agriculture, 1963–64. Membership: American Association of Political and Social Science; American Economic Association; American Farm Economic Association; American Sociological Society; International Association of Agricultural Economists; International Development Society. Research: agricultural economics; land economics; government administration. Author: Land Economics (1958); The Government and Administration of Montana (1959); The Montana Citizen (1960). Language: Spanish 2,3,2,-2; French 2,3,2,2. Home: 1815 Sour Dough Rd., Bozeman, Mont. Office. Dept. of Economics, Mont. State Coll., Bozeman.

RENNIE, ROBERT ALVIN, b. Blackstone, Mass., May 13, 1917. ECONOMICS. A.B., Wesleyan U., 1939; M.A., Harvard U., 1941; Ph. D., 1947. Economist, Latin American Section, Federal Reserve Board, 1946–48; asst. prof., Johns Hopkins U., 1948–51; dir. of research, Nationwide Insurance, 1951–56; secretary-treasurer, Mutual Income Foundation, Inc. (Columbus, Ohio), 1952–55; VICE PRESIDENT, RESEARCH, NATIONWIDE INSURANCE (COLUMBUS, OHIO), 1956– ; VICE PRESIDENT, ECONOMIST, BASIC ECONOMICS, INC. (N.Y.), 1963– . Sheldon traveling fellow (Argentina), 1941–43; member, Klein-Sax economic mission (Lima, Peru), 1948; Insurance Research Subcommittee, International Cooperative Alliance, 1961–63; Board of Directors, American Risk and Insurance Association. Membership: American Economic Association; American Finance Association; Econometric Association. Research: economic development; establishment of financial institutions in developing countries, especially insurance companies, mutual investment funds, and savings and loan associations. Author: Argentina in Crisis (Foreign Policy Reports, May 1944); La política fiscal argentina (Boletín, Banco de México, Sept. 1947); Argentine Fiscal Policy (Inter-American Economic Affairs, June 1947). Language: Spanish 4,3,3,3; Portuguese 1,1,1,1; French 4,3,3,3; German 2,2,2,1. Home: 2583 Wexford Rd., Columbus, Ohio 43221. Office: Nationwide Insurance, 246 North High St., Columbus, Ohio, 43216.

REYNER, ANTHONY STEPHEN, b. Tabor, Czechoslovakia, June 15, 1912. GEOGRAPHY. Doctor, Charles U. (Prague), 1935; Sc. M., U. of Chicago, 1941. Instr., U. of Calif., Berkeley, 1941–42; prof., Grinnell Coll., 1942–43; chief, Portuguese unit, Foreign Economic Administration, 1943–44; prof., chmn., Geography and International Relations, U. of P.R., 1944–46; PROF., CHMN., GEOGRAPHY, HOWARD U., 1946– . International Exchange fellow (United States), 1938; grant (Ecuador), 1948; chief, United Nations Mission to Costa Rica, 1952; grant (Venezuela), 1959; National Science Foundation grant, 1962; consultant, American Council on Education, Foreign Service Institute, and Industrial College of the Armed Forces. Membership: African Studies Association; American Association of University Professors; American Geographical Society; Association of American Geographers; Royal Canadian Geographical Society; Royal Geographical Society. Research: political and economic geography. Author: Surinam Agriculture (Annals, Association of American Geographers, 1963); British Honduras—International Boundaries (World Affairs, Summer 1963). Co-author: World Political Geography (1957). Language: Spanish 5,5,5,5; Portuguese 3,3,2,1; French 5,5,5,5; Czech 5,5,5,5; German 5,5,5,5; Italian 4,3,2,1. Home: 4535 Q Pl., NW., Washington, D.C. 20007. Office: 1098 Howard U., Washington, 20001.

REYNOLDS, CLARK WINTON, b. Chicago, Ill., Mar. 13, 1934. ECONOMICS. A.B., Claremont Men's Coll., 1956; M.A., U. of Calif., Berkeley, 1962; Ph. D., 1962. Asst. prof., Occidental Coll., 1961–62; ASST. PROF., ECONOMICS, YALE U., 1962– . Woodrow Wilson fellow, Mass. Institute of Technology, 1956–57; Danforth Foundation fellow, 1956–60; Rockefeller Brothers theology fellow, Harvard Divinity School, 1957–58; Doherty Foundation and Mills traveling fellow (Chile), 1960–61. Membership: American Economic Association. Research: economic development; international trade; history and growth of Latin American economics; economic structure and growth of Mexico, 1900–1960; Chile and copper exportation. Author: Domestic Consequences of Export Instability (American Economic Review, May 1963). Language: Spanish 4,4,4,3; French 3,3,3,3. Office: Economic Growth Center, Yale U., Box 1987 Yale Station, New Haven, Conn.

RICCIO, GUY JOHN, b. New York, N.Y., Oct. 9, 1920. SPANISH AMERICAN LITERATURE AND LANGUAGE. B.A., Queen's Coll., 1941; M.A., U. of Wis., 1943; U. of Coimbra, 1953; Ph. D., U. of Md., 1963. INSTR., SPANISH AND PORTUGUESE, U.S. NAVAL ACADEMY, 1947– . Membership: American Association of Teachers of Spanish and Portuguese; Modern Language Association. Research: Brazilian Portuguese; Hispanidad and the growth of national identity in contemporary Spanish-American thought. Author: Introduction to Brazilian Portuguese (1957). Language: Spanish 4,4,4,4; Portuguese 4,4,4,4; French 4,3,3,3; Italian 3,4,3,3. Home: 1720 Ritchie Highway, Annapolis, Md. Office: Dept. of Foreign Languages, U.S. Naval Academy, Annapolis.

RICH, ROLLAND GLEN, b. Beaverton, Oreg. LINGUISTICS. B. Th., Biola Coll., 1950; B.A., Lewis and Clark Coll., 1952. LINGUIST, SUMMER INSTITUTE OF LINGUISTICS (PERU), 1954– . Research: language, culture, and customs of the Arabela tribe of northern Peru. Language Spanish 4,4,4,4. Linguistic studies: Arabela. Home and office: Instituto Lingüístico de Verano, Casilla 2492, Lima, Perú.

RICHARDSON, IVAN LeROY, b. Donovan Ill., Dec. 14, 1920. POLITICAL SCIENCE B.A., U. of Ill., 1943; M.A., U. of Iowa, 1948 Ph. D., 1950. Part-time instr., U. of Iowa 1948–50; asst. prof.-prof., Fort Hays, Kans State Coll., 1950–59; administrative an alvst. Legislature. State of Kans., 1958 assoc. prof., School of Public Administration, U. of Southern Calif. Brazil contract 1959–64; PROF., POLITICAL SCIENCE CALIF. STATE COLL. AT FULLERTON

1964– . Consultant, U. of Bahia and U. of Rio Grande do Sul, 1959–64; consultant, Organization of American States (Mexico, P.R., Ecuador), 1965. Membership: American Political Science Association; American Society for Public Administration; Southern California Political Science Association; Western Political Science Association. Research: public administration; developmental agencies and administration; comparative administration; Brazil. Author: Bibliografia brasileira de administração pública (1964); Public Administration Education in Brazil (in Perspectives of Brazilian Public Administration, 1963). Editor: Perspectives of Brazilian State and Local Government (1965). Language: Spanish 3,3,3,1; Portuguese 4,4,4,4. Home: 2853 Mystic Ave., Fullerton, Calif. Office: Dept. of Political Science, Calif. State Coll., 800 North State College, Fullerton.

RICHARDSON, ROBERT WILLIAM, b. Oakland, Calif., Dec. 16, 1906. GEOGRAPHY. A.B., U. of Calif., Berkeley, 1930; Ph. D., 1943. Acting asst. prof., Chico State Coll., 1938–39; asst. prof., San Diego State Coll., 1939–41; asst., Office for the Coordination of Inter-American Affairs, 1942–43; head, Latin American Geography Section, U.S. Office of Strategic Services, 1944–46; technical consultant, U.S. Bureau of the Census (Ecuador), 1946–47; PROF., GEOGRAPHY, SAN DIEGO STATE COLL., 1948– . Consultant on climates of the American tropics, Texas Instruments, Inc. Membership: Association of American Geographers; Association of Pacific Coast Geographers; Pacific Coast Association of Latin American Studies. Research: physical and economic geography; primary agricultural production in the Caribbean; commercial agriculture and plantations in Costa Rica; cultural geography, land tenure and primary production in Mexico. Author: Population Handbook of Latin America (1943); Latin America (in Encyclopaedia Britannica, 1945). Language: Spanish 4,3,3,2; French 2,2,2,1; German 2,2,2,1. Home: 5707 Hardy Ave., San Diego, Calif. 92115. Office: Dept. of Geography, San Diego State Coll., San Diego, 92115.

RIESENFELD, STEFAN A., b. Breslau, Germany, June 8, 1908. LAW. J.U.D., U. of Breslau, 1932; J.U.D., U. of Milan, 1934; LL.B., U. of Calif., Berkeley, 1937; S.J.D., Harvard Law School, 1939. Prof., U. of Minn., 1938–52; PROF., LAW, SCHOOL OF LAW, U. OF CALIF., BERKELEY, 1952– . Senior consultant, Board of Economic Warfare, 1942; consultant, High Commission for Germany, 1950–51; senior consultant, United Nations, 1952; consultant, U.S. Dept. of Defense, 1958; staff, Economic Commission for Latin America (Chile), Summer 1960. Membership: American Bar Association; American Society of International Law; Foreign Law Association; International Law Association. Research: comparative and international law; regional integration; Latin American Free Trade Association. Author: Modern Social Legislation (1950, 1958); Protection of Competition in the European Common Market (1962); Recent Developments in French Labor Law (Minnesota Law Review, Mar. 1939). Language: Spanish 4,3,–,2; Portuguese 3,1,1,1; French 4,–,4,2; German 5,5,5,5; Italian 4,4,–,3. Home: 1129 Amador Ave., Berkeley 4, Calif. Office: School of Law, U. of Calif., Berkeley 4.

RIGBY, PAUL HERBERT, b. Humboldt, Ariz., Aug. 6, 1924. ECONOMICS AND STATISTICS. B.B.A., U. of Tex., 1945; M.B.A., 1948; Ph. D., 1952. Research asst., Bureau of Business Research, U. of Tex., 1947–48; manager, Smithville Chamber of Commerce (Smithville, Tex.), 1948–49; senior price economist, Seattle Regional Office, U.S. Office of Price Stabilization, 1951–52; research assoc., asst. prof., U. of Ala., 1952–54; assoc. prof., dir., Bureau of Business Research, Ga. State Coll., 1954–56; prof., dir., Center for Research, U. of Houston, 1956–62; assoc. prof., Research Center, U. of Mo., 1962–64; PROF., BUSINESS ADMINISTRATION, DIR., BUREAU OF BUSINESS RESEARCH, PA. STATE U., 1964– . Fulbright grant, U. of Mexico, Summer 1962; participant, Ford Foundation workshops for directors of bureaus of business research. Membership: American Economic Association; American Statistical Association; Institute of Management Science; Southwestern Social Science Association. Research: resources and accounting. Author: MANTRAP—Management Training Program (1962); Economic Analysis and Business Management (1964); Conceptual Foundations of Business Research (1965). Language: Spanish 4,4,3,3. Home: 1916 North Oak Lane, State College, Pa., 16802. Office: Coll. of Business Administration, Pa. State U., University Park, 16801.

RILEY, CARROLL LAVERNE, b. Summersville, Mo., Apr. 18, 1923. ANTHROPOLOGY. B.A., U. of N. Mex., 1948; M.A., U. of Calif., Los Angeles, 1950; Ph. D., U. of N. Mex., 1952. Instr., U. of Colo., 1953–54; asst. prof., U. of N.C., 1954–55; ASSOC. PROF., SOUTHERN ILL. U., 1955– . U. of N. Mex. fellow, 1949–50, 1951–52; Social Science Research Council fellow (Venezuela), 1950–51; National Institutes of Health research grants (Mexico), 1957–58, 1958–59, 1960–63; American Philosophical Society research grant, 1959–60. Membership: American Anthropological Association; American Association for Advancement of Science; American Association of Physical Anthropologists; Royal Anthropological Institute of Great Britain and Ireland; Sigma Xi; Society for American Archaeology. Research: ethnology; archeology; Sierra Madre area of Mexico; Venezuela. Author: Noticias sobre los indios Panare (Boletín Venezolano Indigenista, Apr.–June 1953, 1955). Coauthor: The Southwestern Journals of Adolph Bandelier (1964); Diffusion and Discontinuous Distribution (American Anthropologist, Apr. 1958). Language: Spanish 4, 3, 3, 3; Portuguese 3,1,1,1; French 3,1,2,1; German 3,1,2,1; Italian 3,2,3,2. Home: 509 West Walnut St., Carbondale, Ill. Office: Dept. of Anthropology, Southern Ill. U., Carbondale.

RILEY, G. MICHAEL, b. Silver City, N. Mex., Apr. 22, 1934. HISTORY. B.S., Ariz. State U., 1956; M.A., U., of N. Mex., 1961; Ph. D., 1964. Vis. asst. prof., U. of N. Mex., 1963–64; ASST. PROF., HISTORY, COLO. STATE U., 1964– . Social Science Research Council fellow (Spain), 1962–63. Membership: American Historical Association; Conference on Latin American History; Phi Alpha Theta; Phi Kappa Phi. Research: colonial Latin American history; the estate of Fernando Cortés in the Cuernavaca Valley (Mexico) to 1547; archival research in Spain and Mexico. Language: Spanish 4,3,3,3; Portuguese 2,1,1,1; French 3,1,1,1. Home: 133 Harvard, SE., Albuquerque, N. Mex. Office: Dept. of History, U. of N. Mex., Albuquerque.

RILEY, HAROLD M., b. Holton, Kans., Nov. 13, 1922. ECONOMICS. B.S., Kans. State U., 1947; M.S., 1948; Ph. D., Mich. State U., 1954. Asst. prof., Kans. State U., 1948–51; PROF., AGRICULTURAL ECONOMICS, MICH. STATE U., 1953– . Advisor, Coll. of Agriculture, National U. of Colombia, 1960–62; vis. prof., Universidad del Valle (Colombia), 1961; assoc. editor, Journal of Farm Economics, 1962– . Membership: American Farm Economic Association; International Association of Agricultural Economists. Research: agricultural marketing and prices; livestock and meat marketing; problems of market organization in countries in early stages of development. Author: Beef Production in Colombia (1962). Co-author: An Analysis of Operating Costs at Michigan Livestock Auctions (Bulletin, Michigan Agricultural Experiment Station, 1961). Contributor: Economics and Management in Agriculture (1962). Language: Spanish 3,3,3,3. Home: 1351 Albert Ave., East Lansing, Mich. Office: Dept. of Agricultural Economics, Mich. State U., East Lansing.

RIPOLL, CARLOS R., b. Havana, Cuba, Mar. 31, 1922. SPANISH AMERICAN LITERATURE. M.S., U. of Havana, 1944; Ph. D., N.Y.U., 1964. Vice president, Polry, S.A., and Laboratorios Merck (Havana), 1945–50; construction engineer (Havana), 1950–60; INSTR., SPANISH, QUEEN'S COLL., 1964– . Research: literary movements in Latin America; picaresque novel; works of José Martí. Author: La Revista de Avance, 1927–1930, vocero de vanguardismo y pórtico de revolución (Revista Iberoamericana, Dec. 1964). Language: Spanish 5,5,5,5; Portuguese 3,2,1,1; French 4,3,3,3; Russian 1,1,2,2. Home: 1214 Madrid, Coral Gables, Fla.

RIPPY, JAMES FRED, b. Sumner County, Tenn., Oct. 27, 1892. HISTORY. B.A., Southwestern U. of Tex., 1913; A.M., Vanderbilt U., 1915; Ph. D., U. of Calif., 1920; D. Litt. (honorary), Southwestern U. of Tex., 1961. Instr., U. of Chicago, 1920–23; asst. prof., 1923–24; assoc. prof., 1924–26; prof., Duke U., 1926–36; prof., U. of Chicago, 1936–58; PROF. EMERITUS, HISTORY, U. OF CHICAGO, 1958– . Native Sons fellow, U. of Calif., 1917–18; editorial staff, Hispanic American Historical Review, 1926– ; Guggenheim fellow (Central America), 1927; Carnegie fellow (Colombia), 1928; Albert Shaw lectr., Johns Hopkins U., 1928; lectr., Instituto Interamericano of the National U. of Mexico, 1929; American Historical Review, 1933–38; delegate, Pan American Conference on History and Geography, 1935; Walter Fleming lectr., U. of La., 1941; Walker Ames lectr., U. of Wash., 1945; recipient, William Volker award, 1960. Membership: American Academy of Political and Social Science; American Association of University Professors; American Historical Association; Mississippi Valley Historical Association; North Carolina Historical and Literary Society; Phi Alpha Theta; Phi Beta Kappa. Research: the national period in Latin America; the industrial age in Latin America. Author: Modern Latin America (1958); Globe and Hemisphere (1958); British Investments in Latin America (1959). Language: Spanish 5,4,4,–; French 4,3,–,–; German 3,2,–,–; Italian 2,2,–,–. Home: 814 East Forest Hills Blvd., Durham, N.C.

RIPPY, NOBLE MERRILL, b. Fort Worth, Tex., Aug. 8, 1917. HISTORY. A.A., Decatur Baptist Coll., 1936; B.A., Tex. Christian U., 1938; M.A., 1939; Ph. D., U. of Tex., 1950. Teacher-counselor, Fort Worth Public Schools, 1938–45; part-time instr., U. of Tex., 1945–46; asst. prof.-assoc. prof., Tex. Christian U., 1947–53; asst. prof.-assoc. prof., Lamar State Coll., 1954–58; asst. prof.-ASSOC. PROF., HISTORY, BALL STATE TEACHERS COLL., 1959– ; vis. lectr. and researcher, U. of P.R., Summers 1959, 1960, 1961. E. D. Farmer international fellow, Universidad Nacional Autónoma de México, 1947; Ford Foundation post-doctoral fellow, U. of Chicago-U. of Tex., 1952–53; Smith-Mundt exchange prof., U. of Panama, 1956–57; National Defense Foreign Language post-doctoral fellow in Spanish, U. of Calif., Los Angeles, Summer 1963. Membership: American Historical Association; Bolivarian Society of the United States; Conference on Latin American History; Indiana Academy of the Social Sciences; Midwest Council, Association for Latin American Studies; Texas State Historical Association. Research: intellectual history of Mexico and the Caribbean; Spanish origins of Latin American intellectuality. Author: El Petróleo y la Revolución Mexicana (1954); The Mexican Oil Industry (in Essays in Mexican History, 1958); Theory of History: Twelve Mexicans (The Americas, Jan. 1961). Language: Spanish 4,4,4,3; Portuguese 2,2,2,2; French 2,2,2,2. Home: 2613 North Janney Ave., Muncie, Ind. 47304. Office: Dept. of Social Sciences, Ball State Teachers Coll., Muncie.

RITTENHOUSE, FLOYD OLIVER, b. Bozeman, Mont., Mar. 10, 1906. HISTORY. B.A., Andrews U., 1928; M.A., Ohio State U., 1932; Ph. D., 1947. Assoc. prof., Wash. Missionary Coll., 1939–48; prof., Southern Missionary Coll., 1948–52; prof., Andrews U., 1952–63; PROF., HISTORY, PACIFIC UNION COLL.,1963– . Membership: American Historical Association; Phi Alpha Theta. Research: Mexico; the Mexican Revolution, 1910–1920. Language: Spanish 4,3,3,3; French 3,2,2,2. Home: 495 South White Cottage Rd., Angwin, Calif. Office: Dept. of History, Pacific Union Coll., Angwin.

ROBB, JAMES WILLIS, b. Jamaica, N.Y., June 27, 1918. SPANISH AMERICAN AND BRAZILIAN LITERATURES. A.B., Colgate U., 1939; Universidad Nacional de México, 1948; A.M., Middlebury Coll., 1950; Ph. D., Catholic U. of America, 1958. Spanish translator and underwriter, United States Life Insurance Company, 1941–46; U.S. Naval Observer (Belém and Florianópolis, Brazil), 1942–44; instr., Norwich U., 1946–50; ASSOC. PROF., ROMANCE LANGUAGES AND LITERATURES, GEORGE WASHINGTON U., 1950– . Membership American Association of Teachers of Spanish and Portuguese; Instituto Internacional de Literatura Iberoamericana; Modern Language Association. Research: Spanish-American essayists; Mexican and Colombian literature; contemporary Argentine and Chilean literature; works of Alfonso Reyes, J. Vasconcelos, G. Arciniegas, B. Sanín Cano. Author: Imagen y estructura en la obra de Alfonso Reyes (1965); Baldomero Sanín Cano y su obra literaria (Revista Interamericana de Bibliografía, Oct.-Dec. 1961); Imágenes de América en Alfonso Reyes y en Germán Arciniegas (Humanitas, 1963). Language: Spanish 4,4,4,4; Portuguese 4,4,4,4; French 4,4,4,4; Italian 4,3,3,3. Linguistic studies: French; Portuguese; Spanish. Home: 3807 Rodman St. NW., Washington, D.C. 20016. Office: Dept. of Romance Languages and Literatures, George Washington U., Washington, 20006.

ROBBINS, FRANK ERNEST, b. Elmira, N.Y., May 12, 1926. LINGUISTICS. A.B., Houghton Coll., 1949; M.A., Cornell U., 1960. LINGUIST, TRANSLATOR, SUMMER INSTITUTE OF LINGUISTICS (MEXICO), 1950– . National Defense Education Act fellow in Chinantec. Membership: Linguistic Society of America. Research: analyses, description, literacy and translation in Highland Chinantec of Oaxaca, Mexico. Author: Quiotepec Chinantec Syllable Patterning (International Journal of American Linguistics, July 1961). Language: Spanish 4,4,4,4; Chinantec 4,3,3,4. Linguistic studies: Quiotepec Chinantec. Home: Instituto Lingüístico de Verano, Apartado 2975, México 1, D.F. Office: Summer Institute of Linguistics, P.O. Box 1960, Santa Ana, Calif.

ROBE, STANLEY LINN, b. Tangent, Oreg., July 26, 1915. LANGUAGE. B.A., U. of Oreg., 1936; M.A., 1939; Ph. D., U. of N.C., 1949. Investigator, Counter Intelligence Corps, U.S. Army (Panama), 1943–46; part-time instr., U. of N.C., 1946–49; PROF., SPANISH, U. OF CALIF., LOS ANGELES, 1949– . American Council of Learned Societies grant, U. of Chicago, 1941; travel and maintenance grant, U.S. Dept. of State (Mexico), 1947; Fulbright exchange lectr., Seminario Andrés Bello, Instituto Caro y Cuervo (Bogotá), 1961; dir. of studies, U.S. Peace Corps training program for Peru, U. of Calif., Los Angeles, 1963. Membership: American Folklore Society; Folklore Americas; Modern Language Association. Research: dialectology of American Spanish; phonetics; folklore of Spanish America. Author: Coloquios de Pastores from Jalisco, Mexico (1954); The Spanish of Rural Panama (1960); Hispanic Riddles from Panama (1963). Language: Spanish 5,5,5,5; Portuguese 4,3,3,2; French 5,5,4,4; German 2,2,2,2. Linguistic studies: Goajiro; Spanish. Home: 979 South Bundy Dr., Los Angeles, Calif. 90049. Office: Dept. of Spanish and Portuguese, U. of Calif., 405 Hilgard Ave., Los Angeles, 90024.

ROBERTS, WARREN ALDRICH, b. Galva, Iowa, Nov. 28, 1901. ECONOMICS AND POLITICAL SCIENCE. A.B., Gooding Coll., 1924; M.A., U. of Idaho, 1927; Ph. D., Harvard U., 1932. Asst. prof.-assoc. prof., U. of Ariz., 1932–37; chmn., Economics, Cleveland Coll., Western Reserve U., 1937–45; U.S. Dept. of State, 1942–47; PROF.,

POLITICAL SCIENCE AND ECONOMICS, WABASH COLL., 1947– ; Foreign Service Reserve Officer, 1962–64. Guggenheim fellow, 1939; chmn., Political Science, Wabash Coll., 1947–59; Indiana State Education Commission, 1952–56; dir., Special Commission on Public Education (Ind.), 1956; adviser, U.S. representative to Security Council, 1946; U.S. Dept. of State inspection team (Central America), 1962. Membership: American Economic Association; American Political Science Association; American Society of International Law; American Society of Political and Legal Philosophy. Research: government; public finance; economic political development; labor organizations of Mexico; political changes in Guatemala. Author: State Taxation of Metallic Deposits (Harvard Economic Studies, 1944); Community as Matrix (in Community, 1959); Reflections on Political Integrity (in Responsibility, 1960). Language: Spanish 4,3,3,3. Home: 410 Crawford St., Crawfordsville, Ind. Office: Dept. of Political Science and Economics, Wabash Coll., Crawfordsville.

ROBERTS, WILLIAM H., b. Parkersburg, W. Va., Sept. 6, 1914. SPANISH AMERICAN LITERATURE. A.B., Williams Coll., 1936; Université d'Aix-Marseille, 1936–37; M.A., U. of Wis., 1939; Ph. D., 1950. Vis. lectr., Ohio U., 1940–41; officer, Latin American Section, Office of Naval Intelligence, 1943–54; asst. naval attaché (Asunción, Paraguay), 1945–46; instr., Colo. Coll., 1946–47; instr.-PROF., SPANISH AND PORTUGUESE, VANDERBILT U., 1947– ; CHMN., 1962– ; asst. naval attaché (Lisbon), 1951–54. Membership: American Association of Teachers of Spanish and Portuguese; Instituto Internacional de Literatura Iberoamericana; Modern Language Association; Tennessee Teachers of Spanish. Research: literature of the Río de la Plata, 1880 to the present; Portuguese literature. Author: Notes on Recent Portuguese Theatre (Hispania, May 1955); Hacia una tradición indígena en la poesía paraguaya (Hispanófila, Sept. 1961). Translator: Platero y Yo (1956, 1957, 1960). Language: Spanish 5,5,5,5; Portuguese 5,5,4,4; French 5,5,5,5. Home: 4809 Belmont Park Ter., Nashville, Tenn. Office: Dept. of Spanish, Vanderbilt U., Nashville 5.

ROBERTSON, DONALD, b. Elizabeth, N.J., May 12, 1919. ART. B.A., U. of N. Mex., 1942; M.A., Yale U., 1944; Ph. D., 1956. Instr., Queens Coll., 1946–47; asst. prof., U. of Tex., 1947–50; instr., Pomona Coll., 1954–56; vis. asst. prof., U. of Kans., 1956–57; ASSOC. PROF., ART, NEWCOMB COLL., TULANE U., 1957– . Pomona Coll. faculty research grant (Mexico), 1955; Social Science Research Council grant (Costa Rica, Guatemala), Summer 1958; Tulane U. grants (Mexico), Summers 1958, 1962, Winter 1963; American Council of Learned Societies fellow, Summers 1960, 1961; Guggenheim fellow, 1964–65; Social Science Research Council grant, 1964–65; contributing editor, Handbook of Latin American Studies. Membership: College Art Association; Conference on Latin American History; Renaissance Society; Society for American Archaeology; Society of Architectural Historians; Southeastern Conference on Latin American Studies.

Research: pre-Columbian, colonial and modern art, especially of Mexico; Mexican manuscript painting. Author: Mexican Manuscript Painting of the Early Colonial Period: The Metropolitan Schools (1959); Pre-Columbian Architecture (1963); The Relaciones Geográficas of Mexico (Actas, 33rd Congreso Internacional de Americanistas, July 1958). Language: Spanish 4,4,4,1; Portuguese 3,2,2,1; French 4,4,4,1; German 3,2,2,1; Italian 4,3,3,1; Latin 2,1,1,1. Home: 7707 Plum St., New Orleans, La. 70118. Office: Dept. of Art, Newcomb Coll., Tulane U., New Orleans, 70118.

ROBINSON, DOW FREDERICK, b. Weymouth, Mass., June 22, 1928. LINGUISTICS. B.A., Houghton Coll., 1952; B.D., Fuller Theological Seminary, 1955. FIELD WORKER, SUMMER INSTITUTE OF LINGUISTICS (MEXICO), 1956– . Linguistic consultant, Instituto Indigenista Interamericano (Mexico), 1960–62; linguistic consultant, Dirección General de Asuntos Indígenas de la Secretaría de Educación Pública (Mexico), 1963– . Research: phonetics and phonemics. Author: Field Notes of Coatlan Zapotec (1960). Language: Spanish 4,4,4,4; Nahuatl 5,4,4,5; Zapotec 3,2,2,2. Linguistic studies: Nahuatl; Zapotec. Home: 308 Highland Ave., Wollaston, Mass. Office: Summer Institute of Linguistics, Broadway and Walnut, Santa Ana, Calif.

ROBINSON, NELSON MARTIN, b. Grove City, Pa., Oct. 30, 1922. POLITICAL SCIENCE: PUBLIC ADMINISTRATION. A.B., U. of Wis., 1947; M.A., Syracuse U., 1951; Ph. D., 1954. Asst. prof., Albright Coll., 1952–53; asst. prof., U. of Tenn., 1953–59; public personnel adviser, International Cooperation Administration-U. of Tenn. contract (Bolivia), 1956–57; chief of party, 1957–60; assoc. prof., U. of Tenn., 1959–62; chief of party, Agency for International Development-U. of Tenn. contract (Panama), 1960–62; PROF., POLITICAL SCIENCE, ASSOC. DIR., BUREAU OF PUBLIC ADMINISTRATION, U. OF TENN., 1962– ; area studies coordinator, Peace Corps Training Center for Latin America, U. of N. Mex., Summer 1963. Membership: American Political Science Association; American Society for Public Administration; Association for Latin American Studies; Midwest Council of the Association for Latin American Studies; Public Personnel Association; Southern Political Science Association. Research: role of higher education in developing societies; Latin American university organization and administration; the institutionalization of political parties; labor movement, and role of the military in Latin America. Author: Un plan propuesto de clasificación de cargos (1957); Curso de principios de administración pública (1959); Apuntes sobre principios de ciencia política (1962). Language: Spanish 4,4,4,3; Portuguese 1,1,1,1; French 2,1,1,1. Home: 7312 West Ridge Rd., Knoxville 19, Tenn. Office: Dept. of Political Science, U. of Tenn., Knoxville.

ROBOCK, STEFAN H., b. Redgranite, Wis., July 31, 1915. ECONOMICS. B.A., U. of Wis., 1938; M.A., Harvard U., 1941; Ph. D., 1948. Instr., Tufts Coll., 1948–49; chief economist, Tenn. Valley Authority, 1949–54; United Nations economic development adviser, Government of Brazil, 1954–56; manager, Economics Div., Midwest Research Institute (Kansas City), 1956–58; deputy dir., Committee for Economic Development (N.Y.), 1958–60; PROF., INTERNATIONAL BUSINESS, IND. U., 1960– . Wis. scholar, U. of Wis., 1938–39; administration fellow, Littauer School, Harvard U., 1939–40; United Nations economic adviser (Chile), 1955, (Colombia), 1956, (Venezuela), 1959, (Bolivia), Summer 1963; prof. Honoris Causa, U. of Recife (Brazil), 1956; consultant, Latin America Overseas Development Program, Ford Foundation, 1960; Organization of American States adviser, Bank of Northeast Brazil and U. of Ceara, 1960; consultant, Resources for the Future, 1963. Membership: American Economics Association; Regional Science Association; Society for International Development. Research: regional economic planning; economic development; industrialization; Brazil. Author: Nuclear Power and Economic Development in Brazil (1957); Brazil's Developing Northeast: Regional Planning and Foreign Aid (1963); Management in Underdeveloped Countries (Advanced Management, Jan. 1962). Language: Spanish 4,4,4,–; Portuguese 5,5,4,–; French 3,3,2,–. Home: 1900 Ruby Lane, Bloomington, Ind. Office: Graduate School of Business, Ind. U., Bloomington.

ROCA, PABLO, b. Quebradillas, P.R., May 16, 1907. EDUCATION. B.A., U. of P.R., 1933; M.A., U. of Tex., 1948; Ph. D., 1952. Research asst., U. of P.R., 1944–46; asst. chief, Vocational Rehabilitation, Veterans Administration (San Juan, P.R.), 1947; dir. of research and statistics, Dept. of Education (P.R.), 1948–58; dir., Office of Evaluation, Dept. of Education (P.R.), 1959–60; acting chief, Div. of Education, Organization of American States, 1960–64; DIR., TESTING AND GUIDANCE CENTER, INTER AMERICAN U. OF P.R., 1964– . UNESCO education expert (Panama), 1958; consultant, World Bank (Venezuela), 1960–61; project dir., adaptation into Spanish of Modern Arithmetic Through Discovery Series. Membership: American Association for the Advancement of Science; American Educational Research Association; American Psychological Association; Phi Delta Kappa; Psychometric Society; Puerto Rico Teachers Association. Research: construction and validation of psychological tests. Author: Costos de la Educación (La Educación, Jan.–June 1961); Education (in The Economic Development of Venezuela, 1961); Educational Research in Latin America (Phi Delta Kappan, Jan. 1964). Language: Spanish 5,5,5,5; Portuguese 4,4,2,1; French 4,2,2,1. Home: 510 Ana Roque St., Hato Rey, P.R. 00918. Office: Testing and Guidance Center, Inter American U. of P.R., P.O. Box 1293, Hato Rey, 00919.

RODGERS, KIRK PROCTOR, b. Baltimore, Md., Oct. 15, 1932. GEOGRAPHY. B.A., Yale U., 1954; M.S., 1956. Instr. in photo interpretation, U.S. Navy Fleet Air Intelligence Training Center, 1958–59; SENIOR SPECIALIST, NATURAL RESOURCES, PAN AMERICAN UNION, 1960– . Ford Foundation fellow; Conservation Foundation fellow. Membership: Association of American Geographers; Regional Science Association. Research: economic geography; natural resources; demography; cartography; ecology. Author: Integración económica y social del Perú central (1961) ; Informe oficial, Misión 105 a Honduras (1962) ; Survey for the Development of the Guayas River Basin, Ecuador (1964). Language: Spanish 3,3,3,2; French 2,2,2,2. Home: 1421 Stoneybrae Dr., Falls Church, Va. Office: Natural Resources Unit, Dept. of Economic Affairs, Pan American Union, Washington, D.C. 20006.

RODRÍGUEZ, MARIO, b. Colusa, Calif., Oct. 1, 1922. HISTORY. A.B., U. of Calif., Berkeley, 1946; M.A., 1948; Ph. D., 1952. Instr., Tulane U., 1952–54; faculty research adviser, Graduate Seminar in Central America, Tulane U. and U. of San Carlos (Guatemala), Summer 1953 ; instr.-asst. prof., Yale U., 1954–60; assoc. prof.-PROF., HISTORY, U. OF ARIZ., 1960– . Robertson Prize, Conference on Latin American History, 1955 ; Morse Fellowship in History, Yale U., 1958–59; contributing editor, Handbook of Latin American Studies, 1959– . Membership: American Historical Association ; Conference on Latin American History; Pacific Coast Council of Latin American Studies. Research: 19th and 20th century Central American history ; Río de la Plata area. Author: The Livingston Codes in the Guatemalan Crisis of 1837–1838 (1955) ; The Genesis of Economic Attitudes in the Río de la Plata (Hispanic American Historical Review, May 1956) ; Dom Pedro of Braganza and Colônia do Sacramento, 1680–1705 (Hispanic American Historical Review, May 1958). Language: Spanish 5,5,5,5; Portuguese 5,3,3,2; French 5,3,3,2; German 2,2,1,1; Italian 3,3,2,1. Home: 3331 East Waverly St. Tucson, Ariz. Office: Dept of History, U. of Ariz., Tucson.

RODRÍGUEZ-ALCALÁ, HUGO ROSENDO, b. Asunción, Paraguay, Nov. 25, 1917. SPANISH AMERICAN LITERATURE AND PHILOSOPHY. Doctor of Laws, Universidad de Asunción, 1943 ; Ph. D., U. of Wis., 1953. Secretary, Supreme Court of Paraguay, 1943–47; instr., State U. of Wash., 1947–50; acting instr., U. of Wis., 1950–53 ; asst. prof., Dennison U., 1953–54 ; asst. prof., State U. of Wash., 1954–56; asst. prof., Rutgers U., 1956–58; prof., U. of Wash., 1958–63; PROF., SPANISH, U. OF CALIF., RIVERSIDE, 1963– ; CHMN., 1965– . Institute of International Education fellow, 1943–45 ; Editing Committee, Revista Iberoamericana. Membership: Instituto Internacional de Literatura Iberoamericana ; Rocky Mountain Council of Latin American Affairs. Research: Latin American civilization and philosophy ; River Plate essay ; contemporary Mexican literature. Author: Estampas de la guerra (1939) ; Misión y Pensamiento de Francisco Romero (1959) ; Ensayos de Norte a Sur (1960). Language: Spanish 5,5,5,5 ; Portuguese 5,4,–,2 ; French 5,4,–,2. Home: 3827 Gates Pl., Riverside, Calif., 92504. Office: Dept. of Romance Languages, U. of Calif., Riverside.

RODRÍGUEZ-BOU, ISMAEL, b. Orocovis, P.R., Sept. 28, 1911. EDUCATION. B.A., U. of P.R., 1936; M.A., Columbia U., 1938 ; Ph. D., U. of Tex., 1944. Prof., Inter American U., 1938–41 ; asst. superintendent of schools (Mayagüez, P.R.), 1939–40 ; high school principal (Mayagüez), 1940–41 ; asst. prof., U. of P.R., 1941–45; PROF., PSYCHOLOGY, PERMANENT SECRETARY, DIR. OF EDUCATIONAL RESEARCH, SUPERIOR EDUCATIONAL COUNCIL, U. OF P.R., 1945– ; acting dean, Coll. of Social Sciences, 1948–49. Chmn., Permanent Committee on Educational Problems of Teachers Association of P.R., 1936–38, 1944– ; vis. prof., National U. of Panama, Summer 1939 ; representative, American Council on Education (Mexico, P.R., U.S.), 1941–44 ; dir., Pedagogical Mission, Office of Inter American Affairs (Mexico, Honduras, Ecuador), 1945 ; P.R. Delegate, Seminar on Illiteracy and Adult Education (Brazil), 1949 ; Advisory Committee, Regional Center of Fundamental Education for Latin America (Uruguay), 1950 ; UNESCO delegate, Educational Mission (Costa Rica, El Salvador, Guatemala, Bolivia), 1951 ; special adviser, U. of Costa Rica, 1953 ; P.R. delegate, White House Conference on Education, 1955 ; dir., Survey of the Educational System of Panama (Panama), 1956 ; consultant, 6th Seminar of Inter-American Education, 1958 ; adviser on educational programs, Ministries of El Salvador, Guatemala, and Costa Rica, 1961 ; representative of the Special Commission of the Organization of American States for the Programming and Development of Education, Science and Culture in Latin America, Alliance for Progress, 1962, and at the International Conference on Education and the Economic and Social Development in Latin America (Santiago, Chile), 1962 ; Alliance for Progress representative (Nicaragua, Costa Rica, Honduras, Guatemala, Dominican Republic, Haiti), 1962–63 ; adviser, Centro Interamericano de Estudios Económicos y Sociales (Dominican Republic), 1963. Membership: American Educational Research Association ; Phi Delta Kappa ; Sigma Delta Pi ; Teachers Association of Puerto Rico. Research: educational psychology ; school dropouts; test preparation; adult education. Author: Estudio del paralelismo entre el vocabulario inglés y el español (1950) ; Estudio del sistema educativo de Panamá (1956) ; Informe sobre la situación, necesidades y soluciones aconsejables para el desarrollo de la educación superior en América Latina (1963). Language: Spanish 5,5,5,5. Home: 800 Vesta St., Dos Pinos, Río Piedras, P.R. Office: Superior Educational Council, U. of P.R., Río Piedras, 00931.

ROGERS, EDWARD JONATHAN, b. Hanford, Calif., Feb. 9, 1915. POLITICAL SCIENCE. A.B., San Jose State Coll., 1938 ; M.A., Stanford U., 1948 ; Ph. D., 1957. PROF., POLITICAL SCIENCE, SAN JOSE STATE COLL., 1948– . Faculty Research grant, 1963–64. Membership: Hispanic American Society ; International Studies Association ; Northern California Political Science Association. Research: government and politics of Brazil, Argentina, and Mexico. Author: Brazil's Río Doce Valley Project (Journal of Inter-American Studies, Apr. 1959) ; Brazil: New World City Planning Center (Western City Magazine, Mar. 1962) ; The Iron and Steel Industry in Colonial and Imperial Brazil (The Americas, Oct. 1962). Language: Spanish 3,2,2,1 ; Portuguese 3,3,3,3. Home: 150 Branbury

Dr. Campbell, Calif. Office: Dept. of Political Science, San Jose State Coll., San Jose, Calif.

ROGERS, EVERETT M., b. Carroll, Iowa, Mar. 6, 1931. COMMUNICATION AND SOCIOLOGY. B.S., Iowa State U., 1952; M.S., 1955; Ph. D., 1957. Instr., Sociology, Iowa State U., 1954–57; assoc. prof., Rural Sociology, Ohio State U., 1957–64; ASSOC. PROF., COMMUNICATION, MICH. STATE U., 1964– . UNESCO consultant on study of communication in India and Costa Rica, 1963– ; Fulbright lectr., Universidad Nacional (Bogotá), 1963–64. Membership: Colombian Sociological Association. Research; role of diffusion of technological innovations in social change and economic development in developing countries; communication among peasants in Colombia. Author: Social Change in Rural Society (1960); Diffusion of Innovations (1962). Language: Spanish 4,4,4,3. Office: Dept. of Communication, Mich. State U., East Lansing.

ROGERS, PAUL, b. Snohomish, Wash., Jan. 5, 1900. SPANISH AMERICAN LITERATURE AND LANGUAGE. B.S., U. of Miss., 1921; M.A., Acadia U., 1925; Ph. D., Cornell U., 1928. Asst. prof., U. of Mo., 1928–29; asst. prof.–PROF., ROMANCE LANGUAGES, OBERLIN COLL., 1929– ; vis. prof., Pa. State U., 1949; chmn., 1956–62; vis. prof., U. of N. Mex., 1963–64. Membership: American Association of Teachers of Spanish and Portuguese; American Association of University Professors; Modern Language Association. Research: Hispanic Literature; Mexican literature; poetry. Author: English Words in the Spanish of Mexico (Modern Language Forum, June 1932); A Galdosian Parallel for Part of Martín Luis Guzmán's El Águila y la Serpiente (Hispanic Review, Jan. 1950). Editor: Escritores Contemporáneos de México (1949). Language: Spanish 5,5,5,5; Portuguese 2,2,2,2; French 4,4,4,4; Italian 2,2,2,2. Linguistic studies: French; Spanish. Home: 131 Forest St., Oberlin, Ohio. Office: Dept. of Romance Languages, Oberlin Coll., Oberlin.

ROGERS, ROLLAND C., b. Kent, Wash., Mar. 20, 1910. HISTORY. A.B., U. of Wash., 1933; M.A., 1937; Ph. D., Stanford U., 1953. Research asst., Div. of Press Intelligence, Executive Office of the White House, 1935–37; instr., Wash. Public Schools, 1937–46; instr., San Francisco State Coll., Spring 1951; asst. prof., Stanford U., 1951–57; instr., Foothill Coll., 1958–59; asst. prof., San Jose State Coll., 1959–64; ASSOC. PROF., HISTORY, SAN JOSE STATE COLL., 1964– . Membership: American Historical Association; Pacific Coast Council of Latin American Studies. Research: Brazil. Author: Latin American Transportation (in Encyclopedia Americana, 1955). Language: Spanish 2,2,2,1; Portuguese 3,3,3,1; French 2,2,2,1. Home: P. O. Box 3581, Stanford, Calif. Office: Dept. of History, San Jose State Coll., San Jose 14, Calif.

ROGGIANO, ALFREDO ÁNGEL, b. Chivilcoy, Buenos Aires, Argentina, Aug. 2, 1919. SPANISH AMERICAN LITERATURE. P.L., U. of Buenos Aires, 1945; Certificate, Universidad Central de Madrid, 1949. Prof. titular, U. of Tucumán (Argentina), 1946–54; prof., U. of Chile, Summer 1954; lectr., U. of N. Mex., 1955; lectr., U. of Calif., Berkeley, Summer 1955; EDITOR, REVISTA IBEROAMERICANA, 1955– ; assoc. prof., State U. of Iowa, 1956–63; prof. extraordinario, U. of Mexico, Summer 1958; vis. prof., Ind. U., 1959; vis. prof., U. of Calif., Los Angeles, Summer 1963; PROF., ROMANCE LANGUAGES, U. OF PITTSBURGH, 1963– . Comisión Nacional de Cultura (Argentina), 1948–49; Consejo Superior de Investigaciones Científicas (Spain), 1949; State U. of Iowa research prof., 1958. Membership: American Association of Teachers of Spanish and Portuguese; American Association of University Professors; Instituto Internacional de Literatura Iberoamericana; Modern Language Association; Sociedad Argentina de Escritores; Sociedad Internacional de Hispanistas. Research: modernismo; poetry and novels of Chile; colonial and contemporary literature of Mexico. Author: Una obra desconocida del teatro hispanoamericano (1958); Pedro Henríquez Ureña en los Estados Unidos (1961). Co-author: Diccionario de la literatura latinoamericana: Argentina (2 vols., 1960, 1961). Language: Spanish 5,5,5,5; Portuguese 3,3,2,2; French 5,4,4,4. Linguistic studies: Italian; Spanish. Home: Apt. 112, 1412 Centre Ave., Pittsburgh 19, Pa. Office: Cathedral of Learning 1617, U. of Pittsburgh, Pittsburgh 13.

ROGLER, LLOYD HENRY, b. San Juan, P.R. July 21, 1930. SOCIOLOGY. B.A., U. of Iowa, 1951; M.A., 1952; Ph. D., 1957. Research assoc., Human Resources Research Office, George Washington U., 1954–55; instr., U. of Iowa, 1955–57; asst. prof., U. of P.R., 1957–60; ASST. PROF., SOCIOLOGY YALE U., 1960– . Consultant, Dept. of Psychiatry, School of Medicine, U. of P.R. consultant, Dept. of Psychiatry, U. of Valle (Colombia). Membership: American Sociological Association. Research: sociology of developing societies and of medicine mental illness in the slums of San Juan, Puerto Rico. Co-author: Las clases sociales y la comunicación de ideas de los enfermos mentales (Revista de Ciencias Sociales, Mar 1959); The Puerto Rican Spiritualist as Psychiatrist (The American Journal of Sociology, July 1961); La clase social y el lenguaje desarticulado en los enfermos mentales (Revista de Ciencias Sociales, Dec 1961). Language: Spanish 5,5,5,5. Home 110 Blakelsee Ave., North Haven, Conn. Office: Dept. of Sociology, Yale U., New Haven, Conn. 06520.

ROJAS, CARLOS A., b. San Francisco, Mexico Apr. 6, 1901. SPANISH AMERICAN LITERATURE, B.A., Pomona Coll., 1924 M.A., 1925; Ph. D., U. of Wash., 1948 PROF., HISTORY, FRESNO STATE COLL 1928– . Resident dir., Calif. State College International Programs (Madrid, Spain) Membership: American Association of Teachers of Spanish and Portuguese; Foreign Language Association of Northern California; Modern Language Association Sigma Delta Pi. Research: Latin American history; Mexican literature. Language: Spanish 5,5,5,5; Portuguese 5,4,4,4 French 5,4,4,4; Italian 5,3,4,3. Home: 421 North Thorne Ave., Fresno 5, Calif. Office Dept. of History, Fresno State Coll., Fresno 26.

ROMANELL, PATRICK, b. Bari, Italy, Oct. 2, 1912. PHILOSOPHY. B.A., Brooklyn Coll., 1934; M.A., Columbia U., 1936; Ph. D., 1937. Prof., U. of Panama. 1941–44; assoc. prof., chmn., Philosophy, Wells Coll., 1946–52; prof., U. of Tex. (Galveston), 1952–62; PROF., PHILOSOPHY, MEDICAL PHILOSOPHY, U. OF OKLA., 1962– . Cutting traveling fellow, Columbia U. (Mexico), 1945–46; Fulbright prof., U. of Turin, 1952–53; Smith-Mundt prof., U. of Mexico, 1952, Central U. of Ecuador, 1957; lectr., U.S. Dept. of State (Latin America), Summer 1961. Membership: American Association for the Advancement of Science; American Association for the History of Medicine; American Association of University Professors; American Philosophical Association; Instituto Brasileiro de Filosofía; Southwestern Philosophical Society. Research: history and philosophy of medicine; contemporary American and Italian philosophy; history of Mexican philosophy. Author: Can We Agree? (1950); Making of the Mexican Mind (1952); Toward a Critical Naturalism (1958). Language: Spanish 5,5,5,5; Portuguese 3,3,2,2; French 3,3,2,2; Italian 5,5,5,5. Home: 726 McCall Dr., Norman, Okla. Office: Dept. of Philosophy, U. of Okla., Norman.

ROMNEY, ANTONE KIMBALL, b. Rexberg, Idaho, Aug. 19, 1925. ANTHROPOLOGY. A.B., Brigham Young U., 1947; M.A., 1948; Ph. D., Harvard U., 1956. Asst. prof., U. of Chicago, 1955–56; ASSOC. PROF., ANTHROPOLOGY, STANFORD U., 1957– . Center for Advanced Studies in Behavioral Science grant, 1956–57; National Research Council grant; National Institute of Mental Health research grant; Social Science Research Council fellow. Membership: American Anthropological Association. Research: social anthropology; Mexico. Author: Juxtlahuaca (in Six Cultures, 1963). Language: Spanish 3,3,3,2. Home: 790 Gailey, Palo Alto, Calif. Office: Dept. of Anthropology, Stanford U., Stanford, Calif.

RONAN, CHARLES EDWARD, S.J., b. Chicago, Ill., June 1, 1914. HISTORY. A.B., Loyola U. (Ill.) 1940; M.A., 1954; Ph. D., U. of Tex., 1958. Instr., U. of Detroit, 1956–57; asst. prof., Loyola U. (Ill.), 1957–60; asst. prof., Xavier U. (Ohio), 1960–63; ASST. PROF., HISTORY, LOYOLA U. (ILL.), 1963– . Membership: American Division of the Jesuit Institute of History; American Historical Association; Catholic Historical Association. Research: biography of Francisco Javier Clavigero, Mexican Jesuit, 1731–1787; 18th century Latin America. Author: On the Word Gringo (Historia Mexicana, Apr. 1959). Language: Spanish 4,4,4,4; Portuguese 2,2,2,1; French 3,-,-,-; Latin 2,2,3,3. Office: Dept. of History, Loyola U., 6525 Sheridan Rd., Chicago 26, Ill.

RONNING, C. NEALE, b. Kenyon, Minn., Sept. 27, 1927. POLITICAL SCIENCE. B.A., U. of Minn., 1950; M.A., U. of Calif., Berkeley, 1952; Ph. D., U. of Minn., 1958. Instr., Princeton U., 1955–58; asst. prof., 1958–62; ASSOC. PROF., POLITICAL SCIENCE, NEWCOMB COLL., TULANE U., 1962– . Procter and Gamble fellow (Peru, Guatemala, Colombia), 1959; Rabinowitz Foundation fellow (Venezuela), Summers 1961, 1963; assoc. dir. of armament study in Western Hemisphere, Mershon Center for Study in National Security, 1965. Membership: American Association of University Professors; American Political Science Association. Research: Latin American politics and government; international relations of Western Hemisphere. Author: Law and Politics in Inter-American Diplomacy (1963); Punta del Este: Limits of Collective Security in a Troubled Hemisphere (1963); Diplomatic Asylum: Legal Norms and Political Reality in Latin American Relations (1964). Language: Spanish 4,4,4,4; Portuguese 2,2,2,2. Home: 7330 Pitt St., New Orleans, La. 70118. Office: Dept. of Political Science, Newcomb Coll., Tulane U., New Orleans, 70118.

ROOT, WILLIAM CAMPBELL, b. Grass Valley, Calif., Oct. 26, 1903. ANTHROPOLOGY. B.S., U. of Calif., 1925; Ph. D., Harvard U., 1932. PROF., CHEMISTRY, BOWDOIN COLL., 1932– . Membership: American Anthropological Association; American Chemical Society; Royal Anthropological Society; Society for American Archaeology. Research: archeological chemistry; pre-Columbian metallurgy. Author: Metallurgy (in Handbook of South American Indians, 1949). Language: Spanish 2,-,-,-; French 3,-,-,-. Home: 11 Potter St., Brunswick, Maine. Office: Dept. of Chemistry, Bowdoin Coll., Brunswick.

ROOTS, THOMAS PAGE, JR., b. Long Beach, Calif., Aug. 24, 1924. LINGUISTICS. B.A., U. of Calif., Berkeley, 1950. RESEARCH STAFF, HASKINS LABORATORIES, INC., 1959– ; instr., Hunter Coll., 1963–64. Consultant, Ministry of Justice, Government of Venezuela, Summer 1961. Membership: Acoustical Society of America; American Anthropological Association; Linguistic Circle of New York; Linguistic Society of America. Research: acoustic phonetics; speech perception; anthropological linguistics in Venezuela. Language: Spanish 4,3,3,3; French 3,2,2,2; German 3,2,2,3. Linguistic studies: Yaruro. Home: 345 Riverside Dr., New York, N.Y. 10025. Office: Haskins Laboratories Inc., 305 East 43rd St., New York, 10017.

ROSA, ALBERTO MACHADO DA, b. Angra, Azores, Jan. 30, 1924. BRAZILIAN LITERATURE. B.A., U. of Coimbra, 1946; M.A., 1947; Ph. D., U. of Wis., 1953. Instr.-asst. prof., U. of Wis., 1953–59; vis. assoc. prof., dir., N.Y.U. Junior Year in Brazil, U. of Bahia, 1959–60; ASSOC. PROF., SPANISH AND PORTUGUESE, DIR., LUSO-BRAZILIAN DIV., U. OF WIS. 1960– ; dir., U. of Wis. Summer Session in Brazil, 1961, 1962. Consultant, U.S. Peace Corps Training Center for Brazil, U. of Wis., Milwaukee, 1963–64; Committee for Latin American Studies, U. of Wis. Membership: American Association of Teachers of Spanish and Portuguese; Modern Language Association. Research: the poetry of Rosalía de Castro. Author: Uma experiência pioneira (1960); Uma experiência pioneira de intercâmbio cultural (1963); Eca, discípulo de Machado? (1963). Language: Spanish 5,5,4,4; Portuguese 5,5,5,5; French 4,4,3,3. Home: 110 Farley Ave., Madison 5, Wis. Office: Dept. of Foreign Languages, U. of Wis., 540 University Ave., Madison 5.

ROSALDO, RENATO IGNACIO, b. Minatitlán, Mex., Apr. 16, 1912. SPANISH-AMERICAN

LITERATURE. B.A., U. of Ill., 1936; M.A., 1937; Ph. D., 1942. Instr., U. of Ill., 1942–45; vis. prof., U. of Minn., Summer 1945; asst. prof., U. of Wis., 1945–47; acting chmn., Summer 1947; assoc. prof., 1947–55; vis. prof., U. of N. Mex., Summer 1949; vis. prof., Guadalajara Summer School, 1955, 1956, 1958; vis. prof., U. of Ariz., 1955–56; PROF., SPANISH, U. OF ARIZ., 1956– ; vis. prof., U. of Calif., Los Angeles, Summer 1957; HEAD, ROMANCE LANGUAGES, U. OF ARIZ., 1958– . Co-dir., Guadalajara Summer School (Mex.), 1959– ; dir., U. of Ariz.-U. of Sonora (Mex.) Committee; co-ordinator and member, Executive Committee, Ariz.-Mexico West Coast Trade Commission; editor, Amigos; Executive Council, American Association of Teachers of Spanish and Portuguese. Membership: Arizona Foreign Language Association; Pacific Coast Council of Latin American Studies; Rocky Mountain Council for Latin American Studies. Research: 16th, 19th, and 20th century Mexican literature. Author: Flores de Baria Poesía (1952); Menéndez y Pelayo y Roa Bárcena, una disensión académica. Datos para una biografía de Roa Bárcena (Revista Iberoamericana, Oct. 1953); A Decade of Mexican Literature, 1950–60 (Arizona Quarterly, Winter 1960). Language: Spanish 5,5,5,5; Portuguese 4,2,2,2; French 5,4,3,3; German 2,3,2,3; Italian 3,3,2,2. Home: 5424 East 10th St., Tucson, Ariz. Office: Dept. of Romance Languages, U. of Ariz., Tucson, 85721.

ROSE, THEODORE E., b. Long Island, N.Y., May 11, 1931. LANGUAGE AND BRAZILIAN LITERATURE. B.A., Queens Coll., 1952; M.A., N.Y.U., 1955; Ph. D., 1959. Teacher, União Cultural Brasil-Estados Unidos (São Paulo, Brazil), 1953–54; teacher, Forest Hills High School (N.Y.), 1956–59; ASSOC. PROF., SPANISH, PORTUGUESE, AND EDUCATION, U. OF WIS., 1959– . União Cultural Brasil-Estados Unidos grant, U. of São Paulo, 1953–54; Fulbright scholar (Spain), Summer 1963; educational consultant in Spanish for Holt, Rinehart & Winston Company. Membership: American Association of Teachers of Spanish and Portuguese; National Education Association; Wisconsin Education Association; Southern Wisconsin Education Association. Research: Luso-Brazilian studies; Brazilian novel; methods of teaching Spanish and French in the secondary schools. Author: Evaluations of Spanish Periodicals (Top of the News, Mar. 1963): The Role of the Cooperating Teacher (Wisconsin Journal of Education, Apr. 1963): Wedding—A Mnemonic Device for Teaching the Subjunctive (Language Arts News, Spring 1964). Language: Spanish 5,5,5,5; Portuguese 4,5,5,5; French 4,4,5,5; Italian 3,3,2,3. Home: 4633 Tokay Blvd., Madison, Wis. 53711. Office: Dept. of Spanish and Portuguese, U. of Wis., Madison, 53706.

ROSENBERG, BERNARD, b. Detroit, Mich., Nov. 30, 1923. SOCIOLOGY. B.A., U. of Mich., 1945; Ph. D., New School for Social Research, 1949; Columbia U., 1949–52. Instr., Hunter Coll., 1949–52; instr., Brandeis U., 1952–55; asst. prof., Harpur Coll., 1955–56; ASST. PROF., SOCIOLOGY, CITY COLL. (N.Y.) 1956– . Fulbright lectr., U. of Buenos Aires, 1960–61; Social Science Research Council grant; Doherty grant. Membership: American Association of Public Opinion Research; American Sociological Society; Eastern Sociological Society; International Sociological Society. Research: bureaucratic organization; social stratification; juvenile delinquency; urban development; Argentina; Uruguay; Chile. Author: The Values of Veblen (1956); Mass Culture (1957); Mass, Class and Bureaucracy (1964). Language: Spanish 5,4,4,3; Portuguese 1,1,1,1; French 5,4,3,3; Hungarian 5,5,5,5. Office: City Coll., Convent Ave. at 139th St., New York, N.Y. 10031.

ROSS, DAVID F., b. Ann Arbor, Mich., Nov. 27, 1925. ECONOMICS. A.B., Harvard U., 1950; M.A., 1951; Ph. D., 1956. Instr., Colegio de Agricultura y Artes Mecánicas (Mayagüez, P.R.), 1952–53; economist, asst. dir. of research, Administración de Fomento Económico (P.R.), 1953–57; assoc. prof., Fla. State U., 1957–59; prof.-dean Bethany Coll., 1959–64; PROF., ECONOMICS, CUTTINGTON COLL. (SUACOCO, LIBERIA), 1964–67. Consultant, Government of P.R., 1958; Ford Foundation faculty research fellow, U. of Mich., 1960; consultant, Checchi and Company. Membership: American Economic Association. Research: economic growth; history of the Puerto Rican development program; economic development of Honduras. Author: The Costs and Benefits of Puerto Rico's Fomento Programmes (Social and Economic Studies, Sept. 1957); The Future of the Liberal Arts College (Key Reporter, 1963). Co-author: Honduras: a Problem in Economic Development (1960). Language: Spanish 4,2,3,3; French 3,2,2,1 Office: Cuttington Coll., Bishop's House Monrovia, Liberia.

ROSS, MARION DEAN, b. Williamsburg, Pa. June 6, 1913. ARCHITECTURE AND ART B.S. in Arch., Pa. State Coll., 1935; M Arch., Harvard U., 1937. Instr.-asst. prof. Tulane U., 1937–46; asst. prof., Pa. State Coll., 1946–47; PROF., HEAD, ART HIS TORY, U. OF OREG., 1947– . American Institute of Architects Langley fellow (South America), 1941; architect, Harvard Cornell Expedition (Sardis), 1958; Fulbright lectr., Universidad Nacional de Asunción (Paraguay), 1961. Membership American Institute of Architects; Archaeological Institute of America; College Ar Association; Medieval Academy of America Oregon Historical Society; Rennaissance Society of America; Society of Architectural Historians. Research: Baroque architecture and architecture of the 19th and 20th centuries; history of art in Latin America art and architecture in Ecuador, Guatemal Mexico, Peru, Colombia, and Brazil. Author: Oregon Architecture, 1859–195 (1959); Colonial Architecture in Jamaic (Journal, Society of Architectural Histor ians, Oct. 1951); Oregon Architectur 1845–1895 (Oregon Historical Quarterl 1956). Language: Spanish 4,3,3,3; Port guese 2,–,–,–; French 4,3,3,3; Germa 2,2,–,–; Italian 2,2,–,–. Home: 653 Ea 12th Ave., Eugene, Oreg. Office: Dept. Art History, School of Architecture an Allied Arts, U. of Oreg., Eugene, 97403.

ROSS, OLIVER DELL, b. Lorain, Ohi Oct. 12, 1925. HISTORY. B.A., U. Wis., 1948; M.A., 1950; Ph. D., Ohio Sta U., 1953. Manager-PRESIDENT, SA ROSS AND SONS, 1953– . Membershi American Historical Association; Phi Alp Theta. Research: studies of selected Me ican communal institutions in the colonial period. Language: Spanish 4,3,2,3; French 2,-,-,-; German 2,-,-,-. Home: 317 Euclid Ave., Lorain, Ohio. Office: 1351 Broadway, Lorain.

ROSS, STANLEY ROBERT, b. New York, N.Y., Aug. 8, 1921. HISTORY. A.B., Queens Coll., 1942; M.A., Columbia U., 1943; Ph. D., 1951. Asst. prof., U. of Nebr., 1951–57; assoc. prof., 1957–60; vis. assoc. prof., Columbia U., Summer 1960; prof., dir., Latin American Program, U. of Nebr., 1960–62; vis. prof., U. of Colo., Summer 1962; PROF., CHMN., HISTORY, STATE U. OF N.Y., COLL. AT STONY BROOK, 1962– ; ACTING DEAN, COLL. OF ARTS AND SCIENCES, 1963– . U.S. Dept. of State travel grant (Mexico), Summers 1947, 1948; Doherty fellow (Mexico), 1952–53; U. of Nebr. grant (Mexico), Summer 1955; Rockefeller Foundation grants (Mexico), 1958–59, 1961–62. Membership: American Association of University Professors; American Historical Association; Conference on Latin American History; Mississippi Valley Historical Association. Research: 20th century Mexico; effects of revolutionary movement; diplomatic history. Author: Francisco I. Madero, Apostle of Mexican Democracy (1955). Language: Spanish 4,4,4,3; Portuguese 2,3,1,1. Home: Mud Rd., Setauket, N.Y. Office: Dept. of History, State U. of N.Y., Coll. at Stony Brook, Stony Brook.

ROSSI, PIETRO CARLO, S. J., b. San Francisco, Calif., May 30, 1902. LANGUAGE. B.S., U. of Calif., Berkeley, 1923; Ph. D., Gregorian U. (Rome), 1933; Ph. D., U. of Calif., Berkeley, 1940. Prof., U. of San Francisco, 1942–45, 1946–56; dir., Language Lab, National U. of Santo Domingo, 1957; PROF., MODERN LANGUAGES, U. OF SAN FRANCISCO, 1957– . U.S. Dept. of State grant (Brazil), 1946; Oficial, Cruzeiro do Sul, 1949, Comandante, 1952. Research; language and culture of Brazil. Author: Portuguese, The Language of Brazil (1945); Vida Brasileira (1949); Structural French for College (1964). Language: Spanish 5,5,5,5; Portuguese 5,5, 5,5; French 5,5,5,5; German 3,3,3,3; Italian 5,5,5,5. Linguistic studies: French. Home and office: Dept. of Modern Languages, U. of San Francisco, 2130 Fulton St., San Francisco, Calif. 94117.

ROTHBERG, IRVING PAUL, b. Philadelphia, Pa., June 8, 1921. SPANISH AMERICAN LITERATURE. B.S., Temple U., 1948; M.A., Pa. State U., 1951; Ph. D., 1954. Instr., U. of Conn., 1954–58; asst. prof., Temple U., 1958–62; ASSOC. PROF., ROMANCE LANGUAGES, U. OF MASS., 1962– . Fulbright lectr., Universidad del Valle (Cali, Colombia), 1960. Membership: American Association of Teachers of Spanish and Portuguese; Comediantes; Modern Language Association; Renaissance Society. Research: Spanish literature; English as a foreign language. Author: Los temas dominantes en las Minúsculas de González Prada (Iberoamérica, 1962); El agente cómico de Lope de Vega (Hispanófila, Sept. 1962). Language: Spanish 5,5,5,5; Portuguese 2,2,1,1; French 4,2,2,4. Linguistic studies: English; French; Spanish. Home: 18 Van Meter Dr., Amherst, Mass. Office: Dept. of Romance Languages, U. of Mass., Amherst.

ROTHMAN, STANLEY, b. Brooklyn, N.Y., Aug. 4, 1927. POLITICAL SCIENCE. B.S.S., City Coll. (N.Y.), 1949; A.M., Brown U., 1951; Ph. D., Harvard U., 1958. Instr.-ASSOC. PROF., GOVERNMENT, SMITH COLL., 1956– ; instr., Harvard U., Summer 1960; vis. asst. prof., Yale U., Fall 1962. Ford Foundation area training fellow (Chile), 1962–63; consultant, Institute for the Comparative Study of Political Systems (Washington, D.C.). Membership: American Political Science Association; International Political Science Association. Research: comparative politics; Christian Democratic parties in Latin America; community power structures in Latin America. Author: British Labor's New Left (Political Science Quarterly, Sept. 1961): Chile Moves to the Left (The Reporter, June 1964); Chileans and Americans (South Atlantic Quarterly, Summer 1964). Language: Spanish 3,3,3,3; French 3,3,3,3. Home: 101 Crescent St., Northampton, Mass. Office: Dept. of Government, Smith Coll., Northampton.

ROTHWELL, KENNETH JAMES, b. Perth, Australia, Oct. 13, 1925. ECONOMICS. B.A., U. of Western Australia, 1949; M.A., 1954; U. of Stockholm, 1951–52; Ph. D., Harvard U., 1960. Asst. prof., Bucknell U., 1958–61; asst. prof., Darmouth Coll., 1961–63; senior economist, Organization of American States-Inter-American Bank-United Nations Economic Commission for Latin America Fiscal Mission to Ecuador, 1962; ASSOC. PROF., ECONOMICS, U. OF N.H., 1963– . Teaching fellow, Harvard U., 1957; consultant of fiscal studies, Pan American Union; consultant, Foreign Bondholders Protective Council. Membership: American Economic Association; Economic Development Society. Research: international economics; comparative fiscal systems; international portfolio investment; fiscal structure of Ecuador. Author: Export Taxes in Underveloped Countries (Public Finance, 1963); The Extra Borrowing Costs of Fixed Return Over Equity Foreign Capital (Indian Economic Journal, Jan.-Mar. 1964). Language: Spanish 4,3, 2,3; Portuguese 2,1,1,1; French 4,2,2,2; Swedish 4,4,3,3. Home: Box 124, Durham, N.H. Office: Dept. of Economics, U. of N.H., Durham.

ROTTENBERG, SIMON, b. Providence, R.I., Aug. 22, 1916. ECONOMICS. B.A., George Washington U., 1940; M.A., Harvard U., 1948; Ph. D., 1950. Dir., Social Science Center and Labor Relations Institute, U. of P.R., 1947–52; dir., Economic Research Center, Catholic U. of Chile, 1956–58; asst. prof.-assoc. prof., U. of Chicago, 1952–61; DEAN, SCHOOL OF BUSINESS ADMINISTRATION, PROF., ECONOMICS AND INDUSTRIAL RELATIONS, STATE U. OF N.Y., COLL. AT BUFFALO, 1962– . Social Science Research Council fellow, 1949–50; U. of Chicago fellow, 1952–53; commissioner of enquiry, Colony of Antigua, 1960; consultant, U.S. Dept. of Labor, 1962. Membership: American Economic Association; Industrial Relations Research Association; Royal Economic Society. Research: economics of growth; industrial relations; labor economics. Author: Technical Assistance in Latin America: How U.S. Business Firms Promote Technological Progress (1957); Problems in a Latin American

Factory Society (Monthly Labor Review, July 1954); The Meaning of Excess Supplies of Labor (Scottish Journal of Political Economy, Feb. 1961). Language: Spanish 4,4,4,3; French 3,3,2,2; Yiddish 3,4,3,2. Home: 468 Ashland Ave., Buffalo 22, N.Y. Office: School of Business Administration, State U. of N.Y., Buffalo 14.

ROUSE, IRVING, b. Rochester, N.Y., Aug. 29, 1913. ANTHROPOLOGY. B.S., Yale U., 1934; Ph. D., 1938. PROF., ANTHROPOLOGY, YALE U., 1938– . Contributing editor, Handbook of Latin American Studies; Guggenheim fellow; editor, American Antiquity. Membership: American Anthropological Association; National Academy of Sciences; New York Academy of Sciences; Society for American Archaeology. Research: Caribbean archeology. Author: Archeology of the Maniabón Hills, Cuba (1942); Porto Rican Prehistory (1952). Co-author: Venezuelan Archaeology (1963). Language: Spanish 4,4,4,4; French 3,2,2,3. Home: 12 Ridgewood Ter., North Haven, Conn. Office: Dept. of Anthropology, Yale U., Box 2114, Yale Station, New Haven, Conn.

ROWE, JOHN HOWLAND, b. Sorrento, Maine, June 10, 1918. ANTHROPOLOGY AND HISTORY. A.B., Brown U., 1939; M.A., Harvard U., 1941; Ph. D., 1947; Litt. D. (honorary), Universidad Nacional de Cuzco, 1954. Supervisor, Southern Peruvian Project, Institute of Andean Research, 1941–42; prof., dir., Instituto de Arqueología, Universidad Nacional de Cuzco, 1942–43; representative in Colombia, Institute of Social Anthropology, Smithsonian Institution, 1946–48; asst. prof., U. of Calif., Berkeley, 1948–51; assoc. prof., 1951–56; PROF., ANTHROPOLOGY, U. OF CALIF., BERKELEY, 1956– ; CHMN., 1963– ; CURATOR OF SOUTH AMERICAN ARCHEOLOGY, LOWIE MUSEUM OF ANTHROPOLOGY. Peabody Museum fellow (Peru), 1946; Guggenheim fellow (Peru), 1958; research prof., Miller Institute for Basic Research in Science, 1964–65. Membership: American Anthropological Association; Institute of Andean Studies: Sociedad Científica del Cuzco; Sociedad Peruana de Historia; Société des Américanistes; Society for American Archaeology. Research: archeology; ethnology; Peru; Colombia. Author: An Introduction to the Archaeology of Cuzco (1944); Inca Culture at the Time of the Spanish Conquest (in Handbook of South American Indians, 1946); The Incas Under Spanish Colonial Institutions (Hispanic American Historical Review, May 1957). Language: Spanish 5,4,4,4; Portuguese 3,2,1,1; French 4,4,3,2; German 3,1,1,1; Italian 3,1,1,1; Quechua 3,1,1,1. Linguistic studies: Guambian; Quechua. Home: 2137 Rose St., Berkeley, Calif. 94709. Office: Dept. of Anthropology, U. of Calif., Berkeley, 14720.

ROWLAND, DONALD WINSLOW, b. Mariposa, Calif., Jan. 12, 1898. HISTORY. A.B., U. of Calif., Berkeley, 1925; A.M., 1926; Ph. D., 1931. Asst. prof., U. of Hawaii, 1930–35; vis. prof., U. of Oreg., Summer 1933; PROF., HISTORY, U. OF SOUTHERN CALIF., 1935– ; summer vis. prof., U. of Calif., Berkeley, 1935, 1941, 1955, U. of Mich., 1957; political analyst, Office of Coordinator of Inter-American Affairs, 1943–47. Native Sons of the Golden West traveling fellow (Spain), 1927–28. Membership: American Historical Association; Conference on Latin American History; Pacific Coast Council on Latin American Affairs. Research: colonial Latin America. Author: History of the Office of the Coordinator of Inter-Ameriacn Affairs (1947). Contributor: Greater America (1933). Language: Spanish 3,–,2,2. Home: 1205 Chavez St., Burbank, Calif. Office: Dept. of History, U. of Southern Calif., University Park, Los Angeles 7, Calif.

RUBEL, ARTHUR J., b. Shanghai, China, Aug. 29, 1924. ANTHROPOLOGY. B.A., Mexico City Coll., 1951; M.A., U. of Chicago, 1957; Ph. D., U. of N.C., 1962. Ethnologist, U. of Chicago, 1956; research assoc., U. of Tex., 1957–59; research assoc., U. of Chicago, Summer 1961; research assoc., U. of N.C., Summer 1962; anthropologist, U.S. Public Health Service, 1963; ASST. PROF., ANTHROPOLOGY, U. of N.C., 1963–. National Institute of Mental Health research fellow, 1961–62; consultant, Migrant Health Branch, U.S. Public Health Service. Membership: American Anthropological Association; Anthropological Society of Washington; Central States Anthropological Society. Research: public health; beliefs and behavior relevant to health; Mexico. Author: Epidemiology of a Folk Illness: Susto (1960); Concepts of Disease in Mexican-American Culture (American Anthropologist, Oct. 1960); Health and Social Relations (in Handbook of Middle American Indians). Language: Spanish 4,5,4,4; French 2,–,–,–. Linguistic studies: Tzotzil. Home: 927 Carr St., Greensboro, N.C. Office: Dept. of Sociology and Anthropology, U. of N.C., Greensboro.

RUBIN, JOAN, b. Detroit, Mich., June 7, 1932. ANTHROPOLOGY: LINGUISTICS. B.A., U. of Mich., 1954; M.A., 1956; Ph. D., Yale U., 1963. Coordinator, Technical Studies, U.S. Peace Corps Project, Georgetown U., 1963; ASST. PROF., ANTHROPOLOGY, AMERICAN U., 1963–. Cutler fellow, Yale U., 1959–60; National Institute of Mental Health research fellow, 1960–63, (Paraguay), 1960–61. Membership: American Anthropological Association; Linguistic Society of America; Sigma Xi. Research: bilingualism; culture change. Author: Bilingualism in Paraguay (Anthropological Linguistics, Jan. 1962); A Bibliography of Caribbean Creole Languages (Caribbean Studies, Jan. 1963). Language: Spanish 5,5,4,4; Portuguese 5,5,4,4; French 4,5,3,3; Guaraní 3,4,3,3. Linguistic studies: Guaraní. Home: 1722 19th St., NW., Washington, D.C. Office: Dept. of Sociology and Anthropology, American U., Washington, 20016.

RUDERMAN, ARMAND PETER, b. Brooklyn, N.Y., Nov. 19, 1923. ECONOMICS AND STATISTICS. B.S., Harvard U., 1943; M.B.A., U. of Chicago, 1944; Ph. D., Harvard U., 1947. Instr., Colgate U., 1946–47; asst. prof., S. Dak. State Coll., 1947–48; asst. prof., Mont. State U., 1948–50; statistician, International Labour Office (Switzerland), 1950–59; ECONOMIC ADVISER, PAN AMERICAN SANITARY BUREAU, 1960– . Membership: American Economic Association; American Public Health Association; Royal Economic Society. Research: role of public health in social and economic development. Author: Algunos aspectos económicos de la atención médica en las Américas (in Atención Médica, 1963); Inflation and Economic Growth: A Comment (Economic Development and Cultural Change, Apr. 1964); ¿Cómo medir las ventajas económicas de la salud? (Boletín de la Organización Sanitaria de Pan América, Nov. 1964). Language: Spanish 5,5,4,3; Portuguese 4,4,3,2; French 5,5,5,4; German 4,3,3,2; Russian 3,3,3,2. Home: 11006 Montrose Ave., Garrett Park, Md. 20766. Office: Pan American Sanitary Bureau, 1501 New Hampshire Ave., NW., Washington, D.C. 20006.

RUDOLPH, DONNA KEYSE, b. Scott County, Kans., Nov. 3, 1934. LIBRARY SCIENCE. A.B., Stanford U., 1956; M.S. in L.S., Western Resreve U., 1961. Librarian, instr. of Spanish, Garden City Senior High School (Kans.), 1958–59; instr. of Spanish, Garden City Junior Coll., Garden City Senior High School, 1959–60; part-time asst. for periodicals and abstracting, Center for Documentation and Research, Western Reserve U., 1960; part-time asst. for periodicals, Library, Cleveland Museum of Art, 1960–61; gifts and exchange librarian, Library, Harvard Coll., 1961–62; asst. education librarian, Ohio U., 1962–63; instr., Kans. State U., 1964; ASST. INSTR., SPANISH, KANS. STATE U., 1964– . Stanford U. graduate fellow, 1956–58; Western Reserve U. graduate fellow, 1960–61; reviewer for Latin America. Choice: Books for College Libraries, 1964– . Membership: American Library Association. Research: modern Latin American history. Language: Spanish 5,4,4,4; Portuguese 2,2,2,2; French 3,3,3,3; Greek 1,2,2,1. Home: 1510 College Ave., Manhattan, Kans. 66502. Office: Dept. of Modern Languages, Kans. State U., Manhattan, 66504.

RUGGLES, ROBERT THOMAS, b. Waterloo, Iowa, Oct. 11, 1931. ECONOMICS. B.S., N.Y.U., 1954; M.B.A., 1956. Asst. economist, Savings Banks Trust Company, 1957–59; economist and chief statistician, Coty, Inc., 1959–62; economist, International Minerals and Chemicals, 1962–64; ECONOMIST, ANTHES IMPERIAL LIMITED, 1964– . Membership: American Economic Association; American Statistical Association; Industrial Economists Forum, Canadian Chamber of Commerce; National Association of Business Economists. Research: international finance; foreign investment; flow of private funds; uncertainty and risk on foreign investment; economic structure of Mexico. Language: Spanish 3,3,2,2; Portuguese 2,2,1,1; French 3,2,1,1; Italian 3,2,1,1. Home: 8 Champa Dr., St. Catharines, Ontario, Canada.

RUIZ, RAMON EDUARDO, b. Pacific Beach, Calif., Oct. 9, 1921. HISTORY. B.A., San Diego State Coll., 1947; M.A., Claremont Coll., 1948; Ph. D., U. of Calif., Berkeley, 1954. Lectr., U. of Calif., San Francisco, 1953–54; vis. lectr., Claremont Coll., Summers 1954–57; asst. prof., U. of Oreg., 1955–57; asst. prof., Southern Methodist U., 1957–58; assoc. prof., Smith Coll., 1958–64; vis. prof., U. of Tex., Summer 1964; PROF., HISTORY, SMITH COLL., 1964– . John Hay Whitney fellow, 1950–51; Huntington Library grant, 1958; American Philosophical Society grant, 1959. Membership: Conference on Latin American History. Research: political and cultural history of Mexico; rural education in Latin America; the Caribbean, particularly Cuba. Author: An American in Maximilian's Mexico (1959); Mexico: The Challenge of Poverty and Illiteracy (1963); The Mexican War—Was It Manifest Destiny? (1963). Language: Spanish 5,5,5,4. Home: 66 Paradise Rd., Northampton, Mass. Office: Dept. of History, Smith Coll., Northampton.

RUSSELL, ROBERT LEE, b. Akron, Ohio, Nov. 12, 1925. LINGUISTICS. B.A., Wheaton Coll., 1950. LINGUIST, SUMMER INSTITUTE OF LINGUISTICS, 1951– . Research: literacy; translation; linguistic investigations in jungle area of Peru. Author: Syntactotonemics in Amahuaca (1959). Language: Spanish 4,4,4,4; Portuguese 3,2,1,1; French 3,2,1,1; Amahuaca 4,4,4,4. Linguistic studies: Amahuaca. Home: 222 Ohio Ave., Wadsworth, Ohio. Office: Summer Institute of Linguistics, Box 1960, Santa Ana, Calif.

RUST, IRWIN WALTER, b. Batavia, N.Y., July 14, 1909. ECONOMICS. A.B., U. of Redlands, 1932; Ph. D., U. of Md., 1954. Assoc. prof., extension economist, U. of Hawaii, 1949–52; agricultural economist, research asst., U. of Md., 1952–54; AGRICULTURAL ECONOMIST, BRANCH CHIEF, FARMER COOPERATIVE SERVICE, U.S. DEPT. OF AGRICULTURE, 1954– . U.S. Agency for International Development consultant, Ministry of Agriculture (Guatemala), 1964. Membership: American Farm Economic Association. Research: public and personnel relations and management of cooperatives; cooperative education and development in Guatemala. Author: Motor Vehicle Accident Experience and Motor Vehicle Insurance Cost in Maryland (1955); Management Analysis of Maine Potato Growers, Inc. (1956); Sunkist Growers, Inc., A California Adventure in Cooperation (1960). Language: Spanish 3,3,3,3; French 2,1,1,1; German 2,2,1,2. Home: 6426 Dahlonega Rd., Washington, D.C. 20016. Office: Chief, Membership Relations Branch, Farmer Cooperative Service, U.S. Dept. of Agriculture, Washington, D.C. 20250.

RUTH, RICHARD LEE, b. Wichita, Kans., Jan. 13, 1931. ECONOMICS. B.A., U. of Wichita, 1958; M.S., U. of Wis., 1960; Ph. D., 1964. ASST. PROF., ST. BENEDICT'S COLL., 1964– . Woodrow Wilson fellow 1958–59, 1959–60; Land Tenure Center fellow, U. of Wis. Membership: American Economic Association; Economic History Association. Research: international economics; economic development in Latin America; cotton and sugar industries of Mexico and Peru. Language: Spanish 3,2,2,2. Office: Dept. of Economics, St. Benedict's Coll., Atchison, Kans. 66002.

RYAN, HEWSON A., b. New Haven, Conn., June 16, 1922. POLITICAL SCIENCE. B.A., Yale U., 1947; M.A., 1949; Ph. D., U. of Madrid, 1951. Instr., Yale U., 1947–51; dir., Binational Center, U.S. Information Agency (Bogotá, Colombia), 1951–54; cultural affairs officer (La Paz, Bolivia), 1954–56; information officer (Santiago, Chile), 1956–58, public affairs officer (Santiago), 1958–61; ASST. DIR., U.S. INFORMATION AGENCY, 1961– . Sterling fellow,

Yale U., 1949–50; chmn., Chilean Fulbright Commission 1958–61; adviser, U.S. Delegation, V Meeting of Foreign Ministers of the Americas, 1959; II UNESCO Conference on Information, 1960; U.S. Government Latin American Policy Committee, 1962– . Membership: American Academy of Political and Social Sciences. Research: international communications and intercultural problems. Author: Bibliografía Gongorina del siglo XVII (Boletín de la Real Academia Española, 1953); Reflexiones sobre la dialéctica (1956). Editor: Readings for Advanced Students (1954). Language: Spanish 5,5,5,4; Portuguese 3,3,3,2; French 3,2,2,1; German 2,2,1,1. Home: 6109 Robinwood Rd., Bethesda, Md. Office: U.S. Information Agency, 1776 Pennsylvania Ave., NW., Washington, D.C. 20547.

RYDJORD, JOHN, b. Webster, S. Dak., Sept. 5, 1893. HISTORY. B.A., U. of Wis., 1922; M.A., Northwestern U., 1923; Ph. D., U. of Calif., Berkeley, 1925. Head, History, U. of Wichita, 1926–51; vis. prof., George Washington U., Summer 1929, U. of Calif., Berkeley, 1943–44, Northwestern U., Summer 1945, U. of Calif., Los Angeles, 1945–46; dean, Gradaute School, U. of Wichita, 1949–58; PROF. EMERITUS, U. OF WICHITA, 1958– ; vis. prof., U. of Nebr., 1961–62. Bolton Prize Committee; Native Sons of the Golden West traveling fellow; William Smith Mason fellow, Northwestern U. Membership: American Historical Association; Hispanic American Historical Association; Kansas State Historical Association; Phi Alpha Theta; Pi Sigma Alpha. Research: Mexico. Author: Foreign Interest in the Independence of New Spain (1935); French Revolution and Mexico (Hispanic American Historical Review, Feb. 1929); Spanish Defeat of the Napoleonic Confederation (U. of Wichita Studies, Dec. 1944). Language: Spanish 3,3,3,3; French 3,2,2,1; German 3,2,2,1. Home: 1730 North Lorraine, Wichita, Kans. 67214. Office: Dept. of History, Wichita State U., Wichita.

S

SABLE, MARTIN HOWARD, b. Haverhill, Mass., Sept. 24, 1924. LIBRARY SCIENCE. A.B., Boston U., 1946; M.A., 1952; Dr. en Letras, National U. of Mexico, 1952; M.S., Simmons Coll., 1959. Bibliographer, Dodge Library, Northeastern U., 1959–63; part-time reference librarian and guide-interpreter, Office of Latin American Studies, Harvard U., 1962–63; reference librarian, Los Angeles State Coll., 1963–65; RESEARCH ASSOC., LATIN AMERICAN CENTER, U. OF CALIF., LOS ANGELES, 1965– . Fellowship for study at National U. of Mexico, 1952; Committee on Peace Corps Trainee Curriculum, Los Angeles State Coll., 1963. Membership: American Library Association; California Library Association; International Federation of Library Associations; Pacific Coast Council on Latin American Studies. Research: bibliography and acquisitions of Latin American materials: Latin American folklore. Language: Spanish 5,5,4,4; Portuguese 2,2,1,1; French 4,4,3,3; German 2,2,2,2. Home: 416½ North Maple Dr., Beverly Hills, Calif. 90212.

SACKS, NORMAN P(AUL), b. Philadelphia, Pa., Feb. 11, 1914. LANGUAGE AND LINGUISTICS. B.S., Temple U., 1935; M.A., U. of Pa., 1937; Ph. D., 1940. Instr., U. of Hawaii, 1940–42, Temple U., 1945–46; prof., Oberlin Coll., 1946–61; PROF., SPANISH AND PORTUGUESE, DIR., LATIN AMERICAN CENTER, U. OF WIS., 1961– ; vis. prof., U. of Calif., Berkeley, Western Reserve U., U. of Southern Calif., U. of N. Mex., U. of Wis., Harvard U. Consultant, Language Development Program, U.S. Office of Education; dir., Oberlin Summer Program in Mexico; consultant, Modern Language Association. Membership: American Association of Teachers of Spanish and Portuguese; American Association of University Professors; Linguistic Society of America; Modern Language Association. Research: Spanish and Portuguese philology and structural linguistics; Spanish cultural and intellectual history; Hispanic civilization. Author: Latinity of Dated Documents in the Portuguese Territory (1941); Cuentos de hoy y de ayer (1956). Collaborator: Modern Spanish (1960). Language: Spanish 5,5,5,5; Portuguese 4,4,4,4; French 4,4,4,4; German 4,–,–,–; Italian 4,–,–,–; Latin 4,–,–,–. Linguistic studies: English; French; Latin; Portuguese; Spanish. Home: 918 Swarthmore Ct., Madison 5, Wis. Office: Dept. of Spanish and Portuguese, U. of Wis., Madison 6.

SAFA, HELEN ICKEN, b. Brooklyn, N.Y., Dec. 4, 1930. ANTHROPOLOGY. B.A., Cornell U., 1952; M.A., Columbia U., 1958; Ph. D., 1962. Training and evaluation officer, Technical Cooperation Administration, U.S. Dept. of State and Government of P.R., 1954–55; assoc. dir., Research Project, Social Programs Administration, U.S. Dept. of Agriculture and Government of P.R., 1955–56; SENIOR RESEARCH ASSOC., YOUTH DEVELOPMENT CENTER, ASST. PROF. ANTHROPOLOGY, SYRACUSE U., 1962– . U. of P.R. grant, Columbia U., 1957–59; consultant, Urban Renewal and Housing Administration, Government of P.R., 1959–60, Pan American Union (Colombia), 1961; National Institute of Mental Health grants, 1960–61, 1963; housing section, Puerto Rican Conference on the Aging, 1960. Membership: American Anthropological Association; American Ethnological Society; Phi Beta Kappa; Society for Applied Anthropology; Society for International Development. Research: cultural and social anthropology; rural-urban migration and urbanization; housing. Author: The Socio-Economic Conditions of Parceleros Resettled by the Social Programs Administration (1956); A Study of Aged Ineligible Applicants for Public Housing in New York City (1957). Language: Spanish 5,5,5,4; Portuguese 3,2,2,2; French 3,2,2,2; German 3,3,3,3. Home: 231 Houston Ave., Syracuse, N.Y., 13210. Office: Youth Development Center, 926 South Crouse Ave., Syracuse, 13210.

SALER, BENSON, b. Philadelphia, Pa., May 2, 1930. ANTHROPOLOGY. B.A., Princeton U., 1952; M.A., U. of Pa., 1957; Ph. D., 1960. Instr., U. of Conn., 1960–63; ASST. PROF., ANTHROPOLOGY, BRANDEIS U., 1963– . Harrison scholar, U. of Pa., 1957–58; Organization of American States fellow (Guatemala), 1958–59; Harrison special fellow, U. of Pa., 1959–60. Membership: American Anthropological Association. Research: enthnography: culture and personality; Guatemala. Author: Unsuccessful Practitioners in a Bicultural Guatemalan Community (Psychoanalysis and the Psychoanalytic Review, Summer 1962); Migration and Ceremonial Ties Among the Maya (Southwestern Journal of Anthropology, Winter 1962); Nagual, Witch, and Sorcerer in a Quiché Village (Ethnology, Summer 1964). Language: Spanish 3,3,3,3; French 3,2,2,2. Linguistic studies: Kalmuck; Quiché. Home: 7 Fair Oaks Dr., Lexington 73, Mass. Office: Dept. of Anthropology, Brandeis U., Waltham 54, Mass.

SALZ, BEATE R., b. Heidelberg, Germany, Apr. 27, 1913. ANTHROPOLOGY AND SOCIOLOGY. B.A., Ohio State U., 1941; M.S. Sc., New School for Social Research, 1943; Ph. D., 1950. Research asst.-dir. of research; Wenner-Gren Foundation for Anthropological Research, 1945-50; asst. prof., research assoc., U. of N.C., 1952-53; research assoc., asst. prof., U. of Chicago, 1953-54; PROF., CHMN., SOCIOLOGY AND ANTHROPOLOGY, COLL. OF SOCIAL SCIENCE, U. OF P.R., 1954-   ; vis. prof., U. of Pa., 1964-65. Halle fellow, 1943-44; Wenner-Gren research fellow (Peru), 1950-52; Project on Political Behavior, Institute for Research in Social Sciences, U. of N.C., 1952-53. Membership: American Anthropological Association; American Ethnological Society; American Geographical Society. Research: economic development and industrialization in Peru and Ecuador; economic structure and political organization in St. Lucia. Author: The Human Element in Industrialization: A Hypothetical Case Study of Ecuadorean Indians (1955); Indianismo (Social Research, Nov. 1944); Some Psychological Aspects of Industrialization (Revista de Ciencias Sociales, Mar. 1957). Language: Spanish 5,5,4,3; Portuguese 3,2,1,1; French 5,4,2,2; Italian 3,2,1,1. Home: Apt. 9, 179 Las Caobas, Hyde Park, Río Piedras, P.R. Office: Coll. of Social Sciences, U. of P.R., Río Piedras.

AMMONS, RAMON W., b. Windham, Mont., Sept. 14, 1932. ECONOMICS. Th. B., Multinomah School of the Bible, 1960; M.S., Mont. State Coll., 1961; Ph. D., 1964. EXTENSION ECONOMIST, MONT. STATE COLL., 1964-   . International Cooperation Center fellow, Carnegie Foundation Fund (Mexico). Membership: American Farm Economic Association; Rural Sociological Society; Western Farm Economics Association. Research: agricultural economics; land and water; consumer interests. Author: Methods of Marketing Montana Wool (1962); The New Wheat Standards (1964). Language: Spanish 3,2,3,3. Home: R.F.D. 2, Bozeman, Mont. 59715. Office: Dept. of Agricultural Economics, Mont. State Coll., Bozeman, 59715.

AMMONS, ROBERT L., b. Cambridge, Minn., Sept. 6, 1912. ECONOMICS. A.B., George Washington U., 1940; M.A., 1943. Chief, Balance of Payments, U.S. Dept. of Commerce, 1940-53; statistical consultant, P.R. Planning Board, 1953-56; chief, Latin American Section, Board of Governors of the Federal Reserve System, 1956-61; ADVISER, DIV. OF INTERNATIONAL FINANCE, FEDERAL RESERVE SYSTEM, 1961- . Member, Klein-Saks Mission (Peru), 1949; consultant, Inter-American Development Bank (Ecuador), 1962. Membership: American Economic Association. Research: central banking and finance of Latin America; balance of payments. Author: Net Income and Gross Product of Puerto Rico (1956). Language: Spanish 4,4,4,3. Home: 812 Tanley Rd., Silver Spring, Md. Office: Federal Reserve System, 21st St. and Constitution Ave., Washington 25, D.C.

SAMORA, JULIAN, b. Pagosa Springs, Colo., Mar. 1, 1920. SOCIOLOGY. B.A., Adams State Coll., 1942; M.S., Colo. State U., 1947; Ph. D., Wash. U., 1953. Assoc. prof., Adams State Coll., 1949-50, 1952-55; vis. prof., Mich. State U., Summer 1955; asst. prof., U. of Colo. School of Medicine, 1955-57; asst. prof., Mich. State U., 1957-59; assoc. prof., Notre Dame U., 1959-63; PROF., HEAD., SOCIOLOGY, U. OF NOTRE DAME, 1963-   ; vis. prof., Universidad Nacional de Colombia, Fall 1963; vis. prof., U. of Calif., Los Angeles, Summer 1964. John Hay Whitney Foundation fellow; consultant, U.S. Commission on Civil Rights, 1962-64; Ford Foundation grant, 1963; consultant, U.S. Public Health Service, 1963-64. Membership: American Catholic Sociological Society; American Sociological Society; Midwest Council of the Association for Latin American Studies; Ohio Valley Sociological Society. Research: medical sociology; minority groups; Colombia. Co-author: Minority Leadership in a Bi-Cultural Community (American Sociological Review, Aug. 1954); A Medical Care Program in a Colorado Community (in Health, Culture and Community, 1955); Medical Vocabulary Knowledge among Hospital Patients (Journal of Health and Human Behavior, Summer 1961). Language: Spanish 4,4,4,4; Portuguese 2,2,1,1; French 2,1,1,1. Home: 19612 Cowles Ave., South Bend, Ind. Office: Dept. of Sociology, U. of Notre Dame, Notre Dame, Ind.

SÁNCHEZ, GEORGE I., b. Albuquerque, N. Mex., Oct. 6, 1906. EDUCATION. B.A., U. of N. Mex., 1930; M.S. in Ed., U. of Tex., 1931; Ed. D., U. of Calif., Berkeley, 1934. Dir., research div., Julius Rosenwald Fund (Chicago), 1935-37; chief, technical dir., Pedagogical Institute, Ministry of Education (Venezuela), 1937-38; PROF., LATIN AMERICAN EDUCATION, CHMN., HISTORY AND PHILOSOPHY OF EDUCATION, U. OF TEX., 1940-   ; education specialist, Office of Inter-American Affairs, 1943-44. Rockefeller Foundation fellow; Rosenwald fellow; consultant, U.S. Office of Civilian Defense (Dallas), 1942-43; consultant, Inter-American Education Foundation (Washington), 1943-44; editorial consultant, The Nations Schools, 1944-   ; consultant, U.S. Dept. of Health, Education, and Welfare (Venezuela), 1961; consultant, U.S. Agency for International Development (Peru), 1962; National Advisory Council of the U.S. Peace Corps. Membership: League of United Latin American Citizens; National Education Association; New Mexico Education Association; Phi Delta Kappa; Phi Kappa Phi; Progressive Education Association; Sigma Delta Pi; Sociedad Mexicana de Geografía y Estadística; Sociedad Nacional Argentina de Estudios Históricos. Research: rural and higher education in Mexico; Venezuelan and Peruvian education. Author: Mexico:

A Revolution by Education (1936); Forgotten People (1940); The Development of Education in Venezuela (1963). Language: Spanish 5,5,5,5; Portuguese 3,4,3,1; French 2,1,–,–; Italian 3,3,–,–. Home: 2201 Scenic Dr., Austin 3, Tex. Office: Dept. of Education, U. of Tex., Austin 12.

SANCHEZ, JUAN DELGADO, b. Salamanca, Spain, Oct. 7, 1909. ECONOMICS: BANKING. Diploma, American Institute of Banking, 1934; diploma, Graduate School of Banking, 1937; B.B.A., Rutgers U., 1944. Asst. cashier, National Bank of New Jersey, 1930–47; VICE PRESIDENT, OVERSEAS DEPT., FIRST NATIONAL CITY BANK— NEW YORK, 1947– . Research: accounting; credit management; banking in Colombia, Cuba, and Central America. Language: Spanish 4,4,5,4; Portuguese 3,3,3,1; French 3,3,3,1; Italian 3,3,3,1. Home: 296 North 5th Ave., Highland Park, N.J. Office: 399 Park Ave., New York 22, N.Y.

SÁNCHEZ-REULET, ANÍBAL, b. Azul, Argentina, Apr. 13, 1910. PHILOSOPHY AND SPANISH AMERICAN LITERATURE. U. of Madrid, 1934–36; Ph. D., U. of La Plata (Argentina), 1939. Prof., U. of Tucumán (Argentina), 1939–46; dean, Faculty of Philosophy and Letters, 1945–46; chief, Div. of Philosophy, Letters and Sciences, Pan American Union, 1950–58; assoc. prof., U. of Calif., Los Angeles, 1958–64; PROF., SPANISH, U. OF CALIF., LOS ANGELES, 1964– . Guggenheim fellow, 1947; profesor extraordinario, National U. of Mexico, 1949; contributing editor, Handbook of Latin American Studies, 1950– ; dir., editor, Revista Interamericana de Bibliografía, 1952; editorial board, Revista Iberoamericana, 1959–61; advisory board, Handbook of Latin American Studies, 1962– . Membership: American Association of Teachers of Spanish and Portuguese; American Philosophical Association; Instituto Internacional de la Literatura Iberoamericana; Modern Language Association; Pacific Coast Council on Latin American Studies. Research: history of ideas and literature in 19th and 20th century Latin America. Author: Contemporary Latin American Philosophy (1954); Alfonso Reyes, 1889–1959 (Revista Iberoamericana, Jan.–June 1960); La poesía gauchesca como problema literario (Revista Iberoamericana, July–Aug. 1961). Language: Spanish 5,5,5,5; Portuguese 3,3,2,2; French 4,4,4,4; German 3,2,1,1. Office: Dept. of Spanish, U. of Calif., Los Angeles 24.

SANDERS, WILLIAM, b. Durango, Mexico, Apr. 15, 1903. POLITICAL SCIENCE. A.B., Stanford U., 1928; LL.B., Columbus U., 1933; M.A., George Washington U., 1934. New York manager, International Telephone and Telegraph Corporation, 1929–32; chief, Legal Unit, Pan American Union, 1932–42; executive positions: U.S. Dept. of State, 1942–58; seminar lectr., Georgetown U., 1948–53; ASST. SECRETARY GENERAL, ORGANIZATION OF AMERICAN STATES, 1958– . U.S. coordinator, Ninth International Conference of American States (Colombia), 1947; U.S. representative, Inter-American Council of Jurists, 1948–58; chmn., Inter-American Council of Jurists (Brazil), 1950; U.S. representative, Four Power Statement, West Indian Conference and Caribbean Commission, 1950; spokesman on internal security, Fourth Meeting of Consultation of Ministers of Foreign Affairs of the American Republics, 1951; deputy chief of mission, Embassy (Chile), U.S. Dept. of State, 1953–56; U.S. representative, United Nations Committee on the Defining of Aggression, 1956; U.S. coordinator, International Conference on the Law of the Sea, 1957–58; vice chmn., Conference on the Law of the Sea, 1958. Membership: American Bar Association; American Political Science Association; American Society of International Law. Research: international relations and law; international organizations. Author: International Law and International Peace (1940); Sovereignty and Interdependence in the New World (1948). Co-author: The Emergency Advisory Committee for Political Defense (American Journal of International Law, Apr. 1944). Language: Spanish 4,4,- 4,4; Portuguese 3,3,2,1; French 3,3,1,1. Home: 2708 36th St., NW., Washington, D.C. Office: Pan American Union, Washington, D.C. 20006.

SANDERS, WILLIAM TIMOTHY, b. Patchogue, N.Y., Apr. 19, 1926. ANTHROPOLOGY. B.A., Harvard Coll., 1949; M.A., Harvard U., 1953; Ph. D., 1957. Research asst., New World Archaeological Foundation (Mexico), 1953; asst. prof., U. of Miss., 1956–59; ASSOC. PROF., ANTHROPOLOGY, PA. STATE U., 1959– . Carnegie Institution fellow (Mexico), 1954–55; La. State U. research fellow (Mexico), 1957; New World Archaeological Foundation research fellow (Mexico), 1958; Pan American Union fellow (Mexico), 1960; National Science Foundation grants (Mexico), 1961, 1962, 1963, 1964; Fulbright teaching fellow, U. of Cuzco (Peru), 1964. Membership: American Anthropological Association. Research: cultural anthropology; Mexican archeology; human ecology; comparative growths of ancient civilizations. Author: Ceramic Stratigraphy at Santa Cruz Chiapas, Mexico (1961): Cultural Ecology of Nuclear Mesoamerica (American Anthropologist, Winter 1962); Cultural Ecology of the Maya Lowlands (Estudios de Cultura Maya, 1962, 1963). Language: Spanish 5,5,5,5. Home: 2072 North Oak Lane State College, Pa. Office: Dept. of Sociology and Anthropology, Pa. State U., University Park.

SANDS, RICHARD D., b. Chicago, Ill., Jan 14, 1929. GEOGRAPHY. B.A., U. o Minn., 1951; M.S., U. of Wis., 1953; Ph. D. Clark U., 1960. Instr., U. of Del., 1958– 59; asst. prof., State U. of N.Y., Coll. a Buffalo, 1959–60; ASST. PROF., GEOG RAPHY, U. OF NEV., 1960– . Member ship: Association of American Geographers Research: natural resources; regional plan ning; rainfall occurrence in Mexico. Lan guage: Spanish 3,3,3,2. Home: 1925 Castl Ave., Reno, Nev. Office: Dept. of Geolog and Geography, U. of Nev., Reno.

SANDVIG, MAUDA POLLEY, b. London, En; land, July 18, 1901. LIBRARY SCIENC M.A., U. of Calif., 1923; Centro de Estudic Históricos (Madrid), 1927; B.S., Columbi U., 1928. Librarian, instr., Internationa Institute for Girls (Madrid), 1928–29; ass librarian, Seattle Public Library, 1930–37 dir., Library, Office of Coordinator of Inte American Affairs, 1943–46; reference brarian, Library, U.S. Dept. of State, 1946–48; chief, Latin America Area, Information Centers Service, U.S. Dept. of State, 1948–51; subdirector-DIR., U.S. INFORMATION SERVICE CENTERS IN MEXICO, LIBRARIAN, BENJAMIN FRANKLIN LIBRARY, 1951– . Language: Spanish 5,-4,4,4; Portuguese 3,2,2,–; French 3,3,3,3; German 2,2,2,1. Home and office: Benjamin Franklin Library, Niza 53, Mexico 6, D.F.

SANTANA, ARTURO F., b. Santurce, P.R., June 9, 1921. HISTORY. B.A., U. of P.R., 1941; M.A., U. of Chicago, 1942; Ph. D., 1952. Instr., U. of P.R., 1944–49; asst. prof., 1949–54; assoc. prof., 1954–63; PROF., HISTORY, U. OF P.R., 1963– . Board of Directors, Institute of Puerto Rican Culture; consultant in history, Dept. of Education, Commonwealth of Puerto Rico; contributing editor, Handbook of Latin American Studies. Research: early relations between the United States and Puerto Rico, 1790–1830. Language: Spanish 5,5,5,5; French 2,2,2,2. Home: Box 21822, U. of P.R. Station, Río Piedras, P.R. Office: Dept. of History, U. of P.R., Río Piedras.

SAPORTA, SOL, b. New York, N.Y., Mar. 12, 1925. LINGUISTICS AND LANGUAGE. B.A., Brooklyn Coll., 1944; M.A., U. of Ill., 1952; Ph. D., 1955. Asst. Prof., Ind. U., 1955–60; ASSOC. PROF., ROMANCE LANGUAGES AND LINGUISTICS, U. OF WASH., 1960– ; CHMN., LINGUISTICS, 1962– . Social Science Research Council fellow, 1952–53, 1955–56; National Science Foundation grant, 1961–63; consultant, National Defense Education Act, Title VI Program, U.S. Office of Education. Membership: American Association of Teachers of Spanish and Portuguese; Linguistic Circle of New York; Linguistic Society of America; Modern Language Association. Research: psycholinguistics; descriptive linguistics; Hispanic linguistics. Author: Psycholinguistics: A Book of Readings (1961); Morpheme Alternants in Spanish (in Structural Studies on Spanish Themes, 1959). Co-author: Phonological Grammar of Spanish (1962). Language: Spanish 4,4,4,4; Portuguese 3,2,1,1; French 2,1,1,1. Linguistic studies: Spanish. Home: 11721 5th Ave., NE., Seattle, Wash. 98125. Office: Dept. of Linguistics, U. of Wash., Seattle.

SARABIA, ANTONIO ROSAS, b. Chihuahua, Mexico, June 29, 1913. LAW. B.S., Ind. Technical Coll., 1942; J. D., U. of Chicago, 1949. Assoc., Baker, McKenzie & Hightower (Chicago), 1949–52; partner, 1952–62; lectr., University Coll., U. of Chicago, 1959–62; ATTORNEY AT LAW, PRIVATE PRACTICE (CHICAGO), 1962– ; MEMBER OF FACULTY, THE LAWYERS INSTITUTE, JOHN MARSHALL LAW SCHOOL, 1962– . Chmn., International and Foreign Law Committee, Chicago Bar Association, 1959–61; vice-chmn., International Law Section, Ill. State Bar Association, 1964– . Membership: American Arbitration Association; American Bar Association; American Foreign Law Association; American Management Association; American Society of International Law; British Institute of International and Comparative Law; Inter-American Bar Association; International Law Association. Research: private commercial international law dealing with corporate and tax matters. Author: Taxation to Promote Trade and Investment in the Americas (Taxes—The Tax Magazine, July 1956); The United States and Latin America (Chicago Bar Record, Nov. 1961); The European Common Market (The Journal of Accountancy, May 1963). Language: Spanish 5,5,5,5; Portuguese 4,3,3,3; French 4,4,4,3; Italian 4,3,2,2. Home: 270 Wentworth, Glencoe, Ill. 60022. Office: 135 South La Salle St., Chicago, Ill., 60603.

SATRA, JOHN C., b. Engrav, Austria, Feb. 17, 1924. POLITICAL SCIENCE. Dr. Jur., U. of Geneva, 1948; Institute of International Studies (Geneva), 1948–50; Ph. D., U. of Fla., 1961. Document officer, United Nations European Office (Switzerland), 1950–52; native affairs officer, Australian Administration of Papua and New Guinea, 1953–57; ASSOC. PROF., POLITICAL SCIENCE, U. of P.R., 1961– . Membership: American Political Science Association. Research: comparative jurisprudence and administration; Guatemala; Peru. Language: Spanish 5,5,5,4; Portuguese 3,3,3,2; French 5,5,5,5; German 5,5,5,5; Italian 5,5,5,4. Home: 306 Carretera Guanajibo Mayagüez, P.R. Office: Dept. of Social Science, U. of P.R., Mayagüez.

SATTERTHWAITE, LINTON, b. Trenton, N.J., Feb. 8, 1897. ANTHROPOLOGY. B.A., Yale U., 1920; Ph. D., U. of Pa., 1943. Lawyer (N.J.), 1924–28; asst., U. Museum, U. of Pa., 1930–33; asst. curator, 1933–48; lectr., 1938–55; assoc. curator, 1948–55; CURATOR, U. MUSEUM, PROF., ANTHROPOLOGY, U. OF PA., 1955– . Membership: American Anthropological Association; American Association for the Advancement of Science; Asociación Antropológica de Guatemala; Royal Anthropological Institute of Great Britain and Ireland; Seminario de Cultura Maya; Sociedad de Geografía e Historia de Guatemala; Sociedad Mexicana de Antropología; Society for American Archaeology. Research: ancient Maya architecture, hieroglyphs, and astronomy. Author: Piedras Negras Archaeology: Architecture (1943–54); Concepts and Structures of Maya Calendrical Arithmetics (1947); Moon Ages and the Maya Inscriptions: The Problem of Their Seven-day Range of Deviation from Calculated Mean Ages (Proceedings, 29th International Congress of Americanists, 1951). Language: Spanish 3,3,3,3; French 2,–,–,–; German 2,–,–,–. Home: 257 South Van Pelt St., Philadelphia 3, Pa. Office: U. Museum, U. of Pa., 33rd and Spruce Sts., Philadelphia 4.

SAUNDERS, JOHN VAN DYKE, b. Pôrto Alegre, Brazil, Feb. 25, 1930. SOCIOLOGY. B.A., Vanderbilt U., 1951; M.A., 1952; Ph. D., U. of Fla., 1955. Instr., Miss. State U., 1955–56; asst. prof., 1956–59; asst. prof., La. State U., 1959–61; assoc. prof., 1961–62; ASSOC. PROF., SOCIOLOGY, DIR., LATIN AMERICAN LANGUAGE AND AREA CENTER, U. OF FLA., 1962– . Social Science Research Council grant, U. of Chicago, Summer 1956; guest lectr., Organization of American States (Cuba), 1957, 1959; Fulbright lectr., U. of Guayaquil and Central U. (Ecuador), 1958–59; guest lectr., Organization of American States (Mexico), 1960; contributing editor, Handbook of Latin American Studies,

1960– ; area studies coordinator, U.S. Peace Corps, U. of Okla., 1962. Membership: American Sociological Association; Population Association of America; Rural Sociological Society; Southeastern Conference of Latin American Studies; Southern Sociological Society. Research: rural and medical sociology; agrarian reform; demography. Author: Differential Fertility in Brazil (1955); The Population of Ecuador: A Demographic Analysis (1960); Man-Land Relations in Ecuador (Rural Sociology, Mar. 1961). Language: Spanish 5,5,5,4; Portuguese 5,5,5,5; French 4,4,3,3. Home: Box 12603, University Station, Gainesville, Fla. Office: Latin American Language and Area Center, U. of Fla., Gainesville.

SAVELLE, MAX, b. Mobile, Ala., Jan. 8, 1896. HISTORY. A.B., Columbia U., 1925; M.A., 1926; Ph. D., 1932. Instr., Columbia U., 1926–32; prof., Stanford U., 1932–47; PROF., HISTORY, U. OF WASH., 1947– . Fulbright scholar (France), 1950; Fulbright teacher (Spain), 1960–61; Rockefeller Foundation grant (Chile), 1963; editorial board, American Historical Review and Western Humanities Review. Membership: American Historical Association; Mississippi Valley Historical Association; Phi Alpha Theta. Research: United States colonial history; American Revolution. Author: Seeds of Liberty (1948); Short History of American Civilization (1957); Diplomatic History of the Canadian Boundary, 1748–1763 (1960). Language: Spanish 4,3,4,4; Portuguese 2,–,–,–; French 4,3,4,4. Home: 4545 55th Ave., NE., Seattle, Wash. Office: Dept. of History, U. of Wash., Seattle 5.

SAWYER, ALAN REED, b. Wakefield, Mass., June 18, 1919. ART AND ARCHEOLOGY. B.S., Bates Coll., 1941; M.A., Harvard U., 1949. Instr., Tex. State Coll. for Women, 1949–52; curator, Primitive Art, The Art Institute of Chicago, 1952–59; DIR., THE TEXTILE MUSEUM, 1959– . Consultant, Metropolitan Museum of Art. Membership: Archaeological Institute of America; Society of American Archaeology. Research: art history; iconography; formative and florescent periods of ancient Peruvian art; Paracas and Nazca Chronology; Bolivia. Author: Handbook: The Natham Cummings Collection of Ancient Peruvian Art (1954); Paracas and Nazca Iconography (in Essays in Pre-Columbian Art, 1960); Tiahuanaco Tapestry Design (Textile Museum Journal, Dec. 1963). Language: Spanish 3,3,3,2; Portuguese 1,1,1,1; French 3,3,2,2; German 2,2,2,2. Home: 5504 33rd St., NW., Washington 16, D.C. Office: Textile Museum, 2320 S St., NW., Washington, D.C. 20008.

SAYERS, RAYMOND S., b. New York, N.Y., Aug. 29, 1912. BRAZILIAN LITERATURE. B.A., City Coll. (N.Y.), 1933; M.A., Columbia U., 1935; Ph. D., 1952. Asst. dir. of courses, Instituto Brasil-Estados Unidos (Rio de Janeiro), 1946–47; teacher, High School of Music and Art, 1947–55, 1956–59; LECTR., SPANISH AND PORTUGUESE, COLUMBIA U., 1950– ; teacher, Central High School (Santurce, P.R.), 1955–56; ASST. PROF., ROMANCE LANGUAGES, CITY COLL. (N.Y.), 1959– ; vis. prof., U. of Wis., Summer 1961; vis. prof., Harvard U., Summer 1963; vis. prof., N.Y.U., 1963–64. Social Science Research Council grant (Brazil), Summer 1964; Fulbright Hays faculty award (Brazil), Summer 1964; chmn., Portuguese Section, Modern Language Association. Membership: American Association of Teachers of Spanish and Portuguese; Modern Language Association. Research: the Negro as subject and writer in Brazilian and Portuguese literature; 19th century Brazilian and Portuguese literature. Author: The Negro in Brazilian Literature (1956); O Negro na literatura Brasileira (1958); The Romantic Movement: A Selective and Critical Bibliography for the Year 1957—Portuguese Section (Philological Quarterly, Apr. 1958). Language: Spanish 5,5,5,5; Portuguese 5,5,5,5; French 5,4,3,3. Home: 549 West 123rd St., New York, N.Y. 10027. Office: Dept. of Romance Languages, City Coll. of N.Y., 17 Lexington Ave., New York, 10010.

SAYRE, ROBERT MARTION, b. Hillsboro, Oreg., Aug. 18, 1924. ECONOMICS. B.A., Willamette U., 1949; LL.B., George Washington U., 1956; M.A., Stanford U., 1960. Foreign affairs officer, Latin America, U.S. Dept. of State, 1950–57; chief, political section, Embassy (Peru), U.S. Dept. of State, 1957–59; financial adviser, Embassy (Cuba), 1960; officer in charge of Mexican affairs, 1961–63; deputy dir., Caribbean and Mexican affairs, 1963–65; DEPUTY ASST. SECRETARY, BUREAU OF INTER-AMERICAN AFFAIRS, U.S. DEPT. OF STATE, 1965– . Membership: American Economic Association; Foreign Service Association; Military Government Association. Research: private enterprise in economic development of Latin America. Language: Spanish 4,4,3,3; Portuguese 1,1,1,1; French 2,2,2,2. Home: 109 North Nottingham St. Arlington, Va. Office: Bureau of Inter American Affairs, Dept. of State, Washington, D.C.

SAYRES, WILLIAM CORTLANDT, b. Detroit Mich., Apr. 5, 1927. ANTHROPOLOGY AND EDUCATION. A.B., Beloit Coll. 1949; A.M., Harvard U., 1951; Ph. D., 1953 Instr., Yale U., 1954–57; assoc. in educational research, Research Offices, State U of N.Y., 1957–63; ASSOC. PROF., ANTHROPOLOGY, TEACHERS COLL., COLUMBIA U., 1963– ; EDUCATION SPECIALIST IN SURVEY AND EVALUATION PERU PROJECT, 1963– . National Science Foundation fellow. Membership American Anthropological Association American Ethnological Society; New York State Educational Research Association Sigma Xi. Research: cultural anthropology and education; basic educational development and reform in Peru; Colombia. Author: Maestro, conozca su comunidad (1964); Disorientation and Status Change (Southwestern Journal of Anthropology Spring 1956). Co-author: Social Aspect of Education; A Casebook (1962). Language: Spanish 4,4,4,3. Home: 407 Angamos (Miraflores), Lima, Peru. Office: c/ TCCU Team, U.S. Embassy, Lima, Peru.

SCAPERLANDA, ANTHONY EDWARD, b Galveston, Tex., Sept. 29, 1938. ECONOMICS. M.A., U. of Tex., 1963; Ph. D 1964. Asst. prof., St. Cloud State Coll 1963–64; ASST. PROF., ECONOMICS NORTHERN ILL. U., 1964– . Member ship: American Economic Association. Research: international economics; impact of economics; impact of economic integration on economic development; Latin American Free Trade Association's developmental impact; economic structure of Mexico. Language: Spanish 3,2,2,2; Portuguese 1,1,1,1; French 1,1,1,1. Home: 809 East Taylor, De Kalb, Ill. Office: Dept. of Economics, Northern Ill. U., De Kalb.

SCHAEDEL, RICHARD PAUL, b. Newark, N.J., Aug. 17, 1920. ANTHROPOLOGY. B.A., U. of Wis., 1942; Ph. D., Yale U., 1952. Dir., Instituto de Antropología, Universidad de Trujillo (Peru), 1948–51; lectr., N.Y.U., 1951–52; vis. organizing prof., Centro de Estudios Antropólogos, Universidad de Chile, 1953–54; vis. lectr., Universidad de Buenos Aires, 1954; research asst., Human Relations Area Files, Yale U., 1955–56; intelligence research specialist, U.S. Dept. of State, 1956–57; anthropologist, Southern Peru Regional Development (Cuzco), 1957–59; community analyst, U.S. Agency for International Development (Haiti), 1959–62; anthropologist, U.S. Agency for International Development (Venezuela), 1962–64; SOCIAL SCIENCE RESEARCH CONSULTANT, INSTITUTE OF LATIN AMERICAN SUDIES, U. OF TEX., 1964– . Wenner-Gren fellow (Peru), 1952–53; consultant, U.S. Agency for International Development (Nicaragua), 1963. Membership: American Anthropological Association; Archaeological Institute of America; Institute of Andean Research; Phi Beta Kappa; Sigma Xi; Sociedad para la Antropología de Peru; Sociedad Venezolana de Planificación; Society for American Archaeology. Research: archeology in the Andean area; social anthropology; human resource studies in Chile, Peru, Haiti and Venezuela; community development in Haiti, Venezuela and Nicaragua. Author: Major Ceremonial and Population Centers in Northern Peru (Proceedings, 29th Congress of Americanists, 1951); Los recursos humanos del departamento de Puno (in Southern Peru Regional Development Plan, 1960); An Essay on the Human Resources of Haiti (1962). Language: Spanish 5,5,5,4; Portuguese 3,3,2,1; French 4,3,2,2; Creole 4,4,4,3; German 4,3,3,2; Russian 3,3,2,2. Home: 1550 Fairholme Rd., Grosse Pt. Weeds, Mich. Office: Institute of Latin American Studies, U. of Tex., Austin 12, Tex.

SCHAEFFER, WENDELL G., b. Waverly, Ill., Nov. 5, 1917. POLITICAL SCIENCE. B.S. F.S., U. of Southern Calif., 1939; M.A., U. of Calif., Berkeley, 1946; Ph. D., 1949. Asst. prof., U. of Fla., 1948–50; consultant, Public Administration Service (El Salvador, P.R., Nicaragua), 1950–59; prof., assoc. dean, Graduate School of Public and International Affairs, U. of Pittsburgh, 1959–63; DEAN AND CHIEF OF PARTY, ECUADOR PROJECT, U. OF PITTSBURGH FACULTIES IN ECUADOR, 1963– . Consultant, United Nations (Costa Rica), 1959; evaluation mission to Argentina, Brazil, Chile and Uruguay, Organization of American States, 1962. Membership: American Political Science Association; American Society for Public Administration. Research: public administration; administrative theory; economic development. Author: Modernizing Government Revenue Administration (1961). Co-author: The Government of Metropolitan Miami (1954); The Growth and Culture of Latin America (1956). Language: Spanish 4,4,4,4; Portuguese 3,2,2,1; French 3,2,2,2; German 2,2,2,2. Home: U.S. Agency for International Development (Pittsburgh), American Embassy, Quito, Ecuador. Office: Chancellor's Office, U. of Pittsburgh, Pittsburgh 13, Pa.

SCHANZER, GEORGE O., b. Vienna, Austria, Oct. 26, 1914. SPANISH AMERICAN LITERATURE. J.D., U. of Vienna, 1938; M.A., U. of Mo., 1946; Ph. D., State U. of Iowa, 1950. Instr., State U. of Iowa, 1946–47; asst. prof., U. of Kans., 1948–52; PROF., SPANISH, ST. JOHN'S U. (N.Y.), 1952– . Buenos Aires Convention fellow (Uruguay), 1947–48; Fulbright research fellow (Madrid), 1962–63. Membership: American Association of Teachers of Spanish and Portuguese; American Association of University Professors; Hispanic Institute of Columbia U.; Instituto Internacional de Literatura Iberoamericana; International Association of Hispanists; Modern Language Association. Research: Russian-Spanish American cultural relations; literature in Uruguay. Author: Rodó's Notes on Tolstoy's What is Art? (Symposium, Nov. 1951); Parallels between Spanish American and Russian Novelistic Themes (Hispania, Feb. 1952); Bohemia—Revista de Arte, Montevideo 1908–1910 (Revista Iberoamericana, Jan.–June 1962). Language: Spanish 5,5,5,5; Portuguese 3,2,1,–; French 4,4,4,3; German 5,5,5,5; Italian 3,3,3,3; Russian 3–,–,–. Home: 5 Terry Lane, Jericho, N.Y. Office: Dept. of Modern Foreign Languages, St. John's U., Jamaica 32, N.Y.

SCHELLENBERG, THEODORE R., b. Harvey County, Kans., Feb. 24, 1903. HISTORY AND ARCHIVAL MANAGEMENT. A.B., U. of Kans., 1928; A.M., 1930; Ph. D., U. of Pa., 1934. Executive secretary, Joint Committee on Materials for Research, American Council of Learned Societies and Social Science Research Council, 1934–35; history asst., Works Progress Administration, National Park Service, U.S. Dept. of the Interior, 1935; deputy examiner-asst. archivist of the United States, U.S. National Archives, 1935–63; assoc. national dir., Survey of Federal Archives, U.S. Government, 1936; records officer, U.S. Office of Price Administration, 1945–48; RETIRED, 1963– . Fulbright lectr. (Australia, New Zealand), 1954; Rockefeller Foundation consultant in Trinidad and Tobago, 1958; American specialist, International Education Exchange Program (South American countries), 1960; dir., Inter-American Archival Seminar, National Archives, 1961; chmn., Inter-American Archives Council, 1961. Membership: Pan American Institute of Geography and History. Research: preservation and administration of archives; archival situations in South American countries. Author: Archivos modernos: principios y técnicas (1958); Arquivos privados e públicos: arranjo e descrição (1963); Manual de arquivos (1959; 1961). Language: Spanish 3,2,2,1; Portuguese 3,1,1,1; French 3,2,2,1; Dutch 3,3,2,1; German 5,5,4,4. Home: 2637 Military Rd., Arlington 7, Va.

SCHENK, WILLIAM EARL, b. Bozeman, Mont., Nov. 21, 1911. ECONOMICS. B.S.,

Mont. State Coll., 1934; A.M., U. of Mich., 1939; Ph. D., U. of Ill., 1948. Instr-asst. prof., Mont. State Coll., 1933–44; prof., Tex. A. & M. Coll., 1948–49; vis. prof., National U. of El Salvador, 1949–51; INTERNATIONAL ECONOMIST, U.S. AGENCY FOR INTERNATIONAL DEVELOPMENT, 1951– . Consultant, National Tax Equality Association (Chicago), Tex. Senate Finance Committee, Ill. State Tax System Review Project, 1947–49; consultant, Ministry of Economy, El Salvador, 1949–51. Membership: American Economic Association; Geographic Society of Peru; Indian Economic Association; National Economic Association (El Salvador); National Economic Association (Peru); Society for International Development. Research: institutional measures for economic development; planning and execution of development programs; development problems of southern Peru and El Salvador. Author: Pattern of Aid to Underdeveloped Countries in the Sixties (Commerce, Bombay, 1961). Editor: Southern Peru Regional Development Project Reports (Government of Peru, Finance Ministry, 1957–60). Language: Spanish 5,5,4,4; Portuguese 3,2,2,1; French 4,2,2,1; Dutch 3,2,1,1; German 4,4,2,2; Italian 3,2,1,1. Home: 122 South 8th Ave., Bozeman, Mont. Office: U.S. Agency for International Development, American Embassy, New Delhi, India.

SCHIFF, WARREN, b. Pforzheim, Baden, Germany, June 22, 1924. HISTORY. B.S., Georgetown U., 1948; M.A., U. of Calif., Berkeley, 1949; Universidad de la República (Uruguay), 1950–51; Ph. D., U. of Calif., Berkeley, 1957. Assoc. prof., chmn., Div. of Social Sciences, Little Rock U., 1957–61; ASSOC. PROF., HISTORY, COLL. OF THE HOLY CROSS, 1961– . Membership: American Historical Association; Worcester Academy of Historians and Political Scientists. Research: study of German influence in Mexico; Uruguay. Author: German Military Penetration into Mexico during the Late Díaz Period (Hispanic American Historical Review, Nov. 1959); An East German Survey Concerning Recent Soviet Historical Writings on Latin America (Hispanic American Historical Review, Feb. 1960). Language: Spanish 4,4,4,4; Portuguese 2,1,1,1; French 2,1,1,1; German 5,5,5,4. Home: 8 Lenox St., Worcester, 2, Mass. Office: Dept. of History and Political Science, Coll. of the Holy Cross, Worcester.

SCHLESINGER, EUGENE RICHARD, b. New York, N.Y., Mar. 19, 1925. ECONOMICS. A.B., Harvard U., 1947; A.M., 1948; Ph. D., 1950. Economist, Federal Reserve Bank of N.Y., 1948–52; economist, International Bank for Reconstruction and Development, 1952–54; ASSOC. PROF., ECONOMICS, N.Y.U., 1954– . Consultant, Central Bank of Guatemala, 1949–50; consultant, Fiscal Div., United Nations, 1950; consultant, United Nations Economic Commission for Latin America, 1950–51; Ford faculty research fellow, 1960–61; consultant, Fiscal and Financial Branch, United Nations Secretariat, 1962–63. Membership: American Economic Association; American Finance Association; National Tax Association; Society for International Development. Research: international trade and finance; public finance and fiscal policy; development economics. Author: Multiple Exchange Rates and Economic Development (1952); Public Finance and Economic Development in Guatemala (1952); Tax Policy Recommendations of Technical Assistance Missions: Evolution, Pattern, Interpretation (1964). Language: Spanish 1,1,2,3. Home: 7 Bruce Lane, Westport, Conn. 06880. Office: Dept. of Economics, N.Y.U., 100 Trinity Pl., New York 6, N.Y.

SCHMECKEBIER, LAURENCE, b. Chicago, Ill., Mar. 1, 1906. ART. B.A., U. of Wis., 1927; U. of Marburg, 1927–28; Ph. D., U. of Munich, 1930. Asst. prof., U. of Wis., 1931–38; prof., chmn., Fine Arts, U. of Minn., 1938–46; dir., Cleveland Institute of Art, 1946–54; PROF., FINE ARTS, DEAN, SCHOOL OF ART, SYRACUSE, U., 1954– . Advisory editor, College Art Journal, 1934– ; advisory art editor, Encyclopedia Americana, 1952– ; Fulbright research fellow U. of Munich, 1960–61; Accrediting Committee, National Association of Schools of Art, 1962–63; contributing editor, American Artist Magazine, 1963– . Membership: College Art Association; National Association of Schools of Art. Research: history of contemporary artists and art movements in Mexico. Author: Modern Mexican Art (1939); Art in Red Wing (1946); Ivan Mestrovic, Sculptor and Patriot (1959). Language: Spanish 2,2,2,1; Portuguese 1,1,1,1; French 2,2,2,1; German 5,4,4,4; Italian 2,2,2,1. Home: 227 Scottholm Ter., Syracuse, N.Y. Office: School of Art, 309 University Pl., Syracuse, 13210.

SCHMITT, KARL MICHAEL, b. Louisville, Ky., July 22, 1922. HISTORY AND POLITICAL SCIENCE. B.A., Catholic U., 1947; M.A., 1949; Ph. D., U. of Pa., 1954. Asst. prof., Niagara U., 1950–55; analyst for Latin America, Intelligence Research, U.S. Dept. of State, 1955–58; ASSOC. PROF., GOVERNMENT, U. OF TEX., 1958– ; asst. prof., U. of Calif., Los Angeles, Summer 1959. Consultant, U.S. Dept. of State, 1962– ; consultant on education in Central America, U.S. Government, 1963. Membership: Catholic Historical Association; Conference on Latin American History. Research: government and politics of Latin America; Mexico. Author: Evolution or Chaos: Dynamics of Latin American Government and Politics (1963); Communism in Mexico Today (Western Political Quarterly, Mar. 1962); The Catholic Response to the Secular State: The Case of Mexico, 1867–1911 (Catholic Historical Review, July 1962). Language: Spanish 4,3,3,–; Portuguese 2,2,2,–; French 2,2,2,–. Home: 2603 Pinewood Ter., Austin, Tex. Office: Dept. of Government, U. of Tex., Austin.

SCHNEIDER, RONALD MILTON, b. Minneapolis, Minn., Sept. 29, 1932. POLITICAL SCIENCE. B.S., Northwestern U., 1954; M.A., Princeton U., 1956; Ph. D., 1958. Research assistant, Foreign Policy Research Institute (Washington, D.C. and Guatemala), 1956–57; intelligence research specialist, U.S. Dept. of State, 1957–63, Embassy (Brazil), 1962; lectr., Catholic U., 1960–61; vis. assoc. prof., Catholic U., Summer 1963; VIS. ASSOC. PROF., GOVERNMENT, COLUMBIA U., 1963– ; acting asst. dir., Institute of Latin American Studies, Columbia U. Dir., Metropolitan Summer Graduate Field Training Program in Latin America. Research: Latin American comparative politics and government; communism in Latin America; Brazilian politics; Guatemala; Colombia; Panama. Author: Communism in Guatemala, 1944–54 (1959); Introduction (in Evolution or Choas: The Dynamics of Latin American Government and Politics, 1963); Five Years of the Cuban Revolution (Current History, Jan. 1964). Language: Spanish 4,4,3,3; Portuguese 4,4,4,4. Home: 36 East Glen Ave., Ridgewood, N.J. Office: Dept. of Government, Columbia U., 417 West 117th St., New York 27, N.Y.

SCHOENHALS, ALVIN, b. Apr. 15, 1929. LINGUISTICS. B.A., Wheaton Coll., 1953; M.A., U. of Tex., 1962. MISSIONARY LINGUIST, SUMMER INSTITUTE OF LINGUISTICS (MEXICO), 1956– . Research: anthropology; classification of Totontepec Mixe verbs. Language: Spanish 3,3,3,2; German 2,2,2,2. Linguistic studies: Totontepec Mixe. Home and office: Instituto Lingüístico de Verano, Apartado 2975, México 1, D.F.

SCHOENHALS, LOUISE CONETY, b. Mountain Top, Pa., Apr. 27, 1930. LINGUISTICS. B.A., Wheaton Coll., 1953; M.A., U. of Tex., 1963. LINGUISTIC INVESTIGATOR, SUMMER INSTITUTE OF LINGUISTICS (MEXICO), 1956– . Research: anthropology; education; history; cultural change and history of bilingual dictionaries in Mexico; Mixe Indians of Mexico. Author: Mexico Experiments in Rural and Primary Education, 1921–1930 (Hispanic American Historical Review, Feb. 1964). Language: Spanish 3,3,3,3. Linguistic studies: Totontepec Mixe. Home and office: Instituto Lingüístico de Verano, Apartado 2975, México 1, D.F.

SCHOLES, FRANCE VINTON, b. Bradford, Ill., Jan. 26, 1897. HISTORY. A.B., Harvard U., 1919; A.M., 1922; Ph. D., 1943. Instr., Mass. Institute of Technology, 1919–20; instr., U. of N. Mex., 1925–26; asst. prof., Colo. Coll., 1926–27; assoc. prof., U. of N. Mex., 1928–30; prof., 1930–31; investigator, Div. of Historical Research, Carnegie Institution of Washington, 1931–36; prof., History, U. of N. Mex., 1946–63; RETIRED– . Serra Award, Academy of American Franciscan History, 1956. Membership: Academy of American Franciscan History; American Academy of Arts and Sciences; American Anthropological Association; American Historical Association; Phi Beta Kappa; Phi Kappa Phi. Research: colonial history of Latin America. Author: Church and State in New Mexico, 1610–1650 (1937); Troublous Times in New Mexico, 1659–1670 (1942). Co-author: The Maya Chontal Indians of Acalan-Tixchel (1948). Language: Spanish 5,4,4,4; Portuguese 3,2,1,1; French 4,2,2,1; German 4,1,1,1. Home: 115 Harvard Dr., SE., Albuquerque, N. Mex.

SCHOLES, WALTER V., b. Bradford, Ill., July 26, 1916. HISTORY. B.A., U. of Mich., 1938; M.A., 1940; Ph. D., 1943. Prof., Stephens Coll., 1943–45; PROF., HISTORY, U. OF MO., 1945– . Membership: American Historical Association; Conference on Latin American History. Research: 19th century Mexico; early 20th century United States diplomacy. Author: Diego Ramírez Visita (1946); Mexican Politics During the Juárez Regime (1957). Editor: Mexico During the War with the United States (1950). Language: Spanish 3,–,–,–; Portuguese 1,–,–,–; French 3,–,–,–. Home: 1515 Ross, Columbia, Mo. Office: Dept. of History, U. of Mo., Columbia.

SCHOOLER, ROBERT DALE, b. Boone County, Mo., July 7, 1932. ECONOMICS: MARKETING. B.S., U. of Mo., 1957; Ph. D., U. of Tex., 1964. Data processing representative, International Business Machines, 1957–61; registered representative, Reinholdt-Gardner (Joplin, Mo.), 1961; ASST. PROF., BUSINESS MANAGEMENT, U. OF MO., 1964– . National Defense Education Act fellow, 1961–62; Fulbright fellow (Central America), 1964. Research: international business; inter-cultural barriers to trade within the Central American Common Market. Co-author: Selected Bibliography of Latin American Business Literature (1964). Language: Spanish 4,4,4,4. Home: 1801 Sunrise Dr., Columbia, Mo. Office: Dept. of Business Management, School of Business Administration, U. of Mo., Columbia.

SCHULMAN, IVAN ALBERT, b. New York, N.Y., Oct. 4, 1931. SPANISH AMERICAN LITERATURE. B.A., Brooklyn Coll., 1953; M.A., U. of Calif., Los Angeles, 1954; Ph. D., 1959. ASSOC. PROF., ROMANCE LANGUAGES, WASHINGTON U., 1959– ; vis. asst. prof., U. of Oreg., 1961–62; vis. prof., Center for Latin American Studies, U. of Fla., 1965. Mexico-United States Commission on Cultural Cooperation, 1952–53; U. of Calif. fellow, 1958–59; Editorial Board, Duquesne Hispanic Review. Membership: American Association of Teachers of Spanish and Portuguese; Instituto Internacional de Literatura Iberoamericana; Modern Language Association. Research: modernism; stylistics. Author: Símbolo y color en la obra de José Martí (1960); Bécquer y Martí: coincidencias en su teoría literaria (Neuva Revista Cubana, 1962). Co-author: Esquema ideológico de José Martí (1961). Language: Spanish 5,5,5,5; Portuguese 3,3,3,4; French 4,4,4,2. Home: 714 Paddock Ct., St. Louis 26, Mo. Office: Dept. of Romance Languages, Washington U., St. Louis 30.

SCHULTZ, THEODORE W., b. Arlington, S. Dak., Apr. 30, 1902. ECONOMICS. B.S., S. Dak. State Coll., 1928; M.S., U. of Wis., 1928; Ph. D., 1930; LL.D. (honorary), Grinnell Coll., 1949; D. Sc. (honorary), S. Dak. State Coll., 1959; LL.D. (honorary), Mich. State U., 1962. Prof., head, Economics and Sociology, Iowa State Coll., 1930–43; PROF., ECONOMICS, U. OF CHICAGO, 1943– ; chmn., 1946–61. Chmn., U.S. Agricultural Development Mission (Argentina, Brazil, Uruguay), 1941; Board of Directors, National Bureau of Economic Research 1949– ; Center for Advanced Study in the Behavioral Sciences fellow, 1956–57; dir., Studies of Technical Assistance in Latin America, 1953–57; American Economic Association Award of Merit, 1957; Ford Foundation faculty research fellow, 1961–62; adviser, Latin American Science Board of National Academy of Sciences, U.S. Peace Corps, United Nations Food and Agriculture Organization, International Bank for Reconstruction and Development; consultant: Committee for Economic Development,

Twentieth Century Fund, Resources for the Future, Rand Corporation, Ford Foundation, Rockefeller Foundation. Membership: American Academy of Arts and Sciences; American Economic Association; American Farm Economic Association; American Philosophical Society; International Conference of Agricultural Economists; National Planning Association; Royal Economic Society. Research: agricultural economics; economic development of underdeveloped countries; economics of education. Author: The Economic Test in Latin America (1956); Transforming Traditional Agriculture (1964). Co-author: Measures for Economic Development of Underdeveloped Countries (1951). Language: German 3,3,3,–. Home: 5620 South Kimbark Ave., Chicago, Ill. 60637. Office: Dept. of Economics, U. of Chicago, Chicago, 60637.

SCHUSTER, ALICE K., b. Pittsburgh, Pa., Apr. 13, 1903. HISTORY. A.B., U. of Pittsburgh, 1936; M.A., 1938; Ph. D., 1946. Asst. prof., Westminster Coll., (Pa.), 1945-51; instr., Frostburg State Teachers Coll., 1951-57; ASSOC. PROF., SOCIAL STUDIES, EDINBORO STATE COLL., 1957– . Membership: American Historical Association; Conference on Latin American History; Pennsylvania Historical Association. Research: Nicholas P. Trist and peace mission to Mexico. Language: Spanish 2,–,–,–. Home: 340 South Highland Ave., Pittsburgh, Pa., 15206. Office: Dept. of Social Studies, Edinboro State Coll., Edinboro, Pa.

SCHWARTZ, HENRY CHARLES, b. Toledo, Ohio, July 6, 1915. LANGUAGE. A.B., U. of Toledo, 1937; A.M., U. of Mich., 1938; Ph. D., 1954. Prof., U.S. Office of Education and Coordinator of Inter-American Affairs (Haiti), 1943-44; English teacher, Bi-National Centers (Peru), U.S. Dept. of State, 1944-45; dir. of courses (Chile, Brazil), 1946-48; lectr., U. of Mich., 1949-51; prof., Ark. Coll., 1954-59; prof., French Lycée (Savigny), 1956-57; assoc. prof.-PROF., FRENCH AND SPANISH, MARIETTA COLL., 1959– . U. of Mich. fellow, 1940-42, 1949-51; American Council of Learned Societies grant (Peru), 1944-45; Fulbright prof. (France), 1956-57. Membership: American Association of Teachers of French; American Association of Teachers of Spanish and Portuguese; Modern Language Association. Research: English as a foreign language. Author: The Teaching of English as a Foreign Language (Andean Quarterly, 1946). Language: Spanish 5,5,4,4; Portuguese 4,4,4,3; French 5,5,5,5; German 4,4,3,3; Italian 3,3,3,3. Linguistic studies: English; French; Spanish. Home: 722 Seventh St., Marietta, Ohio. Office: Dept. of French and Spanish, Marietta Coll., Marietta.

SCHWARTZ, KESSEL, b. Kansas City, Mo., Mar. 19, 1920. SPANISH AMERICAN LITERATURE. B.A., U. of Mo., 1940; M.A., 1941; Ph. D., Columbia U., 1953. Dir. of cultural center, U.S. Dept. of State (Nicaragua, Ecuador, Costa Rica), 1946-48; instr., Hofstra Coll., 1949-50; Hamilton Coll., 1950-51; Colby Coll., 1951-53; asst. prof., U. of Vt., 1953-57; prof., chmn., Romance Languages, U. of Ark., 1957-62; PROF., CHMN., MODERN LANGUAGES, U. OF MIAMI, 1962– . Membership: American Association of Teachers of Spanish and Portuguese; Modern Language Association. Research: contemporary Spanish literature. Author: The Contemporary Novel of Ecuador (1953); Russian Literature in Ecuadorian Fiction (Kentucky Foreign Language Quarterly, 1956); Barbusse and the Ecuadorian Novel (Romance Notes, Fall 1959). Language: Spanish 5,5,5,5; Portuguese 3,2,1,1; French 5,3,3,2; German 3,2,2,1; Italian 4,3,2,2. Home: 6400 Mayo nada, Coral Gables, Fla. 33146. Office: Dept. of Modern Languages, U. of Miami Coral Gables, 33124.

SCHWARTZ, LOLA ROMANUCCI, b. Hershey, Pa., June 13, 1923. ANTHROPOLOGY. A.B., Ohio U., 1944; M.A., U. of Minn., 1955; Ph. D., Ind. U., 1963. Anthropologist (Mexico), 1958-61; RESEARCH ASSOC. AMERICAN MUSEUM OF NATURAL HISTORY (ADMIRALTY ISLANDS, MELANESIA), 1963– . Membership: American Anthropological Association. Research: community development; mental health and social problems in Mexico; peasant communities in Mexico. Language: Spanish 5,4,4,4; Portuguese 3,2,2,1; French 5,5,4,4; Italian 5,5,4,4. Home: 209 West Granada Ave., Hershey, Pa. 17033. Office: Dept. Anthropology, American Museum of Natural History, New York, N.Y. 10024.

SCHWARTZ, THEODORE, b. Philadelphia, Pa., Sept. 20, 1928. ANTHROPOLOGY. A.B., Temple U., 1950; M.A., U. of Pa., 1951; Ph. D., 1958. Research, Admiralty Island Expedition, American Museum Natural History, 1953-54; instr., U. Mich., 1955-56; instr., U. of Chicago, 1956-57; research prof., field dr., Universidad Nacional Autónoma de México, 1959-61; CO-PRINCIPAL INVESTIGATOR, PROJECT DIR., EXPEDITION TO MANUS AND NEW GUINEA, AMERICAN MUSEUM OF NATURAL HISTORY, 1963– American Museum of Natural History research fellow, 1957-58; Foundation Fund for Psychiatric Research grant, (Mexico) 1959-61; National Institutes of Health research fellow, École Pratique des Hautes Études (Paris), 1961-63. Membership: American Anthropological Association. Research: cultural anthropology; linguistic psychology; community development projects in Mexico; mental health and social problems in Mexican communities. Author: The Paliau Movement in the Admiralty Islands, 1946-1954 (1962); Systems Areal Integration (in Anthropological Forum, 1963). Co-author: The Cult as Condensed Social Process (in Group Processes, 1958). Language: Spanish 4,4,4,4; French 4,4,4,4; German 3,3,3,3. Linguistic studies: Melanesian. Home: 53 Berks St., Philadelphia 31, Pa. Office: Dept. of Anthropology, American Museum of Natural History, New York, N.Y. 1002.

SCHWINDEN, JAMES, b. Vida, Mont., Oct. 27, 1917. ECONOMICS. B.S., U. of Minn., 1953; M.A., 1962; Ph. D., 1963. Research analyst, dir., Tax Research, Dept. of Taxation, State of Minn., 1955-57; asst. prof., Economics, dir., Research Project, of Minn., 1957-63; AGRICULTURAL ECONOMIST, ECONOMIC RESEARCH SERVICE, U.S. DEPT. OF AGRICULTURE (EL SALVADOR), 1963– . Consultant agricultural development in Nicaragua

Public Administration Service, U. of Chicago; consultant, Minneapolis Planning Commission. Membership: American Farm Economics Association; American Statistical Association; Minnesota Planning Association; National Planning Association. Research: agricultural economics; agrarian reform; property taxes; economic effects of highways; recreation. Author: Real Estate Assessment—Principles and Problem (1962); Farm Real Estate Assessment—Practice (1962). Co-author: Highways and the Farmer (1958). Language: Spanish 3,3,3,3; French 2,2,2,2. Home: R.F.D. 2, Forest Lake, Minn. Office: Economic Research Service, U.S. Dept. of Agriculture, c/o U.S. Embassy, San Salvador, El Salvador.

SCOBIE, JAMES ROBERT, b. Valparaiso, Chile, June 16, 1929. HISTORY. A.B., Princeton U., 1950; M.A., Harvard U., 1951; Ph. D., 1954. Part-time instr., U. of Md. Overseas Program, 1956-57; instr.-asst. prof., U. of Calif., Berkeley, 1963-64; vis. prof., U. of Tex., Summer 1961; ASSOC. PROF., HISTORY, IND. U., 1964– . Doherty fellow (Argentina), 1952-53; Social Science Research Council and Organization of American States Faculty research fellow (Argentina), 1959-60; vis. scholar, Institute of Latin American Studies, Columbia U., 1962-63. Membership: American Historical Association; Conference on Latin American History; Pacific Coast Council on Latin American Studies. Research: Río de la Plata area, 1840-1900; 19th and 20th century Argentine development. Author: Argentina: A City and a Nation (1964); Consolidación de la nación argentina, 1852-1862 (1964). Co-author: Correspondencia Mitre-Elizalde (1956). Language: Spanish 5,5,5,4; Portuguese 4,4,3,3; French 5,5,4,3; German 3,3,3,1; Italian 2,2,2,1. Office: Dept of History, Ind. U., Bloomington.

SCOTT, FRANK S., JR., b. Cody, Wyo., Mar. 5, 1921. ECONOMICS. B.S., Oreg. State U., 1943; M.A., U. of Mo., 1947; Ph. D., U. of Ill., 1951. Asst. prof., Stephen F. Austin State Coll., 1947-50; asst. agricultural economist, U. of Nev., 1951-54; assoc. prof., U. of Hawaii ,1954-59; PROF., CHMN., AGRICULTURAL ECONOMICS, U. OF HAWAII, 1962– . Marketing adviser, United Nations Food and Agriculture Organization, (Argentina) 1960-62. Membership: American Farm Economic Association; Hawaii Economic Association; International Conference of Agricultural Economists; Western Farm Economics Association. Research: economics of market development and market potentials for agricultural products; economic development; Argentina. Author: Marketing Aspects of Western Cattle Finishing Operations (1955); An Analysis of Market Development for Frozen Passion Fruit Juice (1958); Basic Considerations in the Development of a System of Research, Extension, and University Training in Agricultural Economics for Argentina (Food and Agriculture Organization of the United Nations Report, 1962). Language: Spanish 4,4,4,4. French 3,2,2,2; German 3,2,2,2. Home: 130 North Kalaheo Ave., Kailua, Hawaii. Office: Dept. of Agricultural Economics, U. of Hawaii, Honolulu, Hawaii.

SCOTT, J. T., b. North Little Rock, Ark., Feb. 22, 1926. ECONOMICS. B.A., La. Polytechnic Institute, 1949; M.B.A., U. of Ark., 1952; Ph. D., Iowa State U., 1957. Instr., Drury Coll., 1952-54; instr.-PROF., ECONOMICS, IOWA STATE U., 1955– ; CHIEF, IOWA STATE U.-U.S. AGENCY FOR INTERNATIONAL DEVELOPMENT CONTRACT (PERU), 1964– . Membership: American Association of University Professors; American Economic Association; American Farm Economic Association. Research: agricultural economics; macroeconomic planning, land reform, agricultural production and marketing, and natural resource planning in Peru. Language: Spanish 3,3,3,3. Office: Dept. of Economics and Sociology, Iowa State U., Ames.

SCOTT, ROBERT E., b. Chicago, Ill., Apr. 27, 1923. POLITICAL SCIENCE. B.A., Northwestern U., 1945; M.A., 1946; Ph. D., U. of Wis., 1949. PROF., POLITICAL SCIENCE, U. OF ILL., 1949– ; researcher, National Council, Episcopal Church of U.S. (Central America and Mexico), 1957, 1958; vis. prof., Yale U., 1962; senior staff member, Brookings Institution, 1963-64. Consultant, El Salvador Unit, Public Administration Service, 1950; Joint Committee on Latin American Studies, Social Science Research Council-American Council of Learned Societies, 1962-63; participant, Summer Institute on Political Development, Committee on Comparative Politics, Social Science Research Council, 1962, 1963. Membership: American Political Science Association; Association for Latin American Studies; Illinois Committee for UNESCO; Midwest Conference of Political Scientists. Research: political development and change; comparative government; political systems of Mexico, Peru, and Central America. Author: Mexican Government in Transition (1959); Legislatures and Legislation (in Government and Politics of Latin America, 1958); Political Culture and Modernization in Mexico (in Modern Political Culture, 1964). Language: Spanish 4,4,4,4; Portuguese 2,2,2,1; French 2,2,2,1. Office: Dept. of Political Science, U. of Ill., Urbana.

SCRUGGS, OTEY MATTHEW, b. Vallejo, Calif., June 29, 1929. HISTORY. B.A., U. of Calif., Santa Barbara, 1951; M.A., Harvard U., 1952; Ph. D., 1958. Instr., U. of Calif., Santa Barbara, 1957-59; ASST. PROF., HISTORY, U. OF CALIF., SANTA BARBARA, 1959– . Membership: Agricultural History Society; American Historical Association; Mississippi Valley Historical Association. Research: United States history; Mexican agricultural labor in the United States; recent Mexican history and culture. Author: Mexican Farm Labor Agreement of 1942 (Agricultural History, July 1960); The United States, Mexico, and the Wetbacks (Pacific Historical Review, May 1961); Mexican Farm Labor Program under the Farm Security Administration (Labor History, Spring 1962). Language: Spanish 3,2,2,2; Portuguese 1,1,1,1; French 2,1,1,1. Home: 6784 Sueno Rd., Goleta, Calif. 93018. Office: Dept. of History, U. of Calif., Santa Barbara.

SEDA-BONILLA E(DWIN), b. July 13, 1927. ANTHROPOLOGY. B.A., U. of P.R., 1948; M.A., City Coll. (N.Y.), 1950; Ph. D., Columbia U., 1951. Dir., Social Science Research Center projects, 1957–60; ASSOC. PROF., ANTHROPOLOGY, U. OF P.R., 1957– ; chmn., Social Science, 1961–63; vis. scholar, Columbia U., 1964. Whitney Foundation fellow, 1953–55. Membership: Academia de Artes y Ciencias de Puerto Rico; American Anthropological Association; American Sociological Association. Research: community interaction and personality; attitude of Puerto Ricans toward civil liberties. Author: Los derechos civiles en la cultura puertorriqueña (1963); Social Structure and Race Relations. Language: Spanish 5,5,5,5; Portuguese 3,3,3,3; French 3,3,3,3. Office: Departamento de Ciencias Sociales, U. of P.R., Río Piedras, P.R.

SEDWITZ, WALTER J., b. Vienna, Austria, Apr. 14, 1925. ECONOMICS. M.A., Columbia U., 1951; Ph. D., 1955. Dir. of research, Federal Reserve Bank of N.Y., 1954–60; dir., Latin American Studies, Council on Foreign Relations, 1960–62; dir., Dept. of Economic Affairs, Organization of American States, 1962–63; ASST. SECRETARY FOR ECONOMIC AND SOCIAL AFFAIRS, ORGANIZATION OF AMERICAN STATES, 1963– . Research fellow, Council on Foreign Relations, 1954. Membership: American Economic Association; Council on Foreign Relations, Inc. Research: aid administration; programming; development economics; Latin American finance; international organization policy on Latin America. Author: Effect of European Common Market on Latin America (1962); Monetary Control in Underdeveloped Countries (1963); Latin American Common Market (Current History, July 1963). Language: Spanish 5,5,5,4; Portuguese 5,3,2,1; French 5,5,5,4; German 5,5, 5,4. Home: 6704 Tulip Hill Ter., Bethesda, Md. Office: Pan American Union, Organization of American States, Washington, D.C. 20006.

SEELEY, E(RWIN) CLAYTON, b. Detroit, Mich., Dec. 3, 1920. EDUCATION. B.A., Columbia U., 1953; M.S., 1954; Ed. D., 1956. Dir., employee training, Firestone Sociedad Anónima (São Paulo), 1947–49; teacher, American Elementary and High School (São Paulo), 1949–52; part-time music dir., American-Brazilian Bi-National Center (São Paulo), 1950–52; asst. to superintendent, public schools (Scarsdale, N.Y.), 1956–58; part-time lectr., N.Y.U., 1956–60; part-time adjunct asst. prof., Hofstra Coll., 1958–60; principal, Gardiners Ave. School (Levittown, N.Y.), 1958–60; superintendent of schools, American Elementary and High School (São Paulo), 1960–62; project dir., Brazilian Study Group, Institute for International Education, 1963; assoc. prof., Newark State Coll., 1963; DIR., LATIN AMERICAN PROJECT, SCHOOL OF EDUCATION, U. OF WIS.-MILWAUKEE, 1963– ; EDUCATIONAL ADVISER, MINISTRY OF EDUCATION (VENEZUELA), U.S. AGENCY FOR INTERNATIONAL DEVELOPMENT-U. OF WIS.-MILWAUKEE CONTRACT, 1964– . Columbia U. alumni fellow; organizer, Association of American Sponsored Bi-National Schools in South America; cultural dir., Brazilian-American Cultural Association (N.Y.); consultant, Association for Supervision and Curriculum Development. Membership: American Overseas Educators Organization; American Association of School Administrators; Association for Student Teaching; Association for Supervision and Curriculum Development; International Institute (Milwaukee); Kappa Delta Pi; Midwest Council for Latin American Studies; National Association of Secondary School Principals; National Education Association; Phi Kappa Delta; Wisconsin Education Association. Research: curriculum development; goals and programs in Venezuela and Dominican Republic educational systems. Author: A Story Festival (Childhood Education, Feb. 1953). Language: Spanish 3,3,3,2; Portuguese 4,4,4,3. Home: 2134 North Lake Dr., Milwaukee, Wis. 53202. Office: School of Education, U. of Wis.-Milwaukee, 3203 North Downer Ave., Milwaukee, 53211.

SENIOR, CLARENCE OLLSON, b. Clinton, Mo., June 9, 1903. SOCIOLOGY. B.A., U. of Kans., 1927; M.A., U. of Kans. City, 1941; Ph. D., Columbia U., 1955. Foreign economic specialist, Foreign Economic Administration, 1942–45; research assoc., National Planning Association, 1943–44; dir., Social Science Research Center, U. of P.R., 1945–48; research assoc., Bureau of Applied Social Research, Columbia U., 1948–51; chief, Div. of Migration, Dept. of Labor (P.R.), 1950–61; LECTR., COLUMBIA U., 1951– ; PROF., SOCIOLOGY, BROOKLYN COLL., 1961– . Organizer of work camp projects, American Friends Service Committee (Mexico), 1939; delegate, Second Inter-American Indian Congress (Peru), 1949; consultant, Secretary of Labor (P.R.), 1949– , United Nations, 1949, United Nations Economic Commission for Latin America, 1949–50, Twentieth Century Fund, 1950, Ford Foundation, 1960–61; adviser, Demographic Conference of the Caribbean Commission, 1957; member, Board of Education of New York City, 1961– . Membership: American Economic Association; American Sociological Association; International Union for the Scientific Study of Population; National Planning Association; Population Association of America; Rural Sociological Society; Society for International Development; Society for the Study of Social Problems. Research: migration, especially in Brazil and Chile; land reform in Mexico; developmental prospects in Costa Rica. Author: Land Reform and Democracy (1958); Strangers—Then Neighbors: From Pilgrims to Puerto Ricans (1961). Co-author: The Puerto Rican Journey: New York's Newest Migrants (1950). Language: Spanish 4,4,4,2; Portuguese 3,3,2,1; French 2,2,1,1; German 2,2,2,1. Home: 15 Claremont Ave., New York, N.Y. 10027. Office: Dept. of Sociology, Brooklyn Coll., Brooklyn 10, N.Y.

SENSABAUGH, LEON F., b. Dublin, Tex., Oct. 9, 1903. HISTORY. A.B., Vanderbilt U., 1925; Ph. D., Johns Hopkins U., 1928. Asst. prof., Birmingham-Southern Coll., 1928–29; prof., Okla. City U., 1929–36; assoc. prof.-prof., Birmingham-Southern Coll., 1936–56; dean, Washington & Lee U., 1956–60; PROF., HISTORY, WASHINGTON & LEE U., 1960– . Rosenwald fellow (Brazil), 1941–42. Membership: Conference on Latin American History; Southern Historical Association. Research: Brazilian diplomatic history; United States-Brazilian relations; Latin American boundary disputes. Author: American Interest in the

Mexican-Guatemalan Boundary Dispute (Birmingham-Southern College Bulletin, Dec. 1940); The Attitude of the United States toward Colombia-Costa Rica Arbitral Proceedings (Hispanic American Historical Review, Feb. 1939); The Coffee-Trust Question in United States-Brazilian Relations (Hispanic American Historical Review, Nov. 1946). Language: Spanish 2,1,1,1; Portuguese 3,2,2,1; French 2,1,1,1. Home: 6 University Pl., Lexington, Va. Office: Dept. of History, Washington & Lee U., Lexington.

SERVICE, ELMAN ROGERS, b. Tecumseh, Mich., May 18, 1915. ANTHROPOLOGY. B.A., U. of Mich., 1941; Ph. D., Columbia U., 1950. Instr.-asst. prof., Columbia U., 1949-53; PROF., ANTHROPOLOGY, U. OF MICH., 1953– . Membership: American Anthropological Association. Research: ethnology; Paraguay; Mexico; Guatemala. Author: Tobatí: Paraguayan Town (1955); Primitive Social Organization (1962); Profiles in Ethnology (1963). Language: Spanish 5,5,4,4; Portuguese 4,3,3,3; French 4,3,3,2. Home: 401 Awixa Rd., Ann Arbor, Mich. 48104. Office: Dept. of Anthropology, U. of Mich., Ann Arbor.

SERVIN, MANUEL PATRICIO, b. El Paso, Tex., Aug. 8, 1920. HISTORY. M.S.W., Boston Coll., 1951; A.M., U. of Southern Calif., 1954; Ph. D., 1959. Instr., El Camino Coll., 1958–60; lectr., Summer School (Mexico), U. of Southern Calif., 1960; ASST. PROF., HISTORY, U. OF SOUTHERN CALIF., 1961– . Del Amo Foundation fellow (Spain), 1957–58; editor, California Historical Society Quarterly, 1961– ; advisory editor, Southern California Quarterly, 1962. Research: colonial church; colonial social history. Author: Religious Aspects of Symbolic Acts of Soverignty (The Americas, Jan. 1957); La toma de posesión inglesa (Revista de Indias, Apr. 1958); The Instructions of Viceroy Bucareli to Ensign Juan Pérez (California Historical Society Quarterly, Sept. 1961). Language: Spanish 5,5,5,5; Latin 1,–,–,–. Home: 1625 Bushnell Ave., South Pasadena, Calif. Office: Dept. of History, U of Southern Calif., Los Angeles 7.

SHAFER, ROBERT JONES, b. South Salem, Ohio, Jan. 29, 1915. HISTORY. B.A., Ohio State U., 1938; M.A., U. of Calif., Los Angeles, 1943; Ph. D., 1947. PROF., HISTORY, SYRACUSE U., 1945– ; vis. prof., U. of Calif., Los Angeles, Summer 1953. U.S. Office of Education research fellow, 1946; Ford Foundation grant (Mexico), 1961–63; consultant on Latin American marketing and data handling problems, Itek Corporation. Membership: American Historical Association; Association for Latin American Studies; Conference on Latin American History. Research: recent economic development; Mexican economic development planning; military institutions in Latin American. Author: The Economic Societies in the Spanish World (1958). Language: Spanish 4,3,3,3; Portuguese 3,–,–,–; French 4,2,2,2. Home: 311 Houston Ave., Syracuse 10, N.Y. Office: Dept. of History, Syracuse U., Syracuse 10.

SHAPIRO, SAMUEL, b. Ellenville, N.Y., Aug. 23, 1927. HISTORY. Ph. D., Columbia U., 1958. Asst. prof., Oakland U., 1960–63; ASST. PROF., LATIN AMERICAN HISTORY, U. OF NOTRE DAME, 1963– . Fulbright prof., Tucumán U. (Argentina), 1959. Membership: American Historical Association; Hispanic American Historical Association; Midwest Council of the Association of Latin American Studies; Mississippi Valley Historical Association; Southern History Association. Research: contemporary Latin America; the Cuban revolution; current economic and political affairs in Argentina. Author: Richard Henry Dana, Jr. (1961); Invisible Latin America (1963); Fidel Castro and John Brown (Columbia University Forum, Winter, 1963). Language: Spanish 5,4,4,4; Portuguese 3,2,3,1; French 5,4,4,4. Home: 1828 Crestwood, South Bend, Ind. Office: Dept. of History, U. of Notre Dame, Notre Dame, Ind.

SHARP, JOHN McCARTY, b. Neenah, Wis., Oct. 24, 1917. LANGUAGE. B.A., Westminster Coll., 1940; M.A., U. of Chicago, 1942; Ph. D., 1949. Instr., Wright Junior Coll., 1942–43; instr., Ind. U., 1947–48; instr., U. of Chicago, 1947–48; PROF., MODERN LANGUAGES, TEX. WESTERN COLL., 1949– ; head, Spanish Workshop for Teachers, U. of N. Mex., Summer 1960; dir., Summer Spanish Program, U. of Southern Calif., 1962. Vis. lectr., Seminar on Latin American Affairs, U. of Ariz., Summer 1961; official interpreter, Seminars on University Affairs for Colombian Educators (Tex. Western Coll. and Ibagué, Colombia), 1962, 1963, 1964; asst. dir., Inter-American Institute, Tex. Western Coll. Membership: American Association of Teachers of Spanish and Portuguese; Modern Language Association; Rocky Mountain Council for Latin American Studies. Research: Spanish and Portuguese language and literature. Co-author: Diario de Navegación (1952). Translator: Juárez, by José Martí (in Literature of the Americas, 1950). Language: Spanish 5,5,5,5; Portuguese 4,5,5,4; French 4,4,3,3; German 3,3,2,2; Italian 4,4,4,4; Russian 3,3,2,2. Linguistic studies: Spanish. Home: 611 Cincinnati St., El Paso, Tex. 79902. Office: Dept. of Modern Languages, Tex. Western Coll., El Paso, 79902.

SHARPE, LAWRENCE ALBRIGHT, b. Burlington, N.C., July 22, 1920. LANGUAGE. A.B., U. of N.C., 1940; Ph. D., 1956. Part-time instr., U. of N.C., 1946–51; dir. of courses, Instituto Brasil-Estados Unidos (Fortaleza), 1951–53; lectr.-ASSOC. PROF., ROMANCE LANGUAGES, U. OF N.C., 1953– . Chmn., Spanish Section V, Bibliography Committee, Modern Language Association. Membership: American Association of Teachers of Spanish and Portuguese; International Phonetic Association; Modern Language Association. Research: linguistics and literature of Brazil, Portugal and Spanish America; interlinguistics; language laboratories. Author: Leonardo Motta and the Cantadores Nordestinos (Unitário, Dec. 1954); Artificial Language Projects (South Atlantic Bulletin, May 1961). Language: Spanish 4,5,4,4; Portuguese 4,5,4,4; French 3,3,3,3; Catalán 3,2,2,3; Danish 3,2,2,3; Dutch 3,2,2,3; Esperanto 3,2,2,3; German 3,3,3,3; Ido 3,2,2,3; Italian 3,2,2,3; Latin 3,–,–,–; Norwegian 3,2,2,3; Swedish 3,2,2,3. Home: 102 Taylor St., Chapel Hill, N.C. Office: 334 Dey Hall, U. of N.C., Chapel Hill.

SHAVER, HAROLD R., b. Rushville, Ill., Jan. 15, 1925. LINGUISTICS. B.S., Western Ill. U., 1948. MISSIONARY, LINGUIST, SUMMER INSTITUTE OF LINGUISTICS (PERU), 1958– . Membership: Wycliffe Bible Translators. Research: linguistic analysis of primitive languages. Language: Spanish 4,4,4,3; Nomatsiguenga 2,2,2,2. Linguistic studies: Nomatsiguenga. Home: R.F.D. 1, Rushville, Ill. 62681. Office: Wycliffe Bible Translators/Summer Institute of Linguistics, P.O. Box 1960, Santa Ana, Calif.

SHAW, MARY ELLEN, b. Pittsburg, Kans., Sept. 15, 1921. LINGUISTICS. B.A., John Brown U., 1948; M.A., Kans. State Teachers' Coll., 1952. ANALYTICAL LINGUIST, TRANSLATOR, SUMMER INSTITUTE OF LINGUISTICS (GUATEMALA), 1953– . Research: analytical and descriptive linguistics; analysis of unwritten Indian languages; preparation of primers. Language: Spanish 3,4,4,4; French 1,1,1,1. Linguistic studies: Achi. Home: Colony, Kans. 66015. Office: Summer Institute of Linguistics, Box 1960, Santa Ana, Calif. 92702.

SHEA, DONALD RICHARD, b. Minneapolis, Minn., July 15, 1926. POLITICAL SCIENCE. B.A., U. of Minn., 1947; M.A., 1949; Ph. D., 1953. PROF., POLITICAL SCIENCE, U. OF WIS.-MILWAUKEE, 1949–; dir., Institute for World Affairs Education, 1960–63; administrator for Peace Corps Programs, 1962– ; special asst. to the provost, 1962–63; dean, International Studies and Programs, 1963– . Doherty fellow (Mexico), 1955–56; dir., Foreign Student Seminar (Twin Lakes, Salisbury, Conn.), Summers 1962, 1963. Membership: American Academy of Political and Social Science; American Political Science Association; American Society of International Law; Midwest Council of the Association for Latin American Studies. Research: international law; Latin American comparative politics; Mexican political structure. Author: The Calvo Clause: A Problem of Inter-American and International Law and Diplomacy (1955). Language: Spanish 4,3,3,3. Home: 2225 East Kenwood Blvd., Milwaukee, Wis. 53211. Office: Dept. of Political Science, U. of Wis.-Milwaukee, 3203 North Downer Ave., Milwaukee, 53211.

SHEAHAN, JOHN BERNARD, b. Toledo, Ohio, Sept. 11, 1923. ECONOMICS. B.A., Stanford U., 1948; Ph. D., Harvard U., 1954. Economist analyst, Economic Cooperation Administration (Paris), 1951–54; ASSOC. PROF., ECONOMICS, WILLIAMS COLL., 1954– ; economist, Development Advisory Service, Harvard U. (Colombia), 1963–65. Brookings Institution national research prof. (France), 1959–60; adviser, Economics Institute, U. of Colo. Research: international trade; industrial organization; economic development; economic planning and current monetary policies of Colombia. Author: Promotion and Control of Industry in Postwar France (1963); International Specialization and the Concept of Balanced Growth (Quarterly Journal of Economics, May 1958). Language: Spanish 4,4,3,3; French 4,4,3,3. Home: Lynde Lane, Williamstown, Mass. Office: Dept. of Economics, Williams Coll., Williamstown.

SHEARER, ERNEST CHARLES, b. Denton, Tex., July 6, 1903. HISTORY. B.A., West Tex. U., 1930; M.A., U. of Colo., 1933; Ph. D., U. of Tex., 1940. Teacher, acting president, Amarillo Coll., 1935–46; chmn., U. of Houston, 1946–56; PROF., HISTORY, SUL ROSS STATE COLL., 1956– ; summer lectr., U. of Tex., 1931, 1932, West Tex. State Coll., 1952, Mexico City Coll., 1954, U. of Tenn., 1956. Research: Mexico. Author: Robert Potter, Remarkable North Carolinian and Texan (1954). Home: Alpine, Tex. Office: Dept. of History, Sul Ross State Coll., Alpine.

SHELTON, DAVID H., b. Winona, Miss., Nov. 30, 1928. ECONOMICS. B.A., Millsaps Coll., 1951; M.A., Ohio State U., 1952; Ph. D., 1958. ASSOC. PROF., ECONOMICS, U. OF DEL., 1958– . Nationwide Mutual Insurance Company fellow; Doherty fellow (Chile, Mexico, Argentina), 1957; consultant, Nationwide Mutual Insurance Company research contract (Brazil), Summer 1959; researcher, Center for Internatioanl Affairs (Mexico), Summers 1961, 1962; consultant, U.S. Agency for International Development-International Economic Services contract (Brazil), Summer 1963. Membership: American Economic Association; Beta Gamma Sigma; Southern Economic Association. Research: economic development; money and banking; economic structure of Brazil, Chile, and Mexico. Author: The Economic Growth of Latin America: Motivations, Prospects, and Problems (Journal of Inter-American Studies, Apr. 1959); Mexico's Economic Growth: A Success of Diversified Development (Southwestern Social Science Quarterly, Dec. 1960); Money, Credit, and the Goal of Growth (in Public Policy and Private Enterprise in Mexico, 1964). Language: Spanish 3,3,3,2; Portuguese 3,2,1,1; French 1,1,1,1; Home: 5 Ferncliff Rd., Newark, Del. Office: School of Business and Economics, U. of Del., Newark.

SHEPARD, MARIETTA DANIELS, b. Mt. Washington, Mo., Jan. 24, 1913. LIBRARY SCIENCE. B.A., U. of Kans., 1933; B.S.L.S., School of Library Service, Columbia U., 1943; M.A., Washington U., 1945. Order asst., Kansas City Public Library, 1934–38; chief of circulation, Library, Washington U., 1938–43; librarian, prof., Escuela Normal Juan D. Arosemena (Santiago, Panama), 1943–46; prof., Universidad Central (Quito, Ecuador), Spring 1944; special asst. to librarian, Hispanic Foundation, Library of Congress, 1946–48; ASSOC. LIBRARIAN, CHIEF OF LIBRARY DEVELOPMENT PROGRAM, COLUMBUS MEMORIAL LIBRARY, PAN AMERICAN UNION, 1948– . Consultant, Sociedad Económica de Amigos del País (Havana, Cuba), 1946; editor, Inter-American Library Relations, 1955– ; secretary, Seminars on the Acquisition of Latin American Library Materials, 1956– ; president, International Executive Council, Inter-American Library School (Medellín, Colombia), 1956– ; consultant, Instituto Tecnológico (Monterrey, Mexico), 1957; consultant, Institute of Caribbean Studies, U. of P.R., 1960; chmn. pro tem, Books for the People Fund, Inc. Membership: Altrusa International; American Library Association; Beta Phi Mu; District of Columbia Library Asociation; Special Libraries Association. Research: libraries, book production, bibliography, educational institutions in Latin America; Latin American literature. Author: Estudios y conocimientos en acción (1958); The Seminars on the Acquisition of Latin American Library Materials: A 7-Year Report (1962); Public and School Libraries in Latin America (1963). Language: Spanish 5,5,5,5; Portuguese 5,5,1,1; French 5,4,3,3. Home: 3025 Ontario Rd., NW., Washington 9, D.C. Office: Pan American Union, 17th & Constitution, NW., Washington, 20006.

HIEBER, BENJAMIN MURRAY, b. New York, N.Y., May 5, 1928. LAW. B.S. Columbia U., 1952; LL.B., 1953; Faculdade de Direito, Universidade de São Paulo, 1962–63. Legal research asst., American Law Institute Federal Tax Project, Harvard Law School, 1953–54; law clerk, U.S. District Court for the Southern District of N.Y., 1954–55; assoc., Winthrop, Stimson, Putnam & Roberts (N.Y.), 1955–56; assoc., General Counsel's Office, International Ladies Garment Workers' Union, 1956–60; assoc., Cohen & Weiss (N.Y.), 1960–62; vis. asst. prof., U. of Okla., Spring 1964; ASSOC. PROF., LAW, SCHOOL OF LAW, LA. STATE U., 1964– . Membership: Association of the Bar of the City of New York. Research: constitutional law; labor law; anti-trust law; administrative law; federal courts of the United States; Brazilian anti-trust law. Author: Abusos do poder econômico—lei e experiência antitruste no Brasil e nos E.U.A. (1964); O conceito de dominação dos mercados nacionais na lei antitruste brasileira (Revista dos Tribunais, Dec. 1963). Co-author: Revision of the Federal Estate and Gift Taxes: The Internal Revenue Act of 1954 (Stanford Law Review, Dec. 1954). Language: Spanish 4,4,3,3; Portuguese 4,4,4,4. Office: School of Law, La. State U., Baton Rouge, 70803.

HELS, W(ILLIAM) EUGENE, S.J., b. Cincinnati, Ohio, Feb. 2, 1897. HISTORY. A.B., Gonzaga U. (Wash.), 1922; M.A., St. Louis U., 1928; Ph. D., U. of Calif., Berkeley, 1933. Instr., Campion Coll., 1923–25; instr., Loyola U. (Ill.), 1930–31; asst. prof., St. John's Coll. (Ohio), 1934–35; assoc. prof., Loyola U. (Ill.), 1935–42; assoc. prof., U. of Detroit, 1944–46; PROF., CHMN., HISTORY, XAVIER U., 1946– . Canisius fellow, 1958–59. Membership: American Catholic Historical Association; American Historical Association; Hispanic American Conference; Mississippi Valley Historical Association. Research: colonial church history in Mexico and Paraguay. Author: Gonzalo de Tapia: Founder of Jesuit Missions of North America (1934; Spanish edition, 1958); King and Church (1961). Language: Spanish 5,3,2,3; French 4,2,2,1; German 3,3,2,1; Latin 5,5,5,5. Office: Dept. of History, Xavier U., Cincinnati 7, Ohio.

OOK, EDWIN MARTIN, b. Newton, N.C., Nov. 22, 1911. ANTHROPOLOGY. Drexel Institute; George Washington U.; Harvard U., 1937–39. Asst. archeologist, research staff, Div. of Historical Research, Carnegie Institution of Washington, 1933–39; archeologist, 1940–58; Cinchona representative for Guatemala, U.S. Government, 1943–46; ARCHEOLOGIST, DIR., TIKAL PROJECT, J. MUSEUM, U. OF PA., 1955– ; research assoc. in archeology, Carnegie Institution of Washington, 1959–61; DIR., GUATEMALA TRAINING PROGRAM, ANTHROPOLOGY, ROCKEFELLER FOUNDATION, 1961– . Coordination Committee for Guatemala, Office of Inter-American Affairs, U.S. Dept. of State, 1942–46; Carnegie delegate, 29th International Congress of Americanists, 1949; Tropical Resources Study Group (Guatemala), 1961; U. Museum delegate, 35th International Congress of Americanists, 1962; Norton lectr., Archaeological Institute of America, 1962. Membership: American Anthropological Association; American Association for the Advancement of Science; Asociación de Antropología de Guatemala; Sociedad de Geografía e Historia de Guatemala; Sociedad Mexicana de Antropología; Society for American Archaeology. Research: archeology of Mesoamerica; archaeological, ethnological, and environmental studies in Mexico, Guatemala, and Honduras. Author: The Present Status of Research on the Preclassic Horizons in Guatemala (Proceedings, 29th International Congress of Americanists, 1951). Co-author: Excavations at Kaminaljuyu, Guatemala (1946): Mound E–III–3, Kaminaljuyu, Guatemala (1952). Language: Spanish 4,4,4,4; Portuguese 2,2,2,2; French 2,2,2,2. Home: Oak Hill Rd., Harvard, Mass. 01451. Office: U. Museum, U. of Pa., 33rd and Spruce Sts., Philadelphia 4, Pa.

SHOUP, CARL SUMNER, b. San Jose, Calif., Oct. 26, 1902. ECONOMICS. A.B., Stanford U., 1924; Ph. D., Columbia U., 1930. PROF., ECONOMICS, COLUMBIA U., 1928– ; research dir., Federal Government of Venezuela, 1958–59; research dir., Federal District (Venezuela), 1959; RESEARCH DIR., COLUMBIA U., 1962– . Fulbright lectr., U. of Paris and U. of Strasbourg, 1953–54; consultant, U.S. Dept. of Treasury; consultant, European Economic Community, 1961–63; consultant, Vargas Foundation (Rio de Janeiro), 1964. Membership: American Economic Association; International Institute of Public Finance; National Tax Association. Research: public finance; fiscal system of Brazil and Venezuela. Author: Principles of National Income Analysis (1948); Ricardo on Taxation (1960). Co-author: Facing the Tax Problem (1938). Language: Spanish 3,1,1,1; Portuguese 3,1,1,1; French 5,3,3,2; German 4,1,1,1; Italian 3,1,1,1. Home: 370 West 245th St., New York 71, N.Y. Office: 512 Fayerweather, Columbia U., New York, 10027.

SIBIRSKY, SAÚL B., b. Montevideo, Uruguay, June 29, 1933. SPANISH AMERICAN LITERATURE. B.A., N.Y.U., 1954; M.A., U. of Wis., 1956; Ph. D., U. of Pittsburgh, 1964. Asst. prof., Cornell Coll., 1956–63; LECTR., DIR., LANGUAGE LABORATORY, U. PITTSBURGH, 1964– . Contributing editor, Handbook of Latin American Studies; editor, Iowa Foreign Language Newsletter, 1961–63; Cornell Coll. grant (Mexico), Summer 1963. Membership: American Association of Teachers of Spanish and Portuguese; American Association of University Professors; Instituto Internacional de Literatura Iberoamericana. Research: culture and literature of the colonial period in Latin American history; educational institutions; novel, essay, and culture in Latin America. Author: Manuel de Castro y su última novela (Revista Iberoamericana, Jan.-June 1960). Language: Spanish 5,5,5,5; Portuguese 3,3,3,2; French 4,4,3,3; German 3,3,3,1; Yiddish 4,5,5,5. Home: 602 South Lang Ave., Pittsburgh 8, Pa. Office: 1617 Cathedral of Learning, U. of Pittsburgh, Pittsburgh, 15213.

SIEGEL, BERNARD JOSEPH, b. Superior, Wis., Oct. 26, 1917. ANTHROPOLOGY. A.B., Harvard U., 1939; M.A., U. of Chicago, 1941; Ph. D., 1943. Instr., Brooklyn Coll., 1944–46; asst. prof., U. of Wyo., 1946–47; asst. prof.-PROF., ANTHROPOLOGY, STANFORD U., 1947– . Duter Prize, Harvard Coll., 1937–38; Social Science Research Council fellow (Brazil), 1949–50; Social Science Research Council faculty research fellow, 1955–58. Membership: American Anthropological Association; American Association for the Advancement of Science; American Ethnological Society; American Sociological Society; Phi Beta Kappa. Research: cultural change; peasant societies; social organization. Author: Slavery During the Third Dynasty of Ur (1947); Implications of Social Structure for Economic Growth in Brazil (in Economic Growth: Brazil, India, Japan, 1955); Social Structure and the Medical Practioner in Rural Brazil and Portugal (Sociologia, Dec. 1959). Language: Spanish 4,4,3,2; Portuguese 5,5,-5,3; French 5,4,3,2. Home: 259 Marvin Ave., Los Altos, Calif. Office: Dept. of Anthropology, Stanford U., Stanford, Calif.

SIEVERS, FLORENCE NIERMAN, b. Wentzville, Mo., Sept. 14, 1913. LIBRARY SCIENCE. B.S. in L.S., Drexel Institute, 1934; M.A., Radcliffe Coll., 1948. Business and social science librarian, Library, U. of Tex., 1935–42; documents librarian, Library, U. of Wash., 1942–43; social science analyst, Special Surveys Div., U.S. Dept. of Agriculture, 1948–51; operations analyst, Operations Research Office, 1951–53; research assoc., Foreign Area Studies Div., American U., 1955–60; science information specialist, Pan American Union, 1960–63; CONSULTANT, 1963– . Research: social psychology; survey research; scientific library and information center development. Author: Science Information in Latin America (1961); Guide to Latin American Scientific and Technical Periodicals, An Annotated List (1962); Latin American Scientific and Technical Journal Publication, A Statistical Analysis (1962). Language: Spanish 3,2,2,2. Home: 5703 Stillwell Rd., Rockville, Md., 20851.

SILSETH, MARTHA JENSINE, b. Minneapolis, Minn., June 14, 1897. LANGUAGE. M.A., U. of Minn., 1938; Columbia U., 1949–53; Ph. D., Inter-American U. (Saltillo, Mexico), 1962. Technician, Special Services, Women's Army Corps, 1944–46; instr., Spanish, Wilkes Coll., 1946–49; teacher, Alianza Cultural (Montevideo, Uruguay), 1949–50; ASST. PROF., SPANISH, CONCORDIA COLL., 1953– ; English instr., Centro Cultural (Costa Rica), Summer 1958; English instr., Instituto Guatemalteco-Americano, Summer 1959. Membership: American Association of University Professors; National Education Association. Research: English as a foreign language; folklore of Mexico, Costa Rica, and Uruguay. Author: Flying Over the Andes (Travelogue Magazine, 1950). Language: Spanish 5,5,5,5; Portuguese 3,-,-,-; French 3,3,3,3. Home: 221 South Seventh St., Moorhead, Minn. Office: Dept. of Spanish, Concordia Coll., Moorhead.

SILVERT, KALMAN HIRSCH, b. Bryn Mawr, Pa., Mar. 10, 1921. POLITICAL SCIENCE. B.A., U. of Pa., 1942; M.A. 1947; Ph. D. 1948. Teacher, Lincoln Coll. Preparatory School, 1946–47; asst. prof-prof., Tulane U., 1948–61; dir. of studies, American Universities Field Staff, 1955– ; PROF., GOVERNMENT, DARTMOUTH COLL., 1962– Penfield traveling fellow (Chile), 1948; Social Science Research Council grant (Guatemala), 1952; Carnegie grant, 1961– . Membership: American Political Science Association. Research: Latin American comparative politics of modernization. Author: A Study in Government: Guatemala (1954) The Conflict Society (1961). Editor: Expectant Peoples (1963). Language: Spanish 5,4,5,4; Portuguese 4,2,2,1; French 4,2,2,1; German 4,4,2,2. Linguistic studies Fanti. Home: Hopson Rd., Norwich, Vt Office: Dept. of Government, Dartmouth Coll., Hanover, N.H.

SIMMONS, GEORGE BENTON, b. Nashville Tenn., Aug. 3, 1931. ECONOMICS ANI BUSINESS. B.A., U. of Louisville, 1953 M.B.A., D.B.A., Ind. U., 1961. Faculty lectr, teaching assoc., Ind. U., 1957–61 asst. prof., U. of Tex., 1961–62; ASST PROF., GRADUATE SCHOOL OF BUSINESS, COLUMBIA U., 1962– . Consultant U.S. Agency for International Developmen (Monterrey, Mexico), 1962. Membership American Economic Association; American Marketing Association; Institute of Management Science; Society for General Systems Research. Research: international business administration; economic development; marketing; management science market potential in underdeveloped countries. Author: A bibliography of International Business (1964). Language Spanish 4,3,3,3; French 3,2,2,2. Home: 8 Morningside Dr., New York, N.Y. 10027. Office: Graduate School of Business, Columbia U., New York, 10027.

SIMMONS, MERLE EDWIN, b. Kansas City Kans., Sept. 27, 1918. SPANISH AMERICAN LITERATURE. A.B., U. of Kans 1939; M.A., 1941; Ph. D., U. of Mich., 1952 Instr.-PROF., SPANISH, IND. U., 1942– American Philosophical Society grant, 1955 American Council of Learned Societies gran (Peru), 1962. Membership: American Association of Teachers of Spanish and Portuguese; American Association of Universit Professors; American Folklore Society Conference on Latin American History Instituto Internacional de Literatura Iberoamericana; Modern Language Association Phi Beta Kappa; Phi Sigma Iota. Research: the romance, folklore, and histor of ideas in Spanish America; U.S. influen and intellectual currents at the time Peruvian independence. Author: The Me ican Corrido as a Source for Interpreti Study of Modern Mexico, 1870–1950 (1957) A Bibliography of the Romance and Relate Forms in Spanish America (1963). La guage: Spanish 5,5,5,5; Portuguese 4, 2,2; French 4,2,2,2; German 2,-,-,-. Hom

4233 Saratoga Dr., Bloomington, Ind. Office: Dept. of Spanish and Portuguese, Ind. U., Bloomington.

SIMMONS, OZZIE GORDON, b. Winnipeg, Canada, Oct. 9, 1919. SOCIOLOGY AND ANTHROPOLOGY. B.S., Northwestern U., 1941; M.A., Harvard U., 1948; Ph. D., 1952. Assoc. prof., School of Public Health, Harvard U., 1953–61; consulting anthropologist, Institute of Inter-American Affairs (Santiago, Chile), 1953; dir. in Peru, Institute of Social Anthropology, Smithsonian Institution, and vis. prof., U. of San Marcos (Lima), 1959–62; PROF., SOCIOLOGY, DIR., INSTITUTE OF BEHAVIORAL SCIENCE, U. OF COLO., 1961– . Sigmund Livingston fellow; Arnold traveling fellow; Committee on Drinking Behavior; Society for the Study of Social Problems; consultant, National Institute of Mental Health, Veterans Administration, 1957– ; assoc. editor, American Sociological Review, 1959–62, Journal of Health and Human Behavior, 1959– ; senior research assoc., Florence Heller Graduate School, Brandeis U., 1962– . Membership: American Anthropological Association; American Association for the Advancement of Science; American Sociological Association; Phi Beta Kappa; Society for Applied Anthropology. Research: behavioral sciences; role of alcohol in mestizo culture; post-hospital experience of mental patients; folk medicine; urbanization processes and assimilation; Peru and Chile. Author: Social Status and Public Health (1958); The Criollo Outlook in the Mestizo Culture of Coastal Peru (American Anthropologist, Feb. 1955). Co-author: The Mental Patient Comes Home (1963). Language: Spanish 4,4,4,4; Portuguese 1,1, 1,1; French 1,1,1,1; German 2,2,2,1. Home: 999 Eighth St., Boulder, Colo. Office: Institute of Behavioral Science, U. of Colo., Boulder.

SIMONSON, WILLIAM N., Richmond, Va., July 26, 1929. POLITICAL SCIENCE. B.A., Coll. of William and Mary, 1951; M.A., Fletcher School of Law & Diplomacy, 1953; Ph. D., 1964. FOREIGN SERVICE OFFICER, U.S. DEPT. OF STATE, 1955– ; RESEARCH ANALYST, DIV. OF RESEARCH AND ANALYSIS FOR THE AMERICAN REPUBLICS, 1955–57, 1960– ; political officer, Consulate (São Paulo, Brazil), 1957–60. Research fellow in American Diplomacy, Fletcher School of Law and Diplomacy, 1954. Membership: American Historical Association; American Political Science Association; Conference on Latin American History. Research: international relations; Nazi infiltration in South America, 1933–45; Brazilian politics and history. Language: Spanish 4,4,3,3; Portuguese 5,5, 5,5; French 4,4,3,3. Home: 306 Raymond Ave., McLean, Va. Office: INR/RAR, Room 7534, U.S. Dept. of State, Washington, D.C.

SIMPSON, GEORGE EATON, b. Knoxville, Iowa, Oct. 4, 1904. SOCIOLOGY AND ANTHROPOLOGY. B.S., Coe Coll., 1926; M.A., U. of Mo., 1927; Ph. D., U. of Pa., 1934. Instr., Wis. State Coll., 1927–28; instr.-asst. prof., Temple U., 1928–39; assoc. prof., chmn., Sociology, Pa. State U., 1939–47; PROF., CHMN., SOCIOLOGY AND ANTHROPOLOGY, OBERLIN COLL., 1947– . Social Science Research Council fellow, 1936–37; American Philosophical Society grant (Jamaica), 1953; chmn., National Advisory Screening Committee for Fulbright lectureships and advanced research awards in sociology, 1960–62; National Institute of Mental Health grant (Trinidad), 1962; Joint Committee on African Studies, National Institute of Mental Health, and American Philosophical Society grants (Nigeria), 1964. Membership: American Anthropological Association; American Sociological Association; Central States Anthropological Association; Phi Kappa Phi; Philadelphia Anthropoligical Society; Royal Anthropological Institute; Sigma Xi. Research: racial and cultural minorities; peasant life, and religious and political cults in Haiti, Jamaica, and Trinidad. Author: Jamaican Revivalist Cults (Social and Economic Studies, Dec. 1956); The Shango Cult in Nigeria and in Trinidad (American Anthropologist, Dec. 1962). Co-author: Racial and Cultural Minorities (1953, 1958). Language: French 3,3,3,2. Office: Rice Hall, Oberlin Coll., Oberlin, Ohio 44074.

SINCLAIR, JOSEPH TREBLE, b. Detroit, Mich., May 17, 1915. GEOGRAPHY. A.B., U. of Mich., 1937; M.A., Columbia U., 1944; Ph. D., U. of Mich., 1959. President, J.T. Sinclair Company (Detroit), 1946–64; asst prof.-ASSOC. PROF., GEOGRAPHY, EASTERN MICH. U., 1957– . Membership: American Association of Science; American Geographic Society; Association of American Geographers; International Geographic Union; Michigan Academy of Science; National Council for Geographic Education. Research: economic, human, and physical geography; Peru. Language: Spanish 3,2, 2,2. Home: 3430 East Huron River Dr., Ann Arbor, Mich. Office: Dept. of Geography, Eastern Mich. U., Ypsilanti, Mich.

SISTO, DAVID THEODORE, b. White Cloud, Kans., Apr. 5, 1910. SPANISH AMERICAN LITERATURE. B.A., U. of Tex., 1930; M.A., 1933; Ph. D., U. of Iowa, 1952. Teacher, Spur High School (Tex.), 1930–42; translator-examiner, U.S. Office of Censorship, 1942–45; teacher, Orange High School (Tex.), 1945–46; instr., U. of Iowa, 1946–54; ASSOC. PROF., SPANISH, U. OF TEX., 1954– . Research: honor code and literature of the gaucho; novel in Spanish America. Author: The Gaucho-Criollo Honor Code in the Theatre of Florencio Sánchez (Hispania. Dec. 1955); A Possible Fictional Source for Don Segundo Sombra (Hispania, Mar. 1959); The String in the Conjurations of La Celestina and Doña Bárbara (Romance Notes, Nov. 1959). Language: Spanish 5,5,4,4; Portuguese 2,2,2,2; German 1,1, 1,1. Home: 3203 Oakmont Blvd., Austin 3, Tex. Office: Dept. of Romance Languages. U. of Tex., Austin 2.

SITTLER, RICHARD CULVER, b. Omaha, Nebr., Oct. 16, 1925. LANGUAGE. B.A., State U. of Iowa, 1946; M.A., 1948; Ph. D., 1952. Instr., Spanish, State U. of Iowa, 1948–52; acting dir., Latin American Institute, Miss. Southern Coll., 1952–53; dir., Associação Cultural Brasil-Estados Unidos (Bahia), 1953–55; dir., Centro Venezolano-Americano (Caracas), 1955–58; dir. of courses, American U. Alumni Language Center (Thailand), 1958–62; DIR., INSTITUTO HISPANO-NORTEAMERICANO (MADRID), 1962– . Membership: American Association of Teachers of Spanish and

Portuguese; Linguistic Society of America. Research: application of structural linguistics to language learning; language teacher training; English as a foreign language. Author: Intermediate English for Thais (1961-62). Language: Spanish 5,5,5,5; Portuguese 4,4,4,4; French 4,4,3,3; German 2,3,2,2; Thai 2,3,3,1. Linguistic studies: Portuguese; Spanish; Thai. Home: c/o Oscar Hellerud, R.F.D. 1, Northfield, Minn. Office: Instituto Hispano-Norteamericano, Calle Fuencarral 123, Madrid (10), Spain.

SKAGGS, EARLE CLAYTON, b. Bloomington, Ill., May 1, 1903. POLITICAL SCIENCE. B. Ed., Western Ill. U., 1938; M.A., U. of Minn., 1946; U. of Southern Calif., U. of Colo. Instr., Woodruff Senior High School (Ill.), 1943-62; INSTR., DIR., SCHOOL OF INTERNATIONAL STUDIES, BRADLEY U., 1962- . Membership: Mississippi Valley Historical Association; Phi Alpha Theta. Research: diplomatic history; international relations; Latin American history; Mexico. Language: Spanish 2,2,2,2. Home: 802 North Orange St., Peoria, Ill. 61606. Office: School of International Studies, Bradley U., Peoria.

SKIDMORE, THOMAS ELLIOTT, b. Troy, Ohio, July 22, 1932. HISTORY. B.A., Denison U., 1954; B.A., M.A., Oxford U., 1956; Ph. D., Harvard U., 1961. Instr., Harvard U., 1960-61; research fellow in Latin American studies, 1961-64; ASST. PROF., HISTORY, HARVARD U., 1964- . Social Science Research Council fellow 1958-59, 1959-60; Harvard U. research fellow (Brazil), 1963-64. Membership: American Historical Association. Research: modern Brazilian history; Brazilian politics, 1889-1918. Author: Survey of Unpublished Sources on the Government and Politics of the Second Empire: 1871-1918 (American Historical Review, July, 1960). Language: Spanish 4,3,2,-; Portuguese 4,4,3,-; French 3,2,2,-; German 4,3,3,-. Home: 55 Frost St., Cambridge 40, Mass. Office: Dept. of History, Harvard U., Cambridge 38.

SKINNER, LEONARD EDWARD, b. Los Angeles, Calif., Feb. 15, 1931. LINGUISTICS. B.A., Wheaton Coll., 1953. LINGUIST, SUMMER INSTITUTE OF LINGUISTICS (MEXICO), 1958- . Research: translation of bilingual reading materials into Chinantec. Author: Usila Chinantec Syllable Structure (International Journal of American Linguistics, Oct. 1962). Language: Spanish 4,4,4,4; Chinantec -,3,3,-. Linguistic studies: Chinantec. Home and office: Instituto Lingüístico de Verano, Apartado 2975, México 1, D.F.

SLEIGHT, FREDERICK WINFIELD, b. Corning, N.Y., Oct. 29, 1918. ANTHROPOLOGY. A.B., U. of Ariz., 1941. Instr., Rollins Coll., 1947-54; archeologist, Navajo Tribal Council (Window Rock, Ariz.), Laboratory of Anthropology (Santa Fe, N. Mex.), 1949-55; DIR., AMERICAN STUDIES, WILLIAM L. BRYANT FOUNDATION, CENTRAL FLORIDA MUSEUM, 1955- ; archeologist, William L. Bryant Foundation (Cuba; Virgin Islands), 1956-58; archeologist, William L. Bryant Foundation and U.S. National Park Service (V.I.), 1959-60. Archeological consultant, Archeological Survey Program, Sociedad de Ciencias Naturales de Lago Chapala (Jalisco, Mexico), 1963-64; president, Southeastern Museums Conference. Membership: Explorers Club of New York; Sociedad de Ciencias Naturales de Lago Chapala; Society of American Archaeology; Southeastern Museums Conference. Research archeology, especially of the Caribbean area. Author: Archaeological Reconnaissance of the Island of St. John, U.S. Virgin Islands (1962); The Krum Bay Site, St Thomas, U.S. Virgin Islands (1963). Language: Spanish 3,3,3,3. Home: 301 West Packwood Ave., Maitland, Fla. Office: Central Florida Museum, 810 East Rollin Ave., Orlando, Fla.

SLONIMSKY, NICOLAS, b. St. Petersburg Russia, Apr. 27, 1894. MUSIC. Conservatory of Music (St. Petersburg). Concert tours, Europe, 1921-22, United State 1923- . South America, 1941-42; instr Eastman School of Music (Rochester, N.Y.) 1923-25; instr., Boston Conservatory o Music, 1925-45; conductor, Pierian Sc dality, Harvard U., 1928-30; vis. prof Colo. Coll., Summers 1940, 1947-49; instr Harvard U., 1946-47; lectr., Simmons Coll 1947-49; Peabody Conservatory, 1956-57 conductor, Apollo Club Chorus, 1947-49 Guest conductor, Paris, Berlin, Budapes Havana, San Francisco, Los Angeles, Hollywood and South America; editor, International Cyclopedia of Music and Musicians 1946-58; Baker's Biographical Dictionar of Musicians, 1958; American Music Editorial Board, Encyclopaedia Britannica 1958- . Membership: American Society Composers, Authors and Publishers; National Association for American Composer and Conductors. Research: native mus of Latin America. Author: Music Sin 1900 (1949); Music of Latin Americ (1945); Lexicon of Musical Invectiv (1953). Language: Spanish 4,3,3,3; Po tuguese 3,2,1,1; German 4,4,3,3; Italia 4,4,3,3; Russian 5,5,5,5. Home: 151 We 88th St., New York, N.Y., 10024.

SLOVENKO, RALPH, b. New Orleans, La Nov. 4, 1926. LAW AND PSYCHIATR LL.B., Tulane U., 1953; M.A., 1955; Ph. D 1965. Research asst., La. Supreme Cou 1953; ASSOC. PROF., LAW, INST PSYCHIATRY, TULANE U., 1953- . F bright scholar (France); Board of Go ernors, La. State Bar Association. Memb ship: American Bar Association; Americ Psychiatry Association; International sociation in Criminology; Louisiana Sta Bar Association. Research: the menta ill and the law; Mexico. Editor: Sy posium on Labor Relations Law (1961 Cases and Materials on Louisiana Securi Rights; the Law of Debtors' and Cre tors' Rights (1962); Oil and Gas Ope tions; Legal Considerations in the Ti lands and on Land (1963). Languag Spanish 5,5,2,-; French 5,5,3,3; Russi 3,5,2,-; Yiddish 1,5,1,-. Office: School Law, Tulane U., New Orleans 18, La.

SLUITER, ENGEL, b. New Holland, S. Da June 30, 1906. HISTORY. B.A., Stanfo U., 1929; M.A., U. of Calif., Berkeley, 193 Ph. D., 1937. Instr., San Francisco St. Coll., 1937-38; project dir., U.S. Wo Progress Administration and Bancr Library, U. of Calif., Berkeley, 1938-3 PROF., HISTORY, U. OF CALIF., BERK LEY, 1940- . Social Science Resea Council grant (Europe), 1935-36; Roc feller Foundation fellow (Latin Americ 1942-43; Guggenheim fellow (Spain, Por gal), 1948–49; Fulbright fellow (Belgium), 1954–55. Membership: American Historical Association; Conference on Latin American History. Research: Dutch-Iberian rivalry in the colonial world; Brazil, decline of the Spanish and Portuguese empires. Author: The Dutch Archives and American Historical Research (Pacific Historical Review, Mar. 1937); Dutch Maritime Rivalry and the Colonial Status Quo, 1585–1641 (Pacific Historical Review, Mar. 1942); Dutch-Spanish Rivalry in the Caribbean Area (Hispanic American Historical Review, May 1948). Language: Spanish 5,5,4,3; Portuguese 5,5,4,3; French 4,3,1,1; Dutch 5,5,5,5; German 5,5,4,3. Home: 214 Yale Ave., Kensington 8, Calif. Office: Dept. of History, U. of Calif., Berkeley, 94720.

SLUTSKY, HERBERT L., b. Chicago, Ill., Nov. 6, 1925. GEOGRAPHY AND PUBLIC HEALTH. B.S., U. of Ill., 1950; M.S., 1951; Ph. D., 1959. ASSOC. PROF., HEAD, GEOGRAPHY, ROOSEVELT U., 1959– ; EPIDEMIOLOGIST, CHICAGO BOARD OF HEALTH, 1962– . National Academy of Science-National Research Council felow (Guatemala), 1957–58. Membership: American Geographical Society; Association of American Geographers; Illinois Geographical Society: Illinois Public Health Society; International Society of Biometeorology; Sigma Xi. Research: medical geography; human ecology; preventative medicine and health education; Guatemala. Author: An Ecological Investigation of Protein Malnutrition and Kwashiorkor in 1,200 Guatemalan Preschool Children (1959). Co-author: Hot Climate Miliaria: Disease or Sign? (in Clinical Selections in Dermatology and Mycology, 1956); The Natural History of the Eccrine Miliarias: A Study in Human Ecology (New England Journal of Medicine, Feb. 1957). Language: Spanish 2,2,2,1; Portuguese 1,1,1,1; French 2,2,2,1; German 2,2,2,1. Home: 1151 Gordon Ave., Deerfield, Ill. Office: Dept. of Geography, Roosevelt U., 430 South Michigan Ave., Chicago 5, Ill.

SMITH, GEORGE E., b. Waukegan, Ill., June 25, 1924. SPANISH AMERICAN LITERATURE AND LANGUAGE. B.A., Mexico City Coll., 1947; A.M., Northwestern U., 1950; Ph. D., Ind. U., 1959. Instr., Wright Junior Coll., 1950–51; assoc. prof., Purdue U., 1951–59, 1962–63; supervisor of foreign languages, Ind. State Dept. of Public Instruction, 1959–61; asst. dir., Chilean Peace Corps Project, U. of Notre Dame, 1961–62; ASSOC. PROF., SPANISH AND PORTUGUESE, DIR., IND. LANGUAGE PROGRAM, IND. U., 1962– . Consultant, U.S. Office of Education, Title VI-Institute Program, 1960, 1963; consultant, Modern Language Association; Board of Directors, Dept. of Foreign Languages, National Education Association; Danforth Teachers' fellow; National Defense Education Act Language Institute evaluator. Membership: American Association of Teachers of Spanish and Portuguese; Indiana Foreign Language Teachers Association; Indiana Schoolmen's Club; Modern Language Association. Research: Chilean literature; public school education; language laboratories; foreign language education in secondary schools. Author: Language Laboratory Manual for El Español al Día (1961); Bibliografía de las obras de Augusto d'Halmar (Revista Iberoamericana, July–Dec. 1962). Co-author: Learning Spanish the Modern Way (1962). Language: Spanish 5,5,5,5; Portuguese 5,3,3,3; French 4,4,3,3. Home: 100 Heritage Rd., Bloomington, Ind. Office: Dept. of Spanish and Portuguese, Ind. U., Bloomington.

SMITH, HALE GILLIAM, b. Jacksonville, Ill., July 24, 1918. ANTHROPOLOGY. B.A., Beloit Coll., 1940; M.A., U. of Chicago, 1945; Ph. D., U. of Mich., 1951. PROF., CHMN., ANTHROPOLOGY, DIR., MUSEUM, FLA. STATE U., 1949– ; archeologist, Fla. State U. (Panama), Summer 1952, (Cuba), Summer 1953; dir. and archeologist, National Park Service (P.R.), Summer 1961. Circum-Caribbean Nomenclature Committee. Membership: American Anthropological Association; Society for American Archaeology. Research: Spanish colonial archeology. Author: Tallahassee (1955); The European and the Indian (Florida Anthropological Society Memoir, 1956); El Morro: Notes in Anthropology (1962). Language: Spanish 2,2,2,1. Office: Dept. of Anthropology, Fla. State U., Tallahassee.

SMITH, MARGARET HARRISON, b. Newport News, Va., Feb. 15, 1907. GEOGRAPHY. A.B., Randolph-Macon Woman's Coll., 1929; M.S., U. of Chicago, 1947; Ph. D., U. of Tex., 1961. Instr., Kans. State U., 1946–61; asst. prof., Winthrop Coll., 1961–63; ASST. PROF., GEOGRAPHY, SOUTHEAST MO. STATE COLL., 1963– . Membership: American Geographical Society; Association of American Geographers; National Geographic Society. Research: lower Rio Grande region in Tamaulipas, Mexico; Puerto Rico. Language: Spanish 2,-,-,-. Home: 1526 Bertling St., Cape Girardeau, Mo. Office: Dept. of Earth Sciences, Southeast Mo. State Coll., Cape Girardeau.

SMITH, MERVIN GEORGE, b. Corunna, Ind., Apr. 6, 1911. ECONOMICS. B.S.A., Purdue U., 1933; U. of Chicago, 1938; Ph. D., Purdue U., 1940. Agricultural attaché, Embassy (Mexico), U.S. Dept. of State, 1942–45; specialist, Ohio Agricultural Cooperative Extension Service, Ohio State U., 1948–53; PROF., CHMN., AGRICULTURAL ECONOMICS, OHIO STATE U., 1953– ; vis. prof., Iowa State U., 1960; DIR., SUPERVISOR, AGRICULTURAL CREDIT RESEARCH, U.S. AGENCY FOR INTERNATIONAL DEVELOPMENT-OHIO STATE U. RESEARCH PROJECT, 1964– . Consultant, International Cooperation Administration, U.S. Dept. of State, 1957, 1958–59, (Latin America), 1959, (Dominican Republic), 1962–64; consultant, Interamerican Institute of Agricultural Sciences, Organization of American States, 1964; Board of Directors, International Voluntary Services, Inc. Membership: Agricultural Missions, Inc.; American Farm Economics Association; International Agricultural Economics Association. Research: agricultural economics; agricultural development, policy, and credit; agricultural credit in Latin America. Author: The Mexican Winter-Vegetable Export Industry (1947); First International Seminar on the Development of Agricultural Marketing and Cooperatives in Latin America and the Caribbean (1959); Adjustments in Agriculture—A National Basebook (1961). Language: Spanish 3,3,3,3; Portuguese 2,2,2,1; French 1,1,1,1. Home: 338 Fallis Rd., Columbus, Ohio 43214. Office: Dept. of Agricultural Economics, Ohio State U., 2120 Fyffe Rd., Columbus, 43210.

SMITH, RALPH ADAM, b. San Augustine, Tex., Apr. 1, 1912. HISTORY. B.A., Stephen F. Austin State Coll., 1934; M.A., U. of Tex., 1936; Ph. D., 1938. Prof., Okla. Coll. for Women, 1939–42; prof., Hardin-Simmons U., 1945–50; PROF., HISTORY, ABILENE CHRISTIAN COLL., 1950– . Membership: Southwestern Historical Association; West Texas Historical Association. Research: Mexico and the American Southwest. Author: Indians in American-Mexican Relations Before the War of 1846 (Hispanic American Historical Review, Feb. 1963). Language: Spanish 2,2,2,–; French 2,–,–,–. Home: 665 NE. 15th St., Abilene, Tex. Office: Dept. of History, Abilene Christian Coll., Abilene.

SMITH, RICHARD VERGON, b. Ada, Ohio, June 28, 1928. GEORGRAPHY. B.A., Miami U., 1951; M.A., Northwestern U., 1952; Ph. D., 1957. Instr., U. of N. Dak., 1954–57; ASST. PROF., GEOGRAPHY, MIAMI U., 1957– . Miami U. faculty research fellow (Mexico), Summer 1958, 1960; consultant, Bureau of Governmental Research, City of Cincinnati. Membership: American Geographical Society; Association of American Geographers; Regional Science Association. Research: urban geography; population and resource relationships. Language: Spanish 3,2,2,2; French 3,3,2,2. Home: 311 West High, Oxford, Ohio. Office: Dept. of Geography, Miami U., Oxford.

SMITH, ROBERT CHESTER, b. Cranford, N.J., Feb. 26, 1912. ART. A.B., Harvard U., 1933; M.A., 1934; Ph. D., 1936. Assoc., U. of Ill., 1937–39; asst. dir., Hispanic Foundation, Library of Congress, 1939–46; PROF., ART, U. OF PA., 1947– . Guggenheim fellow (Brazil), 1946–47; Fulbright fellow, 1961. Membership: College Art Association; Hispanic Society of America. Research: social history; history of Brazilian art. Author: Guide to the Art of Latin America (1947); João Frederico Ludovice (Art Bulletin, 1936); A Talha em Portugal (Lisbon Horizonte, 1962). Language: Spanish 5,5,5,3; Portuguese 5,5,5,5; French 5,5,5,5. Home: 2416 Delancey Pl., Philadelphia 3, Pa. Office: Dept. of Art, U. of Pa., Philadelphia 4.

SMITH, ROBERT ELIOT, b. Arcachon, France, May 24, 1899. ANTHROPOLOGY. B.A., Harvard U., 1922. Staff member, Carnegie Institution of Washington (Guatemala, Mexico), 1932–59; ARCHEOLOGIST, INSTITUTO NACIONAL DE ANTROPOLOGÍA E HISTORIA DE MÉXICO, 1962– . Membership: American Anthropological Association; Sociedad de Geografía e Historia de Guatemala. Research: Mesoamerican archeology; Maya archeology; ceramic analysis and research; pottery of Mayapán, Yucatán, Mexico; ceramic study on pottery from the Great Pyramid of the Sun, Teotihuacan. Author: A Study of Structure A–1 Complex, Uaxactun, Guatemala (1937); Pottery from Chipoc; Alta Verapaz, Guatemala (1952); Ceramic Sequence at Uaxactun, Guatemala (1955). Language: Spanish 5,5,4,3; French 5,5,4,3. Home: 1 Orchard St., Marblehead, Mass. Office: Peabody Museum, Harvard U., Cambridge 38, Mass.

SMITH, ROBERT FREEMAN, b. Little Rock, Ark., May 13, 1930. HISTORY. B.A., U. of Ark., 1952; M.A., 1953; Ph. D., U. of Wis., 1958. Instr., U. of Ark., 1953; asst. prof., Lutheran Coll., 1958–62; asst. prof., U. of R.I., 1962–64; ASSOC. PROF., HISTORY, U. OF R.I., 1964– . Advanced Knapp fellow, U. of Wis., 1957–58. Membership: American Historical Association; Economic History Association; Hispanic American Society; Mississippi Valley Historical Association; Southern Historical Association. Research: Cuban history; United States foreign policy. Author: The United States and Cuba: Business and Diplomacy, 1917–1960 (1960); What Happened in Cuba: A Documentary History (1963); The U.S. and Latin American Revolutions (Journal of Inter-American Studies, Jan. 1962). Language: Spanish 3,2,1,1; Portuguese 1,1,1,1; French 2,1,1,1. Home: Greenwood Dr., Peace Dale, R.I. Office: Dept. of History, U. of R.I., Kingston.

SMITH, ROBERT JACK, b. New Haven, Conn., Apr. 9, 1930. ANTHROPOLOGY. B.A., Yale U., 1951; M.A., 1955; Ph. D., U. of Pa., 1963. Staff anthropologist, Clinical Research Dept., Eastern Pa. Psychiatric Institute (Philadelphia), 1958–61; lectr., Pa. Military Coll., 1958–61; research assoc., Social Systems Project, Kansas State Hospital, National Institute of Mental Health, 1961–63; ASST. PROF., ANTHROPOLOGY, WESTERN MICH. U., 1963– . U. of Pa. research grant (Trinidad), 1957–58; Western Mich. U. faculty research grant (Trinidad), 1964. Membership: American Anthropological Association; American Association for the Advancement of Science; American Council of Latin American Studies; Society for Applied Anthropology. Research: differential response to physical and psychiatric illnesses in Latin America; acculturation and peasant societies in the Caribbean and Latin America; Islam in the Circum-Caribbean area. Author: The Impact of an Innovative Treatment Program on the Structure and Culture of a Large State Mental Hospital (1961). Co-author: Toward a Definition of the Therapeutic Milieu (Psychiatry Digest, Dec. 1963). Language: French 3,3,3,3; German 3,3,3,2. Home: 203 West Cork St., Kalamazoo, Mich. 49001. Office: Dept. of Sociology and Anthropology, Western Mich. U., Kalamazoo, 49001.

SMITH, ROBERT SIDNEY, b. Waterbury, Conn., June 13, 1904. ECONOMICS AND HISTORY. A.B., Amherst Coll., 1927; A.M., 1928; Ph. D., Duke U., 1932. PROF., ECONOMICS, DUKE U., 1932– ; vis. prof., Universidad de San Carlos (Guatemala), Summer 1949, Universidad del Valle (Colombia), 1963. Amherst Memorial fellow, 1930–32; Guggenheim fellow (Mexico), 1942; U.S. Dept. of State grants (Costa Rica), 1945, (Guatemala), 1949, (Latin America), 1955, 1956, 1957; research grant (Peru, Chile), 1946; Ford Foundation fellow (Central America), 1959–60; Rockefeller grant (Colombia), 1963; Board of Editors, Hispanic American Historical Review, 1947–53, Southern Economic Journal, 1959–62. Membership: Academia de Historia del Valle del Cauca; American Economic Association; Economic History Association; Inter-American Statistical Institute; Southern Economic Association. Research: the Consulados in Spain and America; Spanish and Hispanic economic thought, 1500–1850. Author: The Spanish Guild Merchant: A History of the Consulado, 1250–1700 (1940) ; Population and Economic Development in Latin America (Southern Economic Journal, July 1957) ; Population and Economic Growth in Central America (Economic Development and Cultural Change, Jan. 1962). Language: Spanish 4,4,4,4 ; Portuguese 3,1,1,1 ; French 4,2,2,1. Home: 2236 Cranford Rd., Durham, N.C. Office: Dept. of Economics, Duke U., Durham.

SMITH, ROBERT WAYNE, b. Kansas City, Mo., June 6, 1903. HISTORY. B.A., U. of Kans., 1924 ; M.A., U. of Idaho, 1932 ; Ph. D., U. of Calif., Berkeley, 1937. Instr., Yuba Junior Coll., 1937–41 ; PROF., HISTORY, OREG. STATE U., 1943– ; part-time vis. prof., U. of Oreg., 1963–64. Membership: American Association of University Professors ; American Historical Association. Research: Mexico ; South America. Author: Coeur D'Alene Mining War of 1892 (1961). Language: Spanish 4,4,4,4 ; Portuguese 3,3,3,3 ; French 4,3,3,3 ; German 2,2,2,2 ; Italian 2,2,1,1 ; Russian 1,1,1,1. Home: 105 North 32nd St. Corvallis, Oreg. Office: Dept. of History, Oreg. State U., Corvallis.

SMITH, THOMAS LYNN, b. Sanford, Colo., Nov. 11, 1903. SOCIOLOGY. B.S., Brigham Young U., 1928 ; M.A., U. of Minn., 1929 ; Ph. D., 1932. Asst. prof.-prof., head, Sociology, La. State U., 1931–47 ; prof., head, Sociology, dir., Institute of Brazilian Studies, Vanderbilt U., 1947–49 ; GRADUATE RESEARCH PROF., HEAD, SOCIOLOGY, U. OF FLA., 1949– . Social Science Research Council grant; Guggenheim fellow ; Julius Rosenwald fellow ; consultant, Organization of American States, Inter-American Institute of Agricultural Sciences, U.S. Dept. of Agriculture, Government of Colombia, Government of Brazil. Membership: American Sociological Society ; International Population Union ; Population Association of America ; Sociological Research Association ; Southern Sociological Society. Research: demography ; rural sociology of Brazil and Colombia ; land tenure in Latin America. Author: Sociology of Rural Life (1940, 1947, 1953) ; Brazil, People and Institutions (1946, 1954, 1963) ; Fundamentals of Population Study (1961). Language: Spanish 4,4,4,4 ; Portuguese 4,4,4,4 ; French 2,-,-,– ; German 2,2,2,2. Home: 632 SW. 27th Ct., Gainesville, Fla. Office: Dept. of Sociology, U. of Fla., Gainesville.

SMITH, WILLARD HARVEY, b. Eureka, Ill., Oct. 15, 1900 HISTORY. B.A., Goshen Coll., 1928 ; M.A., U. of Mich., 1929 ; Ph. D., Ind. U., 1939. PROF., HISTORY, GOSHEN COLL., 1929– . Dir. of relief work, Mennonite Central Committee (Paraguay), 1944–45, (Mexico), 1954–55. Membership: American Historical Association ; American Political Science Association ; Hispanic American Society ; Mississippi Valley Historical Association. Research: United States-Latin American relations. Author: Paraguayan Interlude-Observations and Impressions (1950) ; Schulyer Colfax, the Changing Fortunes of a Political Idol (1952) ; Mennonites in Latin America (Mennonite Quarterly Review, Oct. 1952). Language: Spanish 3,3,3,3 ; German 3,3,3,3. Home: 1619 South Eighth St., Goshen, Ind., Office: Dept. of History, Goshen Coll., Goshen.

SMOLE, WILLIAM JOSEPH, b. Akron, Ohio, July 30, 1931. GEOGRAPHY. A.B., Kent State U., 1953 ; A.M., U. of Chicago, 1955 ; Ph. D., 1963. Instr., Kent State U., 1956–58 ; vis. prof., Escuela de Geografía, Universidad Central de Venezuela, 1961–64 ; ASST. PROF., GEOGRAPHY, U. of PITTSBURGH, 1964– . Salisbury fellow, U. of Chicago, 1954 ; Fulbright research scholar (Chile), 1959–61. Membership: American Geographical Society of New York ; Association of American Geographers ; Sociedad Argentina de Estudios Geográficos. Research: regional and cultural geography ; Venezuela ; Chile. Author: Physical Geography of the Tri-County Area, Akron, Ohio (1957) ; Owner-Cultivatorship in Middle Chile (1964). Language: Spanish 4,4,4,4 ; Portuguese 2,2,2,1. Home: 5416 Hollywood Ave., Maple Heights, Ohio. Office: Dept. of Geography, U. of Pittsburgh, Pittsburgh, Pa.

SNEARY, EUGENE C., b. Marion, Mich., Oct. 1, 1919. SPANISH AMERICAN LITERATURE. B.S., Central Mich. Coll., 1941 ; M.A., Okla. A. & M. Coll., 1948 ; Ph. D., Tulane U., 1959. Instr., Okla. Baptist U., 1948–49 ; prof., Instituto Caro y Cuervo (Bogotá, Colombia), 1949–50 ; instr., Bethany Coll., 1950–53 ; instr., Tulane U., 1954–59 ; asst. prof., St. Olaf Coll., 1959–60 ; ASSOC. PROF., SPANISH AND FRENCH, CARSON-NEWMAN COLL., 1960– . Okla. A. & M. Coll.-Ministerio de Educación de Colombia exchange fellow, 1949. Membership: American Association of Teachers of French ; American Association of Teachers of Spanish and Portuguese ; Modern Language Association ; Tennessee Philological Association. Research: works of José Martí. Author: Cecil Charles, traductor de Marí (Revista Iberoamericana, Jan.-June 1958). Language: Spanish 5,5,4,5 ; Portuguese 3,2,2,1 ; French 5,4,4,4 ; German 2,2,2,1 ; Italian 4,2,2,1. Home: R.F.D. 2, Jefferson City, Tenn. 37760. Office: Dept. of Foreign Languages, Carson-Newman Coll., Jefferson City, 37760.

SNELL, HAMPTON KENT, b. Harvey, Ill., Mar. 10, 1904. ECONOMICS. B.A., U. of Wis., 1925 ; M.A., 1928 ; Ph. D., Yale U., 1941. Asst. dir. of research, Industrial Coll. of the Armed Forces, 1944–45 ; asst. to vice president, Association of American Railroads, 1945–47 ; PROF., TRANSPORTATION, U. OF TEX., 1947– ; transportation economist, Common Carrier Barge Lines (St. Louis), 1957–58 ; senior transportation economist, U.S. Agency for International Development-Ministério de Planejamento-Escritório de Pesquisas Econômicas Aplicadas (Rio de Janeiro), 1964–65. Strathcona fellow, Yale U. ; consultant, Second Hoover Commission, Commission on Organization of Executive Branch of the Government, 1954 ; consulting transportation economist, United Nations, Government of Egypt, Summer 1959 ; consulting transportation economist, U.S. International Cooperation Administration, Government of Indonesia, 1961, consultant, Office of Transportation Research, US. Dept. of Commerce (Austin, Tex.), 1964. Membership: American Economic Association ; American Society of Traffic and Transportation; National Small Shipments Traffic Conference; Southwest Shippers Advisory Board; Transportation Research Forum. Research: transportation and public utility economics; transportation problems of Brazil. Author: Coordination of River, Road and Rail Transport in Egypt (1960). Co-author: Land Transportation for Indonesia (1961). Language: Spanish 3,2,2,2; French 3,2,2,2; German 3,3,3,3. Home: 3409 Mountain Top Circle, Austin, Tex. 78731. Office: Coll. of Business Administration, U. of Tex., Austin, 78712.

SNOW, PETER GORDON, b. Boulder, Colo., July 3, 1933. POLITICAL SCIENCE. B.A., Tex. Technological Coll., 1958; M.A., 1960; Ph. D., U. of Va., 1963. ASST. PROF., POLITICAL SCIENCE, U. OF IOWA, 1962– . Membership: American Political Science Association; Hispanic American Society; Midwest Conference of Political Scientists. Research: comparison of the radical parties of Argentina and Chile; political parties and elections, especially in Argentina; communist movement in Bolivia. Author: Argentine Radicalism 1957–1963 (Journal of Inter-American Studies, Oct. 1963); Political Party Spectrum in Chile (South Atlantic Quarterly, Oct. 1963); Parties and Politics in Argentina: The Elections of 1962 and 1963 (Midwest Journal of Political Science, Feb. 1965). Language: Spanish 3,3,3,3; Portuguese 1,–,–,–; German 2,2,2,1. Home: 84 Olive Ct., Iowa City, Iowa 52240. Office: Dept. of Political Science, U. of Iowa, Iowa City, 52240.

SNYDER, DAVID ELMER, b. Chicago, Ill., Aug. 26, 1932. GEOGRAPHY. B.A., Valparaiso U., 1954; M.A., Northwestern U., 1956; Ph. D., 1959. Asst. prof., U. of Pa., 1959–62; ASST. PROF., GEOGRAPHY, YALE U., 1962– . Northwestern U. scholarship (Uruguay), 1958; junior faculty summer grant, Yale U. (Latin America), 1963. Membership: American Academy of Political and Social Science; American Geographical Society; Association of American Geographers; Hispanic American Society; National Council for Geographic Education; Regional Science Association. Research: economic geography; urbanization; transportation; regional development. Author: Regiones metropolitanas nodulares de pasajeros (1962); Ciudad Guayana: A Planned Metropolis on the Orinoco (Journal of Inter American Studies, July 1963); Alternative Perspectives on Brasilia (Economic Geography, Jan. 1964). Language: Spanish 4,4,4,4; Portuguese 3,3,3,2; French 3,2,2,2. Office: Dept. of Geography, Yale U., 77 Prospect St., New Haven, Conn.

SOBOL, JOHN ANDREW, b. Worcester, Mass., July 19, 1920. GEOGRAPHY. B.S., Mass. State Teachers Coll., 1942; M.A., Clark U., 1949; Ph. D., U. of Mich., 1961. ASSOC. PROF., GEOGRAPHY, MEMPHIS STATE U., 1956– . Membership: American Association for the Advancement of Science; American Association of University Professors; American Geographical Society; Association of American Geographers; National Council for Geographic Education. Research: industrial development of Huachipato, Chile. Language: Spanish 2,2,2,1. Home: Apt. 3, 1590 Poplar Ave., Memphis, Tenn. 38104. Office: Dept. of Geography, Memphis State U., Memphis, 38111.

SOBRINO, JOSEPHINE, b. San Antonio, Tex., Aug. 1, 1915. ANTHROPOLOGY: FOLKLORE. A.B., Incarnate Word Coll., 1936; M.A., U. of Tex., 1946; Ed. D., U. of Houston, 1960. Chamn., Foreign Languages, Texas Southmost Coll., 1942–60; PROF., CHMN., SPANISH, U. OF HOUSTON, 1960– . U.S. Office of Education fellow (Mexico), 1945. Membership: American Association of Teachers of Spanish and Portuguese; American Association of University Women; International Federation of Catholic Alumnae; Modern Language Association. Research: craft economy, customs and influence of customs on education of seven Indian tribes in Mexico. Language: Spanish 5,5,5,5; Portuguese 4,4,3,3; French 4,5,4,4; Nahuatl –,4,3,–; Tarascan –,4,4,–. Home: 5326 Dannell, Houston, Tex., 77035. Office: Dept. of Spanish, U. of Houston, Cullen Blvd., Houston, 77004.

SOLNICK, BRUCE B., b. New York, N.Y., Sept. 7, 1933. HISTORY. A.B., N.Y.U., 1954; A.M., 1955; Ph. D., 1960. Instr. N.Y.U., Summers 1957, 1958, 1959; instr., Hunter Coll., 1959–61; ASST. PROF., HISTORY, STATE U. OF N.Y., COLL. AT ALBANY, 1961– . Penfield fellow, 1956–57, 1957–58; Samuel S. Fels Fund grant, 1958–59; Research Foundation of the State U. of N.Y., Inc. grant-in-aid (Jamaica), 1962. Membership: American Historical Association; Conference on Latin American History; Society for the History of Discoveries. Research: history of inter-American relations; period of Latin American Independence; American opinion concerning the Spanish American Wars of Independence, 1808–1824. Language: Spanish 4,3,3,3; Portuguese 3,3,2,1; French 2,1,1,1; German 3,2,2,2; Italian 2,2,1,1. Home: 499 Livingston Ave. Albany, N.Y. 12203. Office: Dept. of History, State U. of N.Y., Coll. at Albany, 135 Western Ave., Albany, 12203.

SOLOW, ANATOLE ABRAHAM, b. Davos, Switzerland, Aug. 10, 1913. CITY AND REGIONAL PLANNING. B.A. Arch., Ecole Spéciale d'Architecture (Paris), 1935; M.A. in City Planning, School of Planning and Research for National Development (London), 1939. Research assoc., Committee on the Hygiene of Housing, American Public Health Association, 1940–43; chief, Housing and Planning Div., Pan American Union, 1948–59; adviser on urban and regional planning, U.S. Agency for International Development (Central America), 1959–64; ASSOC. PROF., URBAN AND REGIONAL PLANNING, U. OF PITTSBURGH, 1964– . Consultant, Government of Costa Rica, 1948, Government of Guatemala, 1949, Government of El Salvador, 1949, 1950, Government of Panama, 1955, Government of the Dominican Republic, 1955, National Housing and Planning Agency of Costa Rica, 1956, U. of P.R. and P.R. Planning Board, 1957; adviser to Board of Directors, Inter-American Planning Society; chmn., International Committee, American Institute of Planners; vis. lectr., U. of Pa., 1952–59. Membership: American Institute of Planners; American Society of Planning Officials; British Town Planning Institute; Inter American Planning Society. Research: housing; industrial parks; infrastructure projects in Latin America. Author: Planning Program for the Capital of Costa Rica (1948); Housing in Guatemala (1950); Industrial Location and Industrial Parks in Nicaragua (1962). Language: Spanish 4,4,4,4; Portuguese 2,2,1,1; French 5,5,4,4; German 5,5,4,4; Russian 4,5,4,3. Home: 5476 Darlington Rd., Pittsburgh 17, Pa. Office: Graduate School of Public and International Affairs, U. of Pittsburgh, Pittsburgh, 15213.

SOMMERS, JOSEPH, b. New York, N.Y., June 21, 1924. SPANISH AMERICAN LITERATURE. M.A., U. of Wis., 1960; Ph. D., 1962. ASST. PROF., SPANISH, U. OF WASH., 1963– . Woodrow Wilson fellow, 1959–60; Social Science Research Council fellow (Mexico), 1962–63. Membership: American Association of Teachers of Spanish and Portuguese; Instituto Internacional de Literatura Iberoamericana; Modern Language Association; Phi Beta Kappa; Philosophical Association of the Pacific Coast. Research: contemporary novel; treatment of the Indian and Indian themes in the novels of Mexico, Central America and the Andean highlands. Author: El ciclo de Chiapas: nueva corriente literaria (Cuadernos Americanos, Mar. 1964); Changing View of the Indian in Mexican Literature (Hispania, Apr. 1964); The Indian-oriented Novel in Latin America: New Spirit, New Forms, New Scope (Journal of Inter-American Studies, Apr. 1964). Language: Spanish 5,5,5,5; French 4,4,4,4. Home: 13747 42nd Ave. NE., Seattle, Wash. 98125. Office: U. of Wash., Seattle, 98105.

SORENSON, JOHN LEON, b. Smithfield, Utah, Apr. 8, 1924. ANTHROPOLOGY. B.S., Brigham Young U., 1951; M.A., 1952; M.S., Calif. Institute of Technology, 1952; Ph. D., U. of Calif., Los Angeles, 1961. Archeologist, New World Archaeological Foundation (Chiapas, Mexico), 1953; assoc. prof., Brigham Young U., 1958–64; research analyst, U.S. Naval Ordinance Test Station, 1962–63; MEMBER, TECHNICAL STAFF, DEFENSE RESEARCH CORPORATION, 1964– . National Science Foundation fellow, 1955–58. Membership: American Anthropological Association; American Association of University Professors; Ethnological Society; Sigma Xi; Society for American Archaeology; Utah Folklore Society. Research: social anthropology; urban conditions in relation to development; Mesoamerica. Author: A Chronological Ordering of the Mesoamerican Pre-Classic (Middle American Research Records, 1955); Traditions of Immigration by Sea in the Peopling of Mesoamerica (El México Antiguo, 1955); A Bibliography for Yucatan Medicinal Plant Studies (Tlalocan, 1957); Language: Spanish 3,2,2,1; Portuguese 2,1,1,1; French 1,1,1,1; German 2,1,1,1; Rarotongan 4,3,4,3. Home: 2601 Mesa School Lane, Santa Barbara, Calif. Office: Defense Research Corporation, 4050 State St., Santa Barbara.

SORIA, MARIO T., b. La Paz, Bolivia, Aug. 22, 1927. SPANISH AMERICAN LITERATURE. B.A., Baldwin Wallace Coll., 1950; M.A., Western Reserve U., 1957; Ph. D., 1962. Teacher, American Institute (Bolivia), 1953–54; asst. prof.-ASSOC. PROF., SPANISH, HIRAM COLL., 1959– ; lectr., Cleveland Public Library, 1961–62. Hiram Coll. research grant (Bolivia), 1963. Membership: American Association of Teachers of Spanish and Portuguese; American Association of University Professors; Modern Language Association; Phi Sigma Iota. Research: Bolivian literature. Author: Armando Chirveches A., novelista boliviano (1963); Bolivia Mutilada (Presencia, 1963). Language: Spanish 5,5,5,5; Portuguese 3,2,1,1; French 4,3,2,1. Home: 4238 Colony Rd., Cleveland 21, Ohio. Office: Dept. of Spanish, Hiram Coll., Hiram, Ohio.

SOUZA, RAYMOND DALE, b. Attleboro, Mass., Mar. 11, 1936. SPANISH AMERICAN LITERATURE. B.A., Drury Coll., 1958; M.A., U. of Mo., 1960; Ph. D., 1964. Instr., Kent State U., 1961–62; ASST. PROF., ROMANCE LANGUAGES, U. OF KANS., 1964– . National Defense Education Act fellow, U. of Mo., 1962–63. Membership: American Association of Teachers of Spanish and Portuguese. Research: Cuban literature; Argentine literature. Author: The World, Symbol and Synthesis in Octavio Paz (Hispania, Mar. 1964). Language: Spanish 5,4,4,4; Portuguese 3,2,–,–; French 3,–,–,–. Home: 37 Orange St., Attleboro, Mass. Office: Dept. of Romance Languages, U. of Kans., Lawrence.

SPAETH, CARL B., b. Cleveland, Ohio, May 3, 1907. LAW. A.B., Dartmouth Coll., 1929; B.A. Juris., Oxford U., 1931; B.C.L., 1932. Vice president, dir., and general counsel, Venezuelan Development Corporation (Caracas), 1939–1940; asst. coordinator, Inter-American Affairs, Office of Emergency Management (Washington, D.C.), 1940–42; U.S. member, Emergency Advisory Committee for Political Defense (Uruguay), 1942–44; chief, River Plata Div., U.S. Dept. of State, 1944–45; asst. diplomatic adviser, United Nations Relief and Rehabilitation Administration, 1945; special asst. to Asst. Secretary of State for American Republics, U.S. Dept. of State, 1945–46; prof., dean, School of Law, Stanford U., 1946–62; dir., Overseas Div., Ford Foundation, 1951–52; WILLIAM NELSON CROMWELL PROF. OF LAW, CHMN., COMMITTEE ON INTERNATIONAL STUDIES, STANFORD U., 1962– . Rhodes scholar, Oxford U., 1932; Sterling fellow, Yale U., 1933; Ford Foundation consultant, Indian Legal Studies, 1959, Latin American Studies Survey, 1962– . Membership: American Association of University Professors; American Society of International Law; Association of American Law Schools; International Law Association. Research: international law and organization; legal aspects of inter-American relations. Co-author: The Boyd Case and Section 77 (Illinois Law Review, Mar. 1938); The Emergency Advisory Committee for Political Defense (American Journal of International Law, Apr. 1944). Language: Spanish 4,4,4,3; French 2,2,2,1; German 3,3,2,1. Office: School of Law, Stanford U., Stanford, Calif.

SPECTOR, ROBERT MELVYN, b. Boston, Mass., Mar. 5, 1926. HISTORY AND POLITICAL SCIENCE. A.B., Boston U., 1948; M.A., 1949; LL.B., Boston Coll., 1959; Ph. D., Boston U., 1961. Teacher, William Howard Taft Junior High School (Boston), 1954–56; master, Boston Latin School, 1956–63; lectr., University Coll., Northeastern U., 1960; ASST. PROF., HISTORY, WORCESTER STATE COLL., 1963– . Membership: American Historical Association; Mississippi Valley Historical Association; Worcester Association of Historians and Political Scientists. Research: constitutional history; United States-Latin American relations; judicial structure of Caribbean countries; American investment and expropriation problems in the Caribbean. Language: Spanish 2,1,1,2; French 2,1,1,2. Home: 7 Old Wood Rd., Framingham, Mass. 01704. Office: Dept. of History, Worcester State Coll., 486 Chandler St., Worcester, Mass.

SPELL, JEFFERSON REA, b. Pottsboro, Tex., Nov. 9, 1886. SPANISH AMERICAN LITERATURE. B.A., U. of Tex., 1913; M.A., 1920; Ph. D., U. of Pa., 1931. Prof., U. of Tex., 1920–62; vis. prof., Universidad Nacional de México, 1944–46; PROF. EMERITUS, ROMANCE LANGUAGES, U. OF TEX., 1962– . Harrison fellow, U. of Pa., 1930–31; recipient, diploma de honor, Academia Mexicana. Membership: Institute of Latin American Studies; Instituto Internacional de Literatura Iberoamericana; Modern Language Association. Research: Mexican literature, especially periodicals; Fernández de Lizardi. Author: The Life and Works of José Joaquín Fernández de Lizardi (1931); Rousseau in the Spanish World before 1933 (1938); Tres comedias de Eusebio Vela (1948). Language: Spanish 5,5,–,–; Portuguese 5,–,–,–; French 5,5,–,–. Home: 2108 Hartford Rd., Austin, Tex. 78703. Office: Dept. of Romance Languages, U. of Tex., Austin, 78712.

SPELL, LOTA M., b. Feb. 2, 1885. MUSIC. B.A., U. of Tex., 1914; M.A., 1919; Ph. D., 1923. Cataloger, García Collection, Library, U. of Tex., 1922–29; inscription writer, Historical Monuments, State of Tex., 1936; PRIVATE TEACHING AND RESEARCH, 1936– . Research: Latin American history, literature, and culture. Author: Music in Texas (1936); Research Materials for the Study of Latin America at the University of Texas (1954); Pioneer Printer: Samuel Bangs in Mexico and Texas (1963). Language: Spanish 4,5,4,–; French 3,–,–,–; German 4,5,4,–. Home: 2108 Hartford Rd., Austin, Tex. 78703.

SPICER, EDWARD H., b. Cheltenham, Pa., Nov. 29, 1906. ANTHROPOLOGY. B.A., U. of Ariz., 1932; M.A., 1933; Ph. D., U. of Chicago, 1939. PROF., ANTHROPOLOGY, U. OF ARIZ., 1950– . Guggenheim fellow (Mexico), 1941–42, 1955–56; U. of Ariz.-Rockefeller Foundation Intercultural Exchange Executive Committee, 1958– ; consultant, Interamerican Indian Institute, 1963–64; National Science Foundation fellow (Mexico), 1963–64. Membership: American Anthropological Association; American Association for the Advancement of Science; Interamerican Indian Institute; International Congress of Americanists; Society for Applied Anthropology. Research: cultural anthropology; northwestern Mexico; Yaqui Indian culture and history; processes of cultural change, especially directed change. Author: Pascua: A Yaqui Village in Arizona (1940); Potam: A Yaqui Village in Sonora (1954); Cycles of Conquest: The Impact of Spain, Mexico and the U.S. on the Indians of the Southwest, 1533–1960 (1962). Language: Spanish 3,3,3,3; French 2,2,2,2; German 2,2,2,2 Yaqui –,2,2,–. Linguistic studies: Seri Yaqui. Home. 5344 East Fort Lowell Rd Tucson, Ariz. Office: Dept. of Anthropology, U. of Ariz., Tucson.

SPIEGEL, HENRY WILLIAM, b. Berlin, Germany, Oct. 13, 1911. ECONOMICS J.U.D., U. of Berlin, 1933; Ph. D., U. of Wis., 1939. Asst. prof., Duquesne U., 1939 42; assoc. prof., Catholic U. of America 1943–49; PROF., ECONOMICS, CATHOLIC U. OF AMERICA, 1950– ; lectr., U. of Wis Summer 1947; lectr., Johns Hopkins U 1950; research prof., U. of Idaho, Summer 1958; lectr., U. of Wash., Summer 1961, U of Calif., Berkeley, Santa Barbara, Summer 1962; LECTR., ECONOMICS, U. OF MD 1961– . Guggenheim fellow (Brazil, Argentina, Uruguay), 1945–46; consultant President's Materials Policy Commission 1951, Public Advisory Board for Mutual Security, 1952, Committee on Public Work U.S. House of Representatives, 1962 Membership: American Accounting Association; American Association of University Professors; American Economic Association; American Political Science Association; Pi Gamma Mu. Research: economic development; economic theory and its history. Author: The Brazilian Economy (1949); Development of Economic Thought (1952); Current Economic Problems (1961 Language: Spanish 2,–,–,–; Portuguese 2,–,–,–; French 2,–,2,–; German 5,5,5, Home: 6848 Nashville Rd., Lanham, M Office: Dept. of Economics, Catholic U. of America, Washington, D.C. 20017.

SPIESS, LINCOLN BUNCE, b. Hartford Conn., Nov. 14, 1913. MUSIC. A.B., Harvard U., 1935; A.M., 1937; Ph. D., 194 Asst. organist, Old South Church (Boston 1935–41; lectr., U. of Calif., Los Angeles 1947–48; asst. prof., Miami U., 1948–5 ASSOC. PROF., MUSIC, WASHINGTON U 1951– . Research grant, Summer 196 Membership: American Musicological Society; Archaeological Society of New Mexico; College Music Society; Missouri Historical Society; New Mexico Historical Society. Research: Middle Ages and Renaissance; organ; Latin American musicology; New Mexican mission music, 1598–185 Author: Historical Musicology (1963); The Diatonic Chromaticism of the Enchiriad Treatises (Journal of the American Musicological Society, Spring 1959); Benavid and Church Music in New Mexico in t Early Seventeenth Century (Journal of t American Musicological Society, Summ 1964). Language: Spanish 3,2,2,3; Portuguese 2,1,1,1; French 4,2,2,3; German 4,3,3,3; Italian 3,2,2,3; Latin 3,1,1, Home: 4475 West Pine Blvd. St. Louis, M 63108. Office: Dept. of Music, Washington U., St. Louis, 63130.

SPIRO, BENJAMIN PAUL, b. Concise, Vau Switzerland, June 6, 1917. ECONOMIC Lic. Sc. Pol., U. of Lausanne, 1939; Lic. Ec., 1940; Dr. Sc. Pol., 1941; Columbia 1941–42. Vis. prof., Duke U., 1946–4 financial analyst, operations officer, Wor Bank, 1947–59; president, Bank Fund F eral Credit Union, 1959; program manag International Finance, Stanford Resear Institute, 1959–60; PRESIDENT, FO

286

EIGN ECONOMIC AND FINANCIAL CONSULTANT, BENJAMIN SPIRO ASSOCIATES, INC. OF CALIFORNIA, 1962– . Consultant, International Labor Organization, Caja de Crédito Agrario, Industrial y Minero (Bogotá), Coney Argentina, S.A., Inter-American Development Bank, 1960–64. Membership: American Association of University Professors; American Economic Association. Research: organization and function of development institutions. Author: Organization of Agricultural Credit Institutions in Latin America (1958); A Plan for the Reorganization of the Government Credit Institutions of Paraguay (1960); Small Scale Industry in Latin America, Chile, Peru, Colombia, Puerto Rico (1964). Language: Spanish 5,5,5,5; Portuguese 4,4,3,3; French 5,5,5,5; German 4,4,3,3; Italian 4,4,3,–. Office: Benjamin Spiro Associates, Inc., 24 California St., San Francisco, Calif., 94111.

SPORES, RONALD MARVIN, b. Eugene, Oreg., Jan. 25, 1931. ANTHROPOLOGY. B.S., U. of Oreg., 1953; M.A., U. of the Americas, 1960; A.M., Harvard U., 1963; Ph. D., 1964. ASST. PROF., ANTHROPOLOGY, U. OF MASS., 1964– . Harvard fellow and Kendall fellow, Harvard U.; National Institute of Mental Health fellow; National Defense fellow. Research: archeology; historical documentation pertaining to native Americans; modern community study; culture history of the Mixtec and Zapotec Indians of Oaxaca, Mexico. Author: The Genealogy of Tlazultepec: A Sixteenth Century Mixtec Manuscript (Southwestern Journal of Anthropology, Spring 1964); Mixtec and Zapotec at the Spanish Conquest (in Handbook of Middle American Indians). Language: Spanish 4,4,4,3. Office: Dept. of Sociology and Anthropology, U. of Mass., Amherst.

STAATS, WILLIAM F., b. San Antonio, Tex., Feb. 9, 1938. ECONOMICS: FINANCE. B.S., Tex. Lutheran Coll., 1960; M.B.A., U. of Tex., 1961; Ph. D., 1965. Teacher, U. of Tex., 1961–63; PROF., COMMERCE AND FINANCE, RICE U., 1963– . Membership: American Economic Association; American Finance Association. Research: financial institutions; macroeconomics; banking structures; Mexico. Author: Sale-Leaseback of Real Estate as a Financing Device (1963); Automation of Bank Operations (Texas Business Review, Oct. 1962); Employment Patterns in Texas (Texas Business Review, Sept. 1963). Language: Spanish 3,2,2,2; Portuguese 1,1,1,1; French 2,1,1,1; German 1,2,2,1. Home: 1529 Wirt Rd., Houston, Tex., 77055. Office: Dept. of Commerce, Rice U., Houston, 77001.

STABB, MARTIN S., b. New York, N.Y., Apr. 5, 1928. SPANISH AMERICAN LITERATURE. B.A., Rutgers U., 1949; M.A., U. of Calif., Los Angeles, 1953; Ph. D., 1956. Instr., Colgate U., 1953–55; ASSOC. PROF., SPANISH, U. OF MO., 1955– ; dir., Language Laboratory, 1958–61; dir., National Defense Education Act Summer Language Institute, U. of Mo., Summer 1961. Consultant, Board of Education, City of St. Louis, 1960; American Philosophical Society research grant, 1962; consultant, Language Institute Program, U.S. Office of Education, 1962. Membership: American Association of Teachers of Spanish and Portuguese; Modern Language Association. Research: Spanish American intellectual history; the essay in Spanish American literature. Author: Martí and the Racists (Hispania, Dec. 1957); Indigenism and Racism in Mexican Thought, 1857–1911 (Journal of Inter-American Studies, Oct. 1959); La Bella Dormida: Analysis of the Image (Hispania, May 1963). Language: Spanish 5,5,5,4; Portuguese 4,3,3,3; French 4,2,2,2. Home: 1211 Frances Dr., Columbia, Mo. Office: Dept. of Romance Languages, U. of Mo., Columbia.

STALEY, A. EUGENE, b. Friend, Nebr., July 3, 1906. ECONOMICS. A.B., Hastings Coll., 1925; Ph. D., U. of Chicago, 1928. Asst. prof., U. of Chicago, 1931–37; assoc. prof.-prof., Fletcher School of Law & Diplomacy, 1937–44; economist, U.S. Dept. of State, 1943–44; prof., School of Advanced International Studies, Johns Hopkins U., 1944–45; lectr., Stanford U., 1945–46; research assoc., Stanford U., 1948–50; SENIOR INTERNATIONAL ECONOMIST, DIR. OF BASIC RESEARCH, INTERNATIONAL DEVELOPMENT CENTER, STANFORD RESEARCH INSTITUTE, 1949– ; chief economist, Cuban Mission of the International Bank for Reconstruction and Development, 1950–51. U. of Chicago fellow, 1928–29; Social Science Research Council traveling fellow (Europe), 1929–30, 1930–31; United Nations Conference on International Organization, 1945; consultant, Venezuelan Development Corporation, 1963; team leader, Stanford Research Institute (Colombia), 1962; U.S. delegation to United Nations Conference on the Application of Science and Technology for the Benefit of the Less Developed Areas (Geneva), 1963; consultant, U.S. Agency for International Development (Peru), 1964. Membership: American Economic Association; Council on Foreign Relations; National Planning Association; Society for International Development. Research; economic and social development, including industrial development; human resources development; education in relation to development; small-medium industry development in Peru and Colombia. Author: The Future of Underdeveloped Countries: Political Implications of Economic Development (1954, 1961). Co-author: A Manual of Industrial Development (1954). Editor: Creating an Industrial Civilization (1952). Language: Spanish 3,3,3,3; French 4,3,3,3; Arabic –,1,1,–; German 4,3,3,3; Italian 3,2,2,1: Home: 455 Seale Ave., Palo Alto, Calif. Office: Stanford Research Institute, Menlo Park, Calif.

STALEY, CHARLES EARL, b. Wichita, Kans., Feb. 17, 1927. ECONOMICS. B.A., U. of Kans., 1950; Ph. D., Mass. Institute of Technology, 1956. PROF., ECONOMICS, U. OF KANS., 1953– . Carnegie grant, Kans. U.-Costa Rica faculty exchange, Summers 1960–61; Watkins summer faculty fellow, U. of Kans., 1962; Ford Foundation faculty fellow, 1963–64. Membership: American Economic Association; Midwest Economic Association; Royal Economic Society. Research: international trade; economic development; Central American Common Market. Author: Response to Agricultural Prices in Costa Rica (The Economic Journal, June 1961); Costa Rica and the Central American Common Market (Economia Internazionale, Feb. 1962); Central American Economic Integration (Southern Economic Journal, Oct. 1962). Language: Spanish 4,3,3,3. Office: Dept. of Economics, U. of Kans., Lawrence.

STANISLAWSKI, DAN, b. Bellingham, Wash., Apr. 20, 1903. GEOGRAPHY. A.B., U. of Calif., Berkeley, 1937; Ph. D., 1944. Instr. Syracuse U., 1941–42; instr., U. of Calif., Berkeley, 1942–45; asst. prof., U. of Wash., 1945–47; assoc. prof., U. of Pa., 1947–49; prof., U. of Tex., 1949–62; PROF., CHMN., GEOGRAPHY, U. OF ARIZ., 1962– . Guggenheim fellow, 1952; Social Science Research Council fellow, 1952; Fulbright lectr., U. of Brazil, 1961. Research: historical and urban geography. Author: The Anatomy of Eleven Towns in Michoacan (1950); The Individuality of Portugal (1959); Portugal's Other Kingdom: The Algarve (1963). Language: Spanish 4,4,4,4; Portuguese 3,3,3,3; French 2,2,2,2. Home: 4125 East Roberts Pl., Tucson, Ariz. Office: Dept. of Geography, U. of Ariz., Tucson.

STANLEY, RAYMOND WALLACE, b. Allahabad, India, Oct. 9, 1916. GEOGRAPHY. A.B., U. of Chicago, 1941; M.A., 1947; Ph. D., U. of Calif., Los Angeles, 1954. Asst. prof., George Peabody Coll., 1947–50; instr., Fresno State Coll., 1953–54; asst. prof., Bradley U., 1954–56; ASSOC. PROF., GEOGRAPHY, SAN JOSE STATE COLL., 1956– . Membership: American Geographic Society; Association of American Geographers; Association of Pacific Coast Geographers; California Council of Geography Teachers. Research: political geography; upper Colorado delta of Mexico. Language: Spanish 2,1,1,1. Home: 1177 Husted Ave., San Jose, Calif. 95125. Office: Dept. of Economics and Geography, San Jose State Coll., San Jose, 95114.

STANSIFER, CHARLES LEE, b. Garden City, Kans., Dec. 13, 1930. HISTORY. B.A., Wichita U., 1953; M.A., 1954; Ph. D., Tulane U., 1959. Asst. prof., U. of Southwestern La., 1958–63; ASST. PROF., HISTORY, U. OF KANS., 1963– . Doherty fellow (Chile), 1962–63. Membership: American Association of University Professors; Conference on Latin American History; Mississippi Valley Historical Association. Research: United States relations with Central America; Latin American politics, 1920–40. Author: Cumulative Index to Volumes XXXVI–XLV (1949–1959) of the Mississippi Valley Historical Review (1961); Mexican Foreign Policy in the United Nations: The Advocacy of Moderation in an Era of Revolution (Southwestern Social Science Quarterly, Sept. 1963). Langauge: Spanish 5,4,4,4; Portuguese 4,3,1,1; French 3,2,2,2; Italian 3,2,2,1. Home: 1023 Highland Dr., Lawrence, Kans. Office: Dept. of History, U. of Kans., Lawrence.

STARK, DONALD STEWART, b. Wilkes-Barre, Pa., Oct. 9, 1915. LINGUISTICS. M.A., U. of N. Dak., 1959; Cornell U. Special instr., Wheaton Coll., 1956–59; MEMBER, SUMMER INSTITUTE OF LINGUISTICS, 1941– . National Defense Education Act fellow in Spanish. Research: Mixteco language Bible translation; Pucallpa area in Peru. Author: Boundary Markers in Dakota (International Journal of American Linguistics, Apr. 1962). Language: Spanish 5,4,4,4; Portuguese 3,2,1,1; French 3,2,2,1; Italian 3,2,2,1. Linguistic studies: Dakota; Mixteco. Office: Summer Institute of Linguistics, Box 1960, Santa Ana, Calif.

STARKEY, OTIS PAUL, b. Buffalo, N.Y., Apr. 14, 1906. GEOGRAPHY. B.S., Columbia U., 1927; A.M., 1930; Ph. D., 1939. Asst. prof., U. of Pa., 1931–42; head geographer, Topographic Dept., Military Intelligence, 1942–45; deputy dir., Planning Dept., U.S. Dept. of State, 1945–46; PROF. GEOGRAPHY, IND. U., 1946– . Recipient, Office of Naval Research Contract (Lesser Antilles), 1958–59. Membership: American Association for the Advancement of Science; American Geographical Society; Association of American Geographers; Institute of Caribbean Studies; National Council for Geographic Education. Research: economic geography; the Caribbean. Author: Introductory Economic Geography (1937, 1940, 1956); Economic Geography of Barbados (1939). Language: Spanish 2,1,1,–; Portuguese 1,1,1,–; French 3,2,2,2; German 2,2,2,2. Home: 2602 Browncliff, Bloomington, Ind. Office: Dept. of Geography, Ind. U., Bloomington.

STAUFFER, DAVID HALL, b. Shanghai, China, Nov. 3, 1921. HISTORY. B.A., Amherst Coll., 1946; M.A., Columbia U., 1952; Ph. D., U. of Tex., 1955. Teacher, Kiskiminitas Springs School (Pa.), 1949–51; asst. prof., Union Coll., 1955–56; diplomatic historian, U.S. Dept. of State, 1956–62; REPRESENTATIVE, U.S. PEACE CORPS, 1962– ; dir., U.S. Peace Corps Education Project (British Honduras), 1962–64. Membership: Phi Alpha Theta; Phi Delta Kappa. Research: Brazil; British Honduras. Author: Central American Sections (in Foreign Relations of the United States, Diplomatic Papers, 1943–44); Origin and Establishment of Brazil's Indian Service (Revista de História, São Paulo, 1957). Language: Spanish 3,2,1,1; Portuguese 2,1,1,1; French 2,1,1,1; Chinese –,1,1,–. Office: U.S. Peace Corps, Washington 25, D.C.

STEELE, ARTHUR ROBERT, b. Oakland, Calif., Oct. 28, 1916. HISTORY. A.B., U. of Calif., Berkeley, 1937; M.A., U. of N. Mex., 1950; Ph. D., Duke U., 1957. Asst. prof., State U. of N.Y., Coll. at Buffalo, 1957; instr.-ASSOC. PROF., HISTORY, DIR., UNIVERSITY HONORS PROGRAM, U. OF TOLEDO, 1957– . Doherty fellow (Peru and Chile), 1951–52. Membership: American Historical Association; Conference on Latin American History; Midwest Council of the Association for Latin American Studies. Research: colonial period; intellectual history. Author: Flowers for the King: The Expedition of Ruiz and Pavón and the Flora of Peru (1964). Language: Spanish 4,3,3,3; Portuguese 2,1,1,1; French 3,1,1,1. Office: Dept. of History, U. of Toledo, Toledo, Ohio 43606.

STEELE, HOWARD LOUCKS, b. Pittsburgh, Pa., Jan. 27, 1929. ECONOMICS. B.S., Washington and Lee U., 1950; M.S., Pa. State U., 1952; Ph. D., U. of Ky., 1962. Sales manager, secretary-treasurer, Greenville Dairy Company, 1952–56; asst. agricultural economist-assoc. prof., Clemson U., 1956–64; ASSOC. PROF., AGRICULTURAL ECONOMICS, OHIO STATE-U.S. AGENCY

FOR INTERNATIONAL DEVELOPMENT-BRAZIL CONTRACT (PIRACICABA, BRAZIL), 1964– . Consulting economist, Beverly Farms, Inc. (Pittsburgh, Pa.), Summer 1962; chmn., Technical Committee, Southern Regional Food Marketing Research Project 13, 1962–63; participant, First National Workshop on Improving Undergraduate Instruction in Agricultural Economics, American Farm Economic Association, 1963. Membership: American Association for the Advancement of Science; American Farm Economic Association; American Marketing Association; Association of Southern Agricultural Workers; South Carolina Academy of Science. Research: agricultural marketing; consumption economics; business organization and management. Author: Discussion—Use of Controlled Experiments to Estimate Demand (Proceedings, Association of Southern Agricultural Workers Annual Convention, Feb. 1963); How University, Business and Government Researchers Can Work Together in Doing Market Tests and Collecting Relevant Data on New Products (Proceedings, Fourth National Symposium on Dairy Market Development, Feb. 1964). Co-author: Can We Sell More Milk? (The Sunbelt Dairyman, Jan. 1963). Language: Spanish 2,2,1,1; Portuguese 3,3,3,3; French 2,1,1,2; German 3,3,3,3. Home: 1145 Rua Dr. Alvim, Piracicaba, São Paulo, Brazil. Office: Dept. of Agricultural Economics and Rural Sociology, 2120 Fyffe Rd., Ohio State U., Columbus, Ohio 43210.

STEIGERWALT, ALBERT K., b. New York, N.Y., Dec. 20, 1919. ECONOMICS. B.A., Wayne State U., 1946; A.M., U. of Mich., 1951; Ph. D., 1952. Research assoc., U. of Mich., 1953–57; PROF., BUSINESS ADMINISTRATION, U. OF MICH., 1953– . U. of Mich. fellow, 1950–51; chmn., Conference on Business History, 1954– ; executive committee, Program in International Business; dir., Venezuelan Student Leader Seminar, 1960–63. Membership: American Historical Association; Conference on Business History; Mississippi Valley Historical Association. Research: business and economic development; higher education in Venezuela. Author: Locational Factors in Iron and Steel Industry (1954); The National Association of Manufacturing (1963); Student Tyranny in Latin America (Michigan Quarterly, Autumn 1963). Language: Spanish 3,2,2,2; French 3,2,2,2; German 4,2,2,2. Home: 1535 Stonehaven Rd., Ann Arbor, Mich. Office: Graduate School of Business Administration, U. of Mich., Ann Arbor.

STEIN, STANLEY J., b. New York, N.Y., June 8, 1920. HISTORY. B.A., City Coll. (N.Y.), 1941; M.A., Harvard U., 1948; Ph. D., 1951. PROF., HISTORY, PRINCETON U., 1953– . Social Science Research Council fellow (Brazil), 1948–49; Woodbury Lowery fellow, 1948–49; research fellow, Research Center in Entrepreneurial History, Harvard U., 1950–53; Guggenheim fellow (Mexico), 1958–59; Joint Committee on Latin American Studies, Social Science Research Council-American Council of Learned Societies; Translation Committee, Association of American University Presses. Membership: American Historical Association; Conference on Latin American History. Research: history of Brazil and Mexico, 1750–1900. Author: Vassouras, a Brazilian Coffee County, 1850–1900 (1957); The Brazilian Cotton Manufacture: Textile Enterprise in an Under developed Area, 1850–1950; (1957); Brazilian Historiography (Hispanic American Historical Review, May 1960). Language: Spanish 4,4,4,4; Portuguese 4,4,4,4; French 4,4,3,3. Home: 12 Edgehill St., Princeton, N.J. Office: Dept. of History, Princeton U., Princeton.

STEIN, WILLIAM W., b. Buffalo, N.Y., Oct. 9, 1921. ANTHROPOLOGY. A.B., U. of Buffalo, 1949; Ph. D., Cornell U., 1955. Research asst., Human Relations Area Files, Yale U., 1955–56; asst. prof.-assoc. prof., U. of Miami, 1956–61; asst. prof., U. of Alberta, 1961–63; field instr., Columbia, Cornell, Harvard, Ill. Universities Summer Field Session (Vicos, Peru), 1962; ASST. PROF., ANTHROPOLOGY, U. OF KANS., 1963– . Fulbright lectr., Universidad de San Marcos (Peru), 1959. Membership: American Anthropological Association; Society for Applied Anthropology. Research: social and cultural anthropology; public health; community development; folk cultures of Latin America; cultural change; medical anthropology; culture and language in Latin America; community study of Andean Indian village in Peru. Author: Hualcan: Life in the Highlands of Peru (1961); Patterns of a Peruvian Mental Hospital (International Journal of Social Psychiatry, Summer 1963). Language: Spanish 3,4,4,2; Portuguese 1,–,–,–; French 2,1,2,1; German 2,–,–,–. Linguistic studies: Ancash dialect of Quechua. Home: 637 Tennessee St., Lawrence, Kans. Office: Dept. of Sociology and Anthropology, U. of Kans., Lawrence.

STEPHENS, RICHARD HUNTER, b. Salt Lake City, Utah, May 10, 1920. POLITICAL SCIENCE. B.A., U. of Utah, 1941; M.P.A., Harvard U., 1958; George Washington U. Military intelligence officer, Caribbean Defense Command (Panama), 1942–43; foreign service officer, U.S. Dept. of State, 1945–62; vis. lectr., Yale U., 1961–63; professorial lectr., George Washington U., 1962–64; PRESIDENT, INTERNATIONAL STUDY CENTER, INC., 1962– . Latin American expert, Draper Committee, The White House, 1959. Membership: American Association of University Professors; American Political Science Association; American Studies Association; Rural Sociological Association. Research: political socialization in Latin America; overseas operations of the United States Government; United States Government policies in relation to Latin American intellectuals. Author: Developing an American Diplomatic Tradition (Foreign Service Journal, Jan. 1951); The Impact of Administration on the Foreign Service (Foreign Service Journal, Jan. 1953); American Constitutional System (Australian Quarterly, 1953). Language: Spanish 4,4,4,3; Portuguese 4,3,3,3; French 3,3,3,3. Home: 5415 York Lane, Bethesda 14, Md. Office: International Study Center, Inc., 1755 Massachusetts Ave., NW., Washington, D.C. 20036.

STERN, DAVID SACHS, b. Chicago, Ill., July 27, 1919. LAW. LL.M., N.Y.U., 1949, Doctor de Ciencias Sociales y Derecho Público, U. of Havana, 1957; S.J.D., N.Y.U., 1960. Prof., dir., Interamerican Legal Studies Program, School of Law, U. of Miami, 1950–

63; lectr., U. of Guadalajara (Mexico), 1955–56; lectr., U. of Mexico, Summer 1959; area studies coordinator, U.S. Peace Corps Training Center, U. of Wash., 1963–64; RESEARCH LAWYER, CENTER FOR STUDY OF LAW AND SOCIETY, U. OF CALIF., BERKELEY, 1964– . Membership: American Bar Association; American Foreign Law Association; American Society of International Law; Dade County Bar; Florida Bar; Inter-American Bar Association; Panamanian Academy of International Law. Research: inter-American development; law and politics of Mexico and Cuba. Author: Notes on the History of Puerto Rico's Common Status (Revista Jurídica, 1961). Language: Spanish 5,5,5,5; Portuguese 4,4,4,3; French 3,4,3,3; German 4,4,3,3; Italian 3,4,3,2; Norwegian 3,3,3,2. Home: 1444 Walnut Ave., Berkeley, Calif. Office: Center for Study of Law and Society, U. of Calif., Berkeley.

STERNBERG, HILGARD O'REILLY, b. Rio de Janeiro, Brazil, July 5, 1917. GEOGRAPHY. Ph. D., La. State U., 1956; Doutor, Universidade do Brasil, 1958. Asst. prof., Universidade do Brasil, 1942–44; prof., 1944–64; PROF., GEOGRAPHY, U. OF CALIF., BERKELEY, 1964– . Former dir., Center for Research in Geography of Brazil, Universidade do Brasil; Guggenheim fellow; former representative, Central Directory, National Council of Geography, Ministry of Education (Brazil). Membership: Associação dos Geógrafos Brasileiros; Brazilian Academy of Sciences; International Geographical Union; Gesellschaft für Erdkunde zu Berlin; Société de Géographie (Paris). Research: regional geography, especially of Latin America, Brazil, humid tropics, and arid lands; relations of man and land; pioneer settlements in Brazil; ecological framework and economic significance of trace element deficiencies. Author: A água e o homem na várzea do Careiro (1956); Radiocarbon Dating Applied to Amazonian Morphology (1959); Brasilië (1963). Language: Spanish 4,3,3,3; Portuguese 5,5,5,5; French 4,4,3,3; German 4,4,4,4. Office: Dept. of Geography, U. of Calif., Berkeley 4.

STERNBERG, MARVIN JOHN, b. Minneapolis, Minn., Dec. 1, 1933. ECONOMICS. A.B., U. of Calif., Berkeley, 1955; M.A., 1962; Ph. D., 1962. Acting instr., U. of Calif., Berkeley, 1962; consultant, Inter-American Committee for Agricultural Development, 1962–64; MEMBER DIV., INTERNATIONAL LABOUR OFFICE (GENEVA, SWITZERLAND), 1964– . Inter-American Cultural Committee grant (Chile), 1960–61. Membership: American Economic Association; Asociación de Economistas Agrarias de Chile. Research: economic development; land tenure institutions; agrarian reform; Chilean land tenure. Author: Distribución de los ingresos en la agricultura chilena (Panorama Económico, Dec. 1961). Co-author: Reforma agraria y crédito campesino en Chile (Desarrollo Económico, May–June 1964). Language: Spanish 4,4,4,4; Portuguese 3,2,1,1; French 2,2,2,1. Home: 20 Chemin de L'Esplanade, 1214 Vernier, Suisse. Office: International Labour Office, Co-op Rural and Related Institutions Branch, Geneva, Switzerland.

STERRETT, DELBERT ELLINGSWORTH, b. Allerton, Iowa, Dec. 7, 1911. MUSIC. B.A., Tarkio Coll., 1935; M.A., Columbia U., 1942; Ed. D., Peabody Coll. for Teachers, 1957. Instr., Assiut Coll. (Egypt), 1935–38; instr., American U. (Cairo), 1938–40; professional tenor (N.Y.), 1940–42; Foreign Service Auxiliary, Embassy (Bogotá), U.S. Dept. of State, 1942–45; instr., Adelphi Coll. for Women, 1945–48; prof., U. of Fla., 1948–63; PROGRAM DIR., FLA. UNION, U. OF FLA., 1963– . Julliard School of Music fellow. Membership: Alpha Psi Omega; American Graphological Association; Music Educators National Conference; Music Teachers National Association; Phi Delta Kappa. Research: music education and recreation; choral teaching; recreation for senior citizens of Florida; stage production. Author: Profile of Current Music Activities in Central America (in The Caribbean: The Central American Area, 1961); The Zarzuela (in Encyclopedia Americana, 1963). Language: Spanish 3,3,3,2; French 2,2,1,1; Italian 2,2,2,2. Home: 2100 NW. 8th Ct., Gainesville, Fla. Office: Fla. Union, U. of Fla., Gainesville, 32603.

STEVENS, ROBERT CONWAY, b. Elgin, Ill., Mar. 2, 1924. HISTORY. B.A., U. of Ariz., 1953; M.A., 1954; Ph. D., U. of Calif., Berkeley, 1963. RESEARCH ASSOC., HISTORY, U. OF ARIZ., 1962– . Arizona Historical Convention Committee, 1963–64. Membership: American Historical Association; Pacific Coast Council on Latin American Studies. Research: archival research on northern Mexico; history of Sonora, 1821–1846. Author: A History of Chandler, Arizona (1955). Language: Spanish 4,2,3,1; Portuguese 2,1,1,1; French 2,1,1,1. Home: 7005 East Kingston Dr., Tucson, Ariz. Office: Dept. of History, U. of Ariz., Tucson.

STEVENSON, JOHN R., b. Chicago, Ill., Oct. 24, 1921. LAW. A.B., Princeton U., 1942; LL.B., Columbia U., 1949; D.J.S., 1952. Asst. naval attaché, U.S. Navy (Madrid), 1944–45; political desk officer, Caribbean Div., Office of American Republic Affairs, U.S. Dept. of State, 1946–47; lectr., School of Law, Columbia U., 1949–50; assoc., Sullivan & Cromwell, 1950–55; PARTNER, SULLIVAN & CROMWELL, 1955– . Princeton U. fellow (Chile), 1941; fellow, School of Law, Columbia U., 1949–50; editor-in-chief, Columbia Law Review, 1950; editor, American Journal of International Law, 1963– . Membership: American Bar Association; American Law Institute; Association of the Bar of the City of New York. Research: public international law; law of international transactions; corporate law and finance; international political and financial matters. Author: The Chilean Popular Front (1942); The Relationship of Private International Law to Public International Law (Columbia Law Review, May 1952); Legal Aspects of Public Offering of Foreign Securities in the United States Market (George Washington Law Review, Oct. 1959). Language: Spanish 5,4,4,3; French 3,3,3,2. Home: 1120 Fifth Ave., New York 28, N.Y. Office: Sullivan & Cromwell, 48 Wall St., New York.

STEVENSON, ROBERT MURRELL, b. Melrose, N. Mex., July 3, 1916. MUSIC. M. Mus., Yale U., 1939; Ph. D., U. of Rochester, 1942; B. Litt., Oxford U., 1954. Instr., U. of Tex., 1941–46; faculty member, Westminster Choir Coll., 1946–49; instr.-PROF.,

MUSIC, U. OF CALIF., LOS ANGELES, 1949– ; vis. asst. prof., Columbia U., 1955–56; vis. prof., Ind. U., 1959–60. Buenos Aires Convention fellow (Mexico), 1950; Ford Foundation fellow, 1953–54; Carnegie Foundation grant, 1955–56; Fulbright research fellow (Peru), 1958–59, (Portugal), 1963–64; Organization of American States grant (Colombia, Ecuador), 1960; American specialist, U.S. Dept. of State (Brazil, Argentina), 1962; Guggenheim fellow (Guatemala), 1962. Membership: Inter-American Conference on Musicology; Music Library Association. Research: piano; composition; Latin American and Iberian music. Author: Spanish Music in the Age of Columbus (1960); The Music of Peru (1960); Spanish Cathedral Music in the Golden Age (1961). Language: Spanish 4,4,4,4; Portuguese 4,4,3,3; French 4,4,3,3; German 3,–,–,– ; Latin 3,–,–,–. Home: Apt. 321, 2801 Quebec St. NW., Washington 8, D.C. Office: Dept. of Music, U. of Calif., 405 Hilgard Ave., Los Angeles 24.

STEWART, DONALD EDWARD JAMES, b. La Ceiba, Honduras, Feb. 24, 1932. BIBLIOGRAPHY. B.A., Washington & Lee U., 1955; M.A., George Washington U., 1960. Asst. to the editor, Handbook of Latin American Studies, 1962–64; Foreign Service officer, U.S. Dept. of State, 1964–65; VICE-CONSUL (YOKOHAMA, JAPAN), U.S. DEPT. OF STATE, 1965– . U.S. Dept of State Foreign Service Institute guest lectr.; George Washington U. guest lectr. on international politics of the Western Hemisphere; administrative asst. and dir. of evening programs for participants in the Andean Seminar, International Study Center. Membership: American Historical Association; Association of Latin American Studies; Inter-American Council. Research: Latin American history, especially that of Central America; Latin American bibliography. Language: Spanish 5,5,5,5; Portuguese 4,3,3,1; French 4,4,4,2. Home and office: American Consulate General, FPO, San Francisco, Calif., 96661.

STEWART, NANCY C., b. New York, N.Y., Mar. 10, 1922. LANGUAGE. B.S., U. of Minn., 1944; Litt. D., Universidad Nacional Mayor de San Marcos (Peru), 1950. Teacher, Revillo High School (S. Dak.), 1943–45; teacher, Junior and Senior High Schools (Escanaba, Mich.), 1945–47; teacher, Boulder City High School (Nev.), 1947–48; TEACHER, SPANISH, CENTRAL HIGH SCHOOL (FARGO, N. DAK.), 1951– . Participant, Survey of Foreign Language Offerings and Enrollments in Public Secondary Schools, Modern Language Association, 1958–59; Foreign Language Curriculum Committee, Fargo Public Schools, 1958–62. Membership: American Association of Teachers of Spanish and Portuguese; National Education Association; North Dakota Education Association. Author: La alimentación del pueblo peruano (1950); A Look at a Language Lab (North Dakota Teacher, Mar. 1960); A Look at the Peace Corps (North Dakota Teacher, Sept. 1963). Language: Spanish 5,5,4,5. Linguistic studies: Spanish. Home: 2614 9½ St. North, Fargo, N. Dak. Office: Dept. of Foreign Languages, Central High School, Fargo.

STEWART, NORMAN REGINALD, b. Los Angeles, Calif., Oct. 1, 1928. GEOGRAPHY. B.A., U. of Calif., Los Angeles, 1950; M.A., 1955; Ph. D., 1963. Instr., Los Angeles State Coll., 1959–61; ASST. PROF., GEOGRAPHY, U. OF NEBR., 1962– . National Academy of Science-National Research Council grant (Paraguay), 1958; Fulbright lectr., Universidad de Ayacucho (Peru), 1961–62. Membership: American Geographical Society; Association of American Geographers; Sigma Xi. Research: physical and cultural geography; settlement in Mexico; Paraguay; Peru. Author: Tea: A New Agricultural Industry for Argentina (Economic Geography, July 1960); Foreign Agricultural Colonization as a Study in Cultural Geography (Professional Geographer, Sept. 1962). Language: Spanish 4,4,4,3; German 2,2,1,1. Home: 3331 T. St., Lincoln, Nebr. 68503. Office: Dept. of Geography, U. of Nebr., Lincoln, 68508.

STEWART, THOMAS DALE, b. Delta, Pa., June 10, 1901. ANTHROPOLOGY. A.B., George Washington U., 1927; M.D., Johns Hopkins U., 1931. Aid, Div. of Physical Anthropology, Museum of Natural History, Smithsonian Institution, 1927–31; asst. curator, 1931–39; assoc. curator, 1939–42; curator, 1942–61; head curator, Dept. of Anthropology, 1961–63; DIR., MUSEUM OF NATURAL HISTORY, SMITHSONIAN INSTITUTION, 1 9 6 3– . Membership: American Anthropological Association; American Association of Physical Anthropology. Research: physical anthropology in Mexico, Guatemala, and Peru. Author: Stone Age Skull Surgery: A General Review with Emphasis on the New World (1958); Skeletal Remains from Venado Beach, Panama (Proceedings, XXXIII Congress of Americanists, 1958); A Physical Anthropologist's View of the Peopling of the New World (Southwestern Journal of Anthropology, Sept. 1960). Language: Spanish 2,2,2,2; Portuguese 2,1,1,1; French 2,1,1,1. Home: 4533 Crest Lane, McLean, Va. Office: Museum of Natural History, Smithsonian Institution, Washington 25, D.C.

STEWART, WATT, b. Flatwoods, W. Va., Mar. 21, 1892. HISTORY. B.A., West Va. Wesleyan, 1920; M.A., U. of Chicago, 1925; Ph. D., 1928. Prof., Okla. State U., 1928–40; prof., chmn., History, State U. of N.Y., Coll. at Albany, 1940–57; PROF. EMERITUS, 1957– . Smith-Mundt lectr., U. of Guayaquil, U. of Cuenca, and Central U. (Ecuador), 1957–58; Guggenheim fellow (Costa Rica), 1958–59. Membership: American Historical Association; Conference on Latin American History; Sociedad Chilena de Historia y Geografía; Sociedad Costarricense de Geografía e Historia. Research: Latin American diplomatic relations. Author: Henry Meiggs: Yankee Pizarro (1946); Chinese Bondage in Peru (1951); Keith and Costa Rica (1964). Language: Spanish 4,4,4,3; French 4,3,2,1. Home: F-4 Park Terrace Apts., 1020 Valencia, SE., Albuquerque, N. Mex. Office: Coll. of Education, State U. of N.Y., Albany.

STILLWELL, H. DANIEL, b. Staten Island, N.Y., Mar. 21, 1931. GEOGRAPHY AND FORESTRY. B.S., Duke U., 1952; M.F., 1954; Ph. D., Mich. State U., 1961. Research asst., Oregon Forest Research Center, 1954–57; instr., Eastern Mich. U., 1960–61; asst. prof., U. of Tex., 1961–62; ASST. PROF., GEOGRAPHY, EAST CAROLINA

COLL., 1962- . Pan American Institute of Geography and History fellow (Brazil), 1959. Membership: American Forestry Association; Association of American Geographers; Gamma Theta Upsilon; National Council for Geographic Education; National Parks Association; Sigma Xi. Research: physical geography; national parks; biogeography. Author: Initial Study of Kiln Drying Clear Douglas Fir Planks (Oregon Forest Products Laboratory Report, Jan. 1957); National Parks of Brazil—A Study in Recreation (Annals, Association of American Geographers, Sept. 1963). Language: Spanish 3,2,2,2; Portuguese 3,2,2,2; German 3,2,2,2. Home: 1107 East Wright Rd., Greenville, N.C. Office: Dept. of Geography, East Carolina Coll., Greenville.

STIMSON, FREDERICK SPARKS, b. Newark, Ohio, Jan. 1, 1919. SPANISH AMERICAN LITERATURE. B.A., Ohio State U., 1940; M.A., U. of Mich., 1948; Ph. D., 1952. Vis. prof., Universidad de Antioquia (Medellín, Colombia), 1943-46; dir., Cultural Institute, U.S. Dept. of State (Medellín, Colombia), 1944-46; asst. public affairs officer, Embassy (San Salvador, El Salvador), U.S. Dept. of State, 1947; assoc. prof., Franklin Coll., 1952-54; instr., Northwestern U., 1954-57; asst. prof., 1957-63; ASSOC. PROF., ROMANCE LANGUAGES, NORTHWESTERN U., 1963- . Princeton junior fellow, 1940-41; Ford Foundation grant, U. of Mich., 1951; Northwestern Graduate School research grants (Cuba), 1959-60. Membership: American Association of Teachers of Spanish and Portuguese; American Association of University Professors; Modern Language Association. Research: Spanish influence on North American literature; literature in Cuba; Gabriel de la Concepción Valdés. Author: Orígenes del hispanismo norteamericano (1961). Co-editor: Yo y el ladrón, by Fernández Flores (1957); Moctezuma, el de la silla de oro, by Monterde (1958). Language: Spanish 5,5,5,5; French 4,4,3,4. Home: 2018 Sherman Ave., Evanston, Ill. Office: Dept. of Romance Languages, Northwestern U., Evanston.

STIRLING, MATTHEW W., b. Salinas, Calif., Aug. 28, 1896. ANTHROPOLOGY: ARCHEOLOGY. B.A., U. of Calif., 1920; M.A., George Washington U., 1922; D. Sc., Tampa U., 1943. Dir., Bureau of American Ethnology, Smithsonian Institution, 1928-58; RETIRED, 1958- ; RESEARCH ASSOC., SMITHSONIAN INSTITUTION, 1958- . Recipient, Franklyn L. Burr Award, 1939, 1941, 1958. Membership: American Anthropological Association; American Association for the Advancement of Science; National Geographic Society; Sigma Xi; Society for American Archaeology. Research: archeology and ethnology of Mexico, Panama, and Ecuador. Author: Historical and Ethnographical Material on the Jivaro Indians (1938); Stone Monuments of Southern Mexico (1943); Concepts of the Sun Among American Indians (in Smithsonian Institution Annual Report, 1945). Language: Spanish 3,3,3,3; French 3,2,1,1. Home: 3311 Rowland Pl. NW., Washington, D.C., 20008.

STOCKWELL, ROBERT PAUL, b. Oklahoma City, Okla., June 12, 1925. LINGUISTICS AND LANGUAGE. B.A., U. of Va., 1946; M.A., 1949; Ph. D., 1952. Prof., Language Training Branch, Foreign Service Institute, U.S. Dept. of State, 1952-56; PROF., ENGLISH AND LINGUISTICS, U. OF CALIF., LOS ANGELES, 1956- . American Council of Learned Societies fellow, 1963-64. Membership: Association for Machine Translation and Computational Linguistics; Linguistic Society of America; Modern Language Association. Research: Spanish linguistics; English philology. Author: Patterns of Spanish Pronunciation (1960); The Structures of English and Spanish (1964). Language: Spanish 4,4,4,2; Portuguese 2,2,2,1; French 2,2,2,1. Linguistic studies: English; Portuguese; Spanish; Tagalog. Office: Dept. of English, U. of Calif., Los Angeles, 90024.

STOKES, CHARLES J., b. Washington, D.C., Aug. 17, 1922. ECONOMICS. A.B., Boston U., 1943; A.M., 1947; Ph. D., Harvard U., 1950; Mass. Institute of Technology, 1950-51. Prof., Atlantic Union Coll., 1946-60; dean, 1954-56; dir. of economic research, Office of Price Stabilization, 1951-53; DANA PROF., CHMN., ECONOMICS, U. OF BRIDGEPORT, 1960- ; DIR., LATIN AMERICAN CASE STUDIES, BROOKINGS INSTITUTION, 1963- . Edwards scholar, 1940-43, 1946-47; Fulbright prof., Central U. of Ecuador, U. of Guayaquil, 1958-59, National U. of Litoral (Argentina), 1960 (Chile, Colombia), 1960-61; consultant, Development Program for Latin America, Ford Foundation, 1962; Argentine Government Medal, 1962. Membership: American Economic Association; Midwest Economic Association; Phi Beta Kappa. Research: economic development of Latin America; inflation; transportation. Author: Crecimiento Económico (1963); Theory of Slums (Land Economics, Aug. 1962); Inflación y desarrollo, caso de Argentina (Revista de Economía y Estadística, Jan.–Mar. 1963). Language: Spanish 5,5,5,5; Portuguese 3,3,2,2; French 3,3,2,2; German 2,3,2,2; Italian 4,4,2,2. Home: Pepper Crossing, Stepney, Conn. Office: Dept. of Economics, U. of Bridgeport, Bridgeport, Conn. 06604.

STOKES, WILLIAM SYLVANE, b. Willcox, Ariz., Feb. 21, 1916. POLITICAL SCIENCE. B.A., U. of Calif., Los Angeles, 1938; Ph. D., 1943. Instr.-asst. prof., Northwestern U., 1943-46; assoc. prof-prof., U. of Wis., 1946-58; vis. prof., U. of Calif., Berkeley, 1951-52; prof.-senior prof., Claremont Men's Coll., 1958-62; prof., National War Coll., 1962-63; SENIOR PROF., POLITICAL SCIENCE, CLAREMONT MEN'S COLL., 1963- . Volker Fund fellow; Relm Foundation fellow; Del Amo Foundation fellow; Social Science Research Council fellow; executive council. Inter-American Defense Coll., 1962-63. Membership: American Political Science Association; Western Political Science Association. Research: comparative government; international relations; political institutions and governmental development in Honduras; Cuba; Mexico; Central America. Author: Honduras, an Area Study in Government (1950); Latin American Politics (1959); U.S. Policy and Inter-American Misunderstandings (1964). Language: Spanish 5,5,5,5; Portuguese 4,2,1,1; French 3,1,1,1; German 3,1,1,1. Home: 1401 North Mountain Ave., Claremont, Calif. Office: Dept. of Political Science, Claremont Men's Coll., Claremont.

STONE ZEMURRAY, DORIS, b. New Orleans, La., Nov. 19, 1909. ANTHROPOLOGY. A.B., Radcliffe Coll., 1930. Research fellow in Central American Archeology and Ethnology, Peabody Museum, Harvard U.; research assoc., Tulane U.; member, Permanent Council, International Congress of Americanists. Membership: American Anthropological Association; Sociedad de Geografía e Historia de Guatemala; Sociedad de Geografía e Historia de Costa Rica; Sociedad de Geografía e Historia de Honduras; Society for American Archaeology. Research: New World archeology and ethnology; human ecology; folklore. Author: Archaeology of the North Coast of Honduras (1941); Archaeology of Southern and Central Honduras (1957); The Talamancan Tribes of Costa Rica (1961). Language: Spanish 5,5,5,5; French 3,3,3,1. Linguistic studies: Boruca; Bribri; Cabecar; Lenca. Home: Apartado 1309, San José, Costa Rica. Office: Museo Nacional, San José, Costa Rica; or Peabody Museum, Harvard U., Cambridge, Mass.

STOUDEMIRE, STERLING AUBREY, b. Concord, N.C., Sept. 4, 1902. LANGUAGE. A.B., U. of N.C., 1923; A.M., 1924; Ph. D., 1930. PROF., SPANISH, U. OF N.C., 1930– ; CHMN., ROMANCE LANGUAGES, 1949– . Membership: American Association of Teachers of Spanish and Portuguese; American Name Society; Modern Language Association. Research: Latin American history; Spanish literature. Translator: Oviedo's History of the West Indies (1959). Language: Spanish 5,5,5,5; Portuguese 5,3,3,3; French 5,3,3,3. Linguistic studies: Spanish. Home: 712 Gimghoul Rd., Chapel Hill, N.C. Office: Dept. of Romance Languages, U. of N.C., Chapel Hill.

STRASMA, JOHN D., b. Kankakee, Ill., Mar. 29, 1932. ECONOMICS. B.A., DePauw U., 1953; M.A., Harvard U., 1958; Ph. D., 1960. Expert, U.S. Agency for International Development (La Paz, Bolivia), 1961; Joint Mission, Economic Commission for Latin America-International Development Bank-Food and Agriculture Organization (La Paz, Bolivia), 1962; VIS. PROF., INSTITUTO DE ECONOMÍA, U. OF CHILE, 1960– . Danforth fellow, 1956–60; Fulbright vis. prof. (Chile), 1959; delegate, Conference of Latin American Faculties of Economics (Rosario. Argentina), 1960; contributing editor, Handbook of Latin American Studies, 1962– ; Conference of Social Science Research Council (Santiago), 1962; vis. prof., 2nd International Course for Land Reform Professionals (Santiago), Jan.-Feb. 1963, 4th International Course (Bogotá), Oct. 1963; vis. prof., International Seminar in Agricultural Taxation (Santiago), Nov. 1963; vis. prof., 1st National Course for Land Reform Professionals (Lima, Peru), Apr. 1964. Membership: American Economic Association; American Farm Economic Association; International Development Society; International Public Finance Association; National Tax Association. Research: public finance; tax reform; financing agrarian reform; monetary and fiscal measures in regional economic integration. Author: State and Local Taxation of Industry (1960); Financing Agrarian Reform in Peru (1964). Co-author: Free Trade Zone in Latin America: Some Unsolved Problems (1960). Language: Spanish 5,4,4,4; Portuguese 2,2,1,1; French 2,2,1,1. Home: Casilla 3861, Santiago, Chile. Office: Programa de Estudios Económicos Latinoamericanos para Graduados, Instituto de Economía, U. of Chile, Santiago.

STRASSMAN, W. PAUL, b. Berlin, Germany, July 26, 1926. ECONOMICS. B.A., U. of Tex., 1949; M.A., Columbia U., 1950; Ph. D., U. of Md., 1956. PROF., ECONOMICS, MICH. STATE U., 1956– . Social Science Research Council fellow, 1955–56, 1960–61. Membership: American Economic Association; Economic History Association. Research: economic development; Latin American industry; manufacturing in Mexico and Puerto Rico. Author: Risk and Technological Innovation (1959); Risk, Entrepreneurial Caution, and Business History (Business History Review, Winter 1958); Creative Destruction and Partial Obsolescence in American Economic Development (Journal of Economic History, Sept. 1959). Language: Spanish 4,4,4,4. Home: 1844 Walnut Heights Dr., East Lansing, Mich. Office: Dept. of Economics, Mich. State U., East Lansing.

STRATMEYER, DENNIS, b. Chicago, Ill., Jan. 25, 1932. LINGUISTICS. Diploma, Moody Bible Institute, 1953; B.A., Shelton Coll., 1956; U. of Okla. MISSIONARY, LINGUIST, SUMMER INSTITUTE OF LINGUISTICS (GUATEMALA), 1957– . Membership: American Anthropological Association; American Scientific Affiliation; Lingustic Society of America. Research: ethnology, especially of Mayan groups; Jacaltec tribe. Language: Spanish 4,4,3,3; Jacaltec –,3,3,–. Linguistic studies: Jacaltec. Home: Concepción H., Huehuetenango, Guatemala. Office: Summer Institute of Linguistics, Box 1960, Santa Ana, Calif.

STREET, JAMES H(ARRY), b. New Braunfels, Tex., Nov. 17, 1915. ECONOMICS. B.A., U. of Tex., 1940; M.A., 1947; Ph. D., U. of Pa., 1953; Ec. Sc. D. (honoris causa), National U. of Asunción (Paraguay), 1955. Instr., U. of Pa., 1946–48; asst. prof., Haverford Coll., 1948–52; PROF., ECONOMICS, RUTGERS U., 1952– . Old-right fellow, 1940; economic specialist, U.S. Dept. of State (Argentina), 1955; Smith-Mundt vis. prof., National U. of Asunción (Paraguay), 1955; vis. lectr., economic specialist, U.S. Dept. of State (Buenos Aires), 1957–58; Rutgers Research Council faculty fellow, 1962–63; Fulbright lectr., Peruvian-North American Cultural Institute and U. of San Marcos (Lima, Peru), 1963. Membership: American Economic Association; American Statistical Association; Council for Latin American Affairs; Hispanic American Society; Metropolitan Economic Association (N.Y.). Research: economic development; monetary theory and policy; international economics; agricultural economics; economic development in Argentina; inflation in developing countries. Author: The New Revolution in the Cotton Economy (1957); La inflación en los países en desarrollo (Selección Contable, July-Aug. 1958). Co-author: La Argentina y las firmas norteamericanas (1958). Language: Spanish 4,4,4,3; Portuguese 3,2,1,1; German 2,3,2,1. Home: 11 Lexington Dr., Metuchen, N.J. Office:

Dept. of Economics, U. Coll., Rutgers U., New Brunswick, N.J.

STREET, JOHN M., b. McIntosh, S. Dak., May 28, 1924. GEOGRAPHY. Ph. D., U. of Calif., Berkeley, 1960. Asst. prof., U. of Calif., Davis, 1960; ASST. PROF., GEOGRAPHY, U. OF HAWAII, 1960– . U.S. Office of Naval Research grant (Haiti, Dominican Republic), 1952–53. Membership: American Geographical Society; Association of American Geographers; Association of Pacific Coast Geographers; Hawaiian Academy of Science; Hawaiian Geophysical Society. Research: physical geography of the tropics; tropical agriculture. Author: Feral Animals in Hispaniola (Geographical Review, July 1962). Language: Spanish 4,4,3,3; Portuguese 4,2,3,3; French 4,4,4,4; Creole –,3,3,–; German 3,3,3,3; Japanese –,2,2,–. Home: 2243 Mohala Way, Honolulu, Hawaii. Office: Dept. of Geography, U. of Hawaii, Honolulu.

STRICKON, ARNOLD, b. New York, N.Y., July 19, 1930. ANTHROPOLOGY. B.A., City Coll. (N.Y.), 1952; M.A., Columbia U., 1954; Ph. D., 1960. Asst. prof., U. of Nev., 1960–61; ASST. PROF., ANTHROPOLOGY, BRANDEIS U., 1961– . Doherty fellow (Argentina), 1958–59; Columbia U. fellow, 1959–60. Membership: American Anthropological Association; American Association for the Advancement of Science; American Ethnological Society; Society for Applied Anthropology. Research: modern Latin American cultures; Euro-American ranching in Argentina; local community systems of economics, social stratification and organization and their relationships to national systems. Author: Class and Kinship in Argentina (Ethnology, Oct. 1962). Language: Spanish 3,4,4,4; Portuguese 3,2,1,1; French 2,1,1,1. Home: 22 Freeman St., Arlington, Mass. Office: Dept. of Anthropology, Brandeis U., Waltham 54.

STUBACH, CHARLES N(EFF), b. Yonkers, N.Y., Mar. 15, 1906. LANGUAGE. A.B., U. of Mich., 1928; M.A., 1930; Ph. D., 1937. Instr., La. State U., 1929–30; instr.-PROF., SPANISH, U. OF MICH., 1930– ; CHMN., 1954– ; vis. prof., English, Universidad Javeriana, Universidad Nacional, Institute de la Salle (Bogotá, Colombia), 1944–45; technical adviser, International Communications Foundation, National Defense Education Act Institute Film Project (Beverly Hills, Calif.), Summer 1959; vis. prof., National Defense Education Act Institute, U. of Mo., Summer 1960, Iona Coll., Summer 1962; vis. prof. of applied linguistics, U. of N. Mex., 1963–65. Consultant, Ginn & Company, 1957. Membership: American Association of Teachers of Spanish and Portuguese; Modern Language Association. Research: Spanish language and culture; Spanish-English comparisons; applied linguistics in the teaching of Spanish. Co-author: Revista de América (1943); First and Second Year Spanish (1961); Teaching Spanish: A Linguistic Orientation (1961). Language: Spanish 5,5,5,5; Portuguese 3,3,1,1; French 4,4,4,4; German 2,2,2,-1; Italian 4,2,2,2; Norwegian 2,2,2,1. Linguistic studies: Spanish. Office: Dept. of Romance Languages, U. of Mich., Ann Arbor.

STURMTHAL, ADOLF F., b. Vienna, Austria, Sep. 10, 1903. ECONOMICS. Doctor Rerum Polit., U. of Vienna, 1925. Asst. prof.-prof., Bard Coll., 1940–55; vis. prof., Cornell U., 1953–54; prof., Roosevelt U., 1955–60; vis. prof., Columbia U., 1958–59; PROF. ECONOMICS, U. OF ILL., 1960– ; vis. prof., Yale U., 1962–63. Social Science Research Council fellow; Fulbright research prof.; Ford, Carnegie, and Sloan Foundations grants; Social Science Research Center grant, Cornell U. Membership: American Economic Association; American Political Science Association; Industrial Relations Research Association. Research: industrial relations; economic development planning in non-totalitarian societies; economic development and income distribution in Mexico. Author: Current Manpower Problems: An Introductory Survey (1964); Economic Development, Income Distribution and Capital Formation in Mexico (Journal of Political Economy, June 1955). Co-author: United States Business and Labor in Latin America (Monthly Labor Review, May, June 1960). Language: Spanish 4,2,2,1; French 5,5,5,5; German 5,5,5,5; Italian 4,2,2,1. Home: 61 Greencroft, Champaign, Ill. Office: Institute of Labor and Industrial Relations, U. of Ill., 504 East Armory, Champaign.

SUÁREZ-MURIAS, MARGUERITE C., b. Havana, Cuba, Mar. 23, 1921. SPANISH AMERICAN LITERATURE. B.A., Bryn Mawr Coll., 1942; M.A., Columbia U., 1953; Ph. D., 1957. Asst. in public relations, Medical Div., Johns Hopkins U., 1957–58; asst. prof., Sweet Briar Coll., 1958–59; asst. prof., head of Spanish House, Hood Coll., 1959–60; asst. prof., Catholic U., Summers 1959–62; asst. prof., American U., 1960–62; lectr., Business Council of International Understanding, 1960–62; lectr., Catholic U. of America, Winters 1960–63; ASSOC. PROF., LANGUAGES, AMERICAN U., 1963– , assoc. prof., Catholic U. of America, Summers 1964, 1965. Membership: American Association of University Professors; Inter-American Council; Modern Language Association. Research: novel in Spanish America; novel in Cuba; stylistics. Author: La novela romántica en Hispanoamérica (1963); Variantes autóctonas de la novela romántica en Hispanoamérica (Hispania, Sept. 1960); Las iniciadores de la novela en Puerto Rico (Asomante, July-Sept. 1962). Language: Spanish 5,5,5,5; Portuguese 5,3,–,3; French 5,5,–,–; German 2,1,–,1; Italian 5,3,–,3. Home: 4720 Massachusetts Ave., NW., Washington, D.C., 20016. Office: Dept. of Modern Languages, American U., Washington, D.C., 20016.

SUCHMAN, EDWARD A., b. New York, N.Y., Dec. 5, 1915. SOCIOLOGY AND PUBLIC HEALTH. A.B., Cornell U., 1936; M.A., 1938; Ph. D., Columbia U., 1947. Research dir., Columbia U., 1937–42; research dir., U.S. War Dept., 1942–47; prof., Cornell U., 1947–58; dir. of social science activities, City of New York Dept. of Health, 1958–63; adjunct prof., School of Public Health, Columbia U., 1958–63; RESEARCH DIR., DEMONSTRATION PROGRAM FOR SOCIAL SCIENCE IN PUBLIC HEALTH, P.R. DEPT. OF HEALTH, 1961– ; PROF., SOCIOLOGY, U. OF PITTSBURGH, 1963– . U.S. Public Health Service fellow; Rockefeller Foundation fellow; Social Science Research Council fellow; Ford Foundation fellow; consultant, P.R. Dept.

of Health; assoc. editor, American Sociological Review and Journal of Health and Human Behavior. Membership: American Association for Public Opinion Research; American Association of University Professors; American Public Health Association; American Sociological Association; Sociological Research Association. Research: social aspects of public health and community development; health problems and social change in P.R.; social problems of population control, technological change, and medical care. Author: Introduction to Social Research Methods (1954); Sociology and Field of Public Health (1963). Contributor: Medical and Hospital Care in Puerto Rico (1961). Language: Spanish 4,4,4,4; French 3,3,3,3; German 3,3,3,3. Home: 1175 York Ave., New York, N.Y. Office: Dept. of Sociology, U. of Pittsburgh, Pittsburgh, Pa.

SUHM, LAWRENCE LEE, b. Milwaukee, Wis., Dec. 4, 1930. EDUCATION. B.S., U. of Wis., 1953; M.S., 1959; Ph. D., 1962. Social program dir., U. of Wis., 1957–60; lectr., Brazilian Ministry of Education and Culture (Rio de Janeiro), Summer 1959; liaison officer for international organizations, International Recreation Association (N.Y.), Summer 1960; DIR., CENTER FOR LEISURE RESOURCES DEVELOPMENT, U. OF WIS. EXTENSION DIV., 1962– . U.S. Dept. of State grant, Latin American Center for Community Development (Mexico), 1956–57; National Defense Education Act fellow in Portuguese and Latin American Affairs, U. of Wis., 1961–62. Membership: American Association for the Advancement of Science; American Recreation Society; Midwest Council of the Association for Latin American Studies; National Recreation Association. Research: economic and social implications of mass leisure in underdeveloped areas in Latin America; leisure and recreation as related to community development; Brazilian educational institutions and customs. Author: Recreation or Tortillas (Recreation, Nov. 1957); El papel de la recreación en el desarrollo de la comunidad rural (1959); How the Union Can Serve Foreign Students (1960). Language: Spanish 4,4,4,4; Portuguese 3,3,3,3; French 2,1,1,1. Home: 5105 Sherwood Rd., Madison, Wis., 53711. Office: U. of Wis. Extension Div., 432 North Lake St., Madison, 53706.

SULLIVAN, DOROTHEA F., b. Lawrence, Mass., Apr. 11, 1905. SOCIAL WELFARE. B.A., Trinity Coll., 1926; M.A., Columbia U., 1930; Catholic U. of America, 1941–45. Insular dir., Girl Scouts of P.R., 1930–32; field worker and organizer, Girl Scouts of America, 1932–35; adviser, Girl Scouts of America, 1935–41; ASSOC. PROF., SOCIAL GROUP WORK, CATHOLIC U. OF AMERICA, 1941– ; lectr., Howard U., 1942–47; DIR OF SOCIAL SERVICES, CUBAN CHILDREN'S PROGRAM, CATHOLIC WELFARE BUREAU, 1962– . Adviser, U.S. Children's Bureau (Cuba, Peru), Summers 1950, 1951; social welfare expert, United Nations (Italy), 1956; U.S. Dept. of State Specialists Program (Uruguay, Venezuela, Ecuador), 1960; guest lectr., Washington International Center, 1962; consultant, Regional Workshop for Latin American Women Volunteers (Bogotá), Nov. 1962. Membership: Academy of Certified Social Workers; American Association of University Professors; International Union for Social Work; Catholic Inter-racial Council; Catholic Council on Social Work Education; National Association of Social Workers. Research: child welfare; group and community organization. Author: The Relationship of Group Work to Political Stability and Economic Productivity (Revista Lyceum, Aug. 1950); How To Attend a Conference (1954); Servicio social de grupo (1956). Language: Spanish 4,4,4,3; Portuguese 2,2,2,1; French 4,4,4,4; German 2,2,2,1; Italian 3,3,3,2,1; Latin 4,3,–,3. Home: 8416 Atlantic Way, Miami Beach, Fla. 33141. Office: Catholic Welfare Bureau, Cuban Children's Program, 1325 West Flagler St., Miami, 33135.

SUTTON, ANTONY CYRIL, b. London, England, Feb. 14, 1925. ECONOMICS. B. Sc., U. of London, 1951; U. of Calif., Los Angeles; Ph. D., U. of London, 1965. Economist, Desmoc Exploration Ltd. (Toronto, Canada), 1954–57; market researcher, Great Western Steel Company (Los Angeles), 1957; research economist, Bureau of Business and Economic Research, U. of Calif., Los Angeles, 1959–63; ASST. PROF., ECONOMICS, CALIF. STATE COLL. AT LOS ANGELES, 1963– . Membership: American Economic Association. Research: marketing; iron and steel industry and mining in Latin America. Author: Locational Analysis of the Colombian Iron and Steel Industry (Journal of Business, U. of Calif., Los Angeles, Fall 1960). Language: Spanish 2,1,1,1; French 3,3,3,3; Italian 2,1,1,1; Russian 2,–,–,–. Home: 1810 Las Lunas Pasadena, Calif. Office: School of Business and Economics, Calif. State Coll. at Los Angeles, Los Angeles.

SUTTON, LOIS MARIE, b. Fort Worth, Tex., July 5, 1925. LANGUAGE. B.A., U. of Tex., 1945; M.A., Baylor U., 1946; Ph. D., U. of Tex., 1956. TEACHER, SPANISH AND FRENCH, BAYLOR U., 1945– . National Defense Education Act fellow in Brazilian Portuguese, U. of Tex., Summer 1962; Fulbright lectr., U. of Ceará (Fortaleza, Brazil), 1963. Membership: American Association of Teachers of French; American Association of University Professors; South Central Modern Language Association; Texas Foreign Language Association. Research: Spanish and French; English as a foreign language. Language: Spanish 4,4,4,4; Portuguese 4,4,4,4; French 4,4,4,4. Linguistic studies: French. Home: 3405 Race St., Fort Worth 11, Tex. Office: Dept. of Spanish and French, Baylor U.. Waco, Tex.

SYNNESTVEDT, SIG, b. Bryn Athyn, Pa., Nov. 13, 1924. HISTORY AND INTERNATIONAL RELATIONS. B.A., Mich. State U., 1949; M.A., 1950; Ph. D., U. of Pa., 1959. PROF., HISTORY, ACADEMY OF THE NEW CHURCH, 1950– ; RESEARCH ASSOC., INTERNATIONAL RELATIONS, FOREIGN POLICY RESEARCH INSTITUTE, U. OF PA., 1960– . Asst. to dir., Latin American Project, Foreign Policy Research Institute; post-doctoral fellow, U. of Pa.; editorial staff, Orbis: A Quarterly Journal of World Affairs. Membership: American Historical Association; Conference on Latin American History; Phi Alpha Theta; Phi Kappa Phi. Research: Latin American foreign policy. Author: Public

Service (New Church Life, Nov. 1956) ; Red Drive in Cuba (Current History, Oct. 1963). Langauge : Spanish 3,3,2,2 ; French 2,2,2,2. Home : 660 Woodward Dr., Huntington Valley, Pa. Office : Foreign Policy Research Institute, U. of Pa., 133 South 36th St., Philadelphia 4.

SZÁSZDI, ADAM M., b. Budapest, Hungary, Nov. 16, 1930. HISTORY. B.A., Western Reserve U., 1952 ; M.A., Tulane U., 1954 ; Ph. D., Universidad de Madrid, 1956. Asst. prof., Inter American U. of P.R., 1956–58 ; ASSOC. PROF., HISTORY, HUMANIDADES, UNIVERSIDAD DE P.R., 1958– . Organization of American States grant (Ecuador), Summer 1963. Membership : American Historical Association ; Conference on Latin American History ; Phi Alpha Theta ; Society for the History of Discoveries ; Southeastern Conference of Latin American Studies. Research : colonial Latin America ; archival research in Central America. Author: Nicolas Raoul y la República Federal de Centroamérica (1958) ; La municipalidad de San Germán en Puerto Rico, 1798–1808 (Journal of Inter-American Studies, Oct. 1959) ; Credit—Without Banking—in Early 19th Century Puerto Rico (The Americas, 1962). Language : Spanish 5,5,5,5 ; Portuguese 4,3,2,1 ; French 5,5,4,4 ; German 4,4,3,3 ; Italian 3,2,1,1. Home : Ave. de los Flamboyanes 171 Río Piedras, P.R. Office : Facultad de Estudios Generales, Universidad de P.R., Río Piedras.

SZULC, TAD, b. Warsaw, Poland, July 25, 1926. JOURNALISM. U. of Brazil. United Nations correspondent, United Press Association, 1949–53 ; correspondent, The New York Times, 1953–55 ; chief South American correspondent, The New York Times, 1955–61 ; CORRESPONDENT, LATIN AMERICAN AFFAIRS, WASHINGTON BUREAU, THE NEW YORK TIMES, 1961– . Participant, Cuban Project, The Brookings Institution. Membership : National Press Club ; Overseas Press Club ; Overseas Writers. Research : Latin American politics, history, and economics. Author : Twilight of the Tyrants (1959) ; Winds of Revolution (1963). Co-author : The Cuban Invasion (1962). Language : Spanish 5,5,5,5 ; Portuguese 5,5,5,5 ; Italian 3,3,3,2 ; Polish 5,5,5,5 ; Russian 2,3,3,1. Home : 3218 Woodley Rd., NW., Washington, D.C. Office : The New York Times, 1701 K St., NW., Washington, 20006.

T

TABA, HILDA, b. Estonia, Dec. 7, 1902. EDUCATION. B.A., U. of Tartu (Estonia), 1926 ; M.A., Bryn Mawr, 1927 ; Ph. D., Columbia U., 1932. Asst. prof.-assoc. prof., Ohio State U., Emory U., 1936–42 ; dir., Curriculum Laboratory, U. of Chicago, 1942–45 ; dir., Project on Intergroup Education, American Council on Education, 1945–48 ; assoc. prof., U. of Chicago, 1948–51 ; dir., Center of Intergroup Education, U. of Chicago, 1948–51 ; PROF., EDUCATION, SAN FRANCISCO STATE COLL., 1951– . Staff member, UNESCO Seminar on International Understanding (Paris), 1947 ; UNESCO prof., U. of São Paulo, 1958–59 ; technical consultant, White House Conference, 1960 ; U.S. Dept. of State specialist, U. of Rio Grande do Sul (Brazil), 1962 ; research consultant, Modern Language Association. Membership : American Educational Research Association ; Association of Supervisory and Curriculum Development ; National Social Studies Education Association ; Social Studies Social and Psychological Issue. Research : curriculum research ; teaching strategies. Author : The Dynamics of Education (1932) ; Curriculum Development : Theory and Practice (1962) ; Thinking in Elementary School Children (1964). Language : Spanish 2,2,2,2 ; Portuguese 3,3,3,3 ; French 4,4,4,4 ; Estonian 5,5,5,5 ; Russian 4,4,4,4. Home : 631 Taylor Blvd., Millbrae, Calif. Office : Dept. of Education, San Francisco State Coll., 1600 Holloway Ave., San Francisco, Calif. 94132.

TALBOTT, ROBERT DEAN, b. Centralia, Ill., Feb. 18, 1928. HISTORY. B.A., U. of Ill., 1950 ; M.A., 1955 ; Ph. D., 1959. Instr., Emporia State Teachers Coll., 1958–59 ; assoc. prof., Valley City State Teachers Coll., 1959–62 ; ASSOC. PROF., HISTORY, KEARNEY STATE COLL., 1962– . Membership : American Historical Association. Research : the colonial period in Chile ; history of Chilean boundaries, 1540–1955. Language : Spanish 2,2,1,1 ; Portuguese 1,1,1,1 ; French 2,1,1,1. Home : 903 East 30th Dr., Kearney, Nebr. Office : Div. of Social Science, Kearney State Coll., Kearney.

TAMAGNA, FRANK MARIO, b. Milan, Italy, Apr. 12, 1910. ECONOMICS. LL.D., U. of Pavia (Italy), 1934 ; Columbia U., 1934–35 ; Notre Dame U., 1935 ; Ph. D., Yale U., 1937. Economist, Banca d'Italia, 1937–39 ; instr., Xavier U., 1939–40 ; economist, Federal Reserve Bank of N.Y., 1940–47 ; economist, Board of Governors of the Federal Reserve System, 1947–50 ; professorial lectr., adjunct prof., American U., 1948–58 ; chief, International Finance Operations and Policy, Board of Governors of the Federal Reserve System, 1950–56 ; consultant on savings statistics, Board of Governors of the Federal Reserve System, 1956–58 ; PROF., ECONOMICS, AMERICAN U., 1958– . Lectr., consultant, Center for Latin American Monetary Studies (Mexico, D.F.), 1953– ; consultant, Banco de México, 1959–63 ; consultant, Banco Central de la República Argentina, 1960–64. Membership : American Economic Association. Research : monetary economics, especially central banking, commercial banking systems, and financial institutions ; relation of monetary policy to economic development, economic stabilization, and balance of payments ; financial organization of Mexico and Argentina. Author : Banking and Finance in China (1942) ; La Banca Central en América Latina (1963) ; Processes and Instruments of Monetary Policy (in Monetary Management, 1963). Language : Spanish 5,5,5,4 ; Portuguese 4,3,2,1 ; French 5,5,5,4 ; German 4,4,3,2 ; Italian 5,5,5,5. Home : 7101 Connecticut Ave., Chevy Chase, Md. 20015. Office : Dept. of Economics, American U., Massachusetts and Nebraska Aves., NW., Washington, D.C. 20016.

TANNENBAUM, FRANK, b. Austria, Mar. 4, 1893. HISTORY AND ECONOMICS. B.A., Columbia Coll., 1921 ; Ph. D., Brookings Institution, 1927. Newspaper correspondent (Mexico), 1922–24 ; surveyor in Mexico, Institute of Economics (Washington, D.C.),

1925–27; staff member in P.R., 1928–30; instr., Cornell U., Summer 1932; lectr., Columbia U., 1935–37; assoc. prof., 1937–45; prof., 1945–61; vis. lectr., Universidad de San Marcos (Peru), 1947; PROF. EMERITUS, LATIN AMERICAN HISTORY, COLUMBIA U., 1961– . Guggenheim fellow, 1932–33. Membership: Academy of Political Science; American Economic Association; American Geographical Association; American Historical Association; Instituto Geográfico e Histórico de Bahia (Brazil). Research: economic and social history; Mexico. Author: Mexico, the Struggle for Peace and Bread (1950) ; A Philosophy of Labor (1951) ; Ten Keys to Latin America (1962). Language: Spanish 4,4,4,–; Portuguese 4,4,4,–. Office: Dept. of History, Columbia U., 409 West 117th St., New York 27, N.Y.

TANNER, HELEN HORNBECK, b. Northfield, Minn., July 5, 1916. HISTORY. A.B., Swarthmore Coll., 1937; M.A., U. of Fla., 1949; Ph. D., U. of Mich., 1961. LECTR., EXTENSION SERVICE, U. OF MICH., 1961– . American Association of University Women fellow, 1958–59. Membership: American Historical Association; American Indian Ethnohistoric Conference; Central States Anthropological Society; Conference on Latin American History; Florida Historical Society. Research: Spanish Florida. Author: Zéspedes in East Florida (1963). Language: Spanish 3,2,2,2; French 3,2,2,3; German 3,2,2,3. Home: 1319 Brooklyn Ave., Ann Arbor, Mich. 48104. Office: Extension Service, U. of Mich., Ann Arbor.

TAPIA, FRANCISCO XAVIER, S.J., b. Zaragoza, Spain, Jan. 8, 1925. HISTORY. S.T.B., Woodstock Coll., 1958 ; M.A., Georgetown U., 1961; Ph. D., 1963. ASSOC. PROF., LATIN AMERICAN HISTORY AND GEOGRAPHY, IBERO-AMERICAN STUDIES, SOPHIA U. (JAPAN), 1960– . Private grant for archival research in Central and South America, 1963. Membership: American Historical Association; Hispanic American Society. Research: colonial Spanish America : Latin American economic geography. Author: El cabildo abierto colonial (1964) ; Democracia en el absolutismo (Estudios Americanos, (1960). Language: Spanish 5,5,5,5; Portuguese 4,3,2,1 ; French 3,3,1,1; Italian 4,4,4,3; Japanese 4,4,4,3. Home: 19 Media Lequerica, Madrid 4, Spain. Office: Ibero-American Studies, Sophia U., 7 Kioi Cho. Chiyoda Ku. Tokyo, Japan.

TAPSON, ALFRED JOSEPH, b. Feb. 21, 1909. HISTORY. A.B., U. OF CALIF., Berkeley, 1933 ; M.A., 1942 ; Ph. D., 1952. Teacher, San Francisco Unified School District, 1935–55 ; INSTR., HISTORY, CITY COLL. OF SAN FRANCISCO. Membership : California Historical Society ; Conference on Latin American History; Pacific Historical Society. Research: Argentine plains frontier and other similar frontier areas ; the Indian problem on the Argentine Pampa, 1735–1852. Author: The Sutler and the Soldier (Military Affairs, Winter 1957) ; Indian Warfare on the Pampa During the Colonial Period (Hispanic American Historical Review, Feb. 1962). Language: Spanish 4,3,3,3; Portuguese 3,2,2,1; French 4,3,2,1. Home : 110 Walnut St., San Francisco 18, Calif. Office: Dept. of History, City Coll. of San Francisco, San Francisco.

TARR, TERENCE STEPHEN, b. Everson, Wash., Nov. 17, 1935. HISTORY. B.A., State U. of Wash., 1957 ; M.A., U. of Fla., 1958 ; Ph. D., 1960. Asst. prof., U. of Miss., 1960–62 ; vis. asst. prof., U. of Wash., 1962–63 ; ASST. PROF., HISTORY, U. OF DENVER, 1963– . U. of Fla. fellow, 1957–59; Doherty fellow (Chile), 1959–60. Membership : American Association of University Professors ; American Historical Association ; Conference on Latin American History. Research: modern Chile; military intervention and the civilian reaction in Chile, 1924–1938. Language: Spanish 4,4,4,2; Portuguese 2,3,3,1 ; French 2,2,1,1. Home: 2309 South Columbine, Denver 10, Colo. Office: Dept. of History, U. of Denver, Denver 10.

TATKON, MARVIN DANIEL, b. New York, N.Y., June 4, 1932. ECONOMICS AND GEOGRAPHY. B.A., Dartmouth Coll., 1954; B.S., N.Y.U., 1954; M.A., New School for Social Research, 1960 ; D. Sc., U. of West Indies, 1962. PRESIDENT, ATLAS JEWELERS, INC., 1953– ; LECTR., SOCIAL SCIENCE, NEW SCHOOL FOR SOCIAL RESEARCH, 1958– . Consultant, Halle and Stieglitz (N.Y.), 1959–60 ; consultant, Noyes, Inc. (N.Y.), 1960–62; consultant, M.D. Tatkon Assoc. (Jamaica), 1962–63. Membership: American Association of University Professors ; American Economic Association ; American Geographical Society ; Association of American Geographers ; Explorers Club ; Royal Canadian Geographical Society; Royal Geographical Society. Research : economic development of small businesses and new industries in underdeveloped areas ; marketing ; economic geography ; Caribbean region. Author: Public Utilities (1960) ; Economic Development in Jamaica, West Indies (Jamaica Times, June 1962). Language: Spanish 3,4,3,2 ; Portuguese 1,1,1,1 ; French 4,4,4,4; Russian 3,3,3,3. Home: 323 East 18th St., New York, N.Y. 10003. Office: Dept. of Social Science, New School for Social Research, 66 West 12th St., New York.

TAX, SOL, b. Chicago, Ill., Oct. 30, 1907. ANTHROPOLOGY. Ph. B., U. of Wis., 1931; Ph. D., U. of Chicago, 1935. Ethnologist, Carnegie Institution of Washington, 1934–48 ; PROF., ANTHROPOLOGY, U. OF CHICAGO, 1944– . National Institute of Mental Health research grant (Mexico), 1956–59 ; Carnegie Cross Cultural Education Project grant, 1962–67 ; National Science Foundation grant (Guatemala), 1963–66; editor, Current Anthropology; Executive Committee, U.S. National Commission for UNESCO. Membership : American Anthropological Association ; Royal Anthropological Institute of Great Britain and Ireland. Research: social and cultural anthropology ; North and Middle American Indians ; Guatemala. Author: Penny Capitalism (1963) ; World View and Social Relations in Guatemala (American Anthropologist, Jan.–Mar. 1941). Editor: Heritage of Conquest (1952). Language: Spanish 4,4,4,4; French 1,–,–,–. Home: 5537 South Woodlawn, Chicago, Ill. Office: Dept. of Anthropology, U. of Chicago, Chicago, 60637.

TAYLOR, HARRY WHITE, b. Pittsburgh, Pa., June 2, 1930. GEOGRAPHY. B.S., West Chester State Coll., 1954 ; A.M., Ind. U.,

1955; Ph. D., U. of Md., 1961. Part-time asst. prof., Frederick Community Coll. 1958–60; lectr., U. of Md., 1959–60; ASSOC. PROF., GEOGRAPHY, GLASSBORO STATE COLL., 1960– . Research: cultural and economic geography; patterns of industry in Brazil. Author: Race and Population Patterns in Trinidad (Annals, Association of American Geographers, June 1960); Uma região produtora de sergo nos Estados Unidos (Boletim Paulista de Geografia, July 1958). Language: Spanish 2,2,1,1; Portuguese 4,4,4,3; French 2,1,1,1; German 2,1,1,1. Home: 217 Lakeside Dr., Glassboro, N.J. 08028. Office: Dept. of Geography, Glassboro State Coll., Glassboro, 08028.

TAYLOR, MARTIN CHARLES, b. Brooklyn, N.Y., Feb. 26, 1932. SPANISH AMERICAN LITERATURE. B.A., N.Y.U., 1954; M.A., U. of Calif., Los Angeles, 1956; Ph. D., 1964. LECTR., ROMANCE LANGUAGES, U. OF MICH., 1960– . Solnit Memorial Fund grant, 1959. Membership: Hispanic Institute of New York; Instituto Internacional de Literatura Iberoamericana. Research: Gabriela Mistral; the novel in Mexico, Argentina and Chile; contemporary poetry of Latin America; Agustín Yáñez. Language: Spanish 5,5,5,5; Portuguese 3,3,3,3; French 3,3,3,3; Italian 2,2,1,1. Home: 1807 Fair St., Ann Arbor, Mich. 48103. Office: Dept. of Romance Languages, U. of Mich., Ann Arbor.

TAYLOR, MILTON CECIL, b. Vancouver, Canada, Sept. 24, 1916. ECONOMICS. B.S.A., U. of British Columbia, 1939; M.S.A., 1946; Ph. D., U. of Wis., 1954. Instr., Mich. State U., 1946–49; lectr., U. of P.R., 1951–52; consultant, Dept. of the Treasury, Commonwealth of P.R., 1952–53; asst. prof., Marquette U., 1953–55; research assoc., U. of Wis., 1955–56; PROF., ECONOMICS, MICH. STATE U., 1956– . Taxation adviser, Commonwealth of P.R., 1953–59; taxation adviser, Government of Honduras, 1961; dir. of Fiscal Survey Missions, Joint Tax Program of the Organization of American States and Inter-American Development Bank (Panama), 1962, (Colombia), 1963, (Peru), 1964. Membership: American Economic Association; Midwest Economic Association; National Tax Association; Tax Institute, Inc. Research: public finance; fiscal policy; tax administration. Author: Industrial Tax Exemption in Puerto Rico (1957); Fiscal Survey of Panama (1964). Co-author: Fiscal Reform and Development Needs in Panama (National Tax Journal, June 1964). Language: Spanish 3,2,2,1. Home: 4522 Eastwood, Okemos, Mich. Office: Dept. of Economics, Mich. State U., East Lansing.

TAYLOR, PHILIP BATES, JR., b. Visalia, Calif., Mar. 12, 1921. POLITICAL SCIENCE. A.B., U. of Calif., Berkeley, 1942; M.A., 1947; Ph. D., 1950. Instr., Northwestern U., 1950–51; instr.-asst. prof., U. of Mich., 1951–57; vis. asst. prof., U. of Calif., Berkeley, 1956; assoc. prof., Tulane U., 1957–61; ASSOC. PROF., LATIN AMERICAN AFFAIRS, SCHOOL OF ADVANCED INTERNATIONAL STUDIES, JOHNS HOPKINS U., 1961– . Mills traveling fellow (Uruguay), 1949–50; American Philosophical Society (Mexico), 1955; Rockefeller Foundation grant (Uruguay), 1960; consultant, U.S. Dept. of State (Venezuela), 1961–63; research assoc., U.S. Dept. of State (Venezuela), 1962; consultant, Ford Foundation, 1962. Membership: American Political Science Association. Research: Latin American comparative government and international relations; executive power in Uruguay; Mexico; Venezuela. Author: The Executive Power in Uruguay (1951); Hemispheric Security Reconsidered (1957); Government and Politics of Uruguay (1962). Language: Spanish 4,4,4,3; Portuguese 3,3,1,1; French 3,3,1,1. Home: 8004 Maple Ridge Rd., Bethesda 14, Md. Office: School of Advanced International Studies, Johns Hopkins U., 1740 Massachusetts Ave. NW., Washington, D.C. 20036.

TAYLOR, ROBERT BARTLEY, b. Pendleton, Oreg., Oct. 15, 1926. ANTHROPOLOGY AND SOCIOLOGY. B.S., Wheaton Coll., 1949; M.S., U. of Oreg., 1951; Ph. D., 1960. Instr., Wheaton Coll., 1951–54; instr., Kans. State U., 1957–59; vis. asst. prof., U. of N. Mex., 1959–60; ASST. PROF., ANTHROPOLOGY, KANS. STATE U., 1960– . Wenner-Gren Foundation research fellow. Membership: American Anthropological Association. Research: applied anthropology; cultural change; Mesoamerican ethnology; Mexico. Language: Spanish 3,3,3,3. Home: 3608 Dickens Ave., Manhattan, Kans. 66502. Office: Dept. of Sociology and Anthropology, Kans. State U., Manhattan.

TAYLOR, WALTER WILLARD, b. Chicago, Ill., Oct. 17, 1913. ANTHROPOLOGY. A.B., Yale U., 1935; Ph. D., Harvard U., 1943. Prof., U. of Mérida (Mexico), 1956; prof., Mexico City Coll., 1956–57; prof., Escuela Nacional de Antropología e Historia (Mexico), 1955–58; PROF., ANTHROPOLOGY, SOUTHERN ILL. U., 1958– ; chmn., 1958–63. Hemenway teaching fellow, Harvard U., 1941–42; Rockefeller Foundation fellow, 1945–46; Guggenheim fellow, 1950–51. Membership: American Anthropological Association; American Association for the Advancement of Science; American Association of University Professors; Sociedad Mexicana de Antropología; Society for American Archaeology. Research: archeology; Mexico. Author: A Study of Archeology (1948); Two Archaelogical Studies in Northern Arizona (1958); Archaeology and Language in Western North America (America Antiquity, 1961). Language: Spanish 4,4,4,4; Portuguese 2,2,1,1; French 3,2,2,1; Italian 2,2,1,1. Home: 1005 San Acacio, Santa Fe, N. Mex. Office: Dept. of Anthropology, Southern Ill. U., Carbondale.

TEICHERT, PEDRO C. M., b. Santa Fe, Argentina, Feb. 13, 1925. ECONOMICS. B.A., Mexico City Coll., 1950; M.A., 1951; Ph. D., U. of Tex., 1954. Instr., La. State U., 1954–55; asst. prof., Mich. State U., 1955–57; PROF., ECONOMICS, U. OF MISS., 1957– . Executive Committee of the Latin American Research Society, Mich. State U., 1956–57; Council member, Southeastern Conference on Latin American Studies, 1961–64; National Defense Education Act fellow, 1963. Membership: American Economic Association; Southeastern Conference on Latin American Studies; Southern Economic Association. Research: Latin American economic development. Author: Revolución económica e industrialización en América Latina (1963); Towards a Synthesis of Theory and Policy in Latin American Developmental Economics: The Dynamics of the Economic Policy Revolution in the Transformation of the Periphery (Weltwirtschaftliches Archiv, 1958); Latin America and the Socio-Economic Impact of the Cuban Revolution (Journal of Inter-American Studies, Jan. 1962). Language: Spanish 5,5,5,5; Portuguese 3,2,2,2; French 2,2,2,1; German 5,5,5,5. Home: Box 152, University, Miss. Office: Dept. of Economics, U. of Miss., University.

TePASKE, JOHN JAY, b. Grand Rapids, Mich., Dec. 8, 1929. HISTORY. B.A., Mich. State U., 1951; M.A., Duke U., 1953; Ph. D., 1959. Asst. prof., Memphis State U., 1958–59; asst. prof., Ohio State U., 1959–64; ASSOC. PROF., HISTORY, OHIO STATE U., 1964– . Institute of International Education fellow (Spain), 1956–57; Ford Foundation Foreign Area Training fellow, U. of Calif., Berkeley, 1962–63. Membership: American Historical Association; Conference on Latin American History; Phi Beta Kappa. Research: Peru, Bolivia, and Chile in the 18th century; Spanish Florida. Author: Economic Problems of Governors of Florida, 1700–1763 (Florida Historical Quarterly, July 1958). Co-editor: The Character of Philip II: The Problem of Moral Judgements in History (1963); Explosive Forces in Latin America (1964). Language: Spanish 4,4,3,4; Portuguese 2,–,2,1; French 2,3,2,1. Home: 351 Park Blvd., Worthington, Ohio. Office: Dept. of History, Ohio State U., Columbus 10.

TERRY, EDWARD DAVIS, b. Eclectic, Ala., May 19, 1927. SPANISH AMERICAN LITERATURE. B.A., B.S., U. of Ala., 1949; M.A., 1953; Ph. D., U. of N.C., 1958. Asst. prof., Southern Methodist U., 1958–62; asst. prof., U. of Tenn., 1962–64; ASSOC. PROF., SPANISH, U. OF ALA., 1964– . Rotary Foundation fellow, Universidad Nacional de México, 1951; Southern Fellowships Fund fellow, 1955–56, 1956–57. Membership: American Association of Teachers of Spanish and Portuguese; Instituto Internacional de Literatura Iberoamericana; Modern Language Association; Mountain Interstate Foreign Language Conference; Tennessee Philological Association. Research: short story and poetry in Spanish America; Mexican novel; Spanish American language academies. Author: The Founding Date of the Real Academia Española (Romance Notes, Fall 1960); The Question of the Spanish Dipthong (Hispania, Sept. 1962). Language: Spanish 5,5,4,4; Portuguese 5,4,3,3; French 3,3,3,3; Italian 4,2,2,2. Office: Dept. of Modern Languages, U. of Ala., University.

THOBY-MARCELIN, PHILIPPE, b. Port-au-Prince, Haiti, Dec. 11, 1904. HAITIAN LITERATURE. Licencié, Ecole Nationale de Droit, 1937. Budget officer, Dept. of Public Works (Haiti), 1931–41; executive secretary, 1941–44; translator-reviewer, Pan American Union, 1948–59; AUTHOR, 1959– . Guggenheim fellow, 1951–52. Research: Haiti. Author: Canapé-Vert (1944); The Beast of the Haitian Hills (1945); The Pencil of God (1950). Language: Spanish 4,3,–,–; French 5,5,5,5.

Home: 3439 17th St., NW., Washington, D.C. 20010.

THOMAS, A. J., Jr., b. Sherman, Tex., June 8, 1918. LAW. B.S., Tex. A. & M. Coll., 1939; LL.B., U. of Tex., 1943; LL.M., 1947; S.J.D., U. of Mich., 1951. Vice consul, U.S. Dept. of State (Costa Rica), 1942–45; PROF., LAW, SCHOOL OF LAW, SOUTHERN METHODIST U., 1947– . Dir., Law Institute of the Americas, Southern Methodist U., 1954–59; consultant, Caribbean area, Chance Vought Aircraft Company, Summer 1959. Membership: American Society of International Law; London Institute of World Affairs; Texas Bar Association. Research: international law; constitutional law; inter-American law; the Caribbean; Mexico. Author: Economic Regulation of Air Transport: National and International (1951). Co-author: Non-Intervention: The Law and Its Import in the Americas (1956); The Organization of American States (1963). Language: Spanish 3,–,–,–; Portuguese 3,–,–,–. Home: 3404 Stanford, Dallas, Tex. Office: School of Law, Southern Methodist U., Dallas.

THOMAS, ALFRED BARNABY, b. Belt, Mont., Apr. 14, 1896. HISTORY. A.B., U. of Calif., Berkeley, 1923; M.A., 1925; Ph. D., 1927. Asst. prof.-assoc. prof., U. of Okla., 1927–37; PROF., HISTORY, U. OF ALA., 1937– . Native Sons of the Golden West fellow (Spain), 1925–26; Social Science Research Council-Council of Learned Societies research grants (Mexico); Guggenheim fellow (Spain), 1929–30; historian for the Jicarilla, Mescalero, and Chiricahua Apache Indians, 1959–62; editorial consultant, Arizona and the West-Journal of History. Membership: American Historical Association; Hispanic American Society; Conference on Latin American History; Mississippi Valley Historical Association; New Mexico Historical Society; Southeastern Conference on Latin American Studies. Research: the Spanish Empire under Charles III. Author: After Coronado: Spanish Exploration Northeast of New Mexico, 1696–1727 (1935); Teodoro de Croix and the Northern Frontier of New Spain, 1776–1783 (1941); Latin America: A History (1956). Language: Spanish 3,3,3,3; Portuguese 2,–,–,–; French 3,3,3,3; Rumanian 3,–,–,–. Home: 96 The Highlands, Tuscaloosa, Ala. Office: Dept. of History, Box 1491, U. of Ala., University.

THOMAS, ANN VAN WYNEN, b. The Netherlands, May 27, 1919. LAW. B.A., U. of Rochester, 1940; LL.B., U. of Tex., 1943; LL.M., Southern Methodist U., 1952. Vice consul, U.S. Dept. of State, 1943–46; RESEARCH ASSOC., SOUTHWESTERN LEGAL FOUNDATION, 1949– . Consultant, Caribbean area, Chance Vought Aircraft Company, Summer 1959; special legal consultant, U.S. Civil Rights Commission, 1959–62. Membership: American Society of International Law; Texas Bar Association. Research: international law and politics; the Caribbean; constitutional law and civil rights; Mexico. Author: Communism Versus International Law (1953). Co-author: Non-Intervention: The Law and Its Import in the Americas (1956); The Organization of American States (1963). Language: Spanish 3,3,2,1; Dutch 4,4,4,2. Home: 3404 Stanford St., Dallas 25, Tex. Office: Southwestern Legal Foundation,

School of Law, Southern Methodist U., Dallas 22.

THOMAS, D. WOODS, b. Ebensburgh, Pa., Apr. 28, 1925. ECONOMICS. B.S., Pa. State U., 1950; M.S., 1952; Ph. D., 1954. Asst. prof., Purdue U., 1954–57; assoc. prof., 1957–60; agricultural economist, Purdue-Brazil Project, Institute of Agricultural Economics, Universidade Rural do Estado de Minas Gerais (Brazil), 1960–62; PROF., ECONOMICS, PURDUE U., 1960– . Research fellow, Pa. State U., 1952–53; professor honoris causa, Universidade Rural do Estado de Minas Gerais, 1963; agricultural consultant, Ford Foundation (Brazil, Argentina), 1963. Membership: American Farm Economic Association; Brazilian Society of Agricultural Economists; Gamma Sigma Delta; International Association of Agricultural Economists; Phi Eta Sigma; Pi Kappa Phi; Sigma Xi. Research: agricultural economics; farm management; production economics; economic development. Author: Analysis of Human Attributes and Their Relationship to Performance Level of Farm Tenants (1962); Use of Personal History Questionnaires for Tenant Farm Operators in Predicting Farm Output (1963); Integration as an Adjustment to Risk and Uncertainty (Southern Economic Journal, Apr. 1962). Language: Spanish 3,3,3,2; Portuguese 4,4,4,3; French 1,1,1,1. Home: R.F.D. No. 9, Box 80, Lafayette, Ind. 47901. Office: Dept. of Agricultural Economics, Purdue U., Lafayette, 47907.

THOMAS, EARL W., b. Sumner, Ill., Jan. 22, 1915. BRAZILIAN LITERATURE AND LANGUAGE. A.B., U. of Ill., 1936; M.A., 1917; Ph. D., U. of Mich., 1947. Asst. prof.-ASSOC. PROF., SPANISH AND PORTUGUESE, VANDERBILT U., 1947– . Buenos Aires Convention exchange fellow (Brazil), 1941–42; Ford fellow (Spain and Portugal), 1954–55. Membership: American Association of Teachers of Spanish and Portuguese; Modern Language Association. Research: modern spoken Brazilian language. Author: Brazilian Literature (in Brazil, Portrait of Half a Continent, 1949); Folklore in Brazilian Literature (in Three Papers, 1950); The Changing Brazilian Language (Kentucky Foreign Language Quarterly, 1961). Language: Spanish 5,5,5,4; Portuguese 5,5,5,5; French 4,4,3,2; Finnish 3,2,2,1; Italian 4,3,2,1. Linguistic studies: French; Portuguese; Spanish. Home: 6559 Brownlee Dr., Nashville, Tenn. Office: Dept. of Spanish and Portuguese, Vanderbilt U., Box 1558, Nashville 5.

THOMAS, JACK RAY, b. Youngstown, Ohio, Dec. 23, 1931. HISTORY. B.A., Youngstown U., 1954; M.A., Kent State U., 1960; Ph. D., Ohio State U., 1962. ASST. PROF., HISTORY, WIS. STATE COLL., 1962– . Doherty fellow (Chile), 1961–62. Membership: American Historical Association; Midwest Council of the Association of Latin American Studies. Research: growth of the Socialist Party in Chile and the role of Marmaduke Grove Vallejo in its development; political development of Chile, 1920–40. Language: Spanish 4,3,3,2; French 2,1,1,1. Home: 2121 Agnes St., Eau Claire, Wis. Office: Dept. of History, Wis. State Coll., Eau Claire.

THOMAS, ROY EDWIN, b. Bee Branch, Ark., Jan. 21, 1917. ECONOMICS.: MARKETING; INSURANCE. B.A., B.S., U. of Ark., 1941; Ph. D., U. of Tex., 1961. Special agent, Floyd West & Company (Dallas, Tex.), 1950–52; secretary-manager, Arkansas Association of Insurance Agents, 1952–54; insurance agent, Arkansas Valley Trust Company, 1954–55; staff employee, Little Rock Chamber of Commerce, 1955; special agent, Cobb & Stebbins, Managing General Agents, St. Paul Fire & Marine Insurance Company, 1955–59; asst. prof., Fla. State U., 1961–62; vis. lectr., Mexico City Coll., Summer 1962; asst. prof., U. of Tulsa, 1962–63; ASSOC. PROF., BUSINESS DIV., SOUTHERN ILL. U., 1963– . Membership: American Finance Association; American Marketing Association; American Risk & Insurance Association. Research: international trade; business and personal finance; marketing in Mexico; Brazil. Author: Educación de seguros en los Estados Unidos (Revista Mexicana de Seguros, Mar. 1963); The Mexican Automobile Insurance Problem for Tourists (Journal of Insurance, Dec. 1963); Preparation in College for Career in Finance (Collegiate News and Views, Nov. 1964). Language: Spanish 3,3, 3,3; Portuguese 3,3,3,3; French 2,1,1,1. Home: 100 Victoria Dr., Belleville, Ill. Office: Business Div., Southern Ill. U., East Saint Louis, Ill.

THOMPSON, DONALD ENRIQUE, b. Chicago, Ill., Jan. 2, 1931. ANTHROPOLOGY. A.B., Harvard U., 1953; M.A., 1961; Ph. D., 1962. Field asst., Carnegie Institution of Washington (Mexico), 1965; field asst., Chicago Natural History Museum (Peru), 1956; instr., U. of Wis., 1961–62; ASST. PROF., ANTHROPOLOGY, U. OF WIS., 1962– . Tulane U. fellow (Guatemala), Summer 1951; Harvard U. fellow, 1957–59; Fulbright grant (Peru), 1959–60; lectr., U.S. Peace Corps Training Program; National Science Foundation research grant (Peru), 1964–65. Membership: American Anthropological Association; American Ethnological Society; Society for American Archaeology; Wisconsin Archaeological Society. Research: culture change; archeology; ethnohistory; ethnology; contemporary folk cultures. Author: Maya Paganism and Christianity: A History of the Fusion of Two Religions (1960); The Problem of Dating Certain Stone-faced, Stepped Pyramids on Northern Coast of Peru (Southwestern Journal of Anthropology, Winter 1962); Postclassic Innovations in Architecture and Settlement Patterns in Casma Valley, Peru (Southwestern Journal of Anthropology, Spring 1964). Language: Spanish 4,4,3,3. Home: 1324 Milton St., Madison 5, Wis. Office: Dept. of Anthropology, U. of Wis., Madison, 53706.

THOMPSON, JOHN, b. Talara, Peru, Apr. 21, 1924. GEOGRAPHY. B.A., Stanford U., 1947; M.A., U. of Calif., Berkeley, 1951; Ph. D., Stanford U., 1958. Instr., Stanford U., 1951–59; asst. prof., 1959–62; head, Latin American Studies Staff, Language Development Branch, Office of Education, U.S. Dept. of Health, Education, and Welfare, 1962–64; ASSOC. PROF., GEOGRAPHY, DIR., LATIN AMERICAN STUDIES PROGRAM, U. OF ILL., 1964– . Fulbright grants (Chile), 1958, (Brazil), 1960; Office of Naval Research-U. of Calif. grant (El Salvador), Summer 1959; Asia Foundation grant (Pakistan), Summer 1963. Membership: Association of American Geographers; California Council of Geography Teachers; National Council of Geography Teachers; Pacific Coast Council on Latin American Studies. Research: historical geography; urban food supply programs; contemporary agricultural geography. Author: Studies in the Food Supply of El Salvador (1961); La industria lechera de Chile central (Informaciones Geográficas, 1959); The Fisheries Industry of El Salvador (Journal of Inter-American Studies, July 1961). Language: Spanish 4,4,4,3; Portuguese 4,4,3,2; French 2,2,1,1. Office: Dept. of Geography, U. of Ill., Urbana, 61803.

THOMPSON, J(OHN) ERIC S(IDNEY), b. London, England, Dec. 31, 1898. ANTHROPOLOGY. Winchester Coll. (England), 1912–15; Cambridge U., 1924–25; LL.D., U. of Yucatán, 1958; Litt. H. D., U. of Pa., 1962. Asst. curator, Chicago Natural History Museum, 1926–35; staff archeologist (Central America), Carnegie Institution of Washington, 1935–58; RETIRED, 1959. Member, Seminario de Cultura Maya, Universidad Nacional Autónoma de México, 1959– ; Faculty Board, Archaeology and Ethnology, Cambridge U. Membership: British Academy; Royal Anthropological Institute; Sociedad Mexicana de Estudios Antropológicos; Society for American Archaeology. Research: Middle American archeology, ethnology and colonial history. Author: Maya Hieroglyphic Writing: Introduction (1950, 1960); The Rise and Fall of Maya Civilization (1954); A Catalog of Maya Hieroglyphics (1962). Language: Spanish 5,4,4,4; Portuguese 3,2,1,1; French 3,2,2,2. Home: Ashdon Saffron Walden, Essex, England.

THOMPSON, LAYTON SPENCER, b. Delia, Kans., June 17, 1906. ECONOMICS. B.S., Colo. State U., 1939; M.S., Mont. State Coll., 1940; Ph. D., Mich. State U., 1954. Research asst., Farm Credit Administration (Kans.), 1941–43; PROF., ECONOMICS AND AGRICULTURAL ECONOMICS, MONT. STATE COLL., 1943– . Consultant in El Salvador, Agri Research, Inc. (Manhattan, Kans.), 1962. Membership: American Farm Economic Association; Western Farm Economics Association. Research: land economics, especially land tenure and values, taxation, and crop insurance. Author: Economics of Grain Storage on Montana Farms (1955); Sale Prices of Montana Agricultural Land by Class and Grade (1963). Co-author: Adapting Tax Systems to Great Plains Conditions (1963). Language: Spanish 3,2,3,3. Home: 918 South Tracy, Bozeman, Mont. 59715. Office: Dept. of Economics, Mont. State Coll., Bozeman, 59715.

THOMPSON, MAURY WELDON, b. Richmond, Va., June 14, 1905. EDUCATION. A.B., Coll. of William and Mary, 1928; M.A., George Washington U., 1931; Ed. D., Stanford U., 1946. PROF., EDUCATION, LYNCHBURG COLL., 1947– ; vis. prof., Columbia U., 1953–54. National Defense Education Act fellow in Latin American culture, U. of Calif., Los Angeles, 1962. Membership: Comparative Education Society; Philosophy of Education Society. Research: educational systems of Latin America; comparative education. Author: Education in Honduras (1955); Education in Latin America (Education, Sept. 1963). Language: Spanish 3,3,3,3; French 2,1,1,2. Home: 3889 Peakland Pl., Lynchburg, Va. Office: Lynchburg Coll., Lynchburg.

THOMPSON, RAYMOND HARRIS, b. Portland, Maine, May 10, 1924. ANTHROPOLOGY. B.S., Tufts U., 1947; A.M., Harvard U., 1950; Ph. D., 1955. Asst. dir., Upper Gila Archaeological Expedition, Peabody Museum, Harvard U., 1949; asst. prof., curator, Museum of Anthropology, U. of Ky., 1952–56; asst. dir., Archaeological Field School, U. of Ariz., 1956–61; asst. prof., 1956–58; ASSOC. PROF., ANTHROPOLOGY, U. OF ARIZ., 1958– ; DIR., ARCHAEOLOGICAL FIELD SCHOOL, 1962– . Harvard U. fellow, 1949; Carnegie Institution of Washington fellow (Mexico), 1950–52; editor, American Antiquity, 1958–62; chmn., U. of Ariz. Press Committee, 1958– ; Executive Committee and Memoir editor, Society for American Archaeology, 1962– ; National Science Foundation grant (Mexico), 1962–63; Advisory Panel for Anthropology, National Science Foundation, 1963– . Membership: American Anthropological Association; American Association for the Advancement of Science; American Ethnological Society; American Indian Ethnohistoric Conference; Arizona Archaeological and Historical Society; Phi Beta Kappa; Seminario de Cultura Maya; Sigma Xi; Sociedad Mexicana de Antropología; Society for American Archaeology; Tree-Ring Society. Research: archeology of Mexico and Central America, especially Maya area. Author: The Subjective Element in Archaeological Inference (Southwestern Journal of Anthropology, Autumn 1956); Modern Yucatecan Maya Pottery Making (Memoirs, Society for American Archaeology, Apr. 1958); Un espejo de pirita con respaldo tallado de Uayma, Yucatán (Estudios de Cultura Maya, 1962). Language: Spanish 4,4,4,3; Portuguese 2,1,1,1; German 2,1,1,1. Home: 2637 North Plumer Ave., Tucson, Ariz. 85719. Office: Dept. of Anthropology, U. of Ariz., Tucson, 85721.

THORBECKE, ERIK, b. Berlin, Germany, Feb. 17, 1929. ECONOMICS. Propaedeutical degree, Netherlands School of Economics, 1949; Ph. D., U. of Calif., Berkeley, 1957. Asst. prof., Iowa State U., 1957–60; assoc. prof., 1960–63; PROF., ECONOMICS, IOWA STATE U., 1964– . Adviser, Iowa-Peru Project (Lima), 1963; economic adviser, National Planning Institute of Peru, 1963–64. Membership: American Economic Association; Econometric Society. Research: economic development and planning; economic structure and macroeconomic relationships of Peru. Author: The Tendency Towards Regionalization in International Trade, 1928–1956 (1960); European Economic Integration and the Pattern of World Trade (American Economic Review, May 1963). Language: Spanish 4,4,4,3; French 5,5,5,5; Dutch 5,5,4,4. Home: 2323 Donald St., Ames, Iowa. Office: Dept. of Economics, Iowa State U., Ames.

THORN, RICHARD SEMOUR, b. New York, N.Y., Sept. 20, 1929. ECONOMICS. A.B., Columbia Coll., 1951; M.A., U. of Md., 1952; Ph. D., Yale U., 1958. Economist, International Monetary Fund, 1957–62; assoc.

prof., City Coll., 1963–65; ASSOC. PROF., ECONOMICS, U. OF PITTSBURGH, 1965– . Consultant, Committee of Nine, Organization of American States, 1962–63; head, Inter-American Bank Mission to Bolivia, 1964. Membership: American Economic Association; Econometric Association; Hispanic American Society. Research: Bolivia, Chile, and Mexico; public finance; economic development; money and banking; international trade. Author: Non-bank Financial Intermediaries, Credit Expansion, and Monetary Policy (International Monetary Fund Staff Papers, Nov. 1958); Extension of Trade and Payments Agreements to Third Countries (Weltwirschaftliche Archiv, 1963). Language: Spanish 4,4,4,3; French 4,4,4,4. Home: 68–63 108th St., Forest Hills 75, N.Y. Office: Dept. of Economics, U. of Pittsburgh, Pa.

THORNE, ALFRED P., b. Georgetown, British Guiana, May 4, 1913. ECONOMICS. B. Com., U. of London, 1941; M.S., Columbia U., 1950; Ph. D., 1959. Lectr., U. of P.R., 1955–58; assoc. prof., 1958–63; PROF., ECONOMICS, U. OF P.R., 1963– ; vis. prof., Universidad Mayor de San Andrés (La Paz, Bolivia), 1964. Consulting economist, Planning Board of P.R. and Dept. of Commerce (P.R.), 1955–57, 1961–63, Dept. of Statistics (Dominican Republic), 1963, U.S. Agency for International Development (Jamaica, Trinidad), 1963–64. Membership: American Economic Association; International Association for Research in Income and Wealth; Puerto Rican Economic and Statistic Association; Royal Economic Society. Research: economic development; income theory; public finance and fiscal policy. Author: Size, Structure and Growth of the Jamaican Economy (1955); Sector and National Income Analyses for Latin American and Caribbean Economics—More Appropriate Educations (Review of Economics and Statistics, Nov. 1962). Language: Spanish 4,4,4,3; Portuguese 2,1,1,1; French 4,4,4,4; Italian 2,1,1,1. Home: 1747 California St., San Gerardo, Río Piedras, P.R. 00926. Office: Dept. of Economics, Coll. of Social Sciences, U. of P.R., Río Piedras.

THORNING, JOSEPH FRANCIS, b. Milwaukee, Wis., Apr., 25, 1896. HISTORY. B.A., St. Louis U., 1921; M.A., 1929; Ph. D., Catholic U. of America, 1931. Prof., Mount St. Mary's Seminary and Coll., 1936–46; ASSOC. EDITOR, WORLD AFFAIRS, 1940– ; RECTOR, ST. JOSEPH'S-ON-CARROLLTON MANOR, 1946– ; DIR., INTER-AMERICAN SEMINAR, MARYMOUNT COLL., 1958– . Dir., American Peace Society; consultant, U.S. Congress. Membership: Historical and Geographic Institute of Brazil. Research: inter-faith understanding and cooperation; political organization of Brazil. Author: Religious Liberty (1931); Builders of the Social Order (1941); Miranda: World Citizen (1952). Language: Spanish 4,4,4,4; Portuguese 3,3,3,3; French 4,4,4,4; German 3,3,3,3; Greek 5,5,5,5; Italian 3,3,3,3; Latin 5,5,5,5. Home: St. Joseph's-on-Carrollton Manor, Frederick 1, Md. Office: World Affairs, 1307 New Hampshire Ave., NW., Washington 6, D.C.

THURMAN, MICHAEL E., b. Kansas City, Mo., Oct. 7, 1933. HISTORY. A.B., U. of Southern Calif., 1955; A.M., 1960; Ph. D., 1964. Instr., Naval Reserve Officers' School, U. of Southern Calif., 1959–60; Extension Div., 1960; student professional curator, History Div., Los Angeles County Museum, 1959–60; registrar's asst., U. of Southern Calif., Summer 1961; ASST. PROF., HISTORY, EAST TEX. STATE COLL., 1962– . Del Amo fellow (Spain), 1961–62. Membership: California Historical Society; Montana Historical Society; Pacific Council on Latin American Affairs; Phi Alpha Theta; Western History Association. Research: colonial Mexico; Alta California; 19th century Central America. Author: A New Historical Depository (Los Angeles County Museum Associates Quarterly, Summer 1960); The Naval Department of San Blas and Its Initial Naval Fleet (Hispanic American Historical Review, Feb. 1963). Language: Spanish 4,4,4,4; Portuguese 2,1,1,1; French 2,1,1,1; German 2,1,1,2. Home: 643 Fourth St., Encinitas, Calif. Office: Dept. of History, East Tex. State Coll., Commerce.

TIERNEY, JAMES FRANCIS, b. Fall River, Mass., Oct. 29, 1922. POLITICAL SCIENCE AND EDUCATION. A.B., Boston U., 1948; A.M., Brown U., 1950; Ph. D., 1956; U. of London, 1957–58; Oxford U., 1957–58. Instr., Bowdoin Coll., 1951–55; asst. prof., Dartmouth Coll., 1955–57; asst. prof., Hunter Coll., 1958–59; program assoc., Ford Foundation, 1959–61; ASST. REPRESENTATIVE (MEXICO AND CENTRAL AMERICA), FORD FOUNDATION, 1961– . Ford Foundation survey mission (Mexico), 1960; staff dir., Ford Foundation foreign area fellowship program, 1959–60. Membership: American Political Science Association. Research: public administration; development of universities; political and economic structures and educational institutions of Mexico and Central America. Author: A Coordinating Course in the Political Science Major (American Political Science Review, Dec. 1957); Britain and the Commonwealth (Political Studies, Oct. 1958). Language: Spanish 3,3,3,3; French 3,3,2,2; German 2,2,2,2; Hindi 2,2,1,1. Home: Saratoga 270, México 10, D.F. Office: Ford Foundation, Reforma 243, México, D.F.

TIGNER, JAMES LAWRENCE, b. Los Angeles, Calif., Apr. 18, 1918. HISTORY. A.B., U. of Redlands, 1948; A.M., Stanford U., 1949; Ph. D., 1956. Field assoc. in history, Pacific Science Board, National Academy of Sciences and Hoover Institution, Stanford U., 1951–55; instr., Hoover Institution, 1955; Stanford U., 1956–59; ASSOC. PROF., HISTORY, U. OF NEV., 1959– . Pacific Science Board, National Academy of Sciences, research grant for Ryukyuan Emigration Project in Latin America. Membership: American Historical Association; Conference on Latin American History; Pacific Coast Conference on Latin American Studies. Research: immigration and resettlement in Latin America; Japanese and Ryukyuan communities in Latin America; economic and social history. Author: The Okinawans in Latin America (1955); Shindo Remmel: Japanese Nationalism in Brazil (Hispanic American Historical Review, Nov. 1961); The Ryukyuans in Bolivia (Hispanic American Historical Review, May 1963). Language: Spanish 4,4,4,3; Portuguese 4,4,4,3; French 3,2,2,2. Home: P.O. Box 385, Virginia City,

Nev. Office: Dept. of History, U. of Nev., Reno.

TIMMONS, JOHN F., b. Wheeling, Mo., Oct. 29, 1912. ECONOMICS. B.S., U. of Mo., 1937; M.A., 1938; Ph. D., U. of Wis., 1945. Head, Land Policies Section, U.S. Dept. of Agriculture, 1943–47; PROF., ECONOMICS, IOWA STATE U., 1947– ; DIR., IOWA-PERU PROGRAM, 1962– . Ely scholar, U. of Wis., 1941; consultant, United Nations, 1949, 1954–55; consultant, Agrarian Reform Seminar (São Paulo, Brazil), 1953; adviser, International Cooperation Administration (Peru), 161; consultant, Organization of American States Seminar (San José, Costa Rica), 1962, (São Paulo, Brazil), 1963. Membership: Alpha Zeta; American Association for the Advancement of Science; American Economic Association; American Farm Economic Association; Gamma Sigma Delta; International Development Society; National Academy of Sciences; Phi Kappa Phi. Research: agrarian reform and economic growth; land economics. Author: Improving Agricultural Tenancies (1955); Farm Tenancy (in Encyclopaedia Brittanica, 1960); World Tenancy Systems (in Encyclopedia of the Social Sciences, 1964). Language: Spanish 3,2,2,2; French 3,2,2,2. Home: 832 Brookridge Ave., Ames, Iowa, 50010. Office: Dept. of Economics, Iowa State U., Ames, 50010.

TIMMONS, WILBERT H., b. Springfield, Mo., June 22, 1915. HISTORY. B.A., Park Coll., 1938; M.A., U. of Chicago, 1940; Ph. D., U. of Tex., 1949. Asst. prof., Tex. Western Coll., 1949–53; assoc. prof., 1953–57; PROF., HISTORY, TEX. WESTERN COLL., 1957– ; CHMN., 1962– . Membership: American Historical Association; Southwest Social Science Association. Research: United States diplomatic history; Mexican independence period. Author: Morelos of Mexico: Priest, Soldier, Statesman (1963); Los Guadalupes (Hispanic American Historical Review, Nov. 1950). Language: Spanish 4,2,1,1. Home: 104 Crown Point Dr., El Paso, Tex. 79912. Office: Dept. of History, Tex. Western Coll., El Paso.

TINKER, EDWARD LAROCQUE, b. New York, N.Y., Sept. 12, 1881. HISTORY AND SPANISH AMERICAN LITERATURE. A.B., Columbia U., 1902; LL.B., N.Y. Law School, 1905; Ph. D., Université de Paris, 1933; LL. D. (honorary), Middlebury Coll., 1949; Ph. D., Universidad de Madrid, 1955; Litt. D. (honoris causa), Columbia U., 1962. Lectr., Carnegie Endowment for International Peace (Mexico), 1943; exchange prof., U.S. Dept. of State (Uruguay, Argentina), 1945; PRESIDENT, TINKER FOUNDATION. Palmes Academiques (France), 1933; Chevalier Legion of Honor, 1939; La Orden de Mayo al Mérito (Argentina); Award of the Americas Foundation, 1962; Comendador, Orden de Isabel la Católica, 1963; vice president, Spanish Institute. Membership: American Antiquarian Society; Hispanic Society of America; Instituto González Fernández de Oviedo (Spain); Instituto Histórico y Geográfico del Uruguay. Research: gaucho literature; the Latin American cowboy and his folklore. Author: Los jinetes de las Américas y la literatura por ellos inspirada (1952; English edition, 1953); Corridos y Calaveras (1961); Life and Literature of the Pampas (1961). Language: Spanish 4,4,3,2; French 5,5,4,3. Office: Tinker Foundation, 550 Park Ave., New York 21, N.Y.

TINNERMEIER, RONALD LEE, b. Newton, Iowa, Apr. 15, 1936. ECONOMICS. B.S., Iowa State U., 1958; M.S., Mont. State Coll., 1962; Ph. D., U. of Wis., 1964. RESEARCH ASSOC., LAND TENURE CENTER, U. OF WIS., 1963– . Research fellow, International Cooperation Center, Mont. State Coll., Spring 1961. Membership: American Farm Economic Association. Research: agricultural economics; land economics; agrarian reform; land settlement in Colombia. Language: Spanish 4,4,4,3; French 2,1,1,1. Office: Land Tenure Center, 310 King Hall,, U. of Wis., Madison.

TIRADO, MOISÉS C., Aguadilla, P.R., Apr. 8, 1911. SPANISH AMERICAN LITERATURE. A.B., U. of P.R., 1937; M.A., U. of Ala., 1944; M.L.D., Middlebury Coll., 1953. Instr., U. of Conn., 1946–47; instr., U. of Del., 1947–53; lectr., Hunter Coll., 1954–58; VIS. PROF., SPANISH, HUNTER COLL., 1959– ; ASSOC. PROF., SPANISH, WAGNER COLL., 1959– . Membership: American Association of University Professors; Modern Language Association; Puerto Rico Teachers Association. Research: pedagogical ideas of Eugenio Hostos. Author: P. H. Hernández, poeta del dolor (Revista Iberoamericana, Sept. 1955); How Cultural Organizations Have Helped Puerto Ricans and Others Work for Social Progress (Journal of Educational Sociology, May 1962). Language: Spanish 5,5,5,5; Portuguese 2,2,1,1; French 4,3,3,3; Italian 4,4,-3,2. Home: 32 Margaretta Ct., Staten Island, N.Y. 10314. Office: Wagner Coll., Grymes Hill, Staten Island, 10301.

TITIEV, MISCHA, b. Kremenchug, Russia, Nov. 11, 1901. ANTHROPOLOGY. A.B., Harvard U., 1923; A.M., 1924; Ph. D., 1935. PROF., ANTHROPOLOGY, U. OF MICH., 1936– . Research: ethnology; Chile; Peru. Author: Old Oraibi (1944); Araucanian Culture in Transition (1951); The Science of Man (1963). Home: 910 Heather Way, Ann Arbor, Mich. Office: Dept. of Anthropology, 221 Angell Hall, U. of Mich., Ann Arbor.

TOLEDO, RAYMOND R., b. San Sebastian, P.R., Mar. 7, 1905. ECONOMICS. LL.B., Southwestern U., Los Angeles, 1928; B.S., U. of Southern Calif., 1942; M.B.A., 1943. Owner, Rex Import-Export Company (Los Angeles, Calif.), 1938–40; asst. export manager, International Trading and Advertising Company (Los Angeles), 1940–42; instr., U. of Calif., Los Angeles, 1942–43; superintendent of schools, Emery, S. Dak., 1943–44; asst. prof., Mundelein Coll., 1944–49; assoc. prof., DePaul U., 1949–52; dean, Shell Institute (Chicago), 1952–54; teacher, Spanish, Imperial Calif. School District, 1954–55; assoc. prof., chmn., Economics and Business Administration, Immaculate Heart Coll. (Los Angeles), 1955–64; PROF., ECONOMICS, BRESCIA COLL., 1964– . Labor and economic adviser, Commonwealth of P.R. (Chicago), 1952–54. Membership: American Association of University Professors; American Economic Association. Research: labor economics; international trade. Langauge: Spanish 5,5,5,5; Portuguese 4,4,4,3; French 4,3,4,3. Home: 254

South Gramercy Pl., Los Angeles, Calif. 90004. Office: Dept. of Economics, Brescia Coll., Owensboro, Ky. 42302.

TOLSTOY, PAUL, b. Versailles, France, Sept. 29, 1929. ANTHROPOLOGY. B.A., Columbia Coll., 1951; Ph. D., Columbia U., 1959. Lectr., Hunter Coll., 1960; ASST. PROF., ANTHROPOLOGY, UNIVERSITÉ DE MONTRÉAL, 1961– . Fulbright fellow (Peru), 1958–59; Ogden Mills fellow, American Museum of Natural History, 1960–61; Fulbright lectr., Universidad de la República (Uruguay), 1962. Membership: Society for American Archaeology. Research: archeology of high culture areas in the New World; archeology of Mexico and Peru; Mexico from Preclassic to Aztec times. Author: The Archaeology of the Lena Basin . . . (American Antiquity, Apr. 1958); Surface Survey of the Northern Valley of Mexico: the Classic and Post-Classic Periods (Transactions, American Philosophical Society, Sept. 1958); Cultural Parallels Between Southeast Asia and Mesoamerica in the Manufacture of Bark Cloth (Transactions of New York Academy of Science, Apr. 1963). Language: Spanish 5,5, 4,4; French 5,5,5,5; Russian 5,5,4,4. Home: 12 Henderson Pl., New York 28, N.Y. Office: Département d' Anthropologie. Université de Montréal, Montréal, Quebec, Canada.

TOMASEK, ROBERT DENNIS, b. Chicago, Ill., Jan. 16, 1928. POLITICAL SCIENCE. B.A., Grinnell Coll., 1950; M.A., U. of Mich., 1955; Ph. D., 1957. ASSOC. PROF., POLITICAL SCIENCE, U. OF KANS., 1957– . Doherty fellow (Chile), 1960–61; dir., Junior Year Abroad in Costa Rica, U. of Kans., 1962. Membership: American Political Science Association; Phi Sigma Alpha. Research: Latin American domestic and international politics; Latin American political parties; migrant workers, wetbacks and their effect on United States-Mexican politics; Chile. Author: British Guiana: A Case Study of British Colonial Policy (Political Science Quarterly, Sept. 1959); Defense of the Western Hemisphere: A Need for Reexamination of United States Policy (Midwest Journal of Political Science, Nov. 1959); The Migrant Problem and Pressure Group Politics (Journal of Politics, May 1961). Language: Spanish 4,4,4,3. Home: 838 West 22nd St. Terrace, Lawrence, Kans. Office: Dept. of Political Science, U. of Kans., Lawrence.

TOMLINS, JACK EDWARD, b. El Reno, Okla., Jan. 21, 1929. BRAZILIAN LITERATURE. B.A., U. of N. Mex., 1951; M.A., 1953; Ph. D., Princeton U., 1957. Instr., Princeton U., 1956–59; asst. prof., Wake Forest Coll., 1959–60; asst. prof., Rutgers U., 1960–64; dir. of language instruction, U.S. Peace Corps, Rutgers U., Summer 1961; language instr., U.S. Peace Corps Training Center for Latin America, U. of N. Mex., Summer 1963; ASSOC. PROF., SPANISH AND PORTUGUESE, CHATHAM COLL., 1964– . U.S. Dept. of State grant (Brazil), 1954. Membership: Modern Language Association; Phi Sigma Iota. Research: Brazilian novel and poetry from Modernism to the present day. Author: Four Hallucinated Landscapes, by Mário de Andrade (Approach, Spring 1964). Language: Spanish 5,5,5,4; Portuguese 5,5,5,5. Home: 5702 Solway St., Pittsburgh, Pa. Office: Dept. of Modern Languages, Chatham Coll., Pittsburgh 32.

TORCHIA-ESTRADA, JUAN CARLOS, b. Buenos Aires, Argentina, Jan. 1, 1927. PHILOSOPHY. Certificate, Colegio Libre de Estudios Superiores (Buenos Aires), 1952; American U., 1964–65. Prof., Facultad de Filosofía, Letras y Ciencias de la Educación, Universidad del Litoral (Argentina), 1955–57; prof., Facultad de Humanidades, Universidad de la Plata (Argentina), 1956; research asst., Instituto de Filosofía, Universidad de Buenos Aires, 1956–57; chief, Section of Philosophy, Dept. of Cultural Affairs, Pan American Union, 1957–58; ASST. SECRETARY, FELLOWSHIP AND PROFESSORSHIP PROGRAM, DEPT. OF TECHNICAL COOPERATION, PAN AMERICAN UNION, 1958– . Research: history of ideas in Latin America, especially Argentina. Author: La filosofía del siglo veinte (1955); La filosofía en la Argentina (1961); Francisco Romero: esquema de su itinerario filosófico (in Homenaje a Francisco Romero, 1964). Language: Spanish 5,5, 5,5; Portuguese 4,–,–,–; French 4,–,–,–; German 3,–,–,–; Italian 4,–,–,–. Home: Apt. 616, 4977 Battery Lane, Bethesda, Md. 20014. Office: Dept. of Technical Cooperation, Pan American Union, Washington, D.C. 20006.

TORRES, JOSÉ ARSENIO, b. Aguas Buenas, P.R., Sept. 20, 1926. PHILOSOPHY. B.A., U. of P.R., 1947; M.A., U. of Chicago, 1948; Ph. D., 1954. Instr., U. of P.R., 1949–53; asst. prof., 1954–55; assoc. prof., chmn., General Social Sciences, 1956–60; PROF., POLITICAL PHILOSOPHY, U. OF P.R., 1960– . Rockefeller Foundation research grant (London), 1960–61; consultant, Secretary of Education (P.R.), 1962– . Membership: American Philosophical Association. Research: the political ideologies of modernization in developing countries; problems of university education. Author: Educación liberal y técnica pedagógica (Cuadernos Americanos, Apr. 1958); The Ideological Component of Indian Development (International Journal of Ethics, Jan. 1962). Language: Spanish 5,5,5,5; Portuguese 2,2,1,–; French 3,3,3,–. Home: Box 22091, U. of P.R. Río Piedras, P.R. Office: Dept. of Philosophy, U. of P.R., Río Piedras.

TORRES-RIOSECO, ARTURO, b. Talca, Chile, Oct. 17, 1897. SPANISH AMERICAN LITERATURE. A.B., U. of Chile, 1916; M.A., U. of Minn., 1924; Ph. D., 1931. Instr., Williams Coll., 1919–21; instr., U. of Minn, 1921–24; prof., U. of Tex., 1925–28; PROF., LATIN AMERICAN LITERATURE, U. OF CALIF., BERKELEY, 1928– . Guggenheim fellow, 1932; Rockefeller Foundation fellow, 1953; summer vis. prof., U. of Minn., U. of Mexico, U. of Tex., Stanford U., Columbia U., U. of Colo., U. of N. Mex., U. of Guatemala, U. of Chile, Duke U., U. of Calif. at Los Angeles. Membership: Hispanic Society of America; Academia Mexicana de la Lengua; Modern Language Association; Academia Panameña de la Lengua. Research: comparative literature; the novel; Brazilian and North American literature. Author: Rubén Darío: Casticismo y Americanismo (1931); The Epic of Latin American Literature (1942); Grandes novelistas de América Hispana (1943). Language: Spanish 5,5,5,5; Portuguese 5,5,5,5; French 4,4,4,4. Home: 106

Forest Lane, Berkeley, Calif. Office: Dept. of Spanish and Portuguese, U. of Calif., Berkeley.

TOSI, JOSEPH ANDREW, JR., b. Worcester, Mass., July 1, 1921. GEOGRAPHY. B.S. Mass. State Coll., 1943; M.F., Yale U., 1948; Ph. D., Clark U., 1959. Geographer, Rural Land Classification Program, Dept. of Agriculture and Commerce (P.R.), 1950–51; forester, Technical Assistance Program, Inter-American Institute of Agricultural Sciences, Organization of American States (San José, Costa Rica), 1951–52; forester and ecologist (Lima, Peru), 1952–60; ECOLOGIST, TECHNICAL ASSISTANCE PROGRAM, INTER-AMERICAN INSTITUTE OF AGRICULTURAL SCIENCES, ORGANIZATION OF AMERICAN STATES (SAN JOSÉ, COSTA RICA), 1961– ; ecologist, Central American Field Program, Associated Colleges of the Midwest, 1964. Membership: American Association for the Advancement of Science; Association of American Geographers; Association for Tropical Biology; Caribbean Section, American Horticulture Society; Ecological Society of America; International Society of Tropical Foresters; Society of American Foresters; Tropical Science Center. Research: ecology; forestry; rural economic development; phytogeography; economic botany; tropical forest land utilization and economics; bio-climatology and life zone analysis and mapping; forest ecology of the tropics; tropical environmental productivity; physical geography, agriculture, and natural vegetation of Costa Rica and Peru; bio-climatology and natural vegetation of Colombia, Ecuador, and Venezuela. Author: Zonas de vida natural en el Peru y mapa ecológico del Peru (1960). Co-author: Mapa ecológico de Colombia y formaciones vegetales de Colombia (1963); Some Environmental Factors in the Economic Development of the Tropics (Economic Geography, July 1964). Language: Spanish 5,5,4,4; Portuguese 3,2,1,1; French 3,2,1,2; German 3,2,1,1. Home: Apartado 4359, San José, Costa Rica. Office: Inter-American Institute of Agricultural Sciences, Organization of American States, San José, Costa Rica.

TOTH, JOHN CHARLES, b. Mich., Jan. 30, 1925. PSYCHOLOGY AND EDUCATION. B.A., Mich. State U., 1957; M.A., 1960; Ph. D., 1963. Research asst., U.S. Agency for International Development (Guatemala), 1962–63; ASST. PROF., EDUCATIONAL PSYCHOLOGY, U. OF ILL., 1963– . Vis. prof., U. of San Carlos (Guatemala), 1962; consultant, Ministers of Education and Health (Guatemala), 1962–63. Membership: American Personnel & Guidance Association; National Rehabilitation Association. Research: physical, mental, and social-cultural rehabilitation psychology; Guatemala. Author: Clase social y desarrollo ocupacional (1962); Extraversion-Introversion and Decrement in an Auditory Vigilance Task (in Vigilance, 1963). Language: Spanish 2,2,2,2; Portuguese 1,1,1,1; French 1,1,1,1; Hungarian 2,3,3,2. Home: 1303 South Western Ave., Champaign, Ill. Office: 188R Education Bldg., U. of Ill., Urbana.

TOWNSEND, ELAINE MIELKE, b. Chicago, Ill., Nov. 6, 1915. LINGUISTICS. Chicago Teachers Coll., 1936–39. LITERACY CONSULTANT, SUMMER INSTITUTE OF LINGUISTICS (COLOMBIA), 1942– ; literacy consultant, Ministerio de Educación (Lima, Peru), 1952–63; Ministerio de Gobierno, División de Asuntos Indíjenas, 1963. Research: literacy and writing systems; Mexico; Peru. Author: Accelerating Literacy by Piecemeal Digestion of the Alphabet (Language Learning, July 1948). Language: Spanish 4,4,4,4. Linguistic studies: Amuesha; Aguaruna; Arebela; Bora; Campa; Cashibo; Huambisa; Huitoto; Jebero; Machiguenga; Ocaina; Piro; Shapra; Shipibo; Ticuna; Yagua. Home: 2511 North Drake Ave., Chicago 47, Ill. Office: Instituto Lingüístico de Verano, Apartado Nacional 5787, Bogotá Colombia.

TOWNSEND, WILLIAM CAMERON, b. Riverside County, Calif., July 9, 1896. LINGUISTICS. Occidental Coll., 1914–17. GENERAL DIR., SUMMER INSTITUTE OF LINGUISTICS, 1934– . Research: descriptive and applied linguistics; literacy in Mexico, Peru, and Colombia. Author: Aymará Primer (1946); Lázaro Cárdenas, Mexican Democrat (1951). Language: Spanish 4,4,4,4. Linguistic studies: Cakchiquel. Home: Apartado Nacional 5787, Bogotá, Colombia. Office: Summer Institute of Linguistics, Box 1960, Santa Ana, Calif.

TRAGEN, IRVING GLENN, b. San Francisco, Calif., May 18, 1922. LAW AND ECONOMICS: LABOR. A.B., U. of Calif., 1943; LL.B., 1945; U. of Chile, 1946. Lectr., Mexico City Coll., 1949; personnel officer, Mexico-U.S. Commission to Eradicate Aftosa, 1948–49; chief of personnel, Pan American Sanitary Bureau, 1949–53; labor adviser, International Cooperation Administration (El Salvador), 1953–57, (Chile), 1957–60; labor attaché, Embassy (Venezuela), U.S. Dept. of State, 1960–62; LECTR., INTERNATIONAL RELATIONS, AMERICAN U., 1962– ; DIR., OFFICE OF INSTITUTIONAL DEVELOPMENT, LATIN AMERICAN BUREAU, U.S. AGENCY FOR INTERNATIONAL DEVELOPMENT, U.S. DEPT. OF STATE, 1962– . U. of Calif. Mills traveling fellow (Chile), 1945–46; U.S. Dept. of State fellow (Mexico), 1947–48. Membership: California Bar Association; Foreign Law Society; Phi Beta Kappa. Research: social development problems; labor and social problems of Latin American comparative law; economics of labor. Author: Labor Inspection Manual (1964); Observations on Latin American Labor Law (1960); The Taft-Hartley Law (1961). Language: Spanish 5,5,5,3; Portuguese 3,2,1,–; French 2,1,1,–. Home: 4201 Cathedral Ave., NW., Washington 16, D.C. Office: Office of Institutional Development, Latin American Bureau, Agency for International Development, U.S. Dept. of State, 21st St. and Virginia Ave., NW., Washington.

TRANK, LYNN EDGAR, b. Cook, Nebr., Feb. 24, 1918. ART. B.F.A., U. of Nebr., 1942; B.F.A., Washington U., 1948; M.F.A.; State U. of Iowa, 1950; Ph. D., Ohio State U., 1962. Instr., U. of Nebr., 1946; ASSOC. PROF., ART, EASTERN ILL. U., 1952– . Membership: Illinois Art Education Association; Illinois Education Association; Midwestern College Arts. Research: painting, drawing, and printmaking; native dances and folk art in Mexico; Tarascan culture.

Language: Spanish 3,3,3,2; French 4,3,2,2. Home: 10 West Johnson, Charleston, Ill. 61920. Office: Dept. of Art, Eastern Ill. U., Charleston, 61920.

TRAVIS, MARTIN B., b. Iron Mountain, Mich., Sept. 22, 1917. POLITICAL SCIENCE. A.B., Amherst Coll., 1939; M.A., Fletcher School of Law & Diplomacy, 1940; Ph. D., U. of Chicago, 1948. Asst. prof., Syracuse U., 1948–49; asst. prof., Duke U., 1949–53; assoc. prof., Stanford U.. 1953–61; PROF., CHMN., POLITICAL SCIENCE, STATE U. OF N.Y., COLL. AT STONY BROOK, 1961– . Ford Foundation fellow and Rockefeller grants (Mexico), 1950, (Bolivia, Ecuador, Peru), 1952, 1956–57, 1961; consultant, Standard Oil Company of Calif. Membership: American Political Science Association; American Society of International Law; Council on Foreign Relations. Research: Latin American control of foreign policy and relations; political teaching in Mexico; control of foreign policy in Ecuador, Peru, and Bolivia. Author: Control of Foreign Relations in Modern Nations (1957); Organization of American States: A Guide to the Future (Western Political Quarterly, Sept. 1957); Control of the Panama Canal: An Obsolete Shibboleth? (Foreign Affairs, Apr. 1959). Language: Spanish 4,3,3,3. Home: R.F.D. 1, Syosset, Long Island, N.Y. Office: Dept. of Political Science, State U. of N.Y., Coll. at Stony Brook, Stony Brook.

TREJO, ARNULFO DUEÑES, b. Villa Vicente, Guerrero, Mexico, Aug. 15, 1922. LIBRARY SCIENCE. B.A., U. of Ariz., 1949; M.A., Mexico City Coll., 1951; M.A., Kent State U., 1953; Ph. D., National U. of Mexico, 1959. Librarian, Mexico City Coll., 1953–54; head of public service, Main Library, National U. of Mexico, 1954–55; reference librarian, U. of Calif., Los Angeles, 1955–59; asst. librarian, Long Beach State Coll., 1959–63; DIR., BIBLIOTECA, ESCUELA DE ADMINISTRACIÓN DE NEGOCIOS PARA GRADUADOS (LIMA), STANFORD U.–U.S. AGENCY FOR INTERNATIONAL DEVELOPMENT CONTRACT, 1963– . Membership: American Association of University Professors; American Library Association; Association of California State College Professors; California Library Association. Research: linguistics of the slang of the Mexican underworld; Peru. Author: El argot como medio de expresión en la prosa mexicana (Anuario de Letras, Universidad Nacional Autónoma de México, 1961); El acercamiento entre las Américas a través de la enseñanza y el escrito impreso (in La Literatura del Caribe . . ., 1961); The Street Vendors of My Childhood Days (Arizona Highways, Aug. 1963). Language: Spanish 5,5,5,5; Portuguese 2,2,2,2; French 4,2,2,2. Office: Escuela de Administración de Negocios para Graduados (ESAN), Santo Toribio 210, San Isidro, Lima, Perú.

TREMBLEY, WILLIAM ALBERT, b. Akron, Ohio, June 6, 1920. HISTORY. B.A., U. of Akron, 1942; M.A., U. of Houston, 1953. Asst. prof., U.S. Merchant Marine Academy, 1957–59; ASST. PROF., HISTORY, RESEARCH ASSOC., INSTITUTE OF CARIBBEAN STUDIES, U. OF P.R., 1959– ; vis. lectr., U. of the West Indies (Jamaica), 1962–63. John S. Knight scholarship, U. of Akron, 1943; Ford fellow, 1956; Fulbright fellow (Haiti), 1957. Membership: American Historical Association; Jamaica Historical Society. Research: 19th century Haiti and the French Caribbean. Author: The Status of the Church in Saint-Domingue During the Last Days of the French Monarchy, 1781–1793 (Caribbean Studies, Apr. 1960). Co-author: The Alfred Nemours Collection of Haitian History: A Catalogue (Caribbean Studies, Oct. 1962). Editor: Directory of Caribbean Studies (1962). Language: Spanish 2,3,2,1; French 3,3,3,3. Home: Calle del Sol 4 (Interior), San Juan, P.R. Office: Institute of Caribbean Studies, U. of P.R., Río Piedras.

TREUTLEIN, THEODORE EDWARD, b. San Diego, Calif., Dec. 25, 1906. HISTORY. B.A., San Diego State Coll., 1929; M.A., U. of Calif., 1930; Ph. D., 1934. PROF., HISTORY, SAN FRANCISCO STATE COLL., 1935– ; vis. assoc. prof., Stanford U., 1946. Native Sons of the Golden West traveling fellow in Pacific Coast History, 1932–33. Membership: American Association of University Professors; American Historical Association; California Historical Society; Pacific Coast Council on Latin American Studies. Research: history of Mexico. Author: The Relation of Philipp Segesser (Mid-America, July 1945). Translator and editor: Sonora: A Description of the Province, by Ignaz Pfefferkorn (1949). Language: Spanish 3,3,3,1; German 4,4,4,3. Home: 2215 Marin Ave., Berkeley 7, Calif. Office: Dept. of History, San Francisco State Coll., 1600 Holloway, San Francisco 27, Calif.

TRIBE, PEGGY ANN MILLER, b. Hope, Ark., Dec. 30, 1921. LIBRARY SCIENCE. B.S., Memphis State U., 1942; M.A., La. State U., 1945; B.S. in L.S., 1946. Librarian, La. State U., 1945–47; librarian, Biblioteca Americana (Managua, Nicaragua), U.S. Information Agency, 1947–49; librarian, Biblioteca Lincoln (Buenos Aires, Argentina), 1949–55; reference librarian, Intelligence and Research Library, U.S. Information Agency, 1955–56; information specialist, Information Center Service (N.Y.), U.S. Information Agency, 1956–57; program officer, Reception Center (N.Y.), U.S. Dept. of State, 1957–58; librarian, Junior-Senior High School (West Hempstead, N.Y.), 1958–59; librarian, North Senior High School (Great Neck, N.Y.), 1959–64. Consultant, U.S. Agency for International Development (Venezuela), Summer 1962. Membership: National Education Association. Research: library administration. Language: Spanish 4,4,4,4. Home: c/o Mrs. Rose D. Miller, 692 Watson, Memphis, Tenn.

TRIFFIN, ROBERT, b. Flobecq, Belgium, Oct. 5, 1911. ECONOMICS. LL.D., U. of Louvain (Belgium), 1934; Ph. D., Harvard U. 1939. Instr., Harvard U., 1939–42; senior economist, chief, Latin American Div., Federal Reserve Board, 1942–46; chief, Exchange Control Div., International Monetary Fund, 1946–48; head technical representative in Europe, 1948–49; policy adviser, U.S. Economic Cooperation Administration, 1949–51; PROF. ECONOMICS, PELATIAH PERIT PROF. OF POLITICAL AND SOCIAL SCIENCE, YALE U., 1951– ; vis. prof., Graduate Institute of International Studies (Geneva), 1958–61. Consultant, United Nations Economic Commission for

Latin America, Summer 1952, Council of Economic Advisers, 1953–54, 1961, European Economic Community, 1958– ; Merrill Foundation fellow (Paris), 1954–55. Research: foreign central banking and international monetary policy and institutions; Latin American payments agreement and monetary integration. Author: El oro y la crisis del dólar (1962) ; Una cámara de compensación y unión de pagos latinoamericana (in Cooperación financiera en América Latina, 1963). Co-author: Monetary and Banking Legislation of the Dominican Republic, 1947 (1953). Language: Spanish 5,5,4,4 ; French 5,5,4,5 ; German 4,1,1,1 ; Italian, 4,3,1,1. Home: 97 Loomis Pl., New Haven, Conn. Office: Dept. of Economics, Yale U., 37 Hillhouse Ave., New Haven.

TRIFILO, S. SAMUEL, b. Rodi, Italy, Mar. 8, 1917. SPANISH AMERICAN LITERATURE, B.S., Cornell U., 1940 ; M.A., U. of Buffalo, 1951 ; Ph. D., U. of Mich., 1957. Instr., U. of Mich., 1955–57 ; ASSOC. PROF., SPANISH, MARQUETTE U., 1957–. American Philosophical Society grant (Mexico), 1961 ; Social Science Research Council grant, 1963. Membership: American Association of Teachers of Spanish and Portuguese ; Instituto Internacional de Literatura Iberoamericana ; Modern Language Association. Research: 19th century literature in Argentina, Chile, and Peru ; theater in Mexico. Author: La Argentina vista por viajeros ingleses (1959) ; The Contemporary Theater in Mexico (Modern Language Journal, Apr. 1962) ; Catholicism in Argentina—19th Century (The Americas, Jan. 1963). Language: Spanish 5,5,5,5 ; Portuguese 3,3,3,2 ; French 3,3,3,2 ; Italian 4,5,4,4. Linguistic studies: Spanish. Home: 3625 North 55th, Milwaukee 16, Wis. Office: Dept. of Spanish, Marquette U., Milwaukee 3.

TROIKE, RUDOLPH CHARLES, b. Brownsville, Tex., Jan. 11, 1933. ANTHROPOLOGY: LINGUISTICS. B.A., U. of Tex., 1954 ; M.A., 1957 ; Ph. D., 1959. Instr., asst. prof., Georgetown U. English Language Program (Ankara, Turkey), 1959–62 ; ASST. PROF., ENGLISH, U. OF TEX., 1962–. E.D. Farmer International scholar (Mexico), 1957 ; consultant, Teaching English as a Second Language, Universidad Autónoma de Guadalajara (Mexico), 1963–64. Membership: American Anthropological Association ; Linguistic Society of America, National Association for Foreign Student Affairs ; Texas Archeological Society. Research: applied linguistics ; anthropological linguistics and archeology of northeastern and central Mexico ; American Indian languages ; ethnohistory of Northeast Mexico. Author: Time and Types in Archeological Analysis: The Brainerd-Robinson Technique (Bulletin of the Texas Archaeological Society, 1957) ; Origins of Plains Mescalism (American Anthropologist, Oct. 1962) ; A Contribution to Coahuilteco Lexicography (International Journal of American Linguistics, Oct. 1963). Language: Spanish 3,4,3,3 ; German 2,2,2,2. Linguistic studies: Caddo ; Coahuilteco. Home: 3927 Balcones Dr., Austin 31, Tex. Office: Dept. of English, U. of Tex., Austin 12.

TRUEBLOOD, ALAN STUBBS, b. Haverford, Pa., May 3, 1917. LANGUAGE. B.A., Harvard U., 1938 ; M.A., 1941 ; Ph. D., 1951. Dir., Chile-U.S. Cultural Institute (Santiago), 1942–43 ; instr., Inter-American Meteorological School, 1943 ; instr.-PROF., SPANISH, BROWN U., 1947– ; vis. prof., Harvard U., 1959–60, Summer 1962, Spring 1963. Sheldon fellow (Hispanic America), 1941–42 ; Fulbright research grantee (Chile), 1958. Membership: American Association of Teachers of Spanish and Portuguese ; American Society for Aesthetics ; Modern Language Association ; Phi Beta Kappa. Research: comparative literature: inter-American cultural relations ; Spanish literature. Author: The Case for an Early Dorotea: A Re-examination (Publications of the Modern Language Association, Sept. 1956) ; El silencio en el Quijote (Nueva Revista de Filología Hispánica, Apr.-Jun. 1958) ; La experiencia chilena de un yankee de Rhode Island: Samuel Ward Greene (Revista Chilena de Historia y Geografía, Jan.-Dec. 1962). Language: Spanish 5,5,4, 5 ; Portuguese 4,4,3,3 ; French 5,5,4,4 ; German 3,2,2,2 ; Italian 4,4,3,3 ; Russian 2,2,-2,2. Home: 28 Cushing St., Providence 6, R.I., Office: Dept. of Spanish, Brown U., Providence.

TUCKER, WILLIAM PIERCE, b. Walla Walla, Wash., Dec. 7, 1910. POLITICAL SCIENCE. B.A., Coll. of Puget Sound, 1930 ; M.A., U. of Wash., 1931 ; Ph. D., U. of Minn., 1945. Prof., Macalester Coll., 1942–56 ; part-time prof., U. of Minn., 1946–56 ; ASSOC. PROF., POLITICAL SCIENCE, U. OF P.R., 1956– . Membership: American Political Science Association ; Puerto Rico Political Science Association. Research: Latin American politics and government ; Mexico ; Central America. Author: The Mexican Government Today (1957). Editor: Selected Readings in American Government (1954). Language: Spanish 4,4,4,– ; French 3,–,–,–. Office: Dept. of Political Science, U. of P.R., Río Piedras.

TUDISCO, ANTHONY, b. Brooklyn, N.Y., Aug. 5, 1915. LANGUAGE. B.A., Brooklyn Coll., 1936 ; M.A., Columbia U., 1937 ; Ph. D., 1950. Instr., Long Island U., 1938–41 ; tutor, Queens Coll., 1943–47 ; ASSOC. PROF., SPANISH, COLUMBIA U., 1947– . Regional Interviewing Committee for Teacher Exchange Program, U.S. Dept. of Health, Education, and Welfare. Membership: American Association of Teachers of Spanish and Portuguese ; Conference on Latin American History ; Hispanic Institute ; North East Conference for Latin American Studies ; Sigma Delta Pi. Research: language and literature of Spanish America. Author: América en la literatura española del Siglo XVIII (Anuario de Estudios Americanos, 1954) ; The Land, People, and Problems of America in XVIIIth Century Spanish Literature (The Americas, Apr. 1956) ; America in Some Travelers, Historians, and Political Economists of the Spanish Eighteenth Century (The Americas, July 1958). Language: Spanish 5,5,5,5 ; Portuguese 3,3,1,1 ; French 3,3,1,1 ; Italian 4,4, 4,4. Linguistic studies: Spanish. Home: 601 West 113 St., New York, N.Y. 10025. Office: Dept. of Spanish, Columbia U., New York, 10027.

TUMBLIN, JOHN A., JR., b. Salvador, Brazil, Oct. 4, 1923. SOCIOLOGY. B.A., Wake Forest Coll., 1948 ; M.A., Duke U., 1951 ; Ph. D., 1956. Instr., Randolph-Macon Woman's Coll., 1951–54 ; instr.,

Duke U., 1954–55; asst. prof., Randolph-Macon Woman's Coll., 1955–56; prof., Colégio Americano Batista (Recife, Brazil), 1957–60; prof., Seminário Teológico Batista do Norte do Brasil (Recife), 1957–60; acting president, 1960; PROF., CHMN., SOCIOLOGY AND ANTHROPOLOGY, AGNES SCOTT COLL., 1961– . Membership: American Association of University Professors; American Sociological Association; Omicron Delta Kappa; Phi Beta Kappa; Southern Sociological Society. Research; cultural anthropology; sociology of the professions; ethnography; race relations; Brazil. Author: Alguns comentários sôbre a relação entre a sociologia e o cristianismo (Expositor Teológico, Oct. 1958); Responsibilidades e oportunidades sociais da igreja (Expositor Teológico, Dec. 1960); One Continent, Two Worlds (Agnes Scott Alumnae Quarterly, Fall 1963). Language: Spanish 4,3,3,2; Portuguese 5,5,5,5; French 2,1,1,1. Home: 184 South Candler St., Decatur, Ga. 30030. Office: Dept. of Sociology and Anthropology, Agnes Scott Coll., Decatur, 30030.

TURNER, E(LBERT) DAYMOND, b. Gainesville, Fla., Nov. 15, 1915. LANGUAGE. B.A., Davidson Coll., 1937; M.A., U. of N.C., 1939; Ph. D., 1949. Instr., Ga. Teachers Coll., 1939–41; instr., U. of N.C., 1945–49; asst. prof.-PROF., MODERN LANGUAGES, U. OF DEL., 1949– ; instr., National Defense Education Act Institute, Utah State U., 1963. Membership: American Association of Teachers of Spanish and Portuguese; American Association of Teachers of French; American Association of University Professors; Association of Modern Language Teachers; Modern Language Association. Research: literature of exploration; methods of language teaching. Author: Planning the High School Language Lab (French Review, Dec. 1958); Poltrón y perezoso . . . A Question of Meaning (Delaware Notes, Dec. 1959); Biblioteca Ovetense: A Speculative Reconstruction of the Library of the First Chronicler of the Indies (Papers of the Bibliographical Society of America, June 1963). Language: Spanish 5,4,4,4; Portuguese 3,2,1,1; French 4,2,2,2. Home: 271 West Main St., Newark, Del. Office: Dept. of Modern Languages and Literatures, U. of Del., Newark.

TURNER, GLEN DAVID, b. Trinidad, British West Indies, Dec. 11, 1927. ANTHROPOLOGY; LINGUISTICS. B.A., Westmont Coll., 1949; M.A., Ind. U., 1952; Ph. D. 1958. LINGUIST, TRANSLATOR, SUMMER INSTITUTE OF LINGUISTICS (ECUADOR), 1952– . Membership: American Anthropological Association; Linguistic Society of America. Research: translation; Indian affairs in Ecuador; Jívaro phonology and morphology. Author: Alternative Phonemicization in Jívaro (International Journal of American Linguistics, 1957). Language: Spanish 4,5,4,4; Jívaro 3,3,3,3. Linguistic studies: Jívaro. Home: Box 1960, Santa Ana, Calif. Office: Instituto Lingüístico de Verano, Casilla 1007, Quito, Ecuador.

TURNER, PAUL R., b. Peoria, Ill., June 4, 1929. LINGUISTICS. B.A., Wheaton Coll., 1952; U. of Chicago. LINGUIST, MISSIONARY, SUMMMER INSTITUTE OF LINGUISTICS (MEXICO), 1959– . National Science Foundation-Summer Institute of Linguistics-U. of Okla. grant. Research: descriptive linguistics; phonemes of Highland Chontal; Highland Chontal Indians of Oaxaca, Mexico. Author: Gospel of Mark in Chontal (1964). Language: Spanish 3,3,3,3; French 2,–,–,–; Chontal 3,3,3,3. Linguistic studies: Chontal. Home: 405 West Empire, Freeport, Ill. Office: Instituto Lingüístico de Verano, Apartado 2975, México 1, D.F.

TYSON, BRADY BRADFORD, b. San Antonio, Tex., Aug. 31, 1927. POLITICAL SCIENCE: INTERNATIONAL RELATIONS. B.A., Rice U., 1949; B.D., Southern Methodist U., 1952; Ph. D., American U., 1963. Instr., American U., 1959–61; VIS. PROF., POLITICAL SCIENCE, FUNDAÇÃO ESCOLA DE SOCIOLOGIA E. POLÍTICA; METHODIST CHAPLAIN TO THE UNIVERSITY COMMUNITY (SÃO PAULO), 1961– . Membership: American Political Science Association. Research: Brazil. Author: Catholicism in Brazil (America, May 1964). Language: Spanish 3,3,3,3; Portuguese 4,4,4,4; French 2,2,2,2. Home: 9 Pine Hill Lane, Houston, Tex.

U

ULIBARRI, GEORGE SARRACINO, b. Reserve, N. Mex., May 16, 1916. LIBRARY SCIENCE: ARCHIVAL ADMINISTRATION. B.A., U. of N. Mex., 1943; M.A., 1948; Ph. D., U. of Iowa, 1952. Instr., Spanish and Portuguese, U. of Iowa, 1948–52; prof., Spanish, U. of Wyo., 1952–53; translator and interpreter, Mayo Clinic, 1953; LATIN AMERICAN SPECIALIST, ARCHIVIST, DEPT. OF CIVIL ARCHIVES, NATIONAL ARCHIVES, 1956– . Secretary general, Consejo Interamericano Técnico para Archivos; chmn., Committee on Spanish Archival Terminology; Advisory Committee, Guide to Latin American Materials in the United States. Membership: Consejo Interamericano Técnico para Archivos; Sociedad de Archiveros Peruanos; Society of American Archivists. Research: archival management; novels of Peru, Bolivia, and Ecuador. Author: Semejanzas y diferencias entre archivos y bibliotecas (Revista Interamericana de Bibliografía, Sept. 1962); The Inter-American Technical Council on Archives (American Archivist, Jan. 1964). Translator: Técnicas descriptivas de archivos, by T. R. Schellenberg (1961). Language: Spanish 5,5,5,5; Portuguese 4,3,2,1; French 3,1,1,1. Home: 3960 Pennsylvania Ave., S.E., Washington, D.C. 20020. Office: National Archives and Records Service, Washington, D.C. 20408.

ULIBARRI, SABINE REYES, b. Santa Fe, N. Mex., Sept. 21, 1919. LANGUAGE. B.A., U. of N. Mex., 1947; M.A., 1949; Ph. D., U. of Calif., Los Angeles, 1959. Teacher, N. Mex. Public Schools, 1938–42; ASSOC. PROF., MODERN LANGUAGES, U. of N. MEX., 1947–. Pro-secretary, Instituto Internacional de Literatura Iberoamericana, 1950–55; chmn., Hispanic Literature Section, Philological Association of the Pacific Coast, 1962; dir., National Defense Education Act Language Institute (Ecuador), 1963; consultant, D.C. Heath-Louis de Rochemont project for teaching Spanish on TV. Membership: American Association of Teachers of Spanish and Portuguese; Modern Language Association; Rocky Mountain Modern Language Association. Research: modern Spanish poetry. Author: Fun Learning Elementary Spanish (1961); Al cielo se sube a pie (1961); El mundo poético de Juan Ramón (1962). Language: Spanish 5,5,5,5; Portuguese 4,4,4,4; French 2,2,2,2. Linguistic studies: Portuguese; Spanish. Home: 1601 Valencia Dr., NE., Albuquerque, N. Mex. Office: Dept. of Modern Languages, U. of N. Mex., Albuquerque.

ULRICH, E. MATTHEW, b. Bridgeport, Conn. LINGUISTICS. B.A., Seattle Pacific Coll., 1959. MISSIONARY, LINGUIST, SUMMER INSTITUTE OF LINGUISTICS (GUATEMALA), 1960– . Research: translation of Bible and secular materials. Language: Spanish 3,3,2,2; Mopan Maya 5,4,4,5. Linguistic studies: Mopan Maya. Home: 6037 37th NE., Seattle, Wash. 98115. Office: Summer Institute of Linguistics, Apartado 74, Guatemala, Guatemala.

ULRICH, ROSEMARY DIXON, b. Seattle, Wash., July 5, 1932. LINGUISTICS. B.S., U. of Wash., 1955; B.S. Seattle Pacific Coll., 1955; M.N., U. of Wash., 1958. MISSIONARY, LINGUIST, SUMMER INSTITUTE OF LINGUISTICS (GUATEMALA), 1960– . Research: literacy; public health; nursing; Guatemala. Language: Spanish 4,4,4,3; Mopan Maya 3,4,4,3. Linguistic studies: Mopan Maya. Home: 6039 37th NE., Seattle, Wash. 98115. Office: Instituto Lingüístico de Verano, Apartado 74, Guatemala, Guatemala.

UNDERWOOD, FRANCES WENRICH, b. Philadelphia, Pa., Apr. 10, 1917. ANTHROPOLOGY. A.B., U. of Pa., 1938; Ph. D., Yale U., 1948. Instr.-asst. prof., U. of Conn., 1949–51; lectr., Stanford U., 1953–57; asst. prof., U. of the Pacific, 1957–58; LECTR., ANTHROPOLOGY, STANFORD U., 1960–61, 1963, 1964– . Membership: American Anthropological Association. Research: social anthropology; Caribbean societies; folklore; ethnographic patterns of southern Haitian peasant villages; behavioral analysis of a juvenile detention hall. Author: A Comparison of Socialization and Personality in Two Simple Societies (American Anthropologist, Oct.–Dec. 1947); The Marketing System in Peasant Haiti (1960); Land and Its Manipulation in Peasant Haiti (in Explorations in Cultural Anthropology, 1964). Language: Spanish 3,2,1,3; French 3,3,2,3; German 3,1,1,2. Home: 988 College Dr., San Jose, Calif. 95128.

UNDREINER, GEORGE JOSEPH, RT. REV. MSGR., b. Brooklyn, N.Y., Oct. 28, 1900. HISTORY. A.B., Josephinum Coll., 1920; Josephinum Seminary, 1923–27; Ph. D., U. of Fribourg (Switzerland), 1931. PROF. OF HISTORY AND CHURCH HISTORY, PONTIFICAL COLL. JOSEPHINUM. 1931– . Membership: Academy of American Franciscan History; Conference on Latin American History; New Mexico Historical Society. Research: southwest United States history; Catholic missions. Author: Monsignor Joseph Jessing, 1836–1899 (1936); Church and Culture in the Middle Ages (1956); Fray Marcos de Niza and His Journey to Cibola (The Americas, Apr. 1947). Language: Spanish 4,2,1,2; Portuguese 2,–,–,–; French 4,3,3,3; German 5,5, 4,4. Home and office: Pontifical Coll. Josephinum, Worthington, Ohio.

UPTON, THOMAS GRAYDON, b. Salem, Mass., Mar. 26, 1908. ECONOMICS. A.B., Harvard Coll., 1931; Harvard Business School, 1933. Vice president, Foreign Dept., Philadelphia National Bank, 1951–58; asst. secretary, U.S. Treasury, U.S. dir., World Bank, dir., Development Loan Fund, 1958–60; EXECUTIVE VICE PRESIDENT, INTER-AMERICAN DEVELOPMENT BANK, 1961– . Research: foreign commercial banks; Latin American development finance; Central America. Language: Spanish 4,4,4,3; French 4,3,3,2; German 3,3,3,3. Home: Box 437, Route 2, McLean Va. Office: Inter-American Development Bank, 808 17th St., NW., Washington 25, D.C.

URBANSKI, EDMUND STEPHEN, b. Ostrow, Poland, July 6, 1909. SPANISH AMERICAN LITERATURE. A.B., Classic Coll. (Poland), 1930; M.A., School of Journalism (Poland), 1934; M.A., Universidad Nacional de México, 1943; Ph. D., 1946; diploma, Universidad de Barcelona, 1955; Universidad de San Marcos, 1959. Prof., Universidad Nacional de México, 1942–45; asst. prof., Marquette U., 1946–48; U. of San Francisco, 1948–51; Idaho State Coll., 1951–55; vis. assoc., U. of Notre Dame, 1955–56; asst. prof., John Carroll U., 1956–59; assoc. prof., U. of Buffalo, 1960–62; ASSOC. PROF., FOREIGN LANGUAGES AND LITERATURES, WESTERN ILL. U., 1962– Polish-British Research Council grant, 1943–46; Organization of American States grant (Colombia, Ecuador, Peru, Bolivia), 1959. Membership: American Association of Teachers of Spanish and Portuguese; Association for Latin American Studies; International Congress of Americanists; Modern Language Association. Research: culture and social structure in the Andean region and Mexico; comparative Spanish American and Anglo American civilization. Author: Studies in Spanish American Literature and Civilization (1964); Nuevos aspectos histórico-culturales de Latinoamérica (Cuadernos, July 1963); Tradition and Mobility in Anglo-American and Spanish-American Civilizations: An Essay in Comparative History (Journal of World History, Fall 1963). Language: Spanish 5,5,5,5; Portuguese 3,3,3,–; French 3,3,3,–. Linguistic studies: Spanish. Office: Dept. of Foreign Languages and Literatures, Western Ill. U., Macomb, Ill. 61455.

URIBE, JOSEPH GARCIA, b. Los Angeles, Calif., June 24, 1931. ART AND COMMUNICATION. A.B., U. of Calif., Los Angeles, 1954; M.A., Los Angeles State Coll. 1959. Secondary teacher, Los Angeles City Schools, 1955–59; curriculum consultant in secondary art, 1959–60; ASSOC. PROF., ART, CALIF. STATE COLL., LOS ANGELES, 1960– . Membership: National Art Education Association; Pacific Arts Association; Southern California Art Education Association. Research: cinema; art education films; art design; Mexican art and architecture. Language: Spanish 4,5,5,4; Portuguese 2,2,1,1; French 2,2,1,1; Italian 2,2,1,1. Home: 383 Cherry Dr., Pasadena, Calif. Office: Calif. State Coll., 5151 State College Dr., Los Angeles.

URIST, MARGARET ETHEL, b. Osborne, Kans., Jan. 6, 1920. POLITICAL SCIENCE. B.S.F.S., U. of Southern Calif., 1942; M.A., 1946; Ph. D., 1956. Social science analyst, Library of Congress, 1959–

57; research analyst, External Research and Intelligence, U.S. Dept. of State, 1961; scientific reference analyst, National Institute of Mental Health, 1962-63; co-dir., Mental Health Information Center on Latin America, Pan American Health Organization, 1963-64. Consultant, Caribbean Mental Health Conference (Curaçao), Apr. 1963; Pan American Mental Health Conference (Buenos Aires), Sept. 1963. Membership: American Association for the History of Medicine. Research: international relations; social problems in Latin American area. Language: Spanish 4,4,3,1. Home and office: c/o Harold E. Urist, U.S. Information Agency, 1776 Pennsylvania Ave., Washington, D.C. 20547.

V

VALBUENA-(BRIONES), ÁNGEL JULIÁN, b. Madrid, Spain, Jan. 11, 1928. SPANISH AMERICAN LITERATURE. Licenciado, U. of Murcia (Spain), 1949; Ph. D., U. of Madrid, 1952. Profesor ayudante, U. of Murcia, 1949-51; lectr., Oxford U., 1953-55; profesor ayudante, U. of Madrid, 1955-56; vis. lectr., U. of Wis., 1956-58; asst. prof., Yale U., 1958-60; vis. prof., N.Y.U., Summers 1960, 1961; ELIAS AHUJA PROF., SPANISH LITERATURE, U. OF DEL., 1960- . U. of Wis. Alumni research fellow (Latin America), 1957. Membership: American Association of Teachers of Spanish and Portuguese; Asociación Internacional de Hispanistas; Hispanic Institute; International Federation for Modern Languages and Literatures; Renaissance Society of America; Sigma Delta Pi. Research: Puerto Rican poetry; gaucho literature of Argentina and Uruguay; Central American literature. Author: Obras completas de Calderón (1956, 1959); Literatura Hispanoamericana (1962). Co-author: New Puerto Rican Poetry (1952). Language: Spanish 5,5,5,5; Portuguese 4,4,4,4; French 3,3,3,3; German 2,1,1,1; Italian 3,3,3,3. Home: 203 Nottingham Rd., Newark, Del. 19711. Office: 100 Old College, U. of Del., Newark.

VALDMAN, ALBERT, b. Paris, France, Feb. 15, 1931. LINGUISTICS. A.B., U. of Pa., 1953; M.A., Cornell U., 1955; Ph. D., 1960. Asst. prof., Pa. State U., 1959-60; asst. prof., Ind. U., 1960-62; ASSOC. PROF., FRENCH AND ITALIAN, IND. U., 1962-; CHMN., LINGUISTICS, 1963-; asst. dir., 1964 Linguistic Institute, Ind. U., 1963-64; co-dir., Seminar for College Teachers of French, German and Spanish, Ind. U., 1964. Linguistic Advisory Committee, Sub-committee on Planning and Programs in Latin America; Conference Board of Associated Research Councils. Research: Creole French in the Caribbean. Author: A Manual of Applied Linguistics: French Section (1960); A Drillbook of French Pronunciation (1964); Du créole au français en Haïti (Linguistics, July 1964). Language: Spanish 4,4,4,2; Portuguese 3,2,1,1; French 5,5,5,5; Haitian Creole -,3,2,-. Linguistic studies: French; Haitian Creole. Home: 2411 Fritz Dr., Bloomington, Ind. Office: Dept. of Linguistics, Ind. U., Bloomington, 47405.

VALENCIA, MIGUEL A., b. Utuado, P.R., Oct. 3, 1925. STATISTICS. B.S., U. of P.R., 1946; M.S., N.C. State Coll. 1952; Doctor, Universidad Central de Madrid, 1962. Instr., U. of P.R., 1946-50; research asst. in statistics, Agricultural Experiment Station, U. of P.R., 1950-51; interpreter, Training Center for Latin American Statisticians, Food and Agriculture Organization (Quito, Ecuador), 1952; statistician, Dept. of Agriculture, Government of P.R., 1952-53; statistician, P.R. Planning Board, 1953-57; ASSOC. PROF., INSTITUTE OF STATISTICS, U. OF P.R., 1957-. Membership: American Statistical Association. Research: sample design; sampling and statistical methods; advertising and marketing research. Language: Spanish 5,5,5,5; Portuguese 3,1,1,1; French 3,2,2,2; Italian 3,1,1,1. Home: 598 Sinai, Río Piedras, P.R. 00920. Office: Box 21614-University Station, U. of P.R., Río Piedras, 00931.

VALENZUELA, VICTOR M., b. Chillan, Chile, Oct. 23, 1919. SPANISH AMERICAN LITERATURE. B.A., San Francisco State Coll., 1951; M.A., Columbia U., 1952. Asst. instr. Columbia U., Summer 1952; instr., U. of Conn., 1952-54; instr., Columbia U., 1954-57; ASST. PROF., LATIN AMERICAN LITERATURE, LEHIGH U., 1957- . Consultant, U.S. Dept. of Commerce. Membership: American Association of Teachers of Spanish and Portuguese; American Association of University Professors. Research: Chilean literature and philosophy; Chilean society as seen through the novels of Alberto Blest Gana. Author: Hombres y temas de Iberoamérica (1959); Cuatro escritores chilenos (1960); Time and Progress in the Two Americas (Lehigh Alumni Bulletin, May 1963). Language: Spanish 5,5,5,5; Portuguese 4,4,4,3; French 3,3,3,3; Italian 5,5,5,4. Home: 827 West Broad St., Bethlehem, Pa. Office: Dept. of Spanish, Lehigh U., Bethlehem.

VAN AKEN, MARK JAY, b. Elkhart, Ind., Apr. 9, 1922. HISTORY. B.A., U. of Mich., 1944; M.A., U. of Calif., Berkeley, 1952; Ph. D., 1955. Asst. prof., Memphis State Coll., 1955-56; instr., U. of Calif., Berkeley, Fall 1956; asst. prof., San Diego State Coll., 1957-60; asst. prof.-assoc. prof., Alameda State Coll., 1960-63; ASSOC. PROF., HISTORY, DUKE U., 1963- . U. of Mich.-U. of Tucumán exchange fellow (Argentina), 1947-48; Institute of International Education exchange fellow (Spain), 1953-54; Fulbright fellow (Uruguay), 1963-64. Membership: American Historical Association; Conference on Latin American History; Pacific Coast Council on Latin American Studies. Research: university student movement in 20th century Latin America; Pan-Hispanism in the 19th century; diplomatic history, 19th century; the diplomatic intrigues of General Juan José Flores of Ecuador, 1840-1860. Author: Pan-Hispanism: Its Origin and Development to 1866 (1959); British Policy Considerations in Central America before 1850 (Hispanic American Historical Review, Feb. 1962). Language: Spanish 4,4,4,3; Portuguese 3,2, 2,1. Home: % A. Gomez, 968 Alice Ave., San Leandro, Calif. Office: Dept. of History, Duke U., Durham, N.C.

VANCE, CHARLES MICHAEL, b. Havana, Cuba, Aug. 15, 1916. SPANISH AMERICAN LITERATURE. B.A., U. of Tex., 1941; M.A., 1942. Instr., Colegio Cubano Arturo Montori, 1942-43; instr., U. of Tex., 1945-

49; instr., U. of Wis., 1949–50; instr., Army Language School (Monterey, Calif.), 1951–52; assoc., U. of Calif., Los Angeles, 1955–61; ASSOC. PROF., SPANISH, VANDERBILT U., 1961– . Pan American Round Table scholar, U. of Tex., 1938–40; dir., National Defense Education Act Summer Language Institute, Vanderbilt U., 1963, 1964. Membership: American Association of Teachers of Spanish and Portuguese; American Association of University Professors; Ateneo de la Habana; Instituto Internacional de Literatura Iberoamericana; Modern Language Association; Sigma Delta Pi. Research: short story in Latin America; culture and literature of Cuba and Mexico. Author: Ideas filosóficas en las novelas de Alfonso Hernández Catá (1943); Spanish Drama Collection at University of Texas (1953); Patterns for Reading Spanish (1964). Language: Spanish 5,5,5,5; Portuguese 4,4,3,2; French 4,4,1,1; Italian 5,4,4,2. Home: 488 Brentlawn Dr., Nashville, Tenn. 37220. Office: Dept. of Spanish, Vanderbilt U., Nashville.

VAN DE BUNT, WOUTER, b. Vianen, Netherlands, Dec. 29, 1925. ECONOMICS. Doctorate, Netherlands School of Economics, 1951; Clark U., 1951–52. Economist, KLM Royal Dutch Airlines (The Hague), 1952–59; manager, long range planning, Capital Airlines (Washington, D.C.), 1959–60; executive asst. to general manager, Market Research Planning, KLM Royal Dutch Airlines (N.Y.), 1960–64; MANAGER, MARKET RESEARCH, AMERICAN AIRLINES, INC., 1964– . Fulbright-Smith-Mundt grant, Clark U., 1951–52; guest lectr., Nyenrode Business Coll. (Netherlands), 1954–59; consultant, Sociedad Aeronáutica Medellín (Colombia), 1955. Membership: American Economic Association; National Association of Business Economists; Netherlands America Institute; Netherlands Institute of Economists; The Half Moon (Netherlands). Research: economics of transportation, especially air; economic geography; business administration. Author: Zanzibar—Pearl on the Equator (1949); Latin America (in Winkler Prins Atlas, 1947–); Latin America (in Winkler Prins Encyclopedia, 1950). Language: Spanish 3,2,2,2; Portuguese 1,1,1,1; French 4,3,3,3; Dutch 5,5,5,5; German 3,3,3,3. Home: 7 Martha Ct., Centerport, N.Y. 10017. Office: American Airlines, Inc., 633 Third Ave., New York, N.Y. 10017.

VANDERBURGH, JOHN B., b. San Francisco, Calif., Oct. 12, 1917. HISTORY. A.B., Stanford U., 1938; M.A., 1939; Ph. D., 1954. Junior economic analyst, Embassy (Chile), U.S. Dept. of State, 1941–45; reference asst., Hispanic Foundation, Library of Congress, 1946; teacher, Menlo School (Calif.), 1947–48; instr., chmn. of faculty, Deep Springs Junior Coll., 1948–51; LABOR MARKET ANALYST, DEPT. OF EMPLOYMENT, STATE OF CALIF., 1951– . Inter-American exchange fellow (Chile), 1941. Membership: American Statistical Association. Research: labor market analysis. Language: Spanish 4,4,4,4; Portuguese 2,2,2,1; French 2,2,2,1. Home: 5620 State Ave., Sacramento, Calif. 95819. Office: California Dept. of Employment, 800 Capital Ave., Sacramento, Calif. 95814.

VANGER, MILTON I., b. New York, N.Y., Apr. 11, 1925. HISTORY. B.A., Princeton U., 1948; M.A., Harvard U., 1950; Ph. D., 1958. Instr., Okla. State U., 1956–58; vis. lectr., U. of Wis., Summer 1958; asst. prof., Sacramento State Coll., 1958–62; ASSOC. PROF., HISTORY, BRANDEIS U., 1962– . Princeton U. scholarship; Princeton U. grant (Guatemala), Summer 1947; Harvard U. scholarship; Doherty fellow (Uruguay), 1950–52. Membership: American Historical Association; Conference on Latin American History; Pacific Coast Council on Latin American Studies; Phi Beta Kappa. Research: Uruguay; 20th century Latin America; Latin American historiography. Author: José Batlle y Ordóñez of Uruguay: The Creator of His Times, 1902–1907 (1963); Uruguay Introduces Government by Committee (American Political Science Review, June 1954); Latin America in Perspective (Yale Review, Winter 1959). Language: Spanish 5,5,5,4; Portuguese 4,3,2,1. Home: 32 Gray St., Cambridge Mass. Office: Dept. of History, Brandeis U., Waltham 54, Mass.

VANN, JOHN HERMAN, b. Shreveport, La., Aug. 29, 1921. GEOGRAPHY. B.A., La. State U., 1943; M.S., 1948; Ph. D., U. of Calif., Berkeley, 1960. Instr., San Francisco State Coll., 1950–51; instr., U. of Calif., 1951–52; instr.-asst. prof., La. State U., 1953–63; ASSOC. PROF., GEOGRAPHY, STATE U. OF N.Y., COLL. AT BUFFALO, 1963– . Membership: American Geographical Society; Association of American Geographers; International Geographical Union. Research: physical geography, especially the relationships of soils, vegetation, and land forms in tropical areas; Parras area of Mexico; Brazil. Author: Physical Geography of Lower Coastal Plain of Guianas (1959); Land Form—Vegetation Relationships, Atrato Delta, Colombia (Annals, Association of American Geographers, 1959); Developmental Processes in Laterite Terrain (Geographical Review, July 1963). Language: Spanish 4,3,3,3; Portuguese 2,2, 2,2; French 3,2,2,2. Home: 100 Colvinhurst Dr., Kenmore, N.Y. 14223. Office: Dept. of Geography, State U. of N.Y., Coll. at Buffalo, 1300 Elmwood Ave., Buffalo. 14222.

VAN STAN, INA, b. Alameda, Calif., Jan. 22, 1901. ART. A.B., U. of Calif., Berkeley, 1926; M.A., 1937. PROF., TEXTILES AND CLOTHING, FLA. STATE U., 1941– . Fla. State U. Research Council grants. Membership: American Anthropological Association; Centre International d'Etude des Textiles Anciens; Society for American Archaeology. Research: Peruvian textiles and clothing. Author: A Peruvian Ikat From Pachacamac (American Antiquity, Oct. 1957); A Problematic Example of Peruvian Resist Dyeing (American Antiquity, Oct. 1963); The Fabrics from a Peruvian Mummy Bale Found Beneath the Pachacamac Temple (Bulletin de Liaison du Centre International d'Etude des Textiles Anciens, Jan. 1964). Language: Spanish 2,2,1,1; Portuguese 1,1,1,1; French 2,1,1,1; Dutch 2,1,1,1; German 2,2,1,1. Home: 312 Mayo St., Tallahasse, Fla. 32304. Office: Rm. 211, Sandels Bldg., Fla. State U., Tallahassee, 32306.

VARGAS-BARÓN, ANÍBAL, b. Soatá, Colombia, Nov. 27, 1903. SPANISH AMERICAN LITERATURE. B.A., Asbury Coll., 1926; M.A., U. of Wash., 1929; Ph. D., 1943.

Translator of legal documents, Shell de Colombia (Bogotá), 1938–40; instr.-assoc. prof., U. of Oreg., 1940–49; ASSOC. PROF., SPANISH, U. OF WASH., 1949– . Membership: American Association of Teachers of Spanish and Portuguese; American Association of University Professors; Modern Language Association; Philological Association of the Pacific Coast; Sociedad de Escritores y Artistas de Colombia. Research: Colombian literature. Author: José Joaquín Vargas Valdés: Artículos y ensayos (1963); Altiplano: Novela india (Hispania, Mar. 1956). Contributor: Diccionario de la literatura latinoamericana (1959). Language: Spanish 5,5,5,5; Portuguese 5,5,4,4; French 5,5,4,4; German 2,1,1,1; Italian 5,5, 3,3. Linguistic studies: Spanish. Home: 7508 56th Ave., NE., Seattle 15, Wash. Office: Dept. of Romance Languages, U. of Wash., Seattle 5.

VARNER, JOHN GRIER, b. Mt. Pleasant, Tex., Mar. 30, 1905. HISTORY AND TRANSLATION. B.A., Austin Coll., 1926; M.A., U. of Va., 1932; Ph. D., 1940. Asst. prof., Washington and Lee U., 1938–43; dir., Bi-national Institute (Venezuela), U.S. Dept. of State, 1943–47; asst. cultural attaché, Embassy (Mexico), 1947; ASSOC. PROF., ENGLISH, U. OF TEX., 1947– ; lectr. in South America, U.S. Dept. of State, 1951–52. DuPont teaching fellow, U. of Va., 1930–38; American Philosophical Society and U. of Tex. grants (Spain), 1955. Membership: Real Academia de Ciencias, Bellas Letras, y Nobles Artes de Córdoba (Spain). Research: Peruvian history; El Inca Garcilaso de la Vega. Co-author: English Grammar for Venezuelans (1946). Editor: Edgar Allan Poe and the Philadelphia Saturday Courier (1933). Co-translator: The Florida of the Inca, by El Inca Garcilaso de la Vega (1951, 1963). Language: Spanish 4,4,4,2; Portuguese 2,1,1,1; French 2,1,1,1. Home: 2510 Jarratt Ave., Austin, Tex. Office: Dept. of English, U. of Tex., Austin.

VÁZQUEZ, ALBERTO M., b. Yabucoa, P.R., Mar. 25, 1901. SPANISH AMERICAN LITERATURE AND LANGUAGE. A.B., U. of Idaho, 1925; M.A., 1926; Ph. D., Yale U., 1935. Instr., U. of Idaho, 1925–31; instr., Dartmouth Coll., 1935–37; asst. prof., 1937–42; diplomatic service, U.S. Dept. of State (Washington, D.C.; México, D.F.), 1942–61; lectr., George Washington U., 1945–56; PROF., SPANISH, TULANE U., 1962– ; U.S. REPRESENTATIVE, COMMITTEE FOR CULTURAL ACTION, ORGANIZATION OF AMERICAN STATES (MÉXICO, D.F.), 1962– . Sterling fellow, Yale U., 1932–34; member, U.S. delegation, Inter-American Conference on Financial and Economic Control, 1942; Directing Council, Pan American Institute of Geography and History (México, D.F.), 1959; Third Meeting, Inter-American Cultural Council (San Juan, P.R.), 1959. Research: romance languages and literatures; Latin American affairs. Author: Cartas de don Diego de Mendoza, Diplomatic Correspondence, 1536–1552 (1935); Cuentos de la América Española (1952). Language: Spanish 5,5,5,5; French 4,4,4,4; Italian 4,4,4,4. Home: 1205 St. Charles Ave., New Orleans 13, La. Office: Center for Latin American Studies, Tulane U., New Orleans 18.

VAZQUEZ, MARIO CARLOS, b. Aquía, Peru, Jan. 19, 1926. ANTHROPOLOGY. B.A., U. of San Marcos (Peru), 1948; Ph. D., 1951; M.A., Cornell U., 1955. Research asst., Cornell U., 1955–59; field dir., Cornell-Peru project, Cornell U., 1959–63; vis. prof., Pan American Union, 1960; RESEARCH ASSOC., ANTHROPOLOGY, CORNELL U., 1963– . Consultant, Peruvian Government, 1956–58; adviser, UNESCO (Paraguay), 1961; researcher, U.S. Agency for International Development (Bolivia, Peru), 1963. Membership: American Anthropological Association; American Sociological Association; Society for Applied Anthropology. Research: applied and cultural anthropology; community development; social structure and technological change; Peru; colonization and Indian problem in Bolivia; land reform in Mexico and Paraguay. Author: Hacienda y peonaje en los Andes peruanos (1961); Proceso de migración en una comunidad Andina (in Migración e integración en el Perú, 1963); Transformación de las haciendas en cooperación de producción (1963). Language: Spanish 5,5,5,5; Portuguese 3,2,2,–; Quechua –,5,5,–. Home: Calle Oviedo 123, Pueblo Libre, Lima, Perú. Office: Dept. of Anthropology, Cornell U., Ithaca, N.Y.

VEENSTRA, JOHN G., b. Muskegon, Mich., Jan. 24, 1928. LIBRARY SCIENCE. A.B., U. of Mich., 1955; A.M.L.S., 1957. Bibliographer, U. of Mich., 1957–58; acquisitions librarian, Library, Purdue U., 1958–63; DIR. OF LIBRARIES, UNIVERSIDAD DEL VALLE (CALI, COLOMBIA), 1963– . Committee on U.S. Roving Congresses, American Library Association. Membership: American Association of University Professors; American Library Association; Midwest Academy of Librarians; Ohio Valley Group of Technical Service Libraries. Research: bibliography and acquisition of Latin American materials. Author: When Do You Use a Jobber (College and Research Libraries, Nov. 1962); The Stormy Marriage (Library Journal, July 1963). Co-author: International List of Subscription Agencies (American Library Association, Nov. 1963). Language: Spanish 5,5,5,4; Portuguese 3,3,1,3; French 3,3,3,3; German 4,2,2,2; Italian 3,2,2,2; Russian 2,2,2,2. Office: Departamento de Bibliotecas, Universidad del Valle, Apartado aéreo 2188, Cali, Colombia.

VELÁZQUEZ, GONZALO, b. Caguas, P.R., Nov. 24, 1905. LIBRARY SCIENCE. A.B., U. of P.R., 1928; M.L.S., Columbia U., 1934; LL.B., U. of P.R., 1940. Library asst., U. of P.R., 1926–34; asst. librarian, 1934–43; assoc. librarian, 1943–55; DIR., LIBRARY SERVICES, DEPT. OF EDUCATION (P.R.), 1955– . Delegate, First Assembly of Librarians of the Americas, 1947, Primer Seminario Piloto de Bibliografía (Havana), 1955, Segundo Seminario Piloto de Bibliografía (Panama), 1958, Assembly of State Librarians, 1958. Membership: Agrupación Bibliográfica Cubana José Toribio Medina; American Library Association; Comité Internacional de Catalogación. Research: library organization and administration; bibliography. Author: Anuario bibliográfico puertorriqueño, Indice alfabético de libros, folletos, revistas y periódicos publicados en Puerto Rico (1948–1958); Compilación de encabezamientos de materia para catálogos—diccionarios (1948); La bibliografía en Puerto Rico (in Seminario Piloto de Bibliografía, 1955). Language: Spanish 5,5,5,5; Portuguese 3,2,1,1; French 3,3,3,3. Home: Box 3124, San Juan, P.R. 00904. Office: Director, Library Services, Dept. of Education, Hato Rey, P.R.

VERMEER, DONALD EUGENE, b. Oakland, Calif., Nov. 9, 1932. GEOGRAPHY. A.B., U. of Calif., Berkeley, 1954; M.A., 1959; Ph. D., 1964. Research investigator, Office of Naval Research-U. of Calif., Berkeley (British Honduras, Guatemala), 1957, 1961; ASST. PROF., GEOGRAPHY, U. OF COLO., 1962– . National Science Foundation fellow. Membership: American Association of Geographers; Association of Pacific Coast Geographers; Rocky Mountain Social Science Association. Research: physical geography; geomorphology; tropical geography; hurricane transport of pumice; tropical dietetics; West Africa. Author: The Cays of British Honduras (1959); Effects of Hurricane Hattie, 1961, on the Cays of British Honduras (Zeitschrift für Geomorphologie, Dec. 1963); From the Cam to the Cays (The Professional Geographer, May 1964). Language: Spanish 3,3,3,2; French 4,4,4,3; Afrikaans 4,4,4,3; Dutch 4,4,4,3; German 4,4,4,3; Tiv 2,2,2,1. Home: 1715 Dogwood Lane, Boulder, Colo. 80302. Office: Dept. of Geography, U. of Colo., Boulder, 80304.

VERNON, RAYMOND, b. New York, N.Y., Sept. 1, 1913. ECONOMICS. B.A., City Coll. (N.Y.), 1933; Ph. D., Columbia U., 1941. Dir., Office of Economic Defense and Trade Policy, U.S. Dept. of State, 1952–54; dir., Planning and Control, Rawley and Hoops, Inc., 1954–56; dir., N.Y. Metropolitan Region Study, 1956–59; PROF., INTERNATIONAL TRADE AND INVESTMENT, HARVARD BUSINESS SCHOOL, 1959– ; DIR., DEVELOPMENT ADVISORY SERVICE, HARVARD U., 1962– . Staff member, Joint Presidential-Congressional Committee on Foreign Economic Policy, 1953–54; consultant for economic affairs, Undersecretary of State for Economic Affairs, 1961– . Membership: American Economic Association; Council on Foreign Relations. Research: economic development; international trade policy; economic politics. Author: The Dilemma of Mexico's Development (1963). Editor: Public Policy and Private Enterprise in Mexico (1964). Language: Spanish 4,3,3,2; French 3,2,2,1. Home: 56 Lantern Rd., Belmont, Mass. Office: Harvard Business School, Boston, Mass. 02163.

VESCELIUS, GARY STOCKTON, b. Glen Ridge, N.J., Oct. 16, 1930. ANTHROPOLOGY. A.B., Yale U., 1952; M.A., U. of Mich., 1953. Archeologist, Laboratory of Anthropology, Museum of N. Mex., 1953; archeologist, Early Sites Foundation, 1954–55; research asst., Human Relations Area Files, Yale U., 1955–56; instr., Monterey Peninsula Coll., 1957–58; archeologist, Institute of Ethnology and Archaeology, U. of San Marcos (Lima, Peru), 1958–60; dir., Div. of Archaeological Exploration, Institute of Archaeology and Ethnology, U. of San Augustín (Arequipa, Peru), 1960–61; observer, Smithsonian Astrophysical Observatory (Arequipa), 1960–61; RESEARCH ASSOC., ANTHROPOLOGY, CORNELL U. (LIMA AND VICOS, PERU), **1961–65**. Fulbright fellow (Peru), 1958–59, 1959–60. Membership: American Anthropological Association; American Geographical Society; Society for American Archaeology. Research; prehistoric archeology; prehistory and ethnography of South America and the West Indies; Peruvian geography and archeology; human ecology. Author: Mound 2 at Marksville (American Antiquity, Apr. 1957); Archaeological Sampling: A Problem of Statistical Inference (in Essays in the Science of Culture, 1960); Rasgos naturales y culturales de la costa extremo sur (in Antiquo Perú: Tiempo y espacio, 1960). Language: Spanish 5,5,4,4; Portuguese 4,3,3,3; French 2,2,1,1. Linguistic studies: Quechua. Home: c/o J. S. Lewis, 58 Steele Brook Rd., Watertown, Conn. Office: Dept. of Anthropology, Cornell U., Ithaca, N.Y. 14850.

VICKREY, WILLIAM SPENCER, b. Victoria, Canada, June 21, 1914. ECONOMICS. Ph. D., Columbia U., 1947. Instr.-PROF., ECONOMICS, COLUMBIA U., 1946– ; CHMN., ECONOMICS, 1964– . Tax consultant, Governor of P.R., 1946; tax consultant, Federal District Government (Caracas, Venezuela), 1960. Membership: American Economic Association; American Statistical Association; Econometric Society; Metropolitan Economic Association; National Tax Association; Royal Economic Society; Tax Institute. Research: public finance; transportation; theoretical economics; welfare economics; mathematical economics; tax structure of Puerto Rico and Venezuela. Author: Agenda for Progressive Taxation (1947); Microstatics (1964); Metastatics and Dynamics (1964). Language: Spanish 4,3,3,2; Portuguese 3,2,1,1; French 4,4,4,4; German 3,3,3,2. Home: 162 Warburton Ave., Hastings on Hudson, N.Y. 10706. Office: 501 Fayerweather Hall, Columbia U., New York, N.Y. 10027.

VIDICH, ARTHUR J., b. Crosby, Minn., May 30, 1922. SOCIOLOGY AND ANTHROPOLOGY. B.A., U. of Mich., 1943; M.A., U. of Wis., 1948; Ph. D., Harvard U., 1953. Asst. prof., field dir., Cornell U., 1951–54; asst. prof., U. of P.R., 1954–57; asst. prof., U. of Conn., 1957–60; ASSOC. PROF., SOCIOLOGY AND ANTHROPOLOGY, NEW SCHOOL FOR SOCIAL RESEARCH, 1960– ; vis. prof., Universidad Nacional (Colombia), 1963–64. Fulbright fellow, U. of London, 1950–51; research consultant, Florence Heller School for Advanced Studies in Social Welfare, Brandeis U., 1960– ; research consultant, Centro de Estudios de Desarrollo (Caracas), 1961–63; consultant on research in P.R., National Institute of Mental Health. Membership: American Anthropological Association; American Sociological Society. Research: community and political sociology; changes in rural Puerto Rico; Venezuela; Colombia. Author: Small Town in Mass Society (1958); Identity and Anxiety (1960); Sociology on Trial (1963). Language: Spanish 3,3,3,1; Portuguese 2,2,1,1; French 3,1,1,1. Home: Route 2, Box 257, Storrs, Conn. Office: Graduate Faculty, New School for Social Research, 66 West 12th St., New York, N.Y.

VIGNERAS, LOUIS ANDRÉ, b. Paris, France, May 28, 1903. HISTORY. Lic. en lettres, Bordeaux, 1920; M.A., Princeton, 1922; Ph. D., Harvard, 1934. Instr., Robert Coll. (Turkey), 1925–26, Lycée Français (Beirut,

Lebanon), 1927–28, Ohio State U., 1928–30, De Pauw U., 1930–33, Duquesne U., 1934–36; instr.-prof., U. of Maine, 1936–51; PROF., ROMANCE LANGUAGES, GEORGE WASHINGTON U., 1960– . Research: history of the discovery and exploration of America, particularly of North America and the West Indies. Author: The Journal of Christopher Columbus (1960); The Voyage of Samuel Champlain to the West Indies (Anuario de Estudios Americanos, 1953; Revue d'Histoire de l'Amerique Français, Sept. 1957). Language: Spanish 5,5,4,4; Portuguese 4,3,3,2; French 5,5,5,5. Office: Dept. of Romance Languages, George Washington U., Washington, D.C. 20006.

VIGNESS, DAVID MARTELL, b. La Feria, Tex., Oct. 12, 1922. HISTORY. B.A., U. of Tex., 1943; M.A., 1948; Ph. D., 1951. Instr., U. of Tex., Summer 1951; prof., chmn., Social Sciences, Schreiner Institute, 1951–55; PROF., CHMN., HISTORY, TEX. TECHNOLOGICAL COLL., 1955– . Fulbright lectr., U. of Chile and Catholic U. of Santiago (Chile), 1957–58. Membership: American Historical Association; Conference on Latin American History; Mississippi Valley Historical Association; Rocky Mountain Council on Latin American Studies; Southwestern Social Science Association; Texas State Historical Association; Western History Conference. Research: Mexican history; Chile; Texas history. Author: The Revolutionary Decades (1964); Huatchipato: The Story of Steel in Chile (Southwestern Social Science Association Quarterly, June 1959). Co-author: Documents of Texas History (1963). Language: Spanish 5,5,5,4; Portuguese 4,3,2,2; French 3,2,1,1. Office: Dept. of History, Tex. Technological Coll., Lubbock, 79409.

VILLEGAS, FRANCISCO, b. Heredia, Costa Rica, Nov. 25, 1917. LANGUAGE. M.A. in Ed., U. of Mich., 1944; M.A., 1945; Ph. D., 1952. Asst. prof., Eastern Mich. U., 1950–62; instr., U. of Maine, Summers 1959, 1960; assoc. prof., U. of Calif., Los Angeles, Summer 1961; assoc. prof., U. of Houston, 1962–63; ASSOC. PROF., FOREIGN LANGUAGES, EASTERN MICH. U., 1963– . Ad Hoc Committee for the teaching of foreign languages in the elementary grades in the state of Michigan. Membership: American Association of Teachers of Spanish and Portuguese; American Association of University Professors; Modern Language Association. Research: Spanish; Hispanic American and Spanish literature. Author: El argot costarricense (Hispania, Mar. 1955); The Voseo in Costa Rican Spanish (Hispania, Sept. 1963). Language: Spanish 5,5,5,5; Portuguese 3,4,3,1; French 4,3,1,1. Linguistic studies: Spanish. Home: 406 Awixa Rd., Ann Arbor, Mich. Office: Dept. of Foreign Languages, Eastern Mich. U., Ypsilanti.

VOGT, EVON ZARTMAN, b. Gallup, N. Mex., Aug. 20, 1918. ANTHROPOLOGY. A.B., U. of Chicago, 1941; M.A., 1946; Ph. D., 1948. Instr., Harvard U., 1948–50; asst. prof., 1950–55; assoc. prof., 1955–59; PROF., ANTHROPOLOGY, HARVARD U., 1959– . Advanced Study in Behavioral Sciences fellow, 1956–57. Membership: American Academy of Arts and Sciences; American Anthropological Association; Royal Anthropological Society of Great Britain and Ireland; Sociedad Mexicana de Antropología; Society for American Archaeology. Research: ethnology of Middle America; Tzotzil Indians of Chiapas, Mexico. Author: Modern Homesteaders (1955); Desarrollo cultural de los Mayas (1964). Co-author: Water Witching USA (1959). Language: Spanish 4,4,4,3; Portuguese 3,3, 2,2; French 3,2,1,1; Tzotzil –,2,2,–. Home: 79 Spruce Hill Rd., Weston, Mass. Office: Dept. of Anthropology, Harvard U., Cambridge 38, Mass.

VON WINNING, HASSO LEOPOLD, b. Heidelberg, Germany, Jan. 14, 1914. ANTHROPOLOGY. B.A., U. of Calif., Los Angeles, 1950; M. Sc., U. of Southern Calif., 1952. ASSOC. IN ARCHEOLOGY, SOUTHWEST MUSEUM (LOS ANGELES, CALIF.), 1952– . Membership: American Anthropological Association; Instituto Interamericano; Society for American Anthropology. Research: Mesoamerican archeology; Mexico. Author: Shell Designs on Teotihuacan Pottery (El México Antiguo, Dec. 1949); Teotihuacan Symbols: The Reptile's Eye Glyph (Ethnos, 1961); Figurillas de barro sobre ruedas procedentes de México y el Nuevo Mundo (Amerindia, 1962). Language: Spanish 5,5,5,5; French 4,3,3,3; German 5,5,5,5. Linguistic studies: Nahuatl. Home: 2274 Alcyona Dr., Hollywood 28, Calif. Office: Southwest Museum, Highland Park, Los Angeles 42.

W

WAGLEY, CECILIA ROXO, b. Rio de Janeiro, Brazil, Oct. 18, 1911. LIBRARY SCIENCE. Certificate, National Library (Brazil), 1932. Librarian, National Library (Rio de Janeiro, Brazil), 1934–46; lectr., Barnard Coll., 1947–48; research asst., Hylean Amazon Project, 1948; research asst., State of Bahia-Columbia U. Project, 1950–51; librarian, United Nations, 1951; research asst., research survey on Portuguese Africa, 1960. Brazilian Government fellow, Library School, Columbia U., 1940–41. Research: Brazil. Author: Some Notes on Brazilian Libraries (Special Libraries, Apr. 1941). Language: Spanish 3,3,3,1; Portuguese 5,5,5,5; French 4,4,4,3. Home: 15 Claremont Ave., New York 27, N.Y.

WAGLEY, CHARLES, b. Clarksville, Tex., Nov. 9, 1913. ANTHROPOLOGY. A.B., Columbia U., 1936; Ph. D., 1941; Doutour (honoris causa), Universidade da Bahia, 1962. Instr., Columbia Coll., 1940–41; vis. lectr., Museu Nacional (Brazil), 1941–42; field staff dir., Brazilian Field Party, Institute of Inter-American Affairs, 1942–45; staff, Guggenheim Foundation, 1945–47; asst. prof., Columbia U., 1946–49; staff, Social Science Research Council, 1948–49; assoc. prof., Columbia U., 1949–53; PROF., ANTHROPOLOGY, COLUMBIA U., 1953– ; DIR., INSTITUTE OF LATIN AMERICAN STUDIES, 1961– . Committee on Latin America, National Research Council, 1945– ; Center for Advanced Study in the Behavioral Sciences fellow, 1957–58; Fulbright prof. (Brazil), 1962. Membership: American Anthropological Association; American Ethnological Association; Brazilian Anthropological Association; New York Academy of Sciences. Research: social and cultural anthropology; aboriginal ethnology; community studies; race relations; Brazil, Guatemala and

Mexico. Author: Economics of a Guatemalan Village (1941); Amazon Town: A Study of Man in the Tropics (1953, 1964); Introduction to Brazil (1963). Language: Spanish 4,4,4,4; Portuguese 4,4,4,3; French 3,3,3,2. Linguistic studies: Guaraní; Tupí. Home: 15 Claremont Ave., New York, N.Y. 10027. Office: Institute of Latin American Studies, Columbia U., New York, 10027.

WAGNER, PHILIP LAURENCE, b. San Jose, Calif., Oct. 7, 1921. GEORGRAPHY. A.B., U. of Calif., Berkeley, 1947; M.A., 1950; Ph. D., 1953. Teacher, Far East Program, U. of Calif., Berkeley, 1953–54; research assoc., U. of Chicago, 1954–55; asst. prof., 1955–60; ASSOC. PROF., GEOGRAPHY, U. OF CALIF., DAVIS, 1960– . Membership: American Anthropological Association; American Geographical Society; Association of American Geographers; Pacific Coast Council for Latin American Studies. Research: cultural geography of Costa Rica and Mexico. Author: Nicoya: A Cultural Geography (1958); The Human Use of the Earth (1960). Co-editor: Readings in Cultural Geography (1962). Language: Spanish 5,5,4,4; Portuguese 3,2,2,1; French 5,5,4,4; German 5,4,3,3; Polish 4,4,3,3; Russian 5,4,3,3. Home: 407 1st St., Davis, Calif. Office: Dept. of Anthropology and Geography, U. of Calif., Davis.

WAGNER, W. J., b. Poland, Dec. 12, 1917. LAW. LL.M., U. of Warsaw, 1939; Dr. en Droit, U. of Paris, 1948; LL.M., S.J.D., J.D., Northwestern U., 1950–57. Instr.-prof., School of Law, U. of Notre Dame, 1953–62; vis. prof., International Faculty of Comparative Law (Luxembourg), Spring 1960, Summer 1963; PROF., LAW, SCHOOL OF LAW, IND. U., 1962– ; vis. prof., European Federalist Coll. (Aosta, Italy), Summer 1963. Fulbright vis. prof., U. of Paris, U. of Rennes (France), 1959–60; American specialist, Cultural Exchange Program, U.S. Dept. of State lecture grant (Africa), 1960, (world), 1962; Social Science Research Council summer grant, 1961; Committee on Foreign Exchanges, Association of American Law Schools. Membership: American Society for Legal History; Atlantic Union; American Foreign Law Association; United World Federalists; World Association of World Federalists. Research: American and Latin American federalism; constitutional law; comparisons of legal systems; federal systems and juridical organization of Argentina, Brazil, Mexico, and Venezuela. Author: Les Libertés de l'Air (1948); The Federal States and Their Judiciary (1959); Research in Comparative Law, Some Theoretical Considerations (in Essays in Jurisprudence in Honor of Roscoe Pound, 1962). Language: Spanish 1,1,1,1; French 5,5,5,5; Polish 5,5,5,5. Home: 606 South Park Ave., Bloomington, Ind. Office: School of Law, Ind. U., Bloomington.

WAITS, CARON RICHARD, b. Amarillo, Tex., Sept. 9, 1928. ECONOMICS. B.A., Trinity U., 1949; M.A., U. of Tex., 1951; Ph. D., 1963. Asst. prof., Northwestern State Coll., 1961–62; ASST. PROF., ECONOMICS, TEX. CHRISTIAN U., 1962– . Ford Foundation faculty research fellow (Venezuela), 1961. Membership: Southwestern Social Science Association. Research: financial systems; financial and real growth in Venezuela. Language: Spanish 4,3,3,3; Portuguese 1,1,1,1; French 2,1,1,1. Home: 5729 Wharton, Ft. Worth, Tex. 76133. Office: Dept. of Economics, Tex. Christian U., Ft. Worth, 76129.

WALDORF, PAUL DOUGLASS, b. Syracuse, N.Y., Jan. 13, 1908. SPANISH AMERICAN LITERATURE. A.B., Baker U., 1929; M.A., U. of Kans., 1930; Ph. D., Northwestern U., 1949. Instr., U. of Ariz., 1930–31; teacher, Wentworth Military Academy, 1931–33; asst. prof., McKendree Coll., 1933–36; asst. prof., Ft. Hays Kans. State Coll., 1936–42; teacher, Carleton Coll., 1943–44; personnel worker, Western Electric Corp., 1944–45; asst. prof., Denison U., 1945–47; ASSOC. PROF., SPANISH AND FRENCH, MANKATO STATE COLL., 1947– . Membership: American Association of Teachers of Spanish and Portuguese; American Association of University Professors; Modern Language Association. Research: contemporary short story in Mexico. Author: Veraneo en México (1964). Translator: The Boar Hunt (Texas Quarterly, 1959). Language: Spanish 4,4,4,4; Portuguese 2,2,2,2; French 4,3,3,3; Italian 2,1,-,-. Home: 216 Branson St., Mankato, Minn. Office: Dept. of Modern Languages, Mankato State Coll., Mankato.

WALLACE, DWIGHT T(OUSCH), b. Oakland, Calif., May 25, 1927. ANTHROPOLOGY. B.A., U. of Calif., Berkeley, 1950; Ph. D., 1957. Research anthropologist, U. of Calif., Berkeley (Bolivia, Peru), 1954–55; acting asst. prof., U. of N.C., 1959–60; asst. prof., U. of Ga., 1960–61; ASST. PROF., ANTHROPOLOGY, U. OF OREG., 1961– . U. of Oreg. grant (Mexico), Summer 1954; Fulbright research grant (Peru), 1957–59; Fulbright Project coordinator (Peru), 1958–59. Membership: American Anthropological Association; Pacific Coast Conference on Latin American Studies; Society for American Archaeology. Research: archeology; ethnology; Peru. Author: Proto-Lima Cloths (in Proto-Lima, 1954); Reconocimiento del valle de Chincha (Revista del Museo de Ica, 1959); Cerrillos: An Early Paracas Site in Ica, Peru (American Antiquity, 1962). Language: Spanish 4,4,4,3; Portuguese 1,1,1,1; French 3,1,1,1. Home: 2740 Onyx St., Eugene, Oreg. Office: Dept. of Anthropology, U. of Oreg., Eugene.

WALLICH, HENRY CHRISTOPHER, b. Berlin, Germany, June 10, 1914. ECONOMICS. Oxford U., 1932–33; M.A., Harvard U., 1941; Ph. D., 1944. Export business (Argentina), 1933–35; security analyst, Chemical Bank and Trust Company (N.Y.), 1935–36; security analyst, Hackney, Hopkinson & Sutphen, 1936–40; staff, Foreign Research Div., Federal Reserve Bank of New York, 1941–51; chief, 1946–51; PROF., ECONOMICS, YALE U., 1951– ; asst. to the Secretary of the Treasury, U.S. Treasury Dept., 1958–59; President's Council of Economic Advisers, 1959–61. Membership: American Economic Association; American Finance Association. Research: money and finance; Central America and Caribbean. Author: Mainsprings of the German Revival (1955); The Cost of Freedom (1960). Co-author: Public Finances of a Developing Country (1951). Language: Spanish 4,-,-,-; Portuguese 3,-,-,-; French 3,-,-,-; German 5,5,5,5. Home: 88 Cold Spring St.,

New Haven, Conn. Office: Dept. of Economics, Yale U., 37 Hillhouse Ave., New Haven.

WALSH, DONALD DEVENISH, b. Providence, R.I., Oct. 31, 1903. LANGUAGE. S.B., Harvard Coll., 1925. Teacher, head, Spanish, Choate School, 1928–53; assoc. dir., Foreign Language Program, Modern Language Association, 1953–55; dir. of studies, head, Spanish, Choate School, 1955–59; DIR., FOREIGN LANGUAGE PROGRAM, MODERN LANGUAGE ASSOCIATION, 1959– . Editor, Hispania, 1949–57. Membership: American Association of Teachers of Spanish and Portuguese. Research: Spanish American literature; methods of language teaching. Author: Introductory Spanish (1944; 1946; 1950); Repaso, lectura, gramática, conversación (1948). Editor: Cuentos y versos americanos (1942; 1948). Language: Spanish 5,4,4,4; Portuguese 1,1,1,1; French 4,3,3,3. Home: 69 West 9th St., New York, N.Y. 10011. Office: Modern Language Association, 4 Washington Pl., New York, 10003.

WALTHER, DON H., b. Shandon, Ohio, Mar. 30, 1916. BRAZILIAN LITERATURE. B.A., Miami U., 1938; M.A., U. of N.C., 1940; Ph. D., 1948. Instr., U. of N.C., 1941–42, 1946; special agent, Federal Bureau of Investigation, 1942–46; asst. prof., U. of N.C., 1948–50; Central Intelligence Agency, 1950–52; attaché, Embassy (Madrid), U.S. Dept. of State, 1952–56; chief of training, Armed Forces Experimental Training Activity, U.S. Dept. of Defense, 1956–57; assoc. prof., Purdue U., 1957–60; PROF., SPANISH AND PORTUGUESE, PURDUE U., 1960– ; HEAD, MODERN LANGUAGES, 1962– . U.S. Dept. of State exchange fellow (Costa Rica), 1940; Rockefeller Foundation fellow, 1947–48. Membership: American Association of Teachers of Spanish and Portuguese; Indiana Foreign Language Teachers Association; Modern Language Association; Phi Beta Kappa; Sigma Delta Pi. Author: The Critics and O Missionario (in Romance Studies Presented to William Morton Dey, 1950). Language: Spanish 5,5,4,4; Portuguese 5,5,4,4; French 4,4,3,2. Home: 1419 Ravinia, West Lafayette, Ind. Office: Dept. of Modern Languages, Purdue U., West Lafayette, 47907.

WALTHER, TED, b. Atlantic City, N.J., Aug. 23, 1929. ECONOMICS. B.A., Mexico City Coll., 1955; M.A., New School for Social Research, 1958; Ph. D., 1964. ASST. PROF., ECONOMICS, BATES COLL., 1958– . Membership: American Economic Association; Royal Economic Society. Research: economic development; international trade and policy; stabilization policies in Latin America, 1956–1960. Language: Spanish 3,2,2,2; French 2,1,1,1. Home: 148 Wood St., Lewiston, Maine 04240. Office: Dept. of Economics, Bates Coll., Lewiston, 04240.

WANG, HSIN FU, b. Shantung, China, Mar. 2, 1925. ECONOMICS. B.S., National Central U., 1947; M.S., Mich. State U., 1957; Ph. D., 1960. Economist, Ministry of Commerce (Nanking, China), 1947–49; instr., Taichung Agricultural Vocational Institute (Taiwan, Formosa), 1949–55; marketing research specialist, Anderson, Clayton & Company (São Paulo, Brazil), 1960–62; ASSOC. PROF., ECONOMICS, GREENVILLE COLL., 1962– . Rockefeller Foundation fellow, Cornell U., Summer 1957; General Electric Foundation fellow, U. of Chicago, Summer 1963; Ford Foundation fellow, U. of Chicago, Summer 1964. Membership: American Economic Association; American Marketing Associaiton. Research: international economics; economic development; international trade; market research in Brazil. Author: Seasonal Variation of Food Eaten Away from Home (Michigan State University Bulletin, Mar. 1958); Some Measurements of Income—Expenditure Elasticities of Meals Eaten Away from Home (Michigan State University Bulletin, Mar. 1958); Long-run Forecast of Automatic Washer Production in Brazil (Brazilian Journal, Apr. 1961). Language: Spanish 3,2,2,2; Portuguese 5,4,–,4. Home: 424 East South Ave., Greenville, Ill. 62246. Office: Dept. of Economics, Greenville Coll., Greenville, 62246.

WARMAN, HENRY JOHN, b. Scranton, Pa., Jan. 27, 1907. GEOGRAPHY. B.S., Bloomsbury Teachers Coll., 1932; M.S., Temple U., 1938; Ph. D., Clark U., 1945. PROF., GRADUATE SCHOOL OF GEOGRAPHY, CLARK U., 1945– ; teacher, U. of British Columbia, Summer 1960. Clark U. fellow, 1942–43; Clark Research Fund grants (Central America), 1956, (Colombia, Venezuela, Ecuador, Peru), 1958, (Antilles), 1959–60; field coordinator, High School Geography Project, Association of American Geographers, 1962–63. Membership: American Association of University Professors; American Meteorological Society; Association of American Geographers; National Council for Geographic Education; New England Historical Society; New England-St. Lawrence Geographers Conference. Research: human and cultural geography; education in geography; weather and climate. Author: Geography—Backgrounds, Techniques and Prospects (1957); Map Meanings (Journal of Geography, May 1959); Major Concepts in Geography (Journal of Geography, Sept. 1963). Language: Spanish 3,2,2,2; Portuguese 2,–,–,–; German 2,1,1,1. Home: 193 Lovell St., Worcester, Mass. 01603. Office: Graduate School of Geography, Clark U., Worcester, 01603.

WARREN, BRUCE WILLIAM, b. Lyman, Wyo., Jan. 26, 1928. ANTHROPOLOGY: ARCHEOLOGY. B.A., Brigham Young U., 1958. Archeologist, New World Archaelogical Foundation (Orinda, Calif.), 1955–60; ARCHEOLOGIST, BRIGHAM YOUNG U.-NEW WORLD ARCHAELOGICAL FOUNDATION, BRIGHAM YOUNG U., 1961– . Research: Mexican and Central American archeology. Author: New Discoveries in Chiapas (Archaeology, Summer 1959); The Archeological Sequence at Chiapa de Corzo (Mesa Redonda Papers, Sociedad Mexicana de Antropologia, 1961); A Hypothetical Construction of Mayan Origins (XXXV Congreso Internacional de Americanistas, 1964). Language: Spanish 4,4,3,3. Home: 1509 North 2100 West, Provo, Utah. Office: New World Archaelogical Foundation, Brigham Young U., 544 East 1430 North, Provo.

WARREN, DONALD, JR., b. Boston, Mass., Sept. 5, 1921. HISTORY. B.A., Mexico City Coll., 1947; M.A., 1948; Ph. D., Columbia U., 1959. Lectr., Columbia U., 1955–58; instr., Long Island U., 1958–59;

asst. prof., 1959–64; vis. assoc. prof., State U. of N.Y., Coll. at Buffalo, 1964–65; ASSOC. PROF., HISTORY, LONG ISLAND U., 1965– . Fulbright Summer Seminar (Brazil), 1960; National Institute of Mental Health research grant (Brazil), 1962–63; New York State grant, Columbia U., Summer 1964. Membersip: American Historical Association; Association of Brazilianists; Conference on Latin American History. Research: Brazilian history, especially religion and the freeman in the 19th century. Author: The Red Kingdom of Saxony (1964); Religion, Race, and Poverty in Brazil (Helicon, 1964); The Negro and Religion in Brazil (Race, Jan. 1965). Language: Spanish 5,5,4,4; Portuguese 5,4,3,3; French 4,3,3,3; German 4,4,4,3; Italian 3,2,1,1. Home: 12 West 83d St., New York, N.Y. 10024. Office: Dept. of History, Long Island U., Brooklyn, N.Y. 11201.

WARREN, FINTAN BENEDICT, O.F.M., b. Waterflow, N. Mex., June 30, 1930. HISTORY. B.A., Duns Scotus Coll., 1953; M.A., U. of N. Mex., 1960; Ph. D., 1963. RESIDENT MEMBER, ACADEMY OF AMERICAN FRANCISCAN HISTORY, 1958– ; EDITOR, THE AMERICAS, 1963– . Membership: Phi Alpha Theta. Research: institutional and social history of 16th century Mexico. Author: Don Vasco de Quiroga and His Pueblo-Hospitals of Santa Fe (1963); Jesuit Historians of Sinaloa-Sonora (The Americas, Apr. 1962); The Caravajal Visitation: First Spanish Survey of Michoacán (The Americas, Apr. 1963). Language: Spanish 4,4,3,3; Portuguese 3,2,1,1; French 3,2,1,1; German 3,2,1,1; Italian 3,2,1,1; Latin 4,4,4,3. Home and office: Academy of American Franciscan History, 9800 Kentsdale Dr., Box 5966, Washington, D.C. 20014.

WARREN, HARRIS GAYLORD, b. Lincoln, Nebr., Oct. 10, 1906. HISTORY. B.S., Purdue U., 1926; A.M., Stanford U., 1930; Ph. D., Northwestern U., 1937. Instr., Mountain Home High School (Idaho), 1926–28; clerk, American Legation (Asunción, Paraguay), 1928–29; instr., Joliet High School and Junior Coll. (Ill.), 1930–36; instr., Mich. State Coll., 1938–39; assoc. prof., MacMurray Coll. for Women, 1939–40; asst. prof., La. State U., 1940–46; prof., U. of Miss., 1946–57; PROF., CHMN., HISTORY, MIAMI U., 1957– . University Scholar, Stanford U., 1929–30; University Fellow, Northwestern U., 1936–37; American Philosophical Society grant, 1962; Miami U. research grant, 1962; Mississippi State Historical Commission and Ohio Civil War Centennial Commission. Membership: American Association of University Professors; American Historical Association; Association for Latin American Studies; Mississippi Historical Society; Mississippi Valley Historical Association; Ohio Academy of History; Ohio Historical Society; Southern Historical Association; Western History Association. Research: national period in Paraguay; United States-Latin American diplomacy; recent United States history. Author: The Sword Was Their Passport: A History of American Filibustering in the Mexican Revolution (1943); Paraguay: An Informal History (1949); Herbert Hoover and the Great Depression (1959). Language: Spanish 4,4,3,4; Portuguese 4,2,2,2;

French 4,2,1,1; Italian 3,2,1,1. Home: 1022 South Locust St., Oxford, Ohio. Office: Dept. of History, Miami U., Oxford.

WASHINGTON, S(AMUEL) WALTER, b. Charles Town, W. Va., Sept. 30, 1901. POLITICAL SCIENCE. B.A., Va. Military Institute, 1921; B.A., Oxford U. (England), 1924; M.A., 1927. Foreign Service Officer, U.S. Dept. of State, 1926–53; lectr.-acting prof., U. of Va., 1954–59; VIS. PROF., POLITICAL SCIENCE, HISTORY, U. OF P.R., 1960– . Henry Clay Foundation grants (Mexico), Summer 1957, (Venezuela), Summer 1958, (Cuba, British West Indies), 1959; consultant in Argentina, Independence Foundation, 1960. Membership: American Political Science Association; Political Science Association of Puerto Rico; Southern Political Science Association. Research: international relations; student politics in Venezuela; political relationships and news media in Argentina. Author: Mexican Resistance to Communism (Foreign Affairs, Apr. 1958); Student Politics in Latin America: The Venezuelan Example (Foreign Affairs, Apr. 1959); Crisis in the British West Indies (Foreign Affairs, July 1960). Language: Spanish 4,3,3,2; French 4,3,3,3. Home: P.O. Box 851, Hato Rey, P.R. Office: Coll. of Social Science, U. of P.R., Río Piedras.

WATERMAN, DONALD CALVIN, b. Erie, Pa., Aug. 17, 1928. ART. Diploma, Cleveland Institute of Art, 1952; B.F.A., Syracuse U., 1956; M.F.A., 1959. Head, Design Dept., Industrias Ruiz-Galindo, S.A. (México, D.F.), 1953–55; ASST. PROF., ART, SYRACUSE U., 1955– . Consultant on industrial design, Donald C. Waterman-Consultant Industrial Designer, 1955– ; resident designer, American Pavilion, Zagreb Trade Fair (Yugoslavia), 1956, Bari Trade Fair (Italy), 1957 (Peru), 1959. Membership: American Association of University Professors; Industrial Design Education Association. Research: product design; fabric design; crafts. Author: Un lugar a vivir (Construcción Moderna, June 1955); Milan Trienale—1957 (Industrial Design Magazine, Oct. 1957). Language: Spanish 3,3,3,3. Office: School of Art, Syracuse U., Syracuse 10, N.Y.

WATKINS, RALPH J., b. San Marcos, Tex., Dec. 31, 1896. ECONOMICS. B.A., U. of Tex., 1921; B.B.A., 1922; M.S., Columbia U., 1924; Ph. D., 1927. Prof., U. of Tex., 1927–28; assoc. prof., Ohio State U., 1928–29; research staff, National Bureau of Economic Research, 1929–30; dir., Bureau of Business Research, U. of Pittsburgh, 1930–38; asst. administrator, U.S. Dept. of Labor, 1939; economic adviser-asst. dir., National Resources Planning Board, 1939–43; economic adviser-chief, Lend-Lease Mission, Allied Force Headquarters (Algeria), 1943–44; dir., Marketing and Research Div., Dun and Bradstreet, Inc., 1944–48; dir. of research, 1948–57; lectr., Columbia U., 1947–56; researcher, Brookings Institution, 1957–62; PROJECT DIR., SURVEYS AND RESEARCH CORPORATION, 1962– . Special consultant to the Secretary of the Army, 1950–52; consultant, Port of New York Authority, 1956–61; chmn., Advisory Committee on Statistical Policy, U.S. Bureau of the Budget, 1956– ; chmn., Advisory Committee on Economic and Manpower Studies, National Science Foundation, 1961– .

Membership: American Economic Association; American Statistical Association. Research: economic development; Ecuadorian exports; Mexican steel industry. Author: Economic Development Planning in Taiwan (1961). Co-author: Toward Expansion and Diversification of Ecuador's Exports (1963); The Market for Steel in Mexico (1964). Language: Spanish 4,4,3,3; French 4,4,3,3. Home: 2908 R St., NW., Washington, D.C. 20007. Office: Surveys and Research Corporation, 1030 15th St., NW., Washington, D.C. 20005.

WATLAND, CHARLES DUNTON, b. Albert Lea, Minn., Apr. 26, 1913. SPANISH AMERICAN LITERATURE. B.A., Swarthmore Coll., 1934; M.A., U. of Minn., 1937; Ph. D., 1953. Special instr., Johns Hopkins U., 1939–41; translator, cryptographer, American Embassy (Santiago, Chile), 1942–45; instr., Goucher Coll., 1945–46; asst. prof.-assoc. prof., Union Coll., 1946–62; ASSOC. PROF., CLASSICAL AND MODERN LANGUAGES, MARQUETTE U., 1962– . Exchange fellow, National U. of Chile, 1941; editor, Bulletin, Wis. Association of Modern Foreign Language Teachers. Membership: American Association of Teachers of Spanish and Portuguese; American Association of University Professors; Modern Language Association. Research: Spanish and Spanish American literature, 1850 to World War I; modernism; Rubén Darío. Language: Spanish 5,5,4,5; Portuguese 3,3,3,2; French 5,4,4,3; Italian 3,3, 3,2. Home: 1915 North Prospect Ave., Milwaukee, Wis. 53202. Office: Dept. of Classical and Modern Languages, Marquette U., Milwaukee, 53233.

WATSON, JAMES BENNET, b. Chicago, Ill., Aug. 10, 1918. ANTHROPOLOGY. A.B., U. of Chicago, 1941; A.M., 1943; Ph. D., 1948. Manager, Cámara Americana de Commercio (São Paulo), 1943–45; prof., Escola (Livre) de Sociologia e Política, 1944–45; asst. prof., Beloit Coll., 1945–46; assoc. prof., chmn., U. of Okla., 1946–47; assoc. prof., Wash. U., 1947–55; PROF., CHMN., ANTHROPOLOGY, U. OF WASH., 1955– . Buenos Aires Convention fellow (Brazil), 1943–45; principal investigator, National Science Foundation Project (New Guinea). Membership: American Anthropological Association; American Association for the Advancement of Science; Sigma Xi. Research: cultural anthropology; primitive and peasant societies; Brazil; local economic growth; social and cultural change. Author: Cayua Culture Change (1953); Way Station to Westernization: the Brazilian Caboclo (in Brazil: Four Papers, 1952). Editor: New Guinea: The Central Highlands (American Anthropologist, Aug. 1964). Language: Spanish 4,4,5,4; Portuguese 4,4,4,3; French 3,2,2,2; German 2,2,2,1; Italian 2,2,2,2; Melanesian Pidgin 5,–,–,–. Office: Dept. of Anthropology, U. of Wash., Seattle, 98105.

WATTERS, MARY, b. Haynesville, La., Jan. 24, 1896. HISTORY, A.B. Ouachita Coll., 1917; M.A., Baylor U., 1923; Ph. D., U. of N.C., 1931. Instr., Baylor U., 1926–28; prof., Ark. State Coll., 1931–37; research prof., Mary Baldwin Coll., 1937–47; research editor, Ill. State Historical Library, 1947–51; METHODS & PROCEDURES ADVISER, DEPT. OF MENTAL HEALTH, STATE OF ILL., 1951– . Membership: American Historical Association; Catholic Historical Association; Conference on Latin American History; Southern Historical Association. Research: Venezuela. Author: History of the Church in Venezuela (1933); The Colonial Missions in Venezuela Catholic Historical Review, July 1937); A Venezuelan Educator: Don Feliciano Montenegro Colón (The Americas, Jan. 1947). Language: Spanish 5,3,3,4; French 3,–,–,–. Home: 231 West Monroe St., Springfield, Ill. 62704. Office: Ill. State Dept. of Mental Health, 401 South Spring St., Springfield, 62706.

WAUCHOPE, ROBERT, b. Columbia, S.C., Dec. 10, 1909. ANTHROPOLOGY. A.B., U. of S.C., 1931; A.M., Harvard U., 1933; Ph. D., 1942. Expedition staff member, Div. of Historical Research, Carnegie Institution of Washington (Mexico, Guatemala), 1932, 1934, 1935–36; asst. prof., dir., State Archaeological Survey, U. of Ga., 1938–40; assoc. prof., dir., Laboratory of Anthropology, U. of N.C., 1940–42; PROF., ANTHROPOLOGY, DIR., MIDDLE AMERICAN RESEARCH INSTITUTE, TULANE U., 1942– . Joint Committee, Social Science Research Council-American Council of Learned Societies; Advisory Board, Handbook of Latin American Studies. Membership: American Anthropological Association; Society for American Archaeology. Research: Middle American archeology and ethnology. Author: Modern Maya Houses (1938); Excavations at Zacualpa, Guatemala (1958); Archeological Survey of Northern Georgia (1964). Language: Spanish 3,3,2,2,; French 3,2,2,1; German 2,2,2,1. Linguistic studies: Mam; Quiché; Yucatec. Home: 289 Audubon St., New Orleans 18, La. Office: Middle American Research Institute, Tulane U., New Orleans 18.

WEAVER, MURIEL PORTER, b. San Francisco, Calif., Oct. 4, 1922. ANTHROPOLOGY. A.B., U. of Calif., Berkeley, 1944; M.A., Escuela Nacional de Antropología e Historia (Mexico), 1947; Ph. D., Columbia U., 1951. Prof., Universidad de Oriente (Cuba), 1953–56; prof., U. of Calif., Berkeley, Summer 1953. Wenner-Gren fellow, Columbia U., 1948; Wenner-Gren grant-in-aid, 1949, 1951; American Philosophical Society grant, 1951. Membership: American Anthropological Association; Society for American Archaeology. Research: archeology; Mexican culture, customs and terrain; Cuban educational institutions, culture and terrain. Author: Tlatilco and Preclassic Cultures of the New World (1953); Pipas precortesianas (Acta Antropológica, 1948); Excavations at Chupícuaro, Guanajuato (Transactions of the American Philosophical Society, 1956). Language: Spanish 5,5,5,5; French 3,2,2,1. Home: Avenida P. Blanes Viale 6181, Montevideo, Uruguay.

WEBB, KEMPTON EVANS, b. Melrose, Mass., Dec. 28, 1931. GEOGRAPHY. A.B., Harvard Coll., 1953; M.A., Syracuse U., 1955; Ph. D., 1958. Technical consultant, Technical Office of Studies on the Northeast, Banco do Nordeste do Brasil, Summer 1957; asst. prof., Ind. U., 1958–61; asst. prof., Columbia U., 1961–65; asst. dir., Institute of Latin American Studies, 1962–65; ASSOC. PROF., GEOGRAPHY, ASSOC. DIR., INSTITUTE OF LATIN AMERICAN STUDIES, COLUMBIA U., 1965– . Contributing editor, Handbook of Latin American Studies; consultant, U.S. Peace Corps,

Encyclopaedia Britannica Films, and Time-Life, Inc. Membership: American Geographical Society; Associação dos Geografos Brasileiros; Association of American Geographers; International Geographical Union. Research: cultural geography; processes of landscape evolution; geography of Brazil; market systems in central Mexico; regional development planning. Author: Suprimento de gêneros alimentícios básicos para a cidade de Fortaleza (1957); Geography of Food Supply in Central Minas Gerais (1959); Brazil (1964). Language: Spanish 4,4,4,3; Portuguese 5,5,5,4; French 4,3,3,3. Home: 468 Overbrook Rd., Ridgewood, N.J. Office: Dept. of Geography, Columbia U., New York, N.Y. 10027.

WEBER, FRANCES WYERS, b. Chicago, Ill., May 5, 1931. LANGUAGE. B.A., U. of Chicago, 1950; M.A., U. of Mich., 1957; Ph. D., 1962. English teacher, Mexico City Coll., 1951; private English teacher (Madrid), 1953–55; instr., U. of Mich., 1963–64; ASST. PROF., SPANISH, U. OF MICH., 1964– . Teaching fellow, U. of Mich., 1957–61. Research: contemporary Spanish and Latin American literature. Author: El Acoso: Alejo Carpentier's War on Time (Publications of the Modern Language Association, Sept. 1963); Relativity and the Novel: Pérez de Ayala's Belarmino y Apolonio (Philological Quarterly, Apr. 1964); An Approach to Ortega's Idea of Culture: The Concept of Literary Genre (Hispanic Review, Apr. 1964). Language: Spanish 5,5,5,5; Portuguese 4,4,2,2; French 3,3,2,1; Italian 4,4,3,3. Home: 1106 Lincoln, Ann Arbor, Mich. Office: Dept. of Romance Languages, U. of Mich., Ann Arbor.

WEEKLY, JAMES KEITH, b. Seymour, Ind., Nov. 26, 1933. ECONOMICS AND BUSINESS ADMINISTRATION. B.S., Ind. U., 1959; M.B.A., 1960; D.B.A., 1963. ASST. PROF., ECONOMICS, MACALESTER COLL., 1963– . National Defense Education Act fellow, 1959–62; 1962–63. Membership: American Economic Association; Minnesota Economic Association; Society for International Development. Research: international economics; international business administration; development economics; equity-financing in Colombia. Language: Spanish 3,3,3,3. Office: Dept. of Economics, Macalester Coll., St. Paul, Minn. 55101.

WEIANT, CLARENCE WOLSEY, b. West Haverstraw, N.Y., Nov. 30, 1897. ANTHROPOLOGY. B.S., Columbia U., 1937; Ph. D., 1943. Asst. archeologist, National Geographic Society and Smithsonian Institution (Mexico), 1939–41; lectr., Hunter Coll., 1943–51; dean, Chiropractic Institute of N.Y., 1944–63; lectr., U. of P.R., Summer 1954; lectr., Universidad Interamericana (Saltillo, Mexico), Summer 1957; RETIRED, 1963– . Membership: American Anthropological Association; American Association for the Advancement of Science; New York Academy of Sciences; Sociedad Arqueológica de Bolivia; Society for American Archaeology; Society for Applied Anthropology. Research: archeology and ethnology of Mexico. Author: Introduction to the Ceramics of Tres Zapotes (1943); Digging in Chiapas (Explorers Journal, Fall 1954); The Fiesta of the Patron Saint at San Lorenzo (El México Antiguo, IX, 1961). Language: Spanish 4,–,–,–; French 4,–,–,–. Home: 809 Terrace Pl., Peekskill, N.Y. 10566.

WELLMAN, HARVEY RUSSELL, b. Perry, N.Y., Nov. 16, 1916. LAW. A.B., Cornell U., 1937; B.A. Juris., Oxford U., 1939; LL.B., Cornell Law School, 1940; M.A., 1944. Lawyer, Mudge, Stern, Williams & Tucker (N.Y.), 1940–42; economic analyst, Foreign Service Auxiliary, U.S. Dept. of State (Rio de Janeiro), 1942–45; vice consul, Diplomatic Service (Rio de Janeiro), 1945; third secretary and vice consul, Foreign Service (Havana), 1945–47; second secretary and vice consul (Mexico, D.F.), 1947–50; second secretary and consul (Mexico, D.F.), 1950; acting officer in charge, Caribbean Affairs, Bureau of Inter-American Affairs, 1951–54; officer in charge, 1954; first secretary and consul (Paris), 1954–57; counselor of economic affairs (Oslo), 1957–60; counselor of political affairs and consul (Havana), 1960; dir., Office of East Coast Affairs, 1961–62; consul general, 1962; DEPUTY DIR., OFFICE OF PERSONNEL, U.S. DEPT. OF STATE, 1963– . Rhodes scholar, 1937. Membership: New York Bar Association. Language: Spanish 3,3,3,3; Portuguese 2,2,1,1; French 4,3,3,4; Norwegian 2,2,2,2. Home: 4108 Dunnell Lane, Kensington, Md. Office: Foreign Service, U.S. Dept. of State, Washington 25, D.C.

WELLS, HENRY, b. Macomb, Ill., Dec. 15, 1914. POLITICAL SCIENCE. A.B., U. of Ill., 1937; M.A., La. State U., 1939; Ph. D., Yale U., 1947. Instr., Yale U., 1947–49; vis. prof., U. of P.R., Summer 1949; asst. prof., Yale U., 1949–53; part-time vis. prof., U. of P.R., 1951–52; assoc. prof., research assoc., U. of P.R., 1953–56; ASSOC. PROF., POLITICAL SCIENCE, U. OF PA., 1956– . Social Science Research Council fellow, 1946–47, 1960–61; research staff, Puerto Rican Constitutional Convention, 1951–52; member, Organization of American States technical assistance mission on elections (Dominican Republic), 1961–62, (Honduras), Summer 1963. Membership: American Association of University Professors; American Political Science Association; Pennsylvania Political Science and Public Administration Association. Research: government and politics of Puerto Rico; Latin American electoral laws and procedures. Author: Government Financing of Political Parties in Puerto Rico (1961); Ideology and Leadership in Puerto Rican Politics (American Political Science Review, Mar. 1955); The OAS and the Dominican Elections (Orbis, Spring 1963). Language: Spanish 4,3,3,2; French 2,1,1,1. Home: 221 West Mt. Airy Ave., Philadelphia, Pa., 19119. Office: Dept. of Political Science, U. of Pa., Philadelphia, 19104.

WENDT, PAUL FRANCIS, b. New York, N.Y., Nov. 7, 1908. ECONOMICS. B.S., Lafayette Coll., 1928; M.A., Columbia U., 1935; Ph. D., 1941. Statistician, customers' broker, Goodbody and Company (N.Y.), 1928–39; asst. prof., Maryville Coll., 1939–42; economist, War Production Board (Washington, D.C.), 1942–43; PROF., ECONOMICS, U. OF CALIF., BERKELEY, 1946– . Institute of International Studies fellow (Western Europe, Latin America); consultant, Securities and Exchange Commission; consultant, Calif. State Banking

Commission. Membership: American Economic Association; American Finance Association; Regional Science Association. Research: urban economics; investments and real estate; national housing policies of Chile and Argentina. Author: Real Estate Appraisal (1956); Housing Policy—The Search for Solutions (1963). Language: Spanish 3,3,3,3. Home: Box 384, Diablo, Calif. Office: School of Business Administration, U. of Calif., Berkeley, 94720.

WEST, ROBERT COOPER, b. Enid, Okla., June 30, 1913. GEOGRAPHY. B.A., U. of Calif., Los Angeles, 1935; M.A., 1938; Ph. D., U. of Calif., Berkeley, 1946. Instr., U. of Calif., Berkeley, 1940–41; cartographer, U.S. Office of Strategic Services, 1941–45; cultural geographer, Smithsonian Institution (México, D.F.), 1946–48; PROF., GEOGRAPHY, ANTHROPOLOGY, LA. STATE U., 1948– . Guggenheim fellow (Spain), 1955–56; National Science Foundation Postdoctoral Screening Committee, 1959–62; field supervisor, Coastal Studies Institute, La. State U. (Tabasco, Mexico), 1962–63. Membership: American Anthropological Association; American Association for the Advancement of Science; Association of American Geographers. Research: historical geography; enthnography; Mexico. Author: Cultural Geography of Modern Tarascan Area, Mexico (1948); The Mining Community in Northern New Spain: The Parral Mining District (1949); The Pacific Lowlands of Colombia (1957). Language: Spanish 5,4,4,4; Portuguese 4,2,2,1; French 4,1,1,1; German 3,1,1,1; Italian 3,1,1,1. Home: 4756 Highland Rd., Baton Rouge 3, La. Office: Dept. of Geography and Anthropology, La. State U., Baton Rouge 3.

WEST, STANLEY LeROY, b. Los Angeles, Calif., Jan. 15, 1912. LIBRARY SCIENCE. A.B., U. of Calif., Berkeley, 1933; LL.B., U. of Fla., 1938; B.S. in L. S., Columbia U., 1942. Asst. law librarian, U. of Fla., 1938–40; law librarian, instr., Law, U. of Pittsburgh, 1940–42; asst. to dir. of libraries, Columbia U., 1942–43; assoc. law librarian, 1946; DIR. OF LIBRARIES, PROF., LIBRARY SCIENCE, U. OF FLA., 1946– . Fulbright lectr. (Italy); chmn., Farmington Sub-committee (Latin America), Association of Research Libraries; consultant on Latin American library acquisitions, Hispanic Foundation, Library of Congress. Membership: American Library Association; Association of Research Libraries; Association of Southeastern Research Libraries; Florida Library Association; Southeastern Library Association. Research: law; history of books and printing; library organization and administration and library materials in the Caribbean area. Language: Spanish 2,2,2,–; French 2,2,2,–; Italian 2,2,2,–. Home: 1907 NW. Tenth Avenue, Gainesville, Fla. Office: Libraries, U. of Fla., Gainesville 32603.

WESTERN, DOROTHEA, b. Webster City, Iowa, Mar. 20, 1908. LIBRARY SCIENCE. B.A., U. of Iowa, 1933; B.S. in L.S., U of Denver, 1939. Librarian, West Waterloo High School (Iowa), 1935–38; dir., Library, Thomas Jefferson High School (Iowa), 1938–39; dir., Library, Proviso Township High School (Ill.), 1939–45; librarian, U.S. War Dept. (Germany), 1945–46; dir., Proviso Township High School, 1946–50; dir., Library (Djakarta, Indonesia), U.S. Information Service, 1951–55; bibliographical asst., U.S. Information Agency, 1956–58; ASST. DIR., BENJAMIN FRANKLIN LIBRARY (MÉXICO, D.F.), U.S. INFORMATION AGENCY, 1959– . Membership: American Library Association. Language: Spanish 3,3,3,2; French 1,1,1,2; Indonesian 1,1,1,2. Home: 7325 Maple Ter., Wauwatosa, Wis. 53213. Office: Benjamin Franklin Library, Niza 53, México 6, D.F.

WETHEY, HAROLD EDWIN, b. Port Byron, N.Y., Apr. 10, 1902. ART AND ARCHITECTURE. B.A., Cornell U., 1923; M.A., Harvard U., 1931; Ph. D., 1934. Instr., asst. prof., Bryn Mawr Coll., 1934–38; asst. prof., Washington U., 1938–40; assoc. prof., U. of Mich., 1940–46; PROF., HISTORY OF ART, U. OF MICH., 1946– ; lectr., Escuela de Estudios Hispano-Americanos (Spain), 1948. U.S. Dept. of State vis. prof., U. of Tucumán (Argentina), 1943, (Mexico), Summer 1960; Rockefeller Foundation fellow (Peru, Bolivia), 1944–45; Guggenheim fellow (Spain), 1949; contributing editor, Handbook of Latin American Studies, 1948–59. Membership: Academy of American Franciscan History; College Art Association; Hispanic Society of America; Phi Kappa Phi; Real Academia de Bellas Artes de San Fernando (Madrid); Sociedad Peruana de Historia; Society of Architectural Historians. Research: Spanish colonial architecture and sculpture; Renaissance, Mannerist and Baroque painting in Italy and Spain. Author: Colonial Architecture and Sculpture in Peru (1949); Arquitectura virreinal en Bolivia (1961); Ibero-American Architecture (in Encyclopaedia Britannica, 1961). Language: Spanish 4,4,4,4; French 4,4,4,4; German 3,3,3,3; Italian 4,4,4,4. Home: 2009 Morton Ave., Ann Arbor, Mich. 48104. Office: Dept. of History of Art, Tappan Hall, U. of Mich., Ann Arbor.

WEXLER, SIDNEY FREDERICK, b. Brooklyn, N.Y., Oct. 16, 1912. LANGUAGE. B.S., N.Y.U., 1932; M.A., U. of Colo., 1933; Ph. D., N.Y.U., 1952. Export sales, United Naval Stores Company, Inc., 1934–36; teacher, N.Y. City High Schools, 1936–43; training specialist, U.S. Veterans Administration, 1946–49; ASSOC. PROF., ROMANCE LANGUAGES, U. OF MASS., 1949– . U. of Colo. fellow, 1932–33; language coordinator, U.S. Peace Corps Project, Springfield Coll., Summer 1963. Membership: American Association of Teachers of Spanish and Portuguese; American Association of University Professors; Modern Language Association; New England Modern Language Association; Phi Beta Kappa; Phi Kappa Phi. Language: Spanish 5,5,4,4; Portuguese 3,2,1,1; French 4,4,3,3; German 2,3,1,1; Italian 3,2,1,1. Linguistic studies: French; Spanish. Home: 43 Fearing St., Amherst, Mass. Office: Dept. of Romance Languages, U. of Mass., Amherst.

WEYL, NATHANIEL, b. New York, N.Y., July 20, 1910. JOURNALISM. B.S., Columbia U., 1931. Economist, Board of Governors, Federal Reserve System, 1940–41; executive, Amazon desk, Board of Economic Warfare, 1941–43; economist, U.S. Dept. of Commerce, 1945–46; SELF-EMPLOYED WRITER, 1946– . Membership: American Political Science Association; International Academy of Arts and Letters; Mensa; Phi Beta Kappa. Research: history of communism; political history; ethnology; Brazil, Surinam, and Mexico. Author: Red Star Over Cuba (1960); The Negro in American Civilization (1960); The Geography of Intellect (1963). Language: Spanish 4,4,3,3; Portuguese 1,1,-,-,; French 4,3,3,3; German 4,4,3,3. Home: 4201 South Ocean Blvd., Delray Beach, Fla.

WHEELER, RICHARD G., b. Wethersfield, Conn., July 9, 1917. ECONOMICS. B.S., U. of Conn., 1937; M.S., 1940; A.M., Harvard U., 1949; Ph. D., 1950. Agricultural economist, U.S. Dept. of Agriculture (Pa.), 1940–44; asst. prof., U. of Conn., 1946; ASSOC. PROF., AGRICULTURAL ECONOMICS, MICH. STATE U., 1955– ; LEADER, COLOMBIA PROJECT (MEDELLÍN), MICH. STATE U., 1962– . Research fellow and project leader, Harvard U., 1946–50, 1953–55; consultant, Economic Cooperation Administration (Edinburgh, Scotland; Washington, D.C.), 1951–52; lectr., Agrarian Reform Course (Santiago, Chile), 1963, (San Lorenzo, Peru), 1964. Membership: American Farm Economic Association; International Conference of Agricultural Economists. Research: agricultural economics; farm management; economic development; agriculture economy of Colombia. Author: Administración rural en la reforma agraria y el desarollo económico (Revista de Facultad de Agronomía, Nov. 1963). Co-author: Planning for Successful Dairying in New England (1955); Public Law 480 and Colombia's Economic Development (1964). Language: Spanish 4,4,4,3; Portuguese 2,-,-,-; French 2,-,-,-. Office: Dept. of Agricultural Economics, Mich. State U., East Lansing.

WHETTEN, NATHAN LASELLE, b. Chihuahua, Mexico, July 20, 1900. SOCIOLOGY. A.B., Brigham Young U., 1926; M.A., 1928; Ph. D., Harvard U., 1932. Instr., Brigham Young U., 1926–29; PROF., RURAL SOCIOLOGY, U. OF CONN., 1932– ; DEAN, THE GRADUATE SCHOOL, 1940– ; rural sociologist, U.S. Dept. of State (Mexico), 1942–45, (Guatemala), 1944–45; vis. prof., Yale U., 1950–51. Social Science Research Council fellow, Harvard U., 1930–31; consultant, Pan American Union, 1948–50; Guggenheim fellow (Guatemala), 1952–53; editor, Rural Sociology, 1952–54. Membership: American Sociological Association; Institut International de Sociologie; National Planning Association; Population Association of America; Rural Sociological Society; Sociedad Mexicana de Geografía y Estadística; Sociological Research Association. Research: rural sociology; Mexico; Guatemala. Author: Rural Mexico (1948); Guatemala: The Land and the People (1961); Sociology in Latin America (Sociology and Social Research, Nov.–Dec. 1957). Language: Spanish 5,5,4,4; French 3,2,2,1; German 2,1,1,1. Home: Dog Lane, Storrs, Conn. 06268. Office: The Graduate School, U. of Conn., Storrs, 06268.

WHITAKER, ARTHUR PRESTON, b. Tuscaloosa, Ala., June 6, 1895. HISTORY. B.A., U. of Tenn., 1915; A.M., Harvard U., 1917; Ph. D., 1924. Prof., Fla. State Coll. for Women, 1926–27; vis. prof., Vanderbilt U., 1927–28; assoc. pro., Western Reserve U., 1928–30; prof., Cornell U., 1930–36; PROF., HISTORY, U. OF PA., 1936– ; lectr., U. of San Marcos and Catholic U. (Peru), 1941; vis. lectr., National U. of Colombia (Bogotá), 1946; unit head, U.S. Dept. of State, 1943–45. Amherst Memorial fellow, 1924–26; Guggenheim fellow, 1929, 1950; Council on Foreign Relations fellow, 1958–59; Rockefeller Foundation grants for study of Argentine nationalism, 1959–64; Doherty Fellowship Committee; editorial boards, Hispanic American Historial Review, Hispanic American Report, and Orbis: A Quarterly Journal of World Affairs. Membership: American Academy of Political and Social Science; American Historical Association; American Philosophical Society; Council on Foreign Relations; Hispanic Society of America. Research: nationalism in Argentina; United States diplomatic history. Author: The U.S. and the Independence of Latin America, 1800–1830 (1942); The Western Hemisphere Idea: Its Rise and Decline (1954); Spain and Defense of the West: Ally and Liability (1961). Language: Spanish 4,4, 4,4; Portuguese 3,2,1,1; French 4,4,3,4; German 3,2,1,1; Italian 3,1,1,1. Office: Dept. of History, U. of Pa., Philadelphia 4, Pa.

WHITE, BYRON, b. Syracuse, N.Y., June 21, 1906. ECONOMICS. B.A., U. of N.C., 1928; M.A., U. of Tex., 1954; Ph. D., 1959. Foreign Service officer, U.S. Dept. of State (Mexico, Uruguay, Panama, Cuba), 1941–51; economist, U.S. Dept. of Commerce, 1951–53; prof., dir., Instituto de Investigaciones Económicas, Universidad de Oriente (Cuba), 1954–56; faculty member, Coll. of Agriculture and Mechanic Arts, U. of P.R. (Mayagüez), 1958–59; Appalachian State Teachers Coll., 1959; Arlington State Coll., 1959–60; assoc. prof., East Tenn. State U., 1960–61; prof., U. of P.R., 1961–63; PROF. ECONOMICS, EAST CAROLINA COLL., 1963– . Grant, Universidad de Oriente, 1954, 1955; grant, Instituto de Estudios del Caribe (P.R.), 1960; Ford Foundation grant (Cuba), Summer 1960. Membership: American Academy of Political and Social Science; American Association of University Professors; American Economic Association; American Historical Association; American Political Science Association; American Sociological Association; Economic History Association; Hispanic American Society; National Planning Association; Royal Economic Society. Research: international economics, particularly Latin American; economic development; Caribbean history. Author: Azúcar amargo—un estudio de la economía cubana (1955); El triunvirato de Cuba planificada (Revista de Ciencias Sociales, June 1961); Puerto Rico: A Partial Developmental Model (American Journal of Economics and Sociology, Oct. 1963). Language: Spanish 4,4,4,3; Portuguese 3,2,2,–; French 3,2,2,–. Home: 405 South Library St., Greenville, N.C. Office: Box 1524, East Carolina Coll., Greenville.

WHITEFORD, ANDREW HUNTER, b. Winnipeg, Canada, Sept. 13, 1913. ANTHROPOLOGY. B.A., Beloit Coll., 1937; M.A., U. of Chicago, 1943; Ph. D., 1950. Research dir., U. of Tenn., 1939–42; PROF., ANTHROPOLOGY, DIR., LOGAN MUSEUM, BELOIT COLL., 1942– . U. of Chicago research fellow, 1945–46; Social Science Research Council and Wenner-Gren Foundation research grants (Colombia), 1951–52; National Science Foundation faculty fellow (Spain), 1961–62; Joint Committee on Latin America of the Social Science Research Council and American Council of Learned Societies grant-in-aid (Colombia), 1962; research assoc., Instituto Nacional de Antropología (Bogotá, Colombia). Membership: American Anthropological Association; American Ethnological Society; Central States Anthropological Society; Midwest Council for Latin American Studies. Research; social anthropology; community organization; group relations; culture change; museum administration; university curriculum development; Colombia; Mexico. Author: Two Cities of Latin America: A Comparative Description of Social Classes (1960, 1964); Social Class and Social Change in Popayán, Colombia (1963); Notas sobre la clase media en Popayán, Colombia (Ciencias Sociales, Feb. 1953). Language: Spanish 4,4,4,4. Home: 2550 Hawthorne Dr., Beloit, Wis. Office: Logan Museum of Anthropology, Beloit Coll., Beloit.

WHITTEN, NORMAN EARL, JR., b. Orange, N.J., May 23, 1937. ANTHROPOLOGY. A.B., Colgate U., 1959; M.A., U. of N.C., 1961; Ph. D., 1964. RESEARCH FELLOW (COLOMBIA), ANTHROPOLOGY, TULANE U., 1964– . National Institute of Mental Health fellow, 1959–60, 1960–61, (Ecuador) 1961–64. Membership: American Anthropological Association; American Ethnohistorical Society; American Ethnological Society; American Folklore Society; Society for Applied Anthropology. Research: social anthropology; Negroes; social structure and change; power structures; Ecuador; Colombia. Author: Contemporary Patterns of Malign Occultism Among Negroes in North Carolina (Journal of American Folklore, 1962); Sociocultural Change in Northwest Ecuador (Research Previews, 1962). Language: Spanish 3,3,3,2; French 2,1,1,1. Office: Dept. of Sociology and Anthropology, Tulane U., New Orleans, La.

WHYTE, WILLIAM FOOTE, b. Springfield, Mass., June 27, 1914. SOCIOLOGY. B.A., Swarthmore Coll., 1936; Ph. D., U. of Chicago, 1943. Asst. prof., U. of Okla., 1942–43; asst. prof.-assoc. prof., U. of Chicago, 1944–48; PROF., ORGANIZATIONAL BEHAVIOR, SCHOOL OF INDUSTRIAL AND LABOR RELATIONS, CORNELL U., 1948– ; dir. of research in industrial relations, Creole Petroleum Corporation (Venezuela), 1954–55. Fulbright research fellow (Peru), 1961–62. Membership: American Anthropological Association; American Sociological Association; Industrial Relations Research Association; Society for Applied Anthropology. Research: industrial sociology; industrial relations, culture and social structure in Peru; industrial relations in Venezuela. Author: Men at Work (1961); Human Problems of U.S. Enterprise in Latin America (Human Organization, Summer 1956); Culture, Industrial Relations, and Economic Development (Industrial and Labor Relations Review, July 1963). Language: Spanish 4,4,4,4; French 3,3,2,2; German 4,3,3,3; Italian 3,3,3,2. Home: R.F.D. 3, Trumansburg, N.Y. 14886. Office: N.Y. State School of Industrial and Labor Relations, Cornell U., Ithaca, N.Y.

WICKE, CHARLES ROBINSON, b. Roanoke, Va., Apr. 13, 1928. ANTHROPOLOGY. B.A., U. of Va., 1948; M.A., Mexico City Coll., 1954; Ph. D., U. of Ariz., 1965. ASST. PROF., ANTHROPOLOGY, U. OF THE AMERICAS, 1955– . Buenos Aires Convention grant (Peru), 1957; U.S. Steel Foundation fellow, U. of Ariz., 1962–64. Membership: American Anthropological Association; Sigma Xi; Sociedad Mexicana de Antropología; Society for American Archaeology. Research: development of cities and art styles in Mesoamerica; correlation of art styles and social structure; comparison of growth of civilization in Near East with its development in the New World. Author: Los murales de Tepantitla y el arte campesino (Anales del Instituto Nacional de Antropología e Historia, 1954); The Ball Court at Yagul, Oaxaca: A Comparative Study (Mesoamerican Notes, 1957); Así comían los aztecas (in Esplendor del México Antiguo, 1959). Language: Spanish 4,5,4,3. Home: Avenida Irrigación 32, México 10, D.F., México. Office: U. of the Americas, Apartado Postal 968, México 1, D.F.

WILBERT, JOHANNES, b. Cologne, Germany, July 23, 1927. ANTHROPOLOGY. B.A., U. of Cologne (Germany), 1951; Ph. D., 1955. Dir., Instituto Caribe, Fundación La Salle (Caracas), 1956–62; chmn., Anthropology, 1962– ; ASSOC. PROF., ANTHROPOLOGY, U. OF CALIF., LOS ANGELES, 1962– ; DIR., LATIN AMERICAN CENTER, 1963– . Fulbright grant, Yale U., 1953–54; Foreign Area Fellowship Program, Ford Foundation. Membership: American Anthropological Association: Gesellschaft für Kulturmorphologie (Frankfurt); Sociedad de Ciencias Naturales La Salle; Société des Americanistes (Paris); Southwestern Anthropological Association. Research: peoples of South America; Venezuela. Author: Indios de la región Orinoco-Venturari (1963); Warao Oral Literature (1964). Co-author: El antígeno del sistema sanguíneo Diego (1960). Language: Spanish 5,4, 4,4; French 4,3,2,1; German 5,5,5,5. Linguistic studies: Warao; Ye. Home: 15300 Whitfield Ave., Pacific Palisades, Calif. Office: Center for Latin American Studies, U. of Calif., Los Angeles 24.

WILEY, SELVA C., b. Huntington, W. Va., June 16, 1917. GEOGRAPHY. A.B., Marshall U., 1938; M.A., U. of Nebr., 1948; Ph. D., Ohio State U., 1956. Physical geographer, U.S. Army Research and Engineering Center, 1950–56; technologist, U.S. Army Corps of Engineers, 1956–57; cartographer, U.S. Air Force Aero-Chart and Information Center, 1957; head, Foreign Geography, Dept. of Mines and Technical Surveys (Ottawa, Canada), 1957–60; intelligence research speicalist, Army Map Service, 1960–61; intelligence research specialist, Defense Intelligence Agency, 1961–63; RESOURCES DEVELOPMENT OFFICER, SEMINOLE AGENCY (WEST HOLLYWOOD, FLA.), U.S. DEPT. OF THE INTERIOR, 1963– . Liaison officer, Canadian Geography and Pan American Institute of Geography and History. Membership: Association of American Geographers. Research: resources; cartography; geology; botany. Author: Colonization and Settlement in the Americas (1960); Kashmir (Canadian Geographical Journal, Jan. 1961); Canada's Latin American Neighbours (Canadian Geographical Journal, Sept. 1962). Language: Spanish 4,3,3,3; Portuguese 3,2,2,2; French 3,2,2,2; German 3,2, 2,1; Italian 2,2,1,1; Russian 3,1,1,1. Home: 811 NW. 72nd Ter., West Hollywood, Fla. Office: Seminole Agency, Bureau of Indian

Affairs, U.S. Dept. of the Interior, 6075 Stirling Rd., West Hollywood.

WILFORD, WALTON TERRY, b. Murray, Ky., Sept. 27, 1937. ECONOMICS. B.B.A., Southern Methodist U., 1958; Ph. D., 1964. Asst. prof., U. of Ga., 1962–63; ASST. PROF., U. OF IDAHO, 1963– . Cokesbury Graduate Award, Southern Methodist U., 1958–59; Southern Methodist U. teaching fellow, 1959–62; Ford Foundation research grant, Summer 1964. Membership: American Economic Association; Northwestern Universities Business Association; Omicron Delta Epsilon; Southern Economic Association; Western Economic Association. Research: problems of economic development; macroeconomic theory; money and banking; public finance. Author: Federal Reserve Management of the Discount Rate (Southwestern Social Science Quarterly, Sept. 1960). Language: Spanish 3,3,3,4; Portuguese 2,2,2,2; French 2,2,2,2: Home: 729 Brent Dr., Moscow, Idaho 83843. Office: coll. of Business Administration, U. of Idaho, Moscow, 83843.

WILGUS, A(LVA) CURTIS, b. Platteville, Wis., Apr. 2, 1897. HISTORY. B.A., U. of Wis., 1920; M.A., 1921; Ph. D, 1925. Assoc. prof., U. of S.C., 1924–30; assoc. prof., George Washington U., 1930–40; dir., Center of Latin American Studies, 1932–36; prof., 1940–41; PROF., HISTORY, DIR., SCHOOL OF INTER-AMERICAN STUDIES, U. OF FLA., 1951– . Latin America expert, U.S. Office of Education, 1942; dir., Education and Teacher Aids, Office Coordinator for Inter-American Affairs, 1943–44; Cervantes Medal, Hispanic Institute of Florida, 1954; Chevalier, Le Compagnon Honnaire Croix de Lorraine, 1954. Membership: American Association of University Professors; American Historical Association; Association for Latin American Studies; Committee on Library Cooperation with Latin America; Hispanic Society of America; Inter-American Bibliography and Library Association. Research: the Caribbean; United States foreign relations. Author: Latin American History (1939); Development of Hispanic America (1941); Histories and Historians of Hispanic America (1942). Language: Spanish 4,4,4,1; Portuguese 3,2,1,1; French 4,4,4,1; German 2,3,2,1; Italian 2,3,2,1. Home: 32 SW. 43rd Ter., Gainesville, Fla. Office: School of Inter-American Studies, U. of Fla., Gainesville.

WILKENING, EUGENE A., b. Oak Ridge, Mo. SOCIOLOGY. B.S., U. of Mo., 1937; M.A., 1939; Ph. D., U. of Chicago, 1949. Rural rehabilitation supervisor, Farm Security Administration, U.S. Dept. of Agriculture, 1938–40; asst. prof., N.C. State U., 1946–51; PROF., CHMN., RURAL SOCIOLOGY, U. OF WIS., 1951– . Social Science Research Council fellow, 1947–48; Fulbright research scholar (Australia), 1958–59; research grant (Brazil), U.S. Agency for International Development-Land Tenure Center, U. of Wis., 1963. Membership: American Sociological Society; Midwest Sociological Society; Rural Sociological Society. Research: rural sociology; family living, technological change and communications in rural areas; Brazil. Author: Acceptance of Improved Practices (1952); Adoption of Improved Farm Practices as Related to Family Factors (1953); Commentaries Among Victorian Dairy Farmers (Rural Sociology, June 1962). Language: Portuguese 2,2,2,2. Home: 3 Waupaca Ct., Madison 5, Wis. Office: Dept. of Rural Sociology, U. of Wis., Madison 6.

WILKINS, BILLY HUGHEL, b. Paducah, Tex., July 17, 1931. ECONOMICS. B.B.A., Tex. Coll. of Arts & Industries, 1956; M.S., 1957; Ph. D., U. of Tex., 1962. Asst. prof-ASSOC. PROF., ECONOMICS, OREG. STATE U., 1961– ; assoc. prof., U. of the Americas (Mexico), 1963–64. U. of Tex. fellow, 1959–60, Summers 1959, 1960, Spring 1961; Foundation for Economic Education fellow, Summer 1963. Membership: American Economic Association; Economic History Association; Omicron Delta Epsilon; Southwestern Social Science Association; Western Economic Association. Research: history of economic thought; international economics; organization of petroleum exporting countries; social control of industry; economy of Venezuela and Mexico. Author: Foreign Investment and Internally Generated Funds (Inter-American Economic Affairs, Spring 1963); The Impact of Petroleum Imports on the Economic Development of the Southwest (in Economic Development of the Southwest, Resources for the Future Project, Sept. 1963). Co-author: The Economists of the New Frontier (1963). Language: Spanish 3,2,2,1. Office Dept. of Economics, Oreg. State U., Corvallis.

WILKINS, ERNEST J., b. Franklin, Ariz., Nov. 10, 1918. LANGUAGE. B.A., Brigham Young U., 1947; M.A., Stanford U., 1950; Ph. D., 1953. Missionary (Argentina), 1938–41; research analyst, Howard Hughes Productions 1951–53; prof., Brigham Young U., 1953–60; DIR., LANGUAGE TRAINING MISSION, BRIGHAM YOUNG U., 1960– . Membership: American Association of Teachers of Spanish and Portuguese; Instituto Internacional de Literatura Iberoamericana; Modern Language Association; Rocky Mountain Council for Latin American Studies. Research: Spanish; Spanish American literature and culture. Author: Español para misioneros (1962); Español a lo vivo (1963); Portugués para missionarios (1963). Language: Spanish 5,5,5,5; Portuguese 4,4,4,4; French 4,4,4,4; German 3,3,3,3. Linguistic studies: French; Portuguese; Spanish. Home: 1405 East Oakcrest Lane, Provo, Utah. Office: Language Training Mission, 322 Knight Mangum Hall, Brigham Young U., Provo.

WILKISON, ANDY GEORGE, b. Meeker, Okla., Mar. 1, 1906. LIBRARY SCIENCE. A.B., U. of Calif., Berkeley, 1930; certificate of librarianship, 1933; M.A., 1940. Librarian, U. of Calif., Berkeley, 1933–42; supervisor, Marinship Corporation (Sausalito, Calif.), 1942–45; office manager, John Gibson Travel Agency, 1945–47; Librarian, Biblioteca Benjamin Franklin (Mexico, D.F.), U.S. Information Service, 1947–48; dir. of library services, librarian, Biblioteca Lincoln (Buenos Aires), 1949–54; cultural affairs officer, Embassy (Caracas), U.S. Information Agency, 1954–56; cultural affairs officer (La Paz), 1956–58; CULTURAL AFFAIRS OFFICER, EMBASSY (QUITO), U.S. INFORMATION AGENCY, 1962– . Research: Latin American history. Language: Spanish 4,4,4,3; Portuguese 2,2,1,1; French 2,2,1,1. Home and office: American Embassy, Quito, Ecuador.

WILLEMS, EMILIO, b. Germany, Aug. 18, 1905. ANTHROPOLOGY. DVW, U. of Berlin, 1928; Ph. D., 1930; Livre docencia, U. of São Paulo, 1936. Prof., U. of São Paulo, 1937–49; prof., Escola de Sociologia e Política de São Paulo, 1941–49; PROF., ANTHROPOLOGY, VANDERBILT U., 1949– ; vis. prof., Mich. State U., 1952, U. of Mich., 1952–53, U. of Cologne, 1956, 1962, U. of Calif., Berkeley, 1957, U. of Chile, 1959–60, National U. of Colombia, 1962–63. Guggenheim fellow, 1950; Social Science Research Council grant, 1951, 1954; Rockefeller grant (Brazil), 1959; Fulbright grant (Chile), 1959, 1960; Ford Foundation grant (Colombia), 1962–63. Membership: American Anthropological Association. Research: social anthropology; socio-cultural change in Brazil, Chile and Colombia. Author: A aculturação dos alemães no Brasil (1946); Buzios Island (1952); Uma vila brasileira (1961). Language: Spanish 5,4,4,4; Portuguese 5,5,5,5; French 5,4,3,3; German 5,5,5,5. Home: 163 Kenner Ave., Nashville, Tenn. Office: Box 1510, Vanderbilt U., Nashville.

WILLEY, GORDON R., b. Chariton, Iowa, Mar. 7, 1913. ANTHROPOLOGY. B.A., U. of Ariz., 1935; M.A., 1936; Ph. D., Columbia U., 1942. Senior anthropologist. Bureau of Ethnology, Smithsonian Institution, 1943–50; PROF., ANTHROPOLOGY, PEABODY MUSEUM, HARVARD U., 1950– . Membership: American Academy of Arts and Sciences; American Anthropological Association; National Academy of Sciences; Society for American Archaeology. Research: archeology; especially in Guatemala and Central America. Author: Archaeology of the Florida Gulf Coast (1949); Prehistoric Settlement Patterns in Vinu Valley, Peru (1953); Methods and Theory in American Archaeology (1958). Language: Spanish 4,3,3,2. Office: Peabody Museum, Harvard U., Cambridge, Mass.

WILLIAMS, AUBREY WILLIS, JR., b. Madison, Wis., July 31, 1924. ANTHROPOLOGY. A.B., U. of N.C., 1955; M.A., 1958; Ph. D., U. of Ariz., 1964. Work project dir., American Friends Service Committee (México, D.F.), 1957–58; ethnographer, Land Claims Research, Navajo Tribe (Ariz.), 1961; research asst., U. of Ariz., 1961–62; ASST. PROF., ANTHROPOLOGY, U. OF MD., 1962– . Wenner-Gren fellow, 1962; collaborator, R.S. Peabody Foundation Project (Tehuacán, Mexico), 1964. Membership: American Anthropological Association; Society for American Arcaeology; Washington Society for Anthropology. Research: cultural anthropology; culture change; Mexico and southwestern area of United States. Author: Time Continuum in Eastern U.S.A. Archaeology (Southern Indian Studies, 1957, 1958, 1959). Language: Spanish 3,3,–,–; French 3,2,–,–; Navajo –,2,–,–. Home: 9236 St. Andrews Pl., College Park, Md. Office: Dept. of Sociology, U. of Md., College Park.

WILLIAMS, GERALD EUGENE, b. Aug. 31, 1925. ANTHROPOLOGY: LINGUISTICS. B.A., Yale U., 1949; M.A., U. of Chicago, 1951; Ph. D., 1961. Vis. asst. prof., U. of Chicago, 1960–61; asst. prof., Stanford U., 1961–63; ASSOC. PROF., ANTHROPOLOGY, U. OF ROCHESTER, 1963– . National Institute of Mental Health research grant (Mexico), 1964. Membership: American Anthropological Association; American Ethnological Society; Linguistic Society of America. Research: language and culture; ethnolinguistics in Mexico. Author: Bahasa Inggeris: Spoken English for Indonesians (1954); A Formal Ethnographic Analysis of Tenejapa Ladino Weddings (American Anthropologist, Oct. 1963); Tenejapa Medicine I: The Curer (Southwestern Journal of Anthropology, Summer 1963). Language: Spanish 4,4,3,2; French 4,4,3,–. Linguistic studies: Minangkabau; Tepehua; Tzeltal; Tzotzil. Home: 49 Elmcroft Rd., Rochester, N.Y. 14609. Office: Dept. of Anthropology, U. of Rochester, Rochester, 14627.

WILLIAMSON, ROBERT CLIFFORD, b. Los Angeles, Calif., Apr. 25, 1916. SOCIOLOGY. B.A., U. of Calif., Los Angeles, 1938; M.A., 1940; Ph. D., U. of Southern Calif., 1951. Prof., Los Angeles City Coll., 1946–60; part-time lectr., Los Angeles State Coll., 1955–59; part-time lectr., U. of Southern Calif., 1957–60; vis. assoc. prof., Haverford Coll., 1962–63; PROF., SOCIOLOGY, HEAD, SOCIAL RELATIONS, LEHIGH U., 1963– . Smith-Mundt prof., National U. of El Salvador, 1958; Social Science Research Council grant (Central America), Summer 1960; Fulbright prof., Facultad de Sociología, National U. of Colombia, 1961; Latin America Committee, American Friends Service Committee, 1962– ; Lehigh U. faculty research grant, 1964. Membership: American Psychological Association; American Sociological Association; Eastern Sociological Society; International Sociological Institute; National Council of Family Relations. Research: social psychology; university students and social attitudes in Latin America; values and social class in Bogotá. Author: El estudiante colombiano y sus actitudes (Monografías Sociológicas, Facultad de Sociología, Bogotá, 1962). Co-author: Social Psychology (1958). Language: Spanish 5,4,4,4; Portuguese 3,1,1,1; French 4,4,3,3; German 4,4,3,3; Russian 2,2,2,2. Home: R.F.D. 4, Bethlehem, Pa. 18015. Office: Dept. of Social Relations, Lehigh U., Bethlehem, 18015.

WILLIFORD, MIRIAM, b. Rock Hill, S.C., Mar. 26, 1926. HISTORY. B.A., Winthrop Coll., 1945; M.A., U. of N.C., 1950; Ph. D., Tulane U., 1963. Teacher, Cambridge High School (Md.), 1945–47; ASSOC. PROF., HISTORY, WINTHROP COLL., 1947– ; asst. to dean of the college, 1961– ; dean, Rock Hill Community Coll., 1961– . Organization of American States research fellow (Guatemala), Summer 1962. Membership: American Association of University Professors; American Historical Association; Conference on Latin American History; Hispanic American Society; Phi Alpha Theta; Sigma Delta Pi; Southern Historical Association. Research: the reform program of Dr. Mariano Galvez, chief of state of Guatemala, 1831–1838; adult education program. Language: Spanish 4,4,3,3; Portuguese 2,2,2,1; French 3,3,3,3; Italian 2,2,2,2. Home: Apt. 9, 517 North Wilson St., Rock Hill, S.C. Office: Box 102, Winthrop Coll. Station, Rock Hill.

WILSON, IRIS HIGBIE, b. Los Angeles, Calif., Jan. 9, 1935. HISTORY. B.A., U. of Southern Calif., 1956; M.A., 1957; Ph. D., 1962. Teacher Huntington Beach High School 1957–59; translator of Spanish manuscripts, Los Angeles County Museum,

1959–60; lectr., U. of Southern Calif., 1962– ; INSTR., HISTORY, LONG BEACH CITY COLL., 1962– . University graduate fellow, U. of Southern Calif.; Del Amo fellow (Spain), 1960–62. Membership: American Historical Association. Research: history of science; Spanish scientific expeditions in South and Central America with particular emphasis on native medicinal plants and remedies. Author: Scientists in New Spain—the 18th Century (Journal of the West, July 1962); Investigación sobre la planta maguey (Revista de Indias, 1963). Editor: Pineda's Report on the Beverages of New Spain (Arizona and the West, Spring 1963). Language: Spanish 4,5,4,4; Portuguese 2,2,2,2; French 2,2,1,1; German 2,2,2,1; Italian 2,2,1,1. Home: 328 Amethyst Ave. Balboa Island, Calif. Office: Dept. of History, Long Beach City Coll., 4901 Carson St., Long Beach 8, Calif.

WILSON, LARMAN CURTIS, b. Lincoln, Nebr., Apr. 20, 1930. POLITICAL SCIENCE. B.A., Nebr. State Coll., 1952; M.A., U. of Md., 1957; Ph. D., 1964. Lectr., U. of Md., 1957–64; ASST. PROF., POLITICAL SCIENCE AND ECONOMICS, U. S. NAVAL ACADEMY, 1964– . Membership: American Political Science Association; American Society of International Law; Pi Sigma Alpha. Research: non-intervention in recent inter-American relations; the relationship between economic development and political change. Language: Spanish 4,3,3,1; Portuguese 2,1,1,–; French 2,1,1,–. Home: 46½ Southgate Ave., Annapolis, Md. 21401. Office: Dept. of English, History and Government, U.S. Naval Academy, Annapolis.

WINKLER, MARSHALL BAKER, S.J., b. Norfolk, Va., Mar. 28, 1922. POLITICAL SCIENCE. A.B., St. Louis U., 1945; M.A., 1951; S.T.L., Woodstock Coll., 1954; Ph. D., Georgetown U., 1964. ASST. PROF., POLITICAL SCIENCE, ST. PETER'S COLL., 1960– . Organization of American States fellow (Chile), 1959–60; dir., Fordham Junior Year Abroad Program (Chile), 1961–62. Membership: American Political Science Association; Phi Sigma Alpha; Political Science Academy. Research: comparative government; comparative politics; Christian democratic parties of Latin America. Language: Spanish 5,5,4,4; Portuguese 2,2,2,2; French 4,4,4,3. Home and office: Dept. of History and Political Science, St. Peter's Coll., Jersey City 6, N.J.

WINN, WILKINS BOWDRE, b. Fort Worth, Tex., Jan. 19, 1928. HISTORY. A.B., Howard Coll., 1952; Th. M., Dallas Theological Seminary, 1959; M.A., U. of Ala., 1959; Ph. D., 1964. ASST. PROF., HISTORY, MOBILE COLL., 1963– . Membership: American Anthropological Association; Southern Historical Association. Research: Protestantism in Latin America; Central American missions. Language: Spanish 3,–,–,–; German 1,–,–,–; Greek 3,–,–,–; Hebrew 2,–,–,–. Home: 705 Montclaire Way, Mobile, Ala. 36609. Office: Mobile Coll., P.O. Box 13220, Mobile, 36613.

WINNIE, WILLIAM W., JR., b. Pontiac, Mich., Jan. 27, 1928. GEOGRAPHY. B.S., U. of Fla., 1953; M.A., 1955; Ph. D., 1956. Statistician, U.S. Bureau of the Census, 1956–58, Summer 1959; asst. prof., La. State U., 1958–59; prof., Universidad de Nuevo León (Monterrey, Mexico), 1959–61; social planner, Pan American Union (Washington, D.C.; Lima, Peru), 1962–63; member, Evaluation and Coordination Group, Inter-American Development Bank, 1963–64; POSTDOCTORAL RESEARCH SCHOLAR, GEOGRAPHY, U. OF CALIF., LOS ANGELES, 1964– . General Education Board scholar, 1953–54; U. of Fla. fellow, 1953–56; Fulbright lectr. (Chile), 1961–62. Membership: American Geographical Society; Association of American Geographers; International Development Association; Population Association of America; Rural Sociological Society. Research: land tenure; demography; social development; national planning. Author: The Lower Papaloapan Basin: A Case Study in Tropical Development (Economic Geography, July 1958); La tenencia de la tierra en la cuenca del bajo Papaloapan (Humánitas, 1960); Communal Land Tenure in Chile (Annals, Association of American Geographers, 1964). Language: Spanish 5,5,5,4; Portuguese 3,2,2,1; French 3,2,1,1. Home: 2641 Kelton Ave., Los Angeles, Calif. Office: Dept. of Geography, U. of Calif., Los Angeles.

WINSBERG, MORTON DANIEL, b. Chicago, Ill., Aug. 1, 1930. GEOGRAPHY. B.S., U. of Ill., 1951; M.S., 1954; Ph. D., U. of Fla., 1958. Asst. prof., East Carolina Coll., 1958–62; ASST. PROF., GEOGRAPHY, OHIO U., 1962– . Social Science Research Council fellow (Argentina), 1960–61. Membership: American Geographical Society; Association of American Geographers. Research: settlement patterns in Cuba and Argentina. Author: Jewish Agricultural Colonization of the Argentine Pampas: Colonia Barón Hirsch (1964); Costs, Tariffs, Prices and Nationalization vs. the American Grapefruit Industry, Isle of Pines, Cuba (American Journal of Economics and Sociology, Oct. 1961). Language: Spanish 4,4,4,3. Home: Route 1, Box 331–B, Delray Beach, Fla. Office: Dept. of Geography and Geology, Ohio U., Athens, 45701.

WINTERS, HOWARD DALTON, b. Urbana, A.B., Coll of William and Mary, 1949; M.A., U. of Chicago, 1953. Research asst., U. of Chicago, 1953; staff archeologist (Mexico), Carnegie Institution of Washington (Cambridge, Mass.), 1953–54; curator, Meso-American Archeology, Museum, Southern Ill. U., 1955–60; field dir., Ill. State Museum, 1961–62; INSTR., ANTHROPOLOGY, U. OF VA., 1962– . Board of Directors, Illinois Archaeological Research, Inc., 1956–64; chmn., Conference on Peripheral Areas of Mexican High Cultures, 1957; Board of Directors, Illinois Archaeological Survey, 1958–60; chmn., Midwestern Conference for Archaeology, 1959; Council for Illinois Archaeology, 1961–64; asst. editor on Northern Mesoamerica, Archaeological Abstracts. Membership: Massachusetts Archaeological Society; Society for American Archaeology; Virginia Archaeological Society. Research: archeology of Mesoamerica; settlement patterns and settlement systems in the late Archaic; culture and terrain of Mexico. Author: An Archaeological Survey of the Central Wabash Valley (1963). Co-author: A Revision of the Archaeological Sequence in Sinaloa, Mexico (American Antiquity, 1960); The Tepehuan of Northern Mexico (Southwestern Journal of Anthropology, 1963). Language: Spanish 3,3,3,3; French 4,4,4,4. Home: 611 Rugby Rd., Charlottesville, Va. Office: Dept. of Sociology and Anthropology, U. of Va., Charlottesville.

WISE, MARY RUTH, b. Stuttgart, Ark., Apr. 11, 1929. LINGUISTICS. B.A., Columbia Bible Coll., 1951; M.A., U. of Mich., 1959. LINGUIST, SUMMER INSTITUTE OF LINGUISTICS (PERU), 1952– ; CONSULTANT, 1961– . Research: discourse analysis; culture of Amuesha tribe of Peru. Author: Diverse Points of Articulation of Allophones in Amuesha (Miscelánea Phonética, Dec. 1958); Six Levels of Structure in Amuesha Verbs (International Journal of American Linguistics, Apr. 1963). Coauthor: Contrastive Features of Candoshi Clause Types (Studies in Peruvian Indian Languages, Nov. 1963). Language: Spanish 3,3,3,3; Portuguese 1,1,1,1; French 2,-,-,-; Amuesha 5,5,4,4. Linguistic studies: Amuesha; Candoshi; Machiguenga. Home: 211 West Cross DeWitt, Ark. Office: Instituto Lingüístico de Verano, Casilla 2492, Lima, Peru.

WITHERS, WILLIAM H., b. St. Louis, Mo., Dec. 21, 1905. ECONOMICS. A.B., Columbia U., 1926; A.M., 1928; Ph. D., 1932. Instr., Lehigh U., 1928–29; instr., N.Y.U., 1930–31; research assoc., Columbia U., 1932–33; prof., Columbia U., 1933–36; research dir., Works Progress Administration, 1936–37; PROF., ECONOMICS, QUEENS COLL., 1937– ; research dir., Works Progress Administration, 1941–42. Membership: American Economic Association; Metropolitan Economic Association. Research: public finance; tax problems; corporation finance; business organization; economic development; Latin American economies. Author: Financing Economic Security (1939); Public Finance (1948); The Economic Crisis in Latin America (1964). Language: Spanish 3,3,3,3; Portuguese 2,1,1,2; French 3,3,3,3. Home: 83–45 Vietor Ave., Elmhurst, N.Y. 11373. Office: Dept. of Economics, Queens Coll. of the City U. of N.Y., Flushing 67, N.Y.

WITT, LAWRENCE W., b. Chicago, Ill., July 16, 1914. ECONOMICS. B.S., U. of Wis., 1937; M.S., Iowa State U., 1938; Ph. D., 1941. Assoc., Iowa State U. and Institute of Current World Affairs, 1941–43; research assoc., 1943–46; agricultural economist, U.S. Dept. of Agriculture, 1943–47; assoc. prof.-prof., Mich. State U., 1947–58; dir. of Studies, 1958–61; PROF., AGRICULTURAL ECONOMICS, MICH. STATE U., 1961– . Institute of Current World Affairs grant (Brazil), 1942, 1952; agricultural technical assistance, U.S. Dept. of Agriculture (Ecuador, Colombia), 1943, 1944–45; consultant, United Nations Food and Agriculture Organization, 1951; consultant to dir., Food for Peace, White House Office, 1961; consultant, U.S. Dept. of Agriculture (Colombia), 1962, 1963, Inter-American Institute of Agricultural Sciences; governor, Institute of Current World Affairs. Membership: American Farm Economic Association; International Association of Agricultural Economists. Research: agricultural and economic development; agricultural technology; effects of agricultural surplus shipments. Author: Agriculture in Economic Development (1964); The Effects of United States Agricultural Surplus Disposal Programs on Recipient Countries (Michigan Agricultural Experiment Station Bulletin, 1964). Contributor: Economics and Management in Agriculture (1963). Language: Spanish 4,4,3,4; Portuguese 4,3,3,3; French 3,2,2,1; German 2,3,2,1. Home: 488 Haslett, East Lansing, Mich. Office: Dept. of Agricultural Economics, Mich. State U., East Lansing.

WOGAN, DANIEL SPELMAN, b. New Orleans, La., Nov. 24, 1907. SPANISH AMERICAN LITERATURE. A.B., La. State U., 1931; M.A., Columbia U., 1932; Ph. D., U. of N.C., 1939. Instr., La. State U., 1939–44; asst. prof., 1945–47; assoc. prof., Tulane U., 1947–51; PROF., CHMN., SPANISH AND PORTUGUESE, TULANE U., 1952– . Contributing editor, Handbook of Latin American Studies, 1952–64; vice president, Instituto de Literatura Iberoamericana. Membership: Academia Nicaragüense de la Lengua; American Association of Teachers of Spanish and Portuguese; American Association of University Professors; Instituto Internacional de Profesores de Literatura Iberoamericana; Modern Language Association. Research: the Indian in Mexican poetry. Author: A literatura hispanoamericana no Brasil (1949); Los americanismos de Florencio Sánchez (Revista Iberoamericana, June 1948); Cuatro aspectos de la poesía indigenista (Historia Mexicana, Apr.–June 1953). Language: Spanish 5,5,5,5; Portuguese 5,5,5,5; French 5,5,5,5; German 3,3,4,4; Italian 3,3,4,4. Linguistic studies: Portuguese; Spanish. Home: 1320 Burdette St., New Orleans 18, La. Office: Dept. of Spanish, Tulane U., New Orleans 18.

WOLF, ERIC ROBERT, b. Vienna, Austria, Feb. 1, 1923. ANTHROPOLOGY. B.A., Queens Coll., 1946; Ph. D., Columbia U., 1951. Research assoc., vis. asst. prof., U. of Ill., 1952–55; asst. prof., U. of Va., 1955–58; vis. asst. prof., Yale U., 1958–59; assoc. prof., U. of Chicago, 1959–61; PROF., ANTHROPOLOGY, U. OF MICH., 1961– . U. of P.R. fellow, 1948–49; Viking Fund research grant, 1950–51; Doherty fellow (Mexico), 1951–52; Guggenheim fellow, 1960–61; Fulbright Committee; consultant, Dept. of Social Affairs, Pan American Union, Membership: American Anthropological Association; American Ethnological Soicety; Anthropological Society of Washington; Royal Anthropological Institute of Great Britain and Ireland. Research: culture change; peasant communities; Mexico; Mediterranean Europe. Author: Sons of the Shaking Earth (1959); Types of Latin American Peasantry (American Anthropologist, June 1955); Aspects of Group Relations in a Complex Society (American Anthropologist, Dec. 1956). Language: Spanish 4,4,4,4; French 3,3,3,3; German 5,5,5,4; Italian 3,3,2,2. Linguistic studies: Nahuatl. Home: 1102 Forest, Ann Arbor, Mich. Offices: Dept. of Anthropology, 221 Angell Hall, U. of Mich., Ann Arbor.

WOLFE, GREGORY B., b. Los Angeles, Calif., Jan. 27, 1922. ECONOMICS. A.B., Reed Coll., 1943; M.A., Fletcher School of Law & Diplomacy, 1947; Ph. D., 1961. Instr., Mass. Institute of Technology, 1950–52; case leader, Area Development Div., Arthur D. Little, Inc., 1952–57; executive dir., Greater Boston Economic Study Committee, 1957–61; dir., Latin American Program,

Committee for Economic Development, 1961–64; DIR., OFFICE OF RESEARCH AND ANALYSIS FOR THE AMERICAN REPUBLICS, BUREAU OF INTELLIGENCE AND RESEARCH, U.S. DEPT. OF STATE, 1964– . Adviser to Chief of State, Republic of Honduras, 1955–57; Board of Advisers, Fletcher School of Law & Diplomacy, 1959– ; consultant, Ford Foundation, Organization and Operation of Economic Policy Research Foundation (Madrid), 1962; Maryland Science and Industry Development Advisory Board, 1963– . Research: economic development; politics of Latin America. Author: Financing System for Economic Development: Problems and Prospects in Central America (Journal of Inter-American Affairs, Oct. 1964); Higher Education in Contemporary Central America (Journal of Inter-American Affairs, Oct. 1964). Language: Spanish 5,5,5,4. Home: 10401 Lloyd Rd., Potomac, Md. Office: Office of Research and Analysis for the American Republics, Bureau of Intelligence and Research, U.S. Dept. of State, Washington, D.C.

WONDERLY, WILLIAM LOWER, b. Mt. Lake Park, Md., Mar. 10, 1916. LINGUISTICS. A.B., Bryan Coll., 1936; M.A., Columbia Bible Coll., 1939; Ph. D., U. of Mich., 1948. Translator, Summer Institute of Linguistics (Mexico), 1939–54; instr., Summer Institute of Linguistics, U. of Okla., Summers 1939–54; FIELD ASSOC., AMERICAN BIBLE SOCIETY (CENTRAL AMERICA, MEXICO), 1954– . All-University fellow, Ind. U., 1946–47. Membership: American Anthropological Association; Linguistic Society of America; Society of Biblical Literature. Research: biblical translation in Zoque and in Spanish; Indian languages of Mexico. Author: Zoque: Phonemics and Morphology (International Journal of American Linguistics, July 1951). Language: Spanish 4,4,4,4; Portuguese 3,2,1,1; French 3,1,1,1. Linguistic studies: Quechua; Totonaco; Zoque. Home: Nicolás San Juan 1256, México 12, D.F. Office: Liverpool 65, Apartado Postal 20820, México 6, D.F.

WOOD, BRYCE, b. Everett, Wash., Mar. 13, 1909. POLITICAL SCIENCE. B.A., Reed Coll., 1931; M.A., 1933; Ph. D., Columbia U., 1940. Instr., Columbia U., 1936–42; senior administrative asst., Div. of Political Studies, U.S. Dept. of State, 1942–43; assoc. prof., Swarthmore Coll., 1943–50; asst. dir., Div. of Social Sciences, Rockefeller Foundation, 1947–48; STAFF ASSOC., SOCIAL SCIENCE RESEARCH COUNCIL, 1950– ; vis. prof., Columbia U., 1958–60, 1965; staff, Joint Committee on Latin American Studies, American Council of Learned Societies-Social Science Research Council, 1959–63. Social Science Research Council fellow (Europe), 1935–36; William Bayard Cutting fellow, Columbia U. (Mexico, Argentina, Brazil, Chile), 1939–40; asst. secretary, International Secretariat, United Nations Conference on International Organization, 1945; Board of Editors, International Organization. Membership: American Political Science Association; Conference on Latin American History; Council on Foreign Relations. Research: United States policy in Chaco, Leticia, and Marañón disputes, 1932–1942; civil services in Latin America. Author: Peaceful Change and the Colonial Problem (1940); The Making of the Good Neighbor Policy (1961). Language: Spanish 3,3,3,2; Portuguese 3,2,1,1; French 3,3,3,2; German 2,1,1,1. Home: 4 Putnam Hill, Greenwich, Conn. 06830. Office: Social Science Research Council, 230 Park Ave., New York, N.Y. 10017.

WOOD, JAMES EARL, b. Stanford, Ky., Dec. 14, 1906. ECONOMICS. A.B., U. of the Pacific, 1929; Ph. D., U. of Calif., Berkeley, 1941. Economist, U.S. Government, 1935–41; chief, European Div., Office of International Finance, U.S. Treasury, 1941–54; DIR. OF RESEARCH, PAN AMERICAN COFFEE BUREAU, 1954– . Littauer fellow, Graduate School of Public Administration, Harvard U., 1940–41; consultant, International Coffee Conference (Rio de Janeiro), 1958, Secretariat, International Coffee Agreement (Washington, D.C.), 1958–63, United Nations Coffee Conference, 1962, and International Coffee Organization (London), 1963– . Membership: American Economic Association; Artus. Research: international monetary and exchange problems; currency problems; economic problems of the coffee industry; future world demand for coffee. Author: Coffee in the European Common Market (1960); An Analysis of Coffee Prices, 1953–1963 (1964). Editor and co-author: Annual Coffee Statistics (1954–). Language: Spanish 3,3,3,3; Portuguese 4,4,4,4; French 3,3,3,3. Home: Parsonage Rd., Greenwich, Conn. 06832. Office: Pan-American Coffee Bureau, 120 Wall St., New York, N.Y. 10005.

WOOD, MARIE V., b. Altoona, Pa., Dec. 25, 1921. HISTORY. A.B., Shaw U., 1945; M.A., Howard U., 1946; Ph. D., American U., 1955. Instr., Howard U., 1946–55; research assoc., legislative aide, U.S. Congressman Adam Clayton Powell, House of Representatives, 1955–58; assoc. prof., Del. State Coll., 1958–61; dir., Virgin Islands Teacher Education Project, Hampton Institute and Dept. of Education, Government of V.I., 1961–63; ADMINISTRATIVE ASST. TO PRESIDENT, HAMPTON INSTITUTE, 1964– . John Hay Whitney fellow, Buenos Aires Convention fellow; consultant on Haiti, American Friends Service Committee. Membership: American Historical Association; American Personnel and Guidance Association; Association for Higher Education; College Personnel Association; Conference on Latin American History. Research: the Caribbean; the economic development of Haiti, 1934–53. Language: 2,3, 2,2; French 5,5,4,4; Haitian Creole –,4,4,–. Home: 5206 First St., N.W., Washington, D.C. Office: Hampton Institute, Hampton, Va. 23368.

WOODBURY, NATHALIE FERRIS SAMPSON, b. Humboldt, Ariz., Jan. 25, 1918. ANTHROPOLOGY. A.B., Barnard Coll., 1939; Columbia U., 1939–42. Instr., Brooklyn Coll., 1944–45; dir., Roosevelt County Museum, asst. prof., Eastern New Mexico Coll., 1945–46; instr., U. of Ariz., 1946–47; asst. archeologist, Zaculeu Project, United Fruit Company (Guatemala), 1948–50; instr., U. of Ky., 1951–52; lectr., Barnard Coll., 1952–58; asst. dean, Barnard Coll., 1956–58; RESEARCH ASSOC., ARIZ. STATE MUSEUM, 1959– ; research assoc., Bureau of Ethnic Research, U. of Ariz., 1961–62. Board of Directors, American Ethnological Society; Advisory Board, Barnard Coll., 1959–63. Membership: American Anthropological Association; American Ethnological Society; American Folklore Society; Northern Arizona Society of Science and Art; Society for American Archaeology. Research: ethnology and archeology of the Maya area; Southwest United States ethnology and archeology. Author: History of Zaculeu (in Ruins of Zaculeu, 1953); Societies Around the World (1953); Paperbound Books in Anthropology (Current Anthropology, Oct. 1963). Language: Spanish 3,2,2,1; French 3,1,1,1; German 2,1,2,1. Linguistic studies: Uto-Aztecan (Comanche). Office: Div. of Archeology, U.S. National Museum, Smithsonian Institution, Washington 20025.

WOODBURY, RICHARD BENJAMIN, b. West Lafayette, Ind., May 16, 1917. ANTHROPOLOGY. B.S., Harvard U., 1939; M.A., 1942; Ph. D., 1949. Archeologist, Zaculeu Project, United Fruit Company (Guatemala), 1947–50; assoc. prof., U. of Ky., 1950–52; assoc. prof., Columbia U., 1952–58; assoc. prof., U. of Ariz., 1959–63; ARCHEOLOGIST, SMITHSONIAN INSTITUTION, 1963- . Collaborator, U.S. National Park Service, 1956–57. Membership: American Anthropological Association; American Association for the Advancement of Science; Society for American Archaeology. Research: archeology. Author: Prehistoric Agriculture at Point of Pines, Arizona (1961). Co-author: Societies Around the World (1952); The Ruins of Zaculeu (1953). Language: Spanish 2,2,1, 1. Office: Div. of Archeology, Smithsonian Institution, Washington, D.C. 20025.

WOODS, KENNETH FLINT, b. Randolph, Mass., Oct. 20, 1930. HISTORY. B.S., Ball State Teachers Coll., 1954; M.A., U. of Md., 1959; Ph. D., American U. 1962. Asst. prof., Pa. State Coll., 1960–61; coordinator for Venezuelan Affairs, U.S. Peace Corps, Spring 1962; vis. lectr., Universidad Central del Ecuador, Summer 1962; asst. prof., Old Dominion Coll., 1962–63; ASST. PROF., HISTORY, SAN DIEGO STATE COLL., 1963- . Fellow, Universidad Central del Equador, 1962. Membership: American Historical Association; Conference on Latin American History; Pacific Coast Council on Latin American Studies. Research: problems on inter-American cooperation. Author: Intellectual and Artistic History of Panama (in Handbook of Panama, 1962). Language: Spanish 5,4,4,4; Portuguese 3,2,2,2. Home: 4628 63rd St., San Diego 15, Calif. Office: Dept. of History, San Diego State Coll., San Diego 15.

WOODS, WILLIAM ROBERT, b. Greybull, Wyo., May 6, 1933. LIBRARY SCIENCE. B.A., Claremont Men's Coll., 1955; M.A., Long Beach State Coll., 1957; M.S. in L.S., U. of Southern Calif., 1960. Serials reference librarian, Library, Graduate School of Business Administration, U. of Calif., Los Angeles, 1960–63; LATIN AMERICAN BIBLIOGRAPHER, LIBRARY, U. OF CALIF., LOS ANGELES, 1964- . Assoc. editor, Literature of Executive Management, Special Libraries Association, 1963. Membership: Beta Phi Mu; Special Libraries Association. Research: Latin American history; nineteenth century Mexico and Central America. Language: Spanish 4,3,3,3; Portuguese 2,1,1,1; French 3,1,1,1; German 3,1,1,1. Home: Apt. 2, 638 Kelton Ave., Los Angeles, Calif. 90024. Office: Library, U. of Calif., 405 Hilgard Ave., Los Angeles, 90024.

WOODWARD, RALPH LEE, JR., b. New London, Conn., Dec. 2, 1934. HISTORY. A.B., Central Coll. (Mo.), 1955; M.A., Tulane U., 1959; Ph. D., 1962. Asst. prof., U. of Southwestern La., 1962–63; ASST. PROF., HISTORY, U. OF N.C., 1963- . Doherty fellow (Guatemala), 1960–61. Membership: American Association of University Professors; American Historical Association; Conference on Latin American History; Mississippi Valley Historical Association. Research: Central America; Caribbean; southeastern South America; labor history of Cuba. Author: Octubre: Communist Appeal to the Urban Labor Force of Guatemala, 1950–53 (Journal of Inter-American Studies, July 1962); Political Economy in Guatemala (University of Wichita, Aug. 1962); Communism and Urban Labor: Cuba (Caribbean Studies, Oct. 1963). Language: Spanish 4,4,3,3; Portuguese 4,3,2,1; French 4,2,2,2; German 2,2,1,1; Italian 3,3,1,1; Russian 2,1,1,1. Home: 108 Kenan St., Chapel Hill, N.C. Office: Dept. of History, U. of N.C., Chapel Hill.

WOOLSEY, ARTHUR WALLACE, b. Yoakum, Tex., May 1, 1906. LANGUAGE. B.A., U. of Tex., 1929; M.A., 1930; Ph. D., 1945. Prof., Harding Coll., 1931–33; teacher, Edinburgh High School (Tex.), 1934–41; postal censor, U.S. Office of Censorship (Tex.), 1942–44; PROF., SPANISH, DIR., FOREIGN LANGUAGES, TEX. WOMAN'S U., 1944- . Membership: American Association of Teachers of Spanish and Partuguese; American Association of University Professors; Modern Language Association; Phi Beta Kappa; Phi Sigma Iota; Sigma Delta Pi; Texas Association of College Teachers. Research: Mexican literature and civilization; cultural missions in Mexico. Author: A Course in Mexican Civilization (The Modern Language Journal, Oct. 1952); CREFAL'S Contribution to Rural Community Development (Hispania, Mar. 1963); Cultural Mission No. 53, San Pablo Huixtepec, Oaxaca (The Modern Language Journal, Jan. 1964). Language: Spanish 5,5,5,5; Portuguese 2,2,–,–; French 4,3,3,3. Home: 619 Grove St., Denton, Tex. 76202. Office: Box 3897, Tex. Woman's U., Denton, 76204.

WORCESTER, DONALD EMMET, b. Tempe, Ariz., Apr. 29, 1915. HISTORY. A.B., Bard Coll., 1939; M.A., U. of Calif., Berkeley, 1940; Ph. D., 1947. Asst. prof.-prof., chmn., U. of Fla., 1947–63; PROF., CHMN., HISTORY, TEX. CHRISTIAN U., 1963- . Smith-Mundt vis. prof., U. of Madrid, 1956–57. Membership: American Historical Association; Instituto Paraguayo de Investigaciones Históricas; New Mexico Historical Society; Phi Alpha Theta. Research: independence period in Chile; Brazil. Author: Sea Power and Chilean Independence (1962); The Three Worlds of Latin America (1963). Co-author: The Growth and Culture of Latin America. Language: Spanish 4,4,4,4; Portuguese 3,3,3,3; French 2,2,2,2. Home: 5800 Wedgeworth Rd., Ft. Worth, Tex. 76133. Office: Dept. of History, Tex. Christian U., Ft. Worth, 76129.

WORRELL, ALBERT CADWALLADER, b. Philadelphia, Pa., May 14, 1913. ECONOMICS AND FORESTRY. B.S.F., U. or Mich.,

1935; M.F., 1935; Ph. D., 1953. Assoc. prof., U. of Ga., 1947–55; forest economist, United Nations Economic Committee for Latin America (Santiago, Chile), 1960–61; vis. prof., United Nations Special Fund Projects (Argentina, Brazil), Summer 1963; PROF., FOREST ECONOMICS, YALE U., 1955– . Chmn., Div. of Forest Economics and Policy, Society of American Foresters, 1956; chmn. of committee on national forest timber appraisal policies and procedures, 1963. Membership: American Economic Association; American Forestry Association; Society of American Foresters. Research: forest economics; forest policy; forest resources of Argentina, Brazil and Chile. Author: Economics of American Forestry (1959); Latin American Timber Trends and Prospects (1962); Pests, Pesticides, and People (American Forests, July 1960). Language: Spanish 4,4,4,3; Portuguese 3,3,3,3; French 3,1,1,1; German 3,1,1,1. Home: 81 Hilltop Rd., Cheshire, Conn. Office: School of Forestry, Yale U., 360 Prospect St., New Haven, Conn. 06511.

WRIGHT, ALMON ROBERT, b. Roseville, Ohio, July 23, 1903. HISTORY. Ph. D., Denison U., 1926; A.M., Harvard U., 1928; Ph. D., U. of Ill., 1935. Instr., State U. of Mont., 1928–31; asst. Div. of Classification, U.S. National Archives, 1935–41; asst. chief, 1941–47; chief, Div. of State Dept. of Archives, U.S. National Archives, 1947–49; historian, Historical Office, U.S. Dept. of State, 1949–58; SENIOR HISTORIAN, HISTORICAL OFFICE, U.S. DEPT. OF STATE, 1958– . Membership: American Historical Association; Society of American Archivist. Research: United States foreign policy; Panama-United States relations. Author: German Interest in Panama's Piñas Bay, 1910–1938 (Journal of Modern History, Mar. 1955); Defense Sites Negotiations Between the United States and Panama, 1930–48 (U.S. Dept. of State Bulletin, Aug. 1952). Compiler and editor: Foreign Relations: American Republic, 1940–42 (1961–). Language: Spanish 3,-,-,-; French 3,-,-,-. Home: 3901 North Upland St., Arlington, Va. Office: Historical Office, U.S. Dept. of State, Washington, D.C.

WRIGHT, FREEMAN J., b. Bozeman, Mont., Jan. 22, 1935. POLITICAL SCIENCE. B.S., Mont. State Coll., 1955; M.S., 1960; Ph. D., Johns Hopkins U., 1964. ASST. PROF. POLITICAL SCIENCE, FRESNO STATE COLL., 1963– . Organization of American States fellow (Chile), 1962; research consultant for Dr. Milton S. Eisenhower in preparation of his book, The Wine Is Bitter, 1962–63. Membership: American Political Science Association; American Society of Public Administration; Western Political Science Association. Research: parliamentary government in Chile, 1891–1924; public administration practices in Mexico. Language: Spanish 4,4,4,4. Home: 4722 East Fedora, Fresno, Calif. 93726. Office: Dept. of Political Science, Fresno State Coll., Maple and Shaw, Fresno, 93726.

WRIGHT, HARRY KEISLER, b. Houston, Tex., Sept. 20, 1928. LAW. B.S., Georgetown U., 1949; LL.B., U. of Tex., 1952. Attorney, Baker, Botts & Miranda (Mexico), 1954–57; attorney, Baker, Botts, Shepherd & Coates (Houston), 1957–62; ASSOC. PROF., LAW, SCHOOL OF LAW, U. OF TEX. 1962– . American Society of International Law fellow, 1963–64. Membership: American Bar Association; American Society of International Law; Inter-American Bar Association; State Bar of Texas. Research: private investment and trade in Latin America; Latin American commercial law; legal environment for foreign investment in Mexico. Language: Spanish 4,4,-4,4; Portuguese 2,2,2,2; French 1,1,1,1 Office: School of Law, U. of Tex., 2500 Red River, Austin, 78705.

WRIGHT, IONE STUESSY, b. La Grange, Ill., Mar. 12, 1905. HISTORY, B.A., U. of Richmond, 1926; M.A., U. of Calif., Berkeley, 1937; Ph. D., 1940. Lectr.-PROF., HISTORY, U. OF MIAMI, 1946– . Editor, Journal of Inter-American Studies, 1964– . Membership: American Association of University Professors; American Historical Association; Conference on Latin American History; Historical Association of South Florida; Southeastern Conference on Latin American Studies; Southern Historical Association. Research: 16th century Spanish American history; period of the wars of independence. Author: Voyages of Álvaro de Saavedra Cerón, 1527–1529 (1951); Early Spanish Voyages from America to the Far East, 1527–65 (in Greater America: Essays in Honor of Herbert Eugene Bolton, 1945); Factors Affecting Popular Self-government in the Caribbean (in The Caribbean: Its Political Problems, 1956). Language: Spanish 4,3,3,3; Portuguese 2,1,1,1; French 2,1,1,1. Home: 485 NE. 94th St., Miami, Fla. 33138. Office: Dept. of History, U. of Miami, Coral Gables, Fla. 33138.

WRIGHT, JAMES LEITCH, JR., b. Ashland, Va., Aug. 9, 1929. HISTORY. B.S., Va. Military Institute, 1950; M.A., U. of Va., 1956; Ph. D., 1958. Asst. prof., Va. Military Institute, 1958–61; PROF., HISTORY, RANDOLPH–MACON COLL., 1961– . American Philosophical Society and University Center in Va. grants (Mexico, England, and Spain). Membership: American Association of University Professors; American Historical Association; Southern Historical Association. Research: Anglo-Spanish rivalry in North America. Author: Sixteenth Century English-Spanish Rivalry in La Florida (Florida Historical Quarterly, April 1960); Andrew Ranson, 17th Century Pirate (Florida Historical Quarterly, Oct. 1960). Language: Spanish 4,3,3,3; French 3,-,-,-; German 2,-,-,-. Home: Rt. 1 (Gwathmey), Ashland, Va. Office: Dept. of History, Randolph-Macon Coll., Ashland.

WRIGHT, WINTHROP ROBINS, b. Philadelphia, Pa., Mar. 31, 1936. HISTORY. B.A., Swarthmore Coll., 1958; M.A., U. of Pa., 1960; Ph. D., 1964. ASST. PROF., HISTORY, BIRMINGHAM-SOUTHERN COLL., 1963– . Rockefeller Foundation grant (Argentina), 1960–62. Membership: American Association of University Professors; American Historical Association; Conference on Latin American History. Research: 19th century Argentina; political and economic history of the Río de la Plata area; Argentine nationalism. Language: Spanish 4,4,4,4; Portuguese 3,2,1,1; French 3,2,1,1. Home: 812–A 12th St. West, Birmingham 4, Ala. Office: Dept. of History, Birmingham-Southern Coll., Birmingham 4.

WYATT, JAMES L., b. Enid, Okla., Mar. 7, 1923. LINGUISTICS. B.A., U. of Tex., 1944; Master, National U. of Mexico, 1948; Doctor, 1950; Ph. D., U. of Tex., 1965. Staff correspondent, United Press International (Mexico, D.F.), 1944–47; instr., asst. prof., Arlington State Coll., 1947–51; asst. cultural officer, Embassy (Brazil), U.S. Dept. of State, 1951–53; coordinator of div., Latin American Relations, La. State U., 1953–57; HEAD, FOREIGN LANGUAGES, ARLINGTON STATE COLL., 1957– . U.S. Dept. of State fellow, 1949–50; National Defense fellow, U. of Tex., 1961–62, U. of Wash., Summer 1962. Membership: American Association of Teachers of Spanish and Portuguese; Linguistic Society of America; Modern Language Association; National Association of Foreign Student Advisers. Research: descriptive linguistics; Portuguese; linguistic programming for IBM computers; foreign language teaching, materials, and laboratory operation. Language: Spanish 4,4,4,4; Portuguese 4,4,3,3; French 4,3,3,3. Linguistic studies: Portuguese. Home: 1908 West Second Ave., Arlington, Tex. 76010. Office: Dept. of Foreign Languages, Arlington State Coll., Arlington.

WYCKOFF, THEODORE, b. New York, N.Y., Feb. 24, 1922. POLITICAL SCIENCE. B.A., U. of Calif., Los Angeles, 1942; M.P.A., M.A., Princeton U., 1957. Artillery officer, U.S. Army, Dept. of the Antilles (San Juan, P.R.), 1943–45; artillery adviser, Joint Brazil-United States Military Commission, Ministry of War (Rio de Janeiro), 1946–49; chief, intelligence branch office, chief of special warfare, Dept. of the Army, 1957–58; lectr., U. of Md., 1958–60; chief, World War II Histories Branch, Office of Chief of Military History, Dept. of the Army, 1958–60; battalion commander, logistics officer, Eighth U.S. Army (Korea), 1960–61; prof., Ariz. State U., 1961–64; LT. COL., OPERATIONS, MILITARY ASSISTANCE ADVISORY GROUP, U.S. EMBASSY (BONN, GERMANY), 1964– . Membership: American Political Science Association; Phi Beta Kappa; Pi Sigma Alpha. Research: political parties and public opinion; comparative governments of Latin America; military science and history. Author: The Role of the Military in Latin American Politics (Western Political Quarterly, Sept. 1960). Editor: The Defense of Latin America: The Changing Concept (1964). Contributor: The Dictionary of Political Science (1964). Language: Spanish 5,4,5,5; Portuguese 5,4,5,5; French 4,3,4,4; German 3,3,3,3; Italian 2,2,2,2; Russian 2,2,2,2. Home: 124 Bonita Way, Tempe, Ariz. Office: U.S. Embassy, Bonn, Germany.

WYTHE, GEORGE, b. Weatherford, Tex., Aug. 29, 1893. ECONOMICS. B.A., U. of Tex., 1914; Ph. D., George Washington U., 1938. Dir., American Republics Div., U.S. Dept. of Commerce, 1920–60; commercial attaché, Embassy (Mexico), U.S. Dept. of State, 1925–31; professorial lectr., George Washington U., 1953–60; RETIRED, 1960– . Consultant, Journal of Inter-American Studies; contributing editor, Handbook of Latin American Studies; Advisory Board, Handbook of Latin American Studies. Membership: American Economic Association; American Geographical Society; Conference on Latin American History; Economic History Association; Royal Economic Society. Research: economic development. Author: Industry in Latin America (1945, 1949); Brazil: An Expanding Economy (1949); The United States and Inter-American Relations (1964). Language: Spanish 4,4,4,3; Portuguese 4,3,2,1; French 4,4,4,3. Home: 3042 Cambridge Pl., NW., Washington 7, D.C.

Y

YATES, DONALD ALFRED, b. Ayer, Mass., Apr. 11, 1930. SPANISH AMERICAN LITERATURE AND LANGUAGE. B.A., U. of Mich., 1951; M.A., 1954; Ph. D., 1961. ASST. PROF., SPANISH, MICH. STATE U., 1957– . Horace Rackham fellow, U. of Mich., 1956–57; Fulbright grant (Argentina), 1962–63; general editor, MacMillan Modern Spanish American Literature Series. Membership: American Association of Teachers of Spanish and Portuguese; Instituto Internacional de Literatura Iberoamericana; Modern Language Association. Research: Argentine literature, particularly the detective story; Spanish American literature of imagination and fantasy. Author: Imaginación y fantasía (1960). Translator: Rosa at Ten O'Clock, by Marco Denevi 1964). Co-editor and translator: Labyrinths, by Jorge Luis Borges (1962). Language: Spanish 5,5,5,5; Portuguese 3,3,3,3; French 5,5,5,5. Home: 115 South River St., Eaton Rapids, Mich. Office: Dept. of Spanish, Mich. State U., East Lansing.

YOUNG, FRANK W., b. Chicago, Ill., May 31, 1928. SOCIOLOGY. B.A., U. of Wash., 1950; M.A., Cornell U., 1954; Ph. D., 1957. Asst. prof., San Diego State Coll., 1958–61; asst. prof., U. of Pittsburgh, 1961–62; ASSOC. PROF., RURAL SOCIOLOGY, CORNELL U., 1962– . Social Science Research Council grant-in-aid, 1961. Membership: American Anthropological Association; American Sociological Society; Rural Sociological Society; Society for Applied Anthropology. Research: anthropology; sociological development in Mexico. Author: Initiation Ceremonies (1964); Toward a Theory of Community Development (in Social Problems of Development and Urbanization, 1963). Language: Spanish 3,3,2,2. Home: 106 College Ave., Ithaca, N.Y. Office: Dept. of Rural Sociology, Cornell U., Ithaca.

YOUNG, JORDAN MARTEN, b. New York, N.Y., Sept. 25, 1920. HISTORY. B.A., U. of Calif., Berkeley, 1946; M.A., 1947; Ph. D., Princeton U., 1953. Public health work (Brazil), Coordinator of Inter-American Affairs, 1942–44; instr., Princeton U., 1950–53; trainee, Interamericana Investment Banking (Rio, Brazil), 1953–55; general manager, Industrias Consolidadas (Venezuela), 1955–56; ASSOC. PROF., SOCIAL SCIENCE, PACE COLL., 1956– ; vis. assoc., N.Y.U., 1959– . Doherty fellow (Chile), 1947–48; U.S. Office of Education fellow (Brazil), 1949. Membership: American Historical Association; American Political Science Association; Latin American Historians Association; Pan American Society of New York. Research: contemporary political affairs and history of Chile and Brazil; revolutions of 1930 and 1932 in Brazil. Author: The Brazilian Congressional Elections (Journal of Inter-American Studies, Jan. 1963). Language: Spanish 4,4,4,2; Portuguese 5,5,5,3. Home: 159

Meadowbrook Dr., Princeton, N.J. Office: Dept. of Social Science, Pace Coll., 41 Park Row, New York 38, N.Y.

Z

ZARATE, ALVAN O'NEILL, b. New London, Conn., Oct. 13, 1936. SOCIOLOGY. B.A., U. of Conn., 1958; M.A., 1960; Ph. D., Brown U., Aug. 1965. Research asst., U. of Conn., 1958–60; research asst., Brown U., 1960–62; ASST. PROF., SOCIOLOGY, RESEARCH ASSOC., POPULATION RESEARCH CENTER, U. OF TEX., 1964– . University fellow, Brown U., 1962–63; Population Council fellow (Mexico), 1963–64. Membership: American Sociological Association; Eastern Sociological Association; Population Association of America. Research: population; urbanization, industrialization, and fertility in Mexico. Language: Spanish 4,3,3,3; French 3,1,1,2. Office: Population Research Center, Dept. of Sociology, U. of Tex., 217 Archway, Austin 5, Tex.

ZELINSKY, WILBUR, b. Chicago, Ill., Dec. 21, 1921. GEOGRAPHY. B.A., U. of Calif., Berkeley, 1944; M.A., U. of Wis., 1946; Ph. D., U. of Calif., Berkeley, 1953. Asst. prof., U. of Ga., 1948–54; research assoc., U. of Wis., 1952–54; industrial analyst, Chesapeake and Ohio Railway Company, 1954–59; prof., Southern Ill. U., 1959–63; PROF. GEOGRAPHY, PA. STATE U., 1963– . Membership: American Geographical Society; American Name Society; Association of American Geographers; Population Association of America. Research: cultural geography; cartography; population geography of Central America, West Indies, and the Guianas. Author: A Bibliographic Guide to Population Geography (1962); The Historical Geography of the Negro Population of Latin America (Journal of Negro History, Apr. 1949); Rural Population Dynamics as an Index to Social and Economic Development: A Geographic Overview (Sociological Quarterly, Spring 1963). Language: Spanish 3,2,1,1; Portuguese 2,1,1,1; French 3,2,1,1; German 3,2,1,1; Russian 2,1,1,1. Home: 467 Martin Ter., State College, Pa. 16801. Office: Dept. of Geography, Pa. State U., University Park, 16802.

ZIMDARS, BENJAMIN FRANK, b. Whitehall, Wis., May 20, 1927. HISTORY. B.A., North Central Coll., 1952; M.A., U. of Wis., 1954; Ph. D., U. of Tex., 1965. Teaching asst., U. of Tex., 1956–58; ASST. PROF., HISTORY, MARY WASHINGTON COLL. OF THE U. OF VA., 1965– . Southern fellow, 1959–60. Membership: American Historical Association; Conference on Latin American History. Research: colonial Latin American historiography; colonial social, economic, and intellectual history of Peru; independence period of Mexico. Language: Spanish 4,3,3,2; Portuguese 1,1,1,1; French 3,2,2,1; German 3,3,2,2. Home: 1712–E Rio Grande, Austin, Tex. 78701. Office: Dept. of History, Mary Washington Coll. of the U. of Va., Fredericksburg, Va.

ZIMMERMAN, IRENE, b. Idana, Kans., Feb. 23, 1907. LIBRARY SCIENCE: BIBLIOGRAPHY. B.A., Coll. of Emporia, 1927; M.A., U. of Chicago, 1937; M.A., Columbia U., 1938; M.A. in L.S., U. of Mich., 1951; Ph D., 1956. Librarian, teacher, Ray High School (Ariz.), 1928–37; asst. principal, 1934–37; teacher, Columbia High School (South Orange, N.J.), 1938–39; teacher, Lewis and Clark High School (Spokane, Wash.), 1939–41; teacher, Teaneck High School (N.J.), 1941–43; instr., Spanish and History, Colby Jr. Coll. for Women, 1943–48; asst. prof., Spanish, Bucknell U., 1948–50; ASSOC. LIBRARIAN, LATIN AMERICAN SPECIALIST, REFERENCE AND BIBLIOGRAPHY, LIBRARY, U. OF FLA., 1951– . Acquisitions program participant, Rockefeller grant to U. of Fla. (Cuba, Haiti, Dominican Republic, P.R.), 1956, 1959, 1962; chmn., Subcommittee on Caribbean Acquisitions, Seminars on the Acquisitions of Latin American Library Materials, 1959–63; chmn., Bibliography Committee, 1963– ; Executive Board, Association of College and Research Libraries, 1960–63; consultant, Micro-Photo Div., Bell and Howell. Membership: American Association of Teachers of Spanish and Portuguese; American Association of University Professors; Inter-American Bibliographical and Library Association; Southeast Latin American Association; Southeast Library Association. Research: use of Latin American periodicals as research material; selection, nature, and history of most frequently cited titles, especially Caribbean materials. Author: A Guide to Current Latin American Periodicals: Humanities and Social Sciences (1961); Language Occupations: The Foreign Service (Modern Language Journal, Apr. 1950); Central America: Bibliography, Indexes, Guides (in The Caribbean: The Central American Area, 1961). Language: Spanish 4,3,3,4; Portuguese 2,2,1,1; French 3,2,2,2. Home: 710 NE. Third Ave., Gainesville, Fla. Office: Library, U. of Fla., Gainesville.

ZOOK, DAVID HARTZLER, Jr., b. Bellefontaine, Ohio, Jan. 22, 1930. HISTORY. A.B., Wittenberg U., 1950; M.A., Ohio State U., 1955; Ph. D., 1959; Universidad Nacional Mayor de San Marcos (Peru), 1960. Assoc. prof., U.S. Air Force Academy, 1959–63; INTELLIGENCE OFFICER, U.S. AIR FORCE, 1963– ; assoc. professorial lectr., U. of Md., 1964; professorial lectr., 1965– . Membership: American Historical Association; American Military Institute; Conference on Latin American History. Research: South American military and diplomatic history; west coast South America, Bolivia, and Paraguay. Author: The Conduct of the Chaco War (1960; Spanish edition, 1962); Zarumilla-Marañón: The Ecuador-Peru Dispute (1964); U.S. Military Assistance to Latin America (Air University Review, Sept.-Oct. 1963). Language: Spanish 4,3,3,1; Portuguese 2,2,1,1; French 2,1,1,1. Home: R.F.D. 2, West Liberty, Ohio. Office: 1007th A.I.S.G., U.S. Air Force, Washington 25, D.C.

ZYMELMAN, MANUEL, b. Poland, Jan. 28, 1930. ECONOMICS. M.S., Mass. Institute of Technology, 1956; Ph. D., 1958. Research assoc., Center for International Studies, Mass. Institute of Technology, 1958–59; ASSOC. PROF., ECONOMICS, NORTHEASTERN U., 1959– . Vis. lectr., Universidad del Litoral (Argentina), Summer 1960; vis. lectr., Universidad de Córdoba (Argentina), Summer 1961; consultant, Instituto Torcuato Di Tella

(Buenos Aires), Summer 1961; consultant, Arthur D. Little, Inc., 1961–63. Membership: American Economic Association. Research: manpower planning and development; economic history of Argentina. Author: Cultant Patterns of Labor and Their Significance for Latin America (Review of Interamerican Studies, July 1963). Co-author: Historia del desarrollo económico argentino (1964); Desarrollo de espacios abiertos (El Trimestre Económico, Oct. 1962). Language: Spanish 5,5,5,5; Portuguese 3,3,2,2; French 2,2,2,2. Home: 20 Hope St., Auburndale, Mass. 02166. Office: Dept. of Economics, Northeastern U., Boston 15, Mass.

INDEX OF SUBJECT SPECIALTIES

Index to Subject Specialties

ANTHROPOLOGY

Adams, Richard Edward Wood
Adams, Richard Newbold
Alegria, Ricardo E.
Altschuler, Milton
Anderson, Arthur James Outram
Andrews, David Henry
Andrews, Edward Wyllys, IV
Armillas, Pedro
Baerreis, David A.
Baker, Paul T.
Bartell, Gilbert Duke
Bascom, William (Russel)
Beals, Ralph L(eon)
Bell, Betty Bonita
Bell, Robert E.
Biesanz, John Berry
Bird, Junius Bouton
Boggs, Stanley Harding
Borhegyi, Stephan Francis de
Bourguignon, Erika Eichhorn
Bradley, Charles Henry
Bram, Joseph
Broadbent, Sylvia Marguerite
Bryan, Alan Lyle
Bullard, William R., Jr.
Bullen, Ripley Pierce
Bushnell, John Hempstead
Byers, Douglas Swain
Calkin, Carleton Ivers
Calnek, Edward Eugene
Cancian, Frank A.
Carneiro, Robert L(eonard)
Carr, Robert Franklin
Carrasco, Pedro
Carré, Shirley Deshon
Carter, William Earl
Casagrande, Joseph Bartholomew
Champion, J. Rene
Chowning, Ann
Cline, Howard Francis
Coe, Michael Douglas
Colby, Benjamin N.
Collier, Donald
Comitas, Lambros
Compton, Carl Benton
Cook, Sherburne F.
Cook, Warren L.
Corbett, John Maxwell
Cowgill, George Lewis
Crocker, William Henry
Culbert, T. Patrick
Diaz, May Nordquist
Dibble, Charles Elliot
Diebold, Albert Richard, Jr.
Diggs, Irene
Di Peso, Charles Gorradino
Dixon, Keith Alan
Dobyns, Henry Farmer
Dockstader, Frederick J.
Dole, Gertrude Evelyn
Doughty, Paul L.
Driver, Harold Edson
Dumond, Don Edward
Dutton, Bertha P(auline)
Easby, Dudley T., Jr.
Edmonson, Munro Sterling
Ekholm, Gordon F.
Epstein, Jeremiah F.
Erasmus, Charles John
Evans, Clifford
Ewald, Robert Harold
Ezell, Paul Howard
Faron, Louis C.
Fay, George Emory
Ferdon, Edwin Nelson, Jr.
Ferguson, Thomas Stuart
Fernández-Méndez, Eugenio
Firestone, Homer Leon
Forbes, Jack Douglas
Foster, George McClelland, Jr.
Fried, Jacob
Friedrich, Paul W.
Fuson, Robert Henderson
Gayton, Anna Hadwick
Gillin, John Phillip
Gillmor, Frances
Godfrey, William Simpson, Jr.
Goins, John F.
Golde, Peggy Jean
Goldkind, Victor
González, Nancie L. Solien de
Gorenstein, Shirley Slotkin
Graham, John Allen
Greenfield, Sidney Martin
Griffin, James Bennett
Grollig, Francis Xavier, S.J.
Hahn, Paul G.
Hale, Kenneth Locke
Hammel, Eugene Alfred
Harner, Michael James
Harris, Marvin
Harvey, Herbert R.
Harwood, Ruth
Haury, Emil W.
Heath, Dwight B.
Hermitte, Maria Esther A. de
Hewes, Gordon Winant
Hibben, Frank Cummings
Hickman, John Marshall
Hilger, Mary Inez, O.S.B.
Hinton, Thomas Benjamin
Hoffman, Hans
Hohenthal, William Dalton, Jr.
Holmberg, Allan R.
Hotchkiss, John C.
Hurt, Wesley Robert
Hutchinson, Harry William
Irwin-Williams, Cynthia Cora
Kahl, Joseph A.
Kaplan, Bernice Antoville
Kelley, David Humiston
Kelly, William Henderson
Kenny, Michael
Kensinger, Kenneth M.
Key, Harold Hayden
King, Arden Ross

King, Mary Elizabeth
Krieger, Alex Dony
La Barre, Weston
Ladd, John
Landes, Ruth
Landy, David
Lanning, Edward Putnam
Lasker, Gabriel Ward
Laughlin, Robert Moody
Leacock, Seth
Leeds, Anthony
Leonard, Olen E.
Leslie, Charles M.
Lewis, Oscar
Leyburn, James Graham
Linares de Sapir, Olga
Longyear, John Munro, III
Lothrop, Samuel Kirkland
Lounsbury, Floyd Glenn
McCorkle, (Homer) Thomas, Jr.
McGimsey, Charles Robert, III
McKern, Thomas Wilton
MacNeish, Richard Stockton
McQuown, Norman Anthony
Maday, Bela Charles
Madsen, William
Mangin, William
Manners, Robert Alan
Mason, J(ohn) Alden
Massey, William Clifford
Maxwell, Thomas James
Maybury-Lewis, David H. P.
Mayers, Marvin Keene
Maynard, Eileen A.
Meggers, Betty J.
Meighan, Clement Woodward
Menzel, Dorothy
Metraux, Rhoda
Metzger, Duane Gerald
Miles, Suzanne Whitelaw
Miller, Frank C.
Mintz, Sidney Wilfred
Moore, Sally Falk
Munroe, Robert L.
Murra, John Victor
Nader, Laura
Nash, June C.
Nash, Manning
Nesbitt, Paul H.
Newman, Marshall Thornton
Nicholson, Henry B.
Nida, Eugene Albert
Núñez, Benjamin
Nunez, Theron Aldine, Jr.
Nutini, Hugo G.
Oberg, Kalervo
Officer, James E.
Olmsted, David L.
O'Neill, George Caracena
Osborne, Carolyn M.
Owen, Roger Cory
Padilla, Elena
Parsons, Lee Allen
Patch, Richard W.
Patterson, Thomas Carl
Paul, Benjamin D.
Peñalosa, Fernando
Pendergast, David Michael
Peterson, Fredrick Alvin
Pi-Sunyer, Oriol
Pollock, Harry E. D.
Proskouriakoff, Tatiana
Rands, Robert Lawrence
Ravicz, Robert S.
Reed, Erik Kellerman
Reina, Ruben E.
Riley, Carroll Laverne
Romney, Antone Kimball

Root, William Campbell
Rouse, Irving
Rowe, John Howland
Rubel, Arthur J.
Rubin, Joan
Safa, Helen Icken
Saler, Benson
Salz, Beate R.
Sanders, William Timothy
Satterthwaite, Linton
Sawyer, Alan Reed
Sayers, William Cortlandt
Schaedel, Richard Paul
Schwartz, Lola Romanucci
Schwartz, Theodore
Seda-Bonilla, E(dwin)
Service, Elman Rogers
Shook, Edwin Martin
Siegel, Bernard Joseph
Simmons, Ozzie Gordon
Simpson, George Eaton
Sleight, Frederick Winfield
Smith, Hale Gilliam
Smith, Robert Eliot
Smith, Robert Jack
Sobrino, Josephine
Sorenson, John Leon
Spicer, Edward H.
Spores, Ronald Marvin
Stein, William W.
Stewart, Thomas Dale
Stirling, Matthew W.
Stone Zemurray, Doris
Strickon, Arnold
Tax, Sol
Taylor, Robert Bartley
Taylor, Walter Willard
Thompson, Donald Enrique
Thompson, J(ohn) Eric S(idney)
Thompson, Raymond Harris
Titiev, Mischa
Tolstoy, Paul
Troike, Rudolph Charles
Turner, Glen David
Underwood, Frances Wenrich
Vázquez, Mario Carlos
Vescelius, Gary Stockton
Vidich, Arthur J.
Vogt, Evon Zartman
Von Winning, Hasso Leopold
Wagley, Charles
Wallace, Dwight T(ousch)
Warren, Bruce William
Watson, James Bennet
Wauchope, Robert
Weaver, Muriel Porter
Weiant, Clarence Wolsey
Whiteford, Andrew Hunter
Whitten, Norman Earl, Jr.
Wicke, Charles Robinson
Wilbert, Johannes
Willems, Emilio
Willey, Gordon R.
Williams, Aubrey Willis, Jr.
Williams, Gerald Eugene
Winters, Howard Dalton
Wolf, Eric Robert
Woodbury, Nathalie Ferris Sampson
Woodbury, Richard Benjamin

ARCHITECTURE

Baird, Joseph Armstrong, Jr.
Bunting, Bainbridge
Carr, Robert Franklin, II
Connally, Ernest Allen
DuMoulin, Rockwell King
Harris, Walter DeSalles

Kubler, George Alexander
McAndrew, John
Markman, Sidney David
Ross, Marion Dean
Wethey, Harold Edwin

ART

Baird, Joseph Armstrong, Jr.
Bunting, Bainbridge
Calkin, Carleton Ivers
Castedo, Leopoldo
Compton, Carl Benton
Constantine, Mildred
Deinhard, Hanna
Gómez Sicre, José R.
Grieder, (Ronald) Terence
Haas, Lez Lewis
Holbrook, Hollis Howard
Kelemen, Pál
Kiser, J(esse) Dorrance
Kubler, George Alexander
Lynch, James B., Jr.
McAndrew, John
Markman, Sidney David
Mendelowitz, Daniel M.
Mozley, Loren N.
Neumeyer, Alfred
Proskouriakoff, Tatiana
Quinn, Robert MacLean
Robertson, Donald
Ross, Marion Dean
Sawyer, Alan Reed
Schmeckebier, Laurence
Smith, Robert Chester
Trank, Lynn Edgar
Uribe, Joseph Garcia
Van Stan, Ina
Waterman, Donald Calvin
Wethey, Harold Edwin

CITY AND REGIONAL PLANNING

Alten, Ivan John
Friedmann, John R. P.
Gakenheimer, Ralph A.
Guernsey, James Lee
Harris, Walter DeSalles
Mann, Lawrence Dale
Parker, John Albert
Reich, Larry
Solow, Anatole Abraham

COMMUNICATION

Alisky, Marvin Howard
Carter, Roy Ernest, Jr.
Ely, Donald Paul
Herzog, William A., Jr.
Lassey, William Raymond
McNelly, John Taylor
Myren, Delbert Theodore
Nevins, Albert J., M. M.
Rogers, Everett M.
Uribe, Joseph Garcia

ECONOMICS

Abraham, William I.
Abrahams, Allen E.
Adler, John H.
Alexander, Robert J.
Allen, Robert Loring
Alter, Gerald Milton
Anderson, Dole A.
Andic, Fuat M.
Arellano, Richard Gibbs
Ashby, Joe C.

Austin, Ruben Vargas
Averitt, Robert Tabor
Bachmura, Frank Thomas
Baer, Werner
Bakalanoff, Eric Nicolas
Baquero, José Antonio
Baranson, Jack
Barraclough, Solon Lovett
Bear, Donald Van Twisk
Behrman, Jack Newton
Bell, John Fred
Belshaw, Michael
Beneke, Raymond R.
Bennett, Robert L.
Benninger, Lawrence J.
Berg, Sherwood Olman
Berle, Adolf Augustus
Berman, Barbara R.
Bernstein, Edward Morris
Berry, R. Albert
Blair, Calvin Patton
Blitz, Rudolph C.
Bohan, Merwin L(ee)
Borton, Raymond Eugene
Bothwell, Lyman Dutton
Bradsher, Julian Hill
Brandenburg, Frank R.
Branson, Robert Earl
Brothers, Dwight Stanley
Brown, William Francis
Brownlee, Oswald Harvey
Cameron, Rondo
Canet, Gerardo Alvarez
Cardenas, Leonard, Jr.
Carnes, Hugh Byron
Clark, Ronald James
Clement, Meredith Owen
Cochrane, James David
Cohen, Alvin
Cole, William Edward
Collado, Emilio Gabriel
Cook, Arthur J. D.
Cook, Hugh Lincoln
Cornehls, James Vernon
Costanzo, G. A.
Craven, J. Howard
Crim, Ed Franklin, Jr.
Dabasi-Schweng, Lorand
Danco, Léon Antoine
Daniels, Marion Gordon
Davis, Tom Edward
Davis, William Carlton
De Beers, John Sterling
De Capriles, Miguel (Angel)
DeForest, John Duane
Delaplane, Walter Harold
Delwart, Louis Oliver
Dembitz, Lewis N.
De Rosso, Alphonse
Diaz-Rojas, Armando
Domike, Arthur L., Jr.
Dorner, Peter Paul
Dukes, James Henderson
Dye, Howard Spencer
Dyer, John Martin
Edds, John R., Jr.
Eder, George Jackson
Edminister, Robert Regan
Ellis, Howard S.
Ellsworth, Paul Theodore
Ely, Roland Taylor
Ericson, Anna-Stina Louise
Favell, Thomas Royden
Feder, Ernest
Felix, David
Fetter, Frank Whitson
Feuerlein, Willy J.

Fitchett, Delbert Arthur
Flammang, Robert Arthur
Flumiani, Carlo M.
Frankenhoff, Charles Anthony
Freebairn, Donald K.
Friedmann, John R. P.
Frikart, John M.
Fullmer, Robert G.
Gans, Altha Robert
Garbuny, Siegfried
Gillim, Marion Hamilton
Glade, William P., Jr.
Glick, Milton Louis
Goering, Theodore James
Gomez, Michael Albert
Gordon, Lincoln
Gordon, Wendell C.
Green, James Leroy
Gregory, Gustav Robinson
Gregory, Peter
Grossman, William Leonard
Grunwald, Joseph
Gwin, James Martin
Haag, Herman Martin
Haberstroh, Chadwick John
Hagen, Everett Einar
Hamilton, Earl J.
Hanson, Simon Gabriel
Harberger, Arnold C.
Harrington, David N.
Harston, Clive Richards
Hattwick, Richard E.
Hayn, Rolf
Hein, John
Heller, Jack I.
Henning, Dale A.
Hernández, Martín
Herrick, Bruce Hale
Hildebrand, John Raymond
Hillman, Jimmye Standard
Hirschman, Albert O.
Hoecker, Raymond W.
Hoffman, H. Theodore
Homan, A. Gerlof
Hopkins, John Abel
Horowitz, Morris A.
Hoselitz, Bert Frank
Howell, Herbert B.
Howell, James Melton
Hoyt, Edward Lydig
Hoyt, Elizabeth Ellis
Hunt, Shane John
Hunter, John M.
Kafka, Alexandre
Kagan, Sioma
Kalb, Klaus
Kalmanoff, George
Kanel, Don
Katz, Saul Milton
Keepper, Wendell Edgar
Keller, Frank L.
Kolmer, Lee R.
Komarek, Viola Wyckoff
Kraessel, Alfred
Krause, Walter
Kutish, Francis A.
Kyle, Leonard R.
LaBarge, Richard Allen
Lassey, William Raymond
Lauterbach, Albert
Lewis, Darrell Richard
Lloyd-Jones, Donald J.
Lockley, Lawrence Campbell
Locklin, (David) Philip
McGreeve, William Paul
McNeely, John Gordon
McPherson, Woodrow Wilson

Maddox, James Gray
Maddox, James Robert
Magurn, Joseph John
Mandell, Stuart Lester
Mandelstamm, Allan Beryle
Mansfield, Charles Yarrow
Maritano, Nino
Masson, Francis George
May, Phillip Allan
Mayne, Alvin
Meek, Howard Bagnall
Mestre, José A.
Miles, James Franklin
Mitchell, C. Clyde, Jr.
Monsen, Raymond Joseph, Jr.
Montavon, Paul A.
Moore, Frederick T.
Moore, O. Ernest
Morgner, Aurelius
Morris, James Oliver
Mudie, John Howard
Munn, Henry Lusk
Nekvasil, Edward M.
Nelson, Eastin
Nelson, Michael
Nelson, Paul
Newcomer, Hale Alden
Nicholls, William Hord
Nowotny, Franz A.
O'Connor, James R.
Oldman, Oliver
Olson, Ernest Charles
Otte, Robert Charles
Pauling, Norman George
Pazos, Felipe
Pelissier, Raymond Francis
Penn, Raymond L.
Phillips, Joseph D.
Picó, Rafael
Pincus, Joseph
Poleman, Thomas T.
Pollock, David Harold
Post, Albert
Powelson, John Palen
Prescott, James Russell
Pulver, Glen Curtis
Quintero-Ramos, Ángel Manuel
Randall, Harold M.
Randall, Laura R.
Raup, Phillip M.
Reischer, Otto Richard
Renne, Roland Roger
Rennie, Robert Alvin
Reynolds, Clark Winton
Rigby, Paul Herbert
Riley, Harold M.
Roberts, Warren Aldrich
Robock, Stefan H.
Ross, David F.
Rothwell, Kenneth James
Rottenberg, Simon
Ruderman, Armand Peter
Ruggles, Robert Thomas
Rust, Irwin Walter
Ruth, Richard Lee
Sammons, Ramon W.
Sammons, Robert L.
Sánchez, Juan Delgado
Sayre, Robert Martion
Scaperlanda, Anthony Edward
Schenk, William Earl
Schlesinger, Eugene Richard
Schooler, Robert Dale
Schultz, Theodore W.
Schwinden, James
Scott, Frank S., Jr.
Scott, J. T.

Sedwitz, Walter J.
Sheahan, John Bernard
Shelton, David H.
Shoup, Carl Sumner
Simmons, George Benton
Smith, Mervin George
Smith, Robert Sidney
Snell, Hampton Kent
Spiegel, Henry William
Spiro, Benjamin Paul
Staats, William F.
Staley, A. Eugene
Staley, Charles Earl
Steele, Howard Loucks
Steigerwalt, Albert K.
Sternberg, Marvin John
Stokes, Charles J.
Strasma, John D.
Strassmann, W. Paul
Street, James H(arry)
Sturmthal, Adolf F.
Sutton, Antony Cyril
Tamagna, Frank Mario
Tannenbaum, Frank
Tatkon, Marvin Daniel
Taylor, Milton Cecil
Teichert, Pedro C. M.
Thomas, D. Woods
Thomas, Roy Edwin
Thompson, Layton Spencer
Thorbecke, Erik
Thorn, Richard Semour
Thorne, Alfred P.
Timmons, John F.
Tinnermeier, Ronald Lee
Toledo, Raymond R.
Tragen, Irving Glenn
Triffin, Robert
Upton, Thomas Graydon
Van De Bunt, Wouter
Vernon, Raymond
Vickrey, William Spencer
Waits, Caron Richard
Wallich, Henry Christopher
Walther, Ted
Wang, Hsin Fu
Watkins, Ralph J.
Weekly, James Keith
Wendt, Paul Francis
Wheeler, Richard G.
White, Byron
Wilford, Walton Terry
Wilkins, Billy Hughel
Withers, William H.
Witt, Lawrence W.
Wolfe, Gregory B.
Wood, James Earl
Worrell, Albert Cadwallader
Wythe, George
Zymelman, Manuel

EDUCATION

Alessandro, Joseph Vincent
Angel, Frank, Jr.
Anttila, Earl
Axford, Roger
Barton, Robert Durrie
Berger, Evelyn Miller
Birch, Jack W.
Brown, Stanley B.
Burns, Hobert W.
Bush, Robert Nelson
Butler, George Norwood
Canter, Jacob
Carter, Thomas Pelham
Chiappetta, Michael
Colford, William Edward

Cotner, Thomas Ewing
Dale, George A.
Davis, Russell Gerard
Di Franco, Joseph
Del Río, Fernando
Denemark, George William
Dent, Charles H.
Doudna, Quincy V.
Ely, Donald Paul
Espinosa, José Manuel
Fahs, Ned C.
Farrah, Adelaide Georgiana
Faust, Augustus Finlinson
Gálvez, Luis A.
Gill, Clark C.
Goldman, Frank Perry
Grado, Louis M.
Guerra, Emilio L.
Harrell, William Asbury
Hart, Thomas Arthur
Hauch, Charles Christian
Havighurst, Robert J.
Haydon, Rosa Navarro
Holland, (George) Kenneth
Jordan, John Edward
Kavetsky, Joseph
Leeds, Willard Lodowick
Lipp, Solomon
McAlees, Daniel Clark
McConnell, Thomas Raymond
McNeely, Samuel Sidney, Jr.
Miller, David Lynn
Morton, Luis M., Jr.
Norris, Renfro Cole
Oliver, Covey (Thomas)
Opperman, Henry James
Peck, F. Taylor
Peck, Robert F.
Price, Hartley D'Oyley
Roca, Pablo
Rodríguez-Bou, Ismael
Sánchez, George I.
Sayres, William Cortlandt
Seeley, E(rwin) Clayton
Suhm, Lawrence Lee
Taba, Hilda
Thompson, Maury Weldon
Tierney, James Francis
Toth, John Charles

GEOGRAPHY

Akin, Wallace Elmus
Alexander, Charles S.
Alpert, Leo
Aschmann, (Harold) Homer
Atwood, Rollin Salisbury
Augelli, John P.
Ball, John M.
Barrett, Ward Judson
Basile, David Giovanni
Batchelder, Robert Bruce
Beishlag, George A.
Bennett, Charles Franklin, Jr.
Bergmann, John Francis
Biggs, Arthur Perry
Blick, James Donald
Bruman, Henry J(ohn)
Bushong, Allen David
Canet, Gerardo Alvarez
Carlson, Fred A.
Carmin, Robert Leighton
Carter, George Francis
Chardon, Roland E.
Cline, Howard Francis
Cohen, Saul B.
Cook, Sherburne F.
Courtney, Dale Elliott

Crain, Clark N.
Crist, Raymond E.
Culbert, James I.
Dambaugh, Luella N.
De Laubenfels, David John
Denevan, William M.
Dicken, Samuel Newton
Doerr, Arthur Harry
Doran, Edwin, Jr.
Dozier, Craig Lanier
Drewes, Wolfram U.
Durland, Robert Edwin
Dyer, Donald Ray
Eder, Herbert Michael
Edwards, Clinton Ralph
Eidt, Robert C.
Eiselen, Elizabeth
English, Van H.
Ervin, Roger Edward
Ferdon, Edwin Nelson, Jr.
Finch, William A., Jr.
Foscue, Edwin Jay
Frost, Melvin Jesse
Fuson, Robert Henderson
Gauthier, Howard L., Jr.
Gerlach, Arch C.
Gonzalez, Alfonso
Gordon, Burton Leroy
Guernsey, James Lee
Guzman, Louis Enrique
Guzman-Rivas, Pablo
Haase, Ynez Durnford
Haskins, Edward C.
Hawley, Dorothea Burton
Hegen, Edmund Eduard
Henderson, David Allen
Hill, A. David
Hitchcock, Charles Baker
Holmes, Roland Clifford
Horst, Oscar Heinz
Hoy, Don Roger
James, Preston E(verett)
Jensen, J. Granville
Johannessen, Carl Lewis
Keller, Frank L.
Kennelly, Robert Andrew
Kingsbury, Robert C.
Krause, Annemarie E.
Layton, Robert L.
Lemaire, Minnie Ethel
Lloyd-Jones, Donald J.
Long, Robert Grant
Lounsbury, John Frederick
Lowenthal, David
Ludwig, Armin Konrad
Lyons, Marion, S.C.H.
McBride, George McCutchen
McBryde, Felix Webster
McMurray, John H.
MacPhail, Donald Dugald
Manley, Vaughn Porter
Martin, Gene Ellis
Mather, Eugene (Cotton)
Meigs, Peveril
Miller, E. Willard
Minkel, Clarence W.
Momsen, Richard P., Jr.
Moreno, Laudelino
Morrison, Paul Cross
Mowll, Jack Usher
Nowotny, Franz A.
Nunley, Robert E.
Parsons, James Jerome
Patten, George Phillip
Pearson, Ross Norton
Pennington, Campbell White
Picó, Rafael
Psuty, Norbert Phillip
Rau, Herbert Lawrence, Jr.,

Reyner, Anthony Stephen
Richardson, Robert William
Rodgers, Kirk Proctor
Sands, Richard D.
Sinclair, Joseph Treble
Slutsky, Herbert L.
Smith, Margaret Harrison
Smith, Richard Vergon
Smole, William Joseph
Snyder, David Elmer
Sobol, John Andrew
Stanislawski, Dan
Stanley, Raymond Wallace
Starkey, Otis Paul
Sternberg, Hilgard O'Reilly
Stewart, Norman Reginald
Stillwell, H. Daniel
Street, John M.
Tatkon, Marvin Daniel
Taylor, Harry White
Thompson, John
Tosi, Joseph Andrew, Jr.
Vann, John Herman
Vermeer, Donald Eugene
Wagner, Philip Laurence
Warman, Henry John
Webb, Kempton Evans
West, Robert Cooper
Wiley, Selva C.
Winnie, William W., Jr.
Winsberg, Morton Daniel
Zelinsky, Wilbur

HISTORY

Adams, Eleanor Burnham
Addy, George Milton
Aguilar, Luis Enrique
Alden, Dauril
Allen, Cyril G.
Alvarez-Pedroso, Antonio
Ameringer, Charles D.
Anderson, Conwell A.
Anguizola, Gustave A.
Arena, Carmelo Richard
Arnade, Charles W.
Ashby, Joe C.
Bacarisse, Charles Albert
Bailey, Helen Miller
Baily, Samuel L.
Baker, George William, Jr.
Baker, Maury Davison
Bannon, John Francis, S.J.
Barager, Joseph Rufus
Barnhart, Donald Stanford
Bastert, Russell Henry
Baur, John Edward
Bausum, Henry S.
Beals, Carleton
Beatty, W. Donald
Beck, Warren Albert
Beilharz, Edwin Alanson
Bemis, Samuel Flagg
Benson, Nettie Lee
Berbusse, Edward Joseph, S.J.
Bernstein, Harry
Bernstein, Marvin David
Beyer, Robert Carlyle
Bidwell, Robert Leland
Bierck, Harold Alfred
Billingsley, Edward Baxter
Billman, Calvin James
Bishko, Charles Julian
Blaisdell, Lowell Lawrence
Blanco, Richard Lidio
Blossom, Thomas
Bobb, Bernard Earl
Boehrer, George C. A.
Borah, Woodrow (Wilson)

Bork, Albert William
Boyd, Maurice
Boyd, Willis D.
Brenthett, George
Breymann, Walter Norman
Bristol, William Baker
Brooks, Philip Coolidge
Broussard, Ray F.
Brown, Joseph Robert
Brown, Lyle Clarence
Brubaker, George A.
Brundage, Burr C.
Bumgartner, Louis E.
Burks, David Donald
Burns, E. Bradford
Burr, Robert N.
Burrus, Ernest Joseph, S.J.
Bushnell, Clyde Gilbert
Bushnell, David
Butler, Ruth Lapham
Cadenhead, Ivie Edward, Jr.
Callaghan, Mary Consuela, I.H.M.
Callcott, Wilfrid Hardy
Campa, David L.
Canedo, Lino Gómez, O.F.M.
Cardozo, Manoel
Carey, James Charles
Caughey, John W.
Chamberlain, Robert S.
Chamberlin, Eugene Keith
Chapman, Mary P.
Chatelain, Verne Elmo
Chipman, Donald Eugene
Christiansen, Paige W.
Clegern, Wayne M.
Clendenen, Clarence C.
Cline, Howard Francis
Coleman, William Jackson, M.M.
Conrad, David E.
Cook, Sherburne F.
Cook, Warren L.
Cooper, Donald Bolon
Corbitt, Duvon Clough
Corwin, Arthur F.
Cotner, Thomas Ewing
Crampton, C. Gregory
Criscenti, Joseph Thomas
Cronon, E(dmund) David
Crowley, Florence Joseph
Culver, John William
Cumberland, Charles Curtis
Cummins, Lejeune
Cunningham, James Stewart, Jr.
Cutter, Donald Colgett
Dabbs, Jack Autrey
Dahl, Victor Charles
Davis, Harold Eugene
Davis, Thomas Brabson, Jr.
Davis, William Columbus
Dean, Warren Kempton
De Armond, Louis Cushman
Dearth, John A(rthur)
De Conde, Alexander
De Grummond, Jane Lucas
Delaney, Robert W.
Della Cava, Ralph S.
Devore, Blanche Blue
Diaz-Soler, Luis M.
Diffie, Bailey W.
Dillon, Dorothy R.
Donohue, John Augustine, S.J.
Dozer, Donald Marquand
Dreier, John Caspar
Dulles, John Watson Foster
Duncan, Roland E.
Dusenberry, William Howard
Ealy, Lawrence Orr
Ellis, Joseph Albert

Elsasser, Edward Orr
Ely, Roland Taylor
Ervin, Dwain T.
Espinosa, José Manuel
Esquenazi-Mayo, Roberto
Estep, Raymond
Ewing, Floyd Ford, Jr.
Ewing, Russell Charles
Fagg, John Edwin
Felt, Jeremy Pollard
Finan, John Joseph
Fischman, Jerome
Flaccus, Elmer William
Floyd, Troy Smith
Forbes, Jack Douglas
Forrest, Frederick August
Frankel, Benjamin Adam
Frazer, Robert Walter
Frazier, Charles Edward, Jr.
Gagliano, Joseph Anthony
Gale, Thomas Martin
Gatell, Frank Otto
Gauld, Charles Anderson
Gerassi, Marysa
Gerhard, Peter
Gibson, Charles
Giffin, Donald Warren
Gillaspie, William Roscoe
Gilmore, N(ewton) Ray
Gilmore, Robert Louis
Glauert, Earl Theodore
Gold, Robert Leonard
Goodman, Edward J.
Goodsell, James Nelson
Graham, Richard
Gray, William Henry
Greenleaf, Richard Edward
Greer, Virginia Leonard
Greever, Janet Groff
Griffin, Charles Carroll
Griffith, William J.
Guest, Florian Francis, O.F.M.
Guice, C. Norman
Haddick, Jack Allen
Haigh, Roger Malone
Haight, Charles Henry
Hale, Charles Adams
Hamill, Hugh Maxwell, Jr.
Hammond, George Peter
Hanke, Lewis Ulysses
Hanna, Alfred Jackson
Harrell, William Asbury
Harrison, John Parker
Harrison, Sandas Lorenzo
Hauberg, Clifford A.
Helguera, J. León
Hellyer, Clement David
Henderson, Donald C., Jr.
Hendricks, Frances Kellam
Hendrickson, Embert Julius
Herrick, Jane
Herring, Hubert C.
Hewitt, Clyde Eaton
Hildner, Ernest Gotthold, Jr.
Hill, Lawrence F.
Hillmon, Tommie J.
Hoffman, Fritz Leo
Holleran, Mary Patricia
Holmes, Jack D. L.
Hoskins, Lewis M.
Houseman, Philip Joseph
Huck, Eugene Roger
Hundley, Norris Cecil, Jr.
Hutchinson, Cecil Alan
Jamison, Edward A.
Jeffrey, William H.
Johnson, Donald D.
Johnson, John J.

341

Johnson, Richard A.
Jones, Oakah L., Jr.
Jones, Tom Bard
Jones, Wilbur Devereux
Kaiser, Chester Carl
Karnes, Thomas L.
Keen, Benjamin
Kenyon, Robert Gordon B.
Kiemen, Mathias Charles, O.F.M.
King, James F.
Klein, Herbert Sanford
Knapp, Frank Averill
Knowlton, Robert
Knox, A. J. Graham
Kolinski, Charles James
Korth, Eugene Henry, S.J.
Kroeber, Clifton Brown
Lamb, Ursula Schaefer
Lanning, John Tate
Leonard, Irving Albert
Levett, Ella Pettit
Levy, James Robert
Leitz, Paul Stanton
Lieuwen, Edwin
Liss, Sheldon B.
Logan, Rayford W.
Lou, Dennis Wingsou
Lowenthal, David
McAlister, Lyle Nelson
McCarran, Margaret-Patricia
McCarty, Kieran, O.F.M.
McGann, Thomas Francis
McGarry, Daniel D.
Machado, Manuel Anthony, Jr.
Macleod, Murdo John
MacMichael, David Charles
McNeely, John Hamilton
McNicoll, Robert Edwards
Magner, James A., Rt. Rev.
Malagón Barceló, Javier
Manchester, Alan K.
Manno, Francis J.
Martin, Norman Francis, S.J.
Martinez, John R.
Martínez, Manuel Guillermo
Masur, Gerhard S.
Mathews, Thomas George
Meier, Matt S.
Meyer, Michael Carl
Miller, David Lynn
Miller, Hubert John
Miller, Robert Ryal
Miner, William D.
Minger, Ralph Eldin
Moore, James Maxwell
Moore, John Preston
Moorhead, Max Leon
Morales-Carrión, Arturo
Moreno, Laudelino
Morris, James Oliver
Morse, Richard McGee
Morton, Luis M., Jr.
Moseley, Edward Holt
Motten, Clement Gile
Muller, Herman Joseph, S.J.
Munro, Dana G.
Murdoch, Richard Kenneth
Murray, Paul Vincent
Nasatir, Abraham P.
Nava, Julian
Naylor, Robert Arthur
Newton, Ronald Charles
Newton, Wesley Phillips, Jr.
Nichols, Lawrence Richard
Nichols, Madaline Wallis
Nichols, Theodore Edward
Niemeyer, Everhardt Victor, Jr.

Nunn, Frederick McKinley
Nuttall, Donald Andrew
Ogelsby, John C. M.
Oswald, J. Gregory
Padden, Robert Charles
Page, A. Nayland
Pareja Diezcanseco, Alfredo
Parker, Franklin Dallas
Parkes, Henry B.
Parks, E. Taylor
Patterson, Jerry Eugene
Payne, Walter Arville
Peckham, Edmund T.
Peffer, E. Louise
Perkins, Dexter
Perrigo, Lynn Irwin
Peters, Thelma Peterson
Peterson, Harold F(erdinand)
Pflaum, Irving Peter
Phelan, John Leddy
Pikaza, Otto
Pike, Frederick Braun
Pine, John Crane
Pletcher, David Mitchell
Poole, Richard Stafford, C.M.
Poppino, Rollie Edward
Portell-Vilá, Herminio
Potash, Robert A.
Powell, Philip Wayne
Quirk, Robert E.
Randall, Robert William
Rayburn, John C.
Reinhart, Helen Katherine
Riley, G. Micheal
Rippy, James Fred
Rippy, Noble Merrill
Rittenhouse, Floyd Oliver
Rodríguez, Mario
Rogers, Rolland C.
Ronan, Charles Edward, S.J.
Ross, Oliver Dell
Ross, Stanley Robert
Rowe, John Howland
Rowland, Donald Winslow
Ruiz, Ramón Eduardo
Rydjord, John
Santana, Arturo F.
Savelle, Max
Schellenberg, Theodore R.
Schiff, Warren
Schmitt, Karl Michael
Scholes, France Vinton
Scholes, Walter V.
Schuster, Alice K.
Scobie, James Robert
Scruggs, Otey Matthew
Sensabaugh, Leon F.
Servin, Manuel Patricio
Shafer, Robert Jones
Shapiro, Samuel
Shearer, Ernest Charles
Shiels, W(illiam) Eugene, S.J.
Skidmore, Thomas Elliott
Sluiter, Engel
Smith, Ralph Adam
Smith, Robert Freeman
Smith, Robert Sidney
Smith, Robert Wayne
Smith, Willard Harvey
Solnick, Bruce B.
Spector, Robert Melvin
Stansifer, Charles Lee
Stauffer, David Hall
Steele, Arthur Robert
Stein, Stanley J.
Stevens, Robert Conway
Stewart, Watt
Synnestvedt, Sig

Szászdi, Adam M.
Talbott, Robert Dean
Tannenbaum, Frank
Tanner, Helen Hornbeck
Tapia, Francisco Xavier, S.J.
Tapson, Alfred Joseph
Tarr, Terence Stephen
TePaske, John Jay
Thomas, Alfred Barnaby
Thomas, Jack Ray
Thorning, Joseph Francis
Thurman, Michael E.
Tigner, James Lawrence
Timmons, Wilbert H.
Tinker, Edward Larocque
Trembley, William Albert
Treutlein, Theodore Edward
Undreiner, George Joseph, Rt. Rev.
Van Aken, Mark Jay
Vanderburgh, John B.
Vanger, Milton I.
Varner, John Grier
Vigneras, Louis André
Vigness, David Martell
Warren, Donald, Jr.
Warren, Fintan Benedict, O.F.M.
Warren, Harris Gaylord
Watters, Mary
Whitaker, Arthur Preston
Wilgus, A(lva) Curtis
Williford, Miriam
Wilson, Iris Higbie
Winn, Wilkins Bowdre
Wood, Marie V.
Woods, Kenneth Flint
Woodward, Ralph Lee, Jr.
Worcester, Donald Emmet
Wright, Almon Robert
Wright, Ione Stuessy
Wright, James Leitch, Jr.
Wright, Winthrop Robins
Young, Jordan Marten
Zimdars, Benjamin Frank
Zook, David Hartzler, Jr.

JOURNALISM

Alisky, Marvin Howard
Braschi, Wilfredo
Carter, Roy Ernest, Jr.
Clark, Wesley Clarke
De Onis, Juan
Dubois, Jules
Fernandez, Charles J.
Frantz, Harry Warner
Gardner, Mary Adelaide
Gerassi, John
Goodsell, James Nelson
Graban, Michael
Haverstock, Nathan Alfred
Hellyer, Clement David
MacLeish, William Hitchcock
Marbut, Frederick Browning
Matthews, Herbert Lionel
McNelly, John Taylor
Meek, George D.
Meyer, Benjamin Franklin
Nevins, Albert J.
Pflaum, Irving Peter
Preece, Margot
Purks, James Harris, III
Szulc, Tad
Weyl, Nathaniel

LANGUAGE

Abreu, Maria Isabel
Andersson, Theodore
Arias Larreta, Abraham

Armitage, Richard M.
Barnes, Allen Ray
Batchelor, Malcolm C.
Boggs, Ralph Steele
Bolinger, Dwight LeMerton
Bowen, J(ean) Donald
Boyd-Bowman, Peter Muschamp
Canfield, (Delos) Lincoln
Carrino, Frank G.
Colford, William Edward
Davis, Jack Emory
Davis, Joe Edward, Jr.
Del Rosario, Rubén
Donahue, Francis James
Eastlack, Charles Leonard
Ellison, Fred Pittman
Essa, Robert Newyia
Feldman, David M.
Fernandez, Oscar
Fox, Eugene J.
Gaarder, Alfred Bruce
Gálvez, Luis A.
García-Girón, Edmundo
Guerra, Emilio L.
Hall, Robert Anderson, Jr.
Hamilton, Carlos D.
Hammond, John Hays
Head, Brian Franklin
Henderson, Donald C., Jr.
Herman, J(ack) Chalmers
Hill, Emma May
Hilton, Ronald
Hoge, Henry William
Holzapfel, Tamara Osikowska
Irving, Evelyn Uhrhan
Irving, Thomas Ballantine
Kany, Charles Emil
Kavetsky, Joseph
Key, Richard Michael
Kiddle, Lawrence Bayard
King, Charles Lester
Kirsner, Robert
Larew, Leonor A.
Lopes, Albert R.
Lozano, Anthony Girard
Lund, Harry
McNeely, Samuel Sidney, Jr.
McPheeters, Dean William
Malkiel, Yakov
Martin, John W.
Martins, Heitor Miranda
Matluck, Joseph H.
Mercer, Lucille E.
Meyer, Mary Edgar, O.S.F.
Michel, Joseph
Miller, Gustavus Hindman
Mills, Dorothy Hurst
Moloney, Raymond L.
Morínigo, Marcos A.
Munro, Edwin Clair
Narvaez, Ricardo Augusto
Nason, Marshall Rutherford
Obaid, Antonio H.
Oberhelman, Harley Dean
Orjuela, Héctor Hugo
Paratore, Angela
Pettit, John Albert
Previtali, Giovanni
Raymond, Joseph B.
Reid, J. Richard
Riccio, Guy John
Robe, Stanley Linn
Rogers, Paul
Rose, Theodore E.
Rossi, Pietro Carlo, S.J.
Sacks, Norman P(aul)
Saporta, Sol
Schwartz, Henry Charles
Sharp, John McCarty

Sharpe, Lawrence Albright
Silseth, Martha Jensine
Sittler, Richard Culver
Smith, George E.
Stewart, Nancy C.
Stockwell, Robert Paul
Stoudemire, Sterling Aubrey
Stubach, Charles N(eff)
Sutton, Lois Marie
Thomas, Earl W.
Trueblood, Alan Stubbs
Tudisco, Anthony
Turner, E(lbert) Daymond
Ulibarrí, Sabine Reyes
Vazquez, Alberto M.
Villegas, Francisco
Walsh, Donald Devenish
Weber, Frances Wyers
Wexler, Sidney Frederick
Wilkins, Ernest J.
Woolsey, Arthur Wallace
Yates, Donald Alfred

LAW

Angulo, Manuel R.
Baquero, José Antonio
Barnes, William Sprague
Batiza, Rodolfo
Bayitch, Stoyan Albert
Berle, Adolph Augustus
Butte, Woodfin Lee
Canyes, Manuel
Casad, Robert Clair
Córdova, Efrén Córdoves
Charmatz, Jan Paul
Clagett, Helen L.
Coumes, George Raoul
De Capriles, Miguel (Angel)
De Vries, Henry Peter
Easby, Dudley T., Jr.
Edds, John R., Jr.
Eder, George Jackson
Ericson, Anne-Stina Louise
Fenwick, Charles G.
Ford, Edwin D., Jr.
García-Mora, Manuel R.
Hall, Jerome
Hall, Margaret Esther
Heller, Jack I.
Kaplan, Sheldon Zachary
Karst, Kenneth Leslie
Kozolchyk, Boris
Lutz, E. Russell
Macdonald, William Dickson
Malagón Barceló, Javier
Marchant, Anyda
Mestre, José A.
Miller, Patrick Henry
Moore, Sally Falk
Munster, Joe Henry, Jr.
Myren, Richard Albert
Nattier, Frank E.
Oldman, Oliver
Oliver, Covey (Thomas)
Owen, George Hodges
Palmer, Thomas Waverly
Ray, Philip Alexander
Riesenfeld, Stefan A.
Sarabia, Antonio Rosas
Shieber, Benjamin Murray
Slovenko, Ralph
Spaeth, Carl B.
Stern, David Sachs
Stevenson, John R.
Thomas, A. J., Jr.
Thomas, Ann Van Wynen
Tragen, Irving Glenn

Wagner, W. J.
Wellman, Harvey Russell
Wright, Harry Keisler

LIBRARY SCIENCE AND BIBLIOGRAPHY

Adams, Henry E.
Ashton, Jon R.
Baroco, John V.
Benson, Nettie Lee
Brooks, Philip Coolidge
Butler, Ruth Lapham
Carter, Phyllis G.
Clarke, Berta Lou
Clifford, Kathleen Emmons
Connolly, Brendan, S.J.
Cook, Rosemond F.
Cromwell, Frederick N.
Deal, Carl Wanamaker
De La Garza, Peter J.
Diaz, Albert James
Entrikin, Isabelle Webb
Fabilli, Josephine Caroline
Forrest, Frederick August
Garloch, Lorena A.
Gjelsness, Rudolph H.
Goggin, Margaret Enid
Gormly, Mary
Gosnell, Charles Francis
Gropp, Arthur Eric
Hall, Margaret Esther
Harrington, Charles W.
Heiliger, Edward Martin
Hixson, Imogene
Hodgman, Suzanne
Jackson, William Vernon
Johnson, Annita Ker
Kahler, Mary Ellis
Kidder, Frederick Elwyn
Krumm, Roger Vincent
Kurth, William H.
Langman, Ida Kaplan
Le Doux, Marjorie Elizabeth
Litton, Gaston
Longland, Jean Rogers
Martinez, Angelina
Mayol, Josefina M.
Mesa, Rosa Quintero
Milczewski, Marion Anthony
Miles, Paul M.
Mitchell, Eleanor
Montgomery, James Houston
Moushey, Eugene Wilson
Olivera, Guido Francisco
Orne, Jerrold
Pane, Remigio U.
Pariseau, Earl Joseph
Parsons, Mary Dudley
Patterson, Jerry Eugene
Peñalosa, Fernando
Peraza, Elena Vérez
Peraza Sarausa, Fermín
Pulsifer, Josephine Sturdivant
Ramey, Marilyn Lorraine
Rapp, Marie A.
Rudolph, Donna Keyse
Sable, Martin Howard
Sandvig, Mauda Polley
Schellenberg, Theodore R.
Shepard, Marietta Daniels
Sievers, Florence Nierman
Stewart, Donald E. J.
Trejo, Arnulfo Dueñes
Tribe, Peggy Ann Miller
Ulibarri, George Sarracino
Veenstra, John G.
Velázquez, Gonzalo
Wagley, Cecilia Roxo

West, Stanley LeRoy
Western, Dorothea
Wilkison, Andy George
Woods, William Robert
Zimmerman, Irene

LINGUISTICS

Alsop, John Richard
Anderson, James Maxwell
Anderson, Lambert Lyle
Blair, Robert Wallace
Bolinger, Dwight LeMerton
Borman, Marlytte Bubs
Boyd-Bowman, Peter Muschamp
Bradley, Charles Henry
Brend, Ruth Margaret
Bright, William O.
Burns, Donald H.
Crawford, John Chapman
Croft, Kenneth
Dabbs, Jack Autrey
Davis, Irvine Elwin
Del Rosario, Rubén
Diebold, Albert Richard, Jr.
Eastlack, Charles Leonard
Elson, Benjamin F., Jr.
Feldman, David M.
Firestone, Homer Leon
Friedrich, Paul W.
Grimes, Joseph Evans
Gudschinsky, Sarah Caroline
Hale, Kenneth Locke
Hardman De Bautista, Martha James
Head, Brian Franklin
Hess, Harold Harwood
Hoge, Henry William
Hoogshagen, Searle W.
Kany, Charles Emil
Kensinger, Kenneth M.
Key, Harold Hayden
Key, Mary Ritchie
Kietzman, Dale Walter
Kindberg, Willard Roy
Kirk, Paul Livingston
Kleinecke, David Carman
Lado, Robert
Larson, Mildred Lucille
Lastra, Yolanda
Levin, Norman Balfour
Loos, Eugene Emil
Lounsbury, Floyd Glenn
Lozano, Anthony Girard
McQuown, Norman Anthony
Mak, Cornelia
Malkiel, Yakov
Martin, John W.
Matluck, Joseph H.
Matson, Daniel Shaw
Matteson, Esther L. M.
Mayers, Marvin Keene
Meader, Robert Eli
Merrifield, William Richard
Miller, Walter Scott
Minor, Dorothy Anna Hendrich
Minor, Eugene Edward
Moore, Bruce R.
Murguía, Theodore Infante
Narvaez, Ricardo Augusto
Neuenswander, Helen Lucille
Nida, Eugene Albert
Nordell, Norman Wayne
Núñez, Benjamin
Olmsted, David L.
Olson, Donald W.
Oltrogge, David Frederick
Orr, Carolyn
Osborn, Henry A., Jr.

Paratore, Angela
Peeke, M. Catherine
Pickering, Wilbur Norman
Pickett, Velma Bernice
Pike, Eunice Victoria
Pike, Kenneth Lee
Powlison, Paul Stewart
Reiff, Donald G.
Rich, Rolland Glen
Robbins, Frank Ernest
Robinson, Dow Frederick
Rootes, Thomas Page, Jr.
Rubin, Joan
Russell, Robert Lee
Sacks, Norman P(aul)
Saporta, Sol
Schoenhals, Alvin
Schoenhals, Louise Conety
Shaver, Harold R.
Shaw, Mary Ellen
Skinner, Leonard Edward
Stark, Donald Stewart
Stockwell, Robert Paul
Stratmeyer, Dennis
Townsend, Elaine Mielke
Townsend, William Cameron
Troike, Rudolph Charles
Turner, Glen David
Turner, Paul R.
Ulrich, E. Matthew
Ulrich, Rosemary Dixon
Valdman, Albert
Williams, Gerald Eugene
Wise, Mary Ruth
Wonderly, William Lower
Wyatt, James L.

LITERATURE

Brazilian Literature

Abreu, Maria Isabel
Andrews, Norwood Henry, Jr.
Arora, Shirley Lease
Askins, Arthur Lee-Francis
Barrett, Linton Lomas
Batchelor, Malcolm C.
Beck, Vera F.
Brown, Timothy, Jr.
Caldwell, Helen F.
Carter, Henry Hare
Da Cal, Ernesto Guerra
De Jong, Gerrit, Jr.
Dimmick, Ralph Edward
Ellison, Fred Pittman
Englekirk, John E(ugene)
Fernandez, Oscar
Gates, Eunice Joiner
Griffin, William James
Grossman, William Leonard
Hamilton, Daniel Lee
Hower, Alfred
Hulet, Claude Lyle
Johnson, Harvey Leroy
Kasten, Lloyd A. W.
Kocher, John Berchmans, O.P.
Lopes, Albert R.
Martins, Heitor Miranda
Mary Terese Avila, B.V.M.
Mate, Hubert Emery
Maxwell, Henry James
Mazzara, Richard A.
Menton, Seymour
Miller, Gustavus Hindman
Moser, Gerald Max
Munro, Edwin Clair
Nist, John Albert
Pacheco, Armando Correia

Rabassa, Gregory Luis
Ramírez, Manuel D.
Robb, James Willis
Rosa, Alberto Machado da
Rose, Theodore E.
Sayers, Raymond S.
Thomas, Earl W.
Tomlins, Jack Edward
Walther, Don H.

Haitian Literature

Garrett, Naomi Mills
Thoby-Marcelin, Philippe

Spanish American Literature

Aguilera, Francisco
Aldrich, Earl Maurice, Jr.
Alegría, Fernando
Allen, Richard F.
Alvarez-Pedroso, Antonio
Anderson, Robert R.
Anderson-Imbert, Enrique
Angeles, Philip
Aponte, Barbara Bockus
Arias Larreta, Abraham
Arora, Shirley Lease
Arróm, José Juan
Askins, Arthur Lee-Francis
Astuto, Philip L(ouis)
Avrett, Robert
Balseiro, José Agustín
Bates, Margaret (Jane)
Beck, Vera F.
Belitt, Ben
Benton, Gabriele Von Munk
Bernard, Judith Ann
Boggs, Ralph Steele
Bork, Albert William
Bourgeois, Louis Clarence
Boyer, Mildred Vinson
Brushwood, John Stubbs
Calbick, Gladys Stanley
Campa, Arthur Leon
Campbell, Margaret Virginia
Carter, Boyd George
Case, Thomas Edward
Castañeda, Julio R.
Castillo, Homero
Chang-Rodriguez, Eugenio
Chapman, G. Arnold
Ciruti, Joan E(stelle)
Cobb, Carl Wesley
Cobb, H. Logan
Compton, Merlin David
Coons, Dix Scott
Corbitt, Roberta Day
Cord, William Owen
Corvalán, Octavio E.
Crow, John Armstrong
Da Cal, Ernesto Guerra
Dauster, Frank Nicholas
Davis, Jack Emory
Davison, Ned J.
Debicki, Andrew Peter
Dellepiane, Angela Blanca
De Morelos, Leonardo Calderon
De Onís, Federico
De Onís, José
Deuel, Pauline Brandt
Dulsey, Bernard Martin
Dunham, Lowell
Earle, Peter G.
Edberg, George John
Ellison, Fred Pittman
Englekirk, John E(ugene)
Enguídanos, Miguel

Erickson, Martin Elmer
Esquenazi-Mayo, Roberto
Falconieri, John V.
Fein, John Morton
Ferrer-Canales, José
Flores, Ángel
Floripe, Rodolfo Orozco
Florit, Eugenio
Forster, Merlin Henry
García-Girón, Edmundo
García-Prada, Carlos
Garganigo, John Frank
Gates, Eunice Joiner
Gibbs, Beverly Jean
Gicovate, Bernard
Glickman, Robert Jay
González, Manuel Pedro
Gordon, Bruce R.
Hamilton, Carlos D.
Hammond, John Hays
Haws, Gary Lewis
Head, Gerald Louis
Henning, Eugene Albert
Hernandez, David
Hooker, Alexander Campbell, Jr.
Hulet, Claude Lyle
Iduarte, Andrés
Irby, James East
Irving, Evelyn Uhrhan
Johnson, Ernest Alfred, Jr.
Johnson, Harvey Leroy
Jones, Willis Knapp
Karsen, Sonja Petra
Kerson, Arnold Lewis
Knox, Robert Baker
Kocher, John Berchmans, Sister, O.P.
Kolb, Glen L.
Lamb, Ruth S.
Lancaster, C. Maxwell
Lance, Betty Rita Gómez
Leal, Luis
Leavitt, Sturgis Elleno
Lemus, George
Leonard, Irving Albert
Lewald, Herald Ernest
Lichtblau, Myron I.
Lida, Raimundo
Lipp, Solomon
Lopes, Albert R.
Lowy, Sara Jaroslavsky
Lozano, Carlos
McGrady, Donald Lee
McLean, Malcolm Dallas
McMahon, Dorothy Elizabeth
Manchester, Paul Thomas
Marichal, Juan
Martin, John Lewis
Martínez, Manuel Guillermo
Mate, Hubert Emery
Mazzara, Richard A.
Mead, Robert G., Jr.
Mendez, Margarita Castro
Menton, Seymour
Monguió, Luis
Morello-Frosch, Martha Eugenia
Moreno, Laudelino
Murguía, Theodore Infante
Nason, Marshall Rutherford
Navarro, Joaquina
Neale-Silva, Eduardo
Nemes, Graciela P.
Nichols, Grace Lura
Nichols, Madaline Wallis
Oberhelman, Harley Dean
Olivera, Otto Hugo
Orjuela, Héctor Hugo
Pane, Remigio U.
Pareja Diezcanseco, Alfredo

Phillips, Allen W.
Ponseti, Helena Percas
Previtali, Giovanni
Raab, Mary Ricarda
Rabassa, Gregory Luis
Rael, Juan B.
Ramírez, Manuel D.
Reedy, Daniel Ross
Reid, John T.
Riccio, Guy John
Ripoll, Carlos R.
Robb, James Willis
Roberts, William H.
Rodríguez-Alcalá, Hugo Rosendo
Rogers, Paul
Roggiano, Alfredo Angel
Rojas, Carlos A.
Rosaldo, Renato Ignacio
Rothberg, Irving Paul
Sánchez-Reulet, Aníbal
Schanzer, George O.
Schulman, Ivan Albert
Schwartz, Kessel
Sibirsky, Saúl B.
Simmons, Merle Edwin
Sisto, David Theodore
Smith, George E.
Sneary, Eugene C.
Sommers, Joseph
Soria, Mario T.
Souza, Raymond Dale
Spell, Jefferson Rea
Stabb, Martin S.
Stimson, Frederick Sparks
Suárez-Murias, Marguerite C.
Taylor, Martin Charles
Terry, Edward Davis
Tinker, Edward Larocque
Tirado, Moisés S.
Torres-Rioseco, Arturo
Trifilo, S. Samuel
Urbanski, Edmund Stephen
Valbuena-(Briones), Ángel Julián
Valenzuela, Victor M.
Vance, Charles Michael
Vargas-Barón, Aníbal
Varner, John Grier
Vásquez, Alberto M.
Waldorf, Paul Douglass
Watland, Charles Dunton
Wogan, Daniel Spelman
Yates, Donald Alfred

MUSIC

Barwick, Steven
Catalyne, Alice Ray
Chase, Gilbert
De La Vega, Aurelio
List, George Harold
Luper, Albert T(homas)
Matilla, Alfredo
Orrego-Salas, Juan Antonio
Slonimsky, Nicolas
Spell, Lota M.
Spiess, Lincoln Bunce
Sterrett, Delbert Ellingsworth
Stevenson, Robert Murrell

PHILOSOPHY

Ahumada, Rodolfo
Alexander, Hubert Griggs
Berndtson, C. Arthur E.
Cooper, William Frazier
Ferrater-Mora, José
Fránquiz, José Antonio

Guthrie, Joseph Hunter
Hartman, Robert S.
Kilgore, William Jackson
Krusé, Cornelius
Magner, James A., Rt. Rev.
Pacheco, Armando Correia
Rodríguez-Alcalá, Hugo Rosendo
Romanell, Patrick
Sánchez-Reulet, Aníbal
Torchia-Estrada, Juan Carlos
Torres, José Arsenio

POLITICAL SCIENCE

Alexander, Robert J.
Alisky, Marvin Howard
Anderson, Charles William
Anderson, Robert William
Apter, David E.
Avery, Robert Sterling
Baker, Richard D(on)
Ball, Mary Margaret
Barager, Joseph Rufus
Barber, William Foster
Berbusse, Edward Joseph, S.J.
Blanksten, George I(rving)
Blasier, Cole
Board, Joseph Breckinridge
Brady, Helena Real
Brandenburg, Frank R.
Brown, Lyle Clarence
Burnett, Ben George
Busey, James L(ynn)
Cárdenas, Leonard, Jr.
Carlisle, Douglas Hilton
Chilcote, Ronald Hodell
Christopher, Henry Anthony
Cochrane, James David
Colberg, Severo E.
Cope, Orville G.
Córdova, Efrén Córdoves
Cummins, Lejeune
Davis, Harold Eugene
Davis, William Columbus
Day, Lowell Curtis
Delaney, Robert Finley
Dix, Robert Heller
Donald, Carr Lowe
Dreier, John Caspar
Ealy, Lawrence Orr
Ebel, Roland Hinkley
Evans, Alona E.
Fagen, Richard Rees
Fenwick, Charles G.
Fernández, Juan Ramón
Fitzgibbon, Russell H.
Fortier-Ortiz, Adolfo
Francis, Michael Jackson
García-Mora, Manuel R.
Gil, Federico Guillermo
Glick, Edward B.
Godfrey, Erwina Edwards
Goldrich, Daniel
Goodsell, Charles True
Gordon, Lincoln
Gould, Lyman Jay
Gray, Richard Butler
Greifer, Elisha
Hadley, Paul E.
Hall, John Oliver
Harris, Louis Kenneth
Hawkins, Carroll James
Hayton, Robert Deryl
Herman, Donald Louis
Heubel, Edward J.
Hillmon, Tommie J.
Houston, John Albert

Huntington, Samuel Phillips
Hutchins, John A.
Hyman, Elizabeth Hannan
Johnson, Kenneth Fox
Jordan, David Crichton
Jorrín, Miguel
Kahle, Louis George
Kantor, Harry
Kelso, Paul
Kennedy, John J(oseph)
Kitchen, James D.
Knapp, Frank Averill, Jr.
Lane, George B., Jr.
Larson, David Lloyd
Lehmann, Shirley Jeanne
Lemus, George
Lewis, Frank Marshall
Lott, Leo B.
McAdams, John
McCrocklin, James H.
McDonald, Ronald H.
Manger, William
Martz, John D.
Matilla, Alfredo
Mauck, Elwyn Arthur
Mecham, J(ohn) Lloyd
Menez, Joseph F.
Morales-Carrión, Arturo
Moreno, Laudelino
Morton, Ward McKinnon
Moses, Carl C(alvin)
Neal, Joe West
Needler, Martin Cyril
Nigro, Felix Anthony
Oberlitner, Thomas Billing
Packenham, Robert Allen
Padgett, L. Vincent
Pareja Diezcanseco, Alfredo
Paulson, Belden Henry
Peckham, Edmund T.
Peplow, Marijane Eastman
Peterson, Phyllis Jane
Picó, Rafael
Plank, John Nathan
Raine, Philip
Ramirez, Ezekiel S.
Randall, Harold M.
Reisky De Dubnic, Vladimir
Richardson, Ivan LeRoy
Roberts, Warren Aldrich
Robinson, Nelson Martin
Rogers, Edward Jonathan
Ronning, C. Neale
Rothman, Stanley
Ryan, Hewson A.
Sanders, William
Satra, John C.
Schaeffer, Wendell G.
Schmitt, Karl Michael
Schneider, Ronald Milton
Scott, Robert E.
Shea, Donald Richard
Silvert, Kalman Hirsch
Simonson, William N.
Skaggs, Earle Clayton
Snow, Peter Gordon
Spector, Robert Melvyn
Stephens, Richard Hunter
Stokes, William Sylvane
Synnestvedt, Sig
Taylor, Philip Bates, Jr.
Tierney, James Francis
Tomasek, Robert Dennis
Travis, Martin B.
Tucker, William Pierce
Tyson, Brady Bradford
Urist, Margaret Ethel
Washington, S(amuel) Walter

Wells, Henry
Wilson, Larman Curtis
Winkler, Marshall Baker, S. J.
Wood, Bryce
Wright, Freeman J.
Wyckoff, Theodore

PSYCHOLOGY

Berger, Evelyn Miller
Birch, Jack W.
Fránquiz, José Antonio
Havighurst, Robert J.
Jordan, John Edward
Landsberger, Henry A.
Peck, Robert F.
Toth, John Charles

SOCIAL WELFARE

Farman, Carl Hugo
Jones, Robert Cuba
Lightman, Jacob Ben
Martorell, Irma B.
Putnam, Emilie Baca
Sullivan, Dorothea F.

SOCIOLOGY

Alers, J. Oscar
Alers-Montalvo, Manuel
Alleger, Daniel E.
Andrews, David Henry
Andrews, Wade H.
Biesanz, John Berry
Blumer, Herbert G.
Bouquet, Susana
Brown, Gerardo Castillo
Browning, Harley L.
Burnight, Robert Galen
Cancian, Francesca Micaela
Carter, Roy Ernest, Jr.
Chaplin, David
Cicourel, Aaron Victor
Clear, Val B.
Clifford, Roy Arthur
Collver, O. Andrew
Crawford, William Rex
D'Antonio, William Vincent
Dasilva, José Fabio Barbosa
Davis, Ethelyn Clara
Davis, Kingsley
Delaney, Robert Finley
Demerath, Nicholas Jay
Diggs, Irene
Dotson, Floyd Whitney
Ellenbogen, Bert L.
Ericksen, (Ephraim) Gordon
Feldman, Arnold Sanford
Fliegel, Frederick Christian
Ford, Thomas R.
Goldman, Frank Perry
Goldsen, Rose K.
Greenfield, Sidney Martin
Haddox, Benjamin Edward
Haller, Archibald O.
Hancock, Richard Humphris
Havens, A. Eugene
Hayner, Norman Sylvester
Hernández-Álvarez, José Guillermo
Hopper, Rex D.
Jaffe, Abram J.
Kahl, Joseph A.
Knowlton, Clark S.
Knox, John Ballenger

Kunkel, John Howard
Landsberger, Henry A.
Leonard, Olen E.
Leslie, Charles M.
Leyburn, James Graham
Loftin, Marion T.
Loomis, Charles P.
Luebke, Benjamin H.
McCrary, J. Smith
Maday, Bela Charles
Minnich, R. Herbert, Jr.
Nehnevajsa, Jiri
Nelson, Lowry
Nett, Roger W.
Painter, Norman Wellington
Peñalosa, Fernando
Rogers, Everett M.
Rogler, Lloyd Henry
Rosenberg, Bernard
Salz, Beate R.
Samora, Julian
Saunders, John Van Dyke
Senior, Clarence Ollson
Simmons, Ozzie Gordon

Simpson, George Eaton
Smith, Thomas Lynn
Suchman, Edward A.
Taylor, Robert Bartley
Tumblin, John A., Jr.
Vidich, Arthur J.
Whetten, Nathan Laselle
Whyte, William Foote
Wilkening, Eugene A.
Williamson, Robert Clifford
Young, Frank W.
Zarate, Alvan O'Neill

STATISTICS

Berman, Barbara R.
Carter, Phyllis G.
Davis, Russell Gerard
Mayne, Alvin
Meyer, Morton Allan
Prescott, James Russell
Rigby, Paul Herbert
Ruderman, Armand Peter
Valencia, Miguel A.

Hispanic Foundation Bibliographical Series

1. Latin American Belles-Lettres in English Translation. A selective and annotated guide. 2d revised ed. 1943. 33 p............. Out of print
2. A Provisional Bibliography of United States Books Translated Into Portuguese. 1957. 182 p........................... Out of print
3. A Provisional Bibliography of United States Books Translated Into Spanish. 1957. 471 p .... Out of print
4. William Hickling Prescott. An annotated bibliography of published works. 1958. 275 p. Illus. .... [b] $2.00
5. Latin America in Soviet Writings, 1945–58. A bibliography. 1959. 257 p... [b] 2.00
6. Works of Miguel de Cervantes Saavedra in the Library of Congress. 1960. 109 p. 17 illus....................................... [b] 1.25
7. Ladino Books in the Library of Congress. A bibliography. 1963. 44 p... Out of print
8. Spanish and Portuguese Translations of United States Books 1955–1962. A bibliography. 1963. 506 p..................... [a] 3.00
9. Latin America. A bibliography of paperback books. 1964. 38 p... [a] .35

[a] Available from the Superintendent of Documents, U.S. Government Printing Office, Washington, D.C. 20402.
[b] Available from the Card Division, Library of Congress, Building No. 159, Navy Yard Annex, Washington, D.C. 20541.

Ref.
Z
2685
.H5
no.10

MAR 6 1967